Ramsay's Catalog

British Model Trains

Hornby 4-4-0 T9 LSWR No.120

Warners Group Publications Plc.
The Maltings, West Street,
Bourne, Lincolnshire, PE10 9PH
Phone 01778 391027 Fax: 01778 425437

Published by

BRITISH RAILWAY MODELLING

Compiler & Editor: Pat Hammond

1st Edition Published 1998
2nd Edition Published 2000
3rd Edition Published 2002
4th Edition Published 2004
5th Edition Published 2006
6th Edition Published 2008
7th Edition Published 2011

ISBN 978-1-907292-22-4

Book compiled by Pat Hammond.
Published by Warners Group Publications plc.
Pictures by the author unless otherwise stated.

Front Cover Illustration:
Scene of a vintage Bassett-Lowke layout
by Tony Wright

Contents

Welcome

Welcome to the Seventh Edition of ***Ramsay's British Model Trains Catalogue***. Much time has been spent in updating values of more recently released model.

The high interest in private owner (PO) wagons, as modern collectables, made it necessary to completely revise the suggested values of these in the relevant chapters. In the past, it has been impossible to get prices of these individual wagon models from 'room' auction results as, in this type of auction, they are sold in job lots. Until now, online auction prices have been too erratic to provide dependable information but this is changing as more collectors turn to this method of buying. I have therefore spent much time studying eBay results and found some clear patterns emerging.

While one can generalise in applying suggested values to most wagons, commissioned private owner wagons of the past are much in demand and show some very high prices paid. In some cases, these have risen to these levels in five or less years and, it seems that this has occurred irrespective of the number of models originally released. This particularly applies, for example, to Bachmann 14 ton tank wagons where prices seem to be dictated by how unusual is the name carried on the tanker, rather than by how many of the model were made. So, the suggested values of Bachmann, Replica, Mainline, Airfix, Hornby and Dapol wagons have been completely revised in this edition, some showing substantial increases.

I have also removed the anomaly in the Dapol listing that separated general release 5- and 7-plank wagons from commissioned versions. General release wagons are all to be found in the correct alphabetical position in the main tables, with original railway company wagons included at the end of each list.

In the sixth edition of the book, the prices for Wrenn products were based on those suggested in the book *The Story of Wrenn - From Binns Road to Basildon*, written by Maurice Gunter. The book was published a few years ago and auction prices were suggesting that the time had come to revise those suggested here. Coincidentally, in September 2008, I saw an analysis of Wrenn wagon prices being advertised on eBay, and bought a copy. This was compiled by Malcolm Inston and was the result of recording the end price of every Wrenn wagon sold on eBay over a ten year period. The document, once downloaded, ran to many pages and I spent days working out average prices for both mint boxed and good unboxed examples of every variation that I have listed.

I contacted Malcolm to ensure that he had no objection to my using his list for this purpose and he kindly offered to also supply me with both the locomotive and coach lists as well. This led to a further week's work and so now we have Wrenn prices based on recent sales. It is very rarely that such an intensive study of prices becomes available and, when it does, it is most welcome.

Without doubt, the 6th edition of the book received more praise than any previous edition. This was largely down to the use of colour throughout the book but also the quality of the publication when compared with the binding problems experienced with the previous edition.

For those unfamiliar with the book and buying it for the first time, the editing policy of Ramsay's British Model Trains Catalogue has, as its two priorities, comprehensiveness and fast access to information. It sets out to comprehensively list model railway equipment made for the British market but it cannot cover every make and brand as there are far too many of them. I have tried to cover the main proprietary brands of the last 100 years, that are collected, and I have been adding further brands with each edition of the guide. This time I have added Union Mills (N), Mathieson (N), Darstaed (modern tinplate 0 gauge) and Bachmann Brassworks (0, 1 & 3). Also, Ixion (N) is now listed on its own (previously it was included in the Dapol N gauge chapter). There are around 2000 new entries and several thousand updates included since the last edition.

If there is a brand of collected ready-to-run models (not kits) produced for the British market that you would like to see added, please get in touch with me at the address below. I shall need a comprehensive list of the models made by the company, with all the usual details such as catalogue numbers, running numbers, liveries and dates. I also need advice on market values of the things listed. Notice the word 'collected' as this is supposed to be a collector's guide.

I continue to be dependent on regular suppliers of information and, again, Mike Pincott is supreme amongst those helping. The book has also benefited from his recent reassessment of his own collection of model wagons, which has resulted in the release of a lot more information about, for example, the Lima 00 wagon range.

I am grateful to Mike and all the others whose contributions are vital to the comprehensiveness of this publication. This includes the manufacturers who are always helpful. Dennis Lovett, public relations manager for Bachmann Europe plc., has revised his circulars to the trade and press to include the specific information required for inclusion in this book. He also supplied the Brassworks listing and has searched through company files to provide missing running numbers.

Ramsay's British Model Trains Catalogue is not the result of one man, but a joint effort by collectors and the trade and the acknowledgements list on page 5 reads like a Who's Who of the collecting and model railway community.

My thanks once again to Martin Wrigley of Modelfair.com who has kindly prepared a Market Review for us. As usual, the book contains question marks where knowledge is missing, or where I am not sure of the information given. I would welcome your help in reducing the number of these. If you can help, please email me at Pat@mremag.com or write to me at:

Ramsay's British Model Trains Catalogue,
PO Box 199,
Scarborough
YO11 3GT

It remains for me to thank all those who have helped to make the guide the comprehensive reference book it is today and to thank Warners for the work involved in publishing it. Enjoy it!

Pat Hammond
Scarborough
December 2010

Acknowledgements

A work of this nature cannot be achieved by one man's efforts alone but depends upon many experts sharing their knowledge with us all. The original chapters have been checked and added to by a host of established experts whose very important contribution to this book is acknowledged here. Particular mention should be made of the contributions by:

Colin Albright - Graham Farish N gauge
Rolande Allen - prices
Richard Ashby - Bachmann and Dapol wagons
David Atkins - 00 locomotives
Peter Baker - Lima, Bachmann and Dapol
Peter Berry - Graham Farish 00
Derrick Barratt - Hornby 0 wagons
Mike Black - Graham Farish N
Bowman Circle Members - Bowman
Dave Bracken - Irish versin of models
Richard Bradford - Wrenn
Paul Brookes - MasterModels
Roy Chambers - Hornby 0, Bassett-Lowke, Leeds, Milbro, Exley, Bonds and Bowman
Tony Carder - N gauge
Jim Clark - Bachmann
Alan Cliff - various pre-1940
Tony Colbeck - Anbrico
Peter Corley - Graham Farish 00 and Anbrico
Simon Culverhouse - Minitrix and other N gauge
James Day - Playcraft
Martin Doubleday - Lone Star
Ian Dorrell - Lone Star
Terry Durrant formerly of Lacy Scott & Knight
Merl Evans - Bachmann, Mainline and Airfix
Jeremy Everett - Airfix, Bachmann, Dapol, Mainline
Alan Farrow - Exley 00
Bob Field - Hornby Dublo
Robert Forsythe - various
Clive Gehle - Lone Star
Peter Gomm - Airfix, Mainline etc.
Patrick Gower - modern Hornby
Chris & Julie Graebe - Hornby 0 gauge
Maurice Gunter - Wrenn
Peter Gurd - Bowman, Dublo and Graham Farish 00
Henk Guijt - various N gauge
Martin Hale - Peco Wonderful Wagons
John Hammond - Skytrex
Don Haslow - 00 gauge
Jack Holmes - prices
Graham Hubbard - Bachmann Europe plc.
John Ingram - Bassett-Lowke, Leeds, Milbro, Bonds
Malcolm Inston - Wrenn prices
John Jarvis - Dapol wagons
Darryl Judkins - Dapol & Bachmann listing
John Keane - 00 gauge rolling stock
Stephen Knight - Kitmaster and Playcraft
Simon Kohler - Hornby Hobbies Ltd
Eric Large - Tri-ang TT
Brian Lee of George Kidner (Auctioneers)
Oliver Leetham - Dapol wagons
Bob Leggett - Playcraft, Hornby Railways
Allen Levy - Ace Trains
Mike Little - Bassett-Lowke
Martin Long - unlisted Dapol wagons
Dennis Lovett - N gauge and Bachmann products
Quentin Lucas - Exley 0
Robert Newson - Lone Star
Hugo Marsh of Christie's South Kensington
Brian Martin - N Gauge
Len Mills - Corgi Bassett-Lowke
Keith Moore - Tri-ang Hornby chassis variations
David O'Brien - Trix
Nigel Overington - various 00 gauge
David Peacock - Leeds Model Company
Daniel Pearson - Bachmann diesels
Tony Penn - Peco Wonderful Wagons
Mike Pincott - 00 wagon variations
Barry Potter - prices and photographs
Tony Pritchard - Dapol
Ron Rayner - Hornby Dublo
Matthew Richter - Graham Farish N
Owen Roberts - Bowman and Peco
Paul Rouse - Tri-ang TT
Fleetwood Shaw - Bassett-Lowke
Des Sheppard - Bachmann & Dapol
George Smith of Dapol Ltd
Graham Smith-Thompson - Airfix, Mainline, Replica and Dapol
Nicholas Smith - Tri-ang TT
Nick Sparks - Hornby Dublo
Chris Thornburn - Trix rolling stock
Allan Trotter - BR standard coaches
Barry Turner - Bachmann coaches
John Turner - prices
Vectis Auctions - photographs and prices
Davina Vine - Dapol 00 wagons
Wallis & Wallis (Auctioneers)
Mike Wightman - Airfix
David Wild - Graham Farish N and various 00
Chris Wright - N wagon variations
Martin Wrigley - prices and the Market Review
Martin Wykes - H0 models

Many others have also contributed information used in this book and considerable use was also made of the following books:

Hornby Dublo Trains by Michael Foster published by New Cavendish Books (ISBN 0904568180).
The Hornby 0 Gauge System by Chris & Julie Graebe, published by New Cavendish Books (ISBN 0904568350).
The History of Trix H0/00 Model Railways in Britain by Tony Matthewman, published by New Cavendish Books (ISBN 0904568768).
Let's Stick Together by Stephen Knight, published by Irwell Press (ISBN 1871608902).
The Story of Wrenn by Maurice Gunter, published by Irwell Press (ISBN 1903266424).
The Bassett-Lowke Story by Roland Fuller, published by New Cavendish Books (ISBN 0904568342)
Brilliantly Old Fashioned parts 1 & 2 by Allen Levy published by New Cavendish Books (ISBN 1904562078)
Tri-ang Railways (2nd Edition) (ISBN 1872727298)
Tri-ang Hornby (ISBN 1872727581)
Hornby Railways (ISBN 1904562000)
The above three by Pat Hammond and published by New Cavendish Books
Bachmann Branchline Pocket Guide by Pat Hammond and published by Warners Group Publications (ISBN 1907292170)

Market Review

by Martin Wrigley

It would be impossible to take a look at the model railway industry without reference to the wider global financial situation and surprisingly, in so doing, reveal what a resilient industry it is. Admittedly, there have been casualties in Europe and there have been production difficulties in China which have affected a number of model railway companies. Even the situation in China has started to improve of late and here in Britain we seem to be weathering the storm well.

A hobby like railway modelling may be enjoyed on many different levels, not all of them requiring spending large sums of money. That, and the British love affair with railways, has kept the industry buoyant. The quality of ready-to-run models continues to improve with a level of realism and detail simply unimaginable just a few years ago. The popularity of DCC is growing, bringing new people into the hobby. N gauge has been revitalised by Bachmann and with Dapol also now bringing some stunning models to the market. In gauge 0, the same has happened with the release of the ACE Trains and Darstaed new models.

On the collecting side of the hobby, there is strong interest in quality Hornby Dublo, original Bassett-Lowke, Wrenn and Exley models, with the emphasis always on condition and original packaging. Away from these rarefied heights, the humble 00 gauge wagon is a strong area of collecting with prices to suit almost any budget, you can start a collection of wagons themed on private owner companies, location, wagon type, such as tankers, which are particularly popular with collectors. Some Bachmann examples have sold on Ebay recently for £50 and more.

My advice is always to buy the best you can afford. Top quality models always hold their prices better than cheaper models in poorer condition.

Whether you are a modeller or a collector, the hobby is there to be enjoyed and I wish you well with your model railway projects.

Martin Wrigley (Modelfair.com)

Bachmann Class 9F 92077 from an illustration by Robbie McGavin

How to Use This Catalogue

The catalogue has been designed as a reference work and, as such, a high priority has been the ease with which models can be traced. Having said that, it helps if you have some idea as to what the model is. The book is also principally a listing of locomotives and rolling stock and, with a few exceptions, there is little likelihood that you will be able to use it to identify a lineside accessory.

Most models today have the manufacturer's name on them but this was not so in the case of minor manufacturers in days gone by. Nor is it always the case with non-proprietary models, for it is quite possible that your model was not originally bought ready made but was either scratch built or made from a kit. Such models are not covered by the catalogue, although Kitmaster kits have been included because they are particularly collectable in their unmade state.

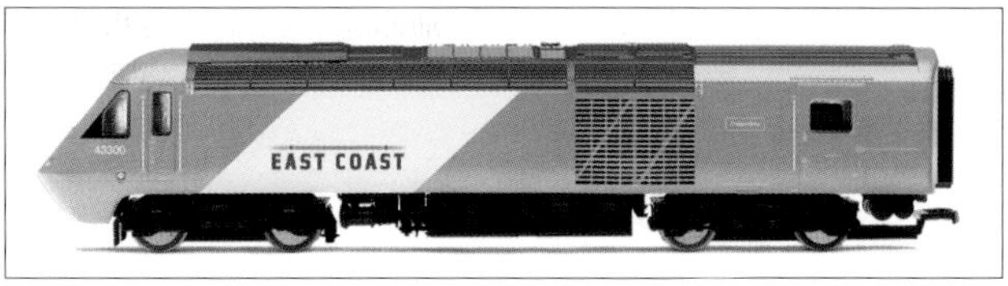

Hornby Class 43 East Coast HST power car (Hornby)

Determine the size

If you do not know the name of the manufacturer, a good starting point is to look at the size of the model. Railway models are governed in size by the gauge of the track they were made to run on. You can determine the gauge of the model by measuring the distance between the backs of the wheels and referring to the section on **Scales and Gauges**.

Having determined the gauge, turn to the **Contents** page where you will find listed all the makes of that gauge that have been included, together with the number of the page on which their listing starts. The contents list is not comprehensive and there is always a chance that the make of the model you are trying to identify has not yet been covered by the catalogue. You will notice that '00' and 'H0' scales are grouped together. This is because both 00 and H0 models use the same gauge track but 00 models are made to a scale of 4mm:1ft and H0 models to 3.5mm:1ft. The former are, therefore, slightly larger than the latter when you compare like subjects.

If, having found the right part of the catalogue, you are still not sure of the make, compare the model with pictures in that section.

Looking for the Number

Having found the section you want, it does help if you know the name of the prototype that has been modelled. This will allow you to find the correct table for that model and to search through it for the model variation that matches your own. If this is not the case, note the number on the side of the locomotive (or its tender) and check through the tables until you find it. This is particularly easy to do in the case of diesel and electric locomotives as these mostly have modern TOPS numbering and have been listed in numerical order.

With three of the largest product ranges (Hornby 0 gauge, Bassett-Lowke and Rovex/Tri-ang/Hornby) 'loco search' tables have been provided. All the known numbers carried by models in each of these groups have been listed in numerical order alongside the number of the table(s) in which they will be found. You will find that this is a very fast way of tracing your model.

Graham Farish N Gauge Class 04

Understanding the Tables

In almost all cases, all the models listed in each table are structurally the same and differ only in the livery they carry or in minor added detail. You will find that the table gives you the catalogue number (if known), the name and number the model carries, its basic colour and livery together with other distinguishing features, either the years it was available in shops or the year of release (*in italics*) and a range of prices you might expect to pay for one (see **Determining Value**).

Some of the information is in code form in order to save space. Where those codes are specific to that model the codes are shown under the title of the table but where the codes are common to many models of that make they may be listed in the introduction to the section. Codes commonly used throughout the catalogue will be found under **Codes and Explanations** in this front section of the catalogue.

The tables also contain information about limited and special editions (Ltd Edn and Sp Edn). Where known, this information includes the number made and, in the case of special editions, the shop or organisation that commissioned it (in brackets).

We hope that the above notes help you to find what you are looking for.

Dapol N gauge weathered 'Silver Bullet' cement tank wagon (anonymous)

Codes and Explanations

Abbreviations

While some sections in the catalogue have their own set of abbreviations, the following codes are common throughout the guide:

Ltd Edn (followed by the number made, if known) = Limited Edition. These are usually initiated by the manufacturer with the undertaking that the model in this form will not be repeated for a number of years. The term does not always mean that only a small number were produced. Indeed, some standard issues have been produced in smaller quantities than limited editions! The absence of a number indicates that we do not have that information.

Sp Edn (followed by the number made, if known) = Special Edition. These are models that have been commissioned by a shop or other interested party and therefore are usually available from only that source. They also have, in brackets, the name of the shop or organisation that commissioned the model. These are also limited editions and usually described as such on the accompanying certificate but to help users of this catalogue to distinguish between them we have adopted the alternative name - 'Special Edition'.

ACE Trains O Gauge Van (Ace Trains)

The following codes are used for decals carried by models:

BRa - 'BRITISH RAILWAYS'.
BRb - lion astride wheel.
BRc - lion holding wheel (in a roundel on multiple units and coaches and a few diesel hydraulics). This is also known as the 'ferret and dart board' logo!
BRd - lion in crown (briefly used on West Coast Main Line electric locomotives)
BRe - double arrow logo
BReLL - double arrow (large logo)

Other abbreviations used in the book include:
ECML = East Coast Main Line
Con = Construction
Dist = Distribution
I-C = Inter-City or InterCity
IC = INTERCITY
ICs = INTERCITY with swallow motif
LH = LoadHaul
LWB = Long wheelbase
Met = Metals
NSE = Network SouthEast
Rft = Railfreight
Reg Rlys = Regional Railways
RES = Rail Express Systems
S&T = Signal & Telegraph
Trans = Transrail
WCML = West Coast Main Line

The following are abbreviations used for railway companies:

Arriva TW = Arriva Trains Wales
Arriva TPE = Arriva Transpennine
BR = British Railways
Cen = Central Trains
CLR = Central London Railway
CR = Caledonian Railway
DRS = Direct Rail Services
DRS (compass) = DRS new livery incorporating a compass
EWS, EW&S = English Welsh & Scottish
FGBRf = First GB Railfreight
FGW = First Great Western (see also GWT)
FNW = First North Western
FScotRail, **FSr** = First ScotRail
GBRf = GB Railfreight
GCR = Great Central Railway
GER = Great Eastern Railway
GNER = Great Northern Eastern Railway
GNR = Great Northern Railway
GWR or **GW** = Great Western Railway
  shirt or **shirt button** = round logo
  () = a crest contained within the inscription
GWT = Great Western Trains (see also FGW)
HR = Highland Railway
LBSCR, LB&SCR = London Brighton & South Coast Railway
LM City = LondonMidland City
LMR = Longmoor Military Railway
LMS = London Midland & Scottish Railway
LNER = London & North Eastern Railway
LNWR, L&NWR = London & North Western Railway
LSWR, L&SWR = London & South Western Railway
LT = London Transport
LYR = Lancashire & Yorkshire Railway

Replica Railways 7-plank wagon

M&GN = Midland & Great Northern Railway
Met = Metropolitan Railway

MML = Midland Mainline
MR = Midland Railway
MSLR = Mid Suffolk Light Railway
NBR = North British Railway
NE = London North Eastern Railway
NER = North Eastern Railway
NLR = North London Railway
NR = Northern Rail
S&D or **S&DJR** = Somerset & Dorset Joint Railway
SECR = South East & Chatham Railway
SER = South Eastern Railway
SR = Southern Railway
SWT = South West Trains
Thames TEx = Thames Trains Express
TPE = TransPennine Express
VT = Virgin Trains
WCR = West Coast Railways

CN = Canadian National, Canadien National
CP = Canadian Pacific
VR = Victorian Railways (Australia)
TA = TransAustralia
TR = Tri-ang Railways
TC = Transcontinental

Tonnage
Older wagons have their weight shown in Imperial tons (T) while more recent wagons have their weight given in Metric tonnes (t).

Colours and Liveries
While some experts on railway liveries may cringe at my use of the term 'red' or 'maroon' (shortened to 'mrn' or 'marn') instead of 'crimson lake' to describe the colour of LMS stock, this has been done so that the description is understood by the non-expert as well those knowledgeable in railway liveries. Likewise, early BR carmine and cream is listed as 'red+cream'. Distinguishing between red and maroon can be difficult especially when the model has not actually been seen.

'Teak' is the description used for LNER coaching stock which was unpainted light wood with a varnish finish. On some models the wood grain has been reproduced by a chemical process in the plastic, but in other cases a yellow-brown paint has been used instead. 'Dark brown and cream' (or just 'brown+cream') is used to describe the GWR coach livery otherwise known as 'chocolate and cream'. A similar colour scheme was used on Pullman cars.

Carette for Gamages O gauge GNR 4-4-0 (Vectis)

GWR locomotives were usually finished in 'Brunswick' green which was darkish and described here simply as 'green' as the same shade became standard on British Railways (BR) locomotives used purely for passenger work. In contrast, LNER locomotives were generally 'Apple' or 'Doncaster' green which was a lot lighter and is sometimes described here as 'light green' (or lt.green). Southern Railway locomotives were usually green but the shade changed over the years and two shades commonly reproduced today on passenger stock are the early 'Olive' green and the later 'Malachite' which is a light slightly bluish green.

The use of the abbreviations '**l.**' or '**lt.**' as a prefix to the colour means that it is a 'light' shade while 'dark' may be referred to by '**d.**' or '**dk.**' prefixes and bright as '**bt.**' and pale as '**pl.**'

Weathering
More recently 'weathered' finishes have been popular and these are identified in the listing with a capital **'W'**, generally after the colour.

Running Numbers
These are the numbers carried on the side (and often the front) of locomotives and also by coaches and wagons. They are useful as a means of identifying a particular model and in a few cases 'loco search' tables have been provided to help you trace a model by its running number. The absence of a number may infer that the model did not carry one but in most cases it is because we did not know what it was. We would therefore welcome this information where it has been left out but please make sure that the number is original and has not been added after leaving the factory.

Bassett-Lowke O gauge 1931 series LNER brake 3rd (Vectis)

Italics
Dates are shown in italics in the tables, in order to make it easier to pick these out.

Motors
All locomotive models are electric powered unless otherwise stated. **c/w** = clockwork

Prices
NA = Not Applicable or Not Available
NPG = No Price Given
(see - **Determining Value - The Impossible Task**).

Detail
The absence of detail in the description of a model is not evidence that the detail is not carried by the model. Furthermore, a feature may be mentioned on one model but not on another that also carries it. Often information is provided only where it is felt that it may be helpful in distinguishing between like models.

Listing Order
The listing of models is not always done in the same way as, in each case, an order of listing has been chosen that best suits the subject and makes it easiest for you to find what you are looking for. The method of listing is normally explained at the start of each section.

Generally speaking, however, there has been a move towards a common system which lists locomotives in the order of tank engines, tender engines, diesels, electric locomotives, DMUs and EMUs. Coaches are listed with pre-nationalised stock first (GWR, LMS, LNER and SR) and then Mk1s, Mk2s, Mk3s and Mk4s. The wagons usually start with flat wagons and follow with timber open wagons, steel open wagons, hoppers, tankers, vans, brake vans and bogie wagons.

Dates

Different systems for dating models have been adopted depending the level of information available. Wherever possible, the span of dates when a model was available have been given but, in some cases, models were produced in batches with hardly any carryover from year to year. This is particularly common today as manufacturers can sell more models by constantly changing their livery or the number they carry. In these cases a single date applies i.e. the year the batch was released.

In the case of earlier models, catalogues were the only source of information as no other records have survived.

Code 3 Models

A Code 3 model is one that has been finished outside the factory by a secondary 'manufacturer'. These are often retailers who buy a quantity of a certain model and re-release it in a modified form. To count as a Code 3 it has to have been produced in the modified form in quantity and to a common specification. This means that one off modifications do not count. Batches of 50 upwards are more usual. These often have a numbered certificate to authenticate them and to indicate how many of them were modified. These have their own niche market and are no longer listed in this guide.

Bachmann TTA tank wagon

'Not Made'

This means that the model did not reach full production. However, it can be confusing when examples of the model turn up. This is usually because, prior to production starting, a small batch of samples was made for individuals to comment on. This is commonly the case where the models are manufactured in the Far East. These samples often find their way on to the market where they can command a high price if the model did not go into full production. This is where it pays to know your subject so that you can recognise the genuine article when you see it.

Pre-Production Models

This is a similar situation except that the models rarely look like production models. They were hand made and hand painted and were produced prior to a decision being taken on whether the subject should be put into production.

With completely new models, the sample may have been built by a model maker using plasticard or may be assembled from a proprietary model kit. It may even have been scratch built using some parts from an existing model in the range. When it was proposed to release an existing model in a new livery, a production model will have been taken off the production line and resprayed and detailed in the new livery as a sample for approval.

Pre-production samples (commonly referred to in the factory as 'prototypes' or 'visuals') were often finished on one side only and the writing and logos are often skilfully hand painted. Where two exist, one would have gone to the studio preparing the catalogue and the other retained in the factory for draughtsmen and engineers to refer to.

Once approved for production a 'proving' model was made. This was structurally identical to what the final production model would be and its component parts would be used in the preparation of the drawings for the toolmaker.

Pre-production models (prototypes, samples and proving models) sometimes come on the market but it is usually a problem proving that they are what someone claims them to be. While many collectors would like to buy them, uncertainty about authenticity can be a disincentive to do so.

This is really an area of collecting which requires a lot of experience in handling examples in order to recognise the genuine from the fake. Where the provenance is good, they can fetch a high price and four figure sums have been known to change hands - but this is not the norm. Where there is no provenance, they may be purchased quite cheaply but there is a risk you could burn your fingers. None of these are listed in this guide.

Heljan OO Class 17 Clayton diesel

Determining Value - The Impossible Task!

For Guidance Only

The first thing to remember about quoted prices is that they are for guidance only. Both at auction and on swapmeet stalls, prices vary enormously and who is to say what is the exact value of a given model? What is worth £200 to one collector may be worth only £150 (or even £100) to another buyer or seller.

Swapmeet Prices

On the whole, stall holders are very knowledgeable about what they sell, but each tends to be a specialist. They sometimes find themselves with models that are outside their specialised area. If advice is not at hand they have to guess at the price to put on it. This can lead to bargains for knowledgeable buyers but can also cause frustration when the object is severely overpriced.

Remember, the price seen on a model at a swapmeet is not necessarily the price at which it sells. Most stall holders are prepared to haggle. So what is the true value of the model; the price at which he bought it in, the price he put on it or the price at which you finally buy it?

Putting an accurate value to individual models is impossible. All we can do is show comparisons and that is all this price guide sets out to do.

Auction Prices

There is, usually, a fair gap between what you pay for a model and what you would expect to get for it when selling it again. We have set out prices at what we think the models will fetch at auction, prior to the addition of the buyer's premium. Even at auction, prices vary erratically depending on who is bidding. As a result of this, we have had to deal with conflicting valuations from different auctions and, in each case, have tried to arrive at a compromise.

Auction prices can be used only for more valuable items as less valuable models are put together in groups to be sold as mixed lots. It is impossible to estimate how much of the hammer price applied to each item in the lot as some would have been more valuable than others.

eBay

Since this price guide was started, on-line auctions have grown in importance, and amongst these, eBay is by far the most used by model railway collectors. Here prices can be more erratic than anywhere else. This is a world-wide auction room and overseas bidders buying into a market they are unfamiliar with will sometimes take a model well over its perceived value. At other times an otherwise valuable model struggles to get anywhere near its 'normal' value. We have largely avoided using eBay prices for this reason.

Our Valuations

Our suggested values are presented in two columns to the right of each table. For reasonably recent releases, where mint boxed items may still be around, the right hand column gives a 'mint boxed' price and the left hand column an 'excellent unboxed' value. If the item was not released on its own, authentically boxed examples are unlikely to exist and so the right hand column carries an 'NA' for 'not available'. Likewise, where a price is given for a boxed set of models, or a train pack, there is an 'NA' in the left hand column.

With many of the older, obsolete, model ranges mint boxed examples are practically an impossibility and so the two columns are used to show the price range for examples in very nice condition. There are cases where there is doubt whether a model actually exists or, alternatively, no example of one having been sold can be found. In these cases the price columns are marked with an 'NPG' for 'no price given'. The guide contains about 25,000 listings and so it is not feasible to trace known prices on each one. A lot of it has to be guesswork.

Effect of Quality

Obviously, value falls as quality falls but not always by the same percentage. It depends how rare the model is and even what make it is. The lack of a box can reduce the value of a model by 40% or more. Generally the rarer the model, the more valuable the box. For poorer quality models the lack of a box has less impact on price.

The gulf between the price first class models are fetching and that paid for those of a lower standard is ever widening and in some ranges the prices of poorer quality models is going down. Models that have had detailing added after leaving the factory (except in the case of Code 3 models) are likely to be of lower value to collectors, even though the detailing has improved the appearance of the model. The same applies to repainted models, although there are very early 0 gauge models for which a professional repaint is acceptable as few if any good unrestored examples exist in reasonable condition.

Fluctuating Prices

Prices can fluctuate from year to year and from decade to decade. With the sale of G&R Wrenn in the early '90s, the price of Wrenn models quickly escalated but, more recently, fell to more modest levels. The publication of the Maurice Gunter book on Wrenn, once again pushed up the prices. The fairly recent end of Lima production saw the almost immediate increase in the demand for Lima models. Thus Lima prices have risen since then.

At auction, the sale of a famous comprehensive collection can bring out top bidders with the result that average prices may rise on the day with rare and common items both selling at figures well above the norm.

High and Low Values

As already indicated, the price gap between rare and common (or poor quality) items is ever widening. This means that rare and top quality models are a much better investment than common or poor quality ones.

Train Packs

Nowadays, some manufacturers sell their models in train packs. These consist of a locomotive and some coaches or wagons but no track, etc. As already indicated, the right hand column price is for the complete train pack. Multiple units (DEMUs, EMUs etc.) are sold as train packs and no price is given for individual parts of these as it is assumed that unboxed the units will be sold together. The price in the left hand column is therefore for the complete 2-car or 3-car unit without its packaging.

The History of Model Train Manufacture

In the Beginning

The first commercially built model railways were imported into Britain from Germany in 1902 and were made for Bassett-Lowke by the German companies, Bing, Carette and Marklin.

Up until the First World War, the most popular gauge was known as gauge 1 but after the war gauge 0 really came into its own.

The war was to have a dramatic effect on the model railway industry as post-war anti-German feeling made German imports unpopular and Bassett-Lowke Ltd were forced to manufacture more of their products themselves. It also created an opportunity for other British manufacturers to enter the fray.

The most successful of these was Meccano Ltd, a company that had been founded in 1908 to manufacture the Meccano engineering construction system. They introduced their toy trains in 1920 and these took the name of the Company's founder - Frank Hornby - and were sold as 'Hornby Trains'. Hornby, from the start, chose to manufacture in 0 gauge and early models constructed with Meccano nuts and bolts soon gave way to tinplate tab and slot construction. Some were direct copies of Bing models.

Other notable manufacturers of the inter-war period were the Leeds Model Company, Mills Brothers, Exley and Bond's - all of which are covered by this book. These principally manufactured their own ranges of 0 gauge models but also produced some gauge 1 equipment and Bond's and Exley branched into 00 scale in later years. All also provided bespoke services for those who wanted specific models built specially for them.

First 00 Scale System

As early as 1922, Bassett-Lowke introduced to Britain a tabletop railway made in Germany by Bing and considered to be 00 gauge - i.e.: half the size of the popular 0 gauge. Within a very short time this was available as an electric system. The Bing company was to fall victim to the rise of Nazi power in Germany and trading became very difficult. Out of these difficulties came a more commercial small scale system known as Trix and this was introduced to Britain in 1936, again with the assistance of Bassett-Lowke.

Within a very short time it was being made by a satellite company of Bassett-Lowke at Northampton. Meccano Ltd could see the way the wind was blowing and quickly responded with their own 00 system which they called Hornby Dublo. This was launched in 1938 and, unlike the Trix Twin system, was initially available in clockwork form as well as electric.

Post World War 2

The Second World War brought to an end all commercial model railway production but post-war Britain saw major changes in both demand and response. It was soon clear that 0 gauge was no longer the leading scale and over the years production of it gradually declined.

The new principal gauge in Britain was 00 and it was to remain so to the present day.

Hornby Dublo returned after the war but while it was the market leader for a while, Meccano Ltd did not recognise the importance of expanding it fast to meet the growing demands from the public. The gap in demand was quickly filled by a new system called Tri-ang Railways which was made by Rovex Scale Models Ltd, a subsidiary of Lines Bros.

The New Contender

The Tri-ang system had several advantages that would play in its favour during the struggle for market domination that lay ahead. It was a two rail system making the track look more realistic, it used plastic mouldings that could show much more detail, it was a lot cheaper while still being reliable and the range expanded quickly to offer the public plenty of choice when building a layout. Within a few years it had become the market leader.

The early post-war years saw many other companies trying to break into the model railway market. Principal amongst these was Graham Farish who marketed an 00 system with some very attractive models but which, initially, were not too reliable mechanically.

Trix in the meantime failed to respond quickly enough to the demand for realism and slowly faded. The business changed hands a few times and new investment resulted in some nice models being produced. One of its problems became obvious in the late '50s and that was its adoption of the Continental H0 scale instead of British 00. This meant that when some excellent models started to arrive they looked out of scale when mixed with those of other makes.

Meanwhile Tri-ang's onslaught was injuring Hornby Dublo and although Meccano Ltd made major improvements to their range, including a 2-rail system and use of plastic mouldings, its response came too late to save the company which was being bombarded on other fronts at the same time.

Big Take-overs

In 1964 Meccano Ltd was taken over by Lines Bros. who renamed their own model railway system 'Tri-ang Hornby' and sold the Hornby Dublo tools to another of their subsidiaries - G&R Wrenn. For the next decade Tri-ang Hornby virtually had the market to itself. The only competition came from a Trix system, which limped along, and Playcraft which was made by Jouef in France and marketed in Britain by Mettoy Ltd. 1973 saw a bid by Lima to break into the British market but they made the mistake of using the smaller H0 scale. Although by 1976 Lima had changed to 00 scale, their day had not yet dawned.

In 1971, the Lines Bros. Group fell apart. Profitable Rovex, the member of the group making Tri-ang Hornby, was sold to Dunbee Combex Marx (DCM) and Tri-ang Hornby was renamed Hornby Railways. Wrenn became an independent company again and continued to manufacture Wrenn Railways for the next 20 years using the former Hornby Dublo tools. The British part of Meccano Ltd (based in Liverpool), who no longer made trains, was sold to Airfix while Meccano France (based in the former Tri-ang factory in Calais) was acquired by General Mills who also owned Palitoy.

New Competition

Both Airfix and Palitoy separately judged that there was a place in the market for better quality model railways and decided to fill it. The Airfix and Mainline (Palitoy) systems were both launched in the mid '70s but it had taken them two years from announcing their intentions to supplying shops and this gave Rovex the breathing space they required to respond with their Hornby Railways system. By 1980 it was a four horse race with Hornby closely chased by Mainline and Airfix and Lima coming up on the outside. Meanwhile, trailing some way behind, was British Trix and Playcraft was now out of view.

This seems an appropriate point at which to stop and look at what else was happening.

Smaller Scales

Tri-ang had seen a need to experiment with yet smaller scales and in 1957 had launched their TT system. This never really caught on although it was well developed as a system and was supported by manufacturers of accessories. It died in the mid '60s.

The even smaller scale of 000 or N gauge was tried by Lone Star as a push-along system in 1957 with an electric system following in 1960. Lines Bros. were invited to buy the system but turned it down and it died out in the 1970s. Lima had produced a more sophisticated N gauge system which they had offered to Lines Bros. in the 1960s and they agreed to market it through their subsidiary, G&R Wrenn. This was sold as Wrenn Micromodels for many years.

Following the purchase of Rovex in 1971 by Dunbee Combex Marx they entered into an agreement with the German Trix company to import their Minitrix system (formerly made at Wrexham by Trix Trains) and sell it as Hornby Minitrix. New models were produced to Rovex's requirements, leaving Rovex free to concentrate on developing Hornby Railways. The arrangement was quite successful and lasted several years.

The only British company to really grasp the N gauge nettle was Graham Farish. Remember them? We last saw them in the 1950s with a nice but not too successful 00 system. This had limped along through the '60s with much shrinkage until they turned their attention to developing an N gauge system at the end of the '60s. In a virtual vacuum, but with a steadily growing demand for good N gauge models at reasonable prices, the Grafar N gauge system has expanded and now offers considerable choice to the N gauge modeller. Many small companies have developed to provide accessories, resprays etc. on the back of this system.

Before returning to 00 gauge it is worth mentioning that 0 gauge virtually petered out in the mid '60s as Hornby, Bassett-Lowke and Leeds production ground to a halt. Despite this, in the mid 1960s, Tri-ang produced their toy-like Big Big trains, the tools for which were later sent to Russia, and Lima produced some acceptable models of British outline.

The Tools Merry-go-round

In 1980 DCM were in the receiver's hands and the future of the Hornby Railway system was once again in question. The same year Airfix went bust and its railway system was taken over by Palitoy and its models absorbed into the Mainline system. By 1981, Hornby Hobbies (formerly Rovex) were an independent company again for the first time in 30 years. Ten glorious years of expansion followed. During the 1980s Lima firmly took hold of the modern image locomotive market bringing out models of many of the better known subjects. Then, in 1990, it all changed again!

In 1984, General Mills, who owned Palitoy, had given up toy production and the assets of their Mainline system, including the Airfix tools, were sold to another up and coming company called Dapol Ltd. They were by then producing their own new, high quality, models of locomotives. Dapol later also purchased the tools and intellectual assets of G&R Wrenn when George Wrenn retired in the early 1990s. However, Palitoy had not owned the tools for the manufacture of their Mainline models as these belonged to Kader of China who had made them.

Enter the Dragon

Kader were interested in expanding their model railway manufacturing and in 1988 took control of the American model company, Bachmann. In 1989 they formed Bachmann Industries Europe Ltd to develop and market models in Europe through bases in Britain and Germany. The Bachmann Branchline range was launched in Britain in 1990, using the former Mainline tools. Building on these, Kader were soon manufacturing models to a quality never before seen in Britain. This was the Blue Riband range.

Once again Hornby found their commanding place in the market threatened and had to respond. To allow them to expand their range fast, and quickly improve the quality of their models, they needed to buy ready-to-use new tooling. As we have seen, Dapol had produced some high quality models of their own but also had the former Airfix tools they had bought from Palitoy along with a few Mainline tools not owned by Kader. Following a major fire which destroyed much of their stock, Dapol needed to raise money quickly and put up for sale some of their tools. In 1996 Hornby bought them and this gave them four years breathing space in which to develop their own new models. In the summer of 2000, the first of these arrived in the shops. with the promise that all new Hornby models would be to the new standard.

Graham Farish was taken over by Bachmann in 2000 and later, Dapol, having extracted the wagon tooling they required to boost their own range, sold the remainder of G&R Wrenn. Efforts at Dapol were now directed towards producing their own quality N gauge system which was launched in 2003.

By 2002 it had become clear that Lima were in difficulties and as they struggled to stay in business the Danish company, Heljan, made a bid for part of the British 00 diesel market. Hornby and Bachmann joined in to pick off Lima's diesel subjects and produce superior versions of them.

The Lima Group went into liquidation and was bought by Hornby in 2004 along with the Lima, Rivarossi, Jouef and Arnold names. They also purchased the leading Spanish company, Electrotren. Lima's British models started to reappear in the Hornby range in 2006

Today, the major 00 market in Britain is dominated by Hornby and Bachmann with Heljan and Dapol retaining a toe-hold as well as relative newcomer ViTrains. The N gauge market is dominated by Graham Farish and Dapol but with Peco showing renewed interest. The 0 gauge market is dominated by Ace Trains, with recent additional competitors in Skytrex and Darstead making themselves felt. Hornby and Bachmann have everything manufactured in China, including their various continental brands. Other model manufacturers also make much of their products in the Far East or in Eastern Europe.

Hornby have launched an 00 scale live steam system and are selling this worldwide. They see their future as an international group and are marketing Electrotren, Lima, Rivarossi, Jouef and Arnold under their own names.

In 2007 Hornby bought Airfix and Humbrol and in 2008 added Corgi Classics to their collection of brands. With Corgi came Bassett-Lowke which brings under one roof the names of the two great pre-war brands - Hornby and Bassett-Lowke. This also opens up some interesting possibilities in 0 gauge.

The future could be very interesting. While shops, clubs and magazines have been commissioning their own versions of models for sometime, a more recent development has been the commisioning of brand new subjects. In some cases the agreement has been a guaranteed purchase of stock in exchange for two years exclusive use of the tooling; in other cases the commissioning organisation pay for and own the tooling. This arrangement appears to be growing in popularity and is increasing the range of models available.

***

This has been a simplified history of the principal manufacturers of ready-to-run models and toy trains and does not reflect the enormous contribution made to the industry by the scores of smaller firms that specialise in kits, materials and accessories. Without them it would be a far less interesting hobby and we hope to cover the products of more of them in future editions.

The History of Collecting

The collecting of toy trains did not really get under way in Britain until the late 1960s when operators of Hornby 0 gauge were looking for additional stock. One way in which the exchange of models was effected was through the organisation of meetings by groups of enthusiasts and this lead to the invention of a new word in the English language - the Swapmeet.

Out of this growth in interest, the Hornby Railway Collectors Association was formed in 1969 and following a period of sometimes heated argument through the pages of the Association's magazine, membership was extended to Hornby Dublo collectors, some of whom had formed the Dublo Circle. The HRCA has steadily grown over the years and is by far the largest club of its kind in the UK. It has also spawned a number of satellite organisations abroad.

The mid 1970s saw a growing interest in collecting of other makes of toy trains and the formation, in 1975, of two more organisations. The first of these was the Tri-ang Hornby Collectors Club which survived for many years, chronicling the diversities of the range, before disbanding. The other new organisation was the Trix Twin Railway Collectors Association which has flourished and remains a well supported organisation producing its own spares, special models for members and an excellent magazine.

It was not until 1979 that collectors in Britain had an organisation that catered for 'any make, any gauge, any age. This is the by-line of the Train Collectors Society which has stuck to its principles and not tried to set close restrictive limits to its member's interests. The result is a very friendly society that does not take itself, or its hobby, too seriously. In recent years the TCS has grown in size and many collectors have seen the value of dual membership (membership of a specialist club and membership of the TCS for the wider interest).

Other specialised clubs followed with the Kitmaster Collectors Club in 1980, the Bassett-Lowke Society in 1991, the Graham Farish Circle in 1994, the Lima Collectors Society in 1995, the Wrenn Railways Collectors Club in 1998 and the Tri-ang Society, with its fairly broad interest in the products of the Lines Bros. Group, in 1999. More recently we have seen an ACE Trains club formed.

Recent years have seen a growing recognition, by the manufacturers, of the expanding market for new models made specially for collectors. To this end, they produce collectors editions of their models. Some, like Bachmann, Hornby, Dapol and Wrenn have their own collectors clubs and Hornby has established collectors centres that exclusively receive some of their limited editions.

Outside the scope of this book are those British clubs that cater for collectors of foreign makes. These include the Fleischmann Model Railway Club and the Lionel Collectors Club UK.

Hornby Standard 4MT 75005 from an illustration by Robbie McGavin

Collectors' Clubs

Anyone interested in collecting railway models should consider joining one of the growing number of specialist collecting clubs. The following are relevant to the systems covered by this guide:

Train Collectors Society

This is a society with a broad interest in toy and model train collecting and has the motto 'Any Make. Any Gauge, Any Age'. Founded in 1978, the Society publishes a 52 page full colour quarterly magazine called *Train Collector* and has a spares and information service, digital magazine index, very active website and listing of known catalogues and price lists. It holds three major gatherings each year but members also exhibit at other events.
Contact : Tony Stanford, tel: 01442 266658
Website : www.traincollectors.co.uk

ACE Trains Class A4 (Wallis & Wallis)

ACE Trains Owners Club

The club was formed in 2007 for collectors of ACE Trains products. It publishes a newsletter four times a year and is independent of the company whose products it promotes.
Contact : webmaster@acetrainsownersclub.org.uk
Website : www.ACETrainsownersclub.org.uk

Bachmann Class G2A

Bachmann Collectors' Club

For a number of years the company sponsored an enthusiasts club called Bachmann Times which operated at arms-length. In 2000 the club was reformed in-house under the name: Bachmann Collectors' Club. Members receive a free wagon each year and a quarterly magazine updating them on development progress and with feature articles related to the models and real railways.
Contact : Bachmann Collectors Club, PO Box 7820, 13 Moat Way, Barwell, Leicestershire LE9 8EY.
Website : www.bachmann.co.uk

Bassett-Lowke Society

The Bassett-Lowke Society, founded in 1992, caters for those who collect and operate Bassett-Lowke models. It publishes a quarterly magazine called *Lowko News* and organises events to which members may take their stock to run. The Society is also sympathetic towards other pre-war 0 gauge brands such as Bonds, Leeds and Milbro.
Contact : Tracy Haydon-White, tel: 0121 5502775
E-mail : tracyhw@blueyonder.co.uk
Website : www.bassettlowkesociety.org.uk

Bassett-Lowke Royal Scot (Vectis)

Dapol Nthusiasts Club

This is a club for Dapol's N gauge customers. On joining you receive a number of promotional freebies and the opportunity of receiving a special club wagon each year. There is a newsletter and access to special releases.
Contact : Through website
Website : www.dapol.co.uk (details in N gauge shop section)

Dapol Class 9F (Dapol)

Hornby Collectors Club

This is a club supported by Hornby Hobbies plc for subscribing customers. The club was formed in 1997 and publishes a full colour bimonthly magazine called *The Collector*. Through the club, members have the opportunity to purchase special collectors editions of models produced by Hornby but also receive a free specially produced loco each year.
Contact : Sarah Woodhouse, Hornby Collectors Club, PO Box 25, Melton Mowbray, Leicestershire. Tel: 0871 248 6000
Website : www.hornby.com

Hornby 'No.2 Special' (Wallis & Wallis)

Hornby Railway Collectors' Association

The HRCA was founded in 1969 and caters for collectors of both Hornby 0 gauge and Hornby-Dublo. It is the largest of the clubs listed here and has overseas associate organisations.

The Association publishes 11 issues of its magazine, called *The Hornby Railway Collector*, each year and has a very well developed spares service.
Contact : John Harwood, tel: 01935-474830
Website : www.hrca.net

Kitmaster 'Deltic' Kits (Dave McCarthy)

Kitmaster Collectors Club
Enthusiasts of the Kitmaster kit range are well catered for by the Kitmaster Collectors Club which was founded in 1980. The club publishes a magazine called *Signal* twice a year and includes in the subjects covered the railway kits by Airfix and Dapol. The magazine is available on the club's website
Contact : Steve Knight
Email : steve@kitmaster.freeserve.co.uk
Website : www.rosebud-kitmaster.co.uk

Leeds Model Company Sentinel Railcar (Vectis)

Leeds Stedman Trust
The Leeds Steadman Trust is an organisation run by David Peacock to help collectors and operators of LMC models to keep them running by supplying spare parts. It is not a club but you can be placed on a mailing list for the annual price list of parts.
Contact : David Peacock, email : dpeacock@btconnect.com
Website : www.leedsstedmantrust.org

Tri-ang Hornby 'Coronation'

Tri-ang Society
The Tri-ang Society was formed in 1999 and caters for all Tri-ang products including Tri-ang Railways, Tri-ang Hornby, Tri-ang Railways TT, Big-Big Trains and Minic Motorway. The Society has a regular magazine called *The Tri-ang Telegraph* and arranges displays at various model shows and vintage events. It also organises two of its own events each year.
Contact : Miles Rowland, tel : 0161 976 5059
Website : www.tri-angsociety.co.uk

Trix Twin Class EM1

Trix Twin Railway Collectors' Association
The Trix Twin Railway Collectors Association (TTRCA) was founded in 1975 and caters for enthusiasts of Trix Twin, Trix Express, Trix Trains and the models of Liliput UK. It publishes a quarterly magazine called *Trix Twin Gazette* and offers a spares service to its members.
Contact : Brian Arnold, te l: 0116 271 5943
Website : www.ttrca.co.uk

Wrenn Collectors Club
The club was founded in 2007 and caters for the collectors of all products of G&R Wrenn Ltd. It publishes two half-colour newsletters each year and offers its members a discount on certain company items and the right to buy the annual wagon release.
Contact : Maurice Gunter, tel : 01707 35459
Website : www.gandr-wrenn.co.uk

Wrenn Railways Collectors Club
The club was founded in 1998 and caters for the collectors of all products of G&R Wrenn Ltd. It publishes a quarterly magazine called *The Wrenn Tracker* and organises gatherings for its members, contributing displays at various vintage events.
Contact : Barry Fentiman, tel : 01628 488455
Website : www.wrennrailways.co.uk

Wrenn BB Class (Wallis & Wallis)

Magazines
As indicated above, many of the collecting organisations publish magazines for their members and there is no better way of keeping in touch with developments and the history of specific makes than through these publications. Since the demise of *Model Railway Enthusiast/Model Railway Collector* there has been no national magazine specifically catering for the toy train and railway model collector but the Train Collectors Society's *Train Collector* tries to fill this gap. Besides this, *British Railway Modelling, Hornby Magazine* and *Model Rail* all carry occasional articles on model railway history while *Collectors Gazette* has a regular monthly column and feature articles on the subject.

Internet
Finally, there are Yahoo chat groups on the Internet with specialisms which marry with those of several of the clubs listed above. These are excellent sources of information, as too are a lot of private websites run by enthusiasts.

In addition, the free *Model Railway Express* magazine at www.mremag.com provides thrice weekly updates of news for collectors and modellers. It also has reviews of newly released models looked at from the collector's point of view. There are book reviews, a classified ads section and a number of articles about specific manufacturers.

TRAIN COLLECTOR

Britain's only comprehensive magazine for the collector of British and overseas brands of model trains.

If you collect trains of any make, gauge or age you should be reading **Train Collector**. It is available by subscription only. Articles from just the last four issues include:-

'Ferris Electric Parcels Van'
'Alresford 2010'
'Tri-ang TT Utility Van'
'Playmobil Railways'
'The Great Trains of Georges Carette'
'Merco'
'Limited Brand Coffee Can Train'
'Mineral Wagons'
'Hafna Steamlined Loco'
'Children's Railway Book Illustrations'
'Early Canadian Tri-ang Sets'
'Shops I Remember'
'Catalogue Covers of Desire'
'Games & Toys Magazine in 1950'
'Bassett-Lowke Steam'
'Milbro Wagons'
'ACEM'
'Bowman Steam'
'The Lure of 0 Gauge Steam'
'Jubb Wagons'
'Ferris B Class Diesels'
'TTR Clairbourg Station'
'TCS Biggleswade 2010'
'The Kemlows Book'
'Japanese 0 Gauge'
'The STC Layout'
'South African Lima H0'
'Hornby 0 Gauge Pullman Cars'
'25 Years of Buying Memories'
'A Lionel Station'
'JH & MSC'
'The Madder Valley Railway'
'Rivarossi & AHM H0 GG1'
'Weimar New Discoveries'
'The Shunting Train from Arnold'
'The 1959 Hornby Dublo Book of Trains'
'New Collectables'
'Brighton Toy Museum Running Day'
'2010 British Model Railway Wish List Poll'
'TCS Leicester 2009'
'Auction Watch' & 'Auction Diary'
'150th TCS News'
'Collecting 0 Gauge Tinplate in London'
'The Winchester Layout'
Years celebrated - 1970, 1959, 1944 & 1910
'Sandy 2010'
'The Zeuke TT Story'
'Collecting Diecast Trains'

Train Collector is published four times a year - December, March, June and September. It costs £20 per annum which also gives you full membership of the Train Collectors Society, access to a substantial spares & repairs service, an index and back issues service, access to TCS events at members' rates, the opportunity to participate in the TCS Internet chat group, discounted museum access and keeps you up to date with train collectors events and auctions held during the year. To subscribe or seek further information, phone: 01442 266658 or go to the TCS website at: www.traincollectors.co.uk. where you can subscribe online.

Further Reading

When toy train collecting was in its infancy, there was a dearth of information about manufacturers and model ranges with the result that any book, however simple, that included text or pictures about toy trains, was pounced on by knowledge hungry collectors.

Two such books were ***'Older Locomotives (1900-42)'*** [ISBN 172132088] by Peter Gomm and ***'Recent Locomotives (1947-70)'*** [ISBN 172132096] by Peter Randall. Both were published in 1970 by Thomas Nelson and Sons Ltd in their Troy Model Club Series for collectors and such was the demand for them that even libraries could not guarantee supplying you with a copy on loan.

While books on British manufacturers remained scarce, those on the international scene started to appear in the '70s. 1972 saw the release in Britain of the English language edition of Gustav Reder's ***'Clockwork, Steam and Electric'***. This is a classic study of early toy train making and is a must for anyone with an international interest in the subject. A better illustrated book with more of a British slant is ***'A Century of Model Trains'*** [ISBN 0517184370] by Allen Levy and published in 1974 by Crescent Books. Another international book which is good for its mouth watering coloured photographs is Udo Becher's ***'Early Tin Plate Model Railways'*** [ISBN 0852426690] which was published by Argus Books in 1980. A much more general history of toy manufacturing is the very detailed ***'The Toy Collector'*** [ISBN 0801578469] by Louis H Hertz and published in 1976 by Hawthorn Books Inc. of New York.

Books specifically for the British collector took a step forward with F.R.Gorham's compilation of extracts from Hornby catalogues published between 1927 and 1932. Titled ***'Hornby Book of Trains'*** [ISBN 0090288820X] it was released by the Oxford Publishing Co. in 1973. This idea of using extracts from old publications was adopted by The Cranbourne Press Ltd. for their booklets. These were made up from Meccano Magazine and Tri-ang catalogue pages and included ***'Main Line Ending'*** by Peter Randall (Hornby 0 Gauge), ***'Hornby Dublo Trains 1938-1939'*** by Ronald Truin and '***A Short History of Tri-ang Railways'*** by Tony Stanford.

Little more was available for several years and then, suddenly, there was an explosion of publishing in the late '70s starting in 1977 with the excellent ***'Collectors Guide to Model Railways'*** [ISBN 0852425295] by James Joyce. This remains, today, one of the best broad-brush studies of the British model railway industry, despite the fact that it needs bringing up to date. It was published by Argus books as, too, was ***'Toyshop Steam'*** [ISBN 085242583X] by Basil Harley, which was released the following year.

That same year saw the release of the first volume of a series of books that was to set the benchmark for specialist books on individual subjects. I refer, of course, to The Hornby Companion Series by New Cavendish. Volume 1 ***'The Products of Binns Road - A General Survey'*** [ISBN 0904568067] by Peter Randall provided us with the first study of Meccano Ltd and, for the first time, included full colour reproductions of three catalogues. The series went on to cover individual toy ranges from this important company as well as their paperwork and publications. There were also compendia published for some of the volumes which provided check lists of products made.

Volume 2 of The Hornby Companion Series was devoted to Meccano super models but Volume 3 was the much awaited ***'Hornby Dublo Trains 1938-1964'*** [ISBN 0904568180] by Michael Foster. I distinctly remember the excitement with which I waited for my volume to arrive and then shutting myself away for a week to study it.

Volume 4 was Mike & Sue Richardson's famous treatise on Dinky Toys and this was followed by what I think is the best written book in the whole series. It is of course Volume 5 ***'The Hornby O Gauge System'*** [ISBN 0904568350] by Chris & Julie Graebe. A better researched and illustrated book would be hard to find. The series went to seven volumes plus five compendia and several of the books have run to second editions.

A magazine popular at the time among collectors was the ***'History of Model & Miniature Railways'*** which built up into two bound volumes. The close-up photography for this was to spawn a number of look-alike books one of which was ***'The World of Model Trains'*** [ISBN 086124009X] edited by Patrick Whitehouse and Allen Levy and published by Bison Books in 1978.

A remarkable book of this period was the ***'International Model Railways Guide'*** [ISBN 3920877160] which was a German publication, written in three languages (German, French and English). This was, in effect, a large catalogue of model railway manufacturers around the world illustrating in colour many (but not all) of the models available at the time (1978-79). I979 also saw the publication of ***'Mechanical Toys'*** [ISBN 0600363317] by Charles Bartholomew and published by Hamlyn, but this had only limited information about toy trains.

Of special interest to Tri-ang Hornby collectors was ***'The Hornby Book of Trains 25 Year Edition'*** [ISBN 095065860X] which was published in 1979. It was edited by S.W.Stevens-Stratten and chapters on everything from real trains to the manufacturing process at Margate were largely written by staff at the factory - much of it by Richard Lines. The book was followed in 1983 by ***'The Art of Hornby'*** [ISBN 071823037X], also written by Richard Lines, which looked at catalogue and leaflet designs by Meccano Ltd for their Hornby Series and Hornby Dublo as well as for Tri-ang Hornby and Hornby Railways.

An important reference series started in 1980 was ***'Cade's Locomotive Guide'*** [ISBN 0905377079] which was written by Dennis Lovett and Leslie Wood. This ran to three volumes [ISBN 0905377117] [ISBN 090537715X] and was re-released in a combined volume in 1988 [ISBN 090537797]. The aim of the series was to provide background information about the real locomotives that are the subjects of models. After each account there were details and photographs of relevant models.

By now articles on model railway collecting were beginning to appear in the model railway press although these remained few and far between. One exception was a series by Peter Gomm called **'Tinplate Topics'** which was a regular feature in *Model Railway News* for several years and looked principally at Hornby 0 gauge. This was followed in 1984 by a series in *Model Railway Constructor* called **'Collector's Corner'** which became a regular feature and ran for several years.

Another attempt at a 'world catalogue' had come in 1983, this time in English, with the publication of ***'The World Guide***

to Model Trains' [ISBN 0722188242] which was compiled by Peter McHoy with the help of Chris Ellis and was published by Sphere Books Ltd.

A new major work appeared in 1984 when Roland Fuller's ***'The Bassett-Lowke Story'*** [ISBN 0904568342] reached the shops. This excellent book, published by New Cavendish Books, contained a considerable number of archive photographs and is a valuable reference work. For quality coloured photographs, the series by Salamanda Books Ltd cannot be beaten. The volume called ***'The Collector's All-Colour Guide to Toy Trains'*** [ISBN 1855010259] (1985) was compiled by Ron McCrindell and contains excellent pictures of many rare items; most of which are in superb condition having been drawn from several famous collections. Following this, in 1986, we had one of the best in depth studies of the subject in ***'Toy Trains - A History'*** by Pierce Carlson [ISBN 0575.3890X] - again with excellent illustrations but virtually restricted to pre WW2 developments.

Now for three New Cavendish books from the early 1990s. The first of these looked at the whole field of British toy manufacturers and, although railway content was small when compared with the rest, the detail provided is so good that it is a 'must' for any toy collector's library. This is ***'British Tin Toys'*** [ISBN 0904568865] by Marguerite Fawdry which was published in 1990 and it covers more than just tin toys!

The next is my own book ***'Tri-ang Railways'*** [ISBN 0904568571] which New Cavendish Books published in 1993. It is the first in a trilogy about the Rovex company better known today as Hornby plc. This first volume deals with the years from 1950 to 1965 when the product was known as Tri-ang Railways.

This was followed the next year by Tony Matthewman's beautiful volume ***'The History of Trix H0/00 Model Railways in Britain'*** [ISBN 0904568768]. For me the book comes a close second to Chris & Julie Graebe's Hornby 0 Gauge book for the excellence of its research and presentation. This, like 'Tri-ang Railways' (and its sequels), was produced in landscape format to match the Hornby Companion Series.

A small book, also released in 1994, was the Shire Series No.255 ***'Toy Trains'*** [ISBN 0747800871] by David Salisbury. And another book published that year was ***'Model Trains - The Collector's Guide'*** [ISBN 1854227807] by Chris Ellis. Published by Magna Books, it contains an easy to follow history and some good photographs.

1996 brought with it Jeff Carpenter's privately produced volume ***'Bings Table Railway'*** [ISBN 1900897008], published by Diva Publishing, which provides not only a full account of the small Bing system but also the histories of many other miniature trains such as those by Karl Bub, Distler and Jep Mignon.

November 1993 had seen the launch of *Model Railway Enthusiast* which was a model railway magazine with some articles for collectors. In February 1998 content for collectors was raised to 50% of the magazine and in November 1999 to 100% when the magazine was renamed *Model Railway Collector.*

1998 saw the release of Donald Troost's first Lone Star guide which, by 2005, was in its 9th Edition and ran to three thick volumes. Independently published, it is the most detailed guide on the subject, to be found.

1998 saw the release of my second book ***'Tri-ang Hornby'*** [ISBN 1-872727-58-1], again by New Cavendish Books, and also the first edition of ***'Ramsay's British Model Trains Catalogue'*** [ISBN 0952835231], published by Swapmeet Publications. In 1999, two useful books on kits were published. The first of these was Steven Knight's excellent study of Kitmaster kits in ***'Let's Stick Together'*** [ISBN 1871608902], published by Irwell Press and the second was Arthur Ward's ***'Airfix Plastic Kits'*** [ISBN 0004723279] published by Harper Collins. It was also in 1999 that ***'Wenman Joseph Bassett-Lowke'*** [ISBN 1900622017] was published by Rail Romances who at the same time released a video recording based on films taken by W.J.Bassett-Lowke, including footage inside the factory. The book had been written by his niece Janet Bassett-Lowke.

In 2000, the first of a series of planned volumes called ***'A History of Locomotive Kits'*** [ISBN 0953772004] by Robert Forsythe was published by Amlor Publishing. This covers kits by K's, Nu-Cast, Wills and South Eastern Finecast. The second edition of Ramsay's Catalogue also appeared that year under new editorship.

Another 2nd edition appeared in 2001 and this was 'Tri-ang Railways' which had had a further 32 pages of information added.

2002 was a bumper year for new books. Harper Collins published Ian Harrison's ***'Hornby - The Official Illustrated History'*** [ISBN 000715173X] and ***'Frank Hornby - News & Pictures'*** was written and published by Jim Gamble [ISBN 095420610X]. The 3rd edition of Ramsay's Catalogue was released - now with comprehensive listing of locos and rolling stock covering some 25 brands produced for sale in Britain over the last 80 years.

The final two books for 2002 were principally aimed at the classic tinplate collector. Firstly there was the excellent ***'Christie's Toy Railways'*** by Hugo Marsh which covers history and development from the earliest times. This was published by Pavilion Books [ISBN 1862055254]. The second is the magnificent English edition of Paul Klein Schiphorst's ***'The Golden Years of Tin Toy Trains'*** published by New Cavendish Books [ISBN 187272759X]. This contains possibly the finest collection of images of early tinplate trains ever to be assembled.

We jump now to 2004 and the release of the long awaited book on G & R Wrenn. Called ***'The Story of Wrenn - From Binns Road to Basildon'*** it was written by Maurice Gunter and published by Irwell Press [ISBN 1903266424]. That year will also saw the publication of my third volume in the Story of Rovex and titled ***'Hornby Railways'***. This was published by New Cavendish Books and covers the years 1972-1996 [ISBN 1904562000]. Also by this publisher and released in 2005 was Allen Levy's book ***'Brilliantly Old Fashioned - The Story of ACE Gauge 0 Trains'*** which provides much information about how ACE came into being and how the products have developed. This was followed in 2010 by **Part 2** which was a compilation of all printed material and publish comment on the ACE Trains range.

2009 saw the release of Paul Brookes' book ***'The Illustrated Kemlows Story'*** (ISBN 0956187901). This includes coloured illustrations of the entire range of Mastermodels and was published by Paul Brookes himself.

Finally, 2010 saw the publication of the first of what is hoped to become a series of comprehensive pocket guides with a list of variations and suggested values. The first in this new series covers an important subject, not previously written about in detail, except in this Ramsay's Guide. The book is the ***'Bachmann Branchline Pocket Guide'*** (ISBN 1907292170) by Pat Hammond.

Thus, from a dearth of books in 1970, today we have quite a library to choose from and there is every indication that the choice will continue to grow as the cost of publishing 'short run' books falls.

ACE Trains

Due to the number of new models added and proposed, it has been necessary to renumber these tables.

HISTORY

ACE Trains originated from an arrangement to produce a limited run of electric Hornby replica 4-4-4 tank locomotives in Southern livery - the colour scheme most in demand with collectors.The parties to this arrangement were Ron Budd (the importer of Darstead Marklin style coaches) and Andries Grabowsky who acquired the Darstead business in the early 1990s.

This arrangement did not come to fruition and Allen Levy agreed to take on and expand the 4-4-4 project which was designated E/1. A company named Alchem Trains Ltd was formed in 1995 which commenced trading under the name ACE Trains.

4-4-2T in LB&SCR livery [L2] (Ace Trains)

The production and assembly of the 4-4-4T was initially concentrated in Taiwan and later at the Grabowsky family factory in Madras, India. Later still it moved to Bangkok. The 4-4-2 derivative of the E/1 followed. The locomotives were designed to run on all types of 3-rail tinplate standard track including that by Hornby, Marklin, Bing, JEP and MDF and also have an interchangeable rear coupling.

The C/1 coach range, covering more railway systems than any former manufacturer, came on the market in 1999. The tin printing for this range was carried out by Cyril Luff in Wales who produced some of the last Hornby 0 gauge and Hornby Dublo tin printed sheets. A five-car Merseyside Express set became the last lithographed toy train product of the twentieth century. The Company introduced the first of a range of EMU units early in 2000.

A Class A4, with its cast alloy body, broke new ground in modern 0 gauge development and was followed by an A3 and a model of the GWR 'Castle' locomotive class.

Some impressive East Coast coach sets, incorporating articulated coaches, arrived in 2004 and 2005 and the first wagons, both petrol and milk tankers, fitted into the same time scale.

In 2005, ACE Trains adopted a practice, common between the wars, of initiating a generic 0-6-0 tender locomotive and changing its more prominent features such as cab, funnel, dome and tender to turn it into different classes of locomotive built by different railway companies.

There was also co-operation with Corgi (Bassett-Lowke), in respect of the Royal Scot boxed set which was a train pack with a Bassett-Lowke loco and ACE coaches.

ACE Trains identified a gap in the market and have been successfully filling it. They have established a market not only in the UK but around the world and have agents in a number of countries.

A major change came when Len Mills, who had been the engineer behind the new Bassett-Lowke locomotives, left Corgi and started to work on the ACE Trains range. His influence can be seen in the beautiful GWR 'Castle' Class and LMS Stanier 2-6-4 tank locomotives, as well as the 'Schools' and Bullied Pacific.

On May 11th, 2004, Alchem Trains Ltd had changed its name to The ACE Electric Train Co. Ltd and in 2008 Andries Grabowsky parted company with ACE Trains. Following the split, in 2009, production moved from Bangkok to China.

Further Reading

Allen Levy's book *Brilliantly Old Fashioned - The Story of ACE Gauge 0 Trains,* published in 2005, provides much information about how ACE came into being and how the products have developed. A second part, published in 2010, provides a collection of all printed material and press references concerning ACE Trains, as well as reproductions of correspondence.

LOCOMOTIVES

Motors - About 10 locos were supplied with 12V motors. 24v was standardised on all ACE Trains locomotives run on 6 - 20V and draw 0.7amp the distinction became academic.

Couplings - All couplings (on locos and coaches) are replaceable except the front hook on the LMS and Metropolitan EMUs and the front buffer couplings on the E/1 and E/2 locos. The Southern EMU units have replaceable couplings throughout but the coaches are without buffers as per the originals.

Cat No.	Company, Number, Colour, Dates	£	£

<u>*Tank Locomotives*</u>

L1. Freelance 4-4-4 Tank Engine (1996)

Made in Taiwan. This E/1 model was based on the No.2 Tank Engine in the pre-war Hornby Series, which went out of production in 1929. The original models were available only with a clockwork mechanism but the E/1 locomotives by ACE Trains have 20v electric mechanisms with remote control in AC/DC. IS = in DC only with isolating switch.

ECR/1	**4-4-4** CR blue gloss or matt IS - *96*	230	250
EMR/1	**108** Metropolitan maroon gloss or matt - *96*	200	220
EGW/1	**7202** GWR green gloss or matt - *96*	180	200
ELM/1	**4-4-4** LMS maroon gloss or matt IS - *97*	180	200
EMB/1	**4-4-4** LMS black gloss or matt - *97*	180	200
ELG/1	**4-4-4** LNER green gloss or matt - *96*	180	200
ELB/1	**4-4-4** LNER black matt - *97*	180	200
ESB/1	**E492** SR black gloss or matt * IS - *96*	250	300
ESG/1	**B604** SR green gloss or matt * IS - *96*	250	300
EET/1	**2-2-2** ETAT black matt - *96*	250	325
EPO/1	**2-2-2** PO grey matt - *96*	250	325
EPL/1	PLM red matt ** - *96*	290	370
END/1	Nord brown matt - *96*	250	294
END/2	Nord green matt - *96*	250	325
EES/1	EST black matt - *96*	250	325
EES/2	EST brown matt - *96*	250	325
ENZ/1	NZR black matt - *96*	300	400

* 44 of the E/1 series in Southern livery were given a very large range of factory produced names at the request of customers (1996/97). These were gold transfers and were said to be in homage to the SR 'River' Class tanks. ** Some of the PLM version carried factory produced names on gold transfer nameplates.

4-4-4T in Caledonian Railway livery [L1] (Ace Trains)

L2. Freelance 4-4-2 Tank Engine (1997)

The E/2 series of locomotives were made in Taiwan, DC only and were fitted with a neutral switch allowing them to stand stationary on live track. They seem to have been based on a LNWR Whale 4-4-2T. 2 cab styles were available for this short lived series. A German style 4-4-2T [E/2G] (after Marklin) with two domes was planned, but not put into production.

E/2LB	**22** LB&SCR brown gloss - *97*	300	425
E/2LN	**40** L&NWR black gloss - *97*	300	400
E/2LM	**6822** LMS maroon gloss - *97*	200	270
E/2S	**2001** Southern green gloss - *97*	320	380
E/2BR	**32085** BR black gloss - *97*	250	320

E/2NZR	green NZR gloss Sp Edn (Railmaster Exports NZ) - *98*	300	400

L3. LNER Class N2 0-6-2T (2011)

Just announced and few details received at the time of going to press. The centre drivers will be flangeless on most models to facilitate tight curves and there will be an option of a smoke unit for an extra £15 . The model is being made by ETS in The Czech Republic.

E/11	? LNER - *11*	350	395
E/11	? BRa black - *11*	350	395
E/11	? BRc black - *11*	350	395

Stanier 2-6-4T in early BR livery [L4] (Ace Trains)

L4. LMS 2-6-4T Stanier 3-Cylinder Tank Engine (2009)

Made in China, these are of all metal construction and have all wheels flanged, sprung oval buffers, sprung bogies, jewelled lamps and removable code discs and reversable destination boards supplied, 2-rail/3-rail switch, firebox glow, smoke generator and 24V DC. Both 2- and 3-cylinder types have been modelled. cn = customised number

E/8	**2546** CR lined gloss blue 2-cylinder - *09*	400	495
E/8	**2524** LMS lined gloss black 3-cylinder - *09*	400	495
E/8	**2529** LMS lined satin black 2-cylinder - *09*	400	495
E/8	**2526** LMS lined satin black 3-cylinder - *09*	400	495
E/8	**2546** LMS lined satin black 2-cylinder - *09*	400	495
E/8	**2465** LMS lined gloss maroon 2-cylinder - *09*	400	495
E/8	LMS lined satin black 3-cylinder cn - *09*	400	495
E/8	LMS lined satin black 2-cylinder cn - *09*	400	495
E/8	**42576** BRa lined gloss black 2-cylinder - *09*	400	495
E/8	**42510** BRa lined gloss black 3-cylinder - *09*	400	495
E/8	**42516** BR? lined gloss black 3-cylinder - *09*	400	495
E/8	**42608** BR? lined gloss black 3-cylinder - *09*	400	495
E/8	**42534** BR? lined satin black 3-cylinder - *09*	400	495
E/8	**42465** BR? lined satin black 2-cylinder - *09*	400	495
E/8	BR? lined satin black 2-cylinder cn - *09*	400	495
E/8	BR? lined satin black 3-cylinder cn - *09*	400	495
E/8	**47546** BRc lined gloss green Ltd Edn - *09*	400	525

Tender Locomotives

L5. Freelance 4-4-0 'Celebration' Class (2006)

Based on the 1920's Hornby 2711 and with Bassett-Lowke leanings. 24V DC electric, working front lights. Isolating switch. 3-rail only and updated version of the E1 mechanism. These were made in Thailand using tooling from previous models. All are numbered 2006 with a GWR style number plate.

E/3	**2006** CR blue (also released in sets with 2 C/1 CR coaches) - *06*	180	200
E/3	**2006** LNWR black (also released in sets with 2 C/1 LNWR coaches) - *06*	180	200

4-4-0 'Celebration' Class [L5] (Ace Trains)

E/3	**2006 *Prince William*** LNWR black (also released in sets with 2 C/1 LNWR coaches) - *06*	180	200
E/3	**2006** NER green - *not made*	NA	NA
E/3	**2006** GCR black - *06*	155	170
E/3	**2006 *John H Kitchen*** GCR black - *07*	180	200
E/3	**2006 *Butler Henderson*** GCR black - *07*	180	200
E/3	**2006** LB&SCR brown - *06*	180	200
E/3	**2006** SECR green - *not made*	NA	NA
E/3	**2006** GWR green - *07*	170	190
E/3	**2006** GWR green with brass dome - *07*	170	190
E/3	**2006** LMS maroon - *06*	160	180
E/3	**2006** LMS black - *06*	160	180
E/3	**2006** LNER green - *06*	160	180
E/3	**2006** LNER black - *06*	160	180
E/3	**2006** SR green - *06*	160	180
E/3	**2006** SR black - *06*	160	180
E/3	**2006** BR blue - *06*	160	180
E/3	**2006 *Prince William*** BRb blue - *06*	160	180
E/3	**2006** BR black - *07*	160	180
E/3	**2006 *Prince William*** BRb black (also released in sets with 2 C/1 BR coaches) - *07*	160	180
E/3	**62360** BR black - *?*	160	180
E/3	**2006 *Jay Beale*** BRb black - *07*	200	249
E/3	**2006** EST black - *not made*	NA	NA
E/3	**2006** ETAT black - *not made*	NA	NA
E/3	**2006** Nord brown - *not made*	NA	NA
E/3	**2006** NSWGR green - *08*	200	249
E/3	**2006** NZR black - *08*	200	249
E/3	**2006** PLM green - *not made*	NA	NA
E/3	**2006** PO grey - *not made*	NA	NA
E/3	**2005** VR maroon - *08*	200	249

'Schools' Class Winchester [L6] (Ace Trains)

L6. SR 'Schools' Class 4-4-0 (2010)

Made in China, the model is fitted with a new 24V DC 4-coupled mechanism and is switchable between 2-rail and 3-rail operation.

E/10	**E900 *Eton*** SR olive green - *10*	NPG	495
E/10	**E900 *Eton*** SR olive green, no smoke deflectors - *10*	NPG	495
E/10	**926 *Repton*** SR olive green - *10*	NPG	495
E/10	**919 *Harrow*** SR sage green - *10*	NPG	495
E/10	**908 *Westminster*** SR wartime black - *10*	NPG	495
E/10	**935 *Sevenoaks*** SR Malachite green - *10*	NPG	495
E/10	**30925 *Cheltenham*** BR gloss black - *10*	NPG	495
E/10	**30928 *Stowe*** BR green - *not made*	NA	NA
E/10	**30903 *Charterhouse*** BR gloss green - *10*	NPG	495
E/10	**1870 *St Fettes*** CR blue ** - *10*	NPG	495
E/10	**1933 *Gordonstoun*** CR blue ** - *10*	NPG	495
E/10	**1885 *Roedean*** navy blue *, female crew - *10*	NPG	495
E/10	**1922 *St Trinneans*** pink, female crew - *10*	NPG	495

*Acknowledging the school's wartime link with HMS Vernon. ** Echoing Marklin's CR version of 1938.

L7a. Cambrian Railways 0-6-0 (2010)

Based on the LMS 4F (below) with modifications, the models are made in China. Fitted with a mechanism similar to that used in the E/8. They have a coal load in the tender, sprung buffers, detailed backhead and interchangeable couplings.

E/5	**849** Great Western gloss green - *10*	NPG	325
E/5	**864** GWR? satin black - *10*	NPG	325
E/5	**873** GWR? gloss black - *10*	NPG	325

L7b. LMS Fowler Class 4F 0-6-0 (2010)

Made in China, the model is fitted with a mechanism similar to that used in the E/8 2-6-4T. They have a coal load in the tender, sprung buffers, detailed backhead and interchangeable couplings.

E/5	**59** S&DJR lined dark blue - *10*	NPG	325
E/5	**4328** LMS maroon - *10*	NPG	325
E/5	**4422** LMS satin black - *10*	NPG	325
E/5	**4454** LMS gloss black - *10*	NPG	325
E/5	**44497** BRa satin black - *10*	NPG	325
E/5	**44252** BRb satin black - *10*	NPG	325

E/5	**44027** BRc gloss black - *10*	NPG	325

L7c. CR McIntosh Class 812 0-6-0 (2011)

Made in China and based on the LMS 4F (above) with modifications. They are fitted with a mechanism similar to that used in the E/8. They have a coal load in the tender, sprung buffers, detailed backhead and interchangeable couplings.

E/5	**?** LMS ? - *11*	NPG	325

L7d. NBR Holmes LNER Class J36 0-6-0 (2011)

Also made in China, this is based on the LMS (above) with modifications. The models are fitted with a mechanism similar to that used in the E/8. They have a coal load in the tender, sprung buffers, detailed backhead and interchangeable couplings.

E/5	**?** LNER ? - *11*	NPG	325

L8a. SR Q Class 0-6-0 (2006)

This was the first of the 0-6-0 range to be released and was made in Thailand. It has an ACE all axle geared chassis incorporating a helical gear drive and have 24 volt DC motors with isolation switch and all axles driven. A 24volt AC version was available to order. The models are of diecast and sheet metal construction with three working front lights which have a sequence changer for route and load type. They have a coal load in the tender, sprung buffers, detailed backhead and interchangeable couplings.

Q Class 0-6-0 SR [L8a] (Vectis)

E/5	**541** SR black with Maunsell chimney - *06*	250	345
E/5	**533** SR black with sunshine lettering - *07*	250	345
E/5	**540** SR green with Maunsell chimney - *06*	250	345
E/5	**30548** BRa black - *08*	250	345
E/5	**30548** BRb black - *06*	250	345
E/5	**30548** SAR black Ltd Edn 20 (Australia) - *08*	250	345
E/5	**30548** NZR black Ltd Edn (N Zealand) - *08*	250	345

L8b. GER/LNER J19 Class 0-6-0

This was advertised at the time of the SR Q Class 0-6-0 (above) and would have used the same basic parts. However, the models did not make it into production despite the fact that ACE Trains had paid for the tooling. This was a key issue in the split that occurred in the company in 2008. The model was later released as a Vintage Trains product by Darstaed. Other 0-6-0 locomotives had been planned with common parts but, around 2007, the decision was taken not to proceed with generic locomotives but to concentrate on more accurate models.

E/5	**8245** LNER green (number on tender) - *not made*	NA	NA
E/5	**8141** LNER black - *not made*	NA	NA
E/5	**64670** BR black - *not made*	NA	NA

L9. GWR 'Castle' Class 4-6-0 (2006)

The first series of 'Castles' were made in Thailand, while later ones, including those produced for Modelfair, were made in China. These are marked with 'C'. Both 2-rail and 3-rail versions are planned. 24V DC (AC to order). Diecast body, twin motors driving all 3 axles through gearbox, working front lights, firebox glow, detailed backhead, new wheel patterns and single and double chimney (dc) versions. In order to simplify construction of the E/7 range, from mid March 2008, the single motor version fitted with the ACE/Mills motor was available at a lower price of £695. There is some reduction in the weight of the ACE/Mills version and a slight reduction in torque characteristics under heavy loads at low speed. dc= double chimney.

Great Western - Green

E/7	**100** ***100 A1 Lloyds*** - *09?*	600	695
E/7	**111** ***Viscount Churchill*** - *09?*	600	695
E/7	**4016** ***Knight of the Golden Fleece*** - *09?*	600	695
E/7	**4073** ***Caerphilly Castle*** - *08*	600	695
E/7	**4079** ***Pendennis Castle*** - *08*	600	695
E/7	**4081** ***Warwick Castle*** - *08*	600	695
E/7	**4082** ***Windsor Castle*** - *08*	600	695
E/7	**4095** ***Harlech Castle*** - *09?*	600	695
E/7	**4096** ***Highclere Castle*** - *09?*	600	695
E7/1	**5000** ***Launceston Castle*** C Sp Edn 5 (Modelfair.com) - *08*	670	695
E7/1	**5001** ***Llandovery Castle*** C Sp Edn 5 (Modelfair.com) - *08*	670	695
E/7	**5002** ***Ludlow Castle*** - *08*	600	695
E/7	**5009** ***Shrewsbury Castle*** - *08*	600	695
E/7	**5011** ***Tintagel Castle*** - *08*	600	695
E7/1	**5013** ***Abergavenny Castle*** C Sp Edn 5 (Modelfair.com) - *08*	670	695
E/7	**5018** ***St.Mawes Castle*** C - *08*	600	695
E/7	**5069** ***Isambard Kingdom Brunel*** C - *08*	600	695
E7/1	**5070** ***Sir Daniel Gooch*** C Sp Edn 5 (Modelfair.com) - *08*	670	695
E7/1	**5072** ***Hurricane*** C Sp Edn 5 (Modelfair.com) - *08*	670	695
E/7	**7007** ***Great Western*** - *09?*	600	695
E/7	**7013** ***Bristol Castle*** - *made?*	NPG	NPG
E/7	**7023** ***Penrice Castle*** - *09?*	600	695
E/7	**7029** ***Clun Castle*** C - *08*	600	695

'Castle' Class [L9] (Wallis & Wallis)

E7/1	**7029** ***Great Western*** C Sp Edn 5 (Modelfair.com) - *08*	670	695

BRc Green

E/7	**4073** ***Caerphilly Castle*** - *08*	600	695
E/7	**4079** ***Pendennis Castle*** - *08*	600	695
E/7	**4081** ***Warwick Castle*** - *08*	600	695
E/7	**4082** ***Windsor Castle*** - *08*	600	695
E7/1	**5000** ***Launceston Castle*** C Sp Edn 5 (Modelfair.com) - *08*	670	695
E7/1	**5001** ***Llandovery Castle*** C Sp Edn 5 (Modelfair.com) - *08*	670	695
E/7	**5002** ***Ludlow Castle*** - *08*	600	695
E/7	**5009** ***Shrewsbury Castle*** - *90?*	600	695
E/7	**5009** ***Leonard Castle*** Sp Edn - *90?*	600	695
E/7	**5011** ***Tintagel Castle*** - *08*	600	695
E7/1	**5013** ***Abergavenny Castle*** C Sp Edn 5 (Modelfair.com) - *08*	670	695
E/7	**5018** ***St.Mawes Castle*** BRb C - *08*	600	695
E/7	**5029** ***Nunney Castle*** - *08*	600	695
E/7	**5043** ***Earl of Mount Edgecumbe*** BRc dc Sp Edn (MAAT) – *08?*	670	750
E/7	**5069** ***Isambard Kingdom Brunel*** BRb C - *08*	600	695
E/7	**5069** ***Isambard Kingdom Brunel*** BRc dc C - *08*	600	695
E7/1	**5070** ***Sir Daniel Gooch*** C Sp Edn 5 (Modelfair.com) - *08*	670	695
E7/1	**5072** ***Hurricane*** C Sp Edn 5 (Modelfair.com) - *08*	670	695
E/7	**7013** ***Bristol Castle*** BRb C - *08*	600	695
E/7	**7013** ***Bristol Castle*** BRc dc C - *08*	600	695
E/7	**7029** ***Clun Castle*** BRb C - *08*	600	695
E/7	**7029** ***Clun Castle*** BRc dc C - *08*	600	695
E7/1	**7029** ***Great Western*** Sp Edn 5 (Modelfair.com) - *08*	670	695
E7/1	**7037** ***Swindon*** - *08*	600	695

BR Experimental 'Pea' Green *

E7/2	**4091** ***Dudley Castle*** BRb C Sp Edn 50 (Modelfair) - *08*	630	725
E7/2	**5010** ***Restormel Castle*** BRb C Sp Edn 50 (Modelfair) - *08*	630	725
E/7	**5010** ***Avondale Castle*** BRa C Sp Edn (Modelfair) - *08*	630	725
E/7	**5023** ***Brecon Castle*** BRa C Sp Edn (Modelfair) - *08*	600	695
E7/2	**7011** ***Banbury Castle*** BRa C Sp Edn 50 (Modelfair) - *08*	630	725

GWR (button) Wartime Plain Green **

E7/3	**5071** ***Spitfire*** C Sp Edn 24 (Modelfair) - *08*	640	725

E7/3	**5079 *Lysander*** C Sp Edn 24 (Modelfair) - *08*	640	725
E7/3	**5080 *Defiant*** C Sp Edn 24 (Modelfair) - *08*	640	725

* In commemoration of the 60th Anniversary of Nationalisation of the railways. ** With plated over cab windows.

L10. LMS 'Duchess' 4-6-2 (2011)

A range of liveries is planned.

?	? ? ? - *11*	NPG	NPG

L11. LMS Streamlined 'Coronation' 4-6-2 (2011)

A range of liveries is planned.

?	? ? ? - *11*	NPG	NPG

L12. LNER A1/A3 Class 4-6-2 (2006)

Based on the A4 chassis with disc wheeled tender, the A3 models were made in Thailand. It is 3-rail with twin 12/24V DC motors (24AC to special order), each driving opposed spindles, power is transferred to all 3 axles through a series of gears. Generally speaking, those locos in Doncaster green have a round dome and those in other liveries have a banjo dome. sd = smoke deflectors. dc = double chimney. In 2006 a batch of one-off models was produced for Modelfair which they advertised for sale in September 2006. These unique models are marked M.

LNER Doncaster Green

E/6	**2500 *Windsor Lad*** - *06*	450	500
E/6	**2502 *Hyperion*** banjo dome M - *06*	700	750
E/6	**2506 *Salmon Trout*** banjo dome M - *06*	700	750
E/6	**2508 *Brown Jack*** banjo dome M - *06*	700	750
E/6	**2545 *Diamond Jubilee*** - *06*	450	500
E/6	**2547 *Doncaster*** - *06*	450	500
E/6	**2550 *Blink Bonny*** - *not made*	NA	NA

LNER Class A1 Flying Scotsman [L12] (Ace Trains)

E/6	**2563 *William Whitelaw*** - *06*	450	500
E/6	**2598 *Blenheim*** - *06*	450	500
E/6	**2743 *Felstead*** - *06*	450	500
E/6	**2744 *Grand Parade*** - *06*	450	500
E/6	**2745 *Captain Cuttle*** - *06*	450	500
E/6	**2748 *Colorado*** banjo dome M - *06*	700	750
E/6	**2749 *Flamingo*** - *06*	450	500
E/6	**2750 *Papyrus*** - *06*	450	500
E/6	**4427 *Flying Scotsman*** - *06*	450	500
E/6	**4427 *Flying Scotsman*** banjo dome - *06*	450	500
E/6	**4427 *Flying Scotsman*** sd as preserved - *06*	450	500
E/6	**4427 *Flying Scotsman*** with 2 tenders (for USA) - *06*	850	900
E/6	**4475 *Flying Fox*** - *06*	450	500

NE Wartime Black

E/6	**2500 *Windsor Lad*** - *06*	450	500
E/6	**2545 *Diamond Jubilee*** - *06*	450	500
E/6	**2550 *Blink Bonny*** - *06*	450	500
E/6	**2744 *Grand Parade*** - *06*	450	500
E/6	**2750 *Papyrus*** - *06*	450	500
E/6	**2752 *Spion Kop*** - *06*	450	500

Post-War LNER Green

E/6	**65 *Knight of the Thistle*** - *06*	450	500
E/6	**60037 *Hyperion*** banjo dome - *06*	450	500
E/6	**60041 *Salmon Trout*** banjo dome - *06*	450	500
E/6	**60043 *Brown Jack*** banjo dome - *06*	450	500
E/6	**60094 *Colorado*** banjo dome - *06*	450	500

BRb Express Blue

E/6	**5 4 57 *Anglo Thai*** (assumed a one-off) - *06?*	700	750
E/6	**60035 *Windsor Lad*** - *06*	450	500
E/6	**60037 *Hyperion*** M - *06*	700	750
E/6	**60038 *FirdaussI*** - *06*	450	500
E/6	**60046 *Diamond Jubilee*** - *06*	450	500
E/6	**60051 *Blink Bonny*** - *06*	450	500
E/6	**60053 *Sansovino*** M - *06*	700	750
E/6	**60061 *Pretty Polly*** - *06*	450	500
E/6	**60063 *Isinglass*** - *06*	450	500
E/6	**60066 *Merry Hampton*** - *06*	450	500
E/6	**60069 *Sceptre*** M - *06*	700	750
E/6	**60090 *Grand Parade*** - *06*	450	500
E/6	**60096 *Papyrus*** - *06*	450	500
-	**60100 *Spearmint*** M - *06*	700	750
E/6	**60103 *Flying Scotsman*** - *06*	450	480

Thompson Blue

E/6	**60084 *Trigo*** - *06*	450	500

BRb Brunswick Green

E/6	**60035 *Windsor Lad*** dc - *06*	450	500
E/6	**60038 *Firdaussi*** dc M - *06*	700	750

BR Class A3 Papyrus [L12] (Ace Trains)

E/6	**60039 *Sandwich*** sd M - *06*	700	750
E/6	**60041 *Salmon Trout*** - *06*	450	500
E/6	**60046 *Diamond Jubilee*** dc - *06*	450	500
E/6	**60048 *Doncaster*** - *06*	450	500
E/6	**60049 *Galtee More*** sd M - *06*	700	750
E/6	**60050 *Persimmon*** sd M - *06*	700	750
E/6	**60051 *Blink Bonny*** dc sd - *06*	450	500
E/6	**60052 *Prince Palatine*** - *06*	450	500
E/6	**60055 *Woolwinder*** - *06*	450	500
E/6	**60058 *Blair Athol*** - *06*	450	500
E/6	**60060 *The Tetrarch*** - *06*	450	500
E/6	**60063 *Isinglass*** dc M - *06*	700	750
E/6	**60064 *Tagalie*** - *06*	450	500
E/6	**60068 *Sir Visto*** - *06*	450	500
E/6	**60070 *Gladiateur*** - *06*	450	500
E/6	**60072 *Sunstar*** dc M - *06*	700	750
E/6	**60073 *St Gatien*** - *06*	450	500
E/6	**60077 *White Knight*** sd M - *06*	700	750
E/6	**60078 *Knight Hawk*** sd M - *06*	700	750
E/6	**60079 *Bayardo*** - *06*	450	500
E/6	**60080 *Dick Turpin*** - *06*	450	500
E/6	**60083 *Sir Hugo*** - *06*	450	500
E/6	**60087 *Blenheim*** - *06*	450	500
E/6	**60088 *Book Law*** sd M - *06*	700	750
E/6	**60090 *Grand Parade*** dc - *06*	450	500
E/6	**60090 *Grand Parade*** dc sd - *06*	450	500
E/6	**60093 *Coronach*** - *06*	450	500
E/6	**60095 *Flamingo*** - *06*	450	500
E/6	**60096 *Papyrus*** dc sd - *06*	450	500
E/6	**60098 *Spion Cop*** - *06*	450	500
E/6	**60100 *Spearmint*** - *06*	450	500
E/6	**60101 *Cicero*** BRb M - *06*	700	750
E/6	**60103 *Flying Scotsman*** dc sd - *06*	450	500
E/6	**60104 *Solario*** dc M - *06*	700	750
E/6	**60105 *Victor Wild*** - *06*	450	500
E/6	**60106 *Flying Fox*** - *06*	450	500
E/6	**60107 *Royal Lancer*** - *06*	450	500
E/6	**60110 *Robert the Devil*** - *06*	450	500
E/6	**60111 *Enterprise*** dc M - *06*	700	750

The locomotive is also available with blank nameplates and unnumbered.

L13. LNER A4 4-6-2 (2002)

All of the A4 models were made in Thailand. Purchasers could choose their own names and numbers and all models were produced in 3-rail only. For the first three years the models were produced as AC/DC but, after that, as DC only. The loco body is pressure diecast and the tender is made from brass (corridor or non-corridor). The loco is fitted with matching twin 24v motors driving all axles and with an isolating switch. Working headlights and firebox glow. Single and double chimney versions available and the second batch had smaller lamps. By the start of 2005 the diecast body had been amended to improve lining band details on fully lined types such as BR and green LNER.

LNER Silver Grey with Valances

E/4	**2509 *Silver Link*** - *04*	550	685
E/4	**2510 *Quicksilver*** - *04*	550	685
E/4	**2511 *Silver King*** - *04*	550	685
E/4	**2512 *Silver Fox*** - *04*	550	685

LNER Class A4 Silver King [L13] (Vectis)

LNER Doncaster Green with Valances

E/4	4463 Sparrow Hawk - 05	550	685
E/4	4467 Wild Swan - 05	550	685
E/4	4482 Golden Eagle - 05	550	685
E/4	4483 Kingfisher - 05	550	685
E/4	4484 Falcon - 05	550	685
E/4	4485 Kestrel - 05	550	685
E/4	4486 Merlin - 05	550	685
E/4	4487 Sea Eagle - 05	550	685
E/4	4489 Woodcock - 05	550	685
E/4	4494 Osprey - 05	600	700
E/4	7143 Frank Hornby* Ltd Edn 4 - 05	800	900
E/4	7144 WJ Bassett-Lowke* Ltd Edn 3 - 05	800	900
E/4	7145 Stanley Beeson* Ltd Edn 2 - 05	800	900
E/4	7146 RF Stedman* Ltd Edn 2 - 05	800	900
E/4	7147 WHG Mills* Ltd Edn 1 - 05	800	900
E/4	7148 Edward Exley* Ltd Edn 2 - 05	800	900
E/4	7149 Gebruder Bing* Ltd Edn 2 - 05	800	900
E/4	7150 Georges Carette* Ltd Edn 3 - 05	800	900
E/4	7151 Gebruder Marklin* Ltd Edn 2 - 05	800	900
E/4	7152 Joshua Lionel Cowen* Ltd Edn 3 - 05	800	900
E/4	7153 J E Fournereau* Ltd Edn - 05	800	900
E/4	7154 Henry Greenly* Ltd Edn - 05	800	900
E/4	7155 Andries Grabowsky* Ltd Edn - 05	800	900
E/4	7156 Count Giansanti Coluzzi* Ltd Edn 1 - 05	800	900
E/4	7157 Marcel Darphin* Ltd Edn 1 - 05	800	900
E/4	7158 Allen Levy* Ltd Edn - 05	800	900
E/4	7159 Leonard W Mills* Ltd Edn - 05	800	900
E/4	7160 Robert Marescot* Ltd Edn - 05	800	900

LNER Garter Blue With Valances

E/4	2512 Silver Fox - 03	550	685
E/4	4462 Great Snipe - 03	550	685
E/4	4464 Bittern - not made	NA	NA
E/4	4466 Sir Ralph Wedgwood - not made	NA	NA
E/4	4468 Mallard - 03	550	685
E/4	4482 Golden Eagle - 03	550	685
E/4	4483 Kingfisher - not made	NA	NA
E/4	4485 Kestrel - not made	NA	NA
E/4	4486 Merlin - not made	NA	NA
E/4	4488 Union of South Africa - not made	NA	NA
E/4	4489 Woodcock - not made	NA	NA
E/4	4489 Dominion of Canada - 03	550	685
E/4	4490 Empire of India - 03	550	685
E/4	4491 Commonwealth of Australia - not made	NA	NA
E/4	4492 Dominion of New Zealand - 03	550	685
E/4	4494 Osprey - 03	550	685
E/4	4495 Golden Fleece - 03	550	685
E/4	4496 Golden Shuttle - not made	NA	NA
E/4	4496 Dwight D Eisenhower - not nade	NA	NA
E/4	4497 Golden Plover - 03	550	685
E/4	4498 Sir Nigel Gresley - 03	550	685
E/4	4901 Capercaillie - not made	NA	NA
E/4	4902 Seagull - not made	NA	NA
E/4	4903 Peregrine - not made	NA	NA
E/4	7160 Terence Cuneo* Ltd Edn 10 - 03	800	900

NE Black Without Valances

E/4	2512 Silver Fox - 05	550	685
E/4	4468 Mallard - 05	550	685
E/4	4469 Wild Swan - 05	550	685
E/4	4467 Sir Ralph Wedgewood - 05	550	685
E/4	4493 Woodcock - 05	550	685
E/4	4494 Andrew K McCosh - 05	550	685
E/4	4498 Sir Nigel Gresley - 03	550	685
E/4	4901 Capercailie - 05	550	685
E/4	4901 Sir Charles Newton - 05	550	685
E/4	4903 Peregrine - 05	550	685

LNER Garter Blue Without Valances

E/4	6 Sir Ralph Wedgwood - not made	NA	NA
E/4	7 Sir Nigel Gresley - 03	550	685
E/4	8 Dwight D Eisenhower - not made	NA	NA
E/4	9 Union of South Africa - not made	NA	NA
E/4	10 Dominion of Canada - not made	NA	NA
E/4	11 Empire of India - not made	NA	NA
E/4	12 Commonwealth of Australia - 03	550	685
E/4	13 Dominion of New Zealand - not made	NA	NA
E/4	14 Silver Fox - 03	550	685
E/4	19 Bittern - not made	NA	NA
E/4	22 Mallard - not made	NA	NA
E/4	23 Golden Eagle - not made	NA	NA
E/4	24 Kingfisher - not made	NA	NA
E/4	27 Merlin - not made	NA	NA
E/4	30 Golden Fleece - not made	NA	NA
E/4	4468 Mallard - 03	550	685
E/4	4469 Sir Ralph Wedgwood - 03	550	685
E/4	4483 Kingfisher - 03	550	685
E/4	4486 Merlin - 03	550	685
E/4	4489 Dominion of Canada - 03	550	685
E/4	4496 Dwight D Eisenhower - 03	550	685
E/4	? Reg Saxton* Ltd Edn 1 - 05	800	900

BRa Garter Blue

E/4	60006 Sir Ralph Wedgwood - 03	550	685
E/4	60022 Mallard - 03	550	685
E/4	60024 Kingfisher - 03	550	685
E/4	60034 Lord Farringdon Ltd Edn 3 - 05	800	900

BRa Thompson Blue (red lining)

E/4	60024 Kingfisher - 03	550	685
E/4	60027 Merlin - 03	550	685
E/4	60028 Walter K Whigham - 03	550	685
E/4	60029 Woodcock - 03	550	685

BRb Express Blue (white lining)

E/4	60007 Sir Nigel Gresley Sp Edn (A4 Society) - 03	550	685
E/4	60010 Dominion of Canada - 03	550	685
E/4	60012 Commonwealth of Australia - 03	550	685
E/4	60020 Guillemot - 03	550	685
E/4	60022 Mallard - 03	550	685
E/4	60032 Gannet - 03	550	685

BRb & BRc Brunswick green

E/4	7160 Terence Cuneo* Ltd Edn 1 (presented to Carol Cuneo) - 05?	800	900
E/4	60003 Andrew K McCosh - 03	550	685
E/4	60007 Sir Nigel Gresley BRb - 03	550	685
E/4	60008 Dwight D Eisenhower BRb - 03	550	685
E/4	60009 Union of South Africa - 03	550	685
E/4	600010 Dominion of Canada - 03	550	685
E/4	60011 Empire of India BRb - 03	550	685
E/4	60012 Commonwealth of Australia - 03	550	685
E/4	60013 Dominion of New Zealand - 03	550	685
E/4	60016 Silver King - 04	550	685
E/4	60017 Silver Fox - 03	550	685

Class A4 special issue of Bittern with double tender [L13] (Vectis)

E/4	60019 Sparrow Hawk - 03	550	685
E/4	60019 Bittern BRb - 03	550	685
E/4	60019 Bittern BRc dc Sp Edn double tender - 05?	1100	1300
E/4	60022 Mallard - 03	550	685
E/4	60024 Kingfisher - 03	550	685
E/4	60025 Falcon - 03	550	685
E/4	60026 Miles Beevor- 03	550	685
E/4	60027 Merlin - 03	550	685
E/4	60029 Woodcock - 03	550	685
E/4	60031 Golden Plover - 03	550	685
E/4	60032 Gannet - 03	550	685

E/4	**60033 *Seagull*** - *04*	550	685
E/4	**60034 *Lord Farringdon*** Ltd Edn 3 - *03*	800	900

* This was fictitious.

In association with John Shawe, a high pressure live steam version of the A4 has been developed which uses the A4 body. Marketed under the name ACE/Shawe, this was developed by The ACE Live Steam Locomotive Company Ltd. It had its inaugural run in 2007 running for over 35 minutes on one filling of spirit. It pulled 15 LNER 'teak' coaches.

L14. SR Class BB/WC 'Spamcan' Bulleid 4-6-2 (2009)

Both 2-rail and 3-rail versions made and fitted with 24V DC motors and isolating switch. All wheels flanged.

	Malachite Green		
E/9	**21C108 *Padstow*** SR - *09*	500	595
E/9	**21C123 *Blackmoor Vale*** SR - *09*	500	595
E/9	**21C136 *Westward Ho*** SR - *09*	500	595
E/9	**21C165 *Hurricane*** SR - *09*	500	595
E/9	**21C167 *Tangmere*** SR - *09*	500	595
E/9	**21C167 *Sir Eustace Missenden*** SR special - *09*	550	635
	Photographic Grey		
E/9	**21C164 *Fighter Command*** SR - *09*	500	595
	BR Green		
E/9	**34001 *Exeter*** - *09*	500	595
E/9	**34015 *Exmouth*** - *09*	500	595
E/9	**34051 *Winston Churchill*** - *09*	500	595
E/9	**34064 *Fighter Command*** - *09*	500	595
E/9	**34066 *Spitfire*** - *09*	500	595

Electric Multiple Units

L15. 3-Car & 4-Car EMUs (1999)

Made in India, all units comprise a powered motor coach (DC only) with 3rd class accommodation, a first class coach and a dummy 3rd class motor coach. All are tin printed and have punched out windows. Extra trailer cars for these sets are available at £55 each.

SR 3-car EMU [L15] (Vectis)

C1E/LM	**LMS** maroon Broad Street - Richmond maroon 3-car unit - *99*	250	295
C1	**LMS** maroon extra trailer car for above - *99*	55	65
C1E/Met	**Metropolitan** brown Baker Street - Harrow 4-car unit - *99*	250	295
C1	**Metropolitan** brown extra trailer car for above - *99*	55	65
C1E/S	**SR 1973 (1528/1664/1783)** green 3-car unit V and L route boards carried, white roof - *00*	370	420
C1E/S	**SR 1973 (1528/1664/1783)** green 3-car unit V and L route boards carried, grey roof - *00*	370	420
C1	**SR 1664** green extra car route boards - *00*	48	55
C/1G	3-car German Triebwagon set with pantograph - *03?*	450	495

L16. 4 CEP/BEP 2-Car EMU (2011)

Units comprise a powered motor coach and a dummy motor coach. To be made in China, they will be sold as a 2-car unit.

C/17	**S61389** motor coach BR SR coach green	NPG	NPG
C/17	**S61388** driving trailer BR SR coach green	NPG	NPG
C/17	above two as set BR SR coach green - *11*	NPG	NPG

L17. Brighton Belle 5-BEL 5-Car EMU (2011)

This model is being made in China and the cars have interiors with working table lamps.

	BR Pullman Chocolate & Cream		
C/17	***No.88*** Motor/Brake livery	NPG	NA
C/17	***No.86*** 3rd Parlour Car	NPG	NA
C/17	***No.89*** Dummy Motor/Brake	NPG	NA
set 3051	above 3 cars for unit 3051 - *11*	NA	NPG
C/17	***Doris*** 1st class kitchen car for unit 3051 - *11*	NPG	NPG
C/17	***Hazel*** 1st class kitchen car for unit 3051 - *11*	NPG	NPG
C/17	***No.90*** Motor/Brake livery	NPG	NA
C/17	***No.87*** 3rd Parlour Car	NPG	NA
C/17	***No.91*** Dummy Motor/Brake	NPG	NA
set 3052	above 3 cars for unit 3052 - *11*	NA	NPG
C/17	***Audrey*** 1st class kitchen car for unit 3052 - *11*	NPG	NPG
C/17	***Vera*** 1st class kitchen car for unit 3052 - *11*	NPG	NPG
C/17	***No.92*** Motor/Brake livery	NPG	NA
C/17	***No.85*** 3rd Parlour Car	NPG	NA
C/17	***No.93*** Dummy Motor/Brake	NPG	NA
set 3053	above 3 cars for unit 3053 - *11*	NA	NPG
C/17	***Gwen*** 1st class kitchen car for unit 3053 - *11*	NPG	NPG
C/17	***Mona*** 1st class kitchen car for unit 3053 - *11*	NPG	NPG

COACHES

Cat No.	Company, Number, Colour, Dates	£	£

C1. 35cm Non-Corridor Stock (1999)

Tin printed and manufactured in India. Some coaches had clerestory roofs and the roofs could be bought separately to convert standard coaches in this range. A total of 11,000 units were made.

C/1	**LNWR** brown+white all 1st - *99*	50	60
C/1	**LNWR** brown+white all 3rd - *99*	50	60
C/1	**LNWR** brown+white brake 3rd - *99*	50	60

Metropolitan coaches [C1] (Vectis)

C/1	**Metropolitan** brown all 1st - *99*	80	100
C/1	**Metropolitan** brown all 3rd - *99*	50	60
C/1	**Metropolitan** brown brake 3rd - *99*	50	60
C/1	above 3 Metropolitan coaches - *00*	NA	450
C/1	**LBSCR** brown+white all 1st - *99*	50	60
C/1	**LBSCR** brown+white all 3rd - *99*	50	60
C/1	**LBSCR** brown+white brake 3rd - *99*	50	60
C/1	above 3 LBSC coaches - *00*	NA	180
C/1	**Caledonian** plum+white all 1st - *99*	50	60
C/1	**Caledonian** plum+white all 3rd - *99*	50	60
C/1	**Caledonian** plum+white all brake 3rd - *99*	50	60
C/1	above 3 Caledonian coaches - *00*	NA	180
C/1	**GWR** dark brown+cream all 1st - *99*	40	45
C/1	**GWR** dark brown+cream all 3rd - *99*	40	45
C/1	**GWR** dark brown+cream brake 3rd - *99*	40	45
C/1	above 3 GWR coaches - *99*	NA	170

C/1CL	**GWR** dark brown+cream clerestory all 1st - *00*	40	45
C/1CL	**GWR** dark brown+cream clerestory all 3rd - *00*	40	45
C/1CL	**GWR** dark brown+cream clerestory brake 3rd - *00*	40	45
C/1CL	3 GWR clerestory coaches - *00*	NA	170
C/1	**LMS** maroon all 1st - *99*	40	45
C/1	**LMS** maroon all 3rd - *99*	40	45
C/1	**LMS** maroon all brake/3rd - *99*	40	45
C/1	above 3 LMS coaches - *99*	NA	130
C/1CL	**LMS** maroon ex-MR clerestory all 1st - *01*	45	55
C/1CL	**LMS** maroon ex-MR clerestory all 3rd - *01*	45	55
C/1CL	**LMS** maroon ex-MR clerestory brake 3rd - *01*	45	55
C/1CL	above 3 clerestory coaches - *01*	NA	150
C/1	**HRCA** maroon all 1st - *99*	40	45
C/1	**HRCA** maroon all 3rd - *99*	40	45
C/1	**HRCA** maroon all brake/3rd - *99*	40	45
C/1	above 3 HRCA 30th Anniversary coaches - *99*	NA	150
C/1	**LNER** 21397 light teak all 1st - *99*	40	45
C/1	**LNER** 1948 light teak all 3rd - *99*	40	45
C/1	**LNER** 21508 light teak brake 3rd - *99*	40	45
C/1	above 3 LNER coaches - *00*	NA	130
C/1CL	**LNER** light teak clestory all 1st - *01*	45	55
C/1CL	**LNER** light teak clestory all 3rd - *01*	45	55
C/1CL	**LNER** light teak clestory brake 3rd - *01*	45	55
C/1CL	above 3 ex-GER teak clerestory coaches - *01*	NA	150
C/1	**Southern** green brake 3rd - *99*	45	50
C/1	**Southern** green all 1st - *99*	45	50
C/1	**Southern** green all 3rd - *99*	45	50
C/1	above 3 Southern coaches - *00*	NA	160
C/1	**BR** M43277 maroon composite - *99*	45	50
C/1	**BR** M43279 maroon all 3rd - *99*	45	50
C/1	**BR** M43278 maroon brake 3rd - *99*	45	50
C/1	above 3 BR coaches - *00*	NA	160
C/1NZ	**NZR** maroon all-2nd Sp Edn (Railmaster Exports NZ)	65	NA
C/1NZ	**NZR** maroon all-1st Sp Edn (Railmaster Exports NZ)	65	NA
C/1NZ	**NZR** maroon brake 2nd Sp Edn (Railmaster Exports NZ)	65	NA
C/1NZ	above 3 NZR coaches - *99*	NA	200
C/1D	3 German Triebwagens - *?*	NA	175
C/1F	**Etat** green clerestory sets of 3 - *99*	NA	175
C/1F	**Est** maroon 1st class	55	NA
C/1F	**Est** green+orange-brown 2nd/3rd	55	NA
C/1F	**Est** orange-brown 3rd class	55	NA
C/1F	above 3 coaches - *99*	NA	175
C/1F	**PO** green set of 3 - *99*	NA	175
C/1F	**Nord** green 1st/2nd composite - *99*	55	NA
C/1F	**Nord** green clerestory all 3rd - *99*	55	NA
C/1F	3 Nord clerestory coaches - *99*	NA	175
C/1F	**PLM** postal car, baggage car and 3 passenger cars set of 5 - *09*	250	300
C/1 Bge	French fourgon khaki - *99*	45	55
C/1F	**SNCF** green 1st/3rd - *99*	55	NA
C/1F	3 SNCF coaches - *99*	NA	175

C2. GWR Collett & Hawksworth Stock (2005)

These coaches use a new 40cm chassis and have rear lights fitted. Made in Thailand they are fitted with insulated wheels and a PCB board for light connection is fitted to one brake end. All are Hawksworth stock except those marked 'C' which are Collett's.

Brown + Cream

C/12	**GWR** 1779 brake end	50	NA
C/12	**GWR** 7798 1st/3rd	50	NA
C/12	**GWR** 8002 1st	50	NA
Set A	above 3 GWR coaches - *05*	NA	160
C/12	**GWR** 7381 brake comp	50	NA
C/12	**GWR** 831 3rd	50	NA
C/12	**GWR** 1297 open 3rd C	50	NA
Set B	above 3 GWR coaches - *05*	NA	160
C/12	**GWR** 9676 buffet car C - *05*	50	60
C/12	**GWR** 295 full brake - *05*	750	60

C3. Merseyside Express Sets (1999)

These coaches, made in India, have domed roofs and litho silver windows. They have Merseyside Express - London (Euston) and Liverpool (Lime Street) name boards in the printing design except where indicated.

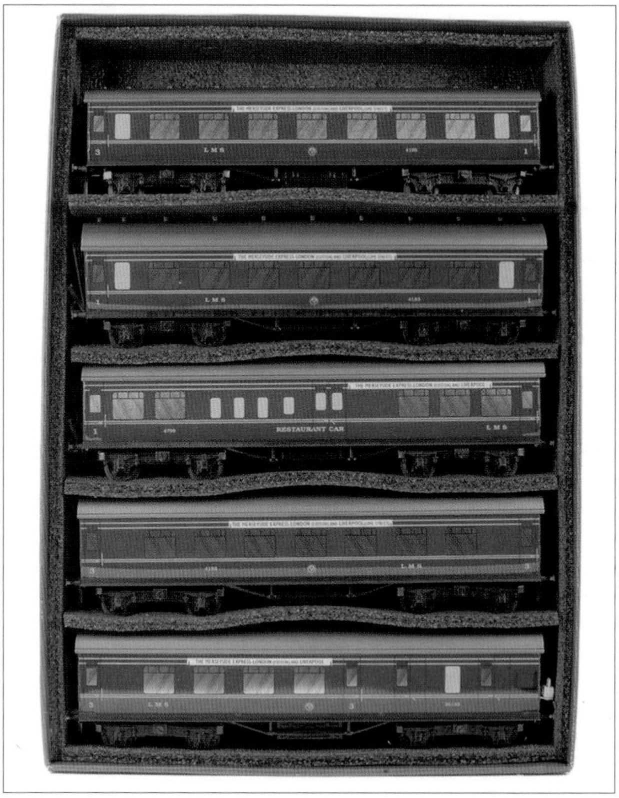

Merseyside 5-coach set [C3] (Vectis)

Maroon

C/2	**LMS** 4195 composite	35	NA
C/2	**LMS** 4195 all 3rd	35	NA
C/2	**LMS** 4799 restaurant car	35	NA
C/2	**LMS** 4183 all 1st	35	NA
C/2	**LMS** 26133 brake 3rd	35	NA
Set A	above 5 coaches Ltd Edn 300 - *99*	NA	180
C/2	**LMS** 4195 composite, no name boards Ltd Edn - *00*	35	40
C/2	**LMS** 4195 all 3rd, no name boards Ltd Edn - *00*	35	40
C/2	**LMS** 26133 brake 3rd, no name boards Ltd Edn - *00*	35	40
Set B	above 3 coaches Ltd Edn - *00*	NA	120

C4. LMS 40cm Stanier Coaches (2008)

Maroon

C/18	**LMS** 8953 all 3rd	NPG	NA
C/18	**LMS** 1083 all 1st	NPG	NA
C/18	**LMS** 5769 brake 3rd	NPG	NA
C/18	above 3 coaches - *08*	NA	NPG

C/18	**LMS** 1935 all 3rd	NPG	NA
C/18	**LMS** 3953 composite	NPG	NA
C/18	**LMS** 5062 brake 1st	NPG	NA
C/18	above 3 coaches – *08*	NA	NPG
C/18	**LMS** 30078 kitchen coach (35cm long) - *08*	NPG	NPG
C/18	**LMS** 3953 all 3rd composite - *08*	NPG	NPG
C/18	**LMS** 125 dining coach - *08*	NPG	NPG

C5. LMS 'Coronation Scot' Coaches (2011)

Made in China. The brake ends have working rear lights.

Blue

C/20	**LMS** 1071 corridor 1st	NPG	NA
C/20	**LMS** 8931 full 3rd	NPG	NA
C/20	**LMS** 5054 corridor brake 1st	NPG	NA
Set A	above 3 Maunsell coaches forming set 209 - *11*	NA	NPG
C/20	**LMS** 7509 corridor 1st	NPG	NA
C/20	**LMS** 9029 full 3rd	NPG	NA
C/20	**LMS** 5814 corridor brake 3rd	NPG	NA
Set B	above 3 Maunsell coaches forming set 250 - *11*	NA	NPG
C/20	**LMS** 3088 35cm dining car - *11*	NPG	NPG
C/20	**LMS** 3089 35cm dining car - *11*	NPG	NPG
C/20	**LMS** 8950 full 3rd - *11*	NPG	NPG

C6. LMS Stanier Main Line Coach Kits (2000)

These Thailand made kits have lower roofs and cut-out windows. They come with a choice of the following destination boards: 'The Royal Scot', 'The Merseyside Express', 'The Mancunian' and 'The Yorkshireman' (16 boards). Apart from the unpainted roofs, all other parts were pre-coloured.

Maroon

AC/C3	**LMS** 4195 1st/3rd - *00*	NA	35
AC/C3	**LMS** 4195 full 3rd - *00*	NA	35
AC/C3	**LMS** 4183 full 1st - *00*	NA	35
AC/C3	**LMS** 26133 3rd brake - *00*	NA	35
AC/C3	**LMS** 4799 restaurant car - *00*	NA	35

C7a. LNER Gresley Stock (printed windows) (2002)

The coaches, made in Thailand, are supplied with slots in the roof and coach roof boards to fit them carrying the name 'Flying Scotsman'. They had black printed windows. A run of only 50 of each were made and there was a rear working light on the brake end.

Teak

C/4/B	**LNER** 6461 all 1st brake	55	60
C/4/B	**LNER** 61639 all 3rd	55	60
C/4/B	**LNER** 1516 brake 3rd	55	60
Set A	above 3 with rear light - *02*	NA	200
C/4	**LNER** 689 teak all 1st brake	55	60
C/4	**LNER** 1865 teak all 3rd	55	60
C/4	**LNER** 62659 teak brake 3rd	55	60
Set B	3 more coaches complimenting Set A - *02*	NA	200
C/4/B	**LNER** 63291 1st/3rd composite - *02*	55	60
C/4/B	**LNER** 650 3rd buffet car - *02*	55	60

C7b. LNER Gresley Stock (clear windows) (2003)

The coaches, also made in Thailand, are supplied with slots in the roof and coach roof boards to fit them carrying the name 'Flying Scotsman'. They has cut-out glazed windows. The first batch made of Set A had no internal partitions (nip) but later ones did or you could have them retrospectively fitted. Rear working light on the brake end.

Teak

C/4/T	**LNER** 6461 all 1st brake nip	55	NA
C/4/T	**LNER** 61639 all 3rd nip	55	NA
C/4/T	**LNER** 1516 brake 3rd nip	55	NA
set A	above three coaches without partitions - *03*	NA	260
C/4/T	**LNER** 6461 all 1st brake	55	NA
C/4/T	**LNER** 61639 all 3rd	55	NA
C/4/T	**LNER** 1516 brake 3rd	55	NA
set A	above three coaches with partitions - *03*	NA	260
C/4/T	**LNER** 62659 brake 3rd	55	NA
C/4/T	**LNER** 1865 all 3rd open	55	NA
C/4/T	**LNER** 689 all 1st open	55	NA
set B	above three coaches - *03*	NA	280
C/4/T	**LNER** 63291 corridor comp - *03*	55	60
C/4/T	**LNER** 650 3rd buffet car - *03*	55	60

LNER buffet car [C7b] (Vectis)

C7c. LNER 1926 Articulated Gresley Cars (2002)

Made in Thailand.

C/6	**LNER** 1204 + 1205 teak sleeping cars, boards (King's Cross - Edinburgh) - *02*	170	200

C8. LNER East Coast Articulated Stock (2004)

These sets comprise articulated units with interior lighting and back light. They were made in Thailand.

Coronation Sets

C/7	**LNER** [C] + [B] blue+white, silver roof	100	NA
C/7	**LNER** [A] + [G] blue+white, silver roof	100	NA
C/7	**LNER** [D] + [H] blue+white, silver roof	100	NA
	above 6 coaches - *05*	NA	495
C/7	**LNER** Beaver Tail blue+white, silver roof - *05*	70	80

1938 Record Breaking Set

C/8	**LNER** 6-car Coronation set Ltd Edn 50 plus ACE/Wright Dynamometer car - *04*	NA	575

West Riding Limited Sets

C/9	**LNER** [C] + [B] blue+white, grey roof	80	NA
C/9	**LNER** [A] + [G] blue+white, grey roof	80	NA
C/9	**LNER** [D] + [H] blue+white, grey roof	80	NA
C/9	above 6 coaches Ltd Edn 50 - *05*	NA	260
C/9	**LNER** Beaver Tail blue+white, grey roof - *05*	70	80

Tourist/Excursion Set

C/10	**LNER** ?+? articulated green+cream	100	NA
C/10	**LNER** ?+? articulated green+cream	100	NA
C/10	**LNER** ? single green+cream	70	80
C/10	**LNER** ? single green+cream	70	80
C/10	above 6 coaches - *05*	NA	495

Silver Jubilee set [C8] (Vectis)

Silver Jubilee Set

C/11 setA	**LNER** [A] + [B] silver - *05*	NA	100
C/11 setB	**LNER** [C] + [D] silver - *05*	NA	100
C/11 setC	**LNER** silver centre kitchen car - *05*	45	60
C/11 setD	**LNER** [E] + [F] silver - *05*	NA	100
C/11	**LNER** Beaver Tail silver - *05*	70	80

C9a. SR Maunsell Pre-War Coaches (2011)

Made in China. The brake ends have working rear lights.

Olive Green

C/22	**SR** 7411 full 1st	NPG	NA
C/22	**SR** 1127 full 3rd	NPG	NA
C/22	**SR** 3722 brake 3rd	NPG	NA
Set A	above 3 Maunsell coaches forming set 209 - *11*	NA	NPG
C/22	**SR** 7674 1st/3rd composite	NPG	NA
C/22	**SR** 1884 full 3rd	NPG	NA
C/22	**SR** 2785 brake 3rd	NPG	NA
Set B	above 3 Maunsell coaches forming set 250 - *11*	NA	NPG
C/22	**SR** 7866 dining car - *11*	NPG	NPG
C/22	**SR** 1450 3rd open - *11*	NPG	NPG

C9b. SR Maunsell Post-War Coaches (2011)

Made in China. The brake ends have working rear lights.

Malachite Green

C/23	**SR** 7229 full 1st	NPG	NA
C/23	**SR** 1123 full 3rd	NPG	NA
C/23	**SR** 3718 brake 3rd	NPG	NA
Set A	above 3 Maunsell coaches forming set 205 - *11*	NA	NPG
C/23	**SR** 7216 1st/3rd composite	NPG	NA
C/23	**SR** 1199 full 3rd	NPG	NA
C/23	**SR** 2781 brake 3rd	NPG	NA
Set B	above 3 Maunsell coaches forming set 248 - 11	NA	NPG
C/23	**SR** 7869 dining car - *11*	NPG	NPG
C/23	**SR** 1445 3rd open - *11*	NPG	NPG

C10. SR/BR Bulleid Coaches (2011)

Made in China. The brake ends have working rear lights.

Malachite Green

C/21	**BR** 7887 restaurant 3rd car	NPG	NA
C/21	**BR** 1457 full 3rd	NPG	NA
C/21	**BR** 4361 brake 3rd	NPG	NA
Set A	above 3 Bulleid coaches forming set 269 - *11*	NA	NPG
C/21	**BR** 7683 restaurant 1st car	NPG	NA
C/21	**BR** 5746 1st/3rd composite	NPG	NA
C/21	**BR** 4362 brake 3rd	NPG	NA
Set B	above 3 Bulleid coaches forming set 269 - *11*	NA	NPG

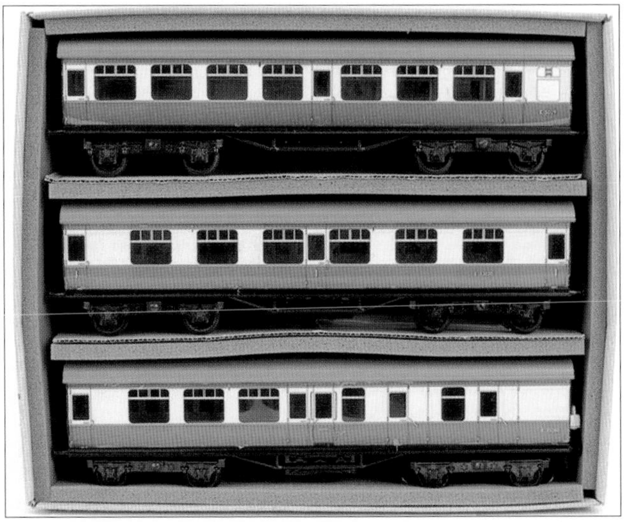

3-coach BR Mk1 set [C11] (Vectis)

C11. BR Mk1 Coaches (2002)

Made in Thailand, these 40cm tin-printed, are as supplied with the Bassett-Lowke 'Royal Scot' train pack (set B). All sets had punched out windows and included internal compartments where appropriate. There were rear working lights on the brake end of Set A and 'The Elizabethan' name boards were included.

Red + Cream

C/5	**BR** E1303 full 1st	50	NA
C/5	**BR** E5029full 3rd	50	NA
C/5	**BR** E35260 brake 3rd	50	NA
Set A	above 3 BR coaches - *02*	NA	150
C/5	**BR** M15578 full 1st	50	NA
C/5	**BR** M24123 full 3rd	50	NA
C/5	**BR** M21089 brake 3rd	50	NA
Set B	above 3 BR coaches - *02*	NA	150
C/5	**BR** E302 restaurant car - *02*	50	60
C/5	**BR** E80675 full brake - *02*	50	60

C12. BR Mk1 Coaches (2005)

Also made in Thailand, these tin-printed coaches use a new 40cm chassis with sprung Commonwealth bogies. They are fitted with insulated wheels and a PCB board for light connection is fitted to one brake end. They are supplied with appropriate destination boards

Brown + Cream

C/13	**BR(WR)** 24165 corridor 2nd	50	NA
C/13	**BR(WR)** 13065 corridor 1st	50	NA
C/13	**BR(WR)** ? 3095 open 1st	50	NA
Set A	above 3 coaches - *06*	NA	140
C/13	**BR(WR)** 34154 brake 2nd	50	NA
C/13	**BR(WR)** 15426 corridor composite	50	NA
C/13	**BR(WR)** 4917 open 2nd	50	NA
Set B	above 3 coaches - *06*	NA	140
C/13	**BR(WR)** 80723 full brake - *06*	50	60
C/13	**BR(WR)** 1728 buffet/restaurant - *06*	50	60

Green

C/13	**BR(SR)** 3068 open 1st	50	NA
C/13	**BR(SR)** 24169 corridor 2nd	50	NA
C/13	**BR(SR)** 13003 corridor 1st	50	NA
Set A	above 3 coaches - *05*	NA	140
C/13	**BR(SR)** 34156 brake 2nd	50	NA
C/13	**BR(SR)** 15032 corridor composite	50	NA
C/13	**BR(SR)** 4375 open 2nd	50	NA
Set B	above 3 coaches - *05*	NA	140
C/13	**BR(SR)** 81039 full brake - *05*	50	60
C/13	**BR(SR)** 1717 buffet/restaurant - *05*	50	60

Maroon

C/13	**BR** 3099 open 1st	50	NA
C/13	**BR** 24147 corridor 2nd	50	NA
C/13	**BR** 13089 corridor 1st	50	NA
Set A	above 3 coaches - *06*	NA	140
C/13	**BR** 34134 brake 2nd	50	NA
C/13	**BR** 15328 corridor composite	50	NA
C/13	**BR** 3754 open 2nd	50	NA
Set B	above 3 coaches - *06*	NA	140
C/13	**BR** 80567 full brake - *06*	50	60
C/13	**BR** 1712 buffet/restaurant - *06*	50	60

C13. Mk1 Pullman Cars (2005)

Made in Thailand, the sets are available with both white and grey roofs.

Dark Brown + Cream

C/14	**Pullman** *Eagle* kitchen 1st	80	NA
C/14	**Pullman** *Amethyst* parlour 1st	80	NA
C/14	**Pullman** *No.351* parlour 2nd	80	NA
Set A	above 3 Pullman cars - *05*	NA	275

Pullman car The Hadrian Bar [C13] (Vectis)

C/14	**Pullman** *Falcon* kitchen 1st	80	NA
C/14	**Pullman** *Emerald* parlour 1st	80	NA
C/14	**Pullman** *No.336* parlour 2nd	80	NA
Set B	above 3 Pullman cars - *05*	NA	275
C/14	**Pullman** *Hadrian Bar,* grey roof - *05*	80	90

C14a. Pullman Cars 1930s Style (2011)

These are being made in China along with the Brighton Belle. The brake ends have a working rear light and all the coaches have interiors with working table lamps.

Dark Brown + Cream

C/15	**Pullman** *Iolanthe* kitchen 1st	80	NA
C/15	**Pullman** *Car No.66* parlour 3rd	80	NA
C/15	**Pullman** *No.65* brake 3rd	80	NA
Set A	above 3 Pullman cars - *11*	NA	275
C/15	**Pullman** *No.68* kitchen 3rd	80	NA
C/15	**Pullman** *Eunice* parlour 1st	80	NA
C/15	**Pullman** *No.62* brake 3rd	80	NA
Set B	above 3 Pullman cars - *11*	NA	275
C/15	**Pullman** *Fingall* kitchen 1st - *11*	80	90
C/15	**Pullman** *No.73* parlour 3rd	80	NA
C/15	**Pullman** *Fingall* kitchen 1st	80	NA
C/15	**Pullman** *Agatha* parlour 1st	80	NA
Set C	above 3 Pullman cars - *11*	NA	275
C/15	**Pullman** *Lorraine* parlour 1st - *11*	80	90
C/15	**Pullman** *Thelma* kitchen 1st - *11*	80	90

C14b. Golden Arrow Pullman Cars (2011)

Made in China. With interiors and working table lamps and working rear lights on the brake ends.

Dark Brown + Cream

C/19	**Pullman** *Adrian* kitchen 1st	NPG	NA
C/19	**Pullman** *Zenobia* kitchen 1st	NPG	NA
C/19	**Pullman** *Niobe* parlour 1st	NPG	NA
Set A	above 3 Pullman cars - *11*	NA	NPG
C/19	**Pullman** *Onyx* kitchen 1st	NPG	NA
C/19	**Pullman** *Montana* brake 1st	NPG	NA
C/19	**Pullman** *Tranon* Bar	NPG	NA
Set B	above 3 Pullman cars - *11*	NA	NPG

ACE/WRIGHT SERIES

This is a small series of ready-to-run special vehicles designed by Brian Wright using overlays and made in Britain. The models are made of lithographed heavily varnished card applied to ACE C/1, C/4, C/5 and C/6 coaches.

CA/W1. Various Stock

ACE/Wright GWR full brake & 'Ocean Mails' [CA/W1] (Vectis)

W1	**LNWR** ? travelling postal van - *05*	70	90
W1	**GWR** 1054 full brake with low roof - *03?*	70	80
W1	**GWR** ? full brake with clerestory roof - *03?*	80	90
W1	**GWR** 1259 Siphon G with pre-war lettering - *03?*	60	70
W1	**GWR** ? Ocean Mails coach - *05*	70	80
W1	**LMS** ? Stanier full brake c1930 - *03?*	60	70
W1	**LMS** ? maroon ex-MR mail van with clerestory roof - *03?*	90	150
W1	**LMS** ? scenery coach - *05*	60	70
W1	**LMS** 30233 Stanier postal van - *05*	70	90
W1	**LNER** 5219 teak full brake The Flying Scotsman - *04*	100	120
W1	**LNER** 23591 teak clerestory dynamometer car ex-set - *05*	75	NA
W1	**LNER** 45412 all 3rd + 45411 brake 3rd articulated pair teak - *?*	80	100
W1	**LNER** beaver tail observation car blue+wht - *07*	120	150
W1	**SR** 2464 parcel van c1930 with ribbed roof - *03?*	70	75
W1	**SR** 1308S cinema coach with 4-wheeled generator van - *05*	70	75

WAGONS

Cat No.	Company, Number, Colour, Dates	£	£

W1. 5-plank Open Wagon (2011?)

Fully detailed chassis.

G/3	grey - *11*	NPG	NPG
G/3	brown - *11*	NPG	NPG

W2a. Petrol/Spirit Tank Wagon (2004)

These are sold in sets of three and they will have interchangeable couplings. The bodies are lithographed in four colours and are fitted to a detailed chassis with brake gear. The tank has cross ties as well as end stays. The chassis has dropout side frames for lubricating axle boxes. The models were made in Thailand.

G/1	**'ACE Trains Oil'** - *04*	35	NA
Set 1	3 tanks (ACE + Esso yellow + Mobiloil) - *04*	NA	120
G/1	**'Esso'** grey	35	NA
G/1	**'Wakefield Castrol'** green	35	NA
G/1	**'Regent'** silver	35	NA
Set 2	above 3 tanks - *04*	NA	120

2 sets of tank wagons [W2a] (Vectis)

G/1	**'Pratt's Spirit'** brown	35	NA
G/1	**'Pratt's Spirit'** green	35	NA
G/1	**'Pratt's High Test Sealed'** orange	35	NA
Set 3	above 3 tanks - *04*	NA	120
G/1	**'Anglo American Oil Co.'** brown	35	NA
G/1	**'Colas'** red	35	NA
G/1	**'BP Motor Spirit'** yellow	35	NA
Set 4	above 3 tanks - *04*	NA	120
G/1	**'Royal Daylight'** grey	35	NA
G/1	**'Redline-Gilco'** dark blue	35	NA
G/1	**'Shell Motor Spirit'** red	35	NA
Set 5	above 3 tanks - *04*	NA	120

G/1	**'National Benzole Mixture'** ochre	35	NA
G/1	**'Pool'** grey	35	NA
G/1	**'Colas'** blue	35	NA
Set 6	above 3 tanks - *04*	NA	120
G/1	**'Esso'** yellow	35	NA
G/1	**'BP Motor Spirit'** grey	35	NA
G/1	**'Power Ethyl'** green	35	NA
Set 7	above 3 tanks - *07*	NA	120
G/1	**'BP British Petrol'** green	35	NA
G/1	**'Mobiloil'** grey	35	NA
G/1	**'Pool'** Fuel Oil black	35	NA
Set 8	above 3 tanks - *07*	NA	120

W2b. Milk Tank Wagon (2005)

These are also sold in sets of three and are the same as the petrol tanks but without cross strapping and riveting. They also have a smaller filler cap with a valve on either side. Made in Thailand.

G/1M	**'United Dairies'** white - *05*	35	NA
G/1M2	3 of above tanks	NA	120
G/1M	**'Express Dairy'** white - *05*	35	NA
G/1M1	3 of above tanks	NA	120
G/1M	**'Nestles Milk'** white - *05*	35	NA
G/1M3	3 of above tanks	NA	120
G/1M4	**'Express Dairy', 'United Dairies', 'Nestles Milk'** - set of 3 - *05*	NA	120

W3. 12T Goods Van (2009)

Fully detailed sprung chassis with sprung wheels. Sold in sets of three. Made in China.

G/2	**'ACE Trains'** dark blue	20	NA
G/2	**LNER** 13897 brown	20	NA
G/2	**LNWR** grey	20	NA
G/2-1	above 3 vans - *09*	NA	99
G/2	**SR** 570027 brown yellow spot banana van	20	NA
G/2	**BR** B755414 brown	20	NA
G/2	**SR** 51298 cream meat van	20	NA
G/2-2	above 3 vans - *09*	NA	99

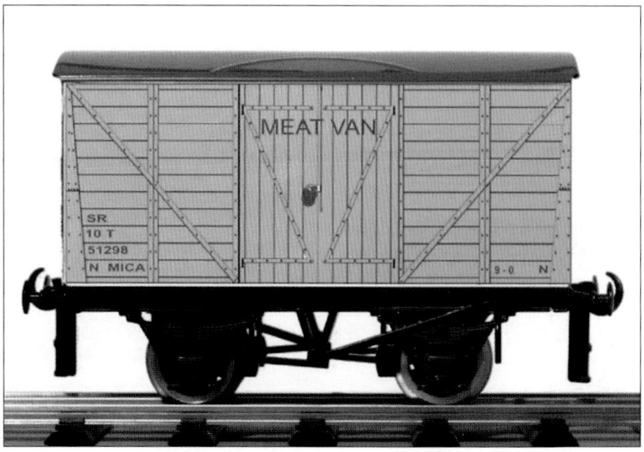

SR meat van [W3] (Vectis)

G/2	**SR** 47375 dark brown	20	NA
G/2	**CR** blue	20	NA
G/2	**GWR** 134053 grey	20	NA
G/2-3	above 3 vans - *09*	NA	99
G/2	**GCR** 727445 light grey	20	NA
G/2	**ED** 7271502 dark green Permenant way Dept.	20	NA
G/2	**LMS** 203975 dark brown	20	NA
G/2-4	above 3 vans - *09*	NA	99
G/2	**BR** S50494 white Insulmeat - *09*	20	NA
G/2-5	3 of the above vans - *09*	NA	99

W4. Brake Van (2007)

Fully detailed chassis. Working gear and internal lighting. 2-rail and 3-rail versions. Made in Thailand.

G/4	brown - *07*	35	47

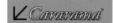

Airfix GMR

HISTORY

Airfix are best remembered for their comprehensive range of plastic construction kits but in 1971, on the collapse of the Lines Group, they had bought Meccano Ltd who, incidentally, had been stripped of all connection with the model railway industry seven years earlier.

Milestones

1971 Airfix buy Meccano Ltd.
1975 Airfix announce the launch of a ready-to-run railway system.
1976 First samples seen at toy fairs.
1976 Class 31 and Doctor X set released for Christmas.
1977 Airfix draw up their production plan.
1979 GMR name adopted and wagon production starts in the UK.
1980 Airfix empire crumbles.
1981 Production ceases and Palitoy acquires the model railway tools.
1985 Tools acquired by Dapol.
1996 Tools pass to Hornby.

In the mid 1970s, Airfix decided to extend their toy range by buying from the American Bachmann company a Wild West adventure train set. This was made by Kader in Hong Kong. To complement it, they decided to add an in-house concept - a Dr X mystery set which was made for them by Sanda Kan, also in Hong Kong, and based on British prototype models - a Class 31 diesel, 'Lowmac' machine wagons and an ex-GWR 'Toad' brake van. When test shots of these models arrived it was realised that they were so well detailed that they would appeal to serious railway modellers. Thus, Airfix saw the potential in expanding the system with some additional models and Airfix Railways was born. The 61XX 2-6-2T, Intercity BSK and 12T van were intended to compliment the set items and test the market too.

So it was that in 1975 Airfix announced their intention of entering the ready-to-run model railway market. Unfortunately for them, the American backed Palitoy toy company had seen a gap in the British market for better quality 00 gauge railway models and decided to fill it.

In the early 1970s, the Hong Kong Trade Development Commission had been looking for business for local factories and this had resulted in the Hong Kong companies, Sanda Kan and Cheong Tak, producing models for Airfix. The Stanier coaches (corridor and non corridor) were made at Cheong Tak who also produced the 'Royal Scot', 4F and were working on the projected 'Compound' to be followed by a 'Crab', 'Black 5' or 8F. Most of the other models were made by Sanda Kan.

The first samples were displayed at the Harrogate and Brighton Toy Fairs in 1976 where they received a cool reception due to their poor quality. They had been cobbled together in a hurry and bore little resemblance to what was to follow.

Mechanically the locomotives were not exceptional but the mouldings were good and brought much praise. The first locomotive release was the Class 31 from the 'Doctor X' set, which arrived in time for Christmas 1976.

In 1977, Airfix drew up an overall programme that was to give a balanced range. There were to be 5 groups: Midland, Western, Southern, Eastern and BR. Each group was going to have an express passenger, mixed traffic, goods, large tank and small tank engines. In addition, the coaches for each group were to be gangwayed (express mainline) and suburban.

The range of locomotives, coaches and wagons expanded in 1978. Other planned models were the N2, 'Dean Goods', 'Schools' and B1 but production delays, due to Hong Kong factories not adhering to Airfix's increasing design requirements, were now affecting future plans.

It was becoming more apparent that communication with Hong Kong and control of the finished product was not very good whereas UK production, although more expensive, would deliver as good a product, on time, to Airfix's specifications, without masses of communication and without so many hidden costs. The company, therefore, produced some wagons themselves in the UK and the success of these proved this point and would have ultimately lead to the phasing out of overseas production.

This change happened in 1979 and, at the same time, the name of the product was altered to GMR which stood for Great Model Railways to better separate the product line from the Airfix kits. The new branding was launched at the Toy Fair at Earls Court and the selling line was 'Precision made by Airfix'.

The GMR assembly line was to be at Charlton (South East London) and the 'Dean Goods' its first locomotive product - 5-plank and 7-pank wagons had been made there since 1978 and the Syphons since 1979. As the 'Dean Goods' was about to go into production in mid 1980, the Airfix empire was crumbling. Other parts of the company were being closed down, moved or sold off. £7M was spent in an attempt to save Meccano and when this failed Airfix went into receivership.

Pre-production model of the Airfix 'Castle' Class locomotive

Airfix/GMR exhibited for the last time at the 1981 Toy Fairs but shortly after this they ceased production. The Airfix model railway interests were acquired by its rival - Palitoy - the makers of Mainline Railways. Many models were made by Palitoy from Airfix tooling and later by Dapol and today Hornby - each adding their improvements.

The moulds used in China had been owned by the Hong Kong factories. When Airfix ceased production, existing UK railway stock and UK tools (R-T-R wagons, 'Siphons' and the Dean Goods loco) went to Palitoy (Mainline) via Humbrol. Dapol were independently dealing with Sanda Kan, to use the Airfix tools owned by them. Dapol also acquired remaining Airfix stock held by Sanda Kan some of which was repackaged by them.

With the exception of the 4F, none of the Cheong Tak models were seen again. However, the 4F has ended up in the Hornby stable along with the Sanda Kan and Palitoy owned models. The 'Royal Scot' and Stanier coach moulds could still be sitting in store somewhere but none of them would be of interest to Hornby today as they have produced their own high quality models of these subjects.

Airfix had started work on the Stanier all 3rd with Cheong Tak and the 12-wheel diner with Sanda Kan. Palitoy did consider them but passed on them. Replica had the all 3rd completed and released some of them, probably through Cheong Tak, while Dapol released the 12-wheel diner through Sanda Kan.

Further Reading

A detailed listing of the Airfix and Mainline model railway systems was produced by the late Charles Manship in the 1980s but it is no longer available. However, there has been a series of articles by Graham Smith-Thompson, in *Model Railway Enthusiast* magazine, profiling the Airfix and Mainline ranges and other systems that later used the tools. There were six parts devoted specifically to Airfix published in the July-December issues in 1998. Later, a detailed history of the Airfix railway range by Pat Hammond was published in *British Railway Modelling*.

Collectors Club

The Airfix Collectors Club caters for collectors of any Airfix product including the model railway range and publishes a newsletter called *Constant Scale*. Further information about this organisation may be obtained from Jeremy Brook at 29 Elley Green, Neston, Nr. Corsham, Wiltshire SN13 9TX (brookjeremy@hotmail.com) or by visiting them at their website which is at http://pws.prserv.net/gbinet.dbjames/acc.htm

Dates - The dates used in the following tables are based on catalogues and price lists and factory records and should not be taken as evidence of availability.

Samples on the Market - Far East manufacturers sent samples to their customers for approval before proceeding with full production. These samples often ended up in collections and today they command a good price. Samples of models that did not reach the production stage are of greater interest to collectors.

LOCOMOTIVES

Listing - The locomotives are arranged in the order of size from smallest to largest, starting with tank engines and finishing with diesels.

Cat No.	Company, Number, Colour, Dates	£	£

L1. GWR Class 14XX 0-4-2T (1978)

0-4-2T GWR Class 14xx [L1]

54152	**1466** GWR green - *78-81*	20	30
54153	**1466** BRb lined green - *78-81*	22	32

The tools for this model passed to Palitoy, then Dapol, and finally Hornby who now make their own versions of the model.

L2. LNER Class N2 Tank 0-6-2T (see Mainline)

54154	**9522** LNER green - *	NA	NA
54155	**69531** BRb black - *	NA	NA

* Arrived too late and were sold by Palitoy in Mainline packaging. The tools for this model passed to Palitoy, then Dapol, and finally Hornby who now make their own versions of the model.

L3. GWR Class 61XX 'Prairie' Tank 2-6-2T (1977)

54150	**6110** Great Western green - *77-81*	18	30
54151	**6167** BRb lined black - *77-81*	20	32

The tools for this model passed to Palitoy, then Dapol, and finally Hornby who now make their own versions of the model.

L4. American 4-4-0s (1977)

54170-5	***Jupiter*** Central Pacific red + silver (CPRR) - *77-80*	20	30
54171-8	**119** Union Pacific RR red + black - *77-80*	20	30

L5. GWR Class 2301 'Dean Goods' 0-6-0 (see Mainline)

The moulds for the plastic parts of this model were made for Airfix by Heller in France and taken over by Palitoy who shipped them out to Sanda Kan in Hong Kong to make. They were sold by Palitoy in Mainline packaging. With the demise of the Mainline range, the tools passed first to Dapol and finally to Hornby who now make their own versions of the model.

54156	**2516** GWR green - *not released by Airfix*	NA	NA
54157	**2538** BRb black - *not released by Airfix*	NA	NA

L6. LMS Class 4F 0-6-0 (1978)

Some Airfix 4Fs had piston tail rod covers on the buffer beam.

54122	**4454** LMS black - *78-81*	25	30
54123	**44454** BRb (small) black - *78-80*	25	35
54122-6	**44423** BRb (small) black - *?*	NPG	NPG
54123	**44454** BRb (large) black - *80-81*	30	40

The tools for this model passed to Palitoy, then Dapol, and finally Hornby who now make their own versions of the model.

L7. LMS Class 'Rebuilt Royal Scot' 4-6-0 (1978)

54120	**6103 *Royal Scots Fusilier*** LMS black - *78-81*	25	40
54121	**46100 *Royal Scot*** green BRb smoke deflectors, badly positioned decals on tender - *78-81*	25	40

L8. GWR Class 4073 'Castle' 4-6-0 (1979)

54124	**4073 *Caerphilly Castle*** Great ( ) Western green - *79-81*	40	60

BR Pendennis Castle [L8]

54125	**4079 *Pendennis Castle*** BRb green incorrectly numbered in cat - *79-81*	40	60

Powderham Castle and *Pembroke Castle* were Airfix models renamed and renumbered by Dapol but sold in original Airfix boxes. These will be found listed under Dapol.

L9. Class 31/4 Diesel A1A-A1A (1977)

54109-9	**D5531** green BRc box code C - *77-81*	15	30
54100-6	**31401** BRe blue, box code IP02 - *77-81*	15	30

Lost and Gone

With Airfix in the hands of the receivers early in 1981, they left plans for new locomotives half finished. Some of these were in a fairly advanced stage of development while others were just a glint in the eye of the designer. They included the following with planned release dates, where known:

SR 'Schools' Class - 1982 *
LNER B1 Class *Mayflower* 1982
LMS 'Compound' - 1982 *

Pre-production sample of LT 1938 stock

LT 1938 Stock Underground train *
GWR 43XX Class 'Mogul' *
SR 'Lord Nelson' Class - 1982
WD 2-8-0 - 1983
SR U Class 'Mogul' - 1983
LNER J69 tank - 1984
LMS 'Crab" Mogul' - 1984
SR ex-LSWR Class O2 Adams tank
LMS 'Black 5'
LMS 8F

* pre-production mock-up exists.

The SR Class O2 Adams tank was to be produced as both a mainland and an Isle of Wight version. An extra chassis was envisaged and the body tool was to have inserts to allow an SR Class G6 0-6-0T to be made. The O2/G6 was to be the next UK produced loco after the 'Dean Goods'.

The underground train was to have been sold as a 4-car set complete with a platform and accessories. It was to have been powered by a specially adapted Mabuchi motor and to this end a testing model was built. This was also to have a non-powered driving end and, in presentation packaging, it would have been aimed at the tourist market. This was going to be tied in with the double decker bus and Austin Taxi model kits.

COACHES

The marketing department had difficulty in getting the production manager to understand the market. He repeatedly rejected tooling for the 2nd class Mk2D coach on the grounds that sales had slowed drastically on the 1st class model. It was thought to be pure folly to do another so similar. He had to be persuaded, that it was needed. The result was the initial run of 7,000 2nd class models sold out immediately and another run of equal size had to be placed straight away.

A similar situation occurred with the 'B' coach. Airfix had large stocks of it in GWR livery, due to over ordering rather than lack of sales. The BR livery version was put off and when permission was finally given, the BR livery 'B' coach sold out immediately. More were to be ordered but factory capacity became a problem at that time.

The Airfix coaches, with very minor exceptions, were excellent scale models, moulded in plastic, assembled, spray painted and tampo printed with accurate detail. They helped to set a new standard in the ready-to-run market of the 1970s. They were the correct length, had flush fitting windows and proper interior detail. Errors did occur and these included the choice of bogies for the two Siphons and the colour of the LMS coaches which was much too dark. The latter was put down to the matt varnish used to finish them. A new batch, in the correct shade, was ordered but these were retained in the store until all the old stock had been cleared. By then, the company was in the liquidators hands and Palitoy inherited the new stock which they sold in the Mainline range.

With the take-over of Airfix railway assets by Palitoy in 1981, many of the Airfix coaches were absorbed into the Mainline range, mostly as new production runs. The tools were then sold on to Dapol in the mid '80s and to Hornby in the mid '90s both of whom produced their own models from them.

At the time of the demise of Airfix there were new coach models in the pipeline in various stages of development but not yet advertised. These included:

SR Bulleid Corridor Stock (3 types) - 1981
LNER Gresley Corridor Stock (3 types) - 1982
SR Birdcage Stock (2 types) - 1983
LMS Sleeper - 1983
LNER Gresley Non-Corridor Stock (2 types) - 1984

Quotes for the Bulleid coaches were obtained in the UK in August 1997 and they were to have been produced in two liveries. A pre-production sample was made up from a Phoenix kit and, finished in BR(SR) green, it was numbered S5806S.

Listing - Earliest styles of coaches are listed first and finishing with more modern British Railways designs.

Cat No.	Company, Number, Colour, Dates	£	£
C1.	**U.S. Passenger Cars** (Bachmann) (1976)		
	These were in the 54051 Wild West set and were made by Bachmann who marketed their version of the set in America.		
(54051)	**CPRR** 3 red saloon car with a trapdoor in roof - *76-78*	10	15
(54051)	**CPRR** 5 red exploding baggage car - *76-78*	12	18
C2.	**GWR Suburban 'B Set' Coach** (1977)		
	B Set coaches were brake ends which were always used in pairs.		
54250	**GWR** 6869 dark brown+cream - *77-81*	10	16
54250	**GWR** 6895 dark brown+cream - *?*	10	16
54250	**GWR** (button) 6896 dark brown+cream - *?*	10	16
54250	**GWR** 4895 dark brown+cream - *78-80*	10	16
54257	**BR** W6894W maroon - *80*	12	22

GWR auto-trailer [C3]

Cat No.	Company, Number, Colour, Dates	£	£
C3.	**GWR Auto-Trailer** (1978)		
54255	**GWR** 187 dark brown+cream - *78-81*	8	14
54256	**BR** W187W maroon Didcot sign - *78-81*	8	14
C4.	**GWR Centenary Stock** (1980)		
54207	**GWR** 6659 dk brown+cream comp* - *80-81*	10	15
54209	**GWR** 4575 dk brn+cream brake 3rd* - *80-81*	10	15
54208	**BR** W6659W maroon composite** - *80-81*	12	18
54208	**BR** W6661W maroon composite** - *?*	12	18
54210	**BR** W4576W maroon brake 3rd** - *80-81*	12	18
	* With 'Cornish Riviera Limited' coach boards (the pre-production sample models had 'Plymouth and Paddington Ocean Express'). ** With 'Paddington, Newport, Cardiff and Swansea' coach boards		
C5.	**LMS Stanier Corridor Stock** (1978)		
	These are LMS Period 3 coaches developed during Stanier's time as CME.		
54202	**LMS** 3935 maroon 1st/3rd 60' - *78-81*	10	16
54202	**LMS** 3935 maroon 1st/3rd 60' - *	NA	NA
54204	**LMS** 5542 maroon brake 3rd 57' - *78-81*	10	16
54204	**LMS** 5542 maroon brake 3rd 57' - *	NA	NA
54258	**LMS** 9072 maroon vestibule 3rd 57'** - *not made*	NA	NA
54203	**BR** M3935M red+cream 1st/3rd 60' - *78-81*	10	16
54205	**BR** M5542M red+cream brake 3rd 57' - *78-81*	10	16
54259	**BR** M9103M red+cream vestibule 2nd 57' * - *not made*	NA	NA
	* These resulted from a colour correction ordered by Airfix but were kept in store until old stocks were used up. They were inherited by Palitoy who boxed and sold them. ** These were in the design stage at Airfix (scheduled for 1982) when they went into receivership and the models were later finished and sold by Replica Railways.		
C6.	**LMS 57' Non-Corridor Stock** (1981)		
54251	**LMS** 19195 maroon 1st/3rd - *79-81*	10	16
54253	**LMS** 15185 maroon brake 3rd - *79-81*	10	16

LMS non-corridor stock [C6]

54253	**LMS** 25250 maroon brake 3rd - *?*	12	20
54254	**LMS** 25250 maroon brake 3rd - *?*	12	20
54252	**BR** M19195M maroon 1st/3rd - *79-81*	12	20
54254	**BR** M25250M maroon brake 3rd - *79-81*	12	20

C7. LMS 68' Dining Car (12 wheels)

These were in the design stage when Airfix went into receivership and Mainline took up the project. They were to have been released by Airfix in 1982. After Palitoy, the project next fell into the hands of Dapol who actually produced the first batch of models. Their tools, thought to have been damaged in a factory fire, were later sold to Hornby who modified them and now make the model. The model was based on an LMS Period 2 coach.

54260	**LMS** - maroon - *not made*	NA	NA
54261	**BR** M236M red+cream - *not made*	NA	NA

C8. BR Mk2d Stock (1977)

Inter-City blue + grey

54201	**BR** E3170 FO 1st open - *77-81*	8	14
54200	**BR** E9479 BSO brake 2nd - *77-81*	8	14
54206	**BR** E5690 TSO 2nd Open - *80*	10	20

WAGONS

The same standards of accuracy that had been applied to locomotives and coaches were also applied to the wagons Airfix produced. However, for the sake of economy, there was standardisation on chassis, wheels etc. 12 of the body types used no more than 4 chassis for a total of 48 models. Only spoked and solid wheels were used and, despite publicity photographs showing metal tyred and white rimmed wheels, neither type was used on production models.

Attention, however, was given to getting liveries reasonably accurate although those on some of the vans were not authentic. These are interesting as some were re-liveried models, done in batches of 7,000 to use up surplus stocks of BR ventilated vans. Not all the liveries were fictitious. The 'English Eggs' one was seen on the LMS and the 'Lyons Tea' livery appeared on some railway containers.

Additionally, some wagons were deliberately done in very small quantities of incorrect colours to generate an interest in collecting them. It had been intended to do a batch 500 of each but the factory manager misunderstood and did only about 20 of each model. These deliberate 'errors' are very rare and therefore command a high price.

Listing - The wagons are arranged in the order of: flats, open wagons, hoppers, tankers, vans, brake vans and bogie stock.

Cat No.	Company, Number, Colour, Dates	£	£

W1. 'Lowmac' MS (1977)

54330	**BR** B904662 red-brown + crate - *77-81*	8	10
54333	**BR** B904662 red-brown 'Conflat' ISO + **'Sea Land'** container - *78-79*	10	16
54334	**BR** B904662 red-brown + **'NCL'** trailer - *78-79*	10	16
(54052)	**BR** B904662 red + **'NCL'** trailer with opening doors from 54052 'Dr. X' pack brown - *77*	14	NA

W2. 'Conflat' with Container (1978)

54331	**GWR** 39005 dark grey + **GW** brown container BK -1829 - *78-81*	7	10
54337	**LNER** 39324, 240749 grey + **'J Miles'** container* - *80-81*	8	12
54332	**BR** B735833, B735700 red brown + **BR** furniture container - *78-81*	8	12

* This was a non-authentic livery although the Leeds-based company existed and had asked for a promotional model for their customers. It is based on the livery of the company's vans.

W3. 5-plank Open Wagon (1978)

Samples based on both LMS and GWR designs were made and the production model was a compromise between the two.

5-plank wagon Devises Sand [W3]

54374	**'Devizes Sand'** 1 grey - *78-79*	6	10
54375	**'Spencer'** 24 red - *78-81*	6	10
54376	**'Arnold'** 156 brown - *78-81*	6	10
54377	**'Harts Hill'** 2 brown - *78-79*	6	10
54388	**'Alloa'** 1124 yellow - *80-81*	6	10
54389	**'ICI'** L3110 grey - *80-81*	6	10
54372	**GWR** 109459 dark grey - *78-81*	6	9
54373	**LMS** 404104 grey - *78-81*	6	9
54364	**BR** M407562 grey - *79-81*	6	9
54365	**BR** M411459 red brown - *79-81*	6	9

W4. 7-plank Open Wagon (1978)

This was a compromise design to allow a range of liveries. This involved stretching what would have been the body of a 9' wheelbase wagon to fit a 10' chassis and stretching the artwork to match.

54380	**'Gloucester Gas Light Company'** 51 black - *78-79*	6	10
54381	**'Broadoak'** 460 brown - *78-79*	6	9
54381	**'Broadoak'** 460 grey Ltd Edn 20 - *78-79*	35	45
54382	**'Highley Mining'** 425 brown - *78-79*	6	9
54382	**'Highley Mining'** 425 grey Ltd Edn 20 - *78-79*	35	45
54383	**'Hales Fuels'** 241 grey - *78-81*	6	9
54383	**'Hales Fuels'** 241 brown Ltd Edn 20 - *78-81*	35	45
54390	**'Carlton'** 4372 black - *80-81*	6	10
54391	**'Stalybridge'** 15 brown - *80-81*	6	10
54391	**'Stalybridge'** 15 grey Ltd Edn 20 - *80*	35	45
54378	**GWR** 29017 dark grey - *78-81*	6	10
54379	**LMS** 40781 grey - *79-81*	6	9
54379	**LMS** 602604 grey - *79-81*	6	9
54366	**BR** P130286 grey - *80-81*	6	10

W5. NE 20T 9-plank Mineral Wagon (1981)

54369	**LNER** 31273 grey - *81*	7	10
54359	**BR** E30995, E10995 grey - *81*	7	10

W6. GWR 20T Steel Mineral Wagon (1979)

?	**'Avon Tyres'*** black - *not made*	NA	NA
54370	**GWR** 83516 dark grey - *79-81*	7	10
54371	**BR** P339371K grey - *79-81*	7	8

* This livery was suggested to Airfix by Palitoy who supplied a picture of it. Airfix prepared the artwork ready for a release in 1981. The artwork was amongst the assets acquired by Palitoy on the demise of Airfix and they brought out the wagon themselves.

W7. NE 21T Hopper Wagon (1980)

54367	**LNER** 193258 grey - *80-81*	7	10
54368	**BR** E289595K grey - *80-81*	7	10

20 ton tank wagon [W8]

W8. 20T Tank Wagon (1979)

This was an authentic model of a 12' chassis tank wagon done from Railway Clearing House drawings but the liveries are not strictly authentic, belonging as they do to other styles of tanker.

54345	**'Esso'** 135 silver - *79-81*	8	14
54346	**'Shell BP'** 3967 black - *79-81*	8	12
54347	**'Shell'** 2373 buff - *79-81*	8	14

W9. BR 12T Planked Single Vent Van (1978)

The private owner versions were mainly re-sprayed and reprinted BR ventilated vans of which there was a large stock unsold. They were done in batches of about 7,000 at the Airfix factory in the UK. For the roofs, six specific greys were stocked, from light grey through very dark grey. Roofs were painted one spray gun full at a time and with each filling another grey was used.

54302	**'Lyon's Tea'** 528163 blue - *78-79*	8	14
54301	**'English Eggs'** 506150 dark blue - *78-81*	9	16
54303	**'Blue Circle'** 520112 yellow - *78-79*	10	16
54310	**'Lyle's Golden Syrup'** 547117 green - *80-81*	8	14
54311	**'Tizer'** 561772 yellow - *80-81*	8	14
54312	**'Spratt's'** 538422 white, name brown - *80-81*	8	14
54312	**'Spratt's'** 538422 white, name in red Ltd Edn 20 - *80*	35	45

Single vent van [W9]

54313	**'Huntley & Palmer'** 566327 green - *80-81*	7	14
54314	**'Persil'** 547921 green - *80-81*	8	14
54315	**'Nestle's Milk'** 531179 blue - *80-81*	8	14
54300	**BR** B751707 red brown, brown roof - *76-80*	6	10
54300	**BR** B751707 red brown, grey roof - *78?*	6	10
54300	**BR** B760563 red brown, grey roof - *78?*	6	10
54300	**BR** B751705 red brown, black roof - *?*	6	10

W10. SR 12T Ventilated Box Van (1979)

54304	**SR** 44392 brown - *79-81*	6	10
54305	**BR** S44437 grey - *79-81*	6	10

W11. LMS 20T Brake Van (1977)

This model had its own unique chassis.

54361	**LMS** 730097 grey - *77-81*	8	12
54362	**BR** 114875 red-brown+yellow - *77-78*	8	12
54362	**BR** B950016 red-brown+yellow - *79-81*	8	12

W12. GWR 20T Brake Van (1977)

This model had its own unique chassis.

54363	**GWR** 114875 dark grey 'Swindon' - *78-81*	8	12
54363	**GWR** 56616 dark grey 'Oxford' - *78-81*	10	14
54360	**BR** 114926 grey - *77-83*	8	12

W13. LNER/BR Standard 20T Brake Van

This was later made by Bachmann in 2001 using the original Airfix drawings.

54386	**LNER** 182922 brown - *not made*	NA	NA
54387	**BR** brown+yellow - *not made*	NA	NA

W14. GWR 'Macaw H' Bogie Bolster Wagon (1981)

54336	**GWR** 107364 dark grey box of 2 - *81*	NA	22
(54336)	as above single unboxed	8	NA
54335	**BR** W107364 grey box of 2 - *81*	NA	22
(54335)	as above single unboxed	8	NA

W15. GWR 'Siphon G' Bogie Milk Van (1980)

As a cost cutting exercise, the two GWR 'Siphons' were fitted with bogies from the GWR 'Centenary' coaches. While authentic, examples on the railways so fitted were rare. The bogies should have been a 9' American type.

54306	**GWR** 1478 dark brown - *80-81*	10	14
54307	**BR** W1452 maroon - *80-81*	10	14

W16. GWR 'Siphon H' Bogie Milk Van (1980)

54308	**GWR** 1437 dark brown - *80-81*	10	14
54309	**BR** W1429 maroon - *80-81*	10	14

W17. US Freight Cars (Bachmann) (1977)

These were in the 54053 Wild West Freight train set and were made by Bachmann who marketed their version of the set in America.

54270	**Union Pacific** 556 red box car - *77-78*	4	NA
54271	**Union Pacific** yellow caboose - *77-78*	4	NA

The last display of new liveries was at the 1981 Toy Fair and included some which Airfix did not have time to produce. These included the 20T steel mineral wagon in the livery of 'Avon Tyres' and the 12T ventilated van finished as 'Meccano', 'Camp Coffee' and 'OXO'. There were also to be a 5-plank 'BAC', a 7-plank 'Perfection Soap' and a 'Conflat' with a 'Frasers' container. Some of these liveries were later taken up by Palitoy.

Also planned for 1982 was an LNER type brake van which was based on vehicle ESR 49028 from which the drawings had been prepared. This was to have been followed by a 9' chassis for more accurately scaled private owner wagons. The model would have been based on a Gloucester design and was due for release during 1981.

Other wagons being considered (with the year of their proposed introduction) were:

SR 25T brake van - 1982
LNER 9' wheelbase fruit van - 1982
GWR Cowans Sheldon 45T mobile crane and jib carrier - 1983
GWR 'Tube' wagon - 1983
GWR 'Ro-Rail' milk wagon - 1983
16T mineral wagon - 1983
'Plate' wagon - 1983

It was also planned to, each year, add further liveries to the 5-plank, 7-plank, tank wagon, container and mineral wagon ranges.

ACCESSORIES

There were very few accessories for the Airfix range but they included, in 1979, a series of card lineside structures which were both available separately and provided in the train sets. The models released that first year were a signal box (54650-6), tunnel (54651-9) and a station (54652-2).

Track was supplied by Peco while Airfix supplied both battery and mains power units. At the end Airfix launched their own version of Zero 1 which was called 'MTC' which stood for Multiple Train Controller

SETS

Airfix tried hard to sell their sets and produced a total of 19 before they went into liquidation. Retailers always wanted sets made up of boxed items so that they could break up sets that did not sell and offer the items individually. As the Airfix range is relatively small and so easy to build a complete collection of, there is a growing interest in Airfix train sets. This particularly applies to those of the pre GMR days. Of special interest are the adventure sets - 'Doctor X' and the two Wild West sets which can fetch as much as £80. Another interesting set is the Cornish Riviera without the gold beading on the splashers of the locomotive or with it applied as printed splasher labels. The latter were done in an emergency to cover a production mistake.

Anbrico 00

HISTORY

The Anbrico name was first used in 1932 in connection with hand-built scale models, in particular 0 gauge railway items for use in the home market. As the years went by, the firm became known as Anbrico Scale Models and all types and sizes were made for sale in countries all over the World.

Beyer-Peacock 'Hymek' B-B diesel [L4]

Anbrico was also producing for other firms in the model trade. Some of the largest models built were coaches in 1:12 scale for use in booking offices around the UK.

In later years, Anbrico Scale Models produced rolling stock for both 0 and 00 gauges but was concentrating more on coaches. After several years, the ranges covering all the various types of BR diesel multiple units and railbuses were introduced with a diesel locomotive series which was added a couple of years later.

The company was based in Pudsey, between Leeds and Bradford, and appropriately the first DMU modelled was that used on the Leeds-Bradford service via Pudsey. Anbrico even supplied the first six twin units to a model shop in Leeds six weeks prior to BR starting up the service.

The DMUs, railbuses and single unit parcels vans were hand-built to customer's orders in 00 and EM scale and the units contained either a destination box or a route number box or both (combined or separate). Any destination, up to 14 letters in length, was included in the price as well as the route number. Appropriate regional stock numbers were also included together with detailed undergear.

Single-link couplings were fitted as standard and each car was fitted out with full interior detail. The motor was well concealed and, on the railbuses, was slung beneath to give the car clear space within.

In 1960, a range of ready-to-run trams was produced in 00 scale which became popular with both customers in the UK and abroad and was available on either 00 or TT gauge chassis.

In 1968, the first range of 00 cast metal bus kits was introduced covering the popular British outline double and single decker buses and coaches. The range was intended to cover the lack of types available for use with model railways, but added interest was found from the enthusiasts who just enjoyed making models of buses and coaches.

An enthusiast group was just starting up at the time and Anbrico was contacted to see if they would be prepared to make some of the types they were interested in and which, by chance, fell in with the survey Anbrico had done earlier on the subject. Sometime later a series of cast metal tramcar kits was introduced in which provision was made for a small motor to be fitted for customers wishing to operate them on their layout.

Before kit production ceased, some 80 were available including some 00 railcar and railbus kits.

Production of parts ceased in September 1987 and the hand-built model section closed sometime later, after the completion of outstanding orders for models and patterns for firms in the model trade. The company had been producing models for 50 years and had 300 sales agents around the world. The factory was sold at the end of 1989 and has since been converted into a house.

All items connected with the scale model business were sold to private collectors when the old premises were emptied for conversion. The models from the showcases in the Pudsey showroom were added to the private collection of one of the business partners and were retained to illustrate the history of the firm since the original models made in 1932.

Prices - As Anbrico models rarely come up for sale at auction and collectors of the range are few and far between, it is very difficult to suggest realistic prices. Hopefully those shown can be modified as information comes in. The prices suggested here show a range of values for models in good condition.

LOCOMOTIVES

The lists shown here is of models available in 1966.

Cat No.	Company, Number, Colour, Dates	£	£
L1.	**Type 1 Diesels**		
-	D8000-8199 English Electric Bo-Bo	80	120
-	D8200-8243 BTH/Paxman Bo-Bo	80	120
-	D8500-8587 Clayton/Paxman Bo-Bo	80	120
L2.	**Type 2 Diesels**		
-	D5000-5299 BR/Sulzer Bo-Bo	80	120
-	D5300-5414 Birmingham RC&WCo Bo-Bo	80	120
-	D5900-5909 English Electric Bo-Bo	80	120
-	D6100-6157 North British Bo-Bo	80	120
-	D6300-6357 North British Bo-Bo	80	120
L3.	**Type 2/3 Diesels**		
-	D5500-5699 Brush A1A-A1A	80	120
L4.	**Type 3 Diesels**		
-	D5600-5697 Birmingham RC&WCo Bo-Bo	80	120
-	D6700-6999 English Electric Co-Co	80	120
-	D7000-7400 Beyer-Peacock ('Hymek') B-B	80	120
L5.	**Type 4 Diesels**		
-	D1-139 BR/Sulzer 1Co-Co1	80	120
-	D200-399 English Electric 1Co-Co1	80	120
-	D400-449 English Electric Co-Co	80	120
-	D1000-1073 'Western' C-C	80	120
-	D1500-1999 Brush Co-Co	80	120
L6.	**Type 5 Diesels**		
-	D9000-9021 English Electric 'Deltic' Co-Co	80	120

AC Railbus [L7] (Paul Colbeck)

Cat No.	Company, Number, Colour, Dates	£	£
L7.	**4-Wheel Railbuses**		
-	British United Traction	90	150
-	AC Cars	90	150
-	Park Royal	90	150
-	Wickham	90	150
-	Bristol/Eastern Coach Works	90	150
-	Waggon und Maschinenbau	90	150
L8.	**Single Unit Parcels Vans**		
-	Cravens Limited 57'	100	160
-	Gloucester RC&W Co. 64' (Western & Midland)	100	160
L9.	**DMUs**		
These were first advertised in 1956.			
-	Metropolitan-Cammell 57' 2-car	220	300
-	Metropolitan-Cammell 57' 3-car	280	350

-	Metropolitan-Cammell 57' 4-car	320	400
-	Cravens 57' 2-car	220	300
-	Cravens 57' 3-car	280	350
-	Cravens 57' 4-car	320	400
-	Gloucester RC&WCo. 57' 2-car	220	300
-	Gloucester RC&WCo. 64' single car	90	150
-	Park Royal Vehicles Ltd 57' 2-car	220	300
-	Birmingham RC&WCo 57' 2-car	220	300
-	Birmingham RC&WCo 57' 3-car	280	350
-	Birmingham RC&WCo 57' 4-car	320	400
-	Birmingham RC&WCo Suburban 64' 3-car	280	350
-	Derby original design 57' single car	90	150
-	Derby original design 57' 2-car	220	300
-	Derby original design 57' 4-car	320	400

BR Derby motor brake 2nd [L9]

-	Derby new style 57' 2-car	220	300
-	Derby new style 57' 3-car	280	350
-	Derby new style 57' 4-car	320	400
-	Derby new style 64' 2-car	220	300
-	Derby Suburban 64' 3-car	280	350
-	Derby Suburban 64' 4-car	320	400
-	Wickham 57' 2-car	220	300
-	Pressed Steel Suburban 64' single car	90	150
-	Pressed Steel Suburban 64' 3-car	280	350
-	Swindon Inter-City 64' 3-car	280	350
-	Swindon Cross Country 64' 3-car	280	350
-	Gloucester RC&WCo. Cross Country 64' 3-car	280	350
L10.	**Sentinel Rail Car**		
-	1928 LNER green+cream	90	150

COACHES

The list shown here is of models available from 1959. BR coaches were offered in maroon, green or chocolate and cream with appropriate regional numbers. A small extra charge was made for rail blue and blue/grey livery.

In 1969, Ambrico Scale Models were also offering a range of 00 scale coach kits taken from their ready-to-run range. These, however, were withdrawn when other competing coach kits came on the market.

Cat No.	Company, Number, Colour, Dates	£	£
C1.	**WCJS Stock**		
-	42' coach	80	120
-	45' coach	80	120

68ft Caledonian Railway dining saloon [C2] (Paul Colbeck)

C2.	**Caledonian Stock**		
-	57' side corridor coach	70	100
-	12-wheel Grampian coach	70	100
C3.	**Midland Stock**		
-	Clerestory 54' side corridor coach	60	90
-	Clerestory 12-wheel diner	60	90
-	Clerestory 12-wheel sleeper	60	90
-	6-wheel 31' stock	60	90
C4.	**LNWR Stock**		
-	57' side corridor coach	60	90
-	12-wheel diner	60	90
-	12-wheel sleeper	60	90
C5.	**SE&CR Stock**		
-	Birdcage stock	70	100
C6.	**GWR Stock**		
-	Clerestory stock	60	90
-	Dreadnought stock	60	90
-	Toplight stock	60	90
-	57' side corridor coach	40	70
-	60' side corridor coach	40	70
-	57' Ocean Mails corridor full brake	40	70
-	50' suburban full brake parcels van	40	70
-	54' suburban 1st	40	70
-	54' suburban 3rd	40	70
-	54' suburban 1st/3rd composite	40	70
-	54' suburban brake/3rd	40	70
-	60' B-set suburban brake/composite	40	70
-	57' bow ended side corridor 1st	40	70
-	57' bow ended side corridor 3rd	40	70
-	57' bow ended side corridor 1st/3rd	50	80
-	57' bow ended side corridor brake/3rd	50	80
-	57' 1st/3rd restaurant car	50	80
-	61' 1st/3rd restaurant car	50	80
-	62' auto-train trailer coach 187-196 series	60	90
C7.	**LMS Stock**		
-	57' side corridor 1st	40	70
-	57' side corridor 3rd	40	70

LMS all-3rd coach [C7] (Paul Colbeck)

-	57' side corridor 1st/3rd	40	70
-	57' side corridor brake 3rd	40	70
-	50' full brake	40	70
-	50' suburban brake	40	70
-	50' parcels van	40	70
-	54' suburban 1st	40	70
-	54' suburban 3rd	40	70
-	54' suburban 1st/3rd	40	70
-	54' suburban brake/3rd	40	70
-	50' kitchen car	40	70
-	57' sleeping car 1st	40	70
-	57' sleeping car 3rd	40	70
-	57' sleeping car 1st/3rd	40	70
-	69' sleeping car 1st	40	70
-	69' sleeping car 3rd	40	70
-	69' sleeping car 1st/3rd	40	70
-	57' centre corridor 1st	40	70
-	57' centre corridor 3rd	40	70
-	57' centre corridor 1st/3rd	40	70
-	57' centre corridor brake/3rd	40	70
-	57' push-pull brake 3rd	40	70
-	57' restaurant car 1st	40	70
-	57' restaurant car 3rd	40	70
-	57' restaurant car 1st/3rd	40	70
-	68' restaurant car 1st	40	70
-	68' restaurant car 3rd	40	70
-	68' restaurant car 1st/3rd	40	70
-	50' engineer's inspection saloon	70	90
C8.	**LNER Stock**		
-	Triplet dining car set	160	240
-	Quint set	220	300
-	Quad set	280	260

-	Clerestory stock	70	100
-	61' drop roof and bow end corridor full brake	60	90
-	61' drop roof bow end centre corridor teak 3rd	60	90
-	61' drop roof bow-ended centre corridor teak restaurant car	60	90
-	61' Gresley teak side corridor 1st	60	90
-	61' Gresley teak side corridor 3rd	60	90
-	61' Gresley teak side corridor 1st/3rd	60	90
-	61' Gresley teak side corridor brake/3rd	60	90

LNER restaurant car [C8] (Paul Colbeck)

-	63' oval window side corridor 1st	50	80
-	63' oval window side corridor 3rd	50	80
-	63' oval window side corridor 1st/3rd	50	80
-	63' oval window side corridor brake/3rd	50	80
-	63' oval window restaurant car	50	80

C9.	**SR Stock**		
-	59' side corridor 1st	50	80
-	59' side corridor 3rd	50	80
-	59' side corridor 1st/3rd	50	80
-	59' side corridor brake/3rd	50	80

C10.	**BR Mk1 Suburban Stock**		
-	57' composite	40	70
-	64' composite	40	70
-	57' brake/2nd	40	70
-	64' brake/2nd	40	70
-	57' 2nd class	40	70
-	64' 2nd class	40	70
-	57' lavatory composite	40	70
-	57' lavatory open 2nd	40	70
-	57' open 2nd	40	70
-	64' open 2nd	40	70

C11.	**BR Mk1 Corridor Stock**		
-	58' corridor full brake	40	70
-	64' corridor 2nd	40	70
-	64' corridor brake/2nd	40	70
-	64' corridor 1st	40	70
-	64' corridor brake/1st	40	70
-	64' corridor 1st/2nd	40	70
-	64' corridor brake/composite	40	70
-	64' corridor sleeper 1st	40	70
-	64' corridor sleeper 2nd	40	70
-	64' corridor sleeper composite	40	70
-	64' corridor open 1st	40	70
-	64' corridor open 2nd	40	70
-	64' corridor open brake 2nd	40	70

C12.	**BR Mk1 Catering Stock**		
-	64' buffet/kitchen (KB)	40	70
-	64' buffet/kitchen (RKB)	40	70
-	64' kitchen car (RK)	40	70
-	64' open 2nd miniature buffet (RMB)	40	70
-	64' restaurant 1st (RF)	40	70
-	64' restaurant 1st (RFO)	40	70
-	64' restaurant 2nd (RSO)	40	70
-	64' restaurant unclassified (RU)	40	70

C13.	**BR Utility Stock**		
-	General utility van (GUV)	50	80

Bachmann Collectors' Club

Club Year 2010-11

For just £20 per year (starting 1st July each year for 12 months ending 30th June) you can be kept up to date with all the developments from Bachmann Europe Plc. Our quarterly club magazine contains news, features and competitions, covering Branchline, Graham Farish and other Bachmann ranges from around the world.

Additionally you will receive:

- A FREE wagon in either OO or N Scale (depending on your preferred choice). These are produced exclusively for the Bachmann Collectors' Club and are highly collectable.

- A FREE 2011 calendar featuring prints by top railway artist Malcolm Root at the end of the year.

- A FREE Branchline or Farish Catalogue.

- The opportunity to purchase locomotives and wagons produced only for Bachmann Club members. During the coming year these will be issued with individually numbered certificates.

With membership now approaching 14,000 there has never been a better time to join the fast growing Bachmann Collector' Club. We look forward to having you on board.

For further information, either log onto:
www.bachmann-collectorsclub.com
or write to:
Bachmann Collector' Club,
PO Box 7820, Barwell,
Leicestershire, LE9 8WZ.
Tel: 01455 841756

BACHMANN BRANCH-LINE

GRAHAM FARISH by BACHMANN

Bachmann Branchline

HISTORY

The name Bachmann came from a German emigrant to the USA who, in 1835, founded a company in Philadelphia. Amongst other things, the company made tinplate toys and, many years later, was one of the pioneers of plastic goods, including toy trains. Bachmann went on to become the largest distributor of toy trains and model railways in America.

Milestones

1835 Bachmann founded in Philadelphia.
1925 Ting Hsiung-chao buys a battery company in Shanghai.
1948 Ting founds Kader in Hong Kong.
1975 Kader start producing Mainline models for Palitoy.
1987 Kader buys Bachmann.
1989 Bachmann Industries Europe Ltd formed.
1990 Bachmann Branchlines launched in UK initially using former Mainline tools.
1993 Kader acquires Liliput.
1998 Bachmann Industries Europe Ltd introduce their Blue Riband range.
2000 Bachmann buy Graham Farish.
2005 Heritage range started in association with the NRM.
2006 Bachmann Europe plc take over UK distribution of Mahano
2009 The demise of Mehano and the end of the agency agreement.

Meanwhile, in 1925, in China, a man named Ting Hsiung-chao bought a battery manufacturing company in Shanghai for US$500. During the civil war between the Nationalist and Communist factions in China he was imprisoned for political reasons by the Communists and was unable to tend to his business, which ultimately collapsed as a result. He was eventually forced to flee from Communist China, to re-establish what became a thriving business in North Point, Hong Kong.

His company, Kader, was founded in 1948 and went on to become the largest manufacturer of toys in the Far East. In the mid 1950s, the Company started manufacturing for Bachmann and by 1987, Kader had bought Bachmann outright.

Kader Industrial Co. Ltd, one of the Kader group of companies, is now based in Kowloon Bay, very near the old airport, Kai Tak.

One British company, for which it manufactured, was Palitoy, the owners of the Mainline Railways range which was prominent in the late 1970s and early 1980s. Palitoy had an arrangement whereby they required the manufacturers to produce their own tools for their products, with the tools remaining in the ownership of the manufacturing company. As a result of this, when Palitoy closed down and its model railway assets were acquired by Dapol, the latter did not acquire the Far East tools of Kader origin.

By the late 1980s, Kader were looking at the European market. With their good collection of tools for making locomotives and rolling stock for the British market (former Mainline range), they decided to form a European company to develop the local potential. Thus, Bachmann Industries Europe Ltd was formed in June 1989 (although it had really started as early as May 1988) and the model railway press in Britain announced the newly launched Bachmann Branchline range in January 1990. Kader also acquired Liliput which is based in Altdorf, near Nuremberg, Germany. A new purpose built block has been added to the Zhong Tang factory complex, in Guang Dong Province, dedicated solely to the manufacture of model railways in various gauges for the UK, Continental Europe, China and US markets. This also included the Graham Farish N gauge range which Bachmann acquired in 2000. While Bachmann models are made at Zhong Tang, the parent company, Kader Industrial Co. Ltd, is still based in Kowloon Bay, Hong Kong.

Although the former Mainline tools formed the basis of the Bachmann British range, the years since then have seen considerable improvements made to the models and, early on, the launch of many new models. This process continues with Bachmann setting a new standard for ready-to-run 00 scale models in the UK which rivals were forced to follow.

Blue Riband Models - With the ever increasing strive for higher quality in their models, in 1998, Bachmann launched their Blue Riband range. This badge is worn only by those models that Bachmann consider to be to the high standard they have set themselves to achieve and it is expected that all completely new models will fall into this category. These are marked with a **(B)** in the headings of the tables below. The name comes from transatlantic shipping where the Blue Riband was awarded to the fastest liner to ply the route.

Further Reading

A series of articles was written by Graham Smith-Thompson, in *Model Railway Enthusiast* and *Model Railway Collector* magazines, profiling the Airfix and Mainline ranges and other systems that later used the tools. The first part on Bachmann models was published before the magazine ceased publication in the summer of 2000 but subsequent parts were not published. The Magazine of the Bachmann Collectors Club (see below) is developing into a useful source of information for further research.

Collectors Club

For a number of years the company sponsored an enthusiasts club called Bachmann Times which operated at arms-length. In 2000 the club was reformed in-house under the name Bachmann Collectors Club (BCC) and members receive a quarterly magazine. Further information about this may be obtained by writing to the Club at Bachmann Europe plc, Moat Way, Barwell, Leicestershire LE9 8EY.

Bachmann frequently offer members limited edition models and these are marked in the tables below with 'BCC'.

Dates - It is difficult to date Bachmann Branchline models by their appearance in catalogues as some models have not been ready for distribution until one or two years after their catalogue launch. As near as possible, in the tables below, we have given the years in which we believe the models first appeared in the shops. Please bear in mind that these may sometimes be incorrect.

A single date has been given because Bachmann operated a batch production supply system. Generally there is only an initial batch of models which, when sold-out, is not repeated. Instead, the model is either dropped from the catalogue or replaced by a similar model renumbered and often improved in finish. Some models have been available in the shops for several years from the date of the initial production - the length of time being dependent on the popularity of the model.

Catalogue Numbers - Generally, the addition of a letter suffix to a catalogue number indicates a modification of some kind to the model. This could be a change of number or an alteration to the chassis. For general release models the letters are taken from the start of the alphabet i.e. 'A', 'B', 'C' etc. but for commissioned models (specials ordered by shops or societies) lettering starts with 'Z' and works upwards from the bottom of the alphabet. (See also the note on 'Wagon Numbers' in the Wagons section, as this may also apply to locos and coaches).

More recently, some locomotive catalogue numbers have received a **'DC'** or **'DS'** suffix. DC indicates that the locomotive already carries a decoder chip and DS that it also fitted for 'sound'.

Buyers should be aware that box numbering errors have sometimes occurred and that boxes with a 'new' number suffix sometimes contain a model with the old number.

Boxes - wooden presentation cases (**wpc**) have been provided for a number of limited or special editions.

Weathering - Bachmann were one of the first to turn out models with a weathered finish (although Tri-ang had tried it in 1965). It started with wagons and spread to locomotive models. To save space, weathered models are coded in the text with a **'W'** after the colour

Heritage Range - From 2005, a number of models, based on subjects in the National Collection, were released by Bachmann in a new 'Heritage Range'.

LOCOMOTIVES

Bachmann took the 'Spectrum' quality of their American range and applied it to the British models to give very superior performance far removed from the old Mainline standard. A skew armature replaceable Mabuchi can motor was fitted with an excellent gear drive and brass flywheel.

'DCC Ready' - (Catalogue No. suffix) - Since 2003, some locomotives have been released ready to receive a DCC decoder ('DCC ready'). This means that they are fitted inside with a blanked-off socket ready to take a DCC decoder (chip).

DC8 or DC21 -This indicates the pins on the decoder that the fitted socket will take. The 21 pin decoders allow for a greater number of functions.

DC Fitted - From 2006 some locomotives were marketed with a DCC decoder already fitted. As mentioned above, these carry a 'DC' catalogue number suffix.

'DS' - From 2006, a selection of locomotives were equipped with DCC sound units and these carry a 'DS' catalogue number suffix.

Cat No.	Company, Number, Colour, Dates	£	£

Tank Engines

L1. Freelance 0-4-0ST (2004)

Originally 'Percy' for the overseas market.

(30-040)DC	**31 *Greg*** red, chip fitted, ex-set - *04*	20	NA
30-905	**311** GWR (shirt-button) green - *05*	20	25

L2. Freelance 0-6-0ST (2007)

0-6-0ST Digby [L2] (Tony Wright)

30-920	**7** LNER green DC8 - *07*	20	26
(30-941)DC	**3 *Digby*** red DC8 ex-set - *07*	20	26

L3. Freelance 0-6-0T (2004)

Originally 'Thomas' for the overseas market.

(30-005)DC	**4 *Billy*** green ex-set - *04*	20	NA
(30-040)DC	**49 *Stuart*** blue ex-set - *04*	20	NA
30-900	**2005** red - *05*	20	25

L4a. GWR Class 57xx 0-6-0PT (ex-Mainline) (1991)

imp = improved chassis. Although shown as solo models in the catalogue from 1993, these may not have seen their debut until later. The plastic used for the first batch of loco bodies was found to be susceptible to damage from lubricating oil and so they were withdrawn.

31-900	**7760** Great Western green - *93*	30	40
31-900A	**7702** GWR green imp - *96*	25	35
31-901A	**8700** GWR (button) green imp - *96*	25	35
31-903*	**L94** London Transport maroon imp Sp Edn 500 (LT Museum) - *99*	40	55
(30-200)	**L91** LT maroon ex-sets - *91*	80	NA
(30-201)	**L99** LT maroon ex-sets - *93*	30	NA
31-901	**5796** BRb black - *93*	30	40
31-902	**7754** BRb black - *93*	30	40
31-902A	**5775** BRc black imp - *96*	25	35

* Box unnumbered.

L4b. GWR Class 57xx 0-6-0PT (B) (2005)

A Collett design of 1929 with a Churchward cab. The model was retooled for re-release in 2005 with new cab and bunker tooling and fitted on the Class 8750 chassis. It was fitted with circular water filler and lamp brackets. Good interior cab detail.

32-215	**5775** GWR green - *10*	45	58
32-210	**5786** GWR green - *05*	40	52
32-213DC	**7788** GWR green DC8 - *07*	55	66
(30-075)	**5764** Great Western green ex-Local Freight set - *10*	50	NA
32-214	**5766** BRb black DC8 - *09*	45	56
32-211	**7739** BRb black DC8 - *05*	40	52
32-212	**5757** BRc black - *05*	40	52
32-210Z	**L99** London Transport maroon Sp Edn 504 (Kernow MRC) - *not made*	NA	NA

Class 57xx Stephenson Clarke [L4b] (Bachmann)

32-210Z	**L95** London Transport maroon Sp Edn 504 (Kernow Model Rail Centre) - *07*	50	60
32-210Y	**7754** NCB green W Sp Edn 504 (ModelZone) - *10*	60	70
32-200K	**3650** Stephenson Clarke blue W Sp Edn 504 (BCC) - *10*	45	56

L4c. GWR Class 57xx (8750) 0-6-0PT (B) (1999)

A heavier later version of the Collett 57xx Class dating from 1929. They had a modified cab with angular windows front and back.

(32-010)	**3705** GWR green ex-Coaler train set - *05*	35	NA
32-200	**9643** GWR green - *99*	35	45
32-200A	**6752** GWR green blue spot - *01*	35	45
32-208	**6757** GWR green - *10*	45	58
32-200B	**3715** GWR green - *03*	35	45
32-204	**4612** Great Western green - *06*	40	52
32-206	**8751** Great Western green DC8 - *08*	40	53
32-201	**8763** BRb lined black - *99*	35	45
32-205	**9736** BRb black DC8 - *06*	40	52
32-200DC	**9759** BRc black DC8 - *06*	52	64
32-207	**9761** BRc black DC8 - *09*	45	56
32-202	**4672** BRc black - *99*	35	45
32-202A*	**9735** BRc black - *02*	40	48
32-202B	**9753** BRc black - *04*	40	48

32-203	**4666** BRc black W - *03*	40	48

* Box found labelled '9735'.

L5. LMS Class 3F 'Jinty' 0-6-0T (B) (2004)

A Fowler development of Johnson's 'Jinty' which became the standard shunting engine on the LMS in 1924. Xkh = without 'keyhole' in the tank sides.

32-226W	**16440** MR red Sp Edn 504 (Cheltenham Model Centre) (32-225W) - *05*	45	56
32-225Y	**18** NCC black Y Class Ltd Edn 250 - *05*	40	55
32-225Z	**19** NCC black Y Class Ltd Edn 250 - *05*	40	55
32-225V	**24** S&DJR blue Sp Edn 504 (Cheltenham Model Centre) - *05*	45	58
32-227	**7524** LMS black - *04*	40	48
32-227A	**7309** LMS black - *09*	45	56
32-226	**47354** BRb black - *04*	40	48
32-229	**47279** BRb black (K&WVR) Xkh - *05*	40	53
(30-016)	**47310** BRb lined black Xkh ex-'Jinty Suburban' set - *06*	40	NA
32-230	**47483** BRb black - *09*	45	56
32-225	**47410** BRc black - *04*	40	48
32-225DC	**47629** BRc black, chip fitted DC8 - *06*	48	62
32-225X	**47357** BRc red Sp Edn 500 *- *05*	65	90
32-228	**47506** BRc black Xkh - *not made*	NA	NA
32-228	**47266** BRc black Xkh - *05*	40	53
32-225U	**47472** BRc black W Sp Edn (Transport Models) - *06*	40	61

* This was initially released at the 2005 Toyfair as a gift for retailers. It is understood that over 100 were distributed this way. The remainder were bought by Bachmann Club members on the basis of a draw held in the autumn.

L6. LNER Class J72 0-6-0T (ex-Mainline) (1990)

Wilson Worsdell 1898 design for goods yard shunting. Similar to the last Mainline J72 but the drive slightly redesigned with an improved open frame motor driving on the centre axle and leaving the cab clear. The wheelsets were also improved and the problem of axles splitting was resolved. * full length ejector pipe

(30-060)	**581** LNER green ex- Kader 60th Anniv, pack - *08*	50	NA
31-050	**8680** LNER green - *90*	28	35
31-050A	**8680** LNER green lined - *99*	30	40
31-054	**2313** LNER black lined * - *96*	25	35
31-057	**8693** LNER black unlined * - *98*	30	40
31-052	**68680** BRb black lined - *90*	28	35
31-055	**68680** BRb green lined * - *96*	25	30

LNER Class J72 0-6-0T [L6]

31-055A	**68737** BRb black W * - *02*	30	45
(30-100)	**68745** BRb plain black Ross 'pop' valves ex-set - *94*	50	NA
31-053	**69012** BRc plain black - *90*	27	35
31-056	**69025** BRc plain black * - *96*	27	35
31-058	**68727** BRc black W - *05*	32	45
31-059	**69022** BRc plain black - *08*	40	51
31-051	**69023** BRc/NER light green - *90*	25	35
31-056	**68723** BRc/NER light green - *05*	30	41

L7. GWR Class 56xx 0-6-2T (B) (2002)

Collett designed heavy freight tank of 1924 to work coal trains in the Welsh valleys. Tall and short safety valve covers have been modelled.

32-076	**6676** Great Western green - *02*	35	45
32-075	**5667** GWR green - *02*	35	45
32-075A	**6600** GWR green - *03*	35	45
32-075B	**6606** GWR green DC8 - *05*	38	51
32-075C	**6623** GWR green DC8 - *10*	38	54
32-075C	**5623** GWR green DC8 - *not made*	NA	NA
32-079	**6624** BRb plain black - *03*	35	45
32-081	**5660** BRb plain black W DC8 - *06*	40	53
32-082	**5639** BRc plain black W DC8 - *10*	40	57
32-076DC	**6671** BRc lined green DC8 - *06*	50	63
32-077	**5658** BRc lined green - *02*	35	45
(30-055)DC	As above with DC8 ex-set - *06*	45	NA
(32-015)	**6622** BRc plain green DC8 ex-set - *06*	35	45
32-080	**5601** BRc plain green - *03*	35	45

L8a. GWR Class 45xx 2-6-2T (B) (2003)

Churchward designed tank dating from 1906. Heavy diecast chassis block, metal chimney, alternative smokebox doors and highly detailed cab interior.

32-127	**4550** GWR green - *03*	40	50
32-127A	**4527** GWR green - *04*	40	54
32-126	**4560** BRb plain black - *03*	40	50
32-128	**4573** BRb plain black W - *04*	45	56
32-129	**4557** BRb lined black - *07*	45	57
32-125DC	**4507** BRc lined green DC8 - *07*	50	69
32-125	**4566** BRc lined green - *03*	40	50
32-125A	**4569** BRc lined green - *04*	40	54

L8b. GWR Class 45xx (4575) 2-6-2T (B) (2004)

Collett modified 45XX tank dating from 1927. They had larger side tanks with sloping tops. Some were fitted for push-pull work. Heavy diecast chassis block and highly detailed cab. Sprung buffers and metal chimney.

32-136	**5555** Great Western green - *04*	40	54
32-135	**5531** GWR green - *04*	40	54
32-135A	**5565** GWR green - *08*	45	57
32-138	**5550** BRc green - *10*	45	64
32-137	**5559** BRb plain black - *not made*	NA	NA
32-137	**5500** BRb plain black - *04*	40	54
32-135Y	**5552** BRc lined green Ltd Edn 504 (Kernow Model Rail Centre) - *04*	45	65
32-135Z	**5553** BRc lined green Ltd Edn 1000 (BCC) - *04*	38	55

L9. LMS Ivatt Class 2MT 2-6-2T (1995)

Ivatt mixed traffic design of 1946. p-p = push-pull equipment.

31-453	**1206** LMS black - *95*	35	48
31-453A	**1202** LMS black - *98*	35	48

Ivatt ex-LMS Class 2MT 2-6-2T [L9]

31-450	**41221** BRb black p-p - *95*	30	44
31-450B	**41281** BRb lined black p-p - *98*	30	44
31-450E	**41273** BRb fine lined black p-p - *02*	40	52
31-451	**41241** BRb lined black - *95*	35	45
31-451A	**41250** BRb lined black - *96*	35	45
31-451C	**41247** BRb lined black - *00*	40	50
31-451D	**41243** BRb lined black - *01*	40	52
31-454	**41286** BRb lined black - *02*	40	50
31-450A	**41272** BRc black p-p plaque as 7000th loco from Crewe - *96*	35	50
31-450C	**41224** BRc lined black p-p - *00*	40	52
31-450D	**41324** BRc fine lined black p-p - *02*	40	52
31-452	**41313** BRc lined black - *95*	30	44
31-452A	**41202** BRc lined black - *96*	35	44
31-452B	**41233** BRc lined black - *98*	35	44
31-452C	**41304** BRc fine lined black - *01*	35	52
31-455	**41212** BRc lined black - *05*	40	52
31-456	**41264** BRc lined black - *08*	47	61
31-450K	**41241** KWVR lined maroon + headboard Sp Edn 650 (BCC) - *08*	47	61

L10. LNER Class V1 & V3 2-6-2T (1992)

Gresley suburban passenger tank locomotive of 1930. hb = hopper bunker. csp = cranked steam pipes. West = Westinghouse pump

31-600	**7684** LNER green (V3) hb - *92*	32	48
31-608	**7684** LNER green hb (V3) - *99*	40	52
31-603	**466** LNER black (V1) hb csp - *92*	34	48

31-606	**448** LNER lined black hb (V1) - *97*	35	48
31-606A	**2911** LNER black csp (V1) - *00*	40	52
31-607	**67684** BRa lined light green hb (V3) - *97*	30	44
31-602	**67664** BRb black (V1) hb - *92*	32	48
31-605	**67610** BRb lined black (V1)* csp - *96*	35	48
31-609	**67673** BRb black West hb (V1)* - *99*	40	52
31-609A	**67669** BRb lined black West hb (V3) - *02*	45	57
31-610	**67645** BRb lined black csp (V1) - *02*	40	52
31-601	**67601** BRc black (V1) csp - *92*	45	57
31-604	**67666** BRc black (V3) hb - *96*	35	48
31-611	**67635** BRc lined black W (V1) - *02*	45	57
31-612	**67682** BRc lined black W West hb - *06*	45	57
31-613	**67628** BRc lined black csp - *09*	50	63

* The box indicates that this was a V3.

L11. BR Class 3MT 2-6-2T (2009)

Riddles mixed traffic tank locomotive of 1952. The model features an opening smoke box door, highly detailed cab interior and different styles of lamp brackets and cab roofs with small or large opening air vents. Models are correctly fitted with either fluted or plain coupling rods and Western Region locomotives feature the extra prototypical handrail on the top of the boiler. It has an 8 pin decoder socket. SR = BR(SR) allocation with extra lamp brackets for white discs.

31-975A	**82020** BRb black - *10*	60	78
31-975	**82029** BRb lined black - *09*	60	76

BR Riddles Class 3MT 2-6-2T [L11]

31-977	**82016** BRb lined black SR - *09*	60	76
31-978	**82019** BRc black - *10*	60	78
31-976	**82005** BRc lined green - *09*	60	76
31-976A	**82030** BRc green - *10*	60	78

L12. LMS Fairburn Class 4P 2-6-4T (B) (2006)

Fairburn designed suburban passenger tank of 1945. DCC ready, heavy internal weights, glazed cab windows and detailed pipework.

32-875	**2691** LMS plain black DC8 - *06*	55	70
32-876	**42096** BRb lined black DC8 - *07*	55	70
32-878	**42691** BRb lined black DC8 - *08*	60	80
32-877	**42073** BRc lined black DC8 - *06*	55	70
32-879	**42267** BRc lined black W DC8 - *08*	55	83
32-875K	**2085** CR blue Ltd Edn 504 (BCC) - *06*	85	100

L13. BR Class 4MT Tank 2-6-4T (B) (2001)

Riddles designed mixed traffic locomotive of 1951. DCC ready, separately fitted water tanks and very detailed cab interior. The original batch of these had a smokebox door that could be opened but, fearing that they would be unable to effect repairs if the door mounting were to get damaged, Bachmann subsequently released them with the door lightly glued in place. The 4MT tanks made from 2002 onwards were fitted with higher quality 3-pole motors and lower gearing.

32-350	**80061** BRb lined black - *01*	45	58
32-350DC	**80009** BRb lined black DC8 - *06*	65	82
32-352	**80032** BRb lined black - *02*	50	64
32-355	**80136** BRb lined black - *03*	50	64
32-358	**80118** BRb lined black DC8 - *08*	60	78
32-359	**80153** BRb black - *10*	65	82
32-351	**80097** BRc lined black - *01*	45	60
32-351DC	**80140** BRc lined black DC8 - *08*	70	92
32-353	**80135** BRc lined green - *02*	50	75
32-354	**80002** BRc lined black - *02*	50	64
32-354A	**80120** BRc lined black W - *03*	55	68
32-356	**80038** BRc lined black W - *04*	55	68
32-357	**80079** BRc lined black DC8 - *06*	55	70

Tender Locos

L14. GWR 'City' Class 37xx 4-4-0 (B) (2009)

Following on from the success of the Prototype 'Deltic' diesel locomotive produced exclusively for the National Railway Museum, the second model ordered by the museum was Great Western 4-4-0 *City of Truro*. This was one of ten locomotives built at Swindon in 1903, with 3440 becoming the 2000th locomotive to be built there. A further ten locomotives were rebuilt from Atbara Class locomotives between 1902 and 1909 to make a total of 20 locomotives in the class.

31-725 NRM	**3440** ***City of Truro*** GWR green with brown chassis Sp Edn (NRM) sold in special platinum box - *09*	90	180

GWR City of Truro 4-4-0 [L14]

31-725 NRM	as above but in a standard box GWR - *10*	90	145
31-725A NRM	**3717** ***City of Truro*** GWR green with Sp Edn (NRM) - *10*	90	150

L15. GWR Class 2251 'Collett Goods' 0-6-0 (B) (1998)

Collett's standard 0-6-0 goods locomotive of 1930. copper capped chimney. ch = Churchward tender.

32-300	**3202** GWR green ch - *98*	35	50
32-304	**2294** GWR (button) green ch - *05*	45	57
32-301	**2260** BRb black - *98*	35	50
32-303	**2251** BRb green - *99*	35	50
32-305	**2217** BRb plain black W ch - *05*	45	59
32-306	**2253** BRb plain black W ch - *10*	45	60
32-300DC	**2244** BRc lined green DC8 ch - *07*	55	70
32-302	**2277** BRc lined green - *98*	35	50

L16. MR Class M (LMS 3F) 0-6-0 (2011)

These were 3F Class 0-6-0 tender locomotives of the Midland Railway, some rebuilt from earlier 2F 0-6-0 types. The Bachmann model is the Midland Railway M Class. Like all 3F Class locomotives they underwent considerable rebuilding during their lifetime and were seen all over the former Midland Railway system. The tender is the modified 3250 gallonJohnson type.

31-627	**3205** LMS plain black - *11*	55	70
31-626	**43186** BRb plain black - *11*	55	70
31-625	**43474** BRc plain black - *11*	55	70

L17. LNER Class J39 0-6-0 (1994)

Gresley's standard 0-6-0 heavy freight locomotive of 1926. st = stepped tender. gst = group standard 4,200 gallon tender

31-850	**1974** LNER lined black - *94*	32	52
31-853	**1996** LNER black - *96*	35	52
31-855	**1856** LNER lined black - *00*	35	54
31-860	**1496** LNER black st - *99*	35	54
31-851	**64964** BRb black - *94*	32	48
31-851A	**64958** BRb black - *96*	35	52
31-854	**64960** BRb black W gst - *05*	40	54
31-861	**64838** BRb black st - *99*	35	48
31-855A	**64897** BRb black gst - *07*	45	59
31-865	**64838** BRc black st - *07*	45	59
31-852	**64967** BRc black - *94*	32	48
31-852A	**64970** BRc black - *96*	35	54
31-862	**64791** BRc black st - *99*	35	54
31-864	**64841** BRc black W st - *05*	40	56

L18a. GWR Class 43xx 2-6-0 (ex-Mainline)(1996)

Churchward's mixed traffic design of 1911. Sprung buffers.

GWR Class 43xx 2-6-0 [L18a]

31-829	**4331** Great () Western lined green - *01*	40	54

31-830	**5321** Great Western green - *06*	48	60
31-825	**4318** GWR green - *96*	30	48
31-827	**5355** GWR (button) green - *96*	30	48
31-828	**5370** BRb lined black red nameplates - *01*	40	48
31-831	**4358** BRb lined green - *08*	50	63
31-826	**6384** BRc unlined green - *96*	30	48
31-827A	**4377** BRc lined green - *03*	40	50
31-2000/2	**5358** BRc lined ex-Cambrian Coast Express set - *01*	65	NA

L18b. GWR Class 93xx 2-6-0 (partly ex-Mainline) (1992)

Collett's 1932 version of the Churchward 43xx mixed traffic locomotive, easily recognised by its cab side windows.

31-801	**9319** GWR green - *92*	35	48
31-802	**9308** BRb black - *92*	35	48
31-803	**7332** BRc green - *92*	35	48

L19. LMS 'Crab' 2-6-0 (B) (2003)

Hughes/Fowler designed mixed traffic locomotive of 1926. DCC ready. cr = coal rail on tender. rt = riveted tender. .

32-175	**13098** LMS maroon - *03*	50	65
32-178	**2715** LMS lined black DC8 - *04*	60	77
32-176	**42765** BRb lined black cr - *03*	50	65
32-179	**42942** BRb lined black W cr, rt DC8 - *04*	60	76
32-177	**42789** BRc lined black cr, rt - *03*	50	65
32-180	**42919** BRc lined black cr, rt - *09*	65	83

L20. LMS Ivatt Class 2MT 2-6-0 (B) (2007)

Ivatt mixed design of 1946. DCC ready. Detailed pipework.

32-827	**6404** LMS black DC8 - *07*	58	72
32-830	**6402** LMS black DC8 - *08*	58	77
32-826	**46440** BRb lined black DC8 - *07*	58	72
32-826Z	**46443** BRc lined black W DC8 Sp Edn 504 (The Signal Box) - *07*	70	85
32-829	**46426** BRc lined black DC8 - *08*	58	77
32-825	**46521** BRc lined green DC8 - *07*	58	72
32-828	**46520** BRc lined green DC8 - *08*	58	77
32-825K	**46441** BRc maroon (livery in preservation) DC8 Sp Edn 504 (BCC) - *07*	65	73
32-829A	**46446** BRc lined black - *10*	68	80

L21. LMS Ivatt Class 4MT 2-6-0 (B)(2005)

Ivatt mixed traffic design of 1947 with the nickname 'Flying Pig'. DCC ready. dc = double chimney. sc = single chimney. tc = tablet catcher.

32-575	**3001** LMS black dc - *05*	60	78
32-575K	**43050** BR lined black Sp Edn (BCC) - *not made*	NA	NA
32-575K	**43050** BR lined black W Sp Edn 1000 (BCC) - *05*	60	77
32-577	**43160** BRb lined black - *05*	60	77
32-578	**43038** BRb lined black dc DC8 - *06*	60	78
32-586DC	**43154** BRb lined black sc tc - *07*	78	93
32-576	**43047** BRc lined black - *05*	60	77
32-579	**43096** BRc lined black sc DC8 - *06*	60	78
32-585	**43106** BRc lined black sc tc DC8 - *07*	65	82
32-580	**43019** BRc lined black W* sc DC8 - *07*	65	82

*Commemorating the last days of steam.

L22. LNER Gresley K3 2-6-0 (B) (2004)

Gresley heavy freight and occasional passenger locomotive of 1929. DCC ready. gst = group standard 4200 gallon tender. st = stepped tender.

32-275	**2934** LNER black gst DC8 - *05*	65	74
32-279	**1935** LNER green gst DC8 - *08*	70	82
32-276	**61932** BRb lined black gst - *04*	65	74
32-277	**61907** BRc lined black st DC8 - *05*	65	74
32-277	**61949** BRc lined black st - *04*	65	74
32-278	**61823** BRc lined black st - *08*	70	86
32-275K	**61811** BRc lined black W st Sp Edn 1,000 (BCC) - *04*	65	77

L23. SR Maunsell Class N 2-6-0 (B) (1998)

Maunsell 'Woolwich' designed mixed traffic locomotive of 1917. Early tenders on this model tended to derail and one batch of locos had footplates distorted which were replaced. wpc - wooden presentation case. sst = slope sided tender. xsd = no smoke deflectors.

32-150/1	**810** SE&CR grey Ltd Edn 1000 - *98*	50	NA
32-150/2	**1863** SR green Ltd Edn 1000 - *98*	50	NA
32-150	above two locos wpc* Kader 50th Anniversary - *98*	NA	165
32-153	**1824** SR olive green - *98*	45	60
32-153A	**1821** SR olive green - *99*	30	52
32-160	**1406** SR olive green xsd sst - *02*	40	62
32-163	**1404** SR olive green sst - *02*	40	62

SR Maunsell Class N 2-6-0 [L23]

32-155	**1854** SR malachite green - *00*	35	58
32-150Z	**31874 *Brian Fisk*** BRb black Sp Edn 500 (Beatties) wpc - *99*	85	145
32-152	**31813** BRb lined black - *98*	35	45
32-156	**31844** BRb lined black W - *02*	40	55
32-161	**31862** BRb lined black sst - *01*	40	55
32-151	**31860** BRc lined black - *98*	35	45
32-151A	**31816** BRc lined black - *99*	35	45
32-154	**31843** BRc lined black - *00*	35	45
32-162	**31401** BRc lined black sst - *01*	40	55
32-164	**31411** BRc lined black sst - *not made***	NA	NA
32-184	31406 BRc lined black sst - *08*	62	76
32-150W	**383** CIE grey+black Class K1 Sp Edn 640 (Murphy's Models) - *00*	45	75
32-150X	**376** (matt), **388** (gloss) CIE black Class K1 Sp Edn 640 (Murphy's Models) - *00*	45	75
32-150Y	**372, 385, 390**** CIE green Class K1 Sp Edn 504 (Murphy's Models) - *00*	50	75
(00651)	CIE green GSR Class K1 ex-set - *04*	60	NA

* Price quoted is for the complete set in a case. ** 3 alternative numbers supplied as transfers. *** 31411 was a right-hand drive loco and so unsuitable, as the model is a left-hand drive one. It was replaced by 31406.

L24. BR Riddles Class 4MT 2-6-0 (B) (2007)

Riddles mixed traffic design of 1953. DCC ready.

32-953DC	**76020** BRb lined blk BR2 tender DC8 - *07*	80	95
32-950	**76053** BRb lined black BR1B tender DC8 - *07*	65	80
32-952A	**76079** BRb lined black BR2 tender DC8 - *09*	70	86
32-951	**76069** BRc lined black BR1B tender DC8 - *07*	65	80
32-952	**76079** BRc lined black BR2 tender DC8 - *07*	68	83

L25. LNER Class V2 2-6-2 (1992)

Gresley express passenger or freight locomotive of 1936. Glazed cab. st = stepped tender. osp = outside steam pipes. wpc - wooden presentation case. dc = double chimney. spn = separate printed nameplates. gst = group standard 4200 gallon tender

Green Arrow

31-550	**4771** LNER green Ltd Edn* 1000 wpc - *92*	80	125
31-550A	**4771** LNER green as preserved *** - *08*	70	90
31-551	**60800** BRb black - *92*	50	65
31-559	**60800** BRc green Ltd Edn 500 - *00*	70	80
31-550	**60800** BRc green dc** - *04*	65	80
31-550	**60800** BRc green gst *** - *06*	68	82
31-555	**4801** LNER green - *92*	45	64
31-558	**4844 *Coldstreamer*** LNER green spn - *96*	50	65
31-560	**4806 *The Green Howard*** LNER green st - *99*	65	80
31-556	**3650** LNER unlined black - *92*	45	64
31-553	**60807** BRa black - *92*	45	64
31-553A	**60807** BRb black - *97*	45	64
31-557	**60884** BRb green osp - *97*	50	65
31-562	**60834** BRb lined black W st - *04*	50	65
31-552	**60964 *The Durham Light Infantry*** BRc green - *92*	50	65
31-554	**60903** BRc green dc - *92*	45	64
31-561	**60825** BRc green osp st - *99*	65	80
31-563	**60865** BRc green osp st - *09*	75	91

*This was Bachmann's 2nd limited edition and the certificates were numbered between 1001 and 2000. **This was incorrectly issued with a double chimney and so Bachmann supplied single chimney bodies, on request, as replacements. *** As preserved and issued as Heritage Range model.

L26. GWR 'Manor' Class 4-6-0 (ex-Mainline) (1991)

A Collett designed locomotive, as a lighter version of a Grange. Coming in 1938, this was quite a late introduction for the GWR. en = etched metal nameplates.

31-300	**7802 *Bradley Manor*** GWR green - *91*	35	58

31-304	**7800 *Torquay Manor*** GWR (button) green - *96*	35	64
31-305	**7805 *Broome Manor*** GWR green - *96*	35	64
(30-021)	**7811 *Dunley Manor*** GWR (shirt-button) green ex-'Cambrian Coast Express' set - *06*	70	NA

Ex-GWR Ramsbury Manor [L26]

31-300Z	**7816 *Frilsham Manor*** BR green, black metalwork en Sp Edn 500 (Brunswick Railways Ltd) - *99*	40	80
31-301	**7820 *Dinmore Manor*** BRb unlined green - *91*	35	52
31-303	**7829 *Ramsbury Manor*** BRb lined black red plates - *91*	35	58
31-303A	**7829 *Ramsbury Manor*** BRb lined black red plates modified chassis - *99*	35	60
31-307	**7813 *Freshford Manor*** BRb black red plates modified chassis - *02*	45	65
(30-061)	**7819 *Hinton Manor***, BRb, black, red plates, modified chassis, ex-GWR 175 Severn Valley Sp Edn 500 (SVR) set in a wood presentation case** - *10*	50	NA
31-302	**7823 *Hook Norton Manor*** BRc lined green - *91*	35	65
31-306	**7822 *Foxcote Manor*** BRc lined green - *96*	35	60
31-308	**7825 *Lechlade Manor*** BRc green - *06*	50	68
31-2000	**7828 *Odney Manor*** BRc green Ltd Edn 1000 + **5358** Class 43XX + 6 Mk1 coaches 'Cambrian Coast Express' set wpc - *01*	NA	140*
31-2000/1	**7828 *Odney Manor*** BRc green from above set - *01*	70	NA

* Price shown is for complete 'Cambrian Coast Express' set (31-2000). ** The model was sold with 4930 *Hagley Hall* as a celebratory set.

L27a. GWR Class 4900 'Hall' 4-6-0 (B) (2005)

Collett introduced the 'Hall' Class in 1924, based on the success of a 'Saint' Class locomotive he had rebuilt. DCC ready. Available with either 4000 gallon Collett tender (Col) or Hawksworth flat-sided tender (Hks).

32-003	**4936 *Kinlet Hall*** Great()Western green Col DC8 - *05*	55	76
32-003Z	**4953 *Pitchford Hall*** Great () Western green DC8 Sp Edn 750 (Buffers) - *07*	75	90
32-004	**4970 *Sketty Hall*** Great () Western green Col DC8 - *09*	75	87
32-004	**9614 *Langton Hall*** Great () Western green Col DC8 - *not made*	NA	NA
(30-061)	**4930 *Hagley Hall***, GWR (button), green, ex-GWR 175 Severn Valley SP Edn 500 (SVR) set in a wood presentation case * - *10*	75	NA
32-002	**5960 *Saint Edmund Hall*** BRb lined black Col DC8 - *05*	55	78
32-000DC	**5927 *Guild Hall*** BRc green Hks DC8 - *07*	75	93
32-001	**6937 *Conyngham Hall*** BRc green Col DC8 - *05*	55	78

* The model was sold with 7819 *Hinton Manor* as a celebratory set.

L27b. GWR Class 6959 'Modified Hall' 4-6-0 (ex-Replica) (1996)

Hawksworth's 'Modified Hall' of 1944. st = stepped tender. Ht = Hawksworth flat sided tender. wpc = wooden presentation case

31-777	**6962 *Soughton Hall*** G()W green st - *96*	35	62
31-779	**6960 *Raveningham Hall*** G()W green, 9ct gold nameplates 9th Ltd Edn 2000 wpc - *97*	40	85
31-778	**6969 *Wraysbury Hall*** BRb green Ht - *96*	35	62
31-775	**6990 *Witherslack Hall*** BRb black red plates - *96*	35	62
31-776	**7915 *Mere Hall*** BRc green st - *96*	35	62
(00639)	***Hogwarts Castle*** red ex-US set - *01*	40	NA

L28. LMS 'Parallel Boiler Royal Scot' 4-6-0 (ex-Mainline) (1994)

Fowler's express passenger, parcel or fitted freight design of 1927. Ft = Fowler 3500 gallon tender with coal rails. St = Stanier 4,000 gallon tender. xsd = no smoke deflectors. wpc - wooden presentation case. cre = coal rail extensions. crest = crest on cabsides and number on tender. The most obvious feature is the boiler with parallel sides (i.e. not tapered).

LMS Maroon

31-275	**6100 *Royal Scot*** St brass bell special nameplates 4th Ltd Edn 1000 (3001>) wpc - *94*	75	125
31-275Z	**6110 *Grenadier Guardsman*** Ft xsd crest Sp Edn 500 (Beatties) wpc - *98*	75	120
31-277	**6112 *Sherwood Forester*** Ft xsd - *94*	40	64
31-279	**6130 *The West Yorkshire Regiment*** Ft cre angled deflectors - *96*	40	64

LMS Royal Scot Class The Lancashire Fusilier [L28]

31-280Z	**6131 *The Royal Warwickshire Regiment*** maroon St Sp Edn (Castle Trains) - *09*	70	85
31-280	**6106 *Gordon Highlander*** St - *98*	50	65
31-281	**6155 *The Lancer*** Ft - *02*	55	70
31-283	**6119 *The Lancashire Fusilier*** Ft - *06*	55	71
31-276	**6134 *The Cheshire Regiment*** LMS black St curved top deflectors - *94*	40	60
31-278	**46148 *The Manchester Regiment*** BRb green St - *95*	40	60
31-282	**46151 *The Royal Horse Guardsman*** BRb green W St - *02*	60	75
31-284	**46165 *The Ranger (12th London Regt)*** BRb green St - *08*	60	76

L29a. LMS 'Rebuilt Royal Scot' 4-6-0 (ex-Mainline) (1996)

Stanier commenced rebuilding the whole of the 'Royal Scot' Class in 1943 and from 1947, smoke deflectors were fitted. The xsd = no smoke deflectors. St = Stanier 4,000 gallon tender. wpc - wooden presentation case.

31-226	**6133 *Green Howards*** LMS black xsd - *97*	50	65
31-225	**46102 *Black Watch*** BRb green etched brass military crest - *96*	45	64
31-277Z	**46159 *The Royal Air Force*** ** BRc green Sp Edn 500 (Jennings Models) - *00*	65	80
31-228	**46141 *The North Staffordshire Regiment*** BRb green - *04*	50	65
31-275X	**46169 *The Boy Scout*** BRb green St - *01*	65	80
31-275W	**46168 *The Girl Guide*** BRc green St - *01*	65	80
31-275Y	Above 2 models Sp Edn 350 wpc (TMC) 'Mancunian' headboard - *99*	NA*	175
31-227	**46162 *Queens Westminster Rifleman*** BRc green - *97*	50	65
(30-020)	**46100 *Royal Scot*** BRb green St ex-'Royal Scot' set - *?*	50	65

* Price quoted is for the pair in the presentation box. ** Commemorating the 60th Anniversary of the Battle of Britain.

L29b. LMS 'Rebuilt Royal Scot' 4-6-0 (B) (2007)

All new tooling. Stanier commenced rebuilding the whole of the 'Royal Scot' Class in 1943 and from 1947, fitted smoke deflectors. The xsd = no smoke deflectors. St = Stanier 4,000 gallon tender. DCC ready.

31-525	**6166 *London Rifle Brigade*** LMS black xsd st - *not made*	NA	NA
31-526	**46115 *Scots Guardsman*** BRb green St - *not made*	NA	NA
31-527DC	**46148 *The Manchester Regiment*** BRc green st - *not made*	NA	NA

L30a. LMS 'Patriot' 4-6-0 (B) (2008)

Fowler's mixed traffic loco of 1930 of which 52 were built. Fowler tender and etched metal smoke deflectors. DCC ready.

31-212	**5541 *Duke of Sutherland*** LMS maroon DC8 - *08*	85	102
31-210	**45503 *The Royal Leicestershire Regiment*** BRb green DC8 - *08*	85	102
31-211	**45543 *Home Guard*** BRc green DC8 - *08*	85	102

L30b. LMS 'Rebuilt Patriot' 4-6-0 (ex-Mainline) (1991)

Ivatt's 1946 rebuild of Fowler's 'Patriot' Class. Stanier 4,000 gallon tender. xsd = no smoke deflectors.

31-202	**5526 *Morecambe and Heysham*** LMS black xsd - *96*	40	64

31-200	**45528** BRa black - *91*	38	64
31-203	**45528 *R.E.M.E*** BRb green - *01*	50	68
31-201	**45545 *Planet*** BRc green - *91*	45	60

L31a. LMS 'Jubilee' Class 5XP 4-6-0 (ex-Mainline) (1990)

Stanier's 1934 standard Class 5 express passenger locomotive for all but the heaviest duties. sc = single chimney. dc = double chimney. en = etched nameplate. Ft = Fowler tender with coal rails. St = Stanier 4,000 gallon tender. wpc = wooden presentation case. Later with sprung buffers.

31-150A	**5699 *Galatea*** LMS maroon St Sp Edn 600 (Loco Marketing Services) red card presentation box - *96*	100	150
31-154	**5721 *Impregnable*** LMS maroon St - *94*	40	64
31-155	**5699 *Galatea*** LMS maroon Ft - *94*	47	64
31-155A	**5699 *Galatea*** LMS maroon Ft - *00*	35	64
31-157	**5684 *Jutland*** LMS maroon St ** - *00*	45	70
31-150	**5552 *Silver Jubilee*** LMS black* 1st Ltd Edn 500 (numbered 501>) wpc - *90*	250	330
31-159	**5711 *Courageous*** LMS black Ft ** - *03*	45	65
31-152	**45568 *Western Australia*** black BRb (small) Ft - *90*	45	66
31-158	**45742 *Connaught*** BRb green St ** - *00*	45	65
31-150X	**45682 *Trafalgar*** BRb green St Ltd Edn 1,000 wpc - *05*	55	96
31-150T	**45670 *Howard of Effingham*** BRb green St en - *01*	45	75
31-150S	**45679 *Armada*** BRc green Ft en - *01*	45	75
31-150Y	above 2 locos wpc Sp Edn 250 (TMC) - *00*	NA	175
31-150V	**45733 *Novelty*** BRb green St en - *01*	45	75
31-150U	**45732 *Sanspareil*** BRc green St en - *01*	45	75
31-150Z	above 2 locos wpc Sp Edn 250 (TMC) 'The Rainham Trials' - *00*	NA	175
31-151	**45552 *Silver Jubilee*** BRc green en St - *90*	40	60
31-153	**45596 *Bahamas*** BRc green dc St - *90*	48	68
31-156	**45715 *Invincible*** BRc green Ft - *97*	40	62
31-156A	**45715 *Invincible*** BRc green Ft - *99*	45	62
31-160	**45697 *Achilles*** BRc green W St - *05*	55	73

* 1930s livery with chrome plated fittings. The chrome plating was applied before the black paint and the latter tends to peel off. ** Single and double chimneys supplied with the model.

L31b. LMS 'Jubilee' Class 5XP 4-6-0 (B) (2007)

Stanier's 1934 standard Class 5 express passenger locomotive. Opening smokebox door and fall plates. All new tooling. sc = single chimney. dc = double chimney. en = etched nameplate. Ft = Fowler tender with coal rails. St = Stanier 4,000 gallon tender (r=riveted, w=welded). DS = fitted with digital sound.

31-185	**5563 *Australia*** LMS maroon Ft DC8 - *07*	80	95
31-175K	**5593 *Kolhapur*** LMS maroon Sp Edn (BCC) - *08*	80	95
31-175	**45611 *Hong Kong*** BRb green sc St(r) DC8 - *07*	80	95
31-175Z	**45637 *Windward Islands*** BRb green St Sp Edn (ModelZone) DC8 - *07*	80	105

Ex-LMS Jubilee Class Baroda [L31b]

31-175Y	**45609 *Gilbert and Ellice Islands*** BRb green Ft Sp Edn 500 (Rails) DC8 - *07*	80	105
31-177DS	**45593 *Kolhapur*** BRb green DS DC21 - *10*	190	225
31-176DC	**45562 *Alberta*** BRc green sc St(w) DC8 - *07*	85	106
31-186	**45587 *Baroda*** BRc green sc Ft DC8 - *09*	85	101
31-176Z	**45596 *Bahamas*** BRc green W dc St Sp Edn 504 (*Hornby Magazine*) - *09*	90	115
31-178DC	**45659 *Drake*** BRc green St(r) sc - *10*	90	114

L32. LMS 'Rebuilt Jubilee' 4-6-0 (1991)

Only two 'Jubilees' were rebuilt with a larger boiler and double chimney and this was in 1942. xsd = no smoke deflectors. Stanier tender.

31-250	**45735 *Comet*** BRa black xsd - *91*	45	64
31-251	**45736 *Phoenix*** BRc green - *91*	45	64

L33. LNER Class B1 4-6-0 (ex-Replica) (1994)

Thompson design mixed traffic loco of 1942.

31-711	**1189 *Sir William Gray*** LNER green - *07*	55	70
31-700	**1264** LNER green - *95*	30	56
31-705	**1306 *Mayflower*** LNER green 9ct gold nameplates wpc 8th Ltd Edn 2000 - *96*	60	85
31-706	**1041 *Roedeer*** LNER lined black - *98*	45	62
31-707	**61002 *Impala*** BRa light green - *98*	45	62
31-712	**61000 *Springbok*** BRb lined black - *07*	55	70
31-701	**61241 *Viscount Ridley*** BRb black - *94*	40	62
31-710	**61251 *Oliver Bury*** BRb lined black, electric lights - *not made*	NA	NA

Ex-LNER Class B1 Gazelle [L33]

31-710	**61251 *Oliver Bury*** BRc lined black, electric lights - *06*	55	67
31-701A	**61399** BRb black - *96*	35	55
31-700Z	**61247 *Lord Burghley*** BRc lined black W Sp Edn 500 (SMC) - *03*	55	95
31-702	**61354** BRc black - *94*	35	55
31-702A	**61190** BRc black - *96*	40	58
31-703	**61010 *Wildebeeste*** BRc black - *96*	35	62
31-708	**61003 *Gazelle*** BRc lined black - *03*	45	64
31-713	**61003 *Gazelle*** BRc lined black - *10*	55	73
31-709	**61008 *Kudu*** BRc black W - *05*	50	65
31-710	**61009 *Hartebeeste*** * BRc black Sp Edn 250 (Rails) wpc - *96*	75	95
31-710A	**61018 *Gnu**** BRc black Sp Edn 100 (Rails) wpc - *96*	95	110

*61009 *Hartebeeste* and 61018 *Gnu* were finished by Fox for Rails of Sheffield and some may therefore consider these to be Code 3 models.

L34. SR 'Lord Nelson' Class 4-6-0 (1992)

The model is based on a Maunsell designed express passenger locomotive of 1926 in its final form as rebuilt by Bulleid. Palitoy had started work on this model before it stopped production on the Mainline Railways range and Bachmann took over the project. There were slight tooling revisions made before the model was re-released in 2006. osc = original small chimney

31-404	**855 *Robert Blake*** SR olive green, osc - *96*	48	72
31-400	**850 *Lord Nelson*** SR malachite green 9ct gold nameplates 3rd Ltd Edn 1000 * wpc - *92*	90	120
31-401	**864 *Sir Martin Frobisher*** SR malachite green - *92*	40	72
31-407	**856 *Lord St.Vincent*** SR malachite - *98*	45	72
31-402	**30851 *Sir Francis Drake*** BRb green - *92*	45	72
31-405	**30852 *Sir Walter Raleigh*** BRb green - *96*	45	72
31-408	**30850 *Lord Nelson'*** BRb green** - *06*	65	82
31-409	**30865 *Sir John Hawkins*** BRb green - *08*	70	83
31-403	**30861 *Lord Anson*** BRc green - *92*	45	72
31-406	**30850 *Lord Nelson*** BRc green - *98*	50	75

* numbering of certificates start at 2001. ** Issued as Heritage Range model.

L35a. BR Class 4MT 4-6-0 (ex-Mainline) (1990)

Riddles designed mixed traffic locomotive of 1951. Sprung buffers. dc = double chimney.

31-100	**75014** BRb black BR2 tender - *96*	35	48
31-100A	**75059** BRb black BR2 tender - *98*	45	55
31-102	**75073** BRb black BR1B tender - *90*	35	48
31-102A	**75072** BRb black BR1B tender - *98*	45	55
31-108	**75063** BRb black W - *not made*	NA	NA
31-108	**75065**** BRb black W BR1B tender - *02*	45	60
31-103	**75020** BRc black dc BR2 tender - *90*	36	48
31-105	**75078** BRc black dc BR1B tender - *90*	36	48
31-105A	**75075** BRc black dc BR2 tender - *98*	45	55
31-101	**75023** BRc green BR2 tender - *96*	35	48
31-104	**75069** BRc green dc BR1B tender - *90*	35	48
31-106	**75029*** BRc green dc BR2 tender - *90*	40	50
31-106A	**75003** BRc green dc BR2 tender - *98*	35	55
31-107	**75027** BRc green BR2 tender - *02*	40	55

*This was supplied with brass nameplates for *The Green Knight* which were made for Bachmann by Jackson Evans. ** The box carries the number '75063' and describes the tender as 'BR18' instead of 'BR1B'.

L35b. BR Class 4MT 4-6-0 (B) (2008)

Riddles designed mixed traffic locomotive of 1951. Sprung buffers. dc = double chimney. sc = single chimney.

(30-060)	**75001** BRc green ex-Kader 60th Anniv, pack - *08*	90	NA
31-117DC	**75074** BRb black BR1B tender sc DC8 - *08*	85	105

BR Riddles Class 4MT 4-6-0 [L35b]

31-115	**75027** BRc green W* sc DC8 - *08*	78	92
31-116	**75069** BRc green BR1B tender dc DC8 - *08*	78	92
31-118	**75033** BRc black BR2 tender sc DC8 - *08*	78	92

*Commemorating the last days of steam.

L36. BR Class 5MT 4-6-0 (B) (2002)

Riddles designed mixed traffic locomotive of 1951. Optional etched nameplates, DCC ready, removable coal load and different tenders and whistle positions. The models were fitted with higher quality 3-pole motors and lower gearing. wp = without Westinghouse pump. sc = single chimney.

32-502	**73082 *Camelot*** BRb black BR1B - *02*	55	65
32-503	**73030** BRb lined black BR1 tender wp DC8 - *03*	70	88
31-503Z	**73050 *City of Peterborough*** BRb lined black BR1G tender Sp Edn 512 (*British Railway Modelling*) - *09*	*75*	*95*
32-500	**73068** BRc green BR1C tender - *02*	55	65
32-501	**73158** BRc black BR1B tender - *02*	55	65
32-504	**73014** BRc lined green BR1 tender DC8 - *02*	70	88
32-505	**73069** BRc plain black W BR1C tender DC8 - *03*	70	88
32-506	**73110 *The Red Knight*** BRc lined black BR1F tender DC8 - *04*	70	88
32-507	**73050** BRc lined black W* sc - *08*	70	88

*Commemorating the last days of steam.

L37. LNER Class A1 4-6-2 (B) (2001)

Peppercorn designed express passenger locomotive of 1948. DCC ready. Removable coal load and optional chimneys. wpc = wooden presentation case.

32-550K	**60163 *(Tornado)*** works grey Sp Edn 504 (BCC), 'w w w.a1steam.com' on tender** - *10*	100	129
32-550A	**60163 *Tornado*** BRa light green** - *10*	90	129
32-554	**60114 *W.P.Allen*** BRa light green - *03*	60	75
32-553	**60161 *North British*** BRb blue - *03*	50	75
32-552	**60147 *North Eastern*** BRb green - *02*	50	75
32-558	**60115 *Meg Merrilies*** BRb green - *09*	90	113
32-551	**60158 *Aberdonian*** BRc green - *01*	50	75
32-555	**60130 *Kestrel*** BRc green - *03*	50	70
32-556	**60156 *Great Central*** BRc green - *05*	70	90
(30-090)	**60143 *Sir Walter Scott*** BRc green ex-Bachmann 15th Anniversary set - *04*	90	NA
32-557	**60144 *King's Courier*** BRc green DC8 - *07*	80	106
32-550	**60163 *Tornado*** BRc green wpc Sp Edn 1000 (A1 Trust) - *03**	95	120
32-559	**60157** Great Eastern BRc green - *10*	92	116

*The motif on the packaging gives the date as 2001 - possibly this was the intended year of release but it got delayed. . ** The 2009 issue of *Tornado* has a different tender top to the production A1s as it has a greater water carrying capacity.

L38. LNER Class A2 4-6-2 (B) (2010)

Peppercorn designed express passenger locomotive of 1948. 8-pin DCC ready. Etched smoke deflectors and nameplates, removable coal load and optional chimneys. wpc = wooden presentation case. sc = single chimney. dc = double chimney.

LNER designed Class A2 No.525 A.H.Peppercorn [L38]

31-525	**525 *A.H.Peppercorn*** LNER light green sc - *10*	90	126
31-527	**60528 *Tudor Minstrel*** BRa light green sc - *10*	90	126
31-526	**60537 *Bachelor's Button*** BRb green sc - *10*	90	126
20-2009	**60532 *Blue Peter*** BRc green dc wpc Ltd Edn - *10*	90	129

L39. LNER Class A4 4-6-2 (1995)

The model is based on the former Trix/Liliput model mouldings, to which 112 minor modifications were made, on a Bachmann split-chassis of standard design principal. dc = double chimney. sc = single chimney. ct = corridor tender. nct = non-corridor tender. v = valances fitted. xv = no valances. bm = blackened metalwork. wpc = wooden presentation case. swb = simulated wood finish box. en = etched nameplate. lcw = large chime whistle.

31-950X	**2509 *Silver Link*** LNER grey Sp Edn 500 (Southampton MC) - *03*	60	100
31-952A	**2512 *Silver Fox*** LNER grey v st - *98*	55	80
31-956	**4482 *Golden Eagle*** LNER green v sc - *97*	55	70
31-950	**4489 *Dominion of Canada*** LNER blue v sc brass bell *** 5th Ltd Edn 2000 wpc - *95*	60	125
31-952	**4903 *Peregrine*** blue LNER v dc st - *96*	50	70
31-952	**4468 *Mallard*** blue LNER v dc**** - *05*	70	90
31-953B	**4496 *Dwight D Eisenhower*** LNER blue sc ct bm Ltd Edn 500 US wpc - *97*	80	120
31-959	**26 *Miles Beevor*** LNER blue xv - *98*	55	70
31-962X	**2510 *Quicksilver*** LNER black Sp Edn 350 (Rails) swb - *99*	80	125
31-962Y	**4496 *Golden Shuttle*** LNER black Sp Edn 350 (Rails) swb - *99*	80	125
31-962Z	**4 *William Whitelaw*** NE black Sp Edn 350 (Rails) swb - *99*	80	125
31-953A	**60008 *Dwight D Eisenhower*** BRb blue sc ct Ltd Edn 500 US wpc - *96*	80	135
31-954A	**60007 *Sir Nigel Gresley*** BRb blue W xv sc - *04*	75	90
31-954	**60007 *Sir Nigel Gresley*** BRb express blue sc - *96*	75	94
31-954	**60007 *Sir Nigel Gresley*** BRb express blue dc - *07*	75	94
31-954A	**60007 *Sir Nigel Gresley*** BRc green dc en Ltd Edn 350, some swb - *00*	55	80
31-950A	**60011 *Empire of India*** BRb green en Ltd Edn 500 (Rails) wpc - *99*	60	135
31-951A	**60009 *Union of South Africa*** BRb green sc ct short run - *96*	55	90
31-955	**60013 *Dominion of New Zealand*** BRb green nct lcw sc - *96*	55	95
31-953C	**60008 *Dwight D Eisenhower*** BRb green sc en Ltd Edn 500 USA wpc - *99*	60	120
31-953	**60008 *Dwight D Eisenhower*** BRc green dc nct en Ltd Edn 250 US wpc - *95*	150	300
31-955	**60013 *Dominion of New Zealand*** BRc green nct lcw sc - *96*	60	120
31-951	**60009 *Union of South Africa*** BRc green dc en and plaques - *95*	100	150
31-951Z	**60009 *Osprey*** ** BRc green Sp Edn (75069 Fund) 350 swb en - *98*	90	145
31-957	**60033 *Seagull*** BRc green dc - *97*	55	70
31-958	**60020 *Guillemot*** BRc green dc - *98*	55	70
31-960	**60017 *Silver Fox*** BRc + 6 BR maroon Thompson coaches, video & book Ltd Edn 1000 Elizabethan set* wpc - *96*	NA	275
(31-960)	**60017 *Silver Fox*** BRc ex above set - *96*	85	NA
31-960A	**60015 *Quicksilver*** BRc green W dc - *03*	75	90
31-963	**60019 *Bittern*** BRc green dc nct - *09*	75	96

31-961/1	**4468 *Mallard*** LNER blue v Ltd Edn 1000 - *98*	65	NA
31-961/2	**60022 *Mallard*** BRc green dc Ltd Edn 1000 - *98*	65	NA
31-961	above 2 locos 60th anniversary release Ltd Edn 1000 wpc - *98*	NA	150

31-2001/1	**4491 *Commonwealth of Australia*** LNER blue from set - *00*	70	NA
31-2001/2	**60012 *Commonwealth of Australia*** BRb blue from set - *00*	70	NA
31-2001/3	**60012 *Commonwealth of Australia*** BRc green dc from set - *00*	70	NA
31-2001	above 3 in Ltd Edn 1000 wpc - *00*	NA	245

* Price given is for complete set. ** The original batch had unacceptable body. mouldings and were re-bodied. However, a few of the original models have survived. *** sterling silver fittings. **** Issued as Heritage Range model.

L40. LNWR Class G2A 0-8-0 (B) (2008)

Webb designed heavy freight locomotive of 1921. DCC ready. Bowen-Cooke tender. bot = back on tender.

31-476	**9301** LMS black DC8 - *not made*	NA	NA
31-476	**9449** LMS black DC8 (G2) - *08*	70	86
31-478	**49287** BRb black DC21 - *09*	75	91
31-475*	**49395** BRb black bot DC8 - *08*	70	86
31-475A	**49064** BRc black bot DC21 - *09*	75	91
31-477DC	**49094** BRc black DC8 - *not made*	NA	NA
31-477DC	**49361** BRc black DC8 - *08*	80	98

* Issued as Heritage Range model and erroneously described as a G2a on the box when it is in fact a G2.

L41. S&DJR Class 7F 2-8-0 (2010)

The 7F 2-8-0 was produced by the Midland Railway at Derby for the Somerset & Dorset Joint Railway. Six locomotives were delivered in 1914 and a further five delivered in 1925, which had larger boilers. All were taken into LMS stock in 1928 and passed to British Railways in 1948. All models feature the smaller boiler and S & D Fowler tender without water pick up apparatus.

31-010	**53806**, BRb, black - *10*	55	70
31-012	**53808**, BRc, black, weathered - *not made*	NA	NA
31-011	**53809**, BRc, black - *10*	55	70
31-012	**53810**, BRc, black, weathered - *10*	55	70

L42a. GCR Class 8K/LNER O4 'ROD' 2-8-0 (B) (2010)

Robinson designed heavy freight locomotive of 1911. DCC ready. Adjustable drawbar length.

31-001Y	**1185** GCR lined black Sp Edn 500 (NRM) - *10*	110	140
31-003	**3693** LNER black DC21 - *not made*	NA	NA

LNER Class O4 2-8-0 [L42a]

31-003	**3291** LNER black DC21 - *not made*	NA	NA
31-003	**6190** LNER black DC21 - *10*	100	125
31-002	**63635** BRb black DC21 - *10*	100	125
32-001*	**63601** BRc black DC21 - *10*	100	125
31-00?	**63743**, BRb black W Sp Edn 512 (Hattons) - *10*	120	145

* Issued as Heritage Range model.

L42b. GWR Class 30xx 'ROD' 2-8-0 (B) (2011)

Having released their model of the LNER Class 04 earlier in the year, in July 2010, Bachmann announced that they would release the model as converted by the GWR. The model has a highly detailed cab and an adjustable drawbar length. Different styles of smokebox door have been modelled and it has a heavy diecast chassis. All are fitted with 21-pin DCC sockets.

31-129	**?** GWR green - *11*	100	128
31-127	**?** BRb plain black - *11*	100	128
31-128	**?** BRc plain black - *not made*	NA	NA
31-128	**?** BR plain black W - *11*	100	128

L43. WD 'Austerity' 2-8-0 (B) (1999)

Riddles designed heavy freight of 1943. Removable coal load and sprung buffers. West = Westinghouse pump fitted.

32-255	**78697** WD 21st Army Transport Group green*** - *00*	75	95
32-255A	**7199** WD WW2 Desert Sand - *02*	80	100
32-250	**400 *Sir Guy Williams*** LMR blue Ltd Edn 2000 wpc - *99*	60	85
32-250W	**90733 *Remembrance - Lest We Forget*** black Sp Edn 500 (K&WVR) - *08*	NPG	120
32-254	**3085** LNER black West - *00*	70	90
32-251	**90274****** BRb black - *99*	70	90
32-253	**90312** BRb black - *00*	70	90
32-257	**90015** BRb black W Ltd Edn - *00*	70	85
32-257A	**90732 *Vulcan*** BRb black - *03*	75	95
32-258	**90423** BRb black - *06*	80	105
32-252	**90445** BRc black W - *99*	75	95
32-252	**90445** BRc black - *99*	75	95
32-252A	**90201** BRc black W - *03*	75	95
32-256	**90566** BRc black - *00*	70	85
32-259	**90630** BRc black W - *06*	85	111
32-?	**90733 *Remembrance - Lest we forget*** BRc black Sp Edn 500 (KWVR Trust) - *06*	90	120
32-250X	**NS4479** NS green North British type Ltd Edn 500 (Tasco Nederland BV) - *03?*	90	110
32-250Y*	**NS4310** NS green Vucan Foundry type Ltd Edn 500 (Tasco Nederland BV) - *00*	45	110
32-250Z	**NS4329** NS green North British type Ltd Edn 500 (Tasco Nederland BV) - *00*	80	100
32-250KCR	**21** Kowloon Canton Railway green+red Sp Edn 1000 (K&CR) - *00*	80	150

* The Dutch agent allocated his own number of 32.259 to this model. ** This was made as a Millennium model for sale in Hong Kong with only 200 being put on sale in the UK. *** Some were originally printed with the red and blue on the shields reversed. **** Box shows '90275'.

L44. BR Class 9F 2-10-0 (B) (2006)

Riddles designed mixed traffic mainly heavy freight locomotive of 1954. DCC ready, etched deflectors, different tenders. dc = double chimney. sc = single chimney

32-854	**92006** BRb black sc BR1G tender DC8 - *07*	95	117

BR Standard 9F 2-10-0 [L44]

32-852	**92116** BRb black BR1C tender - *06*	90	112
32-856	**92002** BRb black sc BR1G tender DC8 - *08*	100	129
32-853	**92044** BRc black W sc BR1F tender DC8 - *07*	100	125
32-850Z	**92240** BRc black W BR1G tender Sp Edn 504 (ModelZone) - *06*	100	125
32-851	**92192** BRc black dc BR1F tender - *06*	90	112
32-850	**92220 *Evening Star*** BRc green BR1G tender * - *06*	90	112
32-850A	**92220 *Evening Star***, BRc, green, BR1G tender, Heritage Range model - *10*	110	135
32-850K	**92203 *Black Prince*** BRc black Sp Edn 504 (BCC) - *06*	90	112
32-855	**92249** BRc black dc BR1B tender DC8 - *07*	95	117
32-857	**92077** BRc black sc BR1C tender DC8 - *08*	100	129
32-858DC	**92185** BRc black W dc BR1F tender DC8 - *08*	100	123

* Issued as Heritage Range model.

Diesels

L45. Freelance Diesel 0-6-0 (2006)

For starter sets.

30-915	**95 *Rusty*** green - *06*	18	25
(30-006)	**25 *Harry*** blue with red wheels DC8 ex-set - *06*	18	NA
(30-041)DC	**5 *Charlie*** yellow+red ex-set - *07*	18	NA

L46a. Class 03 Diesel 0-6-0DS (ex-Mainline) (1991)

No further Class 03 models can now be made from these tools as they were adapted to produce the Class 04 (below). ats = air tanks supplied. xhs = no hazard stripes. cx = conical exhaust. cfc = cast flared chimney

31-350	**D2000** BRc green xhs cx - *91*	35	45
31-351	**D2012** BRc green cx - *91*	35	45
31-353	**03197** BRe blue cfc ats - *91*	35	45
31-352	**03371** BRe blue cx ats - *91*	35	45

L46b. Class 03 Diesel 0-6-0D (2010)

This model is made from all new tooling. ats = air tanks supplied. xhs = no hazard stripes. cx = conical exhaust. cfc = cast flared chimney. The model is fitted with a 6-pin decoder.

31-360	**D2011** BRc green xhs cx - *10*	40	52
31-361	**D2388** BRc green cx - *10*	40	52
31-362	**03066** BRe blue cx ats - *10*	40	52
31-360Y	**03160** BRe blue cfc Sp Edn 512 (*Rail Express Modeller*) - *10*	45	55
31-360X	**03371** BRe blue cx Sp Edn 512 (*Rail Express Modeller*) - *10*	45	55
31-360Z	**03179** NSE blue+white+grey cut-down cab Sp Edn 750 (ModelZone) - *10*	50	60

31-360K	**03179** ***Clive*** WAGN white+black, cut-down cab Sp Edn 504 (BCC) - *10*	45	54

Class 03 diesel shunter [L46b]

L47. Class 04 Diesel 0-6-0DS (1997)

Drewry Car designed loco of 1952 for dockyards and other confined spaces. This model was produced by adapting the former Mainline tools for the Class 03 (above). It has sprung buffers and cab interior. xhs = no hazard stripes.

31-339	**11217** BRb black W xhs - *05*	35	44
31-341	**11222** BRb black xhs - *07*	38	47
31-335	**11226** BRb black xhs - *97*	25	36
31-337A	**D2223** BRc green - *02*	30	40
31-337B	**D2228** BRc green - *02*	30	40
31-337B	**D2228** BRc green W - *04*	35	40
31-338	**D2254** BRe blue W - *05*	35	43
31-336A	**D2258** BRe blue - *02*	35	43
31-342	**D2264** BRc green xhs - *07*	38	47
31-340	**D2267** BRe blue W - *06*	35	43
31-337	**D2280** BRc green - *97*	30	35
31-338	**D2282** BRc green xhs - *99*	30	35
31-336B	**D2294** BRe blue - *04*	35	40
31-336	**D2334** BRe blue - *97*	25	36

L48. Class 08/09 Diesel Shunter 0-6-0DS (B) (2000)

The standard BR diesel shunter dating from 1952. Flywheel drive 5-pole motor and easily converted to DCC. From 2005 they were DCC ready and had an improved pickup design.

32-113	**D3032** BRc plain green hinged door DC8 - *05*	38	51
32-110Z	**D3052** BRb black W Sp Edn (*Model Rail*) - *11*	63	70
32-113Z	**D3232** BRc plain green W hinged door DC8 Sp Edn 508 (Hattons) - *10*	50	62
32-112	**D3336** BRc green hinged door - *04*	35	46
32-101A	**D3586** BRc green hazard stripes - *01*	35	45
32-101	**D3729** BRc green hazard stripes - *00*	30	40
32-101B	**D4192** BRc green hazard stripes - *03*	35	45
32-115	**08173** BRe blue W hgd door, no ladders DC8 - *09*	45	57
32-111	**08243** BRe blue hinged door - *04*	35	46
32-111A	**08375** BRe blue hinged door DC8 - *05*	38	51
32-108V	**08410** FGW green Sp Edn 512 (Kernow Model Railway Centre) - *05*	45	59
32-108VDC	as above but with decoder fitted (taken from above 512 models) - *07*	55	62
32-108VDCS	as above but with Lenz Silver decoder fitted (taken from above 512 models) - *07*	63	70
32-102K	**08484** Captain Nathaniel Darrell Port of Felixstowe blue Sp Edn 504 (BCC) no ladders DC8 - *09*	45	57
32-102Z	**08507** BRe blue W Ltd Edn 1000 (BCC) - *03*	40	50
32-106	**08585** Freightliner green - *02*	35	45
32-102X	**08600** ***Ivor*** early NSE Sp Edn 500 (ModelZone) - *03*	40	50
32-102	**08623** BRe blue no ladders - *00*	30	40
32-102V	**08641** ***Dartmoor*** NSE bright blue Sp Edn 504 (The Signal Box) - *08*	50	60
32-107	**08648** BRe Rft departmental grey - *02*	35	45
32-104	**08653** Rft Distribution grey - *01*	35	45
32-108	**08683** EWS maroon+yellow DC8 - *05*	38	51
32-102B	**08748** BRe blue no ladders - *03*	35	45
32-102A	**08762** BRe blue no ladders - *01*	35	45
32-105	**08800** InterCity swallow grey - *02*	40	50
32-103	**08921** EWS red air comp cabinet new front windows deep springs - *01*	35	45
32-116	**09006** Mainline blue - *02*	35	45
32-110	**13029** BRb black hinged door - *04*	35	46
32-114	**13238** BRb black hinged doors DC8 - *08*	40	56
32-100	**13365** BRc green - *00*	30	40
32-100Z	(***Cambridge***) RES grey+red Ltd Edn 500 (*Model Rail*) * - *01*	40	55
32-102W	**97800** ***Ivor*** BRe blue+red Sp Edn 500 (ModelZone) - *04*	30	40

* This was sold through the magazine and came with a sheet of numbers by Modelmaster and a sheet by Shawplan with 'Cambridge' nameplates and logos.

L49. Class 20 Diesel Bo-Bo (B) (2004)

English Electric loco of 1957. DCC ready, bogies with NEM pockets, wire sand pipes and a choice of bogies. Like the real locomotives, some models have code discs at either end while others have code boxes. In 2005, Bachmann improved windscreen profiles and enhanced radiator grills. A version with tablet catcher recesses (tc) in the cab sides arrived in 2006. DS = fitted with digital sound

32-027	**D8000** BRc green discs - *04*	40	49
32-027Y	**D8000** & **D8001** BRc green, discs, in 504 twin pk Sp Edn (Ian Allan 50th Anniv.) - *07*	NA	110
32-027A	**D8046** BRc green, discs - *04*	40	49
32-042DC	**D8101** BRc green tc DC21 - *07*	52	66
32-040DS	**D8113** BRc green, discs DS tc DC21 - *06*	100	120
32-028	**D8134** BRc green, codeboxes - *04*	40	49
32-033DS	**D8158** BRc green, codeboxes DS DC21 - *08*	130	150
32-034	**D8164** BRc green, codeboxes DC21 - *08*	42	56
32-028A	**D8169** BRc green, codeboxes - *04*	40	49
32-032	**D8307** BRe blue W codeboxes DC - *05*	42	55
32-029	**20023** BReLL Railfreight grey, discs - *05*	40	51
32-041	**20028** BRe blue discs tc DC21 - *07*	40	51
(32-027Z)	**20030** ***River Rother*** BRe green, discs Sp Edn (*Model Rail*) ex-pair - *05*	65	NA
32-035DS	**20034** BRe blue discs DS DC21 - *08*	130	150
32-025TF	**20042** Waterman Railways black Ltd Edn 500 (2004 London Toyfair) - *04*	80	100
32-031	**20052** BRe blue W discs - *05*	42	55
32-031	**20052** BRe blue W codeboxes - *not made*	NA	NA
32-025A	**20058** BRe blue, discs - *04*	40	49
32-025	**20063** BRe blue, discs - *04*	40	49
(32-027Z)	**20064** ***River Sheaf*** BRe green, discs Sp Edn (*Model Rail*) ex-pair - *05*	65	NA
32-027Z	**20030** ***River Rother*** + **20064** ***River Sheaf*** Sp Edn 500 (*Model Rail*) - *05*	NA	124
32-029A	**20090**, BReL Rft red stripe grey, discs - *10*	50	61
32-030	**20132** BReLL red-stripe Railfreight grey codeboxes - *05*	40	51
32-035	**20164** BRe blue, domino headcode DC21 - *09*	45	59
32-027Y	**20188** Waterman Railways black Sp Edn 504 (Basement Models) - *order cancelled and models released as BCC model 32-026K (below)*	NA	NA
32-026K	**20188** Waterman Railways black Sp Edn 504 (BCC) - *07*	65	80
32-026	**20192** BRe blue codeboxes - *04*	40	49
32-026A	**20217** BRe blue codeboxes - *04*	40	50
(32-027X)	**20901** ***Nancy*** Hunslet-Barclay grey Sp Edn 512 (Kernow Model Rail Centre) - *10*	60	NA
(32-027X)	**20904** ***Janis*** Hunslet-Barclay grey Sp Edn 512 (Kernow Model Rail Centre) - *10*	60	NA
32-027X	above two locomotives in twin pack - *10*	NA	140

L50. Class 24 Diesel Bo-Bo (B) (2001)

Mix traffic locomotives introduced in 1958. DCC ready, bogies with NEM pockets (from 2002), roof grill and fan. DS = fitted with digital sound,

Class 24 mixed traffic diesel [L50]

32-430	**D5013** BRc green, discs DS21 - *06*	38	51
32-429	**D5011** BRc green - *03*	35	45
32-430A	**D5030** BRc green DC21 - *09*	40	57
32-427	**D5038** BRc 2-tone green - *not made*	NA	NA
32-426DS	**D5038** BRc 2-tone green discs DS DC21 - *09*	130	155

32-426	**D5054** BRc green - *01*	35	45
32-430B	**D5061** BRc green DC21 - *10*	45	59
32-425Y	**D5072** BRc 2-tone green W Sp Edn 512 (Kernow Model Centre) - *08*	55	70
32-427	**D5085** BRc 2-tone green - *02*	35	45
32-428	**5087** BRe blue - *02*	35	45
32-429DS	**D5100** BRc green DC21 - *10*	130	157
32-425DS	**24035** BRe blue DS DC21 - *07*	100	113
32-425	**24081** BRe blue - *01*	35	45
32-425Z	**97201 *Experiment*** BRe Research Department red+blue Sp Edn 750 (*Rail Express*) - *01*	100	125

L51a. Class 25 (old body style) Diesel Bo-Bo (B) (2001)

Mixed traffic design from 1961. Alternative cab front styles. Roof grill and fan, DCC ready. DS = fitted with digital sound. Bogies with NEM pockets (from 2002). Sno = snow ploughs fitted.

32-325	**D5211** BRc green 25/1 - *03*	35	45
32-325DC	**D5211** BRc green DC21 25/1 - *06*	50	63
32-326Z	**D5218** BRe blue 25/1 Sp Edn 504 (ModelZone) - *07*	44	56
32-328	**D5182** BRc green 25/1 DC21 - *10*	45	59
32-402	**25034 *Castell Aberystwyth/Aberystwyth Castle*** BRe blue 25/1 ex set DC21 - *08*	45	NA
32-327	**25052** BRe blue W DC21 - *08*	44	56
32-326DS	**25054** BRe blue 25/1 - *03*	35	51
(30-050)DC	**25058** BRe blue 25/1 DC21 ex-set - *08*	44	56
32-326DS	**25245** BRe blue 25/2 DS DC21 - *09*	130	155

L51b. Class 25 (new body style) Diesel Bo-Bo (B) (2001)

Mixed traffic design from 1961. The new style body had the various side vents transferred to the roof-line. Roof grill and fan, DCC ready. DS = fitted with digital sound. Bogies with NEM pockets (from 2002). Sno = snow ploughs fitted.

32-411	**D5233** BRc 2-tone green 25/2 - *01*	35	44
(30-045)	As above but chip fitted ex-set sno - *05*	45	NA
32-413	**D5237** BRc 2-tone green 25/2 - *02*	35	44
32-406	**D5255** BRc 2-tone green 25/3 DC21 - *10*	45	59
32-403	**D5269** BRc 2-tone green W 25/2 - *02*	35	44
32-410	**5293** BRe blue 25/2 - *not made*	NA	NA
32-401DS	**D7638** BRc 2-tone green DS DC21 25/3 - *09*	130	155
32-400	**D7645** BRc 2-tone green 25/3 - *01*	35	45
32-405	**D7646** BRc 2-tone green DC21 25/3 - *07*	38	56
32-404	**D7667** BRe blue, sno 25/3 - *02*	40	50
32-402	**D7672 *Tamworth Castle*** BRc 2-tone green 25/3 - *01*	35	60
32-412	**25083** BRe blue W 25/2 - *02*	35	43
32-410	**25087** BRe blue 25/2 - *01*	35	43
32-400DS	**25095** BRe blue with DS DC21 unique livery 25/3 - *06*	90	110
32-401	**25279** BRe blue 25/3 - *01*	35	45
32-402Z	**25322 *Tamworth Castle*** BRe blue, silver roof, yellow cabs 25/3 Sp Edn 750 (*Model Rail*) - *02*	40	75
32-400TF	**ADB97252 *Ethel 3*** IC grey 25/3 Sp Edn 750 (2008 London Toy Fair) - *08*	45	58

L52a. Class 37/0 Diesel Co-Co (B) (2002)

An English Electric mixed traffic design which entered service in 1960. Working LED headlight, metal roof grill and fan and cast or fabricated bogies. Sprung buffers. en = etched nameplates. sno = snow ploughs. ch = centre headcode. sh = split headcode. hye = half yellow ends. rv = refurbished version released in 2006. DCC ready, DS = fitted with digital sound. Upgraded bogies and wheels fitted from start of 2008.

32-375Z	**D6607 *Ben Cruachan*** BRc green 37/4 Sp Edn 900 (BCC) - *02*	80	95
32-776	**D6707** BRc green sh - *04*	45	60
32-776K	**D6717** BRc green W sh hye Sp Edn 1,000 (BCC) - *04*	45	60
32-782	**D6801** BRc green sh - *10*	60	76
32-778	**D6826** BRc green ch - *04*	45	60
32-775Z	**37003** BRe blue Sp Edn 512 (The Class 37 Locomotive Group) - *10*	NPG	NPG
32-780Y	**37025 *Inverness TMD*** BReLL blue Sp Edn 500 (Rails) - *06*	60	75
32-780Y	**37025 *Inverness TMD*** BReLL blue W 500 Sp Edn (Rails) - *07*	55	70
32-779	**37035** BRe Dutch grey+yellow 37/0 sh sno DC21 - *06*	48	62
32-775	**37038** BRe blue sh - *04*	45	60
32-780X	**37038** DRS dark blue 37/0 Sp Edn 512 (Cheltenham Model Centre) - ?	60	75
32-783DS	**37049** BRe blue sh - *10*	150	174
32-781DS	**37057 *Viking*** BReLL blue DS DC21- *07*	120	145
32-775DC	**37114 City *of Worcester*** EW&S maroon sno sh 37/1 DC8 - *06*	60	74
32-777Z	**37142** BRe blue W ch Sp Edn 504 (Kernow Model Rail Centre) - *04*	60	73
32-777ZDC	as above but with decoder fitted (taken from above 504 models) - *07*	76	83
32-777ZDCS	as above but with Lenz Silver decoder fitted (taken from above 504 models) - *07*	66	93
32-780Z	**37207 *William Cookworthy*** BRe blue + Cornish motifs Sp Edn (Kernow Model Rail Centre) - *07*	60	76
32-777	**37238** BRe blue ch - *04*	45	60
32-780	**37239** BRe Rft Coal triple grey 37/2 DC21 - *06*	54	55
32-781	**37251** BRe blue ch domino headcode - *10*	60	76
32-776DS	**37254** BRe Rft Coal blue DS DC21 - *08*	140	164
32-777Y	**97303** Network Rail yellow Sp Edn 500 (*Model Rail*) – *09*	65	80

L52b. Class 37/4 Diesel Co-Co (B) (2006)

Refurbished version. Working LED headlight, metal roof grill and cast or fabricated bogies. Sprung buffers en= etched nameplates sno= snowploughs. DCC ready 08=fitted with digital sound. Upgraded bogies and wheels fitted from start of 2008.

32-384	**37406 *The Saltire Society*** Rft Distribution triple grey 37/4 DC21 - *09*	60	73
32-377	**37408 *Loch Rannoch*** BReLL blue Eastfield motif 700 made - *03*	40	50
32-?	**37409** DRS (compass) blue SP Edn (*Model Rail*) - *10*	NPG	NPG
32-382	**37410 *Aluminium* 100** BReLL blue scottie motif sno en 37/4 DC8 - *07*	48	62
32-381	**37411 *Ty Hafan*** EWS maroon en 37/4 DC08 - *07*	48	62
32-375K	**37411/D6990 *Caerphilly Castle/ Castell Caerfill*** BRc green en 37/4 DC8 Sp Edn 504 (BCC) - *07*	60	75
32-385	**37415** Intercity Executive grey DC21- *10*	60	76
32-375	**37419** EW&S maroon - *03*	40	45
32-381X	**37425 *Pride of the Valleys*** BReLL 37/4 Sp Edn (G.Allison) - *06*	60	75
32-381W	**37426 *Vale of Rheidol*** BReLL blue Sp Edn 504 (Hereford Model Centre) - *10*	60	75
31-381V	**37427 *Highland Enterprise*** Reg Rlys/ ScotRail blue Sp Edn (Rails) - *07*	60	72
32-383	**37428 *David Lloyd George*** Rft Petroleum triple grey 37/4 DC21 - *09*	60	73
32-780V	**37428 *Loch Arkalg*** West Coast maroon Sp Edn 500 (Model Rail) - *10*	65	80

Diesel subclass 37/4 in Railfreight Petroleum livery [L52b]

32-376	**37429 *Eisteddfod Genedlaethol*** Regional Railways blue - *03*	40	45
32-378	**37431 *Bullidae*** IC Mainline /petroleum grey+white sno - *03*	35	40

L52c. Class 37/5 Diesel Co-Co (B) (2008)

Working LED headlight, metal roof grill and fan and cast or fabricated bogies. Sprung buffers. en = etched nameplates. DCC ready, DS = fitted with digital sound.

32-387	**37506** Railfreight red stripe grey BReLL Thornaby depot motif DC21 - *10*	60	76
32-386	**37513** Railfreight triple grey Metals Sector Thornaby depot plates DC21 - *10*	60	76
32-386	**37514** Railfreight triple grey Metals Sector Thornaby depot plates DC21 - *not made*	NA	NA
32-387	**37518** Railfreight red stripe grey BReLL Thornaby depot motif DC21 - *not made*	NA	NA
32-781Z	**37670 *St. Blazey T&RS MD*** EWS maroon W en Sp Edn (Kernow Model Rail Centre) - *07*	60	76
32-781P	**37670 *St. Blazey T&RS MD*** DB Schenker red en		

	Sp Edn 1000 (*Rail Express*) - *10*	60	77
32-781P (DS)	**37670 *St. Blazey T&RS MD*** DB Schenker red en Sp Edn 1000 (*Rail Express*) DS - *10*	145	167
32-380	**37671 *Tre Pol and Pen*** BRe Rft Dist. triple grey sno en, St Blazey plates and nameplates - *03*	40	50
32-375DC	**37672** Transrail triple grey en 37/6 DC8 - *07*	60	74
32-379	**37678** BRe Railfreight red stripe grey sno - *03*	40	45
32-381Y	**37692 *Lass of Ballochmyle*** Rft grey Sp Edn (GMD Models) - *07?*	60	76
32-376DS	**37693** BReLL Rft grey, yellow cabs DS DC21 - *08*	140	164
32-380DS	**37698 *Coedbach*** BRe coal load triple grey DS DC21 en - *07*	120	145
32-?	**37698** Loadhaul black+orange Sp Edn (G. Allison) - *not made* *	NPG	NPG

* The required tooling to produce this variation was unavailable and so it was dropped.

L52d. Class 37/5 (Retooled) Diesel Co-Co (B) (2008)

Exclusively tooled for *Rail Express* magazine. Working LED headlight, metal roof grill and fan and cast or fabricated bogies. There are body variations including either EE or RSH grilles, as well as nose variations. Sprung buffers en= etched nameplates. DCC ready, DS = fitted with digital sound.

(32-381T)	**37501 *Teeside Steelmaster*** British Steel light blue en Sp Edn 504 (*Rail Express*) - *08*	60	NA
(32-381T)	**37502 *British Steel Teeside*** Rft red stripe en Sp Edn 504 (*Rail Express*) - *08*	60	NA
32-381T	above two locos Sp Edn 1000 (*Rail Express*) - *08*	NA	150
32-381S	**37507 *Hartlepool Pipe Mill*** Rft Metals en Sp Edn 672 (*Rail Express*) - *08*	60	75
(32-381U)	**37510** DRS dark blue Sp Edn 504 (*Rail Express*) - *08*	60	NA
32-381R	**37521 *English China Clays*** EWS maroon+yellow W Sp Edn 512 (Kernow MRC) - *10*	60	75
32-381P	**37670 *St. Blazey T&RS MD*** red en Sp Edn 1000 (*Rail Express*) - *10*	60	77
32-381PDS	as above but with a DC21 sound chip fitted (*Rail Express*) - *10*	145	167
(32-381U)	**37688 *Kingmoor TMD*** DRS dark blue Sp Edn 504 (*Rail Express*) - *08*	60	NA
32-381U	**37510** + **37688** together Sp Edn 1000 (*Rail Express*) - *08*	NA	150

L52e. Class 37/7 'Heavyweight' Diesel Co-Co (B) (2010)

The subclass was created in 1986 when 44 Class 37 locomotives were refurbished for heavy freight work and numbered in the 377xx and 378xx ranges. The model of the 37/7 subclass was produced initially exclusively for *Rail Express* magazine. It has a modified body and some were being offered, through the magazine, sound fitted. There are opening cab doors, etched fan grills working LED directional lights, all-wheel drive and fitted with 21-pin DCC sockets.

-	**37702 *Taff Merthyr*** Transrail tripe grey Canton depot logos	70	NA
-	**37798** Mainline blue Stewarts Lane depot logos	70	NA
32-390X	above 2 locos Sp Edn 512 (Rail Exclusive pack E - *10*	NA	170
32-390XDS	above set with locos fitted with sound	NA	330
-	**37713** LoadHaul black+orange	70	NA
-	**37884 *Gartcosh*** LoadHaul black+orange	70	NA
32-390Y?	above 2 locos Sp Edn 512 (Rail Exclusive pack D - *10*	NA	170
32-?DS	above set with locos fitted with sound	NA	330

L52f. Class 37/9 'Slug' Diesel Co-Co (B) (2010)

Produced exclusively for Kernow Model Rail Centre with modified body and roof. Working LED headlight, metal roof grill and fan and cast or fabricated bogies. DCC ready.

-	**37905** Rft Metals triple grey Sp Edn 512 (Kernow Model Rail Centre) - *10*	70	NA
-	**37906** BReLL Rft grey with yellow cabs Sp Edn 512 (Kernow Model Rail Centre) - *09*	70	NA
32-390Z	above two locos - *10*	NA	170

L53. Class 40 Diesel 1Co-Co1 (B) (2004)

English Electric mixed traffic loco introduced in 1958. DCC ready. working LED headlight, metal roof grill and fan, etched metal frost grills and cast or fabricated bogies. After the first batches, the body was lowered slightly to reduce the gap between body and bogies. These improved models were first released late in 2005 but the model was not made DCC enabled until 2010 when the chassis was rebuilt to take it. DS = fitted with digital sound.

32-475Z	**D200/40122** BRe green split headcode, full yell ends Sp Edn 750 (Model Rail) - *04*	75	95
32-478	**D210 *Empress of Britain*** BRc green, discs, the first of the improved models DC8 - *05*	52	66

Class 40 English Electric diesel [L53]

32-480DS	**D211 *Mauretania*** BRc green discs DS DC21 - *10*	135	156
32-477	**D325** BRe green split headcode - *04*	50	63
-	**D326** BRc green Sp Edn (Rails) - *not made*	NA	NA
32-475	**D368** BRc green code boxes - *04*	50	63
(30-090)	**D396** BRc green ex-Bachmann 15th Anniversary set - *04*	60	NA
32-476	**40075** BRe blue discs - *04*	50	63
32-475DC	**40129** BRe blue split codeboxes DC8 - *10*	NPG	NPG
32-475Y	**40145** BRe blue Sp Edn 504 (Class 40 Preservation Society) - *05*	80	95
32-479	**40169** BRe blue domino codeboxes, minus water tanks DC8 - *05*	55	66

L54. Class 42 'Warship' Diesel Hydraulic B-B (B) (1998)

Optional separate apron parts and a buffer beam accessory pack. Despite earlier intensions, the model was not made DCC enabled until 2010 when the chassis was rebuilt to take it. In previous editions of this catalogue, two models (32-050DC and 32-061) were listed as having been released in 2006 but it now seems that these were delayed until 2010.

32-055	**D800 *Sir Brian Robertson*** BRc green - *00*	35	50
32-053	**D804 *Avenger*** BRe blue - *00*	35	48
32-056	**D806 *Cambrian*** BRc maroon - *01*	35	48
32-050DC	**D809 *Champion*** BRc maroon DC21 - *10*	60	73
32-060	**D810 *Vanguard*** BRc maroon W - *04*	40	56
32-061	**D812 *The Royal Naval Reserve 1859-1959*** BRe blue DC21 - *10*	50	62
32-052	**D816 *Eclipse*** BRc green - *99*	35	48
32-050	**D817 *Foxhound*** BRc maroon - *98*	35	45
32-059	**D818 *Glory*** BRc green - *04*	40	56
32-058	**D820 *Grenville*** BRc green - *03*	35	55
32-054	**D831 *Monarch*** BRe blue - *99*	35	48
32-051	**D832 *Onslaught*** BRc green - *98*	35	48
32-057	**D870 *Zulu*** BRe blue - *02*	35	50

A small number of maroon bodies of D827 *Kelly* (not of Mainline origin) have been found.

L55a. LMS Prototype 'Twins' Main Line Diesels (2012)

A year before Nationalisation of the railways, the LMS had announced their intention to build two experimental main line diesel locomotives. No.10000 emerged from Derby Works in November 1947 and was the only one of the two to carry 'LMS' on its sides, which it retained until November 1951. No.10001 arrived in July the following year. The model is being developed in association with Rails of Sheffield, who will have 2 years exclusive use of the tooling.

?	**10000** LMS black - *12*	NPG	NPG
?	**10000** BRb (large) black - *12*	NPG	NPG
?	**10000** BRb (small) black - *12*	NPG	NPG
?	**10000** BRc lined out green - *12*	NPG	NPG
?	**10000** BRc green with partial egg-shell blue waistband - *12*	NPG	NPG
?	**10001** BRb (large) black - *12*	NPG	NPG
?	**10001** BRb (small) black - *12*	NPG	NPG
?	**10001** BRc lined out green - *12*	NPG	NPG
?	**10001** BRc green with partial egg-shell blue waistband - *12*	NPG	NPG
?	**10001** BRc green with full egg-shell blue waistband - *12*	NPG	NPG
?	**10001** BRc green with full egg-shell blue waistband + small warning panel - *12*	NPG	NPG

L55b. Class 44 'Peak' Diesel 1Co-Co1 (B) (2003)

BR mixed traffic locomotives introduced in 1959. DCC ready. Roof grill and fan, buffers mounted on the bogies and etched nameplates.

32-650	**D1 *Scafell Pike*** BRc green DC21 - *03, 05*	52	64

32-652	**44004** ***Great Gable*** BRe blue discs DC21 - *09*	55	74
32-651	**44008** ***Penyghent*** BRe blue - *03, 05*	45	55

L56a. Class 45 'Peak' Diesel Electric 1Co-Co1 (ex-Mainline) (2002)

BR mixed traffic locomotives introduced in 1959. Roof grill and fan, buffers on the bogies and etched nameplates.

31-125Z	**D55** ***Royal Signals*** BRc green W Sp Edn 500 (Southampton MC) - *02*	55	65
31-125	**D67** ***The Royal Artilleryman*** BRc green, cream band - *not made**	NA	NA
31-126	**45114** BRe blue, white roof - *not made**	NA	NA

* These were originally planned in 2002 using the old tooling but not proceeded with as it was decided to retool the model.

L56b. Class 45 'Peak' Diesel 1Co-Co1 (B) (2004)

BR mixed traffic locomotives introduced in 1959. DCC ready. Roof grill and fan, buffers mounted on the bogies and etched nameplates. Retooled nose end from 2006. DS = fitted with digital sound. In 2009 the cabs were retooled to improve detail.

31-675Z	**D55** ***Royal Signals*** BRc green W Sp Edn 500 (Southampton MC) (31-125Z on certificate) - *04*	65	80
32-678DS	**D55** ***Royal Signals*** BRc green DS DC21 - *09*	150	171
32-675	**D67** ***The Royal Artilleryman*** BRc green, cream band DC21 - *04*	50	64
32-679	**D95** BRc green DC21 - *09*	60	75

Class 45 main line diesel [L56b]

32-676Z	**45048** ***The Royal Marines*** BRe blue Sp Edn 504 (ModelZone) - *06*	55	70
32-677	**45053** BRe blue split codeboxes DC21 - *09*	55	74
32-676	**45114** BRe blue, off-white roof DC21 - *04*	50	64
32-677A	**45120** BRe blue, blue roof DC21 - *10*	62	77

L57a. Class 46 'Peak' Diesel 1Co-Co1 (ex-Mainline) (1994)

BR mixed traffic locomotives introduced in 1961. Later models had roof grill and fan, buffers mounted on the bogies and etched nameplates. wpc - wooden presentation case.

31-076A	BRe blue - *95*	25	35
31-081*	**D163** ***Leicestershire and Derbyshire Yeomanry*** BRc green - *not made*	NA	NA
31-080	**D172** ***Ixion*** BRc green Ltd Edn 2000 (Waterman Railway) wpc - *96*	60	75
31-078	**D181** BRe blue - *97*	25	35
31-077	**D193** BRc green - *97*	25	35
31-075	**46026** ***Leicestershire and Derbyshire Yeomanry*** BRe blue - *94*	30	40
31-076	**46045** BRe blue - *94*	25	35
31-0??	**97403** ***Ixion*** Research blue/red Sp Edn (*Rail Express*) - *02*	*90*	*110*

* This was originally planned for 2001 using the old tooling but was not proceeded with as it was decided to retool the model.

L57b. Class 46 'Peak' Diesel 1Co-Co1 (B) (2004)

BR mixed traffic locomotives introduced in 1961. DCC ready. Later models had roof grill and fan, buffers mounted on the bogies and etched nameplates. By 2005 the nose ends had been retooled to include the distinctive seam line as seen first on *Ixion*. wpc - wooden presentation case. DC=DCC fitted

32-700	**D163** ***Leicestershire and Derbyshire Yeomanry*** BRc green - *04*	50	64
32-702DC	**D182** BRc green DC21 - *09*	67	87
32-701	**46053** BRe blue - *04*	50	64
32-700Z	**97403** ***Ixion*** BRe Derby Research Centre blue+red Sp Edn 750 (ModelZone) - *05*	55	70

L58a. Class 47 Diesel Co-Co (B) (2007)

BR built mixed traffic locomotive from 1962. 6-axle drive 5-pole motor, directional lighting, etched nameplates and DCC ready. DS = fitted with digital sound..

32-800	**D1500** BRc green DC21 - *07*	60	72
32-801DS	**D1746** BRc 2-tone green DS DC21 - *09*	150	176
32-801	**1764** BRc 2-tone green, yellow ends and DC21 - *07*	60	72
32-802	**47035** BRe blue illum. marker lights DC21 - *07*	60	72
32-801Y	**47079** ***George Jackson Churchward*** GW150 green 37/0 Sp Edn 512 (Kernow MR Centre) - *not made (see 31-650V in next table)*	NA	NA
32-803	**47148** BRe blue illuminated headcode DC21 - *07*	60	72

Class 47 main line diesel Hadrian [L58a]

32-800Z	**47163** BRe blue + Union Jacks, silver roof Sp Edn 504 (ModelZone) DC21 - *07*	60	72
32-800DS	**47404** ***Hadrian*** BRe blue DS DC21 - *08*	150	176
31-650P	**47406** ***Rail Riders Club*** IC Exec grey DC21 Sp Edn 512 (Gaugemaster) - *09*	65	80
32-800W	**47408** ***Finsbury Park*** BRe blue DC21 Sp Edn 500 (Deltic Preservation Society) - *07*	65	80
31-650T	**47541** ***The Queen Mother*** I-C/Scotrail grey Highland motif Sp Edn (Rails) - *10*	75	90
32-800Y	**47560** ***Tamar*** BRe blue W DC21 Sp Edn 504 (Cheltenham Model Centre) - *07*	60	80
32-650X	**47573** ***The London Standard*** NSE blue DC21 Sp Edn (ModelZone) - *09*	NPG	NPG
?	**47604** ***Pendennis Castle*** Brunswick Green Sp Edn (Rail Exclusive) 57/6 - *11*	NPG	100
?	as above but filled with sound	NPG	200
32-801Z	**47815** ***Abertawe Landore*** BRc green 37/08 Sp Edn 512 (Kernow MRC) - *08*	65	87

L58b. Class 47 Diesel Co-Co (B) (2007)

BR built mixed traffic locomotive from 1962. This version has new roof detail, revised bogie frames and authentic fuel tanks. 6-axle drive 5-pole motor, directional lighting, high intensity centre light, etched nameplates and is DCC ready.

31-650V	**47079** ***George Jackson Churchward*** BRc green, GW150 Sp Edn 512 (Kernow MRC) - *08*	65	87
31-650U	**47145** ***Merddin Emrys*** BRe Tinsley blue Sp Edn (Rails) - *10*	75	90
31-650?	**47461** ***Charles Rennie Macintosh*** Scotrail Sp Edn (Rails) - *10*	75	90
31-652	**47474** ***Sir Rowland Hill*** Parcels red+dark grey DC21 - *08*	60	76
31-650	**47535** ***University of Leicester*** BReLL blue DC21 - *08*	60	76
31.650Z?	**47572** ***Ely Cathedral*** BReLL blue Sp Edn 504 (*Hornby Magazine*) DC21 - *10*	NPG	NPG
31-651	**47612** ***Titan*** BR IC grey DC21 - *08*	60	76
31-650S	**47975** ***The Institution of Civil Engineers*** 'Dutch' grey+yellow DC21 Ltd Edn 512 - *10*	70	88

L59a. Prototype 'Deltic' Diesel Co-Co (B) (2007)

This was produced for the National Railway Museum (NRM).

32-520	***Deltic*** light blue in special box with certificate Sp Edn 500 (NRM) - *07*	100	180
32-520	***Deltic*** light blue Sp Edn 2500 (NRM) - *08*	100	120

L59b. Class 55 'Deltic' Diesel Co-Co (B) (2003)

English Electric express passenger locomotives introduced in 1961. DCC ready. DS = fitted with digital sound. wpc = wooden presentation case. 4 metal roof fans, 5-pole motor/flywheel drive to both bogies and metal sprung buffers. en = etched nameplate.

32-525A	**D9002** ***The Kings Own Yorkshire Light Infantry*** BRc green - *not made*	NA	NA
32-524NRM	**D9002** BRc green (1961 condition) part of a 2 x Deltic set for NRM but a few sold separately - *09*	110	NA
(32-525 TMCH)	**D9003** ***Meld*** BRc green en part of Sp Edn ex-set of two100 (TMC) - *04*	60	NA
32-525U/A	**D9003** ***Meld*** BRc green en 1A16 Sp Edn 252 (Harburn Hobbies) - *05*	60	80
32-525U/B	**D9003** ***Meld*** BRc green W en 1A35 Sp Edn 252 (Harburn Hobbies) - *05*	60	80
32-525	**D9004** ***Queen's Own Highlander*** BRc 2-tone green small yellow panels en - *03*	40	50

32-530	**D9006** (un-named) BRc 2-tone green Ltd Edn 504 (BCC) DC21 - *09*	NPG	NPG
(32-525 TMCH)	**D9007** ***Pinza*** BRc green en part of Sp Edn ex-set of 2 100 (TMC) - *04*	65	NA
32-525DS	**D9007** ***Pinza*** BRc green en DS DC21 - *06*	NPG	NPG
32-525TMCH	**D9003** ***Meld*** + **D9007** ***Pinza*** BRc green wpc en Sp Edn 100 sets (TMC) - *04*	NA	130
TMC189D	**D9013** ***The Black Watch*** BRc green [1A35+ 1A06] Sp Edn 100 (TMC) - *05*	70	90
TMC189DW	as above but weathered Sp Edn 100 (TMC) - *05*	70	90
32-529	**D9017 The** ***Durham Light Infantry*** BRc two-tone green DC21 - *09*	60	77
32-529	**D9019** ***Royal Highland Fusiliers*** BRc green DC21 - *not made*	NA	NA
32-525X	**D9021** ***Argyll & Sutherland Highlander*** BRc green [1A16+1E15] Sp Edn 504 (TMC) - *04*	60	80
32-525Y	as above but weathered Sp Edn 504 (TMC) - *04*	60	70
32-530DS	**55001** ***St. Paddy*** BRe blue DS DC21 - *08*	150	170
32-525A	**55002** ***The Kings Own Yorkshire Light Infantry*** BRc green* - *04*	40	50
32-525Z	**55009** ***Alycidon*** BRe blue en Sp Edn 500 (DPS) - *04*	60	100
31-530ZDS	**55011** ***The Royal Northumberland Fusiliers*** BRe DS DC21 Sp Edn (Rails) - *08*	150	170
32-527	**55012** ***Crepello*** BRe blue - *04*	40	50
32-528	**55013** ***The Black Watch*** BRe blue en ** DC8 - *05*	50	60
32-525V	**55015** ***Tulyar*** BRe blue Sp Edn 750 (DPS) - *05*	60	80
32-525W	**55019** ***Royal Highland Fusilier*** BRe blue W Sp Edn 750 (DPS) - *04*	40	80
32-526	**55020** ***Nimbus'*** BRe blue - *03*	45	55
31-525T	**55022/D9000** ***Royal Scots Grey*** BRe en blue Sp Edn 504 (Beaver Sports) - *06*	65	80

* Also issued as Heritage Range model. **Upgraded diecast metal alloy buffers developed for the Class 66.

L60. Class 57 Diesel Co-Co (B) (2005)

Rebuilds of the Class 47 from 1997. Differing fuel tank styles, working lights, etched roof profile grilles. DCC ready. Early models did not have the Dellner coupling fitted.

32-750	**57008** ***Freightliner Explorer*** Freightliner green DC8 - *05*	55	68
32-750DC	**57010** ***Freightliner Crusader*** 57/0 Freightliner green DC8 - *06*	60	82
32-753	**57011** ***Freightliner Challenger*** 57/0 Freightliner green DC8 - *06*	58	71

Class 57 diesel in DRS (compass) livery [L60]

32-754	**57011** DRS (compass) dark blue 57/0 DC8 - *09*	60	82
32-751	**57301** ***Scot Tracy*** Virgin red and grey - *05*	55	68
32-760Z	**57306** ***Jeff Tracy*** Virgin red and grey, Delner coupling Sp Edn 504 (Hereford Model Centre - *06*	60	78
32-760	**57307** ***Lady Penelope*** Virgin silver+red Delner coupling DC8 - *06*	58	71
32-755	**57315** ***Arriva*** Trains Wales 2-tone blue 57/3 Delner coupling DC8 - *06*	65	82
32-750K	**57601** Porterbrook silver+mauve 57/6 Sp Edn 504 (BCC) - *05*	55	68
32-750?	**57601** West Coast maroon 57/6 DC21 Sp Edn 504 (*Model Rail* magazine) - *09*	65	85
32-752	**57602** ***Restormel Castle*** FGW green 57/6 DC8 - *05*	58	71
32-752Y	**57603** ***Tintagel Castle*** FGW purple 57/6 DC21 Sp Edn 512 (Kernow Model Rail Centre) - *not made*	NA	NA
32-752Y	**57605** ***Totnes Castle***, purple, 57/6, DC21, Sp Edn 512 (Kernow Model Rail Centre) - *10*	75	95

L61a. Class 66 Diesel Co-Co (B) (2005)

General Motors heavy freight design introduced in 1998. DCC ready. Directional lighting (options) en = etched nameplates, 6-axle drive, different light cluster styles and etched roof grill. DS = fitted with digital sound.

32-725DS	**66022** ***Lafarge Charnwood*** EWS maroon DS DC21 - *06*	NPG	NPG
32-733	**66068** EWS maroon+yellow DC21 - *07*	65	80
32-725Z	**66077** ***Benjamin Gimbert GC*** EWS maroon Sp Edn 504 (Rails) - *05*	50	73
32-725	**66135** EWS maroon - *05*	50	73
32-734	**66152** DB Schenker red - *09*	65	84
32-730	**66200** ***Railway Heritage Committee*** EWS maroon - *05*	50	73
32-725W	**66249** EWS maroon W Sp Edn (Hereford Model Centre) - *06*	50	73
32-729	**66405** DRS/Malcolm Logistics Services dark blue - *05*	50	73
32-731	**66407** DRS (compass) blue DC21 - *06*	50	76
32-726Z	**66522** ***East London Express*** Freightliner/ Shanks 2-tone green Sp Edn 504 (Kernow Model Railway Centre) - *05*	65	85
32-726DS	**66522** Freightliner/Shanks 2-tone green 40th Anniv. DS DC21 - *07*	120	157
32-732	**66532** ***P&O Nedlloyd Atlas*** Freightliner green en DC21 - *06*	55	76
32-726K	**66540** ***Ruby*** Freightliner green Ltd Edn 540 (BCC) - *06*	70	90
32-725Y	**66552** ***Maltby Raider*** Freightliner green Sp Edn 504 (Rails) - *05*	50	73
32-726	**66610** Freightliner green - *05*	50	73
32-728	**66612** ***ForthRaider*** Freightliner green - *05*	50	73
32-726Y	**66618** ***Railways Illustrated*** Freightliner green Sp Edn 504 (Ian Allan) - *05*	65	85
32-727	**66701** GBRf blue - *05*	50	73
32-727DS	**66702** ***Blue Lightning*** GBRf blue+yellow en DS DC21- *08*	150	176
32-727Y	**66705** ***Golden Jubilee*** GBRf blue with Union Jack Sp Edn 512 (Kernow) - *08*	70	90
32-727Z	**66709** GBRf 'Medite' blue Sp Edn (Model Rail) - *06*	50	73

L61b. Class 66/9 Diesel Co-Co (B) (2007)

The Class 66 diesel built to meet environmental requirements as a low emission machine. DCC ready. Directional lighting (options) etched nameplates, 6-axle drive, different light cluster styles and etched roof grill. DS = fitted with digital sound.

32-979Y	**66301** Fastline Freight grey W Sp Edn (*Rail Express Modeller*) DS - *09*	75	90
32-979Y (DS)	**66301** Fastline Freight grey W Sp Edn (*Rail Express Modeller*) DS - *09*	150	170
32-977	**66411** ***Eddie the Engine*** DRS/Stobart blue DC21 - *08*	65	84

Class 66/9 low emission diesel in Malcolm Rail livery [L61b]

32-976DC	**66412** DRS (compass) blue DC21 - *07*	75	92
32-979	**66412** DRS/Malcolm Rail dark blue DC21 - *09*	70	85
32-979Z	**66623** ***Bill Bolsover*** Bardon Aggregates violet-blue DC21 Sp Edn 512 (Kernow Model Rail Centre) - *10*	80	100
32-979X	**66722** ***Sir Edward Watkin*** GBRf Metronet violet-blue DC21Sp Edn 500 (*Model Rail*) - *10*	80	98
32-978	**66725** ***Sunderland AFC*** FGBRf violet blue DC21 - *08*	65	80
32-975	**66952** Freightliner green 40th Anniv. DC21 - *07*	65	80

L62. Class 70 'Powerhaul' Co-Co (B) (2011)

The new 75 mph Co-Co 'PowerHaul' locomotives feature innovative designs such as Dynamic Braking and AC traction technology and will be utilised across all parts of the extensive Freightliner route network. The model was developed in co-operation with General Electric and Freightliner and the models have elaborate fan detail, multi-functional lighting control, DCC21 decoder sockets enabling sound to be added.

32-585Z	**70001** ***Powerhaul*** Freightliner green+yellow Sp Edn (Freightliner) - *11*	NPG	NPG
31-586	**70003** Freightliner green+yellow DC21 - *11*	80	95

32-585	**70006** Freightliner green+yellow DC21 - *11*	80	95

Electric Locomotives

L63. Class 85 AC Electric Bo-Bo (B) (2011)

The Class 85 locomotives were built in the early 1960s for the electrification of West Coast Main Line services. They were originally classified as 'Class AL5'. With a capability of 100 mph, the locomotives were used on a variety of mixed traffic work. Later, to work freight trains for Railfreight Distribution, 14 of the class were downgraded to 80 mph capability and renumbered in the 85/1 series.

31-677	**E3056** BRd bright blue twin pantographs - *11*	80	94
31-676	**E3058** BRd bright blue single pantograph - *11*	80	94
31-678	**85026** BRe blue single pantograph - *11*	80	94

Diesel Multiple Units

L64. Class 105 2-Car DMU (B) (2010)

The Class 105s were built in 1956 by Cravens Ltd for branch line and local services. The models have directional and interior lighting and consists of DMBS and DTCL cars. DCC ready.

31-326	**E51254+E56412** BRc green + whiskers DC8 - *10*	75	89
31-325	**E51289+E56463** BRe blue, yellow ends DC8 - *10*	75	89
31-327	**E51296+E56451** BRc green half yellow ends DC8 - *10*	75	89

L65a. Class 107 3-Car DMU (B) (2010)

BR Derby built, from 1960, for Scottish local services, and made up of DMBS+TSL+DMCL cars. The models are 'DCC ready'and have bi-directional lighting, detailed interior with lights and a concealed mechanism.

32-910Z	**107447 (SC52029+SC59792+SC52008)** orange +black, large roof box DC8 Sp Edn 510 (*Model Rail* & Harburn Hobbies) - *10*	85	114

L65b. Class 108 2-Car DMU (B) (2006)

BR Derby built outer suburban trains from 1958. DCC ready, differing cab styles, two roof styles, DMBS and DMCL cars, bi-directional lighting, detailed interior with lights and a concealed mechanism. srb = small roof box. lrb = large roof box.

32-900	**M50628+M56214** BR green, whiskers srb - *06*	60	78
32-900A	**M51928+M52043** BR green, whiskers lrb DC8 - *09*	60	83

Class 108 2-car DMU in Network South East livery [L65b]

32-901	**51909+54271** NSE bright blue lrb DC8 - *06*	60	78
32-902	**54243+53959** BR blue+grey srb - *06*	60	78
32-902A	**51939+52063** BR blue+grey lrb DC8 - *08*	60	82
32-903	**M56231+M50948** BR/GMPTE white+blue srb DC8 - *09*	70	69
32-900Z	**M51908+M56491** AN276 BRe blue Sp Edn 504 (ModelZone) - *06*	70	88
32-900Y	**C970 (56322+54205)** BR blue+grey, red bufferbeams, dragon motif Sp Edn 504 (Hereford Model Centre) - *06*	70	86
32-900B	**M50979+M56262**, green with whiskers, large roof box, DC8 - *10*	60	87

L65c. Class 108 3-Car DMU (B) (2007)

BR Derby built outer suburban trains from 1958. DCC ready, differing cab styles, two roof styles, DMBS+TSL+DMCL cars, bi-directional lighting, detailed interior with lights and a concealed mechanism. srd = small roof box. lrb = large roof box.

32-911	**E50620+E50642+E59386** BR green, small yellow panel srb DC8 - *08*	80	102
32-911A	**E50644+E59388+E50622** BR green, small yellow panel srb DC8 - *09*	85	104
32-910	**M52051+M51936+M59386** BR/GMPTE blue+ grey lrb DC8 - *08*	80	102

L66. Derby 'Lightweight' 2-Car DMU (B) (2011)

This is the original Derby 'Lightweight' of which 97 were built by BR workshops at Derby between 1954 and 1956. They were pioneering units which sped up the retirement of steam locomotives by taking over branch line, cross country and suburban routes. They had the comfort of a city bus and were not to be ridden in for long journeys. As newer units came on stream, they were withdrawn, the last unit disappeared in 1969, and too early to be designated a class under TOPS. They saw extensive use across the country, including the West Riding of Yorkshire, Cumbria, East London, West Midlands, South Midlands, East Anglia and Lincolnshire. Some units passed into departmental service and a 2-car unit has been preserved at the Midland Railway Centre at Butterley. DMBS and DTC cars have been modelled.

32-515	?+? BRc green with full yellow ends DC8 - *11*	75	91
32-516	?+? BRc green with whiskers DC8 - *11*	75	91
32-517	?+? BRe blue DC8 - *11*	75	91

L67. Class 150 2-car DMU (B) (2008)

BREL York built semi-fast passenger trains from 1985. Both subclass, tinted glazing and metal-effect window frames. LED directional lighting and 5-pole motor with flywheel drive. All are DCC fitted as DC21.

32-925K	**150123** ***Richard Crane*** (52123+57123) Silver Link violet+green Ltd Edn 504 (BCC) - *09*	65	88
32-926	**150125** (52125+57125) Central Trains light green +blue 150/1 - *09*	65	88
32-925Z	**150135** (52135+57135) BR Provincial Railways light blue 150/1 Sp Edn 512 (Trains4U) - *10*	75	95
32-925	**150144** (52144+57144) FNW dark blue 150/1 - *09*	65	88

Class 150 2-car DMU in First North Western livery [L67]

(30-046)	**150148** (52148+57148) BR Provincial Railways blue+grey 150/2 ex-Dynamis Digital set - *09*	65	NA
32-935Z	**150207** Regional Railways Merseyrail yellow+ white 150/2 Sp Edn 512 (Hattons) - *09*	75	95
32-935Y	**150252** (52252+57252) ScotRail (Whoosh) violet+pale grey, Sp Edn 500 (*Model Rail* & Harburn Hobbies) - *11*	NPG	NPG
32-935	**150256** (52256+57256) Arriva Trains Wales light blue 150/2 - *08, 10*	65	88
32-936	**150270** (52270+57270) BR Regional Railways blue+grey 150/2 - *08*	65	81

L68a. Class 158 Express 2-Car Units (1996)

Built by BR Derby as outer suburban and cross-country trains from 1989. TPE = Trans-Pennine Express

31-501	**158702** Scotrail Express blue+white - *97*	40	60
31-500Z	**158725** (52725+57725) First ScotRail purple Sp Edn 504 (AMRSS) - *07*	NPG	NPG
31-507	**158726** (52726+57726) ScotRail 'Woosh!' livery - *02*	50	70
31-508	**158739** (52739+57739) First ScotRail/ 'Whoosh!' - *05*	60	75
31-506	**158745** (52745+57745) Wales & West Alphaline silver - *00*	50	70
31-506A	**158746** (52746+57746) Wessex Trains Alphaline silver - *02*	50	70
31-503	**158757** (52757+57757) Regional Railways/ Express blue+white - *97*	40	60
31-505	**158758** (52758+57758) First North Western blue - *00*	50	70
31-510	**158768** (52768+57768) First Transpennine purple+blue - *05*	60	75
31-504	**158783** (52783+57783) Central Trains green - *00*	50	70
31-500	**158791** Regional Railways blue+white - *96*	45	65
31-504A	**158797** (52797+57797) Central Trains green - *02*	50	70
31-510	**158806** First TPE purple+blue - *not made*	NA	NA
31-511	**158823** (52823+57823) Arriva Trains Wales light blue - *09*	75	91
31-500A	**158860** Regional Railways blue+white - *97*	50	70
31-500B	**158868** Regional Railways blue+white - *98*	40	60
31-509	**158905** NR W.Yorks PTE Metro red+silver - *06*	60	75
31-502	**158906** BRe W.Yorks PTE Metro red - *97*	40	60
31-515	**158741** (52741+57741) First ScotRail violet - *08*	65	82
31-514	**158791** (52791+57791) Northern Rail purple+		

	violet - *08*	65	82
31-516	**158782** (52782+57782) Central Trains green - *08*	65	82
(30-051)	**2700** Iarnrod Eiraenn Class 2700 light green ex-set - *10*	65	NA

L68b. Class 158 Express 3-Car Units (1998)

Built by BR Derby as outer suburban and cross-country trains from 1989. TPE = Trans-Pennine Express

31-5??	**158798** Reg Rlys Express blue+grey - *not made?*	NA	NA
31-511	**158809** Reg Rlys Express blue+white - *98*	65	85
31-513	**158811** Transpennine purple+gold - *99*	65	80
31-513A	**158799** Arriva TPE purple+gold? - *02*	65	85

L68c. Class 159 3-Car Units (1998)

31-510	**159001** ***City of Exeter*** NSE bright blue 3-car - *98*	65	85
31-512	**159009** SWT/Stagecoach white 3-car - *98*	65	85
31-514	**159019** SouthWest Trains white 3-car - *01*	65	85

L69a. Class 165/1 'Network Turbo'

Working LED lights and flywheel driven 5-pole motor. This was possibly dropped once Bachmann realised the amount of additional work that would be required to alter the Class 166 tooling.

31-035	**165001** Chiltern Line white 2-car - *not made*	NA	NA

L69b. Class 166 'Network Express Turbo'(1999)

3-car DMUs built by ABB York as semi-fast commuter trains from 1992. Working LED lights and twin flywheel driven 5-pole motor.

Class 166 DMU in First Great Western Link livery [L69b]

31-025	**166202** NSE white+blue+red - *99*	65	85
31-028	**166205** FGW 2006 livery violet+red - *not made*	NA	NA
31-028	**166213** FGW Neon livery violet+red - *08*	80	102
31-026	**166209** Thames Trains Express white+blue - *06*	80	96
31-026	**166212** Thames Trains Express white+blue - *not made*	NA	NA
31-027	**166214** (58135+58614+58114) FGW/Link white +blue+green - *06*	80	96

L70. Class 168/1 'Clubman' DMU (B) (2003)

Adtranx/Bombardier built fast commuter trains from 2000. 3-car DMU. Flywheel drive to both bogies and LED directional lighting.

32-470	**168110** (58160+58460+58260) Chiltern Railways white+violet - *03*	75	90
32-471	**168111** (58261+58461+58161) Chiltern Railways white+violet - *05*	75	93

L71a. Class 170/171 'Turbostar' 2-Car DMU (B) (2001)

ADtranx/Bombardier built fast commuter and inter-regional trains from 1998. Flywheel drive to both bogies and LED directional lighting. Prototypical ribbon glazing and different front apron styles. With a few exceptions, models were DCC ready from 2007.

32-450	**170105** (50105+79105)Midland Mainline teal 170/1 - *01*	50	70
32-453	**170271** (50271+79271) Anglia Railways light blue+white 170/2 - *04*	65	80
32-452	**170301** (50301+79301) SouthWest Trains white+red 170/4 - *01*	50	70
32-452A	**170302** (50302+79302) SWT white+blue+red 170/3 - *04*	65	80
32-466	**170504** (50504+79504) LM City green+black+ pale grey - *09*	70	88
32-451A	**170514** (50514+79514) Central Trains green W 170/5 - *04*	65	80
32-451	**170515** (50515+79515) Central Trains green 170/5 - *01*	55	75
32-460Z	**171721** (50721+79721) Southern green+white 171/7 Sp Edn 504 (Modelzone) - *05*	60	87
32-440DC	Transpennine DC21 170/2 - *not made*	NA	NA

L71b. Class 170/171 'Turbostar' 3-Car DMU (B) (2001)

ADtranx/Bombardier built fast commuter and inter-regional trains from 1998. Flywheel drive to both bogies and LED directional lighting. Prototypical ribbon glazing and different front apron styles. With few exceptions, models were DCC ready from 2007.

32-464	**170202** (50202+56202+79202) Anglia/One blue DC21 170/2 - *09*	80	104
32-463	**170413** (50413+56413+79413) First ScotRail purple 170/4 - *06*	65	80

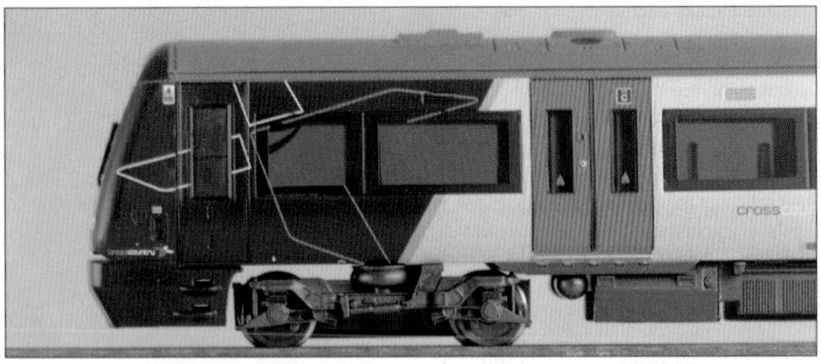

Class 170 Turbostar DMU in Arriva Cross Country livery [L71b]

32-461	**170424** (50424+56424+79424) ScotRail 'Whoosh!' livery 170/3 - *01*	65	85
32-467	**170434?** (?+?+?) Scotrail (Saltaire) 170/4 - *10*	90	112
32-462	**170470** (50470+56470+79470) Strathclyde PTE maroon+cream 170/3 - *03*	65	85
32-460	**170637** (50637+56637+79637) Central Trains green 170/6 - *03*	65	85
32-465	**170102** (50102+55102+79102) Cross Country grey+deep purple 170/2 - *09*	85	102

L71A. Class 205 'Thumper' 2-Car DEMU (B) (2011)

This model was made exclusively for Kernow Model Railway Centre and tooling will allow for backdating this model to as-built condition, and a centre coach will be added during later production runs. The models are fitted with highly detailed interiors and with 21-pin DCC sockets.

K2003	**1108** BR plain green cab front - *11*	NPG	110
K2007	**1115** BR green with all yellow front - *11*	NPG	110
K2006	**1119** BR green with small yellow panel - *11*	NPG	150
K2004	**1121** BR green with small yellow panel - *11*	NPG	150
K2005	**1120** BR blue - *11*	NPG	110
K2005DC	**1120** BR blue with sound chip fitted - *11*	NPG	200
K2001	**205025** NSE bright blue - *11*	NPG	150
K2002	**205012** Connex white+yellow - *11*	NPG	150

L72a. Class 220 'Voyager' DEMU (B) (2002)

Built by Bombardier in 2000 for fast passenger service. Non-tilting 4-car pack. Directional lighting system.

32-600	**220001** ***Maiden Voyager*** (60301 + 60701+ 60201+ 60401) Virgin grey+red 4 car pack - *02*	80	100
(30-600)	**220017** ***Bombardier Voyager*** (60317+60717 +60417) Virgin grey+ red 3-car ex-set - *03*	80	NA
30-602	**220018** ***Dorset Voyager*** (60318+60718+ 60218+60418) Virgin grey+red 4-car pack - *07*	90	110
32-601	**220032** ***Grampian Voyager*** (60332+60732 +60232+60432) Virgin grey+red 4-car pack - *04*	80	103
(30-601)	**220008** ***Draig Gymreig Welsh Dragon*** (60308+ 60208+60408) grey+red 3-car ex-set - *07*	70	NA
32-603	**220017** (60317+60217+60417) Cross Country grey+deep purple - *09*	95	123

L72b. Class 221 'Super Voyager' DEMU (B) (2004)

Tilting 5-car set.

32-626	**221101** ***Louis Bleriot*** (60451+60751+60951 +60351) Virgin grey+red 5-car pack - *04*	80	123
32-627	**221122** ***Doctor Who*** (60472+60772+60872 +60972+60372) Virgin red+silver 4-car pack - *09*	110	130
32-625	**221130** ***Michael Palin*** (60480+60780+60880+60980+60380) Virgin grey+red 5-car pack - *04*	80	120
32-628	**221135** (60485+60785+60885+60985+60385) Cross Country grey+deep purple 5-car pack - *09*	80	138

L72A. BR Class 251 'Blue Pullman' 6-car DMU (B) (2011)

Each six-car unit will comprise 2 power cars, 2 kitchen cars (type 4) and 2 parlour cars (type 6) and will be sold as a 6-car unit. The new model will incorporate today's leading edge technologies and will include a new style close coupling concept, central coach ceiling and table lamp lighting, directional lighting, cab lights, etched fan grilles, a DCC socket and will have provision for added sound.

31-255	**BR Midland Pullman** ? Nanking blue - *11*	NPG	NPG
31-256	**BR Midland Pullman** ? Nanking blue with half yellow ends - *11*	NPG	NPG

Electric Multiple Units

L73. Class 350 'Desiro' 4-car EMU (B) (2011)

Operating on the West Coast, the Siemens Class 350 EMUs are now in service with London Midland City and based in the depot at Northampton. There are 30 4-car units operating from the 25Kv catenary and the first batch originally also had third rail current collection capability. A further 37 units were ordered by London Midland and these do not have third rail provision and have different interiors. They are designated Class 350/2. The Bachmann model represents both versions.

31-032	**350102** London Midland grey+green 4-car pack 350/1 - *11*	110	132
31-030	**350111** ***Apollo*** Silver Link (unbranded) 4-car pack 350/1 - *11*	110	132
31-031	**350238** London Midland grey+green 4-car pack 350/2 - *11*	110	132

L74. Class 411 4-CEP 4-Car EMU (B) (2009)

Built in 1956-63 by BR at Eastleigh as express commuter trains. 4-car set. DCC ready. It is essential for the cars to be assembled in the prescribed order or the unit will not work.

31-425	**7105** (S61230+S70235+S70229+S61229) BR green, whistle DC21 - *09*	100	129
31-427	**7113** (S61908+S70305+S70262+S61909) BR blue+grey, roof horns DC21 - *09*	100	129

Class 411 4-CEP EMU [L74]

31-426	**7126** (S61335+S70318+S70275+S61334) BR green, yellow panel, roof horns DC21 - *09*	100	129
31-426A	**7128** (S61338+S70277+S70320+ S61339) BR green, yellow panel, roof horns DC21 - *10*	100	133
31-427A	**7134** (S61350+S70326+S70283+ S61371) BR blue+grey, roof horns DC21 - *10*	100	133
31-425A	**7141** (S61365+S70290+S70333+ S61634) BR green, whistle DC21 - *10*	100	133
31-427Z	**7119** (S61321+S70268+S70311+S61320) BR blue full yellow ends Sp Edn 504 (ModelZone) DC21 - *09*	110	140

L75. Class 416 2-EPB 2-Car EMU (B) (2011)

Built in 1956-63 by BR at Eastleigh as express commuter trains. 4-car set. DCC ready.

31-376	**5764** (S65378+S77563) BR green DC21 - *11*	80	96
31-375	**5770** (S65384+S77569) BR blue DC21 - *11*	80	96
31-377	**6238** (S65352+S77537) BR blue+grey DC21 - *11*	80	96

COACHES

The earliest coaches were a number of GWR Colletts and LMS types from the former Mainline range but with different stock numbers. Some of these had also been made for Replica Railways by the tool owners - Kader. They were followed by LNER coaches of Thompson design and Bulleid stock of the Southern Region, development of which had been started by Mainline owners - Palitoy. The finest development so far is an extensive range of Mk1 coaches, in the Blue Riband series, which first appeared late in 1999.

Running Numbers - Bachmann tend to give their coaches different stock numbers when they redo a batch and this is usually reflected in the addition of a letter suffix to the catalogue number to denote the change. There have, however, been a few cases where the suffix has been missed off the box and some newly numbered batches have been released in boxes which carry the number used on the earlier release. As always, it is as well to ensure that the contents of the box are what you expect them to be.

Cat No.	Company, Number, Colour, Dates	£	£

GWR Collett Stock

C1a. GWR 60ft All 3rd (2nd) (ex-Mainline) (1991)

This is the ex-Mainline model of a Collett C77 third corridor coach. H = Hawksworth livery

34-050	**GWR** 1107 brown+cream - *91*	12	22
34-050A	**GWR** 1104 brown+cream - *93*	12	20
34-051	**GWR** (button) 1145 brown+cream H - *95*	12	19
(30-021)	**GWR** (button) 1137 brown+cream H ex-set - *06*	14	NA
34-050B	**Great Western** 1118 brown+cream H - *97*	12	17
34-050C	**Great Western** 1155 brown+cream H - *01*	12	17
34-050D	**Great Western** brown+cream H - *not made*	NA	NA
34-052	**Great Western** 1115 brown+cream H - *05*	12	17
34-052A	**Great Western** 1124 brown+cream H - *10*	13	18
34-055	**BR** W1123 red+cream - *95*	12	19
34-056	**BR** W1139W red+cream - *04*	12	17
34-200	**BR** W562W maroon - *91*	12	22

C1b. GWR 60ft Brake 3rd & 1st/3rd (ex-Mainline) (1991)

This is the ex-Mainline model of a Collett E159 brake composite coach. H = Hawksworth livery

34-075	**GWR** 1655 brown+cream 3rd - *91*	12	22
34-075A	**GWR** 1657 brown+cream 3rd - *93*	NPG	NPG
34-076	**GWR** (button) 6600 brown+cream 1st/3rd H - *95*	12	19
(30-021)	**GWR** (button) 6356 brown+cream H ex-set - *06*	14	NA
34-075B	**Great Western** 1656 brown+cream 1st/3rd H - *97*	12	18
34-075C	**Great Western** 6706 brown+cream 3rd H- *01*	12	17
34-075D	**Great Western** brown+cream 3rd H - *not made*	NA	NA
34-076	**Great Western** 6543 brown+cream H - *05*	12	17
34-076A	**Great Western** 6421 brown+cream H - *10*	13	19
34-080	**BR** W6550 red+cream 1st/2nd - *95*	12	19
34-081	**BR** W6608W red+cream - *04*	12	17
34-175	**BR** W1657W maroon 2nd - *91*	12	22

C1c. GWR 60ft All 1st (ex-Mainline) (1990)

This is the ex-Mainline model of a Collett C77 third corridor coach. H = Hawksworth livery

34-100	**GWR** 8095 brown+cream H- *90*	12	22
34-100A	**GWR** 8099 brown+cream - *93*	12	17
34-100B	**Great Western** 8096 brown+cream H - *97*	12	18
34-101	**GWR** (button) 8101 brown+cream - *95*	12	19

C1d. GWR 60ft Composite (ex-Mainline) (1990)

This is the ex-Mainline model of a Collett C77 third corridor coach. H = Hawksworth livery

GWR Collett composite coach [C1d]

34-125	**GWR** 7001 brown+cream - *90*	12	22
34-125A	**GWR** 7003 brown+cream - *93*	12	17
34-125B	**GWR** 7056 brown+cream H - *97*	12	18
34-125C	**Great Western** 7050 brown+cream H - *01*	12	17
34-125D	**Great Western** brown+cream H - *not made*	NA	NA
34-126	**GWR** (button) 7023 brown+cream - *95*	12	19
34-127	**Great Western** 7026 brown+cream H - *05*	12	17
34-127A	**Great Western** 7045 brown+cream H - *10*	15	20
34-076	**G()W** 7025 brown+cream - *04?*	12	17
34-130	**BR** W7021 red+cream - *95*	12	19
34-131	**BR** W7031W red+cream - *04*	12	17
34-150	**BR** W7033W maroon - *90*	12	22

LMS Stock

These include LMS period 1 panelled stock and the period 3 Stanier parcel van.

C2a. LMS Panelled 57ft Brake (ex-Mainline) (1990)

34-226	**LMS** 5312 maroon + end boards - *96*	12	16

34-226A*	**LMS** 5284 maroon + end boards - *00*	12	15
34-226B	**LMS** 5328 maroon + end boards - *03*	12	16
34-226C	**LMS** 5268 maroon + end boards - *08*	13	17
34-276	**LMS** 10199? maroon 1928 livery - *not made*	NA	NA
34-275	**BR** M5267 red+cream - *90*	12	18
34-225	**BR** M5315M maroon - *90*	12	18
34-226Z	**CIE** 1095 green - Sp Edn 300 (Murphy's Models) -*00*	10	15

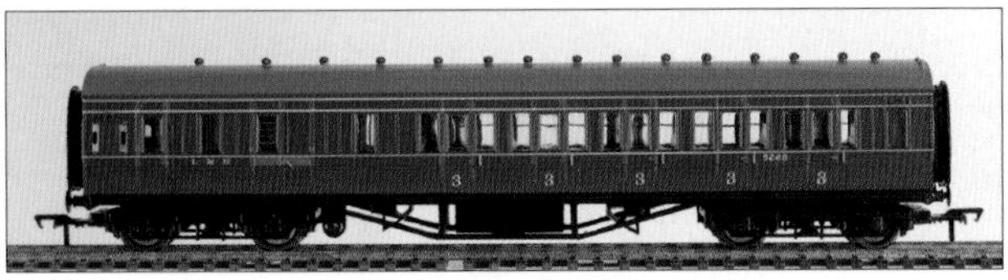

LMS Period 1 brake 3rd coach [C2a]

34-226Y	**CIE** 1087 green - Sp Edn 300 (Murphy's Models) -*01*	10	15
(00651)	**CIE** 1096 green (ex-US Irish set) - *04*	10	NA
74701	**CIE** 1088 green (US solo release) - *?*	10	15

* No 'A' suffix on box.

C2b. LMS Panelled 57ft 1st/3rd (ex-Mainline) (1990)

34-251	**LMS** 3650 maroon + end boards - *96*	12	16
34-251A*	**LMS** 3572 maroon + end boards - *00*	12	15
34-251B	**LMS** 3650 maroon + end boards - *not made*	NA	NA
34-251B	**LMS** 3605 maroon + end boards - *06*	12	16
34-251C	**LMS** 3622 maroon + end boards - *08*	13	17
34-252	**LMS** 3705 maroon + end boards - *96*	12	16
34-252A	**LMS** 3591 maroon - *00*	12	15
34-252B	**LMS** 3650 maroon - *not made*	NA	NA
34-252B	**LMS** 3619 maroon - *03*	12	16
34-252C	**LMS** 3506 maroon - *08*	13	17
34-301	**LMS** 18997 maroon 1928 livery - *not made*	NA	NA
34-302	**LMS** maroon 1928 livery - *not made*	NA	NA
34-300	**BR** M3672 red+cream - *90*	12	18
34-250	**BR** M3565M maroon - *90*	12	18
34-251X	**CIE** 2096 green - Sp Edn 300 (Murphy's Models) -*01*	10	15
(00651)	**CIE** 2097 green (ex-US Irish set) - *04*	10	NA

* No 'A' suffix on box.

C2c. LMS Panelled 57ft 3rd (ex-Mainline) (2000)

34-251Y	**CIE** 1332 green - Sp Edn 300 (Murphy's Models) -*01*	10	15
34-251Z	**CIE** 1336 green - Sp Edn 300 (Murphy's Models) -*01*	10	15
(00651)	**CIE** 1333 green (ex-US Irish set) - *04*	10	NA
74700	**CIE** 1337 green (US solo release) - *?*	10	15

C3. LMS Stanier 50ft Parcels (ex-Mainline) (1990)

34-327	**LMS** 31250 maroon + end board - *96*	12	16

LMS 50ft parcels van [C3]

34-327A	**LMS** 30989 maroon - *01*	12	15
34-327B	**LMS** 31250 maroon + end board - *06*	12	16
34-327C	**LMS** 30966 maroon - *not made*	NA	NA
34-327C	**LMS** 31027 maroon - *09*	13	18
34-325	**BR** M31340M red+cream - *90*	12	18
34-326	**BR** M31319M red+cream + LMS type end boards - *96*	12	16
34-325	**BR** M31386M maroon + LMS type end boards - *96*	12	16
34-325A	**BR** M30980M maroon - *06*	12	16
34-325B	**BR** M31238M maroon - *08*	13	17
34-350	**BR** M31261 maroon - *90*	12	18
34-328	**BR** M31198 blue - *10*	13	17

LNER Thompson Stock

The 1992-93 stock was released in Thompson brown livery but those made in 2000 were in pre-war LNER brown.

C4a. LNER 63ft 3rd (2nd) (1991)

34-377	**LNER** 1047 brown - *92*	12	19
34-375	**BR** E1098E red+cream - *91*	12	19
34-375	**BR** E1056E red+cream - *91?*	12	19
34-379	**BR** E1011E red+cream - *10*	12	19
(31-960)	**BR** E1516E maroon ex-'Elizabethan'* - *96*	14	NA
(31-960)	**BR** E1609E maroon ex-'Elizabethan'* - *96*	14	NA
(31-960)	**BR** E1600E maroon ex-'Elizabethan'* - *96*	14	NA
34-376	**BR** E1497E maroon - *91*	12	19
34-376	**BR** E1001E maroon - *91?*	12	19
34-378	**BR** E1550E maroon - *97*	12	18

* From the 'Elizabethan' limited edition set of which 1000 were made.

C4b. LNER 59.5ft Composite (1991)

34-402	**LNER** 144 brown - *92*	12	19
34-400	**BR** E1207E red+cream - *91*	12	19
34-400	**BR** E1236E red+cream - *91?*	12	19
34-404	**BR** E1224E red+cream - *10*	12	19
34-401	**BR** E1228E maroon - *91*	12	19
34-401	**BR** E1240E maroon - *91?*	12	19
34-403	**BR** E1262E maroon - *97*	12	18

C4c. LNER 63ft Brake Comp (1991)

34-427	**LNER** 138 brown - *not made*	NA	NA
34-427	**LNER** 1142 brown - *92*	12	19
34-427/1	**LNER** 1112 brown - *not made*	NA	NA
34-425	**BR** E1146E red+cream - *91*	12	19
34-425	**BR** E1143E red+cream - *91?*	12	19
34-429	**BR** E1148E red+cream - *10*	12	19
(31-960)	**BR** E1161E maroon ex-'Elizabethan'* - *96*	14	NA
34-426	**BR** E1158E maroon - *91*	12	19
34-426	**BR** E1140E maroon - *91?*	12	19
34-428	**BR** E1151E maroon - *97*	12	18

* From the 'Elizabethan' limited edition set of which 1000 were made.

C4d. LNER 63ft Brake 3rd (2nd) (1991)

34-452	**LNER** 1908 brown - *92*	12	19
34-450	**BR** E1905E red+cream - *91*	12	19
34-450	**BR** E1925E red+cream - *91?*	12	19
34-454	**BR** E1936E red+cream - *10*	12	19
34-451	**BR** E1907E maroon - *91*	12	19
34-451	**BR** E1932E maroon - *91?*	12	19
34-453	**BR** E1910E maroon - *97*	12	18

C4e. LNER 63ft All 1st (1991)

34-477	**LNER** 1132 brown - *92*	12	19
34-477	**LNER** 138 brown - *not made*	NA	NA
34-475	**BR** E1315E red+cream - *91*	12	19
34-475	**BR** E1323E red+cream - *91?*	12	19
34-479	**BR** E1313E red+cream - *10*	12	19
34-476	**BR** E1322E maroon - *91*	12	19
(31-960)	**BR** E1328E maroon ex-'Elizabethan'* - *96*	14	NA
34-476	**BR** E1312E maroon - *91?*	12	19
34-478	**BR** E1320E maroon - *97*	12	18

* From the 'Elizabethan' limited edition set of which 1000 were made.

C4f. LNER 63ft Full Brake BG (1994)

Fitted with end board and step board.

LNER Thompson BG in teak livery [C4f]

34-651	**LNER** brown - *not made*	NA	NA
34-655	**LNER** 11 brown - *00*	12	18

34-651	**BR** E12E red+cream - *95*	12	20
34-651A	**BR** E153E red+cream ** - *00*	12	18
34-653	**BR** E16E red - *96*	12	18
34-653A	**BR** E16E red - *00*	12	18
(31-960)	**BR** E12E maroon also ex-'Elizabethan' pack (31-960)* - *96*	12	NA
34-651	**BR** E12E maroon - *96*	12	18
34-654A	**BR** E14E maroon - *00*	12	18
34-654	**BR** E16E maroon - *97*	12	20
34-650	**BR** E19E maroon - *94*	12	21
34-652	**BR** E18E blue - *95*	12	20
34-652A	**BR** E18E blue - *00*	12	18

* From the 'Elizabethan' limited edition set of which 1000 were made. ** 34-651A has a paler cream band than 34-651.

C4g. LNER All 2nd

Flush end glazing. Proposed for 2002.

34-800	**BR** red+cream - *not made*	NA	NA

C4h. LNER Composite

Flush end glazing. Proposed for 2002.

34-825	**BR** red+cream - *not made*	NA	NA

C4i. LNER Comp Brake

Flush end glazing. Proposed for 2002.

34-850	**BR** red+cream - *not made*	NA	NA

C4j. LNER 2nd Brake

Flush end glazing. Proposed for 2002.

34-875	**BR** red+cream - *not made*	NA	NA

C4k. LNER 1st Corridor

Flush end glazing. Proposed for 2002.

34-900	**BR** red+cream - *not made*	NA	NA

SR/BR Bulleid Stock

C5a. BR(SR) 63ft Semi-Open Brake 3rd (2nd) (1993)

be = brown end door

34-502	**BR** 3960 red+cream - *93*	12	21
34-502	**BR** S3960 red+cream no red cantrail - *93*	12	21
34-502A	**BR** S3960 red+cream - *00*	12	18

Bulleid semi-open brake 2nd coach [C5a]

34-503	**BR** S3962S red+cream - *93*	12	21
34-503A*	**BR** S3957S red+cream - *93*	12	21
34-503A	**BR** S3951S red+cream - *97*	12	18
34-503A	**BR** S3957S red+cream, be - *02*	12	18
34-504	**BR** S3953S green - *06*	12	18
34-500	**BR** S3945S green - *93*	12	21
34-501	**BR** S3948S green - *93*	12	21
34-501A	**BR** S3949S green - *97*	12	19
34-500A	**BR** S3955S green - *97*	12	19
34-500B	**BR** S3962S green - *00*	12	18
34-504A	**BR** S3975S green - *10*	13	20

* No suffix on box.

C5b. BR(SR) 63ft Composite (1993)

be = brown end door

34-550	**BR** S5871S green yellow 1st class line - *93*	12	21
34-550A	**BR** S5870S green yellow 1st class line - *99*	12	18
34-550A	**BR** S5870S green - *97*	12	19
34-550B	**BR** S5810S green yellow 1st class line - *00*	12	18
34-551	**BR** S5890S green - *93*	12	21
34-551A	**BR** S5900S green - *97*	12	19
34-554A	**BR** S5850S green - *10*	13	20
34-552	**BR** S5907S red+cream - *93*	12	21
34-522	**BR** S5???S red+cream no crimson red band - *99*	12	18
34-552A	**BR** S5907 red+cream no red cantrail band - *00*	12	18
34-552A	**BR** S5907 red+cream no red cantrail band, be - *02*	12	18
34-553	**BR** S5868S red+cream - *93*	12	21
34-553A	**BR** S5900S red+cream - *97*	12	18

C5c. BR(SR) 63ft All 3rd (2nd) (1993)

be = brown end door

34-527	**BR** S101 red+cream no red cantrail - *93*	12	21
34-527A	**BR** S101 red+cream - *00*	12	18
34-528	**BR** S114S red+cream - *93*	12	21
34-528A	**BR** S83S red+cream - *97*	12	18
34-528A	**BR** S83S red+cream, be - *02*	12	18
34-525	**BR** S82S green - *93*	12	21
34-529	**BR** S105S green - *06*	12	18
34-526A*	**BR** S108S green - *97*	12	19
34-529A	**BR** S118S green - *08*	13	19
34-525B	**BR** S125S green - *?*	12	18
34-525A*	**BR** S127S green - *97*	12	19
34-526	**BR** S130S green - *93*	12	21

* No suffix on box.

C5d. BR(SR) 63ft Open 3rd (2nd) (1995)

EB = SR end boards.

34-576	**BR** S1493S red+cream EB - 95	12	20
34-576A	**BR** S1493S red+cream - *00*	12	18
34-577	**BR** S1494S green - *06*	12	18
34-577A	**BR** S1488S green - *08*	13	19
34-575A	**BR** S1493S green EB - *00*	12	18
34-575	**BR** S1504S green EB - *95*	12	20

BR Mk1 Suburban Non-Corridor Stock

All the maroon coaches in this section have lining, while the red and blue versions are unlined.

C6a. BR Mk1 57ft Suburban 3rd (2nd) (1993)

34-600	**BR** M46082 red - *93*	12	19
34-600/1	**BR** E56128 red - *94*	12	19
34-601	**BR** M46083 red - *93*	12	19
34-601A*	**BR** M46083 red - *02*	12	18
34-605	**BR** E46109 red - *96*	12	19
34-605A*	**BR** E46109 red - *00*	12	18
34-606	**BR** E46127 red - *96*	12	19
34-606A*	**BR** E46127 red - *00*	12	18
34-602	**BR** M46073 maroon - *93*	12	19
34-602A*	**BR** M46073 maroon - *02*	12	18
34-603	**BR** M46074 maroon - *93*	12	19
34-603A*	**BR** M46074 maroon - *02*	12	18
34-604	**BR** W46199 maroon - *96*	12	19
34-604A*	**BR** W46199 maroon - *00*	12	18
(30-016)	**BR** M46300 maroon ex-set - *06*	12	NA
34-607	**BR** E46087 blue - *06*	12	18
34-607A	**BR** E46200 blue - *06*	12	18

* Straight reissue with later style box and it with slim-line couplings and metal wheels.

C6b. BR Mk1 57ft Suburban Brake 3rd (2nd) (1993)

34-625	**BR** M43259 red - *93*	12	19
34-625A	**BR** M43270 red - *01*	12	18
34-626	**BR** E43130 red - *94*	12	19
34-628	**BR** E53171 red - *96*	12	19
34-628A*	**BR** E53171 red - *00*	12	18

BR Mk1 suburban brake 2nd [C6b]

34-626	**BR** M43257 maroon - *93*	12	19
34-627	**BR** W43102 maroon - *96*	12	19
34-627A*	**BR** W43102 maroon - *00*	12	18
(30-016)	**BR** M43230 maroon ex-set - *06*	12	NA
34-629	**BR** E43112 blue - *06*	12	18
34-629A	**BR** E43138 blue - *07*	12	18
34-730	**BR** blue - *not made*	NA	NA

* Straight reissue with later style box and it with slim-line couplings and metal wheels.

C6c. BR Mk1 57ft Suburban Open 2nd (1996)

34-676	**BR** M48037 red - *96*	12	19
34-676A*	**BR** M48037 red - *01*	12	18
34-675	**BR** W48029 maroon - *96*	12	19
34-675A*	**BR** W48029 maroon - *00*	12	18

* Straight reissue with later style box and it with slim-line couplings and metal wheels.

C6d. BR Mk1 57ft Suburban Composite (1996)

34-701	**BR** M71006 red - *96*	12	19
34-701A*	**BR** M41006 red - *01*	12	18
34-700	**BR** W41058 maroon - *96*	12	19
34-700A*	**BR** W41058 maroon - *00*	12	18
34-702	**BR** E? blue** - *not made*	NA	NA

* Straight reissue with later style box and it with slim-line couplings and metal wheels.
**This was cancelled when it was realised that the BR(ER) coach was to a different design. It was replaced by 34-730 (C6b) at short notice.

BR Mk1 Main Line Corridor Stock

C7a. BR Mk1 SK/TK 3rd (2nd) (B) (1999)

34-727	**BR** red+cream - *not made*	NA	NA
39-027	**BR** M24446 red+cream - *99*	15	22
39-027	**BR** 24813 red+cream - not *made*	NA	NA
39-027A	**BR** M24467 red+cream - *00*	15	21
39-027B*	**BR** E24813 red+cream - *02*	15	20
39-027C	**BR** E24796 red+cream - *03*	15	20
39-027F	**BR** M24135 red+cream - *10*	16	23
39-027D	**BR** M24467 red+cream - *not made*	NA	NA
39-027D	**BR** E24240 red+cream - *06*	15	21
39-027E	**BR** E24159 red+cream - *08*	16	22
39-028	**BR** S24311 green - *00*	15	21
39-028A*	**BR** S24327 green - *02*	15	20
39-028B	**BR** S24305 green - *05*	15	21
39-028C	**BR** S24324 green - *07*	15	22
39-028D	**BR** S24317 green - *10*	15	22
39-029	**BR** W24165 brown+cream - *00*	15	21
39-029A*	**BR** W25051 brown+cream - *02*	15	20
39-029B	**BR** W24747 brown+cream - *05*	15	20
39-029C	**BR** W24165 brown+cream - *not made*	NA	NA
39-029C	**BR** W25200 brown+cream - *06*	15	21
39-029D	**BR** W? brown+cream - *10*	16	23
(31-2000)	**BR** W24750 brown+cream ex-set - *01*	15	NA
(31-2000)	**BR** W25189 brown+cream ex-set - *01*	15	NA
34-726	**BR** maroon - *not made*	NA	NA
39-026	**BR** E24538 maroon - *99*	15	22
39-026A**	**BRc** E25044 maroon - *00*	15	21

BR Mk1 corridor coach [C7a]

39-026B	**BR** M25400 maroon - *01*	15	21
39-026C	**BR** M25704 maroon - *02*	15	20
39-026D	**BR** M24679 maroon - *05*	15	21
39-026E	**BR** M24911 maroon - *06*	15	21
39-026F	**BR** W24165 maroon - *08*	16	22
39-026G	**BR** W24379 maroon - *10*	15	23
39-000W(A)	**BR** W25043 maroon Sp Edn 500 (*Model Rail*) ex-coach set - *06*	18	NA
34-725	**BR** blue+grey - *not made*	NA	NA
39-025	**BR** E25039 blue+grey - *99*	15	22
39-025A	**BR** E26140 blue+grey - *01*	15	21
39-025B	**BR** E26033 blue+grey - *02*	15	20
39-025C	**BR** E25832 blue+grey - *06*	15	21
39-025D	**BR** M24032 blue+grey - *08*	16	22
39-025E	**BR** E25704 blue+grey - *10*	16	23
39-030	**BR InterCity** M18753 grey - *02*	15	21
39-031	**BR NSE** 18752 bright blue - *05*	15	20
39-031A	**BR NSE** 18601 bright blue - *06*	15	21

* Box label wrongly shows running number of the previous release. ** code on box has no suffix.

C7b. BR Mk1 SO/TSO/TTO Open 3rd (2nd) (B) (1999)

34-752	**BR** red+cream - *not made*	NA	NA
39-052	**BR** M3737 red+cream - *99*	15	22
39-052A	**BR** M3788 red+cream - *00*	15	21
39-052B	**BR** E3979 red+cream - *02*	15	20
39-052C	**BR** M4899 red+cream - *not made*	NA	NA
39-052C	**BR** E4260 red+cream - *05*	15	21
39-052D	**BR** E4268 red+cream - *not made*	NA	NA
39-052D	**BR** E3858 red+cream - *06*	15	21
39-052E	**BR** M3741 red+cream - *10*	15	23
39-053	**BR** S3998 green - *00*	15	20
39-053A*	**BR** S4040 green (also 39-053B) - *01*	15	20
39-053B	**BR** S4375 green - *05*	15	21
39-053C	**BR** S3840 green - *07*	15	22
39-053D	**BR** S3824 green - *10*	15	22
39-054	**BR** W3791 brown+cream - *00*	15	20
39-054A	**BR** W4739 brown+cream - *03*	15	21
39-054B	**BR** W3821 brown+cream - *10*	16	23
34-751	**BR** maroon - *not made*	NA	NA
39-051	**BR** E4238 maroon - *99*	15	22
39-051A**	**BR** E3850 maroon - *01*	15	21
39-051B*	**BR** M4414 maroon - *01*	15	20
39-051C	**BR** M4899 maroon - *03*	15	20
39-051D	**BR** M4780 maroon - *05*	15	21
39-051E	**BR** M4929 maroon - *06*	15	21
39-051F	**BR** M3984 maroon - *08*	16	22
39-051G	**BR** W4739 maroon - *09*	15	22
39-000W	**BR** W4746 maroon Sp Edn 500 (*Model Rail*) ex-coach set - *06*	18	NA
(39-000R)	**BR** W3875 maroon Sp Edn 500 (Cheltenham Model Centre) ex-coach set - *09*	20	NA
34-750	**BR** blue+grey - *not made*	NA	NA
39-050	**BR** E4357 blue+grey - *99*	15	22
39-050A	**BR** E5001 blue+grey - *01*	15	21
39-050B	**BR** E4112 blue+grey - *04*	15	20
39-050C	**BR** E4298 blue+grey - *06*	15	21
39-050D	**BR** E4243 blue+grey - *08*	16	22
39-050E	**BR** E? blue+grey - *10*	16	23
39-055	**BR InterCity** 4909 grey - *02*	15	21
39-056	**BR Reg Rlys** 4873 blue+white - *02*	15	21
39-057	**BR NSE** 4920 bright blue - *05*	15	20
39-057A	**BR NSE** 4901 bright blue - *06*	15	21
(39-000X)	**ScotRail - West Highland** 4050 green+cream *see C7k coach sets*	20	NA
(39-000X)	**ScotRail - West Highland** 4494 green+cream *see C7k coach sets*	20	NA
(39-000X)	**ScotRail - West Highland** 4601 green+cream *see C7l coach sets*	20	NA
(39-000Y)	**West Highland Line** IC3767C green+cream - *see C7l coach sets*	20	NA
(39-000Z)	**West Highland Line** IC4912C green+cream - *see C7l coach sets*	20	NA
(39-000Z)	**West Highland Line** IC4911C green+cream - *see C7l coach sets*	20	NA

* Box label wrongly shows running number of the previous release. ** code on box has no suffix.

C7c. BR Mk1 BSK Brake 3rd (2nd) (B) (1999)

34-777	**BR** red+cream - *not made*	NA	NA
39-077	**BR** M34655 red+cream - *99*	15	22
39-077A	**BR** E34226 red+cream - *99*	15	20
39-077B	**BR** E34500 red+cream - *05*	15	21
39-077C	**BR** E34096 red+cream - *06*	15	21

BR Mk1 brake corridor 2nd [C7c]

39-077D	**BR** E34288 red+cream - *09*	15	22
39-078	**BR** S35020 green - *00*	15	21
39-078A	**BR** S35021 green - *00*	15	20
39-078B	**BR** S34974 green - *05*	15	21

39-078C	**BR** S34255 green - *07*	15	22
39-078D	**BR** S34641 green - *10*	15	22
39-079	**BR** W34290 brown+cream - *00*	15	20
39-079A	**BR** W34751 brown+cream - *03*	15	21
39-079B	**BR** W34885 brown+cream - *10*	16	23
(31-2000)	**BR** W34892 brown+cream ex-set - *01*	15	NA
(31-2000)	**BR** W34773 brown+cream ex-set - *01*	15	NA
34-776	**BR** maroon - *not made*	NA	NA
39-076	**BR** E34168 maroon - *99*	15	22
39-076A	**BR** E34007 maroon - *00*	15	21
39-076B*	**BR** M35180 maroon - *00*	15	20
39-076C	**BR** M35486 maroon - *05*	15	21
39-076D	**BR** M34140 maroon - *06*	15	21
39-076E	**BR** W34152 maroon - *08*	16	22
39-076F	**BR** W34315 maroon - *09*	15	22
(39-000W)	**BR** W34751 maroon Sp Edn 500 (*Model Rail*) ex-coach set - *06*	18	NA
(39-000R)	**BR** W34151 maroon Sp Edn 500 (Cheltenham Model Centre) ex-coach set - *09*	20	NA
39-000U	**BR** 99952 maroon Sp Edn 504 (NRM) - *07*	15	25
34-775	**BR** blue+grey - *not made*	NA	NA
39-075	**BR** E35445 blue+grey - *99*	15	20
39-075A	**BR** M35040 blue+grey - *03*	15	20
39-075B	**BR** E35383 blue+grey - *06*	15	21
39-075C	**BR** E35322 blue+grey - *10*	16	23
(39-000K)	**BR** 35402, blue+grey W *see C7l*	16	NA
39-080	**BR InterCity** M35465 grey - *02*	15	21
39-081	**BR Regional Railways** 35452 blue+white - *02*	15	21
39-082	**BR NSE** 35339 bright blue - *05*	15	20
39-082A	**BR NSE** 35464 bright blue - *06*	15	21
(39-000X)	**ScotRail - West Highland** 9312 green+cream *see C7k coach sets*	20	NA
(39-000V)	**BR RTC** RDB975136 'Laboratory 12' red+blue Sp Edn 504 (ModelZone) - *06*	20	NA
(39-000V)	**BR RTC** ADB975051 'Test Car 5' red+blue Sp Edn 504 (ModelZone) - *06*	20	NA
39-000V	above two cars - *06*	NA	50

* Box label wrongly shows running number of the previous release.

C7d. BR Mk1 RU Restaurant Unclassed (B) (1999)

BR Mk1 unclassified restaurant car [C7d]

39-105	**BR** W1900 red+cream - *08*	16	22
39-102	**BR** W1902 brown+cream - *01*	15	20
39-102A	**BR** W1919 brown+cream - *06*	15	21
34-801	**BR** maroon - *not made*	NA	NA
39-101	**BR** E1926 maroon Gresley bogies - *99*	15	20
39-101A	**BR** E1961 maroon - *03*	15	21
39-101B	**BR** E1930 maroon - *07*	15	22
39-101C	**BR** Sc1941 maroon - *10*	16	23
39-103	**BR** W1915 maroon - *01*	15	20
39-103A	**BR** W1944 maroon - *01*	15	21
39-103B	**BR** W1924 maroon - *10*	16	23
39-103C	**BR** W1917 maroon - *10*	16	23
34-800	**BR** blue+grey - *not made*	NA	NA
39-100	**BR** E1938 blue+grey Gresley bogies - *99*	15	20
39-100A	**BR** M1966 blue+grey - *04*	15	21
39-100B	**BR** M1966 blue+grey - *08*	16	22
39-104	**BR InterCity** 1981 grey RBR - *02*	15	21

C7e. BR Mk1 CK Composite (B) (2000)

39-127	**BR** M15019 red+cream - *00*	15	20
39-127A	**BR** E15271 red+cream - *03*	15	20
39-127B	**BR** E15055 red+cream - *06*	15	21
39-127C	**BR** E15192 red+cream - *10*	16	23
39-127D	**BR** M15181 red+cream - *10*	16	23
39-128	**BR** S15904 green - *00*	15	20
39-128A	**BR** S15566 green - *03*	15	21
39-128B	**BR** S15904 green - *08*	16	22
39-129	**BR** W15770 brown+cream - *00*	15	20
39-129A	**BR** W15777 brown+cream - *05*	15	21
39-129B	**BR** W15110 brown+cream - *10*	16	23
(31-2000)	**BR** W15816 brown+cream ex-set - *01*	15	NA
39-126	**BR** E15145 maroon - *00*	15	21
39-126A*	**BR** M16005 maroon - *01*	15	20
39-126B	**BR** M15684 maroon - *05*	15	21
39-126C	**BR** M15916 maroon - *06*	15	21
39-126D	**BR** M15077 maroon - *08*	16	22
39-126E	**BR** W16198 maroon - *10*	16	23
(39-000W)	**BR** W15426 maroon Sp Edn 500 (*Model Rail*) ex-coach set - *06*	18	NA
(39-000R)	**BR** W15066 maroon Sp Edn 500 (Cheltenham Model Centre) ex-coach set - *09*	20	NA
39-125	**BR** E16241 blue+grey - *00, 05*	15	20
39-125B	**BR** E15768 blue+grey - *06*	15	21
39-125C	**BR** M16153 blue+grey - *10*	16	23
39-130	**BR NSE** 7232 bright blue - *05*	15	21

* Box label wrongly shows running number of the previous release.

C7f. BR Mk1 FK All 1st (B) (2000)

39-152	**BR** M13004 red+cream - *00*	15	20
39-152A	**BR** M13110 red+cream - *05*	15	21
39-152B	**BR** E13113 red+cream - *07*	15	22
39-152C	**BR** M13060 red+cream - *10*	15	23
39-153	**BR** S13143 green - *00*	15	20
39-153A	**BR** S13003 green - *05*	15	21
39-153B	**BR** S13086 green - *08*	16	22
39-154	**BR** W13074 brown+cream - *00*	15	20
39-154A	**BR** W13185 brown+cream - *06*	15	21
39-154B	**BR** W13074 brown+cream - *10*	16	23
(31-2000)	**BR** W13187 brown+cream ex-set - *01*	15	NA
39-151	**BR** E13030 maroon - *00*	15	20
39-151A	**BR** M13223 maroon - *03*	15	20
39-151B	**BR** M13070 maroon - *06*	15	21
39-151C	**BR** W13127 maroon - *08*	16	22
39-151D	**BR** M13108 maroon - *10*	16	23
(39-000R)	**BR** W13132 maroon Sp Edn 500 (Cheltenham Model Centre) ex-coach set - *09*	20	NA
39-150	**BR** E13107 blue+grey - *00*	15	20
39-150A	**BR** E13234 blue+grey - *05*	15	21

BR Mk1 corridor 1st [C7f]

39-150B	**BR** M13179 blue+grey - *08*	16	22
39-150C	**BR** M13085 blue+grey - *10*	16	23
39-155	**BR InterCity** M13341 grey - *02*	15	21
39-156	**BR Regional Rlys** 13225 blue+white - *02*	15	21
39-157	**BR NSE** 13328 bright blue - *05*	15	21

C7g. BR Mk1 BG Full Brake (B) (2000)

39-177	**BR** M80541 red+cream - *00*	15	20
39-177A	**BR** E80623 red+cream - *05*	15	21
39-177B	**BR** M81039 red+cream - *07*	15	22
39-177C	**BR** M85065 red+cream - *09*	15	22
39-178	**BR** S81510 green - *00*	15	20
39-178A	**BR** S81292 green - *05*	15	21
39-178B	**BR** S80893 green - *08*	16	22
39-179	**BR** W81205 brown+cream - *00*	15	21
39-179A	**BR** W? brown+cream - *07*	15	22
39-179B	**BR** W80713 brown+cream - *10*	16	23
39-176	**BR** E80798 maroon - *00*	15	21
39-176A*	**BR** M80950 maroon - *01*	15	20
39-176B	**BR** M81300 maroon - *05*	15	21
39-176C	**BR** W80708 maroon - *09*	15	22
39-176D	**BR** M80533 maroon - *10*	16	23
39-175	**BR** E80617 blue+grey - *00*	15	20
39-175A	**BR** M84281 blue+grey NDV - *03*	15	21
39-175B	**BR** M? blue+grey NDV - *08*	16	22
39-175C	**BR** M80906 blue+grey - *10*	16	23

(39-000K)	**BR** 81221 blue+grey W Express Parcels, *see C7l*	16	NA
39-182A	**BR** M80689 blue+grey Newspapers - *06*	15	21
39-182	**BR** 95211 blue Newspapers NCX - *02*	15	20
39-182B	**BR** M81124 blue Newspapers NCV - *10*	16	23
39-180	**BR Inter-City** 92151 grey+beige NEA - *02*	15	21
39-181	**BR Regional Rlys** E92058 blue+white NEA Parcels - *02*	15	21
32-176Z	**NSE** 92315 bright blue Sp Edn 504 (The Signal Box) - *08*	18	24
39-183	**RES** 92322 red+dark grey NEX - *03*	15	21
39-183A	**RES** 92418 red+dark grey NEX - *09*	16	22
39-184	**BR Royal Mail** 92131 red NEA - *03*	15	21

* Box label wrongly shows running number of the previous release.

C7h. BR Mk1 BCK Brake Composite (B) (2001)

39-227	**BR** M21238 red+cream - *made?*	NPG	NPG
39-227	**BR** M21026 red+cream - *02*	15	20
39-227A	**BR** M21030 red+cream - *05*	15	21
39-227B	**BR** E21050 red+cream - *07*	15	22
39-227C	**BR** M21029 red+cream - *10*	15	23
39-228	**BR** S21268 green - *01*	15	20
39-228A	**BR** S21263 green - *05*	15	21
39-228B	**BR** S21272 green - *09*	16	22
39-229	**BR** W21067 brown+cream - *01*	15	21
39-229A	**BR** W21191 brown+cream - *07*	15	22
39-229B	**BR** W21080 brown+cream - *10*	16	23
39-226	**BR** E21202 maroon - *01*	15	20
39-226A	**BR** M21030 maroon - *04*	15	21
39-226B	**BR** W21021 maroon - *09*	16	22
39-226C	**BR** M21026 maroon - *10*	16	23
39-225	**BR** M21241 blue+grey - *01*	15	20
39-225A	**BR** E21222 blue+grey - *05*	15	21
39-225B	**BR** M21236 blue+grey - *08*	16	22
39-230	**BR InterCity** 21266 grey - *02*	15	21
(39-000Y)	**West Highland Line** IC21241C green+cream - *see C7l coach sets*	20	NA

* Box label wrongly shows running number of the previous release.

C7i. BR Mk1 RFO Restaurant 1st Open (B) (2001)

39-252	**BR** M4 red+cream - *01*	15	20
39-252A	**BR** E10 red+cream - *05*	15	21

BR Mk1 1st class open restaurant car [C7i]

39-252B	**BR** W8 red+cream - *08*	16	22
39-253	**BR** S9 green - *01*	18	23
39-253A	**BR** green - *not made*	NA	NA
39-254	**BR** W7 brown+cream - *01*	15	21
39-251	**BR** E3 maroon - *01*	15	21
39-250	**BR** E3 blue+grey - *01*	15	20
39-250A	**BR** M5 blue+grey - *05*	15	21
39-250B	**BR** W9 blue+grey - *10*	16	23

C7j. BR Mk1 RMB Restaurant Mini Buffet (B) (2007)

39-260	**BR** E1852 red+cream - *07*	15	21
39-262	**BR** S1852 green - *not made*	NA	NA
39-262	**BR** S1881 green - *07*	15	21
39-262A	**BR** S1849 green - *10*	16	23
39-263	**BR** W1814 brown+cream - *07*	15	21
39-261	**BR** E1854 maroon - *07*	15	21
39-261A	**BR** W1815 maroon - *09*	15	22
39-264	**BR** E1871 blue+grey - *07*	15	22

C7k. BR Mk1 Super BG Full Brake (B) (2000)

BR Mk1 full brake [C7k]

39-200	**RES** 94474 red+dark grey - *01*	15	20
39-200A	**RES** 94451 red+dark grey - *03*	15	21
39-200B	**RES** 94467 red+dark grey - *09*	16	22
39-201	**RES Royal Mail** 94420 red+dark grey - *01*	15	20
39-201A	**RES Royal Mail** 94520 red+dark grey NBA - *03*	15	21
39-201B	**RES Royal Mail** 94462 red+dark grey NBA - *09*	16	22

C7l. BR Mk1 & Mk2 Coach Sets (B) (2003)

Details of the coaches in the following sets will also be found under the coach type headings where they are individually listed in the tables.

39-000Z	**West Highland Line** 2 x Mk1 SO green+cream Sp Edn 360 (Harburn Hobbies) - *03*	NPG	45
39-000Y	**West Highland Line** Mk1 SO + Mk1 BCK green+cream Sp Edn 360 (Harburn Hobbies) - *03*	NPG	45
39-000X	**ScotRail - West Highland** 3 x Mk1 SO + 1 x Mk1 BSK green+cream Sp Edn 500 *(Model Rail)* - *03*	NPG	90
39-000W	**BR(WR)** maroon Mk1 CK, SK, SO, BSK set of 4 Sp Edn 500 (*Model Rail*) - *06*	NA	99
39-000V	**BR RTC** red+blue Mk1 BSK laboratory car & Mk1 BSK test car Sp Edn 504 (ModelZone) - *06*	NA	50
39-000T	**West Highland Line** 3 x Mk2 TSO, 1 x Mk2 BSO green+ cream Sp Edn 500 (*Model Rail*) - *08*	NA	NPG
39-000S	**BR IC** set of 2 Mk2 blue+grey MTA test coaches Sp Edn 504 (ModelZone) - *08*	NA	55
39-000R	**BR(WR)** maroon Mk1 CK, SO, FK, BSK set of 4 Sp Edn 500 (Cheltenham Model Centre) - *09*	NA	100
39-000L	**Red Bank* Parcels Set 1** - **BR** blue+grey, weathered 2 x Mk1 GUVs, Sp Edn 500 (ModelZone) - *10*	NA	55
39-000K	**Red Bank* Set Parcels 2** - **BR** blue+grey, weathered Mk1 BG & BSK, Sp Edn 500 (ModelZone) - *10*	NA	55

* The name comes from the Red Bank Sidings outside Manchester (Victoria), where the empty coaches were kept.

C8. BR Mk1 GUV (B) (2007)

39-271	**BR** W85470 red - *not made*	NA	NA
39-273	**BR** S86724 green - *08*	15	22
39-273A	**BR** S86791 green - *09*	15	22
39-271	**BR** M86105 maroon - *not made*	NA	NA

BR Mk1 general utility van [C8]

39-271	**BR** W86253 maroon - *07*	15	21
39-271A	**BR** W86148 maroon - *10*	16	23
39-271B	**BR** W86442 maroon - *10*	16	23
39-271Z	**BRe** E86243 maroon, Parcels Express Sp Ed (ModelZone) - *10*	20	26
39-272B	**BR** M86531 blue+grey Express Parcels - *10*	16	23
39-274	**BR** E93326 blue+grey, Motorail - *10*	16	23
(39-000L)	**BR** ? blue+grey W Newspapers, *see C7l*	20	NA
(39-000L)	**BR** ? blue+grey W *see C7l*	20	NA
39-272	**BR** 95211 blue Newspapers NLX - *07*	15	21
39-272A	**BR** W86479 blue Express Parcels - *09*	15	22
39-270	**BR** W86078 blue Express Parcels - *07*	15	21
39-270	**RES** 95199 red+dark grey NOX - *07*	15	21
39-270A	**BR** 95146 red+dark grey NOX - *10*	16	23
39-270Z	**NSE** 93852 bright blue Sp Edn 504 (The Signalbox) - *08*	18	24
39-270Y	**Satlink** KDB977557 red+yellow Sp Edn 504 (*Model Rail*) - *07*	20	25

C9. BR TPO POS Sorting Carriage FK (B) (2010)

Diagram 720 vehicle commissioned by ModelZone

39-420W	**BR** W80300 red (late '50s) Sp Edn (ModelZone) - *10*	28	32

39-420X	**BR** M80300 blue+grey (late '60s > late '80s) Sp Edn (ModelZone) - *10*	28	32
39-420Y	**Royal Mail** W80300 red (late '80s > early '90s) Royal Mail Letters, BR1 bogies, Sp Edn (ModelZone) - *10*	28	32
39-420Z	**Royal Mail** TPO80305 red (early '90s > 2004, Royal Mail Travelling Post Office B4 bogies, Sp Edn (ModelZone) - *10*	28	32

Mark1 Pullman Stock

These have metal bearings within the bogie face and foil-plated window frames The table lamps have fibre optic lighting which, when pulled by a DCC-fitted locomotive, receive constant power.

C10a. BR Mk1 Pullman Kitchen FK (B) (2005)

39-280	**BR** *Eagle* brown+cream - *05*	21	27
39-280A	**BR** *Magpie* brown+cream - *08*	22	28
39-280B	**BR** *Falcon* brown+cream - *10*	22	28
39-281	**BR** E351E grey+blue - *07*	21	27
39-290Z	**BR(RTC)** Wren RDB975427 Laboratory 14 red+blue Sp Edn 504 (ModelZone) - *09*	25	32

C10b. BR Mk1 Pullman 1st FP (B) (2005)

39-290	**BR** *Emerald* brown+cream - *05*	21	27
39-290A	**BR** *Amber* brown+cream - *08*	22	28
39-290B	**BR** *Amethyst* brown+cream - *10*	22	28
39-291	**BR** E326E grey+blue - *07*	21	27

C10c. BR Mk1 Pullman Kitchen 2nd SK (B) (2005)

39-300	**BR** Car No.332 brown+cream - *05*	21	27
39-300A	**BR** Car No.333 brown+cream - *08*	22	28
39-300B	**BR** Car No.334 brown+cream - *10*	20	30
39-301	**BR** E334E grey+blue - *06*	21	27

C10d. BR Mk1 Pullman Parlour 2nd SP (B) (2005)

BR Mk1 Pullman 2nd class parlour car [C10d]

39-310	**BR** Car No.347 brown+cream - *05*	21	27
39-310A	**BR** Car No.348 brown+cream - *08*	22	28
39-310B	**BR** Car No. 349 brown+cream - *10*	22	28
39-311	**BR** E352E grey+blue - *07*	21	27

C10e. BR Mk1 Pullman Bar 2nd BSP (B) (2005)

39-320	**BR** *The Hadrian Bar* brown+cream - *05*	21	27
39-321	**BR** E354E *Nightcap Bar* grey+blue - *07*	21	27

Mark2 Main Line Stock

C11a. BR Mk2 Corridor 1st FK (B) (2006)

39-332	**BR** E13373 maroon - *06*	15	22
39-332A	**BR** W13432 maroon - *10*	16	23
39-333	**BR** S13389 green - *06*	15	22
39-333A	**BR** S13401 green - *10*	16	23
39-330	**BR** S13393 blue+grey - *06*	15	22
39-330A	**BR** S13388 blue+grey - *10*	16	23
39-331	**BR** IC ? blue+grey - *made?*	NPG	NPG

C11b. BR Mk2A Corridor 1st FK (B) (2006)

39-340	**BR** E13472 blue+grey - *06*	15	22
39-341	**BR InterCity** W13456 blue+grey - *06*	15	22
39-342	**NSE** 13443 bright blue - *06*	15	22

C11c. BR Mk2 Open 2nd TSO (B) (2006)

39-350	**BR** M5082 blue+grey - *06*	15	22
39-351	**BR Inter-CityC** E5311* blue+grey - *06*	15	22
39-352	**BR NSE** 5162 bright blue - *06*	15	22
(39-000T)	**BR** 5230 *Corriemoillie* green+cream TSO(T) Sp Edn 500 (*Model Rail*) - *08*	25	NA
(39-000T)	**BR** 5212 *Capercailzie* green+cream Sp Edn 500 (*Model Rail*) - *08*	25	NA
(39-000T)	**BR** 5166 *Clan MacKenzie* green+cream Sp Edn 500 (*Model Rail*) - *08*	25	NA

* Wrongly given a Mk2A number.

C11d. BR Mk2A Open Standard TSO (B) (2006)

39-360	**BR** 5353 blue+grey - *06*	15	22
39-361	**BR Inter-City** E5361 blue+grey - *06*	15	22
39-362	**BR NSE** 5410 bright blue - *06*	15	22
(39-000H)	**Regional Railways** 5316 blue+pale grey	20	NA
(39-000H)	**Regional Railways** 5341 blue+pale grey	20	NA
39-000H	above two models in a twin pack, Sp Edn 500 (*Model Rail*) - *10*	NA	50
(39-000M)	**Regional Railways** 5385 blue+pale grey ex-pair with BSK 35510, Sp Edn (*Model Rail*) - *10*	20	NA

C11e. BR Mk2 Brake Open 2nd BSO (B) (2006)

MTA = mobile track assessment train

39-370	**BR** E9399 blue+grey - *06*	15	22
39-371	**BR Inter City** E9400 blue+grey - *06*	15	22
39-372	**BR NSE** 9409 bright blue - *06*	15	22
(39-000T)	**BR** 9385 *Balmacara* green+cream Sp Edn 500 (*Model Rail*) - *08*	25	NA
39-370Z	**Network Rail** DB977337 yellow test coach Sp Edn (*Model Rail*) - *10*	20	28
(39-000D)	**DRS** (compass) 9419 blue BSO	20	NA
(39-000D)	**DRS** (compass) 9428 blue BSO	20	NA
39-000D	above two nuclear train support vehicles, Sp Edn (*Model Rail*) - *10*	NA	50

C11f. BR Mk2A Brake Open 2nd BSO (B) (2006)

BR Mk2A 2nd class open brake end [C11f]

39-390	**BR** blue+grey - *not made*	NA	NA
39-391	**BR IC** grey - *not made?*	NA	NA
39-380	**BR** E9430 blue+grey - *06*	15	22
39-381	**BR Inter City** Sc9424 blue+grey - *06*	15	22
39-382	**BR NSE** 9422 bright blue - *06*	15	22
39-000M	**Regional Railways** 35510 blue+pale grey, BSK ex-pair with TSO 5385, Sp Edn (*Model Rail*) - *10*	20	NA

C11g. BR Mk2 Brake Corridor 1st BFK (B) (2006)

39-400	**BR** 14033 blue+grey - *06*	15	22
39-401	**BR Inter City** 14080 blue+grey - *06*	15	22
39-401	**BR Regional Railways** blue+grey - *not made*	NA	NA
39-402	**NSE** 17040 bright blue - *06*	15	22

C11h. BR Mk2A Brake Corridor 1st BFK (B) (2006)

39-410	**BR** 17063 blue+grey - *06*	15	22
39-411	**BR Inter City** 17093 blue+grey - *06*	15	22
39-421	**BR Regional Railways** blue - *not made*	NA	NA
39-432	**BR NSE** bright blue - *not made*	NA	NA
39-412	**NSE** 17079 bright blue - *06*	15	22

C11i. BR Mk2z Test Coaches (B) (2008)

These are former brake 2nd open vehicles.

(39-000S)	**BR IC** DB977377 modified blue+grey MTA (dormitory coach) Sp Edn 504 (ModelZone) - *08*	20	NA
(39-000S)	**BR IC** DB977378 modified blue+grey MTA (brake & stores coach) Sp Edn 504 (ModelZone) - *08*	20	NA
39-000S	above two coaches - *07*	NA	55

C11j. BR Mk2 Irish Coaches (B) (2008)

These were produced for sale by Murphy Models of Dublin.

(MM4101)	**IR** 4101 orange + black - *06*	18	NA
(MM4101)	**IR** 4108 orange + black - *06*	18	NA
MM4101	above 2 coaches Sp Edn 504 (Murphy Models)	NA	50

(MM4102)	**IR** 4102 orange+black - *06*	18	NA
(MM4102)	**IR** 4110 orange + black - *06*	18	NA
MM4102	above 2 coaches Sp Edn 504 (Murphy Models)	NA	50
(MM4108)	**IE** 4101 orange + black - *06*	18	NA
(MM4108)	**IE** 4108 orange + black - *06*	18	NA
MM4108	above 2 coaches Sp Edn 504 (Murphy Models)	NA	50
(MM4110)	**IE** 4102 orange + black - *06*	18	NA
(MM4110)	**IE** 4110 orange + black - *06*	18	NA
MM4110	above 2 coaches Sp Edn 504 (Murphy Models)	NA	50
MM1072	**RSPI** 301 green (TSO 2nd class) Sp Edn 500 (Murphy Models) - *08*	25	NA
MM1071	**RSPI** 180 green (Mk2A FK 1st class) Sp Edn 500 (Murphy Models) - *08*	25	NA
MM1073	**RSPI** 460 green (Mk2 BSO brake) Sp Edn 500 (Murphy Models) - *08*	25	NA

C12. 'Voyager' Centre Car (B) (2005)

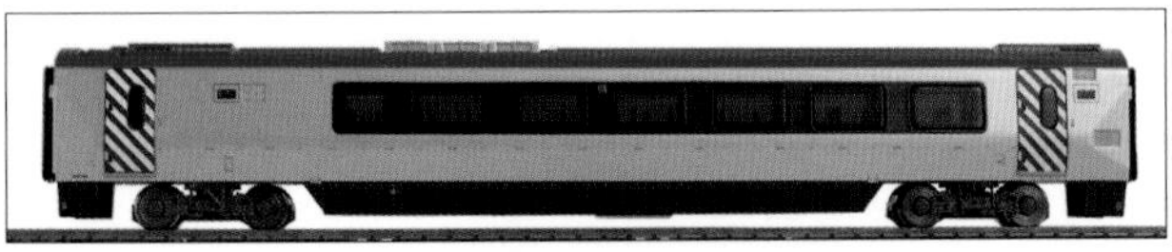

'Voyager' centre car [C12]

30-625	**Virgin** 60217 (*Bombardier Voyager*) red+silver - *05*	20	25
30-625A	**Virgin** 60708 (*Welsh Dragon*) red+silver - *07,09*	20	26

WAGONS

As with the locomotives and coaches, wagons started with Mainline originals reproduced in a selection of new liveries. A new development was the sets of themed coal wagons and petrol tankers which are likely to become more collectable than single wagons.

The Blue Riband wagons are the 'bee's knees' of the ready-to-run wagon world and the range is expanding fast. Besides the greater body and chassis detail, the private owner open wagons now have the more correct 9ft wheelbase instead of the 10ft one. There have been many commissioned models (nearly all private owner open wagons) and some of these are likely to become much sought after in years to come.

Several wagons were issued with detachable loads. These containers, transformers and boilers, used as loads on wagons, were also sold separately as accessories.

Confusion surrounds some of the wagons produced in 2000 and 2001 particularly as far as their catalogue numbering goes. This is because when ordered they were allocated a 33-XXX number but by the time they arrived their specification had been raised to that of the Blue Riband range although they had not been given catalogue numbers in the 37-XXX series.

Wagon Numbers - WARNING! The numbers on wagons are mostly taken from catalogues which is not ideal as, in compiling their catalogues, Bachmann sometimes use pictures of earlier examples but with the new catalogue number. Where pre-production models or photographs of real wagons have been used there is no guarantee that the production model will carry the same number. The best advice is to treat numbers quoted in this section with caution. We are keen to hear from you with suggested corrections.

Missing Wagons - People are often confused at not finding listed here certain wagons which have 'Bachmann Hong Kong' on the underside of the chassis. It could be that they will be found in the chapter titled 'Replica Railways'. This is because the early Replica Railways models were made by Kader in Hong Kong who also owned and made Bachmann. To avoid making a new chassis for the wagons that Replica had ordered, they used ones from the Bachmann production line - thus the confusion.

Set of 3 - A lot of private owner wagons were sold in sets of three different models (Coal Classics). If you cannot find your model in the table you expect, have a look in the 'sets' tables. The Midlander commissioned a number of private owner wagons for delivery in 2000 but the order was cancelled and the batches were split up to be sold by several other retailers. The supplier is shown as 'various' in the tables.

Prices - There is a rising demand for Bachmann's private owner open wagons and 14T tank wagons which is spilling over onto other wagons in the Bachmann range. Since the last edition of this catalogue, the wagon prices have been revised and include some substantial rises. These are based on actual prices achieved on eBay over the last year. Especially high climbers are wagons commissioned for release at Warley shows.

Cat No.	Company, Number, Colour, Dates	£	£

Flat Wagons

W1a. 'Conflat A' (1996)

Early 'Conflat' with poorer chassis.

-	**BR** B702201 brown - *96*	8	NA
-	**BR** B706709 brown - *96*	5	NA
33-335	above 2 'Conflats' - *96*	NA	18
-	**BR** B505461 brown - *98*	8	NA
-	**BR** B505432 brown - *98*	8	NA
33-335A	above 2 'Conflats' - *98*	NA	18

W1b. 'Conflat A' + BD Container (1995)

Early 'Conflat' with poorer chassis and larger container.

33-329	**GW** 36876 dark grey + dark brown GWR container B1775 - *95*	10	12

BR 'Conflat A' with BD container [W1b]

33-325	**BR** B704789 brown + brown **BR** container BD42724B - *not made*	NA	NA
33-325	**BR** B704739 brown + brown **BR** container BD46724B - *95*	10	12
33-325A	**BR** B701283 brown + brown **BR** container BD46541B - *98*	9	11
33-326	**BR** B506033 brown + maroon **BR** container BD6600B - *95*	10	12
33-326A	**BR** B702326 brown + maroon W **BR** container BD6698B - *99*	9	11

W1c. 'Conflat A' + AF Container (1995)

Early 'Conflat' with poorer chassis and one or two small containers.

33-327	**BR** B703760 brown + light blue **BR** container AF66008B - *95*	10	12
33-327A	**BR** B704933 brown + light blue **BR** containers AF65137B + AF66187B - *98*	9	11
33-328	**BR** B704477 brown + white **BR** container AF65098B - *95*	10	12
33-330	**BR** B702201 brown + white **BR** containers AFU16320B, AFU16327B - *?*	10	12
33-330	**BR** B503829 brown + white **BR** containers AFU1632CB, AFU16327B - *96*	10	12

W1d. 'Conflat A' (B) (2001)

Blue Riband 'Conflat' with improved chassis.

1	**BR** B709437 brown Conflat A	9	NA
2	**BR** B737642 brown Conflat A	9	NA
37-980	above two wagons - *01*	NA	18
1	**BR** brown Conflat A	NA	NA
2	**BR** brown Conflat A	NA	NA
37-980A	above two wagons - *not made*	NA	NA
37-980Z	**BR** TDB708135 pale yellow shunter's running wagon 'Norwich Loco' Sp Edn 500 (Pennine Models) - *01*	18	24

W1e. 'Conflat A' + BD Container (B) (2001)

Blue Riband 'Conflat 'with improved chassis and large container.

(30-075)	**GWR** 39612 dark grey + dark brown **GWR** (shirt button) container B1788 ex-Local Freight set - *10*	9	NA
37-950	**BR** B708315 brown + grey+yellow **BR** '**Speedfreight**' container BD47381B - *01*	9	11
37-950A	**BR** B505569 brown + grey+yellow **BR** '**Speedfreight**' container BD46491B - *05*	9	11
37-950Z	**BR** B705400 brown + cream+red 'Man-Tainor' container BD.105 Sp Edn 500 (*Model Rail*) - *05*	22	30
37-951	**BR** B705549 brown + maroon **BR** container BD48964B - *01*	9	11
37-951A	**BR** B704954 brown + maroon **BR** container BD479301B - *not made*	NA	NA
37-951A	**BR** B709708 brown + maroon **BR** container BD50150B - *05*	9	11
37-951B	**BR** B709076 brown + maroon **BR** container BD50165B - *10*	6	8
37-951C	**BR** B709007 brown + **BR** red container BD50311B - *10*	6	8

W1f. 'Conflat A' + AF Containers (B) (2001)

Blue Riband 'Conflat' with improved chassis and small container.

37-975	**GW** 39354 dark grey + white **GWR** container AF-2098 - *01*	9	11

GWR 'Conflat A' with AF container [W1f]

37-975A	**GW** 39326 dark grey + white **GWR** container AF-2111 - *05*	8	10
37-976	**BR** B704954 brown + white **BR** AF16098B + pale blue BR AF16392B containers - *01*	9	11
37-977	**BR** B706709 brown + pale blue **BR** container AF66008B - *08*	6	8

W1g. 'Conflat A' with BA Container (B)

Blue Riband 'Conflat' with improved chassis and sliding door container from Trix range.

37-985	**BR** B708315 brown + silver BA **BR 'Speedfreight'** container - *not made*	NA	NA

Planked Open Wagons

W2a. 1-plank 10T-13T Wagon (ex-Mainline) (1990)

33-405	**'Bath Stone Firms Ltd'** 10T - cream - *97*	14	16
33-401	**'Corsham Quarrying Co.'** 70 maroon - *92*	12	15
33-400	**'H Lees & Son'** 101 red - *90*	8	10
33-400A	**'H Lees & Son'** 96 red - *92*	9	11
33-404	**LMS** 460531 brown - *97*	8	10
33-402	**BR** M460648 brown Lowfit - *92*	8	10
33-403	undecorated light grey - *91*	5	7

W2b. 1-plank 12T Wagon + Vehicle Load (1997)

33-410	**BR** B450023 brown + white Ford Transit Van (Herpa) load - *97*	13	15
33-411	**BR** B450050 brown + blue or red Ford Capri (Herpa) load - *97*	13	15
33-412	**BR** B450141 brown + green Triumph TR3 (Herpa) load - *97*	13	15

W2c. 1-plank 12T Wagon + Small Container (1991)

33-951	**GW** 70031 dark grey + white **GWR** container AF-2121 (box says LMS) - *91*	10	12
33-953	**LMS** 209340 brown + white **LMS** container E5 - *93*	10	12
33-950	**BR** B450027 brown + white **BR** container AFU16320B (box says LNER) - *91*	10	12
33-952	**BR** B450300 brown + white **BR** container AF12 - *92*	10	12

W2d. 1-plank Wagon 12T + Large Container (1992)

33-975	**LMS** 209341 grey + maroon **LMS** container BD1641 - *92*	10	12
33-976	**NE** 203169 brown + blue **LNER** container BD1465 - *94*	9	11
33-977	undecorated dark grey - *not made* *	NA	NA

* planned for the Crewe Open Day in 1996.

W2e. 1-plank 'Lowfit' Wagon (B) (2001)

1-plank wagon 'H.Lees' [W2e]

37-476	**'H Lees & Sons'** 105 red - *02*	9	11
37-476A**	**'Morris & Griffin'** 1 brown - *03*	8	10
37-475Z	**G&KER** 31 grey Sp Edn 504 (Toys 2 Save) - *03*	11	13
37-475	**LMS** 200345 grey - *01*	7	9
37-475A*	**LMS** 209346 grey - *03*	6	8
37-477	**BR** B450032 brown - *07*	6	8
37-477A	**BR** B450262 brown - *09*	5	7
37-477B	**BR** B450394 brown - *10*	5	7

* Boxes labelled 37-475. ** Also listed as 37-476B.

W3a. 3-plank Wagon (ex-Mainline) (1991)

33-450	**'Cammell Laird & Co'** 630 maroon - *92*	9	11
33-451	**'James Carter'** 170 grey - *91*	9	11
33-451A	**'Evan Davies'** 25 light grey - *96*	9	11
33-450A	**'Easter Iron Mines'** 4 brown - *96*	9	11
33-450Z	**M&GN** 470 brown + **LNER** container BD1466 On Loan to M&GN blue Sp Edn 500 (North Norfolk Railway) - *97*	15	18
33-454	**SR** 62948 dark brown - *96*	8	10
(30-200*	**LT** BW231 dark grey ex-set - *91*	15	NA
33-452	**BR** W36459 brown - *92*	8	10
(30-100)	**BR** B478450 brown ex-set - *91*	8	NA
33-453	undecorated light grey - *91*	5	7

* Box unnumbered.

W3b. 3-plank Wagon (B) (2001)

(30-005)	**'English China Clays'** 490 red ex-set - *05*	8	NA
37-925	**'ICI Buxton Lime'** 48 light grey - *02*	9	11
37-928	**'United Stone Firms'** 41 pale grey - *05*	8	10
37-926	**BR** M470105 brown - *01*	7	9
37-926A*	**BR** M470105 brown (2nd batch) - *03*	6	8

* No 'A' on box end label.

W3c. 3-plank Wagon + BD Container (B) (2005)

37-929	**NE** 535962 brown + dark blue **LNER** container BD1460 - *05*	8	10

37-927	**BR** M470105 brown + maroon **BR** container BD48592B - *not made*	NA	NA

LNER 3-plank wagon with LNER container [W3c]

37-927	**BR** B457200 brown + maroon **BR** container BD6534B - *05*	8	10
37-930A	**BR** B457203 brown + brown **BR** container BD47324B - *10*	6	8
37-930	**BR** M475184 brown + red **BR** container BD6534B - *08*	7	9
37-930B	**BR** M? brown + red **BR** container BD????B - *10*	6	8

W4a. 5-plank 13T China Clay Wagon + Hood (1991)

The model was based on real china clay open wagons and the hoods are made of stitched light blue canvas and kept in shape by a removable moulded plastic frame. The models correctly have 9ft wheelbases.

33-075	**BR** B743267 brown - *91*	9	12
33-075A	**BR** B743321 brown - *94*	9	11
33-075B	**BR** B743169 brown W - *98*	9	11
33-075C	**BR** B743197 brown W - *99*	8	10
33-075D	**BR** B743615 brown W - *01*	8	10
33-075E	**BR** B743124 brown W - *not made*	NA	NA
33-076	**BR** B743752 brown - *92*	9	11
33-076A	**BR** B743238 brown - *94*	9	11
33-076B	**BR** B743156 brown W - *98*	9	11
33-076C	**BR** 743127 brown W - *99*	8	10
33-076D	**BR** B743597 brown 7405 - *02*	8	10
33-076E	**BR** B743597 brown - *not made*	NA	NA
33-080	**BR** B743169 brown W - *04*	7	9
33-080A	**BR** B743802 brown W 7405 - *09*	6	7

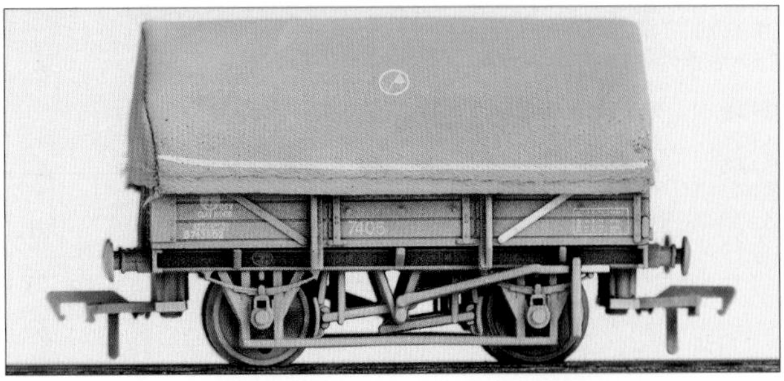

Weathered china clay wagon with hood [W4a]

33-080B	**BR** B743378 brown W 7405 - *10*	6	8
33-081	**BR** B743141 brown W - *04*	7	9
33-081A	**BR** B743420 brown W - *09*	6	7
33-081B	**BR** B743155 brown W - *10*	6	8

-	BR B743689 brown W	7	NA
-	BR B743790 brown W	7	NA
-	BR B743808 brown W	7	NA
33-080Y	above 3 wagons Sp Edn 512 (Kernow MRC) - *10*	NA	30

W4b. 5-plank 13T China Clay Wagon Ex-hood (1992)

33-078A	**GW** 92873 dark grey (light grey inside) - *00*	7	9
33-078B	**GW** 92947 dark grey W (heavy) - *02*	7	9
33-079	**GW** 92971 dark grey - *96*	8	10
33-079	**BR** B743096 grey - *03*	6	8
33-079A	**BR** W42833 grey - *10*	6	8
33-077	**BR** B743236 brown - *92*	8	10
33-077A	**BR** B743620 brown W - *00*	7	9
33-077B	**BR** B743221 brown W 7449 - *02*	7	9
33-078	**BR** P270732 brown - *92*	8	10
33-082	**BR** B743357 brown W 7401 - *04*	6	8

* No 'A' on box end label.

W5a. 5-plank Wagon (ex-Mainline) (1990)

This model was based on a 17'6" open wagon.

33-051	**'Cefnmawr & Rhosymedre'** 12 red - *92*	10	12
33-054	**'English China Clays'** 490 red - *95*	10	12
33-050	**'Hinckley Gas Works'** 4 red - *91*	10	12
33-050A	**'Pounsbery'** 1 green - *94*	10	12
(30-041)	**'Pounsbery'** 1 green (2nd release) ex-set - *08?*	10	NA
33-056	**'Stevenson'** 10 blue (see table W5c - 37-051) - *not made*	NA	NA
33-055	**'Worcester New Coop'** 20 red+black (see table W5c - 37-052) - *not made*	NA	NA
33-050Z	**M&GN** 822045 brown Sp Edn 500 (North Norfolk Railway) - *94*	12	14
33-051A	**SR** 28422 dark brown (see table W5c - 37-050) - *not made*	NA	NA
33-052	**BR Dept** DW280 dark grey - *90*	8	10
33-053	unfinished light grey - *91*	6	8

W5b. 5-plank Wagon - Steel Floor (B) (1998)

37-026A	**'Arenig Granite'** 207 red - *03*	7	9
37-033	**'John Arnold & Son'** 156 red - *10*	5	7
37-032	**'Constable Hart'** 1004 black** - *07*	8	10
37-034	**'James Durnford'** 30 black - *10*	5	7
37-025A	**'James Durnford'** 37 black - *03*	8	10
37-028	**'ICI Lime'** 3034 light grey* - *00*	9	11
37-029	**'Hopton-Wood'** 2 grey - *00*	9	11
37-025X	'WJ **King'** 38 black Sp Edn 504 (Buffers) - *06*	9	11
37-031	**'Lilleshall'** 1750 red - *06*	8	10
37-027A	**'George Lovegrove'** 215 red-brown - *03*	8	10
37-027	**'Penderyn Limestone'** 336 grey - *99*	9	11
37-025	**'Quarrite'** 306 red - *98*	10	12
37-025Y	**'SLB'** 702 pale grey - *(See W30a)*	-	-
37-025Z	*see below under 5-plank wagons with wooden floors*	-	-
37-026	**'Tarslag (1923)'** 836 grey - *98*	10	12
37-030	**'Harry Whitehouse'** 16 red - *00*	9	11

* Reappeared in 2004 in the 30-045 Digital Freight Set. ** Box label misprint 'SREEL' for 'STEEL'.

W5c. 5-plank Wagon - Wooden Floor (B) (1998)

37-059	'Nathanial **Atrill'** 6 black - *07*	8	10
(37-080N)	'S **Bookman'** 30 light grey Sp Edn (ModelZone) - *07*	8	NA
37-050Z	**'Birmingham Railway Carriage & Wagon Co.'** 26892 brown Sp Edn (Warley Model Railway Club) - *00*	30	38

5-plank wagon 'R.Fred Cole' [W5c]

37-056Y	**'Cafferata'** 18 brown Sp Edn (Access Models) - *01*	12	14
37-050V	'AF **Chainey'** 1 brown Sp Edn 504 (Buffers) - *06*	10	12
(37-080P)	**'Chapman & Sons'** 22 black ex-pack - *06*	8	NA
37-060	'R.Fred.**Cole'** 11 red - *08*	7	9
37-050Z	**'Forfar Victoria Coal Society'** 24 dark brown Sp Edn 500 (Virgin Trains) - *05*	22	30
37-050W	**'Goodland & Sons'** 1 black Sp Edn 504 (Buffers) - *06*	8	10

37-056	'**Joshua Gray**' 3 dark brown - *02*	9	11
37-056	'Joshua **Gray**' 3 red-brown ex-set - *05*	8	NA
37-050Y	'TS**Hanson**' 1 red Sp Edn 500 (B&H Models) - *00*	13	15
37-050W	'**Hill Craig**' 6 brown Sp Edn 500 (Harburn Hobbies) - *00*	28	34
37-056Z	'**Hucknall**' 3422 red Sp Edn 500 (Sherwood Models - *01*	13	15
37-056W	'JC **Kew** 14 grey Sp Edn (Access Models) - *01*	12	14
37-050A*	'Hugh **Lumley**' 21 grey - *00*	9	11
37-056A	'AE **Moody**' I dark brown - *03*	8	10
37-050X	'**Newark Corporation**' 4 brown Sp Edn 500 (Access Models) - *00*	13	15
37-025Z	'**Ogilvy Brothers**' 1 dark brown Sp Edn 500 (Virgin Trains) - *04*	12	15
37-050X	'**Ralls & Son**' 51 grey Sp Edn 504 (Buffers) - *06*	10	12
37-062	'**Salt Union**' 91 grey - *10*	5	7
37-050U	'J **Sheppard & Son**' 3 black Sp Edn 504 (Salisbury Model Centre) - *08*	8	10
37-050A	'FH **Silvey**' 191 brown - *not made*	NA	NA
37-050B	'FH **Silvey**' 191 brown - *03*	8	10
37-051	'EA **Stevenson**' 10 blue - *98*	7	9
37-057	'J&R **Stone**' 245 blue grey - *03*	8	10
37-055	'**Wadsworth**' 53 light grey - *00*	9	11
37-050Y	'Fred **Whiteman**' 503 red-brown Sp Edn 500 (Virgin Trains) - *05*	10	12
37-053	'JR **Wood**' 33 orange-yellow - *99*	9	11
37-052	'**Worcester New Co-operative & Industrial Society**' 20 red - *98*	9	11
37-050	**SR** 28422 dark brown - *99*	7	9
37-054	**BR** P143165 grey - *99*	7	9
37-058	**BR** M254661 grey - *06*	6	8
37-061	**BR** M318256 grey - *09*	7	9
37-061A	**BR** P252247 grey - *10*	5	7

* No 'A' on the box end label.

W6a. 12T 'Shocbar VB' Shock Wagon (1992)

33-225	**BR** B721326 brown Shock - *92*	7	9
33-226	**BR** B721385 brown Hybar - *94*	7	9
33-227	**BR** B724180 brown Hybar W - *94*	7	9

W6b. 13T 'Shocbar VB' Shock Wagon (B) (2006)

Fitted with sheet rails.

BR shock wagon 'Shockbar VB' [W6b]

37-875	**BR** B721326 brown - *not made*	NA	NA
37-875	**BR** B722620 brown - *06*	6	8
37-876	**BR** B721385 brown - *not made*	NA	NA
37-876	**BR** B723176 brown - *06*	6	8
37-877	**BR** B721326 brown - *10*	5	7

W7a. 7-plank Wagon (ex-Mainline) (1991)

33-105	'**Anderson**' Whitstable 76 brown - *95*	10	13
33-101A	'**Barnsley Main**' 528 brown - *93*	10	12
33-100U	'**Blidworth**' 2444 light grey Sp Edn 500 (The Midlander) - *97*	14	16
33-100X	'**Bolsover**' 1190 brown Sp Edn 500 (The Midlander) - *96*	14	16
33-100PP	'W **Clarke**' 100 red Sp Edn 500 (B&H Models) also seen listed as 33-100c) - *96*	14	16
33-100A	'JL **Davies**' 121 brown - *94*	10	12
33-100T	'**Dinnington Main**' 641 blue Sp Edn 500 (Geoffrey Allison No3) - *97*	14	16
33-100XX	'**Eckington**' 2801 red-brown Sp Edn 500 (The Midlander) - *99*	13	15
33-100K	'**Firbeck**' 787 brown Sp Edn 500 (Geoffrey Allison) - *98*	18	30
33-104A	'**Flower & Sons**' 7 dark grey - *96*	10	12
33-100Q	'**Forth**' 104 light grey Sp Edn 500 (Harburn Hobbies No2) - *96*	16	21
33-100F	'WH **Garton**' 23 brown Sp Edn 500 (B&H Models) - *99*	13	15
33-100C	'**Gedling**' 2598 red Sp Edn 500 (Gee Dee Models No1) - *99*	13	15
33-100ZZ	'**Hardwick**' 637 brown Sp Edn 500 (The Midlander) - *99*	13	15
33-100	'**Hickleton**' 1408 red-brown - *91*	10	12
33-100D	'**Hucknall No1 Colliery**' 7071 brown Sp Edn 500 (Sherwood Models No1) - *99*	13	15
33-100H	'**Hull Corporation**' 112 light grey Sp Edn 500 (53A Models) - *98*	14	16
33-100M	'J **Kime & Son**' 5 black Sp Edn 500 (B&H Models) - *98*	14	16
33-100W	'**James Lewis**' 19 bright red Sp Edn 500 (B&H Models) - *97*	14	16
33-100E	'**Linby Colliery Co.**' brown Sp Edn 500 (Sherwood Models No2) - *99*	13	15
33-100V	'**Lincoln Corporation**' 9 brown Sp Edn 500 (B&H Models) - *97*	14	16

7-plank wagon 'Manton' [W7a]

33-100N	'**Lincoln Wagon & Engine**' light grey Sp Edn 500 (B&H Models) - *97*	12	14
33-100B	'**Manton**' 891 red-brown Sp Edn 500 (Geoffrey Allison) - *95*	14	16
33-100WW	'**North Norfolk Railway**' 8572 green Sp Edn 500 (NNR) - *93*	18	25
33-100J	'**Nunnery**' 1574 black Sp Edn 500 (Geoffrey Allison) - *98*	14	16
33-100R	'**Ormiston Coal Coy**' 199 blue Sp Edn 500 (Harburn Hobbies No3) - *96*	26	32
33-100G	'JW **Pinner**' 12 red-brown Sp Edn 500 (B&H Models) (also seen listed as 33-100K) - *99*	13	15
33-100S	'**Rossington**' 2054 light grey Sp Edn 500 (Geoffrey Allison No4) - *97*	14	16
33-100Y	'**Sheepbridge** 5101' pale red Sp Edn 500 (The Midlander) (also listed as 33-100Y) - *96*	14	16
(30-006)	'**Sheepbridge**' 6091 red ex-train set - *?*	6	NA
33-101	'**Shirebrook Colliery**' 159 dark red - *91*	10	12
33-100Z	'**Shireoaks**' 4241 brown Sp Edn 500 (Geoffrey Allison No1) - *97*	18	25
33-100YY	'**Staveley**' 4994 black Sp Edn 500 (The Midlander) ('33-100' on box)- *99*	10	12
33-104	'R **Taylor & Sons**' 451 brick red - *92*	10	12
33-105A	'Richard **Webster**' 107 red (see table W5c) - *not made*	NA	NA
33-100L	'**Welbeck**' 2692 black Sp Edn 500 (The Midlander No3) - *97*	20	36
33-100NN	'WS **White & Co**'. 15 grey Sp Edn 500 (B&H Models) - *96*	14	16
33-100P	'**Woodhall**' 220 green Sp Edn 500 (Harburn Hobbies No1) - *96*	15	20
33-102	'**Wyken Colliery Co.**' 441 soft brown- *92*	10	12
33-102A	**LMS** 609545 soft brown - *96*	8	10
33-106	**NE** 138455 grey (see table W7c) - *not made*	NA	NA
33-101A	**BR** M608163 grey - *96*	8	10
33-103	undecorated light grey - *91*	6	8

W7b. 7-plank Wagon - End Door (B) (1998)

See also W8b for wagons in triple sets.

7-plank wagon 'Aberpergwm' [W7b]

37-075K2	**'Aberpergwm'** 941 red-brown Sp Edn 750 (BCC) - *06*	20	25
37-080Z	**'Annesley'** 195 brown Sp Edn 500 (Sherwood Models) - *01*	12	14
37-080T	**'Arniston'** 617 brown Sp Edn (Harburn Hobbies) - *01*	12	14
37-100Y	**'Babbington'** 3144 black Sp Edn 500 (Gee Dee Models) - *00*	13	15
37-078X	**'Bachmann'** 89-99 blue Ltd Edn (Bachmann) 10th Anniversary - *99*	13	14
37-075Y	**'Balgonie'** 226 brown Sp Edn 500 (Harburn Hobbies) - *00*	13	14
(30-045)	**'Barnsley Main'** 528 brown ex-set - *04*	8	NA
37-084Z	**'Blaenavon'** 1457 grey W Sp Edn 504 (Pontypool & Blaenavon Railway Society) - *10*	6	8
37-080Y	**'Blidworth'** 2323 red Sp Edn 500 (Gee Dee Models) - *01*	12	14
37-083	**'Bradleys (Weardale)'** 246 brown - *06*	8	10
37-079V	**'Butterley'** 2301 brown Sp Edn (various)* - *01*	12	14
37-075K3	**'Cain'** 3 black Sp Edn 750 (BCC) - *06*	10	12
37-079U	**'Clay Cross'** Sp Edn 500 (various)* - *01*	12	14
37-080L	**'Coventry'** 1497 black Sp Edn 504 (Castle Trains) - *08*	8	10
37-085	**'Crane & Company'** 107 red - *10*	5	7
37-080W	'The **Derbyshire Carriage & Wagon'** 110 brown Sp Edn (BCC) - *01*	12	14
37-076A	**'Douglas Bank Colliery'** 454 brown - *03*	8	10
37-076K	'Edward **Eastwood'** 2 green Sp Edn (BCC) - *08*	8	10
37-080R	**'Edinburgh'** 313 grey Sp Edn (Harburn Hobbies) - *01*	12	14
37-075K1	**'Fife Coal'** 1655 dark brown Sp Edn 750 (BCC) - *06*	10	12

7-plank wagon 'Gellyceidrim' [W7b]

37-082	**'Firestone'** 2004 dark blue - *06*	8	10
37-076	**'Gellyceidrim'** 719 light grey - *98*	14	15
37-075A	**'Goldendale Iron'** 598 blue-grey - *03*	8	10
37-084	**'Harrisons'** 5038 grey - *08*	9	11
37-080G	**'Highley Mining Co.'** 425 brown Sp Edn 504? (Severn Valley Railway) - *09*	7	9
37-2009K	'Thomas **Hunter'** brown Sp Edn (BCC) - *09*	9	12
37-077	**'ICI Salt Works'** Stafford 326 red-brown - *99*	9	11
37-2003	'James **Kenworthy'** 47 brown Ltd Edn (BCC) - *03*	11	13
37-075Z	**'Kinneil'** 189 brown Sp Edn 500 (Harburn Hobbies) - *00*	13	15
37-078	**'Kobo'** 15 grey - *99*	9	11
37-080H	**'Leadbeter'** 211 dark red Sp Edn 504 (Pontypool & Blaenavon Railway) - *08*	20	24
37-075S	**'Micklefield Coal & Lime Co.'** 423 red-brown Sp Edn (NRM) - *07*	9	11
37-080S	**'Moore'** 113 brown Sp Edn (Harburn Hobbies) - *01*	12	14
37-075W	**'Newstead'** 2281 grey Sp Edn (Sherwood Models) - *00*	12	14
37-080U	**'Niddrie'** 491 grey Sp Edn (Harburn Hobbies) - *01*	12	14
37-2010K	**Pickering** [R.Y.] & Co. 1002, ?, Sp Edn (BCC) - *10*	NPG	NPG
37-080V	**'Renwick, Wilton & Dobson'** 77 red-brown Sp Edn 500 (Warley Show) - *03*	11	13
(30-006)	**'Sheepbridge'** 6091 red ex Harry the Hauler set - *10*	8	NA
37-075K	**'Standard Wagon'** (Cambrian Wagon Company Ltd) 1923 pale yellow Ltd Edn (Bachmann Times) - *99*	25	33
37-080V	**'Swanwick'** 2383 brown Sp Edn 500 (various*) - *01*	12	15
37-075X	**'Thorne - Pease & Partners'** 1336 brown Sp Edn (Rails) - *00*	13	15
37-078B	**'Wimberry Colliery Co.'** 2 black (also seen as '37-078A') - *03*	8	10
37-075V	**'Tom Wright'** 19 brown Sp Edn 504 (Midland Railway Society) - *03*	11	13
37-080	'JR **Wood'** 346 orange - *00*	9	11
37-080A	'JR **Wood'** 346 orange - *03*	NPG	NPG
37-079	**GW** 09244 dark grey - *00*	7	9
37-075	**NE** 158486 light grey - *98*	8	10
37-081A	**BR** M608163 grey - *06*	7	9
37-081B	**BR** P60084 grey - *08*	5	7
37-081C	**BR** P938099 grey - *09*	5	7
37-081D	**BR** P36147 grey - *10*	5	7

*Originally commissioned by The Midlander but order subsequently cancelled. The order was then taken over jointly by Sherwood Models, Geoffrey Allison, Gee Dee Models and C&B Models.

W7c. 7-plank Wagon - Fixed End (B) (1998)

See also W8b for wagons in triple sets.

37-101X	'The **Arley Colliery Co.'** 27 red Sp Edn 504 (Castle Trains) - *08*	8	10
37-100L	**'Awsworth'** 86 light grey Sp Edn 504 (Sherwood Models) - *03*	11	13
37-????	**'Awsworth + Shipley'** Sp Edn (Sherwood Models) - *03*	NA	18
37-100G	**'Bassil King & Co.'** 5 red Sp Edn 504 (Buffers) - *06*	10	12
37-104	**'Birch Coppice'** 927 red - *00*	9	11
37-108	'Frederick **Biss'** 3 grey - *08*	7	9

7-plank wagon 'B.W. & Co Moorgreen Colliery' [W7c]

37-105X	**'Butterley'** 0820 grey Sp Edn 500 (various)* - *01*	12	14
37-105W	**'BW&Co Moorgreen Colliery'** 1466 light grey Sp Edn 500 (Gee Dee Models) - *01*	12	14
37-100E	'Thos.J **Clarke'** 602 dark brown Sp Edn 504 (Buffers) - *06*	11	14
37-100U	**'Clifton'** 2121 brown Sp Edn 504 (Sherwood Models) - *00*	13	15
37-101Z	'Jebez **Cole'** 17 black Sp Edn 504 (Frizinghall Model Railways) - *07*	8	10
37-109	'DV **Costick'** 1 blue - *08*	7	9
37-111	**'Eales & Roberts'** 6 red-brown - *10*	5	7
37-105	**'George & Matthews'** 5 black - *00*	9	11
37-101A	'The **Great Western Railwaymen's Coal Association'** 1 light grey - *03*	8	10
37-105U	**'Kimberley'** 4151 brown Sp Edn 500 (Warley MRC) - *01*	12	14

37-100M	**'Kirriemuir Coal Society'** 2 brown Sp Edn 500 (Virgin Trains) - *04*	20	27
37-105V	**'Lakeside & Haverwaithe'** Sp Edn (L&HR) - *not made*	NA	NA
37-100J	'S **Loney & Co.'** 50 dark grey Sp Edn 504 (Buffers) - *06*	10	12
37-100	**'Marcroft Wagons'** 761 black Sp Edn (BCC) - *02*	12	14
37-101	**'Parkend'** 312 black - *98*	10	12
37-100V	'GE **Parker'** 1 brown Sp Edn 500 (British Railway Modelling) - *00*	13	15
37-100D	'Thos.S **Penny'** 2 red Sp Edn 504 (Buffers) - *06*	10	12
37-100X	**'Pinxton'** 718 black Sp Edn 500 (Gee Dee Models) - *00*	13	15
37-075R	'HJ **Redgate'** 47 brown, Ltd Edn 504 (Sherwood Models) - *10*	8	10
33-101U	**'Ridley's Coal & Iron Co.'** 1 grey Sp Edn 504 (Model Junction) - *08*	8	10
37-106	**'Royal Leamington Spa'** 22 red-brown - *06*	8	10
37-110	**'Shaka Salt'** 580 red-brown - *10*	5	7
37-100N	**'Shipley'** 1522 red-brown Sp Edn 504 (Sherwood Models) - *03*	11	13
37-103	'James H **Smart'** 1 black - *00*	9	11
37-100W	'TE **Smith'** 9 dark red Sp Edn 500 (B&H Models) - *00*	13	15
37-150?	**'Teifi Valley/Henllan'** Sp Edn (Teifi Valley Railway) - *not made*	NA	NA
37-101V	'WH **Thomas & Son'** 119 olive green Sp Edn 504 (Buffers) - *06*	8	10
37-100H	'WH **Thomas & Son'** 120 olive green Sp Edn 504 (Buffers) - *06*	10	12
37-100F	'William **Thomas & Co.'** 2 black Sp Edn 504 (Buffers) - *06*	11	14
37-105Y	**'Waleswood'** 606 red-brown Sp Edn (Geoffrey Allison) - *01*	NPG	NPG
37-101Y	**'Walker & Rodgers'** 3 red Sp Edn 504 (Castle Trains) - *08*	8	10
37-2002	'NA **Walton'** 1 grey Sp Edn 500 (Warley MRC) - *02*	12	14
37-101T	**'Warwick Gas Light Co.'** 6 grey Sp Edn 504 (Castle Trains) - *09*	6	8
37-105A	**'Webb, Hall & Webb'** 19 blue - *03*	8	10

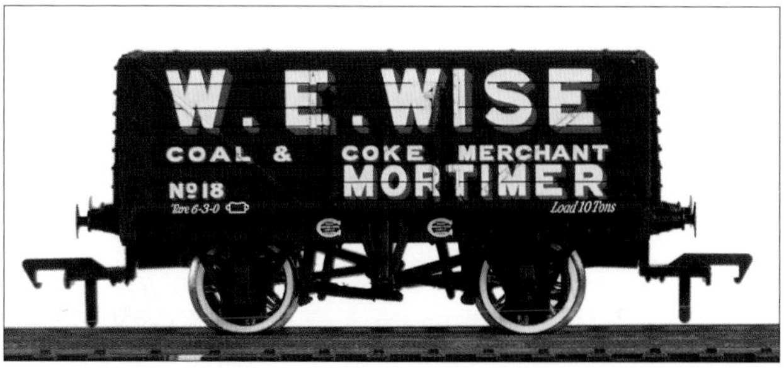

7-plank wagon 'W.E.Wise' [W8a]

37-100	'Richard **Webster'** 107 red - *98*	10	12
37-100A	'WE **Wise'** 18 black - *03*	8	10
37-100Z	**'Wollaton'** 79 red Sp Edn 500 (Gee Dee Models) - *00*	13	15
37-102	**BR** P156142 grey - *99*	7	9
37-107	**BR** E454941 grey - *06*	6	8

*Originally commissioned by The Midlander but order subsequently cancelled. The order was then taken over jointly by Sherwood Models, Geoffrey Allison, Gee Dee Models and C&B Models.

W8a. Early Coal Trader Packs (1995)

All of these wagon packs contain pre-Blue Riband 7-plank wagons. They were sold in sets of three different wagons which were unique to the set. We provide below the mint boxed value of the set and the 'excellent' unboxed value of the individual wagons.

33-025	**'Ammanford Colliery'** 48 brown	9	NA
33-025/1	**'Cambrian Mercantile'** 114 light grey	9	NA
33-025/2	**'Berthlwyd'** 385 dark green	9	NA
33-025	Wales Coal Traders above set of 3 - *95*	NA	30

A	**'Chapman, Fletcher & Cawood'** 980 black	9	NA
B	**'Rothervale'** 2563 grey	9	NA
C	**'Sheffield & Eccleshall'** 13 red	9	NA
33-025W	Coal Traders above set of 3 Sp Edn 500 (Rails) 1st set - *97*	NA	30
A	**'Dearne Valley'** 61 light blue	9	NA
B	**'Cortonwood'** 751 brown	9	NA
C	**'Monkton'** 1771 black	9	NA
33-025X	Dearne Valley Coal Traders above set of 3 Sp Edn 500 (Geoffrey Allinson No.8) - *99*	NA	28
A	**'Thos. Black'** 49 brown	9	NA
B	**'Tinsley Park'** 2241 brown	9	NA
C	**'Thorncliffe'** 3751 black	9	NA
33-025Y	Coal Traders above set of 3 Sp Edn 500 (Rails) 2nd set - *98*	NA	28
A	**'Staveley'** Bleaching Powder 4728 grey	9	NA
B	**'Staveley'** Caustic Soda 7230 black	9	NA
C	**'Staveley'** Sand Spun Pipes 9249 grey	9	NA
33-025Z	Coal Traders above set of 3 Sp Edn 500 (The Midlander No.4) - *98*	NA	30
-	**'Oxcroft'** 721 black	9	NA
-	**'Sherwood'** 575 brown	9	NA
-	**'Ilkeston & Heanor'** 17 dark blue	9	NA
33-026	Derby/Notts Coal Traders above set of 3 - *95*	NA	30

Early Coal Traders set - London area [W8a]

-	**'Phorpres' Bricks'** London Brick 988 dark grey	8	NA
-	**'Lowe & Warwick'** 42 red+yellow	8	NA
-	**'HC Bull & Co.'** 101 dark red	8	NA
33-027	London Coal Traders above set of 3 - *95*	NA	26
-	**'Blackpool Cooperative'** 32 dark grey	9	NA
-	**'Wigan Coal'** A147 red-brown	9	NA
-	**'JB Scholes - Cosy Fires'** 778 light grey	9	NA
33-028	North West Coal Traders above set of 3 - *96*	NA	30
-	**'Hartnell & Son'** 22 black	9	NA
-	**'Dunkerton'** 1117 dark grey	9	NA
-	**'Milton'** 10 dark brown	9	NA
33-029	West Country Coal Traders above set of 3 - *96*	NA	30
-	**'H Fulcher'** 10 brown	9	NA
-	**'Mellonie & Goulder'** 307 grey	9	NA
-	**'Wrights'** 135 red	9	NA
33-030	East Anglia Coal Traders above set of 3 - *96*	NA	30
-	**'Florence'** 1017 dark grey	9	NA
-	**'Grazebrook'** 49 red	9	NA
-	**'Lunt'** 724 grey	9	NA
33-031	West Midlands Coal Traders above set of 3 - *97*	NA	30
-	**'Newbold & Martell'** 180 red	9	NA
-	**'Whitwick'** G55 black	9	NA
-	**'Stockingford'** 9 dark grey	9	NA
33-032	East Midlands Coal Traders above set of 3 - *97*	NA	30
-	**'Wm Shaw & Sons'** 137 red	9	NA
-	**'Flockton Coal Co.'** 94 grey	9	NA
-	**'Sycobrite - The South Yorkshire Chemical Works'** 650 black+yellow	9	NA
33-033	Yorkshire Coal Traders above set of 3 - *97*	NA	30

W8b. Later Coal Trader Packs (B) (2000)

These wagon packs contained Blue Riband quality wagons, almost always of one type and all are 7-plank unless otherwise stated.

37-075JA	**'Parkend'** 312 black W	6	NA
37-075JB	**'Parkend'** 374 black W	6	NA
37-075JC	**'Parkend'** 380 black W	6	NA
37-075J	above 3 wagons Sp Edn 504 (Totally Trains) - *09*	NA	21
-	**'Fleetwood Fish'** 2 red-brown	10	NA
-	**'Guard Bridge Paper Co.'** 67 grey	10	NA
-	**'Lewis Merthyr Navigation Colliery'** 674 black	10	NA
37-075K4	set of above 3 Sp Edn 750 (BCC) - *07*	NA	40

Later Coal Traders set [W8b]

	'St Helens Industrial Coal Department Co-operative Society' 17 grey 7-plank	6	NA
-	**'Lochgelly'** 1898 red-brown 5-plank	6	NA
-	**'T Jenkerson & Sons'** 277 black 8-plank	6	NA
37-075K5	set of above 3 Sp Edn 504 (BCC) - *08*	NA	21
-	**'J Manning & Sons'** 2 black W	8	NA
-	'Geo **Mills & Sons'** 40 black W	8	NA
-	'A **Vitti & Son'** 9 red-brown W	8	NA
37-075T	Coal Traders set of above 3 Sp Edn 500 (Froude & Hext) - *05*	NA	30
-	**'Lincoln Corporation'** 200 maroon	9	NA
-	**'Lincoln Corporation'** 201 maroon	9	NA
-	**'Lincoln Corporation'** 202 maroon	9	NA
37-075U	set of above 3 Sp Edn 500 (B&H Models) - *04*	NA	33
-	**Pilkington Brothers** 1412, red	8	NA
-	**Smith Anderson & Co.** 10, brown	8	NA
-	**Jones [David] & Sons** 650, black	8	NA
37-077K	set of 3, Sp Edn 500 (BCC) - *10*	NA	21
X	**'Walter Boynton'** 982 red-brown	10	NA
Y	**'Walter Woodthorpe'** 15 red-brown	10	NA
Z	**'Walter Boynton'** 01029 red-brown	10	NA
37-079X	Coal Traders set of above 3 Sp Edn (B&H Models) - *01*	NA	36
-	**'Cambrian'** 1410 black	6	NA
-	**'Stuart Coal Coy'** 95 dark brown	6	NA
-	**'Victoria Coal Co.'** 10 grey	6	NA
37-080J	Cardiff Coal Traders set of above 3 wagons Sp Edn 504 (Lord & Butler) - *08*	NA	21
-	'S **Bookman'** 30 grey 5-plank	7	NA
-	'WW **Milton'** 6 black	7	NA
-	**'Whitwill Cole & Co.'** 708 black	7	NA
37-080N	West Country (Bristol) set of above 3 Sp Edn 500 (ModelZone) - *07*	NA	27

Later Coal Traders set - East Midlands area [W8b]

-	**'Snibston'** 585 red-brown	7	NA
-	**'South Leicester'** 373 red	7	NA
-	**'Wood & Co.'** (5-plank) 15 grey	7	NA
37-080M	East Midlands (Leicester) set of above 3 Sp Edn 500 (ModelZone) - *07*	NA	27
	'Chapman & Sons' 22 black 5-plank	8	NA
-	**'Fear Bros.'** 95 brown	8	NA
-	'H **Syrus'** I red	8	NA
37-080P	Surrey & Sussex Coal Traders set of above 3 Sp Edn 504 (ModelZone) - *06*	NA	30

-	'Fred C **Holmes'** 104 red-brown	8	NA
-	'MA **Ray & Sons'** 123 light grey	8	NA
-	'FW **Wacher'** 6 black 5-plank	8	NA
37-080Q	Kent Coal Traders set of above 3 Sp Edn 504 (ModelZone) - *06*	NA	30
-	**'Denaby'** 900 red	8	NA
-	**'Nostell'** 375 black	8	NA
-	**'Wath Main'** 1320 red-brown	8	NA
37-080T	South Yorkshire Coal Traders set 4 of above 3 Sp Edn 500 (Geoffrey Allison) - *05*	NA	30
-	'W **Clarke & Son'** 405 brown	9	NA
-	'W **Clarke & Son'** 101 black	9	NA
-	'Wm **Clarke & Son'** 281 brown	9	NA
37-080UU	set of above 3 Sp Edn (B&H Models) - *03*	NA	33
-	**'Manchester'** 8697 brown	11	NA
-	**'Manchester'** 8725 brown	11	NA
-	**'Manchester'** 8780 brown	11	NA
37-080X	Coal Traders set of above 3 Sp Edn 500 (TMC) - *00*	NA	39
-	**'Brodsworth Main'** 350 red	9	NA
-	**'Waleswood'** 606 red-brown	9	NA
-	**'Yorkshire Main'** 9417 red-brown	9	NA
37-080X	set of above 3 Sp Edn (G Allison) - *01*	NA	27
-	**'Barkby Jolliffe'** 606 black	11	NA
-	**'Birley'** 662 grey	11	NA
-	**'Marshell Bros.'** 7 black	11	NA
37-080Y	Coal Traders set of above 3 Sp Edn 500 (Rails) - *00*	NA	39
-	**'Bulcroft'** 288 dark red	11	NA
-	**'Kiveton'** 2041 dark grey	11	NA
-	**'Maltby Main'** 298 brown	11	NA
37-080Z	South Yorkshire Coal Traders set 1 of above 3 Sp Edn 500 (G Allison No9) - *00*	NA	39
-	**'Murphy Brothers'** 29 brown	10	NA
-	**'Murphy Brothers'** 32 brown	10	NA
-	**'Murphy Brothers'** 33 brown	10	NA
37-105Z	Coal Traders set of above 3 Sp Edn 300 (Murphy Models) - *01*	NA	36
-	**'Murphy Brothers'** 14 red-brown	7	NA
-	**'Murphy Brothers'** 19 red-brown	7	NA
-	**'Murphy Brothers'** 22 red-brown	7	NA
MM1704	above three wagons Ltd Edn 504 (Murphy Models) - *08*	NA	28

Later Coal Traders set [W8b]

-	**'Barrow Barnsley'** 1708 yellow	9	NA
-	**'BW & Co.'** black 8-plank	9	NA
-	**'Hatfield Main'** 1213 brown 8-plank	9	NA
37-105Y	South Yorkshire Coal Traders set 3 of above 3 Sp Edn 500 (G Allison) - *03*	NA	33
-	**'City of Bradford Co-operative Society'** 118 brown	9	NA
-	**'Cleckheaton Industrial Co-operative Society'** 61 brown	9	NA
-	**'Hillhouses Co-operative Society'** 29 black	9	NA
37-075N	above three Yorkshire area wagons Sp Edn 504 (National Railway Museum) - *10*	NA	27

-	**'Birmingham Industrial Co-operative Society'** 13 black	9	NA
-	**'Derby Co-operative Provident Society'** 149 grey	9	NA
-	**'Melton Mowbray Co-operative Society'** 3 red-brown (8 plank)	9	NA
37-075P	above three Midlands are wagons Sp Edn 504 (National Railway Museum) - *10*	NA	27
-	**'CWS'** 85 red	9	NA
-	**'Neasden Co-operative Coal Society'** 3 black	9	NA
-	**'Royal Arsenal Co-operative Society'** 144 brown	9	NA
37-075Q	above three London area wagons Sp Edn 504 (National Railway Museum) - *10*	NA	27

W9a. 7-plank Coke Wagon + Top Rails (ex-Mainline) (1991)

33-150	**'Abbott'** 3607 grey - *91*	9	10
33-155	'JA **Bartlett'** 2 red-brown - *94*	9	10
33-152A	**'Benzol & Byproducts'** 1104 brown - *not made (see table W9b - 37-177)*	NA	NA
33-156	**'Coalite'** 401 red - *95*	9	10
33-151	**'Flockton'** 567 black - *92*	9	10
33-152	**'Lancashire Steel'** 993 grey - *92*	12	17
33-158	**'Modern Transport'** 1206 dark grey - *not made (see table W9c - 37-204)*	NA	NA
33-151A	**'POP'** 217 grey - *not made (see table W9b - 37-176)*	NA	NA
33-154	**'Roberts Davy'** 25 dark grey - *95*	9	10
33-157	**'Stringer & Jagger'** 226 red - *not made (see table W9b - 37-178)*	NA	NA
33-150A	**BR** 368545 grey - *not made (see table W9b - 37-175)*	NA	NA
33-153	undecorated light grey - *91*	4	6

W9b. 7-plank Coke Wagon + Top Rails (B) (1998)

37-177	**'Benzol & By-products'** 1104 red - *98*	10	12
37-175Z	'SJ **Claye'** 822 red Sp Edn 1000 (BCC) - *00*	13	15
37-183	**'Dorchester Gas & Coke'** 6 red-brown - *06*	8	10
37-182	**'Elders Navigation'** 515 black - *06*	8	10
37-182A	**'Elders Navigation'** 588 black - *09*	7	9
37-184	'TL **Hale (Tipton)'** 1533 grey - *10*	5	7
37-179	**'New Cransley'** 166 red - *99*	10	12
37-180	'S **Mosley & Son'** 58 grey+maroon - *00*	9	11
37-176	**'POP.'** 217 grey - *98, 05*	8	10
37-180	**'POP.'** 217 grey - *not sold with this cat.no.*	NA	NA
37-180A	**'POP'** 215 grey - *08*	7	9
37-181	**'South Wales & Cannock Chase'** 901 red-brown - *06*	8	10
37-178	**'Stringer & Jagger'** 226 red - *98*	10	12
37-2002	'NA **Walton'** 1 grey Sp Edn (Warley 2002) - *02*	12	15
37-175	**BR** P368515 grey - *98*	8	11
37-175A	**BR** P167248 grey - *01*	7	10

W9c. 8-plank Coke Wagon + Top Rails (B) (1998)

37-205	**'Bedwas'** 621 grey - *00*	9	11
37-203	**'Birley'** 1605 black - *00*	9	11
37-206	**'Elders'** - *not made*	NA	NA
37-202	'The **Gas Light & Coke Co.'** 821 grey - *99*	9	11
37-207	'TL **Hale'** ? grey - *not made (see table above)*	NA	NA
37-204	**'Modern Transport'** 110 black - *00*	9	11
37-206	**'Reading Gas Company'** 112 black - *06*	8	10
37-200	**'Stamford Gas Light & Coke'** 101 light grey - *98*	10	12
37-201	**'Suncole'** 5062 black - *98*	10	12

W10a. 8-plank Wagon - End Door (B) (1998)

8-plank wagon - 'Boston Deep Sea' [W10a]

37-130	**'Bagley'** 38 red - *00*	9	11
37-125	**'Boston Deep Sea'** 86 blue (2 batches) - *98+99*	10	12
37-125K	'T **Burnett & Co.'** 1907 red Sp Edn (BCC) - *07*	8	10
37-125Z	**'Carlton'** 4727 black Sp Edn 500 (The Midlander) - *00*	13	15
32-175Z	**'Charles Roberts'** 70001 black Sp Edn (BCC) 1st version (no number on box label) - *98*	10	12
37-131	**'Great Mountain'** 980 brown - *06*	8	10
37-127	**'Hinckley Gas Works'** 19 red-brown - *99*	9	11
37-134	**'Ketton Cement - Thos W Ward'** S89 red+blue - *10*	6	8
37-129	**'SC'** 7961 grey - *99*	8	10
37-129A	**'SC'** ? grey - *03*	NPG	NPG
37-130Z	**'Shelton'** 2298 red Sp Edn 500 (Haslington Models) - *01*	12	14
37-126	**Thorncliffe Izal** 2915 black - 98	10	12
37-132	**'Thorne (Pease & Partners Ltd)'** 740 red-brown - *06*	10	12
37-?	'JN **Walker & Co.'** 256 black, Ltd Edn 504 (Sherwood Models) - *10*	7	9
37-128	**BR** P238934 grey - *99*	7	10
37-133	**BR** P63984 grey - *06*	6	8

* No 'Z' suffix on the box label.

W10b. 8-plank Wagon - Fixed End (B) (1998)

37-150Z*	**'Cooperative Society'** 71 brown Sp Edn 500 (The Midlander) - *00*	13	15
37-156	**'Firestone Tyres'** - *not made (see 37-082)*	NA	NA
37-160	**'Ketton Cement'** red+blue (*see table above*)	NA	NA
37-150K	**'Metropolitan'** 188 red Sp Edn (BCC) - *06*	10	12
37-154	**'Musgrave'** 2 dark grey - *00*	9	11
37-156	**'Osborne & Son'** 10 green - *06*	8	10
37-155	**'Partington'** 184 light grey - *00*	9	11
37-153	**'Quibell Brothers'** 10 red - *00*	9	11
37-152	'AJ **Salter'** 202 red-brown - *00*	9	11
37-150	**'Stewarts and Lloyds'** 6159 grey - *98*	9	11
37-157	**'Stewarts & Lloyds'** 6301 dark grey - *06*	8	10
37-151	**'Charles Ward'** 4265 red - *98*	9	11
37-159	'William **Wood & Sons'** 1006 maroon - *09*	5	6
33-158	**BR** P308236 grey - *07*	6	8
33-158A	**BR** P308328 grey - *10*	5	7

* There was no 'Z' suffix on the box label.

W11a. OBA 31t 5-plank Wagon - Low-Ends (B) (2006)

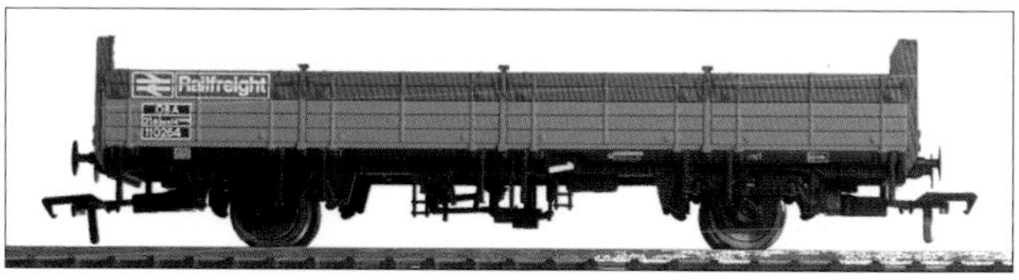

OBA planked open wagon - Railfreight [W11a]

38-040	**EWS** 110456 maroon+yellow - *not made*	NA	NA
38-040	**EWS** 110678 maroon+yellow - *06*	11	14
38-040A	**EWS** 110332 maroon+yellow - *09*	12	15
38-041	**BRe Rft** 110264 grey+red - *06*	11	14
38-041A	**BRe Rft** 110583 grey+red - *09*	12	15
38-040Z	**BR(S&T) Sat-Link** KDC110588 ZDA red+yellow Sp Edn 504 (*Model Rail*) - *06*	14	17

W11b. OBA 31t 5-plank Wagon - High-Ends (B) (2006)

38-042	**BR 'Plasmore Blockfreight'** 110547 red+ grey - *06*	11	14
38-042	as above but 110701 - *06*	11	14
38-043	**EWS** 110436 maroon+yellow - *06*	11	14
38-043	as above but 110636 - *06*	11	14

Steel Mineral Wagons

W12a. 16T Steel Mineral Wagon (ex-Mainline) (1990)

33-751	**BR** M620248 grey - *92*	8	10
33-752C	**BR** M622128 brown Iron Ore - *98*	8	10
33-751/1	**BR** M620233 grey in London Transport sets 30-200 & 30-201 - *91*	14	NA

33-750	**BR** B88643 brown - *90*	8	10
33-750A	**BR** B88647 brown - *94*	8	10
33-750B	**BR** B68919 brown - *96*	8	10
33-750C	**BR** B160415 brown MCV - *98*	8	10
33-751A	**BR** B84198 grey - *94*	8	10
33-751B	**BR** B279900 grey - *95*	8	10
33-751C	**BR** B560287 grey - *96*	8	10
33-751D	**BR** B156124 grey - *97*	8	10
33-752	**BR** B68837 dark grey Coalight - *91*	9	11
33-752A	**BR** B68833 dark grey Coalite - *94*	9	11
33-752B	**BR** B68342 dark grey Coalite - *96*	9	11
33-753	undecorated - *made**	NPG	NPG

W12b. 16T Steel Mineral - Top Flap (B) (1998)

With end door and top flaps above the side doors

37-227	**BR** B106979 grey W - *00*	6	8
37-227A	**BR** B106979 grey W - *02*	6	8
37-225	**BR** B100071 (2 batches) grey - *98+99*	7	9
37-225A*	**BR** B77701 grey - *02*	6	8
37-225B	**BR** B80200 grey - *03*	6	8
37-225C	**BR** B106979 grey - *not made*	NA	NA
37-225C	**BR** B168553 grey - *06*	5	7
37-225D	**BR** B591270 grey - *08*	5	6
37-225E	**BR** B80285 grey - *09*	5	7
37-225F	**BR** B87019 grey - *10*	5	7
-	**BR** B219829 grey W	7	NA
-	**BR** B571730 grey W	7	NA
-	**BR** B119161 grey W	7	NA
37-225X	above set of three Sp Edn 504 (TMC) - *09*	NA	27
(37-225Y)	**BR** B82219 grey W	7	NA
(37-225Y)	**BR** B257058 grey W	7	NA
(37-225Y)	**BR** B140952 grey W	7	NA
37-225Y	above set of three Sp Edn (Hattons) - *08*	NA	24

BR 16 ton steel mineral wagon with top flap [W12b]

37-226	**BR** B68900 brown - *98*	7	9
37-226A	**BR** B69007 brown (37-226 on box) - *01*	6	8
37-226B	**BR** B68901 brown - *?*	5	7
37-226C	**BR** B47202 brown - *06*	5	7
37-226D	**BR** B64026 brown - *08*	5	7
37-226E	**BR** B68919 brown - *09*	5	7
37-226F	**BR** B551677 brown - *10*	5	7
37-228	**BR** B69190 brown W - *00*	6	8
37-228A	**BR** B68998 brown W - *02*	6	8

* No suffix letter on box.

W12c. 16T Steel Mineral - End Door (B) (1998)

With end door and no top flaps above the side doors

37-250	**BR** B38066 grey - *98*	7	9
37-250A*	**BR** B22571 grey - *00*	6	8
37-250B	**BR** B227229 grey - *03*	6	8
37-250C	**BR** B25005 grey MCO - *02*	6	8
37-250D	**BR** B60544 grey - *08*	5	6
37-250E	**BR** B37236 grey - *09*	5	7
37-250F	**BR** B27871 grey - *10*	5	7
37-251	**BR** B258683 light grey MCO - *98*	7	9
37-251A	**BR** B8258683 light grey MCO - *not made*	NA	NA
37-251A	**BR** B229637 light grey MCO - *01*	6	8
37-251B	**BR** B121830 grey MCO - *02*	5	7
37-251C	**BR** B229637 light grey MCO - *06*	5	7
37-253	**BR** B24809 grey W - *not made*	NA	NA
37-253	**BR** B34807 grey W - *00*	6	8
37-253A	**BR** B25311 grey W - *03*	6	8
(37-225Z)	**BR** B203500 grey W Sp Edn (*ex-ModelZone set see table 12b*) - *07*	7	NA
37-252	**BR** ADB562927 olive green ZHV - *99*	6	8
37-252A	**BR** B77701 olive green ZHV - not *made*	NA	NA
37-252B	**BR** B561754 brown - *06*	5	7
37-252C	**BR** B574829 brown MXV - *08*	5	7
37-252D	**BR** B577541 brown MXV - *10*	5	7
37-254	**BR** B266298 brown W Coal - *not made*	NA	NA
37-254	**BR** B564872 brown W Coal - *00*	6	8
37-254A	**BR** B564872 brown W Coal - *not made*	NA	NA
37-254A	**BR** B561754 brown W Coal - *03*	6	8

* No 'A' on box label.

W12d. 16T Pressed Steel Mineral (B) (1999)

With end door. Ends look as if they have been pressed out of a single sheet of steel.

37-375	**BR** B100768 grey - *99*	6	8
37-375A	**BR** B101676 grey - *01*	6	8
37-375B	**BR** B241057 grey - *03*	6	8
37-377	**BR** B100245 grey W - *00*	6	8
37-377A	**BR** B38751 grey W - *03*	6	8
37-377B	**BR** B24890 grey W - *08*	5	6
37-377C	**BR** B61926 grey - *08*	5	7
37-377D	**BR** B80220 grey - *09*	5	7
37-377E	**BR** B82688 grey W - *09*	5	7
37-377F	**BR** B100925 grey W - *10*	5	7
37-376	**MoT** 3308 brown - *not made*	NA	NA
37-376	**MoT** 33011 brown - *99*	6	8
37-376A	**MoT** 3327 brown - *03*	6	8
37-376B	**MoT** 33322 brown - *10*	NA	NA

W12e. Mineral Mixed Wagon Set (B) (2006)

-	**BR** B84198 grey W top flaps	7	NA
-	**BR** B88430 grey W no top flaps	7	NA
-	**BR** B203500 grey W top flaps	7	NA
37-225Z	above set of three wagons Sp Edn 504 (ModelZone) - *06*	NA	24

W13a. 13T Steel Sand Tippler Wagon (B) (1999)

BR steel sand tipper wagon [W13a]

37-351	**BR** B746609 grey Sand - *99*	6	8
37-351A	**BR** B746576 pale grey Sand - *02*	6	8
37-353	**BR** B746548 grey W Sand tare 9-6 - *02*	6	8
37-353A	**BR** B746548 (smaller) grey W Sand tare 7-9 - *02*	6	8
37-354	**BR** B746576 light grey Sand - *not made*	NA	NA
37-354	**BR** DB746638 light grey ZCO - *07*	5	7
37-354A	**BR** B746724 grey - *09*	5	6
37-354B	**BR** B746777 grey - *not made*	NA	NA
37-354B	**BR** B746674 grey - *10*	5	6
37-350	**BR** B746752 brown Sand - *not made?*	NA	NA
37-350	**BR** B746591 brown Sand - *99*	6	8
37-350A	**BR** B746736 brown Sand - *02*	6	8
37-352	**BR** B746426 brown W Sand - *00*	6	8
37-352A	**BR** B746548 brown W Sand - *02*	6	8
37-355	**BR** KDB746058 brown Sand - *07*	5	7
37-355A	**BR** B746350 brown Sand - *09*	5	6
37-355B	**BR** B746103 brown - *10*	5	7

W13b. 27T Steel 'Tippler' Wagon (B) (1998)

Small standard size steel mineral wagon with no doors at all.

37-275	**BR** B381500 grey Iron Ore - *98*	7	9
37-275A**	**BR** B381934 grey Iron Ore - *01*	6	8
37-275B	**BR** B383560 grey Iron Ore - *03*	6	8

37-275C	**BR** B382833 grey Iron Ore - *08*	5	6
37-375D	**BR** B386369 grey Iron Ore - *08*	5	6
37-275E	**BR** B381818 grey Iron Ore - *10*	5	7
37-277	**BR** B383476 grey W Iron Ore - *00*	6	8
37-277A	**BR** B380005 grey W Iron Ore - *02*	6	8
37-276	**BR** B381293 grey Chalk - *98*	7	9
37-276A	**BR** B382888 grey Chalk - *02*	6	8
37-276B	**BR** B380510 grey Chalk - *10*	5	7
37-278	**BR** B381366 grey W Chalk tare 7-8 - *00*	6	8
37-278A	**BR** B381366* grey W Chalk tare 7-4 - *02*	6	8

* Larger numbers. ** No 'A' on the box.

W14. 16T Slope-Sided Steel 'Tippler' (B) (2001)

37-400A	**BSCO** 9426 grey - *03*	6	8
37-400	**BSCO** BSCO20142 grey - *01*	6	8
37-401	**BSCO** BSCO20068 grey W - *01*	6	8
37-401A	**BSCO** BSCO9446 grey W - *03*	6	8

W15a. 16T Slope-Sided Pressed Steel Mineral (B) (2001)

16 ton slope-sided steel mineral wagon - 'Denaby' [W15a]

37-425K	**'Charles Roberts'** 4 brown Sp Edn (BCC) - *04*	10	12
37-427	**'Denaby'** 9151 black - *04*	10	12
37-425	**BR** B197525 grey - *01*	6	8
37-425A	**BR** B8707 grey - *03*	6	8
37-426	**BR** MoT23743 brown - *not made*	NA	NA
37-426	**BR** MoT23768 brown - *01*	6	8
37-426A	**BR** MoT31763 brown - *not made*	NA	NA
37-426A	**BR** MoT24000 brown - *03*	6	8
37-426B	**MoT** 23866 brown - *10*	5	7

W15b. 16T Slope-Side Riveted Steel Mineral (B) (2001)

37-450	**BR** B11816 grey - *not made*	NA	NA
37-450	**BR** B8128 grey - *01*	6	8
37-450A	**BR** B11532 grey - *03*	6	8
37-451	**MWT** 11532 brown - *01*	6	8
37-451A	**MWT** 9512 brown - *04*	6	8
37-451B	**MWT** 9505 brown - *10*	6	8

Steel Box Open Wagons

W16a. LNER High-Sided Steel Wagon Type 1 (B) (2010)

The dimples, seen on the sides and ends of wagons in this table, accommodate rings on the inside of the wagon, to which ropes could be tied when securing a load.

38-325	**BR** E480768 brown (early livery) - *10*	6	8
38-326	**BR** E480215 brown (late livery) - *10*	6	8

W16b. LNER High-Sided Steel Wagon Type 2 (B) (2010)

The side doors on this type of wagon were made of steel and there were no dimples in the sides of the wagons.

38-327	**BR** E281227 brown (early livery) - *10*	6	8
38-328	**BR** E281604 brown (late livery) - *10*	6	8

W16c. LNER High-Sided Steel Wagon Type 3 (B) (2010)

The side doors on this wagon type were made of wooden planks (six planks on iron straps).

38-359	**NE** 278785 grey - *10*	6	8

W17. OCA Steel Drop-Side Open Wagon (B) (2007)

38-055	**BR** Departmental 112115 grey+yellow - *07*	10	13
38-056	**BRe Rft** 112342 red - *07*	10	13
38-056A	**BR Rft** 112391 red - *10*	12	15

Railfreight OCA steel drop-side open wagon [W17]

38-057	**EWS** 112256 maroon+yellow - *07*	10	13
38-055Z	**BR S&T** KDC112182 red+yellow Sp Edn (*Model Rail*) - *10*	10	13

W18. MTA Open Box Mineral Wagon (B) (2005)

38-050	**EWS** 395112 maroon+yellow - *not made*	NA	NA
38-050	**EWS** 365154* maroon+yellow - *05*	6	8
38-050A	**EWS** 395118 maroon+yellow - *09*	7	9
38-051	**EWS** 395090 maroon+yellow W - *09*	7	9

* an erroneous number.

W19a. MFA Open Box Mineral Wagon (2002)

This model was based on a 17'6" open wagon.

33-025	**EWS** 391102 blue+yellow (ex-Mainline) - *02*	6	8
33-026	**EWS** 391572 maroon+yellow - *02*	6	8
33-027	**EWS** 391070 grey (ex-Rft Coal) - *02*	6	8
33-028	**EWS** 391223 black (ex-LoadHaul) - *02*	6	8

W19b. MFA Open Box Mineral Wagon (B) (2004)

Features new chassis upgrade.

38-010	**EWS** 391170 maroon W - *04*	5	7
38-010A	**EWS** 391572 maroon W - *06*	5	7
38-010B	**EWS** 391257 maroon W - *09*	6	8
38-011	**EWS** ex-Mainline - *not made*	NA	NA
38-011	**EWS** 391225 black ex-LoadHaul - *04*	5	7
38-011A	**EWS** 391222 black ex-LoadHaul - *09*	5	7
38-012	**EWS** 391077 dark grey+yellow ex-Rft - *04*	5	7
38-013	**EWS** 391374 maroon W - *09*	6	8
38-013A	**EWS** 391271 maroon W - *10*	6	8

W20a. MEA 45t Steel Box Body Mineral Wagon (1995)

b = Barry WRD motifs

33-375	**BR Rft** Coal 391045 grey+yellow b - *95*	7	9
33-375A	**BR Rft** Coal 391014 grey+yellow b - *96*	7	9
33-376	**BR Rft** Coal 391010 grey+yellow - *95*	7	9
33-376A	**BR Rft** Coal 391042 grey+yellow - *96*	7	9
33-375B	**Transrail** 391008 grey+yellow W b - *01*	6	8
33-377	**BR** M391158 blue - *96*	7	9
33-379	**BR** M391229 black+white - *97*	7	9
33-378	**Mainline** M391139 blue+yellow - *96*	7	9
33-378A	**Mainline** 391143 blue W - *02*	6	8
33-380	**EWS** Wagon ews 391262 maroon - *98*	7	9
33-380A	**EWS** Wagon ews 391250 maroon - *99*	6	8
33-380B	**EWS** Wagon ews 391444 maroon - *02*	6	8
33-380C	**EWS** Wagon ews 391389 maroon - *03*	5	7

W20b. MEA 45t Steel Box Mineral (B) (2005)

38-061	**Mainline** M391155 blue - *05*	5	7
38-060	**EWS** 391327 maroon+yellow W - *05*	5	8
38-062	**EWS** 391374 maroon+yellow W - *09*	5	8

W21a. PNA 34T Ballast/Spoil 5 Rib Wagon (B) (2007)

Railtrack PNA ballast and spoil wagon [W21a]

38-095	**Railtrack** CAIB3627 green – *07*	5	7
38-095A	**Railtrack** CAIB3727 green - *08*	6	7
38-095B	**Railtrack** CAIB3693 green - *10*	6	8

W21b. PNA 34T Ballast/Spoil 7 Rib Wagon (B) (2007)

38-100	**Railtrack** CAIB3619 green - *07*	5	7
38-100A	**Railtrack** CAIB3603 green - *08*	6	8

W22. ZKA 34t Limpet Ballast Wagon (B) (2006)

38-085	**BR** DC390153 grey+yellow - *06*	5	8
38-085A	**BR** DC390226 grey+yellow - *07*	6	8
38-085B	**BR** DC390312 grey+yellow - *10*	7	9
38-086	**BR** DC390168 grey - *06*	5	8
38-086A	**BR** DC390190 grey - *10*	7	9
38-087	**BR** DC390268 black+orange - *06*	5	8

W23. POA/MKA 46t Box Mineral Wagon (B) (2005)

37-552	**ARC** TRL5323 yellow - *05*	6	8
37-552A	**ARC Tiger** TRL5321 yellow - *09*	6	8
37-550	**Tiger** TRL5157 pale grey - *05*	6	8
37-550A	**Tiger** TRL5377 pale grey - *09*	7	9
37-551	**Yeoman** TRL5352 light grey - *05*	6	8
37-554	**Yeoman** Tiger TRL5154 grey POA - *05*	6	8
37-553	**Loadhaul** 393030 black+orange MKA - *05*	6	8

W24. POA/SSA 51t Iron & Steel Scrap Wagon (1995)

lsb = later style body. 'SR' stands for 'Standard Railfreight'

33-425	**SR** 470068 pale blue POA - *not made*	NA	NA
33-425	**SR** RLS5098 pale blue POA - *97*	7	9
33-430	**SR** RLS5068 pale blue POA lsb SR - *99*	6	8
33-430A	**SR** RLS5091 pale blue POA lsb SR - *04*	5	7
33-432	**SR** 470005 pale blue SSA lsb SR - *not made*	NA	NA

'Standard Railfreight' iron and steel industry scrap wagon [W24]

33-426	**SR** 470058 pale blue SSA - *not made*	NA	NA
33-426	**SR** 470096 pale blue SSA - *95*	7	9
33-426A	**SR** 470034 pale blue W SSA - *99*	6	8
33-431	**SR** 470005 pale blue SSA lsb - *99*	6	8
33-431A	**SR** 470181 pale blue SSA lsb - *not made*	NA	NA
33-431A	**SR** 470161 pale blue SSA lsb - *04*	5	7
33-433	**SR** 470181 pale blue SSA lsb - *not made*	NA	NA
33-434	**SR** RLS5059 pale blue SSA lsb - *07*	6	8
33-435	**SR** 470014 pale blue W SSA - *09*	6	8
33-435A	**SR** 470014 pale blue W SSA - *10*	6	8

Open & Covered Hopper Wagons

W25a. 24T Ore Hopper Wagon (ex- Mainline) (1990)

33-252	**'BISC'** 665 black - *92*	10	12
33-254	**'South Durham Steel'** 1010 black - *97*	10	12
33-255	'Richard **Thomas'** 9451 brown - *97*	10	12
33-252	**LMS** grey - *not made*	NA	NA
33-250	**BR** P209938 grey Iron Ore - *90*	12	15
33-251	**BR** B435906 brown - *90*	8	11
33-253	undecorated light grey - *91*	6	9

W25b. 24T Ore Hopper Wagon (B) (2002)

37-504	**'Millom Ironworks'** 261 brown - *07*	7	9
37-501	**'RT & Co.'** 2016 brown - *02*	8	10
37-503	'Richard **Thomas'** 9452 brown - *06*	7	9
37-500	**BR** B437491 grey Iron Ore - *02*	6	8
37-500A	**BR** B437491? grey Iron Ore - *made?*	NPG	NPG
37-502	**BR** B436166 grey Iron Ore - *06*	5	7
37-502A	**BR** B435339L grey Iron Ore - *09*	5	7
37-502B	**BR** B436549 grey Iron Ore - *10*	5	7
37-505	**BR Civil Engineers** DP101453 red ZEO - *10*	5	7

W26a. HEA/HSA/HBA 46t Hopper Wagon (ex-Mainline) (1992)

It is assumed that these are HEAs unless otherwise indicated.

33-550	**BR Rft** 360075 brown HSA - *92*	8	10
33-550A	**BR** 360234 brown W HBA - *02*	7	9
33-551	**BRe Rft** 361862 red+grey HEA - *92*	8	10
33-551A	**BRe Rft** 360694 red+grey W - *94, 01*	8	9
33-551B	**BRe Rft** 361992 red+grey HSA has Scottish Saltaire flag marking - *94*	8	10
33-551C	**BRe Rft** 360320 red+grey W HEA - *02*	8	9
33-551Z	**BRe Rft** 36? red+grey Sp Edn (Pennine Models) - *01*	10	12
33-552	**Railfreight** 360601 grey+black HEA - *93*	8	10
33-552A	**Railfreight** Coal 361554 grey+yellow W HES - *02*	7	9
33-554	**Transrail** 361874 grey - *96*	8	10
33-553	**Mainline** 360955 blue - *97*	8	10
33-556	**ex-Mainline** 360940 blue W graffiti one side only - *03*	6	8

Graffiti covered HEA hopper wagon in Mainline livery [W26a]

33-555	**EWS** Wagon ews 361870 maroon - *98*	8	10
33-555A	**EWS** Wagon ews 361328 maroon - *99*	7	9
33-555B	**EWS** Wagon ews 360677 maroon - *02*	7	9
33-555C	**EWS** Wagon ews 360042 maroon - *03*	6	8

W26b. HEA/HSA 46t Hopper (B) (2004)

Features new chassis upgrade.

38-002	**BR** 360226 brown W HSA - *04*	6	8
38-005	**BR** 360008 brown W HSA - *09*	7	9
38-005A	**BR** 361257 brown W HSA - *10*	7	9
38-001	**BR Rft** 391493 red+grey HEA - *04*	6	8
38-006	**BR Rft** 391481 red+grey HEA - *09*	7	9
38-006A	**BR Rft** 360166 red+grey HEA - *10*	7	9
38-003	**Mainline** 360643 blue HEA - *04*	6	8
38-000	**EWS** 360392 maroon W HEA - *04*	6	8
38-004	**EWS** 960392 maroon W HEA - *not made*	NA	NA
38-004	**EWS** 361859 maroon W HEA - *07*	6	8

W27a. CEA 46t Covered Hopper Wagon (2000)

33-575	**LoadHaul** 361845 orange+black - *not made*	NA	NA
33-575	**LoadHaul** 361841 orange+black - *00*	7	9
33-575A	**LoadHaul** 361845 orange+black W - *02*	7	9
33-576	**EWS** 360791 maroon - *not made*	NA	NA
33-576	**EWS** 360726 maroon - *00*	7	9
33-576A	**EWS** 361024 maroon - *01*	7	9
33-576B	**EWS**360955 maroon - *03*	6	8
33-577	**EWS** 361024 maroon W - *not made*	NA	NA
33-577	**EWS** 361896 maroon W - *02*	7	9

W27b. CEA 46t Covered Hopper (B) (2006)

Features new chassis upgrade.

38-021	**LoadHaul** 360663 black + orange - *06*	6	8
38-020	**EWS** 360726 maroon - *not made*	NA	NA
38-020	**EWS** 361087 maroon - *06*	6	8

W28. BRT 35T Bulk Grain Wagon (1994)

33-125	**BRT 'Grainflow'** BRT7690 green+grey - *94*	10	12
33-127A	**BRT 'Grainflow'** BRT7785 green+grey - *97*	10	12
33-130	**BRT 'Haig'** 5864 blue W - *02*	9	11
33-127	**BRT 'Johnnie Walker'** 5820 blue - *?*	10	12
33-127	**BRT 'Johnnie Walker'** 5819 blue - *94*	10	12
33-126A	'The **Maltsters Association'** 6026 yellow - *96*	10	12
33-126	**BRT 'Vat 69'** 5819 blue - *94*	10	12
33-129	**BRT 'White Horse'** 5818 blue - *97*	10	12
33-125A	**BRT** 7617 brown - *96*	9	11
33-125B	**BRT** 7586 brown - *06*	9	11
33-128	**BRT** 7580 grey - *94*	9	12

W29. 20T/22T 'Presflo' Bulk Powder Wagon (B) (2009)

These are very detailed models. Bachmann have included variations in their tooling which include either one vacuum cylinder (20T) or two (22T). Other differences will be found in buffers, brake levers and vacuum discharge pipes. Some also have an additional notice board on the solebars.

BR 'Presflo' leased to Blue Circle Cement [W29]

38-270	**'Blue Circle'** B873364 red-brown 22T - *10*	7	9
38-260	**'Bulk Tunnel Cement'** B888113 red-brown 20T - *10*	7	9
38-271	**'Cement Marketing Company'** ('Blue Circle') PF100 grey 22T - *10*	7	9
38-261	**Bulk Cement** ('Crown Cement') B888229 red-brown 20T - *10*	7	9
-	**'Blue Circle'** B873150 red-brown W 22T	8	NA
-	as above but numbered B887879	8	NA
-	as above but numbered B888803	8	NA
38-270Z	above 3 wagons Sp Edn 512 (Hattons) - *10*	NA	31
-	**Bulk Cement** B873110 brown	9	NA
-	as above but numbered B873344	9	NA
-	as above but numbered B873295	9	NA
38-275Y	above 3 wagons Sp Edn 504 (Lord & Butler)* - *10*	NA	31

* Lord & Butler also offered these weathered, a finish provided at the shop and so, strictly speaking - code 3.

Tank Wagons

33-500 Series Tank Wagons Guide

The numbering of small tank wagons became a little confusing and so we provide here an index to show where you will find models numbered 33-500 to 33-512:

cat. no.	table				
				33-505	W30a
33-500	W30a	33-501A	W30b	33-505A	W30d
33-500A	W30b	33-502	W30c	33-506	W30b
33-500W	W30c	33-502A	W30b	33-507	W30b
33-500X	W30c	33-502B	W30c	33-508	W30c
33-500Z	W30c	33-503	W30c	33-509	W30c
33-500Z	W30c	33-504	W30b	33-510	W30d
33-501	W30a	33-504A	W30c	33-512	W30d

W30a. 14T Tank Wagon (Early Type 1) (ex-Mainline) (1990)

This model has broad ladders (8mm across), an 8' gantry (32mm long) and 'kettle' manhole cap (9mm across) either side of which there are two small projections (a hand wheel type control valve and a ring). The end stanchions are linked together by a horizontal wire which also ties them down to the frame. It was made using the original Mainline tooling.

33-505	**'Castrol Oil'** 131 green - *92*	15	20
33-501	**'Esso'** 3123 black - *90*	20	25
33-500	**'Royal Daylight'** 1534 red - *92*	15	20

W30b. 14T Tank Wagon (Early Type 2) (1992)

This second version has an 8' gantry (32mm long) and 'kettle' manhole cap (8mm across) but no ladders. The hand wheel control valve and ring projections are again either side of the cap but the wheel is extended higher than with type 1. The end stanchions are again linked together by a horizontal wire which also ties them down to the frame. This is the 2nd type of tank wagon based on the former Mainline tooling.

33-502A	**'Berry Wiggins'** 106 black - *95*	14	16
33-502A	as above but name missing from tank sides (misprint) - *95*	NPG	NPG
33-500A	**'BP'** 22 silver - *94*	12	14
33-507	**'DCL'** 241 silver - *96*	14	16
33-504	**'Fina'** 135 silver - *92*	10	13
33-506	**'Shell Electrical Oils'** 3102 dark brown - *94*	14	18
33-501A	**'Swindon United Gas Co.'** 5 maroon - *96*	18	23

W30c. 14T Tank Wagon (Early Type 3) (1991)

This third version of the 14T tank wagon, from the Mainline tooling, has a 'kettle' manhole cap (7mm across) but no ladders or gantry. Beside the cap is a hand wheel control valve at the top of a column.. This must have been particularly vulnerable as wagons are often found with this broken off short. The end stanchions are again linked together by a horizontal wire which also ties them down to the frame. Slimline couplings are now being used.

33-500W	(see 33-500Z in table W30e and footnote)	NA	NA
33-502B	**'Berry Wiggins'** 116 silver - *98*	10	12
33-509	**'BOCM'** B7 brown - *98*	10	12
33-500X	**'Briggs'** 18 black Sp Edn 750 (Harburn Hobbies) - *99*	20	30
33-500Y	**'Briggs'** 38 black Sp Edn 750 (Harburn Hobbies) - *98*	30	50
	'Briggs' 20 black (see table W30f)	NA	NA
33-500Z	**'Esso'** 1634 buff Dalkeith posters Sp End 750 (Harburn Hobbies) - *98*	18	25
33-502	**'NCB'** Tar 597 black - *92*	18	25
33-504A	**'Trent Oil Products'** 6 buff+brown - *97*	15	18
33-508	**'The Yorkshire Tar Distillers'** 597 black - *98*	15	18
33-503	undecorated light grey - *91*	8	10

W30d. 14T Tank Wagon (Early Type 4) (1998)

This fourth version of the 14T tank wagon from the Mainline tooling has ladders which are much narrower (4.5mm), a 6' gantry (23mm) each side of the manhole the cover of which is flat rather than domed like the others. The cover appeares more detailed. It too has just a hand wheel control valve projection beside it. The end stanchions again are linked together by a horizontal wire which also ties them down to the frame.

33-505A	**'Brotherton'** 908 blue - *98*	25	30
33-510	**'M.O.S.'** 195 buff - *98*	17	22
33-512	**'Shell BP Lubricating Oil'** A7287 black - *99*	20	27

W30e. 14T Tank Wagon (Early Type 5) (1999)

The fifth and final original version of the model has a raised manhole with a domed cap (10mm across). It has a short projection beside it that looks like a shortened hand wheel control valve column. However, the main difference between this and the other four early model types is that the tank is held in place by cross stays.

33-676	**'BP Ethyl'** 1448 buff - *99*	12	15
33-675W	**'Briggs'** 20 black *(see 37-675W)*	-	-
33-677	**'Esso'** 981 black - *99*	17	22
33-675Y	**'Kalchester'** 101 red Sp Edn 500 (TMC) - *00*	30	40
33-675Z	**'Manchester & Sheffield Tar Works'** 19 black Sp Edn 500 (Rails) (numbered 33-657) - *99*	30	40
37-675A	**'Mobil'** 5294 black - *09*	6	8

14 ton tank wagon - 'Power' [W30e]

33-675X	'Michael **Nairn'** 503 yellow *(see 37-675X)*	-	-
33-675	**'Power'** 115 silver - *99*	12	15

33-500Z*	**'Sheffield Chemical Co.'** 33 black Sp Edn 500 (Rails) - *00*	25	37

* This was the number carried on the box although it had already been used on another tank wagon. Bachmann literature also recorded this tank wagon as 33-500W. To make matters worse, it was one of a number of tank wagons given 33-XXX numbers that should have been in the 37XXX series as they were to Blue Riband quality. It should have been 37-675V but this has now been used on something else.

W30f. 14T Tank Wagon (Revised Type 3) (B) (2000)

This is the Blue Riband version of the early Type 3 and so it has a 7mm domed manhole cap, a tall hand wheel control valve and horizontal stays tieing the end stanchions together. The body appears to be from the old tooling and the chassis has had two modifications. The brake handles are now a separate moulding and the couplings are in NEM pockets allowing them to be easily changed.

37-651	**'Bitumuls'** 12 black - *00*	15	23
37-679	**'BP'** 5075, buff - *03*	9	11
37-679R	**'BP Shell'** 5075, buff * - *05*	8	10
37-653	**'Burmah'** 118 black - *02*	12	15
37-652	'Joseph **Crosfield & Sons'** 3 blue - *00*	12	15
37-650	**'ICI'** 315 maroon - *not made*	NA	NA
37-650	**'ICI'** 313 maroon - *00*	14	18
-	**'ICI'** 313 maroon, ex-set - *04*	14	NA
37-656	**'ICI'** 159 dark blue-green - *05*	5	7
37-650V	**'Lane Brothers'** 101 black Sp Edn 500 (Warley 2008) - *08*	30	50
37-650W	**'Lane Brothers'** 102 black W Sp Edn 500 (Warley 2008) - *08*	30	65
37-675	**'Mobil'** 1624 black - *00*	15	25
37-675A	**'Mobil'** 5294 black - *09*	6	8
37-675B	**'Mobil'** 5291 black - *10*	6	8
37-659	**'National Benzole'** 654 yellow? - *not made*	NA	NA
37-660	**'National Fertilizers'** 501, brown - *10*	6	8
37-655	**'Pratts Spirit'** 1613 buff - *02*	15	20
37-650K	'Charles **Roberts'** 9876 buff Sp Edn (BCC) - *05*	10	12
37-654	**'Ronuk'** 38 black+blue - *02*	15	20
37-657	**'Rothervale'** 48 black - *05*	8	10
37-679A	'Jas. **Williamson & Son'** 21 buff - *05*	8	10

W30g. 14T Tank Wagon (Revised Type 4) (B) (2000)

Here we have the Blue Riband version of the early Type 4 tank wagon but with the modified chassis as described above. So it has narrow ladders (4.5mm wide), a 6' gantry (23mm) each side of the flat 7.5mm detailed manhole cover, a hand wheel control valve projection beside it and horizontal stays tieing the end stanchions together.

37-690Y	**Brotherton** 900, blue+red, Sp Edn 500 (Warley 2007) - *07*	35	40
37-690Z	**Brotherton** 806, red-brown, Sp Edn 500 (Warley 2007) - *07*	35	40
37-656	**ICI** 159, dark blue-green - *05*	5	7
37-500Z*	**Shell-Mex-BP** A5281, Sp Edn 500 (Pennine Models) - *02*	25	34

* Box marked '37-500Z'. The label was stuck over one for '24T Hopper BR Grey'. Was this due to a change in the order?

W30h. 14T Tank Wagon (Type 4.5) (B) (2009)

This is the same as Blue Riband Type 4 but has no ladders and may carry logo boards mounted on its sides.

37-659	**National Benzole** 755, silver - *09*	6	8
37-659A	**National Benzole** 757, silver - *10*	6	8

W30i. 14T Tank Wagon (Revised Type 5) (B) (2000)

We come finally to the Blue Riband version of the large cap tank (Type 5). It has the Type 5 body on the modified chassis with its separate brake handles and coupling NEM pockets. So it has the raised 10mm manhole cover and small hand wheel control valve column and cross stays.

37-676	**'Acme Dominion'** 25 lemon - *00*	12	15
37-679	**'BP Shell'** 5075 buff - *02*	9	11
37-679R	**'BP Shell'** 5075 buff * - *05*	8	10
37-675W *	**'Briggs'** 20 black Sp Edn (Harburn Hobbies) (33-675W) - *00*	15	25
37-677	**'Carburine'** Motor Spirit 6 buff - *01*	12	15
37-682	**'Crosfield Chemicals'** 129 dark green - *10*	10	12
37-680	**'Esso'** 1210 silver - *02*	12	16
37-680R	**'Esso'** 1210 silver * - *05*	8	10
37-680	**'Fina'** 136 silver - *05*	8	10
37-680A	**'Fina'** 136 silver - *05*	8	10

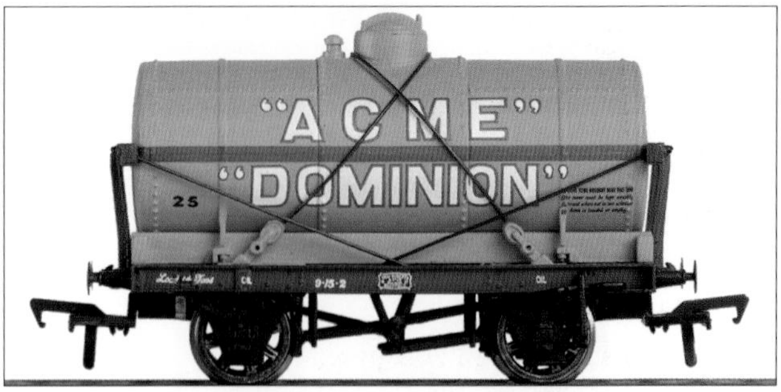

14 ton tank wagon - 'Ace Dominion' [W30i]

37-658	**'Fina'** 140 black - *09*	6	8
37-658A	**'Fina'** 141 black - *10*	6	8
37-679	**'Lancaster Tar'** - *not made*	NA	NA
37-675S	**'Lane Bros'** 186 black Sp Edn 500 (Warley 2009) - *09*	15	22
37-675T	**'Lane Bros'** 187 black W Sp Edn 500 (Warley 2009) - *09*	12	20
37-650X	**'Lee & Green'** 1 blue-green Sp Edn 750 (*British Railway Modelling*) - *02*	25	30
37-650Y	**'Lindsey & Kesteven Chemical Co.'** 2 black Sp Edn 500 (B&H Models) - *02*	14	17
37-650Z	'Morris **Little's Sheep Dips'** 3 black Sp Edn 500 (B&H Models) - *01*	14	17
-	above two wagons - *03*	NA	24
37-675ZZ	**'Major & Co.'** 87 brown (Only one 'Z' printed on the box) Sp Edn (Warley 2005) - *05*	30	42
37-675Z	**'Midland Tar Distillers'** 278 black Sp Edn 500 (Warley 2004) (no 'Z' on box) - *04*	40	55
37-675X	'Michael **Nairn & Co.'** 503 yellow Sp Edn (Harburn Hobbies) - *00*	14	17
37-681	**'OCO'** (Olympic Cake & Oil) 202 brown - *07*	10	12
-	**'Sheffield Chemical Co.'** 33 black (see table W30e)	NA	NA
37-678	**'United Molasses'** 13 brown - *02*	12	15
37-683	'John **Robinson & Co,'** 3 brown - *10*	6	8
37-675Y	**War Office A6** 86, buff, Sp Edn 504 (Castle Trains) - *09*	6	8
37-675V	'The **West Midlands Sugar Co.'** 2 dark blue Sp Edn (Warley Show 2006) - *06*	30	42

* It seems these two wagons, in error, were sent instead of 'Lancaster Tar' and 'Fina' and so were given an 'R' suffix and sold as new models after the boxes had been re-labelled. Early releases from the store were not re-labelled and so do not carry the 'R' suffix and some retailers added the suffix by hand. 'Lancaster Tar' was then dropped and replaced by 'Jas. Williamson & Son'.

W30j. 14T Tank Traffic Classics Sets (Mixed) (1997)

Using pre-Blue Riband tank wagons.

Set of 3 'Shell BP' 14 ton tank wagons [W30j]

(33-525)	**'Shell BP'** A5066 pale grey	8	NA
(33-525)	**'Shell BP'** 4886 black	8	NA
(33-525)	**'Shell'** 4417 silver	8	NA
33-525	Tank Traffic above set of 3 - *97*	NA	30
(33-525Z)	**'Esso'** 301 buff	10	NA
(33-525Z)	**'Power Ethyl'** 116 green	10	NA
(33-525Z)	**'Royal Daylight'** 1531 red	10	NA
33-525Z	Tank Traffic above set of 3 Sp Edn 500 (Alton Model Centre) - *98*	NA	35
(33-526)	**'National Benzol'** 734 silver	9	NA
(33-526)	**'National Benzol'** 2023 black	9	NA
(33-526)	**'National Benzol Mixture'** 576 buff	9	NA
33-526*	Tank Traffic above set of 3 - *98*	NA	32

(33-527)	**'Esso'** 1829 black	8	NA
(33-527)	**'Esso'** 2232 silver	8	NA
(33-527)	**'Esso'** 303 buff	8	NA
33-527*	Tank Traffic above set of 3 - *98*	NA	30
(33-528)	**'Berry Wiggins'** 150 black	10	NA
(33-528)	**'Berry Wiggins'** 119 silver	10	NA
(33-528)	**'Berry Wiggins'** 109 black	10	NA
33-528	Tank Traffic above set of 3 - *99*	NA	35

* The factory list gives the set number to the first wagon listed and a '1' suffix to the second and a '2' suffix to the third.

W30k. Sets of 14T Tank Wagons (B) (2002)

Using Blue Riband tank wagons.

-	**'BP'** A3472 silver twin logos	10	NA
-	**'BP'** 36 silver single logo boards	10	NA
-	**'BP/Shell'** 1223 silver, words	10	NA
37-665	set of above 3 wagons - *02*	NA	35
-	**'Esso'** 1945 black W	9	NA
-	**'Esso'** 1343 black W	9	NA
-	**'Esso'** 1921 black W	9	NA
37-666	set of above 3 wagons - *05*	NA	32
-	**'Esso'** 1485 black W large cap	8	NA
-	**'Esso'** 2338 black W small cap	8	NA
-	**'Esso'** 2184 black W small cap	8	NA
37-666A	set of above 3 wagons - *06*	NA	29
-	**'Esso'** 1231 black W large cap	7	NA
-	**'Esso'** 1855 black W small cap	7	NA
-	**'Esso'** 1869 black W small cap	7	NA
37-666B	set of above 3 wagons - *09**	NA	26
-	**'Esso'** 2878 silver W large cap	9	NA
-	**'Esso'** 303 silver W small cap	9	NA
-	**'Esso'** 3060 silver W gantry + ladder	9	NA
37-668	set of above 3 weathered wagons - *05*	NA	32
-	**'Shell'** BP A4294 black W large cap	8	NA
-	**'Shell'** BP 5101 black W large cap	8	NA
-	**'Shell'** BP 3973 black W gantry + ladder	8	NA
37-669Z	set of above 3 wagons Sp Edn (ModelZone) - *11*	NA	30

Set of 3 'Lion' 14 ton tank wagons [W30k]

-	**'Lion'** C15 black W	9	NA
-	**'Lion'** C24 black W	9	NA
-	**'Lion'** C66 black W	9	NA
37-665Z	set of above 3 weathered wagons Sp Edn 250 (Hereford Model Centre) - *07*	NA	32
-	**'Shell BP'** 3971 black small cap	8	NA
-	**'Shell BP'** 5103 black ladders	8	NA
-	**'Shell BP'** A4282 black large cap	8	NA
37-669	set of above 3 wagons - *06*	NA	29
-	**'Tarmac'** 58 black W large cap	7	NA
-	**'Tarmac'** 60 black W large cap	7	NA
-	**'Tarmac'** 66 black W large cap	7	NA
37-670	set of above 3 wagons - *09*	NA	24
-	**'Tarmac'** 55 black W large cap	7	NA
-	**'Tarmac'** 68 black W large cap	7	NA
-	**'Tarmac'** 69 black W large cap	7	NA
37-670A	set of above 3 wagons - *10*	NA	26

-	**'War Office A6'** 83 buff (Castle Trains)	10	NA
-	**'War Office A6'** 84 buff (Castle Trains)	10	NA
-	**'War Office A6'** 85 buff (Castle Trains)	10	NA
37-675Y	above three models as a set Sp Edn 504 (Castle Trains) - *09*	NA	28

* This set was released early in 2009 in the standard all-blue packaging and then reissued at the end of 2009 in the new blue and red box.

W31. 45t TTA 'Monobloc' Tank Wagon (B) (2005)

37-575M	**'Amoco'** PR58123 pale grey Sp Edn 250 (Frizinghall Model Railways) - *08*	10	13
37-575M/W	**'Amoco'** PR58123 pale grey W Sp Edn 250 (Frizinghall Model Railways) - *08*	10	13

'BP' TTA 'Monobloc' tank wagon [W31]

37-581	**'BP'** BPO53724 black (gas oil) - *06*	6	8
37-575	**'BP'** BPO53774 green, petroleum logos - *05*	7	9
37-575A	**'BP'** BPO37086 green, petroleum logos - *10*	7	9
37-575R	**'BP' Chemicals** 5557 grey W Sp Edn (Cheltenham Model Centre) - *07*	10	12
37-575N	**'BP' Jet A1** BPO60880 green aviation fuel Sp Edn 500 (Model Rail) - *07*	10	12
37-575P	**'BP' Jet A1** BPO60586 green aviation fuel Sp Edn 500 (Model Rail) - *07*	10	12
37-575Q	**'BP' Jet A1** BPO60873 green aviation fuel Sp Edn 500 (Model Rail) - *07*	10	12
37-576	**'Esso'** 57575 light grey BRT - *05*	7	9
37-576A	**'Esso'** 5961 light grey BRT - *10*	7	9
37-576X	**'Esso'** 5925 pale grey W Sp Edn 504 (ModelZone) - *07*	10	12
37-576Y	**'Esso'** 5959 pale grey W Sp Edn 504 (ModelZone) - *07*	10	12
37-576Z	**'Esso'** 5970 pale grey W Sp Edn 504 (ModelZone) - *07*	10	12
37-576W	Above 3 Esso tank wagons individually boxed - *07*	NA	32
37-582	**'Fina'** 3 silver - *06*	7	9
37-575S	**'Gulf'** 731 grey W Sp Edn (Cheltenham Model Centre) - *07*	10	12
37-578	**'ICI Petrochemicals & Plastics'** 54365 white - *05*	8	10
37-583	**'Mobil'** 57305 pale grey - *09*	7	8
37-583A	**'Mobil'** 57303 pale grey - *10*	7	9
37-577	**'Shell BP'** 67391 light grey - *04*	7	9
37-577A	**'Shell BP'** 582 light grey - *10*	7	9
37-577Z	**'Shell BP'** 5165 black Sp Edn 504 (Hereford Model Centre) - *07*	10	12
37-582A	**'Shell BP'** 3452 black - *10*	7	9
37-575X	**'Shell'** 65537 black W Sp Edn (TMC)* - *05*	10	12
37-575Y	**'Shell'** 65543 black W Sp Edn (TMC)* - *05*	10	12
37-575Z	**'Shell'** 65709 black W Sp Edn (TMC)* - *05*	10	12
37-579	**'Shell'** SUKO60705 pale grey - *05*	7	9
37-580	**'Total'** PR58278 grey Caib - *06*	7	9
C	CC55526 black, Water only	10	12
B	CC55529 black, Water only	10	12
A	CC55530 black, Water only	10	12
D	CC55536 black, Water only	10	12
37-575L	above 4 wagons, Sp Edn 512 (Kernow MRC) - *10*	NA	45

Unbranded Grey

37-575T	56050 W	9	NA
37-575U	56039 W	9	NA
37-575V	56177 W	9	NA
37-575W	56103	9	NA
37-575T	set of above 4 wagons Sp Edn 512 (Kernow MR Centre) - *05*	NA	40

* Initially sold only as a set of the three. ** From a Chipman weed killing train. Individually boxed.

Vans

W32. Covered Lime Van (B) (2004)

A wooden floor 5-plank wagon with a separate roof section in the box.

37-025Y	**'SLB'** 702 grey Sp Edn 500 (Geoffrey Allinson) - *04*	11	13

W33. 10T Covered Salt Wagon (1992)

33-177	**'Chance & Hunt'*** 333 dark brown - *92*	10	12
33-178	**'DCL'** 52 light grey - *02*	9	11
33-180	**'Falk Salt'** 2521 green - *06*	8	10
33-178	**'ICI Salt'** 3781 green blue - *92*	10	12
33-179	**'ICI Salt'** 326 maroon - *06*	8	10
33-179A	**'ICI Fleetwood Salt'** 12 maroon - *09*	5	7
33-177X	**'Leith General Warehousing Co.'** ** 120 red-brown, Sp Edn 500 (Harburn Hobbies) - *03*	10	12
33-177W	**'LGW'** ** 118 red-brown Sp Edn 500 (Harburn Hobbies) - *03*	10	12

Pitched roof van 'North British Storage' [W33]

33-177	**'Mangers Salt'** 180 green - *not made*	NA	NA
33-177	**'Mangers Salt'** 121 green - *02*	9	11
33-177Y	**'North British Storage'** ** 56 grey Sp Edn 500 (Harburn Hobbies) - *03*	10	12
33-176	**'Saxa Salt'** 255 orange-yellow - *92*	10	12
33-176A	**'Saxa Salt'** 251 yellow - *96*	10	12
33-179	**'Shaka Salt'** 168 blue - *92*	10	12
33-182	**'Snowdrift Salt'** 306 light green - *09*	5	7
33-181	**'Stafford Salt Works'** C28 red - *94*	10	12
33-175	**'Stubbs Salt'** 35 maroon - *92*	10	12
33-177Z	**'The Distillers Co.'** ** 46 light grey Sp Edn 500 (Harburn Hobbies) - *03*	11	13
33-180	**'Union Salt'** 2713 grey - *92*	10	12
33-177	**'Winsford Salt'** - *not made*	NA	NA

* sold in a box marked 'Winsford Salt'.** This was based on the 10T covered salt wagon and not an accurate representation of the Scottish grain wagons the models represent. These were in use between 1903 and 1969.

W34. 8T/12T GWR/BR Cattle Wagon (B) (2009)

37-711	**GW** 106881 dark grey - *09*	6	7
37-711A	**GW** 106909 dark grey - *10*	6	7
37-710	**BR** 134209 brown - *not made*	NA	NA
37-710	**BR** B893343 brown - *10*	6	7
37-710A	**BR** B893111 brown - *10*	6	7
37-712	**BR** B893085 brown XP - *10*	6	7
37-712A	**BR** B893268 brown late livery XP - *10*	6	7
-	**GWR** 106699 dark grey W	7	NA
-	**GWR** 106855 dark grey W	7	NA
-	**GWR** 106901 dark grey W	7	NA
37-711Z	above 3 wagons Sp Edn (Hereford Model Centre) - *10*	NA	27
-	**GWR** 106750 dark grey	7	NA
-	**GWR** 106838 dark grey	7	NA
-	**GWR** 106917 dark grey	7	NA
37-711Y	above 3 wagons Sp Edn (Hereford Model Centre) - *10*	NA	27
-	**BR** B893603 brown W	7	NA
-	**BR** B893455 brown W	7	NA
-	**BR** B893682 brown W	7	NA
37-710Z	above 3 Sp Edn 504 (ModelZone) - *09*	NA	26
-	**BR** B893007 brown W	7	NA
-	**BR** B893510 brown W	7	NA
-	**BR** B893370 brown W	7	NA
37-712Z	above 3 wagons Sp Edn 504 (TMC) - *10*	NA	27

W35a. 12T GWR Fruit Van (ex-Mainline) (1991)

33-202	**GW** 134209 dark grey - *94*	8	10
33-202	**LMS** 134209 grey - *not made*	NA	NA
33-201	**BR Fisons** W134195 brown * - *91*	8	10
33-204	**BR** W134265 brown W - *99*	7	9
33-200	**BR** B875274 brown + chalk marks - *90*	8	10
33-203	undecorated light grey - *91*	6	8

* box says BR grey with chalk marks.

W35b. 12T GWR Fruit Van (B) (2001)

GWR fruit van [W35b]

37-751	**GW** 134281 dark grey - *01*	7	9
37-751A	**GW** 134209 dark grey - *02*	7	9
37-751B	**GW** 134330 dark grey - *03*	7	9
37-751C	**GW** 134139 dark grey - *05*	6	8
37-750	**BR** W134143 brown - *01*	7	9
37-750A*	**BR** W134143 brown - *02*	7	9
37-750B	**BR** W134333 brown - *03*	7	9
37-752	**BR** W134330 brown - *05*	6	8
37-754	**BR** W134150 brown - *06*	6	8
37-754A	**BR** W134214 brown - *09*	5	7
37-754B	**BR** W134211 brown - *10*	5	7
(37-726Y)	**BR** W134201 brown W 'Pembroke Dock/ Carmarthen' ex-set of 3 Sp Edn 504 (Modelzone) - *06*	9	NA

W36a. 12T GWR 'Mogo' Van (ex-Mainline) (1991)

33-702	**GW** 126981 dark grey - *94*	8	10
33-704	**GW** 126342 dark grey W - *99*	7	9
33-700	**BR** W126981 brown - *91*	8	10
33-700A	**BR** W126981 brown with chalk marks - *?*	NPG	NPG
33-701	**BR** W126901 dark grey - *91*	14	18
33-703	undecorated light grey - *91*	6	8

W36b. 12T GWR 'Mogo' Van (B) (2001)

37-778	**GW** 127000 dark grey - *06*	6	8
37-778A	**GW** 126450 dark grey - *09*	5	7
37-778B	**GW** 123955 dark grey - *10*	5	7
37-775	**BR** W133971 grey - *01*	7	9
37-776	**BR** W126884 brown - *01*	7	9
37-776	**BR** W123956 brown - *01*	7	9
37-776A	**BR** W123954 brown - *02*	7	9
37-776B	**BR** W124000 brown - *03*	7	9

37-777	**BR** W105666 brown - *05*	6	8
37-779	**BR** W105737 brown - *06*	6	8
37-779A	**BR** W105666 brown - *09*	5	7
37-779B	**BR** W126428 brown - *10*	5	7
(37-726Y)	**BR** W126337 brown W 'Return to Cowley' ex-set of 3 Sp Edn 504 (ModelZone) - *06*	9	NA

W37a. 12T GWR Double Vent Van (ex-Mainline) (1991)

33-602	**GW** 134089 dark grey - *91*	8	10
33-604	**GW** 35065 dark grey W - *99*	7	9
33-600	**BR** W145548 brown with chalk marks - *91*	8	10
33-601	**BR** W133977 grey - *91*	8	10
33-603	undecorated light grey - *91*	6	8

W37b. 12T GWR Double Vent Van (B) (2001)

37-725	**GW** 139956 dark grey - *01*	7	9
37-725A	**GW** 112787 dark grey - *03*	6	8
37-727	**GW** 112787 dark grey Parto - *not made*	NA	NA
37-727	**GW** 112754 dark grey Parto - *04*	6	8
37-730	**GW** 126129 dark grey - *06*	6	8
37-730A	**GW** 142335 dark grey - *09*	5	7
37-775	**BR** W133971 light grey - *01*	7	9
37-775A	**BR** W133971 light grey - *not made*	7	9
37-775B	**BR** W134030 light grey - *02*	7	9
37-775C	**BR** W142220 light grey - *05*	6	8
37-731	**BR** W133980 light grey - *09*	5	7
37-731A	**BR** W142220 light grey - *10*	5	7
37-726	**BR** W124480 brown - *01*	7	9
37-726A	**BR** W142689 brown - *03*	6	8
37-726B	**BR** W14150 brown - *05*	6	8
37-728	**BR** W142689 brown - *not made*	NA	NA
37-728	**BR** W142218 brown - *04*	6	8
37-729	**BR** W101090 brown - *06*	6	8
37-729A	**BR** W126140 brown - *08*	5	7

Ex-GWR double vent van [W37b]

(37-726Y)	**BR** W126725 brown W 'M/T Hither Green' ex-set of 3 Sp Edn 504 (ModelZone) - *06*	9	NA
-	**BR** W114521 brown W 'Plymouth/Bristol TM'	9	NA
-	**BR** W112818 brown W 'Crewe'	9	NA
-	**BR** W116296 brown W	9	NA
37-726Z	above three Sp Edn (TMC) 500 - *03*	NA	32
37-800Z	**Virgin Trains** 220 white Sp Edn 500 (Virgin Trains) - *01*	8	10

W38a. LMS Cattle Wagon (ex-Mainline) (1991)

33-652	**LMS** M14400 grey small letters - *92*	8	10
33-652A	**LMS** M14407 grey small letters - *94*	8	10
33-652C	**LMS** 292372 grey large letters (boxed as 'LMS Brown') - *98*	8	10
33-655	**LMS** 243606 grey W - *not made*	NA	NA
33-655	**LMS** M143820 grey W **** - *00?*	NPG	NPG
33-652B	**LMS** 214875 brown medium letters - *95*	8	10
33-651A	**NE** 502460 grey - *94*	8	10
33-651A	**NE** 55787 grey (box says 'brown') - *95*	8	10
33-651B	**NE** 55787 grey large letters - *96*	8	10
33-651	**NE** 502680 brown large letters - *91*	12	17
33-651.1	**NE** 502676 brown *** - *made?*	NPG	NPG
(30-100)	**NE** 502676 brown ex-set (33-650Z?) - *?*	8	NA
33-655	**BR** M143820 brown W **** - *00*	7	9
33-650	**BR** M14398 brown - *90*	8	10
33-650A*	**BR** M14390 brown - *93*	8	10
33-650B	**BR** M266640 brown - *95*	8	10
33-650C	**BR** M14400 brown - *98*	7	9
33-650.1	**BR** M14398 brown + chalk marks - *made?*	NPG	NPG
33-650.2	**BR** 12098 brown - *made?*	NPG	NPG
33-656**	**BR** M143820 brown W - *made?*	NPG	NPG
33-656	**BR** 243606 brown W - *00*	7	9
33-652Z	**BTU** yellow tool van Sp Edn (ModelZone) - *10*	NPG	NPG
33-653	undecorated light grey - *91*	6	8

* No 'A' suffix on box label. ** 33-655 box relabelled. *** no number on box. **** The box was marked - 'BR B/GREY WEATHERED'.

W38b. 12T LMS 10T HBO Cattle Wagon (B) (2002)

37-701	**LMS** M14390 grey - *02*	7	9
37-701A	**LMS** 230909 grey - *04*	6	8
37-703	**LMS** 12098 grey - *05*	6	8
37-705	**LMS** 69453 grey - *07*	6	8
37-700A	**BR** M292722 brown - *04*	6	8

Ex-LMS cattle wagon [W38b]

37-702	**BR** M230909 brown - *05*	6	8
37-704	**BR** M239381 brown - *07*	6	8
37-700	**BR** B891416 brown - *02*	7	9
-	**BR** M292750 brown W	6	NA
-	**BR** M301600 brown W	6	NA
-	**BR** M302349 brown W - *04*	6	NA
37-700Z	above 3 Sp Edn 504 (TMC) - *04*	NA	22

W39a. 12T LMS Single Vent Van (ex-Mainline) (1992)

The doors are fixed shut.

33-625	**LMS** 511470 grey - *92*	8	10
33-626	**BR** M283322 light grey - *92*	8	10
33-628	**BR** M504891 light grey W - *99*	7	9
33-627	**BR** B751782 brown Sunday Times - *92*	8	10

W39b. 12T LMS Single Vent Van (B) (2001)

This LMS type had a flatter roof and corrugated ends.

37-800	**LMS** 505969 grey (blue label on box) - *01*	7	9
37-800A	**LMS** 505969 grey (white label on box) - *02*	7	9
37-800B*	**LMS** 52946 grey - *03*	6	8
37-803	**LMS** 506818 grey - *07*	6	8
37-803A	**LMS** 518520 grey - *09*	5	7
37-803	**LMS** 505969 brown - *not made*	NA	NA
37-801	**BR** M518972 brown - *01*	7	9
37-801A	**BR** M508587 brown** - *03*	7	9
37-801B*	**BR** M508894 brown - *03*	6	8
37-802	**BR** M501723 brown - *05*	6	8
37-802A	**BR** M518113 brown - *09*	5	7
37-802B	**BR** M509355 brown - *10*	5	7

* shown with a 'B' suffix in the catalogue but an 'A' suffix on the box. ** Box marked as '37801' with no suffix. Reappeared in 2004 in the 30-045 Digital Freight Set.

W40. Set of Mixed Vans (B) (2006)

-	**BR** W134201 brown W fruit van	7	NA
-	**BR** W126725 brown W vent van	7	NA
-	**BR** W126337 brown W Mogo van	7	NA
38-726Y	above three vans Sp Edn 504 (ModelZone) - *06*	NA	25

W41. 12T LNER Ventilated Fruit Van (2010)

These were built of wood and had louvres taking up the bottom half of each end wall to ensure good air circulation.

38-385	**BR** E222599 brown (early) - *10*	6	8
38-386	**BR** E222334 brown (late) - *10*	6	8

W42a. 12T LNER Vent Van (Planked Ends) (2010)

Early standard LNER ventilated vans were built on wooden frames and with all planked bodies.

New LNER ventilated van with planked ends [W42a]

38-375	**NE** 236824 brown - *10*	6	8
38-376	**BR** E236698 brown (early) - *10*	6	8

W42b. 12T LNER Vent Van (Corrugated Ends) (2010)

These became the standard design for LNER ventilated vans from the mid 1930s.

38-380	**BR** E256948 brown (early) - *10*	6	8
38-381	**BR** E211308 brown (late) - *10*	6	8

W43a. 12T SR Planked Vent Van (B) (2005)

38-070	**SR** 48679 dark brown large letters - *05*	6	8
38-070A	**SR** 48501 dark brown large letters - *06*	6	8
38-070B	**SR** 48293 dark brown large letters - *08*	6	8
38-070C	**SR** 48329 dark brown large letters - *09*	6	8
38-070D	**SR** 48467 dark brown large letters - *10*	6	8
38-071	**BR** S49091 brown - *05*	6	8
38-071A	**BR** S49186 brown Parto - *06*	6	8
38-071B	**BR** S49230 brown - *08*	6	8
(38-071Z)	**BR** S49226 brown W ex-ModelZone set 'Waterloo-Nottingham Empty' - *05*	7	NA

W43b. 12T SR 2+2 Planked Vent Van (B) (2005)

38-080	**LMS** 521202 light grey - *05*	6	8
38-083	**GWR** 144293 dark grey - *10*	5	7
38-080A	**LMS** 521191 light grey - *09*	6	8
38-081	**BR** M523538 light grey - *05*	6	8
38-081A	**BR** M521144 light grey - *08*	6	8
38-081B	**BR** M523351 light grey - *10*	6	8
38-082	**BR** S54239 brown - *08*	6	8
38-082A	**BR** S59123 brown - *09*	6	8
(38-071Z)	**BR** S65981 brown W ex-ModelZone set 'Loaded Basingstoke' - *05*	9	NA

W43c. 12T SR Plywood Vent Van (B) (2005)

Ex-SR plywood ventilated van [W43c]

38-075Z	**'Arnold & Hancock'** 1 buff Sp Edn 504 (Buffers) - *06*	10	12
38-075Y	**'Arnold & Hancock'** 2 buff Sp Edn 504 (Buffers) - *08*	7	8
38-075X	**'Axminster Carpets'** B895008 pale grey Sp Edn 504 (Buffers) - *08*	7	8
38-075	**SR** 54409 dark brown small letters - *05*	6	8
38-075	**SR** 57002 dark brown small letters - *not made*	NA	NA
38-075A	**SR** 50933 dark brown small letters - *06*	6	8
38-076	**BR** B752698 brown - *05*	6	8
38-076A	**BR** S54273 brown - *06*	6	8
38-076B	**BR** B752909 brown - *08*	6	8
(38-071Z)	**BR** B753001 brown W ex-ModelZone set 'M/T Brighton' - *05*	9	NA

W43d. 12T BR(SR) Set of Vans (2005)

-	**BR** S49226 brown W 'Waterloo-Nottingham Empty'	9	NA
-	**BR** S65981 brown W 'Loaded Basingstoke'	9	NA
-	**BR** B753001 brown W 'M/T Brighton'	9	NA
38-071Z	above 3 vans with chalk marks Sp Edn 504 (ModelZone) - *05*	NA	26

W44a. 12T BR 'Vanwide' Box Van (B)

37-825	**BR** B784873 brown - *not made*	NA	NA
37-826	**Railfreight** 230506 red+grey - *not made*	NA	NA

W44b. 12T BR Planked Ventilated Van (B) (2008)

38-160	**BR** B763964 brown - *not made*	NA	NA
38-160	**BR** B762361 brown - *08*	6	8
38-160A	**BR** B755845 brown (early) - *09*	6	8
38-161	**BR** B755180 brown - *08*	6	8
38-161A	**BR** B758582 brown - *09*	6	8
38-161B	**BR** B760289 brown (late) - *10*	6	8
38-160X	**BR** KDB767014 brown W St Blazey Eng. Stores Sp Edn 504 (Kernow MRC) - *08*	9	11
38-160Y	**BR** B755772 brown W St Blazey Eng. Stores Sp Edn 504 (Kernow MRC) - *08*	9	11

-	**'Bachmann'** 175 white+red	7	NA
-	**'Liliput'** 60 grey+blue	7	NA
-	**'Kader'** 60 grey+orange	7	NA
38-160K	above 3 vans Sp Edn 504 (BCC) - *09*	NA	23

-	**BR** B758515 brown W	7	NA
-	**BR** B758948 brown W	7	NA
-	**BR** B759129 brown W	7	NA
38-160W	above 3 vans Sp Edn 504 (Hattons) - *09*	NA	28

-	**BR** B755822 brown, 'ICI Fertilizer' posters	10	NA
-	**BR** B760065 brown, 'Blue Circle' posters	10	NA
-	**BR** B765001 brown, 'Carrs Biscuits' (Mogo van - see W36b)	10	NA
38-160Z	above 3 vans Sp Edn 504 (Modelzone) - *08*	NA	43

-	**BR** B770968 brown W chalk marks Bedford	8	NA
-	**BR** B758185 brown W chalk marks Walsall	8	NA
-	**BR** B779954 brown W chalk marks Reading	8	NA
38-161Z	above 3 weathered vans Sp Edn 504 (TMC) - *09*	NA	30

W44c. 12T BR Planked Vent Van (Plywood Doors) (2009)

BR ventilated van with plywood doors [W44c]

38-230	**BR** B773727, brown - *09*	6	8
38-230A	**BR** B774447, brown (early livery) - *10*	6	8
38-231	**BR** B774238, brown - *09*	6	8
-	**Bachmann Branchline** 1989 20th Anniversary, blue+red	7	NA
-	**Grafar** 60th Anniversary 1949, blue+yellow	7	NA
-	**Graham Farish** 90th Anniversary 60, white+black	7	NA
38-230K	set of above 3 vans, Sp Edn 504 (BCC) - *09*	NA	23
-	**BR** B773667 early brown	7	NA
-	**BR** B773642 early brown	7	NA
-	**BR** B773594 early brown	7	NA
38-230Z	set of above 3 weathered vans, Sp Edn 504 (Hattons) - *10*	NA	28
-	**BR** B775312 late brown	7	NA
-	**BR** B774316 late brown	7	NA
-	**BR** B775058 late brown	7	NA
38-231Z	set of above 3 weathered vans, Sp Edn 504 (Hattons) - *10*	NA	28

W44d. 12T BR Plywood Ventilated Van (B) (2008)

38-170	**BR** B772170 brown - *08*	6	8
38-170A	**BR** B772139 brown - *09*	6	8
38-170B	**BR** B777586, brown (early) - *10*	6	8
38-171	**BR** B765477 brown - *not made*	NA	NA
38-171	**BR** B765759 brown - *08*	6	8
38-171A	**BR** B765351 brown - *09*	6	8
38-171B	**BR** B775719 brown (late) - *10*	6	8
38-170Z	**BR** ADB766234 olive green 'Vanfit' (EMU spares) Sp Edn 504 (*Model Rail*) - *09*	8	10

W44e. 12T BR Fruit Van (B) (2008)

38-180	**BR** B875800 brown - *08*	6	8
38-180A	**BR** B875726 brown - *09*	6	8
38-180B	**BR** B875716 brown (early) - *10*	6	8
38-181	**BR** B875640 brown - *08*	6	8
38-181A	**BR** B875649* brown - *09*	6	8
38-181B	**BR** B875823 brown (late) - *08*	6	8

* Number correctly printed at an angle as on the original wagon.

W44f. 10T BR Insulated Van (B) (2008)

BR insulated van in ice blue [W44f]

38-190	**BR** B872208 pale blue - *08*	6	8
38-190A	**BR** B872016 pale blue - *09*	6	8
38-191	**BR** B872187 white - 08	6	8
38-191A	**BR** B872112 light cream - *09*	6	8
-	**BR** B872011 white W	8	NA
-	**BR** B872039 white W	8	NA
-	**BR** B872129 white W	8	NA
38-191Z	above 3 wagons Sp Edn 504 (Frizinghall Model Railways) - *08*	NA	30
-	**BR** B872156 pale blue W	8	NA
-	**BR** B872072 pale blue W	8	NA
-	**BR** B872191 pale blue W	8	NA
38-190Z	above 3 wagons Sp Edn 504 (TMC) - *09*	NA	30

W45a. 12T GWR Shock-Absorbing Van (1994)

Early GWR double vent van with shock absorbing chassis and 3 white stripes.

33-725	**GW** 139576 dark grey Shock Absorbing Van No.39 - *95*	15	20
33-726	**BR** W139556 brown 3 medium thin vertical stripes (return to Fishguard) - *95*	15	20
33-727	**BR** W139594 dark grey 3 long thin vertical stripes 'Shock Van No.57' (return to Britton Ferry) - *95*	15	20

W45b. 12T BR Standard Shock-Absorbing Van (1994)

Early single vent van with shock absorbing chassis, corrugated ends and 3 white stripes. Short fat stripes date the finish to 1964 onwards.

33-735	**BR** B852193 brown 3 short thick vertical stripes (post 1964) - *94*	15	20
33-736	**BR** B850605 brown 3 medium thin vertical stripes - *94*	15	20
33-737	**BR** brown 3 medium thin vertical stripes - *not made*	NA	NA

W45c. 12T GW R Shock Absorbing Van (B) (2006)

Blue Riband double vent van with planked ends and 3 white stripes.

37-900	**BR** B851440 brown - *not made*	NA	NA
37-900	**BR** B859554 brown - *not made*	NA	NA
37-900	**BR** W139600 brown - *06*	6	8
37-902	**BR** W139556 brown - *09*	5	7

W45d. 12T BR Standard Shock Absorbing Van (B) (2005)

Blue Riband single vent van with corrugated ends and 3 white stripes.

37-901	**BR** B851778 brown - *not made*	NA	NA
37-901	**BR** B850005 brown - *not made*	NA	NA
37-901	**BR** B851692 brown - *05*	6	8
37-903	**BR** B852353 brown - *09*	5	7

W46a. VAA 45T BR Sliding Door Box Van (B) (2007)

c/w vents.

38-120	**Railfreight** B200116 red+grey - *07*	12	15
38-120A	**Railfreight** B200102 red+grey - *09*	11	14
38-121	**Railfreight** B200119 red-brown - *07*	12	15

W46b. VBA 45T BR Sliding Door Box Van (B) (2007)

38-125K	**LoadHaul** 200600 black+orange Sp Edn 504 (BCC) - *07*	12	15
38-125	**EWS** 200241 maroon - *07*	12	15
38-126	BR 200289 red-brown - *07*	12	15
38-143	**EWS** 200731 maroon - *09*	13	16

W46c. VDA 29T BR Sliding Door Box Van (B) (2008)

Transrail grey VDA van [W46c]

38-141	**BR Rft** 200077 brown Cov AB - *08*	12	16
38-140	**BR Rft** 210380 grey+red - *08*	12	16
38-142	**BR Rft** 200834 grey+yellow - *08*	12	16
33-140K	**Transrail** T210195 grey * Sp Edn 504 (BCC) - *08*	12	16
33-140Z	**BR Civil Link** DC200660 grey+yellow ZRA Sp Edn 504 (*Model Rail*) - *08*	15	19

* carries Carlisle Currock wagon shop motifs (running fox).

W47. OTA BR Timber Carrier Wagon (B) (2011)

These were cut-down VDAs. The models are supplied with a lumber load.

38-300	**BR Rft** ? brown - *11*	15	19
38-301	**EWS** ? maroon - *11*	15	19

W48a. VGA 46t Sliding Wall Van (1998)

33-275	**BRe Speedlink** 210595 grey+red - *98*	12	15
33-276	**BR Rft Distrib** 210614 grey+yellow* - *98*	12	15
33-277	**Transrail** 210572 silver+yellow* - *98*	12	15

* Carries Carlisle Currock wagon shop motifs (running fox).

W48b. VGA 46t Sliding Wall Van (B) (2000)

37-601A	**BRe Rft Speedlink** 210595 grey+red - *not made*	NA	NA
37-601A	**BRe Rft Speedlink** 210452 grey+red - *02*	12	15
37-602	**Rft Distribution** 210614 grey+red - *00*	12	15
37-602A	**Rft Distribution** 210639 grey+yell W - *02*	12	15
37-603	**Rft Distribution** 210614 grey+yellow - *not made*	NA	NA
37-603	**Rft Distribution** 210632 grey+yellow - *00*	12	15
37-604	**Rft Distribution** 210592 silver+yellow - *06*	11	14
37-605	**Rft Distribution/Gi** 210572 grey+yellow W + graffiti (one side) VKA - *07*	11	14
37-607	**Railfreight Dist.** 210493 silver+yellow W - *10*	13	16
37-601	**Transrail** grey+yellow - *00*	12	15
37-600	**EWS** 210444 maroon - *00*	12	15
37-600A	**EWS** 210626 maroon - *03*	11	14
37-603	**EWS** 210632 maroon - *06*	11	14
37-606	**EWS** 210430 maroon - *09*	12	15
37-607	**EWS** 210493 maroon W - *10*	12	16
-	**'Lovat Spring'** 210527 grey+yell	15	NA
-	**'Lovat Spring'** 210622 grey+yellow	15	NA
37-601Z	above 2 vans as a set Sp Edn (Harburn) - *02*	NA	40

Brake Vans

W49. 20T GWR 'Toad' Brake Van (ex-Mainline) (1990)

33-300B	**GW** 56683 dark grey 'Severn Tunnel Junc' RU - *01*	7	9
33-300C	**GW** 68690 grey 'Dowlais Cae Harris' - *03, 05*	6	8

GWR brake van [L49]

33-300D	**GW** 68690 grey 'Dowlais Cae Harris' - *06*	6	8
33-300E	**GW** 68751 dark grey 'Berkenhead' - *07*	6	8
33-301	**GW** 114926 grey 'Cardiff' - *90*	8	10
33-301A	**GW** 56368 dark grey 'Paddington RU' - *97*	8	10
33-301B	**GW** 114800 dark grey W 'Rhymney' - *99*	7	9
33-301Z	**GW** 56368 grey W 'Toddington' * Sp Edn 500 (Cotswold Steam Preservation) - *01*	7	9
(30-010)	**GW** 56590 dark grey 'Oswestry' ex-set - *04*	6	NA
30-301W	**GW** 68897 dark grey 'Stratford-Upon-Avon' Sp Edn 504 (Classic Train & M. Bus) - *05*	6	8
33-301R	**GW** 68684, dark grey, 'Hayle RU', Sp Edn 504 (Kernow MR Centre) - *09*	7	10
33-300	**BR** W68805 grey - *90*	8	10
33-300A	**BR** W68875 grey - *97*	8	10
33-301X	**BR** B950609 grey 'St Blazey RU' Sp Edn 504 (Kernow MR Centre) - *05*	9	11
33-301S	**BR** W68474 light grey 'Truro RU' Sp Edn 504 (Kernow MR Centre) - *09*	7	10
33-301U	**BR** W68568 grey 'St Erth & St Ives RU' Sp Edn 504 (Kernow MR Centre) - *07*	9	11
33-305	**BR** W35960 grey 'Shrewsbury (Cotton Hill) RU' - *01*	7	9
33-305A	**BR** W114925 grey 'Oxford RU' - *03*	7	9
33-306	**BR** W35918 grey 'Bristol West Depot RU', No.2 Western - *05*	6	8
33-306A	**BR** W68834 light grey 'Stourbridge RU' - *09*	5	7
33-306B	**BR** W68476 grey 'Roath Basin Junction RU' - *10*	8	10
33-301C	**BR** W17390 brown 'Westbury (Wilts)' - *04*	6	8
33-301D	**BR** W68870 brown 'Tavistock Jcn RU' - *06*	6	8
33-301E	**BR** W114854 brown 'Birkenhead RU' - *09*	5	6
33-301F	**BR** W17444 brown - *10*	8	10
33-301T	**BR** W68856 brown 'Penzance RU' Sp Edn 504 (Kernow MR Centre) - *07*	9	11
33-302	**BR** DW17455 brown ST - *94*	8	10
33-304	**BR** W114961 brown - *98*	8	10
(30-700)	? brown ex-set - *?*	6	NA
33-301Y	**Virgin Trains** 2003 Warley red+silver Sp Edn 500 (Virgin Trains) - *03*	7	9
33-303	undecorated light grey - *91*	8	10

* This was also being offered by the Gloucester & Warwickshire Railway with bespoke different station names.

W50. 20T 12ft LNER 12ft Brake Van (ex-Mainline) (1990)

This was a design built by the LNER from 1929.

33-800	**NE** 162030 brown large letters ex-sets - *90*	8	NA
33-800.1	**NE** 108001 brown - *90*	8	NA
33-802	**NE** 108061 brown small letters - *02*	8	10
33-802	**NE** E178513 brown small letters - *91*	8	10
33-801	**BR** E168064 grey** - *91*	8	10
33-801B*	**BR** E167830 grey - *01*	7	9
33-801D	**BR** E178499 grey - *03*	7	9
33-803	**BR** E178510 grey unfitted - *04*	6	8
33-805	**BR** E175613 grey - *07*	6	8
33-801A*	**BR** E178569 brown unfitted - *00*	7	9
33-801C	**BR** E167830 brown - *02*	7	9
33-802	**BR** E178513 brown - *02*	6	8
33-804	**BR** E178500 brown - *04*	6	8
33-806	**BR** E.178499 brown - *07*	6	8

* No 'A' on the box label. ** Reappeared in 2004 in the 30-045 Digital Freight Set. ** factory list marks this as "no number on box. Planned for the Crewe Open Day in 1996."

W51a. 20T 16ft LNER/BR Standard Brake Van (ex-Mainline) (1990)

LNER 16ft brake van [W51a]

33-351	**NE** 182908 brown large letters - *92*	8	10
33-352	**NE** 260922 brown small letters, box labelled 'NE Grey' - *90*	8	10
33-352	**EN** (error)*** 260922 brown - *92*	15	18
(30-201)**	**LT** B582 dark grey also (30-200) - *91*	18	20
33-350	**BR** B950880 grey (error) (1st issue) - *90*	12	16
33-352A	**BR** B951759 grey unfitted - *96*	8	10
33-350	**BR** B950880 brown (1st issue) - *90*	8	10
33-350.1	**BR** B950880 brown with chalk marks - made*?*	NPG	NPG
33-350A*	**BR** B953087 brown (2nd issue) - *93*	8	10
33-350Aa	**BR** B955044 brown fitted - *96*	8	10
33-350B	**BR** B952103 brown fitted - *99*	7	9
33-354	**BR** B955136 brown+yellow - *92*	8	10
33-354	**BR** P0016149 brown+yellow - made*?*	NPG	NPG
33-355	**BR Rft Distribution** B964885 grey+red CAR - *not made*	NA	NA
33-355	**BR Rft Distribution** B954673 grey+red CAR - *94*	8	10
33-355A	**BR Rft Distribution** 201205 B954132 dark grey with yellow end panels CAR - *99*	7	9
33-353	undecorated light grey *** - *not made*	NA	NA

* No 'A' on box label. ***The wrongly printed bodies were withdrawn before issue but were later sold off to the public and so may turn up occasionally, possibly fitted to a spare chassis. ** Box unnumbered. It also appeared in set 30-200.

W51b. 20T 16ft LNER/BR Standard Brake Van (B) (2002)

37-527	**BR** NE260922 brown small letters, fitted - *02*	7	9

37-529	**NE** 178705 brown, large letters - *05*	6	8
37-527Z	**LT** B583 light grey with red ends Sp Edn 504 (Kernow MRC) - *07*	10	12
37-526	**BR** B950002 grey - *not made*	NA	NA
37-526	**BR** B951480 grey - *02*	7	9
37-528	**BR** B950884 grey - *05*	6	8
37-528A	**BR** B951504 grey - *10*	5	7
37-525	**BR** B954762 brown fitted - *02*	7	9
37-527Y	**BR** KDB954164 red+yellow ZTR S&TD Sp Edn 504 (*Model Rail*) - *05*	6	8

W51c. 20T BR Standard Brake (flush ends) (B) (2003)

37-538	**BR** Departmental LDB954219, grey - *05*	6	8
37-537	**BR** B950388 brown fitted - *05*	6	8
37-537A	**BR** B953810 brown fitted - *08*	6	8
37-535	**BR Rft** B955247 CAR grey+red - *03*	7	9
37-535A	**BR Rft** B955143 CAR grey+red - *07*	5	7
37-527A	Rft Dist B954661 grey+yellow - 07	5	7

W51d. 20T BR Standard Brake (flush sides & ends) (B) (2002)

37-536	**BR** B955055 CAP brown - *02*	7	9
37-535Z	**BR** B955010 RES CAR red+grey Sp Edn 500 (*Model Rail*) - *02*	10	12
37-535	**BR** Rft B955247 CAR grey+red - *not made*	NA	NA

Bogie Wagons

W52. 25T 'Queen Mary' Brake Van (1996)

33-827	**SR** 56282 dark brown large letters - *96*	12	14
33-827B	**SR** 56294 dark grown large letters - *98*	12	14

SR 'Queen Mary' 'bogie brake van [W52]

33-827A	**SR** 56299 dark brown small letters - *97*	12	14
33-830A	**SR** 56301 dark brown - *04*	11	13
33-830B	**SR** 56291 dark brown - *07*	11	13
33-825	**BR** S56297 brown - *96*	12	14
33-825A	**BR** S56302 brown - *97*	12	14
33-825B	**BR** S56299 brown - *98*	12	14
33-825C	**BR** S56288 brown - *04*	11	13
33-825D	**BR** S56306 brown - *06*	11	13
33-825E	**BR** S56298 brown - *09*	12	15
33-825F	**BR** S56303 brown - *10*	12	15
33-826	**BR** ADS56296 olive green+yellow S&T Department - *96*	15	18
33-826A	**BR** ADS56299 green+yellow S&T Depart - *97*	15	18
33-829	**BR** S56302 stone - *97*	14	17
33-828	**NSE** ADS56304 blue - *97*	15	18
33-825Z	**BR Satlink** KDS56305 red+yellow VZW Sp Edn 504 (Model Rail magazine) - *07*	15	18
33-830	**EWS** ADS56299 maroon - *99*	12	14

W53. 'Intermodal' Bogie Wagon

33-475	**BR Railfreight** Distribution with ISO dry freight steel container - *not made*	NA	NA

W54a. 'Intermodal' ('Euro Twin') (B) (2001)

Like the real thing, these come as a pair of bogie flat wagons, semi-permanently joined, designed to carry 45' 'Swap Body' containers. The wagon frames are diecast.

37-300	**Rft Dist.** 31 70 4938 115-8 + 3170 4938 121-1, green, plus two maroon 45ft **ECS European Containers** containers: ECBU452607[0] + ECBU450600[6] - *01*	22	27
37-300A	**Rft Dist.** 31 70 4938 002-3 + 3170 4938 002-5, green, plus two 45ft **Consent Leasing** containers: NEVU220181[8] + NEVU220200[7] - *02*	20	25
37-300B	**Rft Dist.** 31 70 4938 121-1, green, plus two 45ft **ECS** containers: ECDU450106[7] + ECDU850805[6] - *02*	20	25
37-301	**Rft Dist.** 33 70 4938 713-3, green, plus 45ft containers: **Power Box** PWRU450209[2] and **Sea Wheel** SWLU450001[3] - *01*	22	27
37-301A	**Rft Dist.** 33 70 4938 531-9, green, plus two 45ft **Axis** containers: AXIU716457[4] + AXIU716309 - 02	20	25
37-301B	**Rft Dist.** 33 70 4938 713-3, black, plus two green 45ft **Sea Wheel** containers: SWLU451349[8] + SWIU965245[0] - *03*	22	27
37-302	**Rft Dist.** 31 70 4938 113-8, green, plus two 45ft **Seaco** containers: SCZU146450[1] + SCZU147551[1] - *01*	22	27
37-302A	**Rft Dist.** 33 70 4938 519-4, green, plus two 45ft **EFS** containers: EFSU452044[8] + EFSU452047[4] - *03*	20	25
37-302B	**Rft Dist.** 31 70 4938 113-8, green, plus two dark blue 45ft **Seaco** containers: SCZU146922[6] + SCZU147605[6] - *02*	20	25

Intermodal 'Euro Twin' with 2 'Asda' 45ft containers [W54a]

37-303	**Rft Dist.** 33 70 4938 523-6, green, plus two green+white 45ft **Asda** containers: (WHMU450819[1] + WHMU 450825[2]) - *07*	20	27
37-310	**Rft Dist.** 31 70 4938 217-7, green, plus two 20ft **Hamburg Sud** containers: SUDU370512[2] + SUDU369632[9]) - *03*	22	27
37-311	**Rft Dist.** 33 70 4938 319-9, green, plus two 20ft **P&O** containers: POCU050018[4] + POCU041942[6] - *02*	20	25
37-312	**Rft Dist.** 31 70 4938 006-3, black, plus two 20ft **Mediterranean Shipping Co.** containers: MSCU116371[3] + MSCU251438[7] - *03*	20	25
37-315	**Rft Dist.** 70 4938 012 2 (two flats), black - *03*	15	19
37-316	**Rft Dist.** 33 70 4958 135-0 (two flats), green, weathered - *06*	15	19
37-308	**EWS** 33 70 4938 130-2, green, plus two dark blue 45ft **Geest** containers: GNSU597748[4] + GNSU451546[0] - *10*	32	30
37-320	**EWS** 33 70 4938 300-9, plus two red 20ft **K Line** green+red containers: KKTU740516[4] + KKTU741006[2] plus two 20ft **MOL** grey containers: MOAU052613[8] + MOAU046387[3] - *10*	25	31
37-309	**EWS** 33 70 4938 324-9, green, plus two dark blue 45ft **Samskip** containers: SANU798868[0] + SANU799037[3] - *10*	25	30
37-321	**EWS** 33 70 4938 326-4, green + two red 20ft **Hyundi** containers: HDMU217810[1] + HDMU235691[8] plus two blue 20ft **CMA CGM** containers: ECMU196946[4] + ECMU217218[2] -*10*	25	31
37-304	**EWS** 33 70 4938 510-3, green, plus two 45ft, navy blue, **Malcolm Logistics** containers: WHMU450015[9] + WHMU450020[4] - *07*	20	27
37-305	**EWS** 33 70 4938 535-0, green, plus two 45ft, yellow, **DHL** containers: DZ5141 KDG1 + DZ7005 LEG1 - *07*	20	27
37-305A	**EWS** 33 70 4938 ?-?, green, plus two 45ft, yellow, **DHL** containers: DZ? + DZ? - *10*	25	30

W54b. 'Intermodal' Containers (only) (B) (2002)

36-100	2 x yellow 45' containers **'P&O Ferrymasters'** FMBU 001799[1] + **'P&O Ferrymasters - Container Services'** FMBU 001260[2] - *02*	5	8

36-101	2 x dark green 45' containers **'Eucon'** (45') EUCU 459120[1] + EUCU 459026[8] - *06*	5	8
36-102	2 x blue 45' containers **'Dream Box'** JOKU 000921[3] + JOKU 450273[7] - *06*	5	8

2 'Eucon" 45' containers [W54b]

36-125	2 x **'China Shipping'** green CCLU 314404[5] + CCLU 304949[6] - *03*	5	7
36-126	2 x grey containers **'Maersk'** APMO282700[1] + **'Maersk Sealand'** MSKU206820[0] - *03*	5	7
36-127	2 x grey containers **'Cosco'** CBHU3281860[8] + CBHU328736[5] - *03*	5	7

W55a. 30T GWR 'Macaw B'/'Bogie Bolster C' Wagon (ex-Mainline)(1992)

cb = commonwealth bogies. db = diamond bogies. BBC = Bogie Bolster C.

33-852	**GW** 70247 dark grey 'Macaw B' db - *92*	10	12
33-852A*	**GW** 56302 dark grey 'Macaw B' db - *not made*	NA	NA
33-850A	**LMS** 314064 grey db - *02*	9	11
33-850B	**LMS** 720717 brown db - *04*	9	11
33-857	**LMS** 314000 grey db - *05*	8	10
33-857A	**LMS** 301326 grey db - *09*	7	8
33-850	**BR** ADB997648 dark grey BBC S&T Dept. cb - *91*	10	12
33-851	**BR** B943134 grey cb - *?*	8	10
33-851A*	**BR** M290075 grey BBC db - *97*	12	16
33-855	**BR** B940751 grey BBC cb - *99*	9	11
33-856A	**BR** B922150 grey BBC cb - *not made*	NA	NA
33-856A	**BR** B943405 grey - *05*	8	10
33-856B	**BR** B940050 grey - *09*	7	8
33-856C	**BR** B943501 grey - *10*	7	9
33-853	**BR** B943293 brown (warped) - *97*	10	12
33-853A	**BR** B943293 brown db - *97*	10	12
33-854	**BR** KDB997653 red S&T 'Prawn' cb - *97*	10	12
33-854A	**BR** DB997636 Gulf red S&T 'Prawn' - *04*	9	11
33-856	**BR** B943359 brown BBC cb - *02*	9	11

* No 'A' on box label.

W55b. 30T Bogie Bolster Wagon + Load (ex-Mainline) (1991)

Fitted with diamond bogies.

33-927	**GW** 70240 grey + girder - *92*	14	16
33-926	**LMS** 301326 grey + brown girder - *92*	14	16
33-925	**BR** M290034 grey + girder - *91*	14	16
33-928	**BR** B946405 grey + brown girder - *not made*	NA	NA
33-928	**BR** B943500 grey + brown girder - *10*	8	10
33-929	**BR** B943439 grey + pipe load - *10*	8	10

W56a. BDA 80T Bogie Bolster Wagon (B) (2008)

Fitted with diamond bogies.

Loadhaul BDA bogie bolster wagon [W56a]

38-150	**BR Loadhaul** 950414 black+orange - *08*	12	16
38-151	**BR Railfreight** 950954 red girder - *08*	12	16
38-151A	**BR Railfreight** 951163 red - *09*	12	16
38-150Z	**BR Departmemtal** DC950064 yellow YAA 'Brill' Sp Edn 504 (*Model Rail*) - *08*	14	18
38-152	**EWS** 950026 maroon - *08*	12	16
38-152A	**EWS** 950049 maroon - *10*	13	17

W56b. BDA 80T Bogie Bolster Wagon + Load (B) (2010)

These are the same as the wagons in the above table but with a load added.

38-158	**BR** 950000 maroon + steel pipes - *10*	17	21
38-159	**BR** Railfreight 950991 + steel beams - *10*	17	21

W57a. 45T/65T GWR 'Crocodile H' Well Wagon (ex-Mainline) (1991)

Fitted with commonwealth bogies. BR strengthened the floor of the well wagon to increase its capacity from 45T to 65T. A new shorter coupling was introduced in 2004.

33-900	**GW** 41900 dark grey 'Crocodile H' 45T - *92*	12	15
33-900A	**GW** 41973 dark grey 'Crocodile H' 45T - *98*	10	12
33-900B	**GW** 41900 dark grey 'Crocodile H' 45T - *02*	8	10
33-900C	**GW** dark grey 'Crocodile H' - *not made*	NA	NA
33-900D	**GW** 41901 dark grey 'Crocodile H' 45T - *05*	6	8
33-900E	**GW** 41974 dark grey 'Crocodile H' 45T - *09*	6	8
33-901	**LMS** grey - *not made* *	NA	NA
33-901A	**BR** W41973 grey 'Weltrol WH' 65T - *98*	10	12
33-901B	**BR** W41900 grey 'Weltrol WH' 65T - *00*	8	10
33-901C	**BR** W41973 grey 'Weltrol WH'* 65T - *04*	6	8
33-901D	**BR** W41974 grey 'Weltrol WH' * 65T - *04*	6	8
33-901E	**BR** W41900 grey 'Weltrol WH' * 65T - *10*	6	8
33-902	**BR** W41973 grey 'Weltrol WH' 65T - *91*	12	15

* Factory record says "planned for the Crewe Open Day in 1996".

W57b. 45T/65T Bogie Well Wagon with Load (ex-Mainline) (1991)

Diamond bogies.

33-875	**NE** 77823 grey 'Flatrol M' + boiler **'Riley Bros.'** 3780 brown - *91*	18	23
33-879	**NE** 736919 grey 'Flatrol M' + boiler brown - *10*	8	10
33-876	**BR** W41975 black 'Weltrol WH' + boiler 1877 black 65T - *92*	17	20
33-877	**BR** W41843 grey 'Weltrol WH' + green transformer - *92*	17	20
33-878	**LMS** 299882 grey + grey transformer - *92*	17	20

W58. IPA Bogie Car Transporter (B) (2010)

Four axle car carriers introduced by STVA in 1993 for cross-channel traffic. Soon after, side blinds were fitted following cases of vandelism and thefts.

38-250	**'STVA'** 23 87 4392 692-1 TAL489 Wincar red - *10*	23	29

'STVA' IPA bogie twin car transporter [W58] (Bachmann)

W59. FNA Nuclear Flask Wagon (B) (2011)

38-345	**DRS** 550014 ? flat floor, round buffers - *11*	20	24
38-346	**DRS** 550023 ? sloping floor, changeover valve, oval buffers - *11*	20	24
38-347	**DRS** 550038 ? sloping floor, round buffers - *11*	20	24

W60. MBA/MBB 'Megabox' (High-sided) (B) (2010)

Knuckle couplers are included in the box.

38-240	**EWS** 500028 maroon MBA with buffers - *10*	15	20
38-241	**EWS** 500178 maroon MBA without buffers - *10*	15	20

W61. MOA 'Megabox' (Low-sided) (B) (2010)

Knuckle couplers are included in the box.

EWS MOA 'Megabox' open wagon [W61]

38-245	**EWS** 500327 maroon - *10*	15	20

W62. BAA/BZA Open Steel Coil Carriers (B) (2011)

38-350	**Railfreight** ? brown? + steel coil load - *11*	16	20
38-351	**Railfreight** ? red+black + steel coil load - *11*	16	20
38-352	**EWS** ? maroon + steel coil load - *11*	16	20

W63a. BYA 102t 'Thrall' Steel Coil Carriers (B) (2002)

37-625	**EWS** 960015 maroon - *02*	16	20

W63b. BRA 102t 'Thrall' Steel Strip Carriers (B) (2002)

37-626	**EWS** 964014 maroon - *02*	16	20
37-627	**EWS** 966018 maroon - *06*	16	20
37-628	**EWS** 964007 maroon W - *04*	16	21
37-628A	**EWS** 964040 maroon W - *09*	18	23

W64. JGA 90t JGA Bogie Hopper Wagon (B) (2001)

37-327	**'Buxton'** BLI19206 white+blue - *01*	17	19
37-327A	**'Buxton'** BLI19218 white+blue - *01, 05*	17	19
37-327B	**'Buxton'** BLI19211 white+blue - *02, 05*	17	19
37-326	**'RMC'** RMC19241 orange - *01*	17	19
37-326A	**'RMC'** RMC19228 orange - *01*	17	19
37-326B	**'RMC'** RMC19238 orange - *02*	17	19
37-328	**'Tarmac'** NACO19174 pale grey, green+yellow flash - *02*	17	19
37-328A	**'Tarmac'** NACO19177 off-white, blue line - *03*	17	20
37-328B	**'Tarmac'** NACO19199 off-white, blue line - *not made*	NA	NA
37-328B	**'Tarmac'** NACO19175 off-white, green+yellow flash - *10*	17	20
37-325	**'Tilcon' NACCO** NACO19184 grey - *01*	17	19
37-325A	**'Tilcon'** NACCO NACO19175 grey - *02*	17	19
37-325B	**'Tilcon' NACCO** NACO19188 grey - *02*	17	19

W65. HTA 102t 'Thrall' Bulk Coal Hopper (B) (2003)

EWS HTA 'Thrall' bulk coal hopper [W65]

37-850	**EWS** 310222 maroon - *03*	16	20
37-851	**EWS** 310223 maroon W - *04*	16	21
37-852	**EWS** 310077 maroon - *05*	16	21
37-853	**EWS** 310103 maroon - *06*	16	21
37-854	**EWS** 310384 maroon W - *09*	18	23
37-854A	**EWS** 310148 maroon W - *10*	20	26

W66. HHA 100t Bogie Hopper Wagon (B) (2007)

sed = non-working sliding end door. hed = non-working hinged end doors

Freightliner Heavy Haul

38-030	370258 silver+green sed - *07*	15	20
38-030B	370270 silver+green sed - *10*	17	22
38-03A	370429 silver+green sed - *07*	15	20
38-031	370043 silver+ green hed - *not made*	NA	NA
38-031	370001 silver+ green hed - *07*	16	21
38-032	370169 silver+ green W hed - *08*	18	23

W67. YGA/B/H 40t 'Seacow'/'Sealion' (B) (2007)

This model is based on the earlier riveted type of 'Seacow'.

38-130	**BR** DB982582 olive green YGH - *07*	14	18
38-131	**BR** DB982473 grey+yellow YGB - *07*	14	18
38-131A	**BR** DB? grey+yellow YGB - *10*	16	20
38-132	**EWS** DB982696 maroon YGA - *07*	14	18
38-132A	**EWS** DB980220 maroon YGA - *10*	16	20
38-133	**Loadhaul** DB982582 black+orange YBH - *10*	16	20

W68. JPA Bogie Cement Wagon (B) (2010)

'Lafarge'/VTG JPA bogie cement tank wagon [W68]

38-201	**VTG/'Castle Cement'** VTG12461 pale grey - *10*	18	23
38-200	**VTG/'Lafarge Cement'** VTG12434 chrome - *10*	18	23

W69. TEA 100T Bogie Tank Wagon (B) (2007)

38-112	**'BP'** BPO87467 grey - *07*	16	20
38-111	**'BP'** BPO87887 green - *07*	16	20
38-111A	**'BP'** BPO? green - *10*	20	25
38-113	**'Esso'** 20059 pale grey - *09*	18	23
38-113A	**'Esso'** 20062 pale grey - *10*	20	25
38-114	**'Gulf'** GULF 85021 pale grey - *09*	18	20
38-114Z	**'Gulf'** GP628 black W Sp Edn 504 (TMC) - *10*	22	27
38-110	**'Shell'** SUKO87317 grey - *07*	16	20
38-110A	**'Shell'** SUKO? grey - *10*	20	25

W70. TEA 100T Crude Oil Bogie Tanker (B) (2009)

These tankers have conical ends.

38-222	**'Amoco'** AMOC85020 black - 09	18	22
38-220	**'BP'** BP083377 black - *09*	18	22
38-221	**'Shell/BP'** BPO7500 black - *09*	18	22

TRACK MAINTENANCE EQUIPMENT

T1. Plasser 'Tamper' Machine (2001) (H0)

36-160	**BRe** DX73205 yellow no motor - *01*	12	18
36-160A	**BRe** DX73205 yellow no motor - *08*	12	19
36-165	**EWS** DX73205 yellow motorised - *03*	32	42
36-165A	**EWS** DX73205 yellow motorised - *08*	32	44

T2. Plasser OWB10 with Crane (2001) (H0)

36-150	**BRe** DX68200 yellow no motor- *01*	12	18
36-151	**BRe** DX68200 yellow motorised crane - *06*	25	32

T3. JJA Railtrack 'Auto-Ballaster' Mk2 (B) (2010)

38-210	**Railtrack** GERS12976 blue+buff (outer) with generator - *10*	20	29

Railtrack JJA 'Auto-ballaster' Mk2 [T3] (Bachmann)

38-211	**Railtrack** GERS13005 blue+buff (inner) - *10*	20	29
38-212	**Railtrack** GERS12967 blue+buff (outer) - *10*	20	29

T4. MPV (Multi-Purpose Vehicle) Class 416 (B) (2011)

Built in 1998-2001 by Windhoff GmbH for use by Railtrack for maintenance work. Master and slave units, alternative on-board equipment and directional lighting, DCC ready.

31-575	**Network Rail** DR98909? blue+yellow DC21 - *11*	95	110
31-576DC	**Network Rail** DR989?? blue+yellow DC21 - *11*	95	110
31-577	**Railtrack** DR989?? ? DC21 - *11*	95	110

SETS

Initially, Bachmann sets came with a circle of track, an inexpensive controller, a standard range locomotive and rolling stock drawn from what was available at the time. None of these are of particular interest to collectors but interest in them will almost certainly grow in future years as they were not sold in very great quantities and many sets were broken up by retailers in order to sell the contents separately.

An exception to the general run was the London Transport set (30-201) of 1991 which contained the early pannier tank in LT livery and three wagons. Another exception is the 'Cambrian Coast Express' set (31-2000), which was originally planned by Palitoy for their Mainline range. The Bachmann set had two locomotives and six coaches together with accessories.

In 2004, Bachmann introduced some special sets with a view to introducing beginners to a simple form of digital command control (DCC).

Underground Ernie

The Underground Ernie range was introduced in 2006 with the launch of the children's television series. However, this ran to only one series and, as such, could not establish itself as a marketable product worldwide. Without overseas sales, the project was abandoned and in the summer of 2009, Bachmann cleared their warehouse of remaining stock. It also meant that they did not complete their development plans and several of the models were not released.

TRAIN SETS

S1. Sets (2006)

Containing train, track etc.

UE101	Circle Electric Train Set - *06*	NA	60

STOCK

L1. Trains (2007)

UE201	(***Hammersmith & City)*** twins - *07*	28	35
UE202	(***Bakerloo)*** & trailer car - *07*	28	35
UE203	(***Victoria)*** & trailer car - *07*	28	35
UE204	(***Jubilee)*** & trailer car - *07*	28	35
UE205	(***Circle)*** & trailer car - *08*	28	35
UE207	(***Brooklyn)*** & trailer car - *07*	28	35
UE208	(***Paris)*** & trailer car - *not made*	NA	NA
UE209	(***Moscow)*** & trailer car - *not made*	NA	NA
UE210	(***Osaka)*** & trailer car - *not made*	NA	NA
UE211	(***Sydney)*** & trailer car - *not made*	NA	NA

Underground Ernie series - Victoria [L1]

L2. Mobile Equipment (2008)

UE206	(***Ernie 1)*** inspection vehicle - *08*	16	20

BUILDINGS ETC.

B1. Stations etc. (2007)

UE301	International station - *07*	NA	28
UE302	control centre - *not made*	NA	NA
UE303	train home - *not made*	NA	NA
UE304	Mr Rails' repair shop - *not made*	NA	NA
UE305	turntable - *not made*	NA	NA
UE306	Seaside station with cafe and bridge - *not made*	NA	NA
UE307	Botanical Garden station with trees - *not made*	NA	NA
UE308	Mystery Mansion station - *08*	NA	27
UE309	Sports Stadium station - *07*	NA	25
UE310	Airport station - *not made*	NA	NA
UE311	industrial units - *08*	NA	15
UE312	International tunnel - *not made*	NA	NA

TRACK

T1. Track Packs (2007)

UE201	track pack A - *07*	NA	20
UE201	track pack B - *07*	NA	14
UE201	track pack C - *07*	NA	16
UE201	track pack D - *07*	NA	12

Bachmann A2 Batchelors Button 'Starting' by Robbie McGavin

Bachmann Brassworks

HISTORY

These high quality brass models are produced by San Cheng in China, exclusively for Bachmann Europe Plc. Randolph Cheng, the MD of San Cheng, is a former Vice-president of Bachmann USA. Painted versions are produced without numbers or insignia etc. They are supplied as ready to run, but allowing the owner to customise each model as required.

GAUGE 0

LOCOMOTIVES

These are to 1:43 scale.

Cat No.	Company, Number, Colour, Dates	£	£

0 gauge Class J94 0-6-0ST in brass finish [L0-1]

L0-1. LNER J94 0-6-0T (2001)

Cat No.	Company, Number, Colour, Dates	£	£
BW005	unpainted brass, high bunker - *06*	250	324
BW006	black, high bunker - *06*	280	369
BW007	unpainted brass, standard bunker (also YO94) - *01*	250	324
BW008	black, standard bunker - *06*	280	369

L0-2. BR Standard 2-6-4T (2008)

Cat No.	Company, Number, Colour, Dates	£	£
BW065	unpainted brass - *08*	750	830
BW066	unlined black - *08*	780	865

L0-3. GWR 2251 Collett Goods 0-6-0 (2009)

Cat No.	Company, Number, Colour, Dates	£	£
BW085	unpainted brass - *09?*	NPG	NPG
BW086	unlined black - *09?*	NPG	NPG
BW087	unlined green - *09?*	NPG	NPG

L0-4. LMS 4F 0-6-0 (2002)

Cat No.	Company, Number, Colour, Dates	£	£
BW015	unpainted brass (also YO4F) - *02*	390	469
BW016	black (also YO4FP) - *05*	475	549

L0-5. LMS Crab 2-6-0 (2005)

Cat No.	Company, Number, Colour, Dates	£	£
BW025	unpainted brass (also YOCRAB) - *05*	600	685
BW026	black (also YOCRABP) - *05*	635	712

L0-6. LMS Ivatt 2MT 2-6-0 (2008)

Cat No.	Company, Number, Colour, Dates	£	£
BW075	unpainted brass - *08*	945	1019
BW076	unlined black - *08*	975	1057
BW077	unlined green - *09*	975	1057

L0-7. LNER A3 Class 4-6-2 (2006)

Cat No.	Company, Number, Colour, Dates	£	£
BW035	Flying Scotsman as preserved unpainted brass - *06*	725	800
BW036	LNER Doncaster green as preserved Flying Scotsman - *06*	890	964
BW041	LNER Doncaster green with GN tender, banjo dome, double chimney and smoke deflectors - *06*	890	964
BW045	unpainted brass with non-corridor tender, banjo dome, single chimney - *06*	725	800
BW046	BR green with non-corridor tender, banjo dome, single chimney - *06*	890	964
BW047	Doncaster green with non-corridor tender, banjo dome, double chimney, smoke deflectors - *06*	890	964
BW048	unpainted brass with GN tender, banjo dome, single chimney - *06*	725	800
BW049	BR green with GN tender, banjo dome, single chimney - *06*	890	965
BW050	Doncaster green with GN tender, banjo dome, single chimney - *06*	890	965
BW052	BR Brunswick green with non-corridor tender, domed top feed, single chimney - *06*	890	964
BW053	BR Doncaster green with non-corridor tender, domed top feed, single chimney - *06*	890	964
BW055	BR Brunswick green with GN tender, domed top feed, double chimney - *06*	890	964
BW056	LNER Doncaster green with GN tender, domed top feed, double chimney - *06*	890	964
BW057	unpainted brass with non-corridor tender, domed top feed, double chimney - *07*	725	800
BW057PL	LNER Doncaster green supplied fully lined with non-corridor tender, domed top feed, double chimney - *07*	1100	1175
BW058	BR green supplied fully lined with non-corridor tender, domed top feed, double chimney - *07*	1100	1175
BW059	with non-corridor tender, domed top feed, double chimney and smoke deflectors - *07*	890	964
BW059PL	with non-corridor tender, domed top feed, double chimney and smoke deflectors - *07*	1100	1175
BW069	LNER Doncaster green with non-corridor tender, banjo dome, single chimney - *07*	890	964
BW070	unpainted brass with GN tender, domed top feed, single chimney - *07*	725	800
BW071	BR green with GN tender, domed top feed, single chimney - *07*	890	964
BW072	LNER Doncaster green with GN tender, domed top feed, single chimney - *07*	890	964

L0-8. Class 03 (2006)

Cat No.	Company, Number, Colour, Dates	£	£
BW250	unpainted brass with flower pot chimney - *06*	300	377

0 gauge Class 03 diesel shunter in brass finish [L0-8]

Cat No.	Company, Number, Colour, Dates	£	£
BW250A	unpainted brass with flower pot chimney, air tanks - *06*	300	377
BW251	BR green with wasp stripes, flower pot chimney - *06*	335	412
BW252	BR blue with wasp stripes, flower pot chimney - *06*	335	412
BW253	unpainted brass, cone chimney, air tanks - *06*	300	377

L0-9. Class 04 (2007)

Cat No.	Company, Number, Colour, Dates	£	£
BW260	unpainted brass - *07*	300	377
BW261	BR blue with wasp stripes - *07*	335	412
BW262	BR green with wasp stripes - *07*	335	412
BW263	BR black - *07*	320	395

L0-10. Class 08 (2002)

Two types (A & B) were available. The A Type is the earlier version.

Cat No.	Company, Number, Colour, Dates	£	£
YO08	unpainted brass - *02*	275	349
YO09	unpainted brass (type B) - *04*	275	349
BW270	BR blue with wasp stripes (type B) - *07*	425	505

BW169	BR green (type A) (also YOO8PG) - *07*	425	505

L0-11. Class 24/0 (2001)

YO24	unpainted brass - *01*	275	349
BW275	BR green - *09?*	NPG	NPG
BW276	BR blue - *09?*	NPG	NPG

L0-12. Class 25/3 (2001)

YO25	unpainted brass - *01*	275	349
BW285	BR green - *09?*	NPG	NPG
BW286	BR blue - *09?*	NPG	NPG

L0-13. Class 101 2-Car DMU (2008)

These vehicles were supplied ready-to-run. They were unpainted brass and required painting, glazing and interiors to be fitted by the purchaser.

YO101	unpainted brass - *99*	320	395
BW295	BR green - *08*	570	645
BW296	BR blue - *08*	570	645

L0-14. Class 106 2-Car DMU (2001)

These vehicles were supplied ready-to-run. They were unpainted brass and required painting, glazing and interiors to be fitted by the purchaser.

YO106	unpainted brass - *01*	335	409
BW295	BR green - *08*	570	645
BW296	BR blue - *08*	570	645

L0-15. Class 121 ('Bubble Car') (2000)

These vehicles were supplied ready-to-run. They were unpainted brass and required painting, glazing and interiors to be fitted by the purchaser.

0 gauge Class 121 'Bubble Car' in paint finish [L0-15]

YO122	unpainted brass - *00*	220	295
BW325	BR green - *08*	435	510
BW326	BR blue - *08*	435	510

L0-16. Wickham Trolley & Trailer (2009)

BW305	unpainted brass - *09?*	NPG	NPG
BW306	painted - *09?*	NPG	NPG

COACHES

These coaches were supplied ready-to-run. They were unpainted brass and required painting, glazing and interiors to be fitted by the purchaser. At the time of their introduction they were the first ready-to-run 0 gauge coaches to be introduced since the demise of the underscale Lima Mark 1 coaches and the only alternative had been kit built coaching stock.

The coaches were later available only through Tower Models and were incorporated into the Tower Brass range for a number of years.

Cat No.	Company, Number, Colour, Dates	£	£
C0-1.	**BR MK1 Stock** (1999)		
	All are unpainted brass models.		
Y7-96-001	SK corridor 2nd - *99*	120	159
Y7-96-002	SO open 2nd - *99*	120	159
Y7-96-003	FO 1st open - *99*	120	159
Y7-96-004	FK corridor 1st - *99*	120	159
Y7-96-005	RMB miniature buffet - *99*	120	159
Y7-96-006	BSK corridor 2nd - *99*	120	159
Y7-96-007	BCK corridor composite brake - *99*	120	159
Y7-96-008	full brake - *99*	120	159
Y7-96-009	CK corridor 2nd - *99*	120	159
Y7-96-010	SO/SK suburban 2nd - *99*	120	159
Y7-96-011	suburban 2nd brake - *99*	120	159

WAGONS

These vehicles were supplied ready-to-run. They were unpainted brass and required painting by the purchaser

Cat No.	Company, Number, Colour, Dates	£	£
W0-1.	**MEA 46t Steel Box Mineral Wagon** (2000)		
Y555	unpainted brass - *00*	45	59
W0-2.	**HEA 46t GLW Hopper Wagon** (2000)		
Y380	unpainted brass - *00*	45	59
W0-3.	**12T Tank Wagon** (2001)		
Y650	unpainted brass with ladder and cat walk - *01*	45	59
Y651	unpainted brass with large filler and straps - *01*	45	59
Y652	unpainted brass without ladder or cat walk - *01*	45	59
W0-4.	**20T Tank Wagon** (2001)		
Y675	unpainted brass - *01*	50	64

GAUGE 1

LOCOMOTIVES

Cat No.	Company, Number, Colour, Dates	£	£
L1-1.	**GWR Class 57xx 0-6-0PT** (2007)		
BW1021	unpainted brass - *07*	580	655
BW1020	black - *07*	650	722
BW1022	green - *07*	650	722
L1-2.	**GWR Class 8750 0-6-0PT** (2009)		
BW1005	unpainted brass - *09?*	NPG	NPG
BW1005	black - *09?*	NPG	NPG
BW1007	green - *09?*	NPG	NPG
L1-3.	**LMS Johnson 1F 0-6-0T** (2009)		
BW1015	unpainted brass closed cab - *09?*	NPG	NPG
BW1016	unlined black closed cab - *09?*	NPG	NPG
BW1017	unpainted brass open cab - *09?*	NPG	NPG
BW1018	unlined black open cab - *09?*	NPG	NPG
L1-4.	**LMS Class 3F 'Jinty' 0-6-0T** (2006)		

1 gauge LMS 'Jinty' 0-6-0T in paint finish (pre-production model) [L1-4] (Tony Wright)

BW1010	unpainted brass - *06*	485	560
BW1011	unlined black - *06*	535	610
L1-5.	**LNER J94 0-6-0T** (2006)		
BW1000	unpainted brass, high bunker - *06*	425	499
BW1001	black, high bunker - *06*	485	560
BW1002	unpainted brass, standard bunker - *06*	425	499
BW1003	black, standard bunker - *06*	485	560

L1-6.	**GWR Class 45xx 2-6-2T** (2008)		
BW1100	unpainted brass - *08*	650	725
BW1102	unlined green - *08*	700	775
L1-7.	**GWR Class 4575 2-6-2T** (2008)		
BW1150	unpainted brass - *08*	650	725
BW1152	unlined green - *08*	700	775
L1-8.	**LMS Class 5MT ('Black Five') 4-6-0** (2008)		
	Paired with a 4,000 gallon Stanier tender.		
BW2001	unpainted brass riveted tender - *08*	1100	1200
BW2002	unpainted brass smooth tender - *08*	1100	1200
L1-9.	**Class 03** (2008)		
BW1075	unpainted brass, flower pot chimney, air tanks - *08*	500	575
BW1077	unpainted brass, flower pot chimney, air brakes - *08*	570	645
BW1077A	green, flower pot chimney - *08*	570	645
BW1078	unpainted brass, conical exhaust - *08*	570	645
BW1078A	unpainted brass, cone chimney, air tanks - *08*	500	575
BW1080	blue, conical exhaust - 08	570	645
L1-10.	**Class 04** (2008)		
BW1024	BR green - *08*	570	645
BW1025	BR blue - *08*	570	645

GAUGE 3

LOCOMOTIVES

Cat No.	Company, Number, Colour, Dates	£	£
L3-1.	**GWR Class 45xx 2-6-2T** (2008)		
BW1160	green - *08*	1350	1475

COACHES

This vehicle was supplied ready-to-run. They were unpainted brass and required painting, glazing and interiors to be fitted by the purchaser. They normally ran in pairs.

Cat No.	Company, Number, Colour, Dates	£	£
C3-1.	**GWR B Set** (2009)		
BW1161	unpainted brass - *09*	750	840

NARROW GAUGE

These were built to 1:19th scale to run on garden railways. Both 32mm and 45mm track gauge options were available

LOCOMOTIVES

Cat No.	Company, Number, Colour, Dates	£	£
LN-1.	**Double Fairlie 0-4-4-0** (2008)		

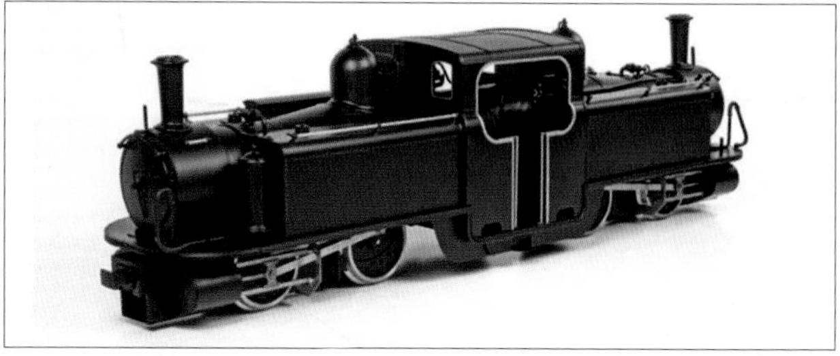

Narrow gauge Double Fairlie 0-4-4-0 in paint finish [LN-1]

BW1500	green 32mm gauge - *08*	1100	1220
BW1545	green 45mm gauge - *08*	1100	1220

Bachmann ex-LMS unrebuilt 'Patroit' The Royal Leicestershire Regiment by Robbie McGavin

Bassett-Lowke 0

HISTORY

Wenman Joseph Bassett-Lowke was born in December 1877 and was a member of the boiler making family, J T Lowke & Co Ltd. After the death of Tom Lowke, his wife had married one Absalom Bassett who adopted her son Joseph Tom Lowke. He got on well with his stepfather and when he married and had three sons of his own he gave them all 'Bassett' as their middle name. The two surviving sons grew up using the surname Bassett-Lowke. Wenman, for some reason, took the name Whynne but was often referred to simply as 'WJ'.

Milestones

1899 Bassett-Lowke sets up his company with Harry Franklin.
1899 B-L produces his first mail order catalogue at the age of just 22.
1900 Paris Exhibition and B-L enters into an import agreements with Stefan Bing and George Carette.
1901 B-L takes delivery of his first supply from Bing.
1901 Henry Greenly appointed Consulting Engineer and Designer to B-L.
1902 Track developed by George Winteringham.
1902 First comprehensive catalogue produced containing railway items.
1905 First exhibition stand at the Model engineering Exhibition in London.
1905 *Model Railway Handbook* first published.
1907 'Lowko' motor introduced.
1908 Winteringham Ltd formed as a subsidiary.
1908 B-L opens his first shop in Holborn, London.
1910 Bassett-Lowke Ltd becomes a public company.
1912 First Continental retail agency opens in Paris.
1913 Acquire Carson models etc.
1916 Acquire C Butcher's stock.
1919 Mass production plant installed for small gauge models.
1920-23 Winteringham's trademark appears on some items.
1922 Introduction of Bing 'Table Top Railway'.
1922 Edinburgh shop opens.
1922 First American agency established in New York.
1924 Smallest model railway in the world made for Queen's dolls house.
1925 Cast loco paperweights.
1927 BDV gift coupon scheme sells 30,000 locos.
1927 Manchester shop opened.
1931 Robert Bindon Blood joins B-L, later to design many of the better models.
1932 Franz Bing emigrates to England.
1932 Trix Ltd founded in the UK with W J Bassett-Lowke as a Director.
1935 Launch of Trix Twin Railway.
1941 Founding of Precision Models Ltd.
1946 Reappearance of models after the war.
1949 50th Anniversary celebrations.
1950 New BR livery appears on a B-L locomotive.
1953 Death of W J Bassett-Lowke.
1963 Last Bassett-Lowke catalogue released.
1965 Bassett-Lowke Ltd ceases trading.
1968 Bassett-Lowke Railways produce some prototype models.
2000 Corgi Classics re-launch the range.
2008 Hornby acquire the brand.

Whynne Bassett-Lowke trained in the family business but wanted to strike out on his own. With his father's book keeper, Harold Franklin, he founded his own model engineering company in 1899 while still serving an apprenticeship with his father. This became a limited company in 1910 with a factory base in Northampton. The Company was never large although its output was considerable. This was achieved by contracting out work to other companies that Bassett-Lowke became associated with. One of these was Winteringham Ltd, which had been established by George Winteringham in 1908 as a subsidiary, and this became Bassett-Lowke's main manufacturer.

WJ had been to the 1900 Paris Exhibition and been much impressed by the products of German manufacturers such as Marklin, Carette and Bing. A year later, all three had agreed to manufacture models to Bassett-Lowke's designs for the latter to sell in the UK. The first supply arrived in 1901 and the first locomotive was a gauge 3 model of a LNWR 4-4-0 named *Black Prince*. WJ supplemented the supplies he received from Germany with models built within his limited facilities although, initially, these were mainly freelance subjects. By 1904 a range of 40 locomotives were being offered!

In 1913, when James Carson & Co. abandoned model engineering, Bassett-Lowke purchased their stock but the only 0 gauge locomotive in this range was an LNWR 4-6-0 'Experiment'. Since 1910, they had been marketing some of Carson's larger scale models which remained in the Bassett-Lowke catalogue until 1925. They also advertised the Carson roller test-rig in the early '20s.

The same thing happened in 1916 when C Butcher & Co. of Watford, who had previously been making high quality models for Bassett-Lowke, gave up model railway production and sold Bassett-Lowke their remaining stock.

Stanier LMS Class 4P 2-6-4T No.2603 [L21] (Vectis)

The German supplies ceased during the First World War but Bing and Marklin both produced models to Bassett-Lowke's requirements after the war. However, it took Germany sometime to recover from the war and there was now considerable anti-German feeling in Britain, particularly among Bassett-Lowke's affluent middle class whose boyhood ranks had been so tragically decimated.

When German supplies did resume, Bassett-Lowke removed German trademarks and stamped the models 'Foreign Made'. Any models marked 'Bing' or 'Marklin' are likely to be from stocks supplied before the First World War. They even supported the sentiments against German products in their advertising! Eventually, around 1930, Winteringham's took over production and Bassett-Lowke became less reliant on imported products.

Model railways in gauges 0, 1, 2 and 3 were only part of the Bassett-Lowke business. They also made stationary engines, model ships and miniature railways. A man who became closely linked with Bassett-Lowke for many years was Henry Greenly and he was responsible for the design of some of their engines as well as the British liveries used on German models made for the British market. Another famous name associated with Bassett-Lowke was the model maker EW Twining who illustrated catalogues for them and later joined the company.

Year-by-year the Bassett-Lowke catalogue grew and was split into different interest sections. Besides the large range of railway locomotives, rolling stock, accessories, track and sets being offered, there were the drawings and parts to enable you to construct your own models in one of a number of gauges. Models were also available with a choice of power units; namely steam, clockwork or electric.

The range of locomotives available before and immediately after the First World War was considerable and some were available for many years. Amongst the favourites were the 'Precursor' tank, *George the Fifth*, *Sydney*, Deeley Compound (which was also available as a kit from 1909), GNR 'Atlantic' and the Great Central locomotive *Sir Sam Fay*.

In the early 1920s, Bassett-Lowke and Henry Greenly were instrumental in introducing 00 scale to Britain in the form of the Bing Table Top Railway. This started life as a clockwork system but was soon available with electric motors. In the mid 1930s they assisted Trix to establish a company in Britain and this became closely associated with Winteringham's where the models were made.

A different approach to marketing had been made in 1927 through

Godfrey Phillips BDV cigarettes, where sons were encouraged to get their fathers to smoke themselves to death to collect enough tokens for the Bassett-Lowke model of the 'Duke of York'! Bassett-Lowke made 30,000 locomotives for this promotion. It was in October this year that Bassett-Lowke opened a shop at 28 Corporation Street, Manchester. A branch they had opened earlier in Fredrick Street, Edinburgh, was closed in 1930.

LNWR 4-4-0 George the Fifth by Bing (for B-L) [L35c]

As the years passed, the demand for the larger gauges fell away and 0 gauge became the mainstay of Bassett-Lowke Ltd, especially after the First World War. Likewise, interest in electric traction grew and that in steam and clockwork lessened especially after the Second World War.

Some of the finest and most famous Bassett-Lowke locomotives were built during the late 1920s and 1930s; many designed by Robert Bindon Blood. Popular subjects included *Flying Scotsman, Royal Scot, Lord Nelson*, a 'Jubilee', *Princess Elizabeth*, a 'Duchess', a range of A4s with different names, a Midland 'Compound', the 0-6-0 and 0-4-0 Standard tanks and, of course, the much loved 'Moguls'.

Production in Northampton ceased during the Second World War and restarted sometime after the cessation of hostilities. The new British Railways livery made its appearance on Bassett-Lowke models in 1950 and, the following year, the 4-4-0 *Princess Elizabeth* was replaced by *Prince Charles.* Notable post-war locomotives were the rebuilt 'Royal Scot', *Spitfire* ('Castle'), *Britannia*, the Classes 5, 8F and 9F and a 'Deltic'. These were mostly built in brass for Bassett-Lowke by Mr V Hunt and some were later rebuilt to a higher quality by Mr V Reader. These compare favourably with today's finescale 0 gauge models.

The final catalogue was published in 1963 and trading ceased in 1965; although there was a short lived attempt at reviving the company in the late 1960s under the name Bassett-Lowke Railways.

In the mid 1990s, a range of white metal models, in 1:43 scale, was produced under the Bassett-Lowke name by the then owners. These were of steam land vehicles such as a 'Clayton' steam lorry, a 'Burrell' steam roller and others. A showman's engine had been planned but deposits for this had to be returned when the name and intellectual assets of the company were acquired by Corgi. This acquisition provided an interesting link with the past. Corgi had been a product of Mettoy, a company which started life in 1933 in the basement and ground floor of the Winteringham factory. At the time Winteringham Ltd was, of course, the production arm of Bassett-Lowke Ltd!

At the 2000 British Toy and Hobbies Fair at Olympia, Corgi Classics launched the first of a new range of Bassett-Lowke 0 gauge locomotives and the subject chosen for the re-launch was a steam powered 'Mogul'. All subsequent models produced by Corgi were electric powered.

In 2008, Hornby bought Corgi Classics and with it Bassett-Lowke.

Further Reading

The standard work is *The Bassett-Lowke Story* by Roland Fuller, published by New Cavendish Books (ISBN 0-904568-34-2). This is out of print but available through the public library service. A book of value to researchers is *Wenman Joseph Bassett-Lowke* by his late niece Janet Bassett-Lowke and published by Rail Romances (ISBN 1-900622-01-7). This same publisher has also released a video tape showing footage taken by WJ himself which includes factory scenes.

Collectors Club

The Bassett-Lowke Society caters for those who collect and operate Bassett-Lowke models. The Society publishes a quarterly magazine called *Lowko News* and organises events to which members may take their stock to run. For further information about the Society, ring the secretary on 01473 437713.

Prices - There is very limited information about prices of Bassett-Lowke models except through auctions. Where auction prices are known, the latest is given but it should be remembered that some of these are now 4 or 5 years old. These will be added to as more information becomes available. The two prices suggest a range for a model in good condition.

Codes - The following codes are peculiar to this section:
(F) = Freelance design. Also, 'Standard' normally implies freelance.
(B) = Made by Bing for Bassett-Lowke.
(C) = Made by Carette for Bassett-Lowke.
(H) = Made by Hunt for Bassett-Lowke.
(L) = Made by Leeds Model Company for Bassett-Lowke.
(M) = Made by Marklin for Bassett-Lowke.
litho = lithographed (printed as opposed to painted) locomotives.

Dates - The dates when models were available are very difficult to determine so long after the event and should not be taken too seriously. They also ignore breaks in availability during the two World Wars when the company was engaged in war work.

LOCOMOTIVES

Pre-WW1 - Not listed here are a number of imported 0 gauge locomotives listed in Bassett-Lowke's catalogues before the First World War. These bore little resemblance to any real locomotives and included 0-4-0Ts, 0-4-0s, 2-2-0Ts, 2-2-0s and 4-4-0s. However, in the larger gauges 1, 2, 3 and 4, greater realism could be found as early as 1902 including quite authentic British liveries. Both steam powered and clockwork versions were available from the start.

4-4-0 'Enterprise' steam powered loco [L28] (Vectis)

Hand-Built Locomotives - In 1933, Bassett-Lowke announced a range of hand-built locomotives which could be made to order. The models would be to a very high specification including all solder construction, all external and visible details and full painting and lining. Locomotives could be had either with variable speed clockwork drive, 8-10v DC or 20v AC electric mechanisms. These are listed together below in Table L97.

'Nu-Scale' - In 1957, Bassett-Lowke introduced both a 2-rail electric control system and a 'Nu-Scale' service. Nu-Scale was Bassett-Lowke's response to a changing market which required an improved, more scale, appearance for model railway locomotives which would run on BRMSB gauge 0 scale track, as well as standard Bassett-Lowke track. The changes, which increased prices by 30 to 40%, included replacing the alloy wheels with 10-spoke iron ones on the front bogie wheels, thinner driving wheel profiles (.200"), Stuart Turner wheel castings and iron ones on the tender. It also meant sprung close-coupled tender drawbars, lamp brackets and lamps, whistles and extra handrails. All the standard range of locomotives, in 2 or 3-rail, were available with these improvements except for *Prince Charles*.

Warning! - Be careful when buying models alleged to be 'Nu-Scale' versions as the term is often misused to describe a locomotive which has had some or all of its wheels changed or thinned down, has been converted to 2-rail electric or has had non-standard details added. These conversions could actually reduce the value of the model on the collector's market, rather than increase it as would be the case with a genuine 'Nu-Scale' model.

The 'Nu-Scale' service does not appear to have been well used judging by the infrequency with which these models turn up at auction. That said, particularly the iron 10 spoke front bogie wheels, do appear on 'Compounds', *Prince Charles* and *Flying Scotsman* locomotives where these have been obtained separately by individual customers. Collectors are advised to check the provenance most carefully.

Missing Tables - it will be noticed that some tables appear to be missing. This is a result of rationalisation resulting from further research. Renumbering of the tables will take place in a future edition of the book to take account of this.

Loco Search

The following table will help you to trace that elusive model. If you know the running number on the side of the locomotive or its tender you can look it up in the following table and the adjacent column will tell you in what section you will find it.

Loco Nos.	Tables	Loco Nos.	Tables	Loco Nos.	Tables
1	L88	773	L51	2495	L62
10	L3	773	L76	2509	L81
11	L12	850	L75	2510	L81
23	L90	851	L62	2511	L81
25	L3	864	L60	2512	L81
33	L57	866	L60	2524	L20
36	L3	903	L61	2526	L20
41	L10	910	L47	2531	L20
44	L10	930	L52	2531	L21
45	L9	947	L13	2536	L20
63	L3	955	L26	2603	L20
73	L13	982	L57	2603	L21
77	L37	999	L30	2663	L35a
78	L13	1000	L38	2663	L35b
78	L16	1000	L35	2664	L35a
88	L3	1017	L2	2664	L35b
89	L12	1036	L39	2670	L22
94	L17	1063	L39	2700	L55
100	L2	1067	L39	2838	L72
101	L2	1082	L39	2848	L72
103	L80	1106	L4	2871	L62
112	L1	1108	L39	2945	L57
142	L36	1113	L39	3064	L93
211	L1	1190	L39	3400	L39
251	L49	1425	L49	3410	L44
298	L14	1442	L49	3433	L35c
335	L13	1448	L53a	3433	L44
433	L13	1456	L54	3536	L20
440	L27	1652	L94	3611	L9
441	L5	1864	L57	3611	L18
483	L40	1902	L33	3800	L45
504	L9	1927	L31	3801	L45
504	L42	1930	L31	4072	L53
504	L35c	1931	L31	4079	L73
513	L34	1931	L53	4256	L54
513	L35c	2066	L58	4331	L59
596	L9	2241	L11	4390	L42
601	L41	2265	L32	4417	L55
650	L24	2350	L48	4420	L25

Loco Nos.	Tables	Loco Nos.	Tables	Loco Nos.	Tables
4431	L59	6100	L67	41109	L39
4460	L51	6101	L19	41125	L39
4460	L63	6105	L18	41611	L13
4472	L51	6200	L77	41613	L13
4472	L64	6201	L77	42603	L21
4472	L80	6202	L77	42608	L21
4481	L2	6220	L78	42980	L56
4489	L81	6225	L78	43871	L54
4490	L81	6232	L79	45126	L71
4498	L81	6285	L28	45295	L62
4844	L61A	6311	L7a	46100	L68
4853	L70	6508	L51	46232	L79
5071	L73	6508	L65	48209	L85
5320	L35	6560	L94	60103	L80
5374	L13	6750	L25	61324	L63
5524	L62	6810	L10	62078	L32a
5552	L69	7100	L13	62136	L32a
5573	L69	7083	L92	62453	L32a
5600	L66	8851	L25	62759	L28
5701	L69	8851	L51	63871	L54
5712	L69	8872	L50	64193	L54
5765	L15	8937	L13	68211	L13
6000	L74	9405	L42a	70000	L82
6027	L74	13000	L55	92220	L87
6100	L19	13007	L56		

Cat No.	Company, Number, Colour, Dates	£	£

Tank Engines

L1. L&SWR Class S14 0-4-0T (by Bing) (1921)

Cat No.	Company, Number, Colour, Dates	£	£
53/0	**112** LNWR black steam - *21-29*	NPG	NPG
21/0	as above c/w - *21-29*	NPG	NPG
37/0	**211** LNWR black electric - *21-29*	325	350
53/0	**112** GNR green steam - *21-29*	NPG	NPG
21/0	as above c/w - *21-29*	NPG	NPG
21/0	as above electric - *21-29*	NPG	NPG
37/0	**211** GNR green electric - *21-29*	NPG	NPG
53/0	**112** MR red steam - *21-29*	NPG	NPG
21/0	as above c/w - *21-29*	NPG	NPG
37/0	**211** MR red electric - *21-29*	NPG	NPG
53/0	**112** NER brown steam - *21-29*	NPG	NPG
53/0	**112** CR blue steam - *21-29*	NPG	NPG
21/0	as above c/w - *21-29*	NPG	NPG
31/0	as above electric - *21-29*	NPG	NPG
37/0	**211** CR blue electric - *21-29*	NPG	NPG
21/0	**112** GWR green c/w - *21-29*	400	600
21/0	**112** LMS maroon c/w - *24-29*	NPG	NPG
21/0	**112** L&NER green c/w - *24-29*	NPG	NPG

L2. Peckett 0-4-0ST (by Carette and Bing) (1907)

The Carette version was slightly smaller than the Bing one.

Cat No.	Company, Number, Colour, Dates	£	£
3104/0	**100** MR maroon (B) c/w - *?*	450	650
3104/0	**101** LNWR black (B) c/w - *07-09-?*	400	550
3104/0	**101** MR maroon (B) c/w - *07-09-?*	350	550
3104/0	**101** GNR green (B) c/w - *07-?*	500	650
3104/0	**1017** green (C) c/w - *24-34*	300	400
3104/0	as above (C) electric - *24-34*	500	600
-	**4481** green electric - *24-34*	400	450

Standard 0-4-0T LNER No.88 [L3] (Vectis)

L3. Standard Tank 0-4-0T (1937)

-	**10** LMS black DC electric - *37-?*	300	360
4730/0	**25** LMS black litho c/w - *37-?*	NPG	NPG
-	as above electric - *37-?*	NPG	NPG
4730/0	**36** LMS black litho c/w - *37-?*	200	250
-	as above electric - *37-?*	300	450
4730/0	**36** LNER black litho c/w - *37-?*	NPG	NPG
-	as above electric - *37-?*	NPG	NPG
-	**88** LNER green DC electric - 37-?	NPG	NPG
-	as above but black - 37-?	300	400
4730/0	**63** Southern black litho c/w - *37-?*	NPG	NPG
-	as above electric - 37-?	NPG	NPG

L4. GWR Class 11XX Class Dock Tank 0-4-0T (1961)

These were made to order.

-	**1106** GWR green (only about 3 made) electric - *61-63*	NPG	NPG

L5. NER Class 0 Passenger Tank 0-4-4T (by Bing) (1914)

-	**441** NER green c/w - *14-19*	NPG	NPG

L6. GNR Suburban Tank 0-4-4T (by Marklin) (1907)

-	GNR c/w - *07-?*	NPG	NPG

L7. L&SWR Class M7 Tank 0-4-4T (by Bing) (1909)

-	**109** LSWR yellow-green c/w - *09-13*	750	900

L7A. GWR Tank 2-4-2T (by Bing) (1911)

-	**3611** GWR green c/w - *11-13*	1900	2800
-	as above electric - *13-16*	1900	2800

L8. 4-4-0T (Freelance) (by Bing) (1920)

Also known as a 'Short Precursor'.

-	GNR green c/w - *20-26*	NPG	NPG
23593/0	L&NWR black c/w - *20-26*	NPG	NPG
-	MR red c/w - *20-26*	NPG	NPG
-	CR blue c/w - *20-26*	NPG	NPG
-	GWR green c/w - *20-26*	NPG	NPG
-	NBR brown c/w - *20-26*	NPG	NPG

'Short Precursor' 4-4-0T in North British livery [L9]

L9. Short 'Precursor' Tank 4-4-0T (by Bing) (1921)

-	GNR lined green c/w - *21-?*	360	500
-	CR blue c/w - *21-?*	NPG	NPG
-	Great Western green c/w - *21-?*	450	550
-	MR red c/w - *21-?*	NPG	NPG
-	**3611** L&NWR black c/w - *21-?*	NPG	NPG
-	**45, 4221** LMS maroon c/w - *23-?*	400	600
-	**504** LNER green c/w - *?*	550	900
-	**3611** LNER black c/w - *23-?*	400	450
-	**596** SR lined green - *?*	600	1000

L10a. L&NWR 'Precursor' Tank 4-4-2T (by Marklin) (1909)

-	**44** L&NWR black c/w - *09-10*	450	550
-	as above electric - *09-10?*	450	550

L10b. L&NWR 'Precursor' Tank 4-4-2T (Enamelled) (by Bing) (1911)

3101/0	**44** L&NWR black c/w - *11-19?*	350	450
-	as above *3-rail 4-8v DC - 11-14?*	350	450

L10c. L&NWR 'Precursor' Tank 4-4-2T (Litho) (by Bing)

3101/0	L&NWR black c/w - *20?*	350	450
-	as above *3-rail 4-8v DC - 20?*	350	450

L10d. L&NWR 'Precursor' Tank 4-4-2T (1921)

3101/0	**44** L&NWR black c/w - *21-c23*	300	400
-	as above electric - *21-c23*	300	400
-	**6810** L&NWR black c/w - *21-?*	NPG	NPG
-	as above electric - *21-c23*	NPG	NPG
- *	as above electric over-painted 'LMS' - *c25*	400	500

LNWR 'Precursor' 4-4-2T No.44 by Marklin (for B-L) [L10d] (Vectis)

3101/0	**6810** LMS red c/w - *25-28*	250	400
2/0	as above electric 3-rail 12vDC - *25-28*	300	450
-	**41** M&GN yellow electric - *64*	NPG	NPG
-	**9*** M&GN yellow electric - *?*	NPG	NPG

* Special order

L11. GWR 'County' Tank 4-4-2T (1950)

-	**2241** GWR green one-off electric - *c50*	NPG	NPG

L12a. LBSCR I2 Class 4-4-2T (by Bing) (1911)

4/0	**11** LB&SCR umber c/w - *11-25*	350	550
-	as above electric - *11-25*	450	600

L12b. LBSCR I3 Class 4-4-2T (1969)

-	**89** LB&SCR umber electric - *69*	500	650

L13. Standard Tank 0-6-0T (Freelance) (1933)

All the 0-6-0 standard tanks were lithographed. Some electric locomotives were fitted with a super reduction gear (40:1) for shunting and locos can be found with automatic (track operated) couplings. Likewise, some models are found with smoke units driven by a cam on the front axle. The LMS versions had a capuchon on the chimney. Pre-war electric models did not have key holes or control rod holes in the cab rear plate while post-war examples usually did, until late production orders. Catalogue number 4305/0 was used until 1940 for electric locos fitted with junior permag mechanisms.

3305/0	**5374** LMS black lined red c/w - *33-38*	250	350
4305/0	as above electric - *33-38*	350	450
4305/0	as above with Walschaerts valve gear electric - *33-38*	450	650
3305/0	**61** LMS black lined red c/w - *38-50*	250	350
5305/0	as above electric - *38-50*	350	450
5505/0	as above electric 20vAC - *38-50*	350	450
3305/0	**78** LMS black lined red c/w - *38-50*	250	350
5305/0	as above electric - *38-50*	350	450
3305/0	**7100** LMS black lined red electric - *?*	250	350
3305/0	**335** LNER black lined red c/w - *33-38*	250	350
5305/0	as above electric - *33-38*	350	450
3305/0	**433** LNER black lined red c/w - *38-50*	250	350
5305/0	as above electric - *38-50*	350	450
3305/0	**533** LNER black lined red c/w - *47-50*	250	350
5305/0	as above electric 12vDC - *47-50*	250	350
5305/0	**8937** LNER black lined red electric 12vDC - *47-50*	300	430
5305/0	**9033** LNER black lined red electric - *48-50*	450	550

Strandard 0-6-0T in BR black livery [L13] (Vectis)

3305/0	**947** Southern black lined green c/w - *38-50*	350	400
5305/0	as above electric 12vDC - *38-50*	400	500
3305/0	**68211** BRb black lined red c/w - *51-67*	250	350
5305/0	as above electric 12v DC 3-rail - *51-67*	300	350
2305/0	as above 2-rail electric - *51-67*	350	400
3305/0	**41611** BRb black lined red c/w - *51-67*	250	350
5305/0	as above electric - *57-67*	400	500
2305/0	as above 2-rail electric - *51-67*	400	500
-	as above electric Nu-Scale** - *57-65*	550	650
3305/0	LMS black lined red c/w - *59-61*	400	450
5305/0	as above electric - *59-61*	450	550
2305/0	as above 2-rail electric - *59-61*	450	550
3305/0	LNER black lined red c/w - *59-63*	400	450
5305/0	as above electric - *59-63*	450	550
2305/0	as above 2-rail electric - *59-63*	450	550
-	**41613-41617*** Longmoor Military Railway (LMR) blue electric - *?*	450	750

* used for training at Longmoor Military Railway. It is understood that they were numbered in sequence from 41613 to 41617. ** See note on Nu-Scale in the Introduction to this chapter.

L14. Hudswell Clarke Ex-Bury Port 0-6-0T (1968)

-	**298** black prototype only, steam - *68*	NPG	NPG

L15. GWR Class 27XX Pannier Tank 0-6-0PT

-	GWR green 2/3 rail electric - *?-50-57?*	NPG	NPG

L15A. GWR 57XX Pannier 0-6-0PT (by Hunt) (1958)

-	**5765, 5775** * Great Western green electric - *58-63*	1600	2000

* Made to order. Other numbers probably exist.

L16. LMS Class 3P Suburban Tank 2-6-2T (1941)

This model was listed only in the 1941/42 catalogue.

3620/0	**78** LMS black lined red c/w - *41-42*	1800	2200
5620/0	**78** LMS black lined red 8-10vDC - *41-42*	1800	2200
5720/0	**78** LMS black lined red 20v AC - *41-42*	1800	2200

L17. LMS Fowler 'Prairie' Tank 2-6-2T

-	**94** LMS black lined red c/w - *?*	2100	2900
-	as above electric 3-rail AC - *?*	2100	2900

L18. GWR 61XX Class 'Prairie' 2-6-2T (1937)

3609/0	**6105** GWR button green c/w - *37-41?*	1100	2200

GWR 2-6-2T No.6104 by Hunt (for B-L) [L18] (Vectis)

A4609/0	as above electric AC - *37-41?*	1100	2200
5609/0	as above electric DC - *37-41?*	1100	2200

L19. GWR 61XX Class 'Prairie' 2-6-2T (by Hunt) (1955)

Hand-built to order. Other numbers probably exist.

-	**6100, 6101, 6104** Great Western green electric 2/3 rail - *55-63*	800	2400

L20. Stanier 3-Cylinder 4P 2-6-4T (by Marklin) (1935)

This was an early Stanier design and had a combined dome and water feed pipe on top of the boiler, a taper to the front footplate and a pronounced curve to the rear of the cab doorway aperture.

913/0/C	**2524** LMS black c/w - *35-?*	1800	2100
913/0/A	as above electric AC - *35-?*	1800	2400
913/0/D	as above electric DC - *35-?*	1800	2400
913/0/C	**2526** LMS black c/w - *c37*	2300	2800
913/0/A	as above electric AC - *c37*	2300	2800
913/0/D	as above electric DC - *c37*	2300	2800
913/0/C	**2531** LMS black c/w - *c39*	1100	1600
913/0/A	as above electric AC - *c39*	1100	1600
913/0/D	as above electric DC - *c39*	1100	1600
913/0/C	**2536** LMS black c/w - *c37*	1800	2300
913/0/A	as above electric AC - *c37*	1800	2300
913/0/D	as above electric DC - *c37*	1800	2300

L21. LMS Stanier 2-Cylinder 4P Tank 2-6-4T (1940)

This was a later Stanier design with separate dome and water feed manifold on top of the boiler and parallel framing to the footplating. The upper edge of the cab doorway had a pronounced recess.

3618/0	**2531** LMS black c/w - *40-c50*	1000	1200
5618/0	as above electric 12vDC - *40-c50*	1100	1700
5718/0	as above electric 20vAC - *40-c50*	1100	1700
913/0	**2602** LMS black electric AC - *40-c50*	750	900
913/0	as above electric DC - *40-c50*	750	900
-	**2603, 2606** LMS black c/w - *40-c50*	1100	1700
913/0	as above electric AC - *40-c50*	1100	1700
913/0	as above electric DC - *40-c50*	1100	1700
-	**42603** BRb black c/w - *c50-?*	1300	1900
-	as above electric - *c50-?*	1600	1900
3618/0	**42608** BRb black c/w - *c52-c59*	850	1400
5618/0	as above electric 2/3 rail - *c52-63*	1100	1400
-	as above * Nu-Scale - *57-60*	1600	2200

* See note on Nu-Scale in the Introduction to this chapter.

L22. Bowen-Cooke Superheater 4-6-2T (by Bing) (1914)

This was a tank version of the LNWR Prince of Wales Class built in 1911.

-	**2670** L&NWR black c/w - *14*	800	1100

Tender Engines

L23. *Der Adler* 2-2-2 (by Marklin) (1935)

-	***Der Adler*** electric - *35-?*	NPG	NPG

L24. MR Johnson 'Spinner' 4-2-2 (by Bing) (1914)

-	**650** MR maroon litho c/w - *14-20*	800	1600

Midland Railway Johnson 4-2-2 'Spinner' No.650 [L24] (Vectis)

-	**650** MR maroon litho 4V electric - *20*	1000	1800
-	**650** MR red litho c/w - *14*	1400	1500

L25. Freelance 0-4-0 (by Bing?) (1928)

4734/0	**4420** GWR green c/w - *c28*	NPG	NPG
4735/0	**6750** LMS maroon c/w - *c28*	NPG	NPG
4732/0	**8851** LNER green c/w - *c28*	NPG	NPG
4733/0	Southern c/w - *c28*	NPG	NPG

L25A. Freelance 0-4-0 (ex-Carette) (1928)

Produced from Carette tooling acquired after Carette closed down in 1917. All were steam driven.

6460/0	green lined in yellow - *c28*	NPG	NPG
6460/0	maroon lined in yellow - *c28*	NPG	NPG
6460/0	blue lined in white - *c28*	NPG	NPG
6460/0	black lined in red - *c28*	NPG	NPG

L26. L&NWR 'Charles Dickens' 2-4-0 (by Marklin) (1903)

-	**955 *Charles Dickens*** L&NWR black c/w - *03 -?*	1600	2200
-	as above electric - *03 -?*	1600	2200

L27. Standard Express 4-4-0 (Freelance) (by Bing) (1922)

All were steam driven.

48/0	**440** LSWR green - *22-29*	NPG	NPG
48/0	**440 *Greater Britain*** CR blue -*22-29*	NPG	NPG
48/0	**440** L&NWR black - *22-27*	NPG	NPG
48/0	**440** MR red - *22-29*	NPG	NPG
48/0	**440** GNR green - *22-29*	NPG	NPG
48/0	**440** GWR green - *22-29*	NPG	NPG

L28. Enterprise Express 4-4-0 (Freelance) (1931)

All were steam driven.

	Loco kit - 31-?	NPG	NPG
?	SR green lined white - *31-40?*	NPG	NPG
6690/0	**6285** on tender red - *31-40*	250	300
6690/0	as above black - *31-40*	350	550
6690/0	as above green - *31-40*	250	270
6690/0	as above LNER green - *31-40*	250	400
6690/0	**62759** BRb green lined white - *c54*	300	350
6690/0	as above blue lined orange - *c54*	400	450
6690/0	as above black lined orange - *c54*	300	350
6690/0	as above black lined white - *c54*	250	300

L29. Bogie Express 4-4-0 (Freelance) (by Bing) (1911)

All were steam driven.

61/250/0	GWR green - *11*	NPG	NPG
61/250/0	LMS red - *24-26*	NPG	NPG
61/250/0	LNER green - *24-26*	NPG	NPG
61/250/0	GWR green - *24-26*	NPG	NPG

L30. Midland Class 999 'Compound' 4-4-0 (by Bing) (1910)

17/0	**999** MR maroon c/w - *10-14, ?-30*	1100	1600
No.0	**1000** MR maroon steam - *10-14**	850	1300

* Remainder stock was being cleared in 1927.

L31. 'Duke of York' 4-4-0 (Freelance) (1927)

All examples of this model have a lithographed body. Only LMS versions carried a company designation. The 1927 locos had coupling rods with 'marine' Bing style big ends while later coupling rods were of a simplified shape. Electric models with a key hole have been converted to electric operation after purchase.

1927 green Duke of York [L31] (Vectis)

	1927 Duke of York		
61/4710/0	light green lined black+white c/w - *27-29*	300	450
61/4710/0	as above electric - *27-29*	300	650
61/4710/0	dark green lined black+white c/w- *27-29*	300	450
61/4710/0	as above electric - *27-29*	300	650
61/4710/0	olive green lined black+white c/w - *27-29*	300	450
61/4710/0	as above electric - *27-29*	300	600
61/4710/0	red lined black+yellow c/w - *27-29*	300	450
61/4710/0	as above electric - *27-29*	300	650
	1930 Duke of York		
3301/0	light green lined black+white c/w - *30*	350	550
4301/0	as above electric - *30*	400	650
3301/0	dark green lined black+white c/w - *30*	350	550
4301/0	as above electric - *30*	400	650
3301/0	olive green lined black+white c/w - *30*	350	550
4301/0	as above electric - *30*	400	650
3301/0	red lined black+yellow c/w - *30*	350	550
4301/0	as above electric - *30*	400	650
	1931 Duke of York		
3301/0	light green lined black+white c/w - *31-32*	300	450
4301/0	as above electric - *31-32*	300	650
3301/0	dark green lined black+white c/w - *31-32*	300	450
4301/0	as above electric - *31-32*	300	650
3301/0	olive green lined black+white c/w - *31-32*	300	450
4301/0	as above electric - *31-32*	400	650
3301/0	red lined black+yellow c/w - *31-32*	300	450
4301/0	as above electric - *31-32*	300	650

The green *Duke of Yorks* were intended to represent the LNER (Apple [light] green), GWR (Brunswick [dark] green) and SR (olive green). None had any distinctive company features such as a copper capped chimney for the GWR version.

L32a. 'Princess Elizabeth' 4-4-0 (Freelance) (1932)

The alloy wheels on this model were prone to metal fatigue and disintegration with the result that many have been re-wheeled. In such a case, if original period Bassett-Lowke iron replacement wheels have been fitted, add £50 to the value. Electric models with a key hole have been converted to electric operation after purchase. All models are lithographed.

3301/0	**2265 *Princess Elizabeth*** LMS red crest on cab c/w - *32-35*	250	350
4301/0	as above electric - *32-35*	300	550
3301/0	**2265 *Princess Elizabeth*** LNER green c/w - *32-35*	250	350
4301/0	as above electric - *32-35*	300	550

L32b. 'Prince Charles' 4-4-0 (Freelance) (1951)

All models were lithographed and all had a key hole whether clockwork or electric.

3313/0	**62078 *Prince Charles*** BRb blue c/w - *51-53*	250	400
4313/0	as above electric - *51-53*	300	550
3313/0	**62136 *Prince Charles*** BRb dark green lined black+white c/w - *52-54*	250	400
4311/0	as above electric - *52-54*	300	550

4-4-0 Prince Charles - BR blue [L32b] (Vectis)

3313/0	**62453 *Prince Charles*** BRb dark green lined black+white c/w - *51-55*	250	400
4311/0	as above electric - *51-55*	300	500
3313/0	**62453 *Prince Charles*** BRb Brunswick green lined black+orange c/w - *54-64*	250	350
4311/0	as above electric 3r - *54-64*	300	450
2311/0	as above electric 2r - *57-64*	300	550

L33. L&NWR 'Black Prince' 4-4-0 (by Bing) (1910)

Lubricator in the smokebox and reversing motion in the cab.

26/0	**1902 *Black Prince*** L&NWR black steam - *10-19**	700	900

* Remainder stock was being cleared in 1927.

L34. L&NWR 'Precursor' 4-4-0 (by Marklin) (1907)

-	**513 *Precursor*** L&NWR black c/w - *07-?*	450	550

L35a. L&NWR 'George the Fifth' 4-4-0 (by Bing) (1911)

Soldered construction and hand painted. This model was also sold in the UK under the Bing name.

11/0	**2663 *George the Fifth*** L&NWR black c/w - *11-13*	300	350
11/0	as above electric - *11-19*	300	350
-	**2664 *Queen Mary*** L&NWR black painted c/w - *11*	NPG	NPG
-	as above electric - *11*	NPG	NPG

L35b. L&NWR 'George the Fifth' 4-4-0 (by Carette) (1911)

Litho model by Carette who were more extravagant with rivet detail than Bing.

-	**2663 *George the Fifth*** L&NWR black c/w - *11*	NPG	NPG
-	as above electric - *11*	NPG	NPG

L35c. L&NWR 'George the Fifth' 4-4-0 (by Bing) (1919)

This litho model was also sold in the UK under the Bing name and also under the Gamages name and by other shops that imported it. These included other names such as *Apollo*, GWR 3343 *Mercury*, LMS 513 *Mercury*, LNER 8551, LNER 504 *King George V* and LMS 1924 as well as versions similar to those listed below. Marklin also made a rather ugly *George V* which too was not marketed through Bassett-Lowke.

2663/0	**2663 *George the Fifth*** L&NWR black c/w - *19-23*	250	300
2663/0	as above electric - *19-23*	250	300
-	**1000** MR red c/w - *19-23*	NPG	NPG
-	**2664 *Queen Mary*** L&NWR black painted c/w - *21?-?*	800	950
-	as above electric - *21?-?*	800	950
61/4710/0	**5320 *George the Fifth*** LMS maroon c/w - *24-27*	300	400
61/BL/0	as above electric - *24-27*	350	450
-	**5320** LMS maroon no name c/w - *24-27*	300	400
-	**513 *George the Fifth*** LMS maroon c/w - *26?*	NPG	NPG

-	as above electric - *26?*	NPG	NPG
-	**3433 *City of Bath*** GWR green c/w - *24-27*	250	300
-	as above electric - *24-27*	250	300
-	**504** LNER green c/w - *24-27*	250	300
-	as above electric - *24-27*	250	300

L36. CR McIntosh Class 140 'Dunalastair IV' 4-4-0 (1911)

This model had an 8-wheel tender.

-	**142** C()R blue (B) c/w - *11-16*	1600	1900
142/0	**142** C()R blue c/w - *25-35*	1500	1800
142E/0	as above electric - *25-35*	1600	1900

L37. CR Pickersgill Class 72 4-4-0 (by Leeds) (1922)

This model had a 6-wheel tender.

Caledonian Railway Pickersgill Class 72 4-4-0 (repaint) by Leeds (for B-L) [L37] (Vectis)

77/0	**77** C()R blue c/w - *22*	NPG	NPG
77E/0	as above electric - *22*	NPG	NPG

L38. MR Deeley 4P 'Compound' 4-4-0 (by Bing) (1912)

-	**1000** MR maroon c/w - *c21-23*	NPG	NPG
-	as above steam - *12-14?, c21-23*	NPG	NPG
-	as above electric - *c21-23*	NPG	NPG

L39. LMS Standard 'Compound' 4-4-0 (1928)

Pre-war electric models did not have key holes and had their handrails cranked where they passed over the front edge of the firebox. After the war, all Compounds had key holes whether clockwork or electric and the handrails were straight. Pre-war models could be had with 20v AC mechanisms (Cat. No. A5502/0). sBt = small Bing type tender. B-Lst = Bassett-Lowke standard tender. crt = coal rail tender

3302/0	**1190** LMS maroon litho sBt c/w - *28-35*	300	450
4302/0	as above 6-8v DC - *28-35*	300	650
-	as above 20v AC - *28-35*	300	650
3302/0	**1108** LMS maroon litho B-Lst c/w - *36-40*	300	450
4302/0	as above 6-8v junior premag - *36-40*	300	650
5302/0	as above 8-10v stand premag - *36-40*	300	650
A5502/0	as above 20vAC - *36-40*	300	650
3302/0	**1108** LMS maroon litho crt c/w - *36-40*	300	450
4302/0	as above electric - *36-40*	300	650
3302/0	**1108** LMS maroon litho crt c/w - *46-47*	300	450
5302/0	as above electric - *46-47*	300	650
3302/0	**1036** LMS maroon litho crt c/w - *48-50*	300	450
5302/0	as above electric - *48-50*	300	650
3302/0	**1036** LMS brown litho crt c/w - *48-50*	300	450
5302/0	as above electric - *48-50*	300	650
3302/0	**1063** LMS brown litho crt c/w - *48-50*	300	450
5302/0	as above electric - *48-50*	300	650
3302/0	**1063** LMS maroon litho crt c/w - *48-50*	300	450
5302/0	as above electric - *48-50*	300	650
3302/0	**1082** LMS maroon litho crt c/w - *48-50*	300	450
5302/0	as above electric - *48-50*	300	650
3302/0	**1082** LMS black painted over 1082 litho red lined c/w - *48-50*	300	450
5302/0	as above electric - *48-50*	300	650
3302/0	**1082** LMS black painted over 1063 litho red lined c/w - *48-50*	300	450
5302/0	as above electric - *48-50*	300	650
3302/0	**41109** BRb black litho lined red+grey c/w - *51-65*	300	450
5302/0	as above electric 3-rail - *51-65*	300	650
2302/0	as above electric 2-rail - *57-68*	350	750
5312/0	**41109, 41125** BRb black litho electric Nu-Scale* - *57-68*	500	850
3302/0	**41125** BRb black litho lined red+grey c/w - *60-64*	300	450
2302/0	as above electric 3-rail 12vDC - *60-64*	300	650
3302/0	**3400** GWR dark green painted over 1190 litho c/w - *34-35*	450	850
5302/0	as above electric - *34-35*	450	850
3302/0	**3400** GWR dark green painted over 1108 litho c/w - *36-39*	450	850
5302/0	as above electric - *36-39*	450	850

Pre-war hand-built quality models of the 'Compound' will be found in Table L97. These had numbers to the customer's choice as could post-war 'Compounds' and 41107 and 41108 are known to exist. * See note on 'Nu-Scale' in the Introduction to this chapter.

L40. LMS Class 2P 4-4-0 (1926)

17/0	**483** LMS maroon c/w - *26?-28-?*	NPG	NPG
66/0E	as above electric - *c26-28-?*	NPG	NPG

L41. LMS Class 2P 4-4-0 (altered 'Compound') (1936)

These were former 1108 'Compound' models that were over-painted. They have had their outside cylinders removed and plated over, and steam chest fairings on each side of the smokebox mounting also removed (the tin tab slots for the fairings can still be seen). The electric models were often fitted with lamp brackets not found on the 'Compounds'.

LMS Class 2P No.809 [L41] (Vectis)

3306/0	**601** LMS black c/w - *36-40*	300	450
4306/0	as above electric - *36-40*	300	600
5506/0	as above electric - *36-40*	300	600
4306/0AC	as above electric 20vAC - *36-40*	300	600
4306/0P	as above electric - *36-40*	300	600

L42. Ex-GNR Ivatt Express 4-4-0 (by Bing) (1924)

L2103/0	**504** LNER green litho c/w - *24-25*	550	850
LE2103/0	as above electric - *24-25*	550	850
L2103/0	**4390** LNER green litho c/w - *27-30*	330	400
LE2103/0	as above electric - *c26-28-?*	330	400

L42A. LNER 'Glen' Class 4-4-0

This was a model built by the reformed Bassett-Lowke Railways in the late 1960s.

-	**9405 *Glen Spean*** LNER green 3-rail - *late 60s?*	NPG	NPG

L43. GWR 'Atbara' Class 4-4-0 (by Bing) (1904)

The models did not have outside cranks.

-	**3410 *Sydney*** GWR green c/w - *04-10*	750	1100

L44. GWR 'City' Class 4-4-0 (by Bing) (1913)

The models had outside frames and cranks and were of an all soldered construction. Brass bogie wheels, nameplates and safety valve cover. Typical Bing buffers with tapered shank and nickel plated.

-	**3433 *City of Bath*** Great Western green with incorrect yellow and black lining c/w - *13-15*	4200	6000
-	as above electric - *14*	4200	6000

L45. GWR Churchward 'County' 4-4-0 (by Leeds) (1922)

3800/0	**3800 *County of Middlesex*** GWR green c/w - *22-25*	NPG	NPG
3800E/0	as above electric - *22-25*	NPG	NPG
3800/0	**3801 *County of Carlow*** GWR green c/w - *22-25*	400	550

Other names exist.

L46. SE&CR Wainwright Class D 4-4-0 (by Bing) (1914)

-	SE&CR green c/w - *14*	1900	2700

L47. SR 'Schools' Class 4-4-0 (by Marklin) (1934)

910/0/C	**910 *Merchant Taylors*** Southern green c/w - *34-37-?*	950	1600
910/0/A	as above electric AC - *34-36-?*	1100	1700
910/0/D	as above electric DC - *34-36-?*	1100	1700

L48. NYC Vauclain 'Compound' 4-4-0 (by Carette) (1905)

2350C/0	**2350** NYC c/w - *05-?*	NPG	NPG

L49. GNR 'Atlantic' 4-4-2 (by Carette or Bing) (1907)

251/0	**251** GNR green (C) c/w - *07-09*	800	1100
-	as above (C) electric - *07-?*	NPG	NPG

Great Northern Railway Atlantic No.1442 by Bing (for B-L) [L49] (Wallis & Wallis)

9/0	**1425** GNR green (B) c/w - *13-14?*	500	650
-	as above (B) electric - *12-14?*	500	650
-	**1442** GNR green litho (C) c/w - *11-?*	500	850
-	as above (C) electric - *11-?*	500	850

L50. NBR Class C1 'Atlantic' 4-4-2 (1955)

-	**8872 *Auld Reekie*** LNER green elec - *c55*	NPG	NPG

L51. Goods Loco 0-6-0 (by Bing) (1927)

4736/0	**773** Southern green litho c/w - *28-?*	NPG	NPG
4736/0	**4460** GWR green litho c/w - *28-?*	NPG	NPG
-	**4472** LNER green litho c/w - *27-?*	NPG	NPG
4736/0	**6508** LMS maroon litho c/w - *28-?*	NPG	NPG
4736/0	**8851** LNER green? c/w - *28-?*	NPG	NPG

L52. L&NWR 'Cauliflower' 0-6-0 (by Bing) (1912)

-	**930, 1269** L&NWR black c/w - *12-14*	NPG	NPG
-	GNR black c/w - *12-14*	NPG	NPG

L53. LMS Fowler 4F 0-6-0 (1927)

This model was of soldered construction with a paint finish.

3204/0	**4072** LMS black lined red c/w - *27-33*	400	650
4204/0	as above electric - *27-33*	400	750
5302/0	**1931** GWR green lined + copper capped chimney elec. - *27-33*	350	500

L54. LNER Gresley J39 0-6-0 (1927)

This model was of soldered construction with a paint finish.

3205/0	**1448** LNER black lined red c/w - *27-35*	350	600
4205/0	as above electric 12v - *27-35*	350	600

L55. Standard Goods Locomotive 0-6-0 (1936)

This model was of tab construction and lithographed. The LMS version had a capuchon on the chimney. The non-BR locos had a Bing type tender without the horizontal fluting found on passenger locomotives. The BR model has the later standard Bassett-Lowke tender.

The following were lined in red

?	**4256** black c/w - *36?*	250	450
3307/0	**4256** LMS black c/w - *36-40*	300	500
4307/0	as above 12vDC - *36-40*	350	500
A4307/0	as above 20vAC - *36-40*	350	550
5307/0	as above spur drive - *36-40*	350	550
?	**4417** LMS black c/w - *?*	250	450
4308/0	**156** LNER black electric - *36-40*	350	550
4308/0	**1448** LNER black 3-rail 12vDC - *36-40*	450	600
3308/0	**1456** LNER black c/w - *36-40*	300	450
4308/0	as above electric - *36-40*	350	550
A4308/0	as above 20vAC - *36-40*	350	550
5308/0	as above spur drive - *36-40*	350	550

Nuscale Standard 0-6-0 in BR black No.64193 [L55]

The following were unlined

3308/0	**63871** BRb black c/w - *55-67*	250	450
5308/0	as above electric 3-rail - *55-67*	300	500
3308/0	**64193** BRb black c/w - *55-67*	250	450
5308/0	as above electric 3-rail - *55-67*	300	500
2308/0	as above electric 2-rail - *57-67*	300	500
-	as above electric * - *57-65*	550	650
3308/0	**43871** BRb black c/w - *55-67*	250	450
5308/0	as above electric 3-rail - *55-67*	300	500
2308/0	as above electric 2-rail - *57-67*	300	500

* See note on Nu-Scale in the Introduction to this chapter.

L56. LMS Hughes 'Crab' 2-6-0 (1925)

-	**2700** LMS maroon steam - *25-?*	NPG	NPG
-	as above c/w - *25-?*	NPG	NPG
-	as above electric - *25-?*	NPG	NPG
-	**2700** LMS black steam - *25-?*	NPG	NPG
-	as above c/w - *25-?*	NPG	NPG
-	as above electric - *25-?*	NPG	NPG
6660/0	**13000** LMS maroon steam - *25-39*	600	750
6670/0	as above steam - *25-39*	600	750
3601/0	as above c/w - *25-33*	550	700
4601/0	as above electric - *25-33*	700	900
4602/0	as above electric - *25-33*	700	900
4601/0 4602/0	as above number on cabsides and tender 3-rail 12vDC - *25-33*	700	900
6660/0	**13000** LMS black steam - *25-39*	650	900
6670/0	as above steam - *25-39*	650	900
3601/0	as above c/w - *25-33*	600	800
4601/0	as above electric - *25-33*	800	1100
4602/0	as above electric - *25-33*	800	1100

L57. LMS Stanier 'Mogul' 2-6-0 (1934)

Standard models had the Greenly derived motion but both clockwork and electric models were available with full Walschaerts valve gear.

	2945 LMS Maroon		
6660/0	steam - *34-c41*	350	550
-	steam kit - *c39-c49*	650	800
-	c/w - *34-c41*	300	400
-	c/w kit - *c39-c49*	400	500
6660/0	c/w with Walschaerts valve gear - *35-40*	450	550
4601/0	electric - *34-c41*	300	400
-	electric kit - *c39-c49*	400	500
4601/0	electric with Walschaerts valve gear - *35-40*	650	750
	2945 LMS Black		
6660/0	steam - *34-c41*	350	550
-	steam kit - *c39-c49*	650	800
-	c/w - *34-c41*	300	400
-	c/w kit - *c39-c49*	400	500
6660/0	c /w with Walschaerts valve gear - *35-40*	450	550
4601/0	electric - *34-c41*	300	400
-	electric kit - *c39-c49*	400	500
4601/0	electric with Walschaerts valve gear - *35-40*	650	750
	42980 BRb Black		
6661/0	lined grey+red steam - *c52-64*	550	800
-	as above c/w - *?*	NPG	NPG
-	as above electric - *?*	NPG	NPG
-	**5524** LMS maroon steam Fowler tend - *?*	NPG	NPG
-	**13007** LMS maroon steam - *68-69*	NPG	NPG
-	**42981** BRb black steam - *?*	NPG	750

L58. LNER Gresley Class K3 'Mogul' 2-6-0 (1925)

LNER Class K3 2-6-0 No.1864 live steam [L58] (Vectis)

6670/0	**33** LNER green steam - *25-41*	1100	1400
3602/0	as above c/w - *25-41*	850	1400
4602/0	as above electric 12vDC - *25-41*	850	1400
6670/0	**33** LNER black steam - *25-41*	1600	1900
3602/0	as above c/w - *25-41*	1300	1700

4602/0	as above electric - *25-41*	1100	1500
6670/0	**982** LNER green steam - *26-c38*	NPG	NPG
3602/0	as above c/w - *26-28-?*	NPG	NPG
4602/0	as above electric - *26-28-?*	NPG	NPG
6670/0	**982** LNER black steam - *26-c38*	NPG	NPG
3602/0	as above c/w - *26-28-?*	NPG	NPG
4602/0	as above electric - *26-28-?*	NPG	NPG
-	**1864** LNER green steam - *46-?*	400	550
-	as above c/w - *46-?*	450	550
-	as above electric - *46-?*	450	550
-	**1864** LNER black steam - *46-50-?*	550	1050
-	as above c/w - *46-50-?*	550	1050
-	as above electric - *46-50-?*	550	1100

Another model described which fits this section was numbered '56' but the colour and type of drive are unrecorded.

L59. LNER Gresley Class K4 'Mogul' 2-6-0

-	**2066 *Deer Stalker*** LNER green elec - *c69*	450	550

L60. GWR Churchward Class 43XX 'Mogul' 2-6-0 (1925)

All carried Great (crest) Western on their tenders.

6680/0	**4431** green steam - *25-28-?*	420	450
3603/0	as above c/w - *25-36?*	500	550
4603/0	as above electric - *25-36?*	500	550
6680/0	**4431** black steam - *25-28-?*	NPG	NPG
3603/0	as above c/w - *25-28?*	NPG	NPG
4603/0	as above electric - *25-28?*	NPG	NPG
3603/0	**4331** green c/w - *25-36?*	500	550
4603/0	as above electric - *25-36?*	500	550

L61. SR Maunsell Class N 'Mogul' 2-6-0 (1926)

6685/0	**864** Southern green steam - *26-c38*	NPG	NPG
3644/0	as above c/w - *26-28-?*	NPG	NPG
4644/0	as above electric - *26-28-?*	NPG	NPG
6685/0	**864** Southern black steam - *26-c38*	NPG	NPG
3644/0	as above c/w - *26-28-?*	NPG	NPG
4644/0	as above electric - *26-28-?*	NPG	NPG
6685/0	**866** Southern green steam - *26-c38*	NPG	NPG
3644/0	as above c/w - *26-c38*	NPG	NPG
4644/0	as above electric- *26-c38*	NPG	NPG

L61A. LNER Gresley Class V2 2-6-2

Made to order.

-	**4844 *Coldstreamer*** LNER green c/w - *?*	NPG	NPG

L62. CR 'Cardean' 4-6-0 (floor model) (by Carette) (1909)

-	**903 *Cardean*** C()R blue c/w - *09-?*	450	550

L63. Super Enterprise 4-6-0 (Freelance) (1937)

6655/0	**851** Southern green steam *37-?*	NPG	NPG

LNER No.2871 4-6-0 'Super Enterprise' live steam [L63] (Vectis)

6655/0	**2495** black steam *37-40*	NPG	NPG
6655/0	**2871** LNER green steam *37-40*	NPG	NPG
6655/0	**5524** LMS maroon steam *37-40*	350	NPG
-	**45295** BRb green steam *?*	250	400
-	**45295** BRb black steam *51-56*	250	420
-	**61324** BRb black steam *?*	250	400

L64. 4-6-0 (Freelance) (by Bing) (1928)

All were litho printed and clockwork.

4737/0	**4460 *Windsor Castle*** GWR green - *28-32*	NPG	NPG
4737/0	**4472 *Flying Fox*** LNER green - *28-32*	NPG	NPG
4737/0	**6508 *Royal Scot*** LMS maroon - *28-32*	NPG	NPG
4737/0	**773 *King Arthur*** Southern green - *28-32*	1100	1300

L65. L&NWR 'Prince of Wales' 4-6-0 (by Bing) (1924)

49/0	**5600 *Prince of Wales*** LMS maroon c/w - *24-25*	NPG	NPG

L66. LMS 'Royal Scot' Class 4-6-0 (1929)

Ft = Fowler tender. St = Stanier tender. sd = smoke deflectors fitted.

LMS 6100 *Royal Scot*

3303/0	maroon litho Ft c/w - *29-37*	850	1450
3611/0	maroon St c/w - *37-52*	850	1450
3622/0	black St c/w - *c48-52*	1300	1900
A4303/0	maroon litho Ft AC - *29-37*	550	700
4303/0	maroon litho Ft DC - *29-37*	550	700
5611/0	maroon St and sd AC - *37-52*	750	950
5711/0	maroon St and sd DC - *37-52*	750	950
5622/0	black St and sd 3-rail 12vDC - *c48-52*	1300	1600

L67. LMS Rebuilt 'Royal Scot' 4-6-0 (1953)

Stanier tender and re-profiled smoke deflectors.

BRb 46100 *Royal Scot*

-	green c/w - *53-?*	1300	1800
5622/0	green 3-rail 12vDC - *53-56-?*	2600	3200
-	green 2-rail 12vDC - *57-?*	2600	3200
-	green electric* Nu-Scale - *57-60*	2100	3700

* See note on 'Nu-Scale' in the Introduction to this chapter.

L68a. LMS 'Jubilee' Class 4-6-0 (by Marklin) (1935)

911/0	**5552 *Silver Jubilee*** LMS black + silver c/w - *35*	3100	4200
911/0/A	as above electric AC - *35*	3100	4200
911/0/D	as above (M) electric DC - *35*	3100	4200
911/0	**5610 *Gold Coast*** LMS maroon c/w - *35-?*	2850	3700
911/0/A	electric AC - *35-?*	2850	3700
911/0/D	electric DC - *35-?*	2850	3700
911/0	**5573 *Newfoundland*** LMS maroon c/w - *35-40?*	2850	3700
911/0/A	as above electric AC - *35-40?*	2850	3700
911/0/D	as above electric DC - *35-40?*	2850	4700
911/0/C	**5682 *Trafalgar*** LMS maroon c/w (also 3607/0) - *36-40-?*	4200	5500
5607/0	as above electric - *36-40-?*	4200	5500

L68b. LMS 'Jubilee' Class 4-6-0 (1936)

The 'Jubilee' model built by Bassett-Lowke had a top-feed projection on top of the boiler which was missing from the Marklin model. The locomotive looked longer and the tender a more realistic shape.

LMS 'Jubilee' Class 4-6-0 No.5701 Conqueror [L68b] (Vectis)

911/0/C	**5701 *Conqueror*** LMS maroon c/w (also 3607/0) - *36-40?*	2700	5200
911/0/A	as above electric AC - *36-40?*	3000	5700
911/0/D	as above electric DC - *36-40?*	3000	5700
911/0/C	**5712 *Victory*** LMS maroon c/w (also 3607/0) - *36-40-?*	3900	5200
5607/0	as above electric DC - *36-40-?*	4200	5700

L69. LMS 'Black 5' 4-6-0 (1935)

Some were rebuilt from Marklin Jubilees but others are clearly Bassett-Lowke models.

	4853? LMS black c/w - *35-c40*	800	1100
-	**5294** LMS black elec 12vDC 3-rail - *35-c40*	800	1100
-	**5241** LMS black elec 12vDC 3-rail - *35-c40*	NPG	2500

L70. Ex-LMS Class 5MT 4-6-0 (1959)

-	**45126** BR black electric 2/3 rail - *59-63*	NPG	NPG

L71. LNER Class B17 4-6-0 (1936)

-	**2838 *Melton Hall*** LNER green c/w - *36-c39*	4700	6200
-	as above electric 3-rail 12vDC - *36-c39*	4600	6200
3608/0	**2848 *Arsenal*** LNER green c/w - *36-c39*	5000	9200

A4608/0	as above electric AC - *36-c39*	5200	9200
5608/0	as above electric DC - *36-c39*	5200	9900
3608/0	**2853 *Huddersfield Town*** LNER green c/w - *36-c39*	4200	5200
A4608/0	as above electric AC - *36-c39*	4200	5200
5608/0	as above electric DC - *36-c39*	4200	5200

L72. GWR 'Castle' Class 4-6-0 (1930)

-	**4079 *Pendennis Castle*** GWR green using Mogul parts c/w - *30-?*	1350	1600
-	**4079 *Pendennis Castle*** GWR green c/w - *39-51*	1600	2100
-	as above electric - *39-51*	1600	2100
-	as above electric (H) - *c55*	2100	2600
-	**5071 *Spitfire*** GWR green electric 2/3 rail - *55-63*	2100	2600
-	**5071 *Spitfire*** BRb green (H) - *c55*	2100	2600

GWR 'Castle' Class No.5071 Spitfire by Hunt (for B-L) [L72] (Vectis)

-	**5015 *Kingswear Castle*** * Great Western green electric 3-rail 12vDC - *50s?*	3200	3700
-	**5003 *Lulworth Castle*** * Great Western green electric 3-rail 12vDC - *50s?*	3200	4200

* Examples of special order models that have been sold at auction.

L73. GWR 'County' Class 4-6-0 (by Hunt) (1957)

-	**1003 *County of Wilts*** BRc green electric 3-rail 12vDC *57-63?*	NPG	NPG

L74. GWR 'King' Class 4-6-0 (1935)

912/0/C	**6000 *King George V*** Great()Western green (M) c/w - *35-37-?*	3200	4700
612/0/A	as above electric AC (M) - *35-37-?*	4200	5450
912/0/D	as above electric DC (M) - *35-37-?*	4200	5450
-	**6027 *King Richard*** GWR green electric 2/3 rail hand built - *c60-63**	2700	3200

* Made to order.

L75. SR 'Lord Nelson' 4-6-0 (from litho Royal Scot) (1935)

-	**850 *Lord Nelson*** Southern green c/w - *35-?*	1300	1600
-	as above electric - *35-?*	1300	1600

L77. LMS 'Princess Royal' Class 4-6-2 (1935)

	LMS 6200 *The Princess Royal*		
3605/0/C	maroon c/w - *35-?*	3100	4200
3605/0/A	maroon electric AC Fowler tender - *35-?*	3100	4200
3605/0/D	maroon electric DC Fowler tender - *35-?*	3100	5000
	LMS 6201 *Princess Elizabeth*		
3605/0	maroon c/w - *36-39-?*	3100	5200
A4605/0	maroon electric AC - *36-39-?*	3100	4700
5605/0	maroon electric DC - *36-39-?*	3600	4700
-	**6202** LMS maroon Turbomotive c/w - *36-c50*	NPG	NPG
-	as above but 3-rail 12v electric (only one known) - *c37*	10000	12000

L78. LMS Streamlined 'Princess Coronation' (1937)

LMS 'Coronation' Class (streamlined) 6225 Duchess of Gloucester [L78] (Vectis)

-	**6220 *Coronation*** LMS blue c/w - *37-c48*	4200	7200
-	as above electric - *37-c48*	4200	8700
3606/0	**6225 *Duchess of Gloucester*** LMS maroon c/w - *38?-c48*	4200	5200
4606/0	as above electric AC - *38?-c48*	4200	7200
5606/0	as above electric DC - *38?-c48*	4200	7200
-	**6227 *Duchess of Devonshire*** LMS maroon c/w made to order* - *?*	NPG	8700

* Made for Harold Elliott's sea-front layout at Scarborough.

L79. LMS 'Princess Coronation' Class 4-6-2 (1939)

sd = with smoke deflectors fitted.

	LMS 6232 Duchess of Montrose		
3613/0	maroon c/w - *39-49*	2100	3200
5613/0	maroon electric 12vDC 3-rail - *39-49*	2100	3200
	BRb 46232 Duchess of Montrose		
3613/0	blue sd c/w - *c52*	3700	5200
3613/0	green sd c/w - *c54-c58*	2600	3200
-	blue sd electric - *c52*	4200	5200
2613/0	green sd electric 2-rail - *c57-c58*	3000	4500
5613/0	green sd electric 3-rail - *c54-c58*	3100	4700
-	green sd electric Nu-Scale ** 2-rail - *57-63*	3000	4500
-	green sd electric Nu-Scale ** 3-rail - *57-65*	3000	4500
-	**46245 *City of London*** * BRb black smoke deflectors 3-rail 12vDC - *50s*	3100	3700
-	**46257 *City of Salford*** * BRb black smoke deflectors 3-rail 12vDC - 50s	1300	1500

* Special order. ** See note on Nu-Scale in the Introduction to this chapter.

L80. LNER A1/A3 'Pacific' 4-6-2 (1933)

	LNER A1 4472 *Flying Scotsman*		
3304/0	green litho c/w - *33-c41*	750	1400
4304/0	green litho electric 8vDC - *33-c41*	850	1400
5304/0	green litho 8vAC - *33-c41*	850	1400
5504/0	green litho electric 20vAC - *33-c41*	850	1400
6304/0	green litho electric 20vAC - *33-c41*	850	1400
-	green litho electric Nu-Scale - *57-65*	1600	2000
	LNER A3 103 *Flying Scotsman*		
-	green litho c/w - *c47-c50*	1300	1900
-	green litho electric - *c47-c50*	1300	1900
	BRb A3 60103 *Flying Scotsman*		
3310/0	blue litho c/w - *50-52*	1300	1600
-	blue litho electric 12vDC 3r - *50-52*	1300	1600
3310/0	green litho c/w - *c53-c58*	800	1300
5310/0	green litho electric 12vDC 3-rail - *c53-c58*	800	1300
2310/0	green litho electric 12vDC 2-rail - *c57-c58*	1300	1700
-	green litho electric 12v DC 3-rail Nu-Scale** - *57-c63*	2000	2500
-	green litho electric 12v DC 2-rail Nu-Scale** - *57-c63*	2000	2500

** See note on Nu-Scale in the introduction to this chapter.

L81. LNER A4 'Pacific' 4-6-2 (1936)

2507/0	**2509 *Silver Link*** LNER silver c/w - *36-c40*	4700	8200
4606/0	as above electric AC - *36-c40*	4700	8200
5606/0	as above electric DC - *36-c40*	4700	8200
2507/0	**2510 *Quicksilver*** LNER silver c/w - *36-c40*	4700	8200
4606/0	as above electric AC - *36-c40*	4700	8200
5606/0	as above electric DC - *36-c40*	4700	8200
2507/0	**2511 *Silver King*** LNER silver c/w - *36-c40*	4700	8200
4606/0	as above electric AC - *36-c40*	4700	8200
5606/0	as above electric DC - *36-c40*	4700	8200
2507/0	**2512 *Silver Fox*** LNER silver c/w - *36-c40*	4700	8200
4606/0	as above electric AC - *36-c40*	4700	8200
5606/0	as above electric DC - *36-c40*	4700	8200
2507/0	**4489 *Dominion of Canada*** LNER blue c/w - *c38-c40*	4700	8200
4606/0	as above electric AC - *c38-c40*	4700	8200
5606/0	as above electric DC - *c38-c40*	4700	8200
2507/0	**4490 *Empire of India*** LNER blue c/w - *c38-c40*	4700	8200
4606/0	as above electric AC - *c38-c40*	4700	8200
5606/0	as above electric DC - *c38-c40*	4700	8200
2507/0	**4498 *Sir Nigel Gresley*** LNER blue c/w - *c38-c40*	4700	8200
4606/0	as above electric AC - *c38-c40*	4700	8200
5606/0	as above electric DC - *c38-c40*	4700	8200

L82. BR 'Britannia' Class Pacific 4-6-2 (by Hunt) (1958)

-	**70000 *Britannia*** BRc green hand built electric 2/3-rail - *58-?*	5200	8200

L83. German State Railways 4-6-2 (by Marklin) (1934)

MG/0	German State Railways electric - *34-36-?*	NPG	NPG

L84. New York Central 4-6-4 (by Marklin) (1934)

AK/0	**AK70/12920 *Commodor Vanderbilt*** New York Central black electric - *34-36-?*	NPG	NPG

L85. LMS Class 8F 2-8-0 (1960)

-	**48209** BRc black electric 2/3-rail - *60-63*	NPG	NPG

L86. French 'Mountain' 4-8-2 (by Marklin) (1934)

MF/0	ETAT electric - *34-36-?*	NPG	NPG

L87. BR Class 9F 2-10-0 (Hunt for Bassett-Lowke) (1961)

-	**92220 *Evening Star*** BRc green electric 2/3-rail - *61-63*	2300	3200
-	BRc black electric - *61-63*	NPG	NPG

Diesel and Electric Locomotives

L88. SECR Steam Railmotor (by Carette) (1907)

-	**1** litho steam brown - *07-09-?*	1600	1900

L89. 'Deltic' Diesel Co-Co (1959)

It is believed that fewer than 10 Deltics were made.

Model of the prototype of the 'Deltic' Class [L89] (Bassett-Lowke Society)

-	***Deltic*** electric blue twin electric motor bogies 3-rail 12vDC - *59-63*	2100	4700
-	***Deltic*** BRc green - *?*	NPG	NPG

L90. Steeplecab Electric 0-4-0 (by Bing & Marklin) (1903)

-	**23** CLR blue (M) electric - *03-?*	1600	1900
-	**23** CLR blue (B) electric - *04-?*	500	650

L91. Swiss Pantograph Electrics (by Marklin)

-	SBB 4-6-2 electric - *35-?*	NPG	NPG
-	SBB 4-4-2 electric - *35-?*	NPG	NPG
-	SBB 0-4-0 electric - *35-?*	NPG	NPG

L92. LT London Underground Standard EMU (1937)

Made all of brass.

-	**7073 +?+ 7072** London Transport red +cream 3-car electric 35 12vDC - *37-38*	2600	5200
-	**7073 + 7072** London Transport red+cream 2-car electric 35 12vDC - *37-38*	950	1400

L93. Southern EMU (by Bing) (1928)

1457/0	**2601** Southern green 3-car set elec - *c28*	1400	1600

L94. LMS Euston-Watford 1927 Stock EMU (1930)

104/0	**1652/3416/6560** LMS maroon 3-car * litho electric 3-rail 12vDC - *30-35*	1100	2000

* The centre car was a 1st/3rd.

L95. Southern EMU (by Exley) (1953)

These were 3-car sets with 12V DC Bassett-Lowke motor bogies and B-L coach bogies.

?	**3072/3086 (11165 + ?)** Southern green Portsmouth 3-car set - *?*	1300	1600
?	**3072/3074** Southern green 4RES 3-car suburban set - *53-57*	1300	1600
?	**3091/3071** Southern green 4RES 3-car suburban set - *53-57*	1600	2100
?	LMS maroon ex-Southern 4RES 3-car EMU (fictional) about 10 sets made as a special order - *c55*	1600	2200

London Underground 3-car EMU [L92]

L96. 'Brighton Belle' Pullman EMU

The cars were made-to-order and had metal sides, metal window frames, wooden floors and roof, brass handrails, B-L bogies and full internal fittings.

-	**88** Pullman dark brown+cream driver	NA	NA
-	**87** Pullman dark brown+cream driver	NA	NA
-	***Hazel*** Pullman dark brown+cream 1st	NA	NA
-	***Doris*** Pullman dark brown+cream 1st	NA	NA
-	**86** Pullman dark brown+cream 3rd	NA	NA
-	the above 5 cars	2600	4200

Miscellaneous

L97. Hand-Built Locomotives (1933)

In 1933, Bassett-Lowke announced a range of hand-built locomotives which could be made to order. The models would be to a very high specification including all solder construction, all external and visible details and full painting and lining. Locomotives could be had either with variable speed clockwork drive, 8-10v DC or 20v AC electric mechanisms. Customers could choose their own running numbers and those given below are examples seen or advertised.

-	GWR 2-6-0 'Mogul' - *33-35*	NPG	NPG
-	GWR 2-6-2T - *33-35*	NPG	NPG
-	**2793** GWR 0-6-0T - *33-35*	NPG	NPG
-	LMS 2-6-0 'Mogul' - *33-35*	NPG	NPG
-	**6100** LMS 4-6-0 'Royal Scot' Class - *33-39*	NPG	NPG
-	LMS 4-6-0 'Patriot' Class - *33-39*	NPG	NPG
-	LMS 4-6-0 Rebuilt 'Claughton' Class - *33-35*	NPG	NPG
-	**1067** LMS 4-4-0 Midland 'Compound' - *33-35*	450	650
-	LMS 4-6-2T CR Pickersgill - *33-35*	NPG	NPG
-	LMS 2-6-2T - *33-39*	NPG	NPG
-	LMS 2-6-4T - *33-39*	NPG	NPG
-	LMS 0-6-0 goods tender loco - *33-39*	NPG	NPG
-	**4472 *Flying Scotsman*** LNER 4-6-2 A1/A3 Class - *33-39*	NPG	NPG
-	LNER 0-6-0 goods tender loco - *33-35*	NPG	NPG
-	**453 *King Arthur*** SR N15 Class - *33-35*	NPG	NPG
-	**850 *Lord Nelson*** SR LN Class - *33-35*	NPG	NPG
-	PLM French 'Windcutter' 'Pacific' - *33-35*	NPG	NPG
	2300 CP 4-6-2 Canadian Pacific loco - *33-35*	NPG	NPG

COACHES

As with the locomotives, many of the early coaches were imported from Germany where they were made by Bing, Marklin or Carette but, by the 1930s, Bassett-Lowke were manufacturing their own.

Carette coaches produced for Bassett-Lowke were all made before the First World War and, consequently were all in pre-grouping liveries. Some of these were toy-like but so-called 'scale' model coaches arrived in 1910. Some of Carette tools were later acquired by Bassett-Lowke to produce the LNWR and LMS travelling post offices and 12-wheeled diners in the 1920s.

Bing lithographed coaches dominated the '20s and are known as the 1921 Series. These were all steel and were produced in the pre-grouping liveries of GNR, LNWR, MR and GWR (lake). A year after the grouping in 1924, the coaches were produced in the post-grouping liveries of LMS, LNER (teak), SR and GWR (chocolate and cream) and were fitted with corridor connections.

The first coach made by Bassett-Lowke themselves appeared in 1930 and was part of the Watford EMU set. First class corridor and brake thirds were made in the liveries of all four railway companies but the LMS and SR EMUs (see 'Locomotives' section) also received a pair of suburban coaches. These were available separately as too was an LMS travelling post office.

A new design of coach was introduced after the Second World War in BR red and cream. These new coaches were made by Precision Models in Northampton who were also manufacturing the Trix Twin system at that time. Exley also made coaches for Bassett-Lowke from 1936 and these had the Exley trademark carefully removed and were packed in Bassett-Lowke boxes. More about these later.

Cat No.	Company, Number, Colour, Dates	£	£

C1. Early Coaches (by Carette) (1908)

These coaches were 10" and 12" long respectively and fitted with Mansell type wheels and double windows. All but the GNR ones had clerestory roofs.

1910 GWR full brake coach by Carette (for B-L) [C1] (Vectis)

-	**GNR** 1321 teak 1st/3rd - *08-19*	200	230
-	**GNR** 1331 teak brake - *08-19*	200	230
	with Clerestory Roof		
-	**MR** 1323 maroon 1st/3rd - *10-19*	200	230
-	**MR** 1333 maroon brake - *10-19*	200	230
-	**GWR** 1324 dark brown+cream /3rd - *08-19*	200	230
-	**GWR** 1334 dark brown+cream full brake - *08-19*	200	230
-	**GWR** 1334 dark brown+cream full brake red cross hospital coach - *14-19*	1000	1500
-	**LNWR** 1322, 1325 brown+cream 1st/3rd - *08-19*	200	230
-	**LNWR** 1334, 133 brown+cream full brake - *08-19*	200	230

C1A. 6-wheel 'Clemenson' Coaches (by Bing)

These coaches had embossed sides and three pairs of wheels. The centre pair were the Clemenson type and so slid from side to side to allow for tight curves. The coaches were also available as a set of three permanently close coupled and had standard couplings at the end of the trio. The set consisted of two composite coaches and a brake 3rd at both ends.

-	**LNWR** 13212 black+crm 1st/3rd composite - *10-?*	200	230
-	**LNWR** 13312 black+cream brake/3rd - *10-?*	200	230
-	**LNWR** 13312 black+cream full brake - *?*	200	230

C2. Early Freelance Coaches

These were designed to be whatever you wanted them to be and were finished for the customer accordingly. They had a curved roof which was fitted with torpedo ventilators. The windows were glazed with glass, including ground glass for the lavatory compartments. They were 13" long and the bodies and underframes were made from hard wood, the door handles were gold plated brass. The doors did not open but the coaches could be bought in kit form.

601E	teak various 1st/2nd/3rd - *?-19*	200	230
602E	teak various brake - *?-19*	200	230

C3. 1921 Series Bogie Coaches (by Bing) (1921)

These coaches were 13" long and of tinplate construction. They had embossed sides and compensated heavy gauge steel bogies. The black painted wheels were a heavy alloy, Mansell type, with thick flanges and ran loose on crimped axles which were retained in covered axle boxes by crimped on washers. The roofs were clipped on and there was no provision for corridor connectors. They were fitted with Bing couplings with long single drop links, cast oval alloy buffers riveted on, with two gas cylinders and underframe stays. The coaches could be had with turned cast iron wheels and are often found with the later superior Bassett-Lowke 612/0 bogies with large diameter turned cast iron Mansell pattern wheels and cast axle boxes. Stocks lasted well after the introduction of the later '1924' series coaches.

60/0	**MR** lake 1st corridor - *22-26*	170	250
61/0	**MR** 2783 lake 3rd/brake - *22-26*	170	250
62/0	**GWR** 132 lake 1st corridor - *22-26*	170	250
63/0	**GWR** 133 lake 3rd/brake - *22-26*	170	250
64/0	**LNWR** 1921 brown+cream 1st corridor - *21-26*	170	250
65/0	**LNWR** 1921,1334 brown+cream 3rd/brake - *21-26*	170	250

1921 GWR all-1st corridor coach by Bing (for B-L) [C3] (Vectis)

65/0	**LNWR** 1334 brown+cream full /brake - *21-26*	170	250
66/0	**GNR** teak 1st (12" long) - *21-26*	170	250
67/0	**GNR** teak full brake (12" long) - *21-26*	170	250
64/0	**LSWR** 1308? brown+salmon 1st/3rd corridor - *21-26*	170	250
65/0	**LSWR** brown+salmon 3rd/brake - *21-26*	170	250

C4. 1924 Series Bogie Coaches (by Bing) (1924)

These were also 13" long and were to the same specification as the 1921 Series (table C3) except for livery and provision of corridor connections. Each coach had one overscale bellows type coach connector made in black camera cloth which spanned between adjacent coaches. The connections were hollow and brake end coaches were provided with a clip-on closure plate. Early examples had brass buffers and brass Bing couplings and, again, improved bogies and cast iron wheels could be fitted.

60/0	**LMS** 2784 maroon 1st - *25-31*	170	200
61/0	**LMS** 2783 maroon 3rd/brake - *25-31*	170	200
62/0	**GWR** 132, 1235N, 8271 cream+dark brown 1st - *28-31*	200	230
63/0	**GWR** 133, 1921, 3251 cream+dark brown 3rd/brake - *28-31*	200	230
66/0	**Southern** 2601, 5180, 7001 green 1st * - *26-31*	220	270
67/0	**Southern** 7000, 7716 green 3rd/brake* - *26-31*	220	270
68/0	**LNER** 1235N teak 1st - *25-31*	170	200
68/0	**LNER** 601 teak all 1st - *25-31*	170	200
69/0	**LNER** 1234N teak 3rd/brake - *25-31*	170	200

*SR coaches introduced in 1926 were repaints of GWR lake coloured ones.

C5. 12-Wheel Dining Cars (Carette design) (1921)

14" long, these had uncompensated folded tinplate bogies, a battery box (instead of gas cylinders), no axle boxes, cast alloy buffers riveted on, recessed vestibules, a clip-on roof, underframe stays, heavy alloy wheels running loose on crimped axles and embossed tinplate sides.

1921 12-wheel LMS diner by Carette (for B-L) [C5] (Vectis)

94/0	**LNWR** 13210 cream+brown - *21-24*	250	370
94/0	**GNR** 3040 teak - *21-24*	250	370

94/0	**LMS** 13210 maroon - *24-34*	250	370

C6. Post Office Mail Vans (Carette design) (1922)

The length of these vans was 12.25" and they had no corridor connections. They had 4-wheel uncompensated folded tinplate bogies, gas cylinders, no underframe stays, cast buffers riveted on and a long ducket along one side. The coach had an operating pickup 'net' and delivery arm and an activating trigger beneath the coach which engaged with a ramp which was operated by the lineside delivery apparatus. Coaches came complete with mail bags and ground apparatus, electric or clockwork. The ground apparatus could be either on tinplate or wooden sleepered track.

95/0	**LNWR** 1339 cream+brown - *22-24*	220	240
95/0	**LMS** 1924 maroon - *24-31*	180	200

C7. Post Office Mail Van - Wooden (1930)

This was to a similar specification to that used for the Carette model (table C6), with identical mechanical features, but with the coach body made of wood and with the livery transferred on. The roof was solidly fixed in place and there appeared to be no easy way of retrieving mail bags from inside the coach.

-	**LMS** 1930 maroon - *30*	300	330

C8. Short Bogie Coaches (1925)

These were to a similar specification as the 1921 and 1924 Series coaches but were only 9.5" long. They were fitted with folded tinplate Carette style bogies and reduced size Bing style couplings. They were also fitted with a transverse mounted single gas cylinder.

100/0	**LNER** 524 teak full brake - *25-32*	120	250
101/0	**LNER** 525 teak 1st - *25-32*	120	250
103/0	**LNER** 526 teak 3rd - *25-32*	120	250
160/0	**LNER** teak 1st/3rd - *30-32*	120	250
160/0	**LMS** maroon 1st/3rd - *30-32*	120	250
260/0	**LNER** teak full brake, opening doors - *30-32*	120	250
260/0	**LMS** maroon full brake, opening doors - *30-32*	120	250

C9. Short Pullman Coaches (by Bing) (1928)

These were 12.25" long and were of tinplate construction with hinged roofs. They were interior fitted with tables and chairs and had vestibule ends, underframe trusses with two transverse gas cylinders and battery box as well as brass couplings and buffers. Bing style bogies with axles retained by press-on washers in axle covers and heavy alloy spoked wheels, were fitted. There were similar GWR, LMS and LNER coaches in this range but they were not listed in the Bassett-Lowke catalogues.

195/0	**Pullman** *Minerva* brown+cream - *28-32*	100	120
195/0	**Pullman** *Cassandra* brown+cream - *28-32*	100	120

C10. Prototypical Scale Wooden Coaches (1921)

Bassett-Lowke offered a high quality range of wooden coaches, of scale length, at least until around 1938. By this time, Edward Exley Ltd were supplying top of the range quality coaches. Most of the models in the Bassett-Lowke quality range were made to customer's own specifications including choice of livery and panelled and moulded sides. Bogies were the current top of the range ones consisting of 601/0, 607/0 (6-wheel) or 612/0 as appropriate. 57' and 70' coaches were available in LMS, LNER and GWR livery.

G621/0	brake 3rd - *21-38*	NPG	NPG
G621/0	1st/3rd composite corridor - *21-38*	NPG	NPG
G621/0	dining car - *21-38*	NPG	NPG
G621/0	sleeping car - *21-38*	NPG	NPG

C11. Wooden Modern Coaching Stock Bodies (1928)

These were quality coach bodies that could be bought and finished by the purchaser. They were supplied without bogies and the body and roof were made of wood. They came ready for painting.

625/8/0	**LMS** 54' corridor 3rd/brake, old type - *28-32*	NPG	NPG
623/7/0	**LMS** 54' corridor 1st/3rd, old type - *28-32*	NPG	NPG
625/5/0	**LMS** 57' centre corridor 1st - *28-32*	NPG	NPG
625/1/0	**LMS** 57' centre corridor 1st/3rd - *28-32*	NPG	NPG
625/2/0	**LMS** 57' centre corridor 3rd/brake - *28-32*	NPG	NPG
625/3/0	**LMS** 57' centre corridor 3rd - *28-32*	NPG	NPG
625/4/0	**LMS** 50' kitchen car - *28-32*	NPG	NPG
625/28/0	**LMS** sleeping car 1st - *30-32*	NPG	NPG
625/29/0	**LMS** passenger brake van - *30-32*	NPG	NPG
625/13/0	**GWR** 57' corridor 1st/3rd - *28-32*	NPG	NPG
625/14/0	**GWR** 57' corridor 3rd/brake - *28-32*	NPG	NPG
625/15/0	**GWR** 57' diner 1st/3rd - *28-32*	NPG	NPG
625/25/0	**GWR** 70' corridor 1st/3rd - *28-32*	NPG	NPG
625/26/0	**GWR** 70' 3rd/brake - *28-32*	NPG	NPG
625/27/0	**GWR** 70' diner 1st/3rd - *28-32*	NPG	NPG
627/1/0	**GWR** 57' corridor 1st/3rd, old type - *28-32*	NPG	NPG
627/2/0	**GWR** 57' 3rd/brake, old type - *28-32*	NPG	NPG
627/10/0	**LNER** 60' corridor 1st/3rd - *28-32*	NPG	NPG
627/11/0	**LNER** 60' corridor 3rd/brake - *28-32*	NPG	NPG
627/12/0	**LNER** 60' diner 1st/3rd - *28-32*	NPG	NPG
628/1/0	**GWR** 38'9" suburban 1st/3rd - *28-32*	NPG	NPG
628/2/0	**GWR** 38'9" suburban 3rd/brake - *28-32*	NPG	NPG
626/1/0	**Pullman** 76' saloon car - *28-32*	NPG	NPG
626/2/0	**Pullman** 76' kitchen car - *28-32*	NPG	NPG

C12. 1931 Series Coaches (by Winteringham) (1932)

1931 LNER 1st class by Winteringham (for B-L) [C12] (Vectis)

These were 13" long and of a similar specification as the earlier steel 1921 and 1924 Series. They had a lower roof line, simplified uncompensated bogies, battery box (instead of gas cylinders), underframe trusses and lighter diecast alloy wheels pressed onto splined axles. The clip-on roofs had under-scale ventilators and rain strips. The buffers were cast alloy, riveted on and the couplings were Bing style with the long link. They also had detachable concertina corridor connections at each end of the coach. At extra cost, the coaches could be bought with improved bogies (612/0) and cast iron wheels.

-	**GWR** 9174 dark brown+cream 1st corridor - *32-40*	170	220
-	**GWR** 9310 dark brown+cream 3rd brake corridor - *32-40*	170	220
-	**LMS** 3490 maroon 1st corridor - *32-40*	140	170
-	**LMS** 9343 maroon 3rd brake corridor - *32-40*	140	170
-	**LNER** 36232 teak 1st corridor - *32-40*	140	170
-	**LNER** 62362 teak 3rd brake corridor - *32-40*	140	170
-	**LMS** 3416 maroon suburban 1st/3rd (13.75") - *32-40*	140	170
-	**LMS** 6560 maroon suburban 3rd/brake (13.75") - *32-40*	140	170
-	**Southern** 7411 green 1st corridor - *32-40*	200	240
-	**Southern** 3722 green 3rd brake corridor - *32-40*	200	240

C13. LMS Post Office Mail Van (by Winteringham) (1932)

This was 13" long and of a similar specification to the 1931 Series coaches in table C10 above. However the pickup and delivery mechanism was the same as that for the earlier Carette mail van. The concertina clip-on corridor connections were offset from the centre and the coach came with mail bags and ground operating apparatus which were the same as those for earlier TPOs. The coaches could be bought separately and were suitable for both electric and clockwork systems. There were no underframe trusses and but one battery box. Bogies and wheels were the same as for the 1931 Series. It seems that the royal cipher of 'G(crown)R' on a red post box, carried on the sides of the coach, was not changed in 1937 with the change of monarch.

107/0	**LMS** 3251 maroon - *32-40*	200	220

C14. Standard BR Coaches (by Precision Models) (1950)

These were 13.75" long and featured tinplate concertina corridor connections. Called 'third class', the coaches never featured a '3' on the doors and so strictly speaking they were standard class. They had the simplified Fox pattern bogies (611/0) with MFD/0 disc pattern alloy wheels although they are often found with the better running TS/0 turned steel disc wheels or synthetic plain disc wheels for 2-rail running which was available from 1957. A particular characteristic of these coaches was the overlong, blackened, round-headed, turned brass buffers. Standard Bassett-Lowke black hook and short single link couplings were used. Curiously, these coaches did not carry a Bassett-Lowke trademark.

1950 BR corridor first class by Precision Models (for B-L) [C14] (Vectis)

110/0**	**BR** 3995 red+cream 1st corridor - *50-61*	140	200

112/0	**BR** 26233 red+cream 3rd/brake - *50-61*	140	200
113/0	**BR** 9272 red+cream 3rd corridor - *50-61*	140	200

** 1st class coaches (110/0) are sometimes found in boxes labelled '111/0 1st Class Corridor Coach', but it is clear that the number '111/0 was never used for this series of coaches.

Coaches by Edward Exley Ltd

Bassett-Lowke bought in complete coach bodies from Exley, fitted their own bogies and wheels, removed any Exley labelling and sold them in Bassett-Lowke labelled boxes. Towards the end of production, the LMS maroon lake was becoming distinctly red and plastic components were being used. For example, battery boxes, coach ends, dynamos and vacuum tanks were introduced and, right at the end (1963-65), Bassett-Lowke (617/0) plastic bogies were used.

There were two types of coach, the K5 and the K6. The differences, for the Bassett-Lowke marketed Exley coaches, were principally the windows. The earlier K5s had the window ventilators painted on whereas the later K6s had them punched out. On K5s and K6s coaches they sold themselves, Exley used their own bogies whereas Bassett-Lowke fitted to them with 616/0 Fox or 618/0 Gresley pattern bogies with turned steel disc wheels (Mansell MCF/0 or plain disc TS/0). From 1957, synthetic plain disc wheel sets were available for 2-rail operation.

The following tables list the Exley coaches sold by Bassett-Lowke in their own boxes. They were produced in batches and were not all available at the same time. The running numbers varied and, because Exley coaches were sold through various retail outlets, it is not easy to determine whether any particular running numbers were unique to Bassett-Lowke.

C15. Pre-WW2 Coaches (by Exley) (1936)

These were quality coaches made for Bassett-Lowke by Edward Exley Ltd. The original labels were removed and the coaches were sold in Bassett-Lowke boxes, fitted with the appropriate Bassett-Lowke bogies and wheels (usually 612/0). These coaches continued to be shown in the catalogues after the Second World War until 1950 but availability would have been both doubtful and, at best, intermittent. cc = centre corridor. sc = side corridor.

	Pullman Dark Brown & Cream		
-	*Hazel* 1st class 19" - *36-40*	250	270
-	3rd class 19" - *36-40*	250	270
-	3rd/brake 19" - *36-40*	250	270
	LMS Maroon		
-	Royal Mail TPO 17" with non-working apparatus - *36-40*	250	270
-	1st sc 15.5" - *36-40*	250	270
-	3rd sc 15.5" - *36-40*	250	270
-	1st sc brake 15.5" - *36-40*	250	270
-	3rd sc brake 15.5" - *36-40*	250	270
-	dining/kitchen car 2050 16.5" - *36-40*	250	270
	SR Green		
-	1st sc 16.5" - *36-40*	320	350
-	3rd sc 16.5" - *36-40*	320	350
-	1st sc brake 16.5" - *36-40*	320	350
-	3rd sc brake 16.5" - *36-40*	320	350
	LNER Teak		
-	dining/kitchen 16.5" - *36-40*	250	270
-	1st sc 15.5" - *36-40*	250	270
-	3rd sc 15.5" - *36-40*	250	270
-	1st sc brake 15.5" - 36-40	250	270
-	3rd sc brake 15.5" - *36-40*	250	270
	GWR Dark Brown & Cream		
-	sc 16.5" long - *36-40*	300	320
-	sc brake end (16.5" long) - *36-40*	300	320

C16. Early Post-WW2 Coaches (by Exley) (1947)

These early post-war coaches predate the introduction of the K5 and K6 types. cc = centre corridor. sc = side corridor.

	LMS Maroon		
-	57' cc - *47-50*	120	170
-	57' cc brake - *47-50*	120	170
-	5091 54' 5091 sc 3rd - *47-50*	120	170
-	3921 54' 3921 sc brake comp - *47-50*	120	170
-	restaurant car - *47-50*	140	200
-	sleeping car - *47-50*	120	170
	LNER Teak		
-	54' sc - *47-50*	120	170
-	54' sc brake end - *47-50*	120	170
-	54' luggage van and brake end - *47-50*	120	170
-	restaurant car - *47-50*	140	200

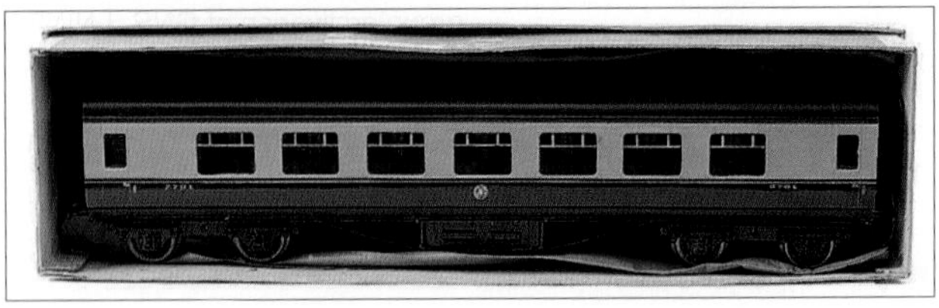

Post-war GWR side corridor 3rd by Exley (for B-L) [C16] (Vectis)

	GWR Dark Brown & Cream		
-	2791 57' sc 3rd - *47-50*	120	150
-	7172 57' sc 1st - *47-50*	120	150
-	57' sc brake - *47-50*	120	150
-	full brake - *47-50*	120	170
-	restaurant car - *47-50*	140	200

C17. Post-WW2 LMS Coaches (by Exley) (1950)

There were no listed LMS side-corridor 1st/brakes (K6) version from Bassett-Lowke, neither was there an LMS Engineer's inspection saloon. The LMS livery was crimson lake (maroon) of late style lined in yellow and black. The LMS decal was carried in the centre of each side. The roofs and underframing were black. cc = centre corridor. sc = side corridor.

	LMS Maroon		
-	54' sc 3rd - *50-54*	120	230
-	54' sc 1st - *50-54*	120	230
-	54' sc brake/3rd - *50-54*	120	230
-	54' sc brake/1st - *50-54*	120	230
-	57' cc 3rd (K5) - *50-54*	120	230
-	57' cc 1st (K5) - *50-57*	170	320
-	57' cc brake/3rd (K5 - *50-57*	170	320
-	57' cc brake/1st (K5) - *50-57*	170	320
-	57' sleeper, 1st/3rd 716 - *50-67*	140	280
-	TPO 30244 (K6) - *54-65*	170	470
-	suburban non-corridor 3rd - *54-62*	140	280
-	suburban non-corridor brake/3rd - *54-62*	140	280
-	suburban non-corridor 1st/3rd - *54-62*	140	280
-	corridor full brake (K5) - *54-57*	140	280
-	corridor kitchen (K5) - *54-57*	200	320
-	non-gangwayed full brake - *54-57*	140	280
-	non-gangwayed parcels van - *54-57*	140	280
-	buffet car + pantry (K5 & K6) - *54-60*	200	300
-	suburban 6-wheeled 3rd - *54-57*	170	310
-	suburban 6-wheeled 1st/3rd - *54-57*	170	310
-	suburban 6-wheeled brake/3rd - *54-57*	170	310
-	sc 3rd (K5) - *54-57*	140	320
-	sc 1st (K5) - *54-57*	140	270
-	sc brake/3rd (K5) - *54-57*	140	290
-	sc brake/1st (K5) - *54-57*	140	280
-	sc 1st (K6) - *57-67*	140	280
-	sc 3rd (K6) - *57-67*	140	280
-	sc brake/3rd (K6) - *57-67*	140	280
-	restaurant 1st/3rd 44 (K5) - *54-57*	170	320
-	restaurant 1st (K5) - *54-57*	170	310
-	restaurant 1st (K6) - *57-65*	200	300
-	cc 3rd (K6) - *57-62*	200	300
-	cc 1st (K5&K6) - *57-62*	200	320
-	cc brake/3rd (K6) - *57-62*	200	300
-	cc brake/1st (K6) - *57-62*	200	300
-	sc1st/3rd composite - *?*	200	300

C18. Post-WW2 GWR Coaches (by Exley) (1950)

There was no listed GWR K6 side corridor 1st/brake from Bassett-Lowke. The GWR livery was chocolate brown and cream with 'Great(crest)Western' at the centre of the coach sides. Roofs and underframing were black. cc = centre corridor. sc = side corridor.

	GWR Dark Brown & Cream		
-	57' sc 3rd (K5) - *50-57*	120	260
-	57' sc 1st (K5) - *50-57*	120	210
-	57' sc 3rd/brake (K5) - *50-57*	120	220
-	57' sc 1st/brake - *50-54*	120	220
-	57' restaurant car 1st/3rd (K5) - *50-62*	170	310

-	57' restaurant car 1st/3rd (K6) - *50-62*	170	310
-	57' cc 3rd (K5) - *54-57*	120	220
-	suburban 3rd - *54-64*	120	220
-	suburban 3rd/brake - *54-64*	120	220
-	suburban 1st/3rd - *54-64*	120	220
-	Ocean Mail parcel van - *54-57*	120	220
-	parcels train full brake - *54-57*	120	220
-	corridor full brake - *54-57*	140	280
-	sleeping car 5550? 1st - *54-57*	140	310
-	sleeping car 3rd - *54-57*	140	280
-	buffet car with pantry - *54-57*	140	280
-	TPO - *54-57*	200	310
-	6-wheel suburban 3rd - *54-57*	200	310
-	6-wheel suburban 3rd/brake - *54-57*	140	280
-	6-wheel suburban 1st/3rd - *54-57*	150	300
-	57' sc 3rd (K6) - *57-62*	210	310
-	57' sc 1st (K6) - *57-62*	210	310
-	57' sc 3rd/brake (K6) - *57-62*	210	310
-	57' cc 3rd - *57-62*	230	330

C19. Post-WW2 SR Coaches (by Exley) (1954)

The Southern Railway coaches had green sides and black ends, roofs and underframes. The name 'Southern' was printed in yellow as a logo in the centre of the coach sides. cc = centre corridor. sc = side corridor.

SR suburban all-3rd coach by Exley (for B-L) [C19]

SR Green

-	sc 3rd - *54-57*	230	390
-	sc 1st - *54-57*	230	390
-	5600 cc 1st - *54-57*	230	390
-	sc 3rd/brake - *54-57*	230	390
-	suburban 3rd - *54-57*	210	330
-	suburban 3rd/brake - *54-57*	210	330
-	suburban 1st/3rd - *54-57*	210	330

C20. Post-WW2 LNER Coaches (by Exley) (1950)

LNER coaches were not listed in Bassett-Lowke catalogues but details could be supplied on request. Two separate liveries are known to exist - Gresley/Thompson teak and LNER tourist stock green and cream. Note that the LNER Exley coaches have square cornered windows (any found with round cornered windows may be repainted LMS or GWR coaches which are more common). LNER coaches should be fitted with Gresley type bogies (618/0).

-	**LNER** teak *50-59*	140	270
-	**LNER** green+cream *55-5?*	550	750

C21. Post-WW2 BR Coaches (by Exley) (1955)

British Railways coaches by Exley were not listed in the Bassett-Lowke catalogues but for a short period (1955-57) Bassett-Lowke offered to supply any of the post-grouping coaches painted in BR livery, to order. Examples are known to exist in both carmine & cream and crimson lake (maroon) livery. Look out for crimson lake examples as they are easy to miss as they look similar to LMS stock. They have slightly different lining and no decals. The coaches should be fitted with the standard Bassett-Lowke Fox pattern bogie (616/0) and either steel turned wheels or post 1957 synthetic plain disc wheels for 2-rail operation.

BR Red & Cream

-	standard centre corridor 9272 - *55-57*	280	380
-	1st class - *55-57*	280	380
-	brake end - *55-57*	280	380
-	full brake - *55-57*	280	380
-	restaurant car - *55-57*	280	380
-	M660 sleeping car (K5) - *55-57*	280	380

BR Maroon

-	centre-corridor standard - *55-57*	200	300
-	1st class - *55-57*	200	300
-	brake end - *55-57*	200	300
-	full brake - *55-57*	200	300
-	restaurant car - *55-57*	200	300
-	sleeping car - *55-57*	200	300

WAGONS

Up until the First World War, Carette of Nuremberg produced wagons in tinplate to Bassett-Lowke's order in 0 gauge and gauge 1. They were first introduced in 1909 with new additions to the range, and reissues, appearing each year until 1913. A photograph showing these wagons has survived in the Bassett-Lowke archives and they are listed and individually illustrated in the early catalogues.

Carette went out of business at the time of the First World War but Bassett-Lowke must have acquired the tooling and litho-printing artwork because most of the range was reissued after the war with the Bassett-Lowke name in the tinprinting, usually on the ends.

Both wooden and tinplate wagons were produced and were available side by side. The latter were mostly post-grouping examples and in wood. You could buy a range of scale handmade wagons at a price four times that of a tinplate equivalent. Even the standard wooden wagons could be twice the price of tinplate ones. After the Second World War, some wooden wagons were available in kit form.

Today, the value of wagons has reversed with tinplate ones selling for twice the price of wooden ones. Look particularly for the 2-rail versions fitted with synthetic wheels and the 3-rail ones which have top quality Bassett-Lowke iron spoked wagon wheel sets.

Cat No.	Company, Number, Colour, Dates	£	£

W1a. Pre-WW1 Tinplate Wagons (by Carette) (1909)

These wagons had the 'grotesque' style large Carette couplings and separate cast iron axleguards. They could be supplied with either heavy iron spoked wheels or lighter tinplate wheels. Although slightly underscale in length, the tin-printing was particularly fine and accurate to prototype. Most wagons carried the drop-signal Bassett-Lowke emblem on the solebars and the date of issue was included in the tin-printing. Thus it is possible to have variations of the wagons showing different issue dates (e.g. the MR cattle van was issued in 1909 and 1913). The Bassett-Lowke catalogue number was also included in the tin-printing in tiny numbers, usually on the wagon end but sometimes on the solebars. In this table is given the catalogue numbers and decoration of each wagon to which it relates.

1341/35	**LNWR** grey brake van 'Crewe' - *09-14*	100	150
1344/35	**LNWR** light grey van - *09-14*	100	150
1345/35	**LNWR** off-white refrigerator van - *09-14*	100	150
1346/35	**LNWR** 530 grey 4-plank 7T goods wagon - *09-14*	50	80
1346/35	**LNWR** 1914 530 grey 4-plank 7T goods wagon - *14*	100	150
13410/35	**LNWR** 1909 grey 2 x timber bolster trucks - *09-14*	200	250
13426/35	**LNWR** 670 dark brown 'Fruit & Milk Traffic' van - *09-14*	450	550
13427/35	**LNWR** 329 dark brown horse box - *09-14*	450	550
13429/35	**LNWR** 1043 dark brown open carriage truck - *09-14*	100	150
13447/35	**LNWR** grey brake van 'Camden' - *11-14*	100	150
13448/35	**LNWR** grey van - *11-14*	100	150

1909 LNWR van by Carette (for B-L) [W1a] (Keith Bone)

13449/35	**LNWR** 640 grey 4-plank 10T Loco Coal wagon - *13-14*	50	80
13444/35	**LNWR** 15591 brown gunpowder van lithographed in England - *11-14*	300	400
13445/35	**LNWR** 13445 dark brown motor car van - *11-14*	700	900

13442/35	**MR** grey brake van one open and one closed verandah - *09-14*	100	150
13343/35	**MR** grey large cattle truck - *09-14*	150	200
1347/35	**MR** grey 5-plank wagon - *09-14*	150	200
13417/35	**MR** bogie steel loco coal wagon grey - *09-14*	200	250
13433/35	**MR** dark grey 7-plank Loco Coal - *11-14*	80	120
13434/0	**MR** open wagon loco coal - *09-14*	NPG	NPG
13436/35	**MR** 35626 grey ventilated van - *11-14*	150	200
13438/35	**MR** grey 3-plank ballast wagon - *11-14*	150	200
13442/35	**MR** 68 brown Eng. Dept. (ED) ballast wagon lithographed in England - *11-12*	100	150
13442/35	**MR** 68 brown Eng. Dept. (ED) ballast wagon - *?-14*	150	200

1913 Caledonian Railway 4-plank wagon by Carette (for B-L) [W1a] (Keith Bone)

13443/35	**CR** 71908 brown 4-plank wagon lithographed in England - *?-14*	100	150
13443/35	**CR** 71908 brown 4-plank wagon - *13-14*	150	200
13434/35	**LYR** 418, grey 3-plank ballast wagon - *11-14*	150	200
13412/35	**GNR** 1909 red-brown van - *09-14*	150	200
13421/35	**GNR** 10959 brown 10T brake van - *09-14*	200	250
13422/35	**GNR** 39284 brown 8T banana van - *09-14*	150	200
13423/35	**GNR** 18335 brown 15T 6-plank wagon - *09-14*	150	200
13424/35	**GNR** 27451 brown 5T fish van - *09-14*	150	200
13431/35	**NBR** grey 8T 4-plank wagon - *11-14*	100	150
13432/35	**GCR** grey 8T 4-plank wagon - *11-14*	100	150
13439/35	**NER** 3192 grey Flatrol M + brown boiler **'JT Lowke & Sons'** - *11-14*	600	900
13446/35	**GER** 14096 grey 4-plank wagon - *11-14*	100	150
13436/35	**LB&SCR** 9083 light grey open wagon + sheet rail + LB&SCR tarpaulin - *11-14*	250	350
13414/35	**GWR** 56452 grey brake van 'Paddington' - 'Guard Greenly' - *09-14*	100	150
13415/35	**GWR** 16613 grey ventilated van - *09-14*	100	150
13416/0	**GWR** 8T banana van - *not made*	NA	NA
13416/35	**GWR** 23464 grey 8T 4-plank Loco coal wagon - *09-14*	50	80
13420/35	**GWR** 59761 off-white Mica B refrigerated meat van - *09-14*	150	200
1348/35	**'EWJ Greaves Blue Lias Lime/Portland Cement'** 130 grey pitched roof wagon - *09-14*	200	250
1349/35	No.1909 black Tar Wagon - *09-14*	200	250
13411/35	**'Anglo American Oil Co.'** 405 red tanker - *09-14*	120	150
13413/35	**'Bassett-Lowke'**, Northampton' 165 red-brown 8-plank - *09-10*	450	550
13413/35	**'Bassett-Lowke'**, Northampton' 165 black 8-plank - *13-14*	100	120
13413/35	**'Bassett-Lowke Ltd'**, London & Northampton' 6285 red-brown, diagonal stripe, 8-plank lithographed in England - *11-12*	150	250
13413/35	**'Bassett-Lowke Ltd'**, London & Northampton' 6285 light grey, diagonal stripe, 8-plank - *13-14*	150	250
13425BL/35	**'WJ Bassett-Lowke & Co.'** yellow 8T van - *09-14*	900	1200
13418/35	**'WH Hull & Son'** 405 light grey 10T 7-plank - *09-14*	250	300
13425M/35	**'Colman's Mustard Traffic'** yellow van - *09-14*	800	1000
13425S/35	**'Colman's Starch Traffic'** yellow van - *09-14*	800	1000
13428/35	**'City of Birmingham Gas Dept.'** 1201 red-brown 12T 8-plank coal wagon Sp Edn (Hull & Son) - *09-14*	250	350
13430/35	**'City of Birmingham Gas Dept.'** 779 grey steel coke hopper - *09-14*	250	350

W1b. Pre-WW1 Cheap Tinplate Wagons (by Carette) (1912)

In 1912, a cheaper range of wagons, very similar to those listed in W1a, was supplied by Carette for Bassett-Lowke. These wagons had tin-printed axleguards integral with the solebars and were supplied only with tinplate wheels. They were, therefore, lighter than the wagons listed in table W1a but appear very similar in general style. This range was restricted to the eleven vehicles listed here. The '35' at the end of the catalogue number refers to the gauge in millimetres.

13470-35	**MR** 35626A grey ventilated van - *12*	120	150
13471-35	**GNR** 18335 brown 15T open wagon - *12*	40	60
13472-35	**GNR** brown covered van - *12*	120	150
13473-35	**MR** grey short 'Large' cattle van - *12*	120	150
13474-35	**LNWR** grey goods van - *12*	120	150

1912 LNWR refrigerator van by Carette (for B-L) [W1b] (Vectis)

13475-35	**LNWR** white refrigerator van - *12*	120	150
13476-35	**LNWR** grey 7T open wagon - *12*	40	60
13477-35	**MR** grey open wagon - *12*	40	60
13492-35	**GNR** 13492 brown 20T brake van - *13*	150	180
13493-35	**LNWR** grey 10T brake van, Willesden - *13*	150	180
13479-35	**MR** grey 10T brake van - *13*	150	180

W2. Post-WW1 Tinplate Wagons (B-L from Carette Tooling) (1923)

These tinplate wagons were made by Bassett-Lowke using Carette tooling and so resemble the pre-WW1 Carette wagons. They were a restricted range having the Bassett-Lowke name included in the tinprinting at their ends. They had a mixture of Bassett-Lowke and Carette style couplings with cast spoked wheels. The issue of these wagons spanned the Grouping of the railways and so pre- and post-Grouping designs were used. The wagons were of an excellent quality but had distinctly short proportions - 5" long and 2.25" wide.

1346/0	**LNWR** 850, 44865 grey 10T 5-plank open wagon - *23-26*	20	30
13447/0	**LNWR** grey 10T brake van, single end verandah - *23-26*	35	45
13448/0	**LNWR** grey covered goods van - *23-26*	45	55
13433/0	**MR** 45321 grey 12T 7-plank open wagon, Loco Coal - *23-26*	20	30
1346/0	**LMS** 24320 grey 10T 5-plank open wagon - *26-30*	20	30
13433/0	**LMS** 45321 grey 12T 7-plank open, Loco Coal Only - *26-30*	45	55
13447/0	**LMS** 152540 grey 10T brake van, single end verandah - *26-30*	35	45
13448/0	**LMS** 4132 grey 10T covered goods van - *26-30*	35	45
13416/0	**GW** (large) 91694 light grey 10T 5-plank open wagon - *23-30*	20	30

1923 GWR open wagon with tarpaulin (from Carette tooling) [W2] (Vectis)

13416/0	**GW** (small) 91694 light grey 10T 5-plank open wagon - *23-30*	20	30
?	**GW** 35642 green 16T brake van 'Exeter' - *23-30*	35	45
13413/0	**'Bassett-Lowke'** London & Northampton 6285 red-brown 8-plank - *23-30*	80	100
13413/0	**'Bassett-Lowke'** London & Northampton 6285 light grey 7-plank - *23-30*	80	100
13413/0	**'Bassett-Lowke'** London, Northampton & Edinburgh 6285 light grey 8-plank - *23-30*	80	90

Several of the Bing tinplate wagons were not listed in the Bassett-Lowke catalogues including 'Explosives', NE 'Refrigerator', NE cattle, LMS fish and the bogie vans - 'Fish Traffic' and 'Milk Traffic'.

W3. Cheap Tinplate Wagons (by Bing) (1928)

These tinplate wagons were 5" long and 2.25" wide and were of a simplified appearance but with good quality litho printing. . They had either Bing automatic couplings or standard Bing drop link hooks with a drop link at one end only. The bases were common for both vans and wagons and carried a running number on the solebars. 73923 was the number often used but 163581, 356204 and 425071 are also found. The wheels were tinplate on spragged axles but some had Bassett-Lowke heavy alloy spoked wheels. The vans were issued with either opening or non-opening doors. The wagons are also found without any company lettering, sometimes with a solebar number on the lower left planking.

	Dark Grey 7-Plank		
592/0	**GW** - *28-32*	25	35
592/0	**LMS** - *28-32*	25	35
592/0	**NE** - *28-32*	25	35
592/0	**SR** - *28-32*	25	35
593/0	No letters*, number on solebars - *28-32*	50	60
593/0	No letters*, 231462 on lower left - *28-32*	50	60
	Dark Grey Van		
593/0	**GW** - 28-32	30	40
593/0	**LMS** - 28-32	30	40
593/0	**NE** - *28-32*	30	40
593/0	**SR** - *28-32*	30	40

* Bassett-Lowke may have ordered some blank wagons so that customers could add their own lettering.

W4. Tinplate Standard Wagons (by Winteringham) (1930)

These were 5.75" long and 2.25" wide and made in tinplate. They were of scale proportions with Bing style hook and long link couplings. The wagons had heavy metal spoked wheels on splined axles and cast buffers that were riveted on. There was no representation of brake gear or vee-hangers and the wheels were painted black. The range, with the exception of the LMS open wagon, covered van and guards van, ceased in 1940 with the outbreak of the Second World War. The design of the LMS wagons was changed in 1938 and continued after the war until 1960. The wheels on these changed to the new post-war design which had a neater, more scale, appearance. They carried the Loko logo on the sole bars.

1352/0	**LMS** 24468 grey 5-plank - *30-38*	35	40
1360/0	**LMS** 62306 grey 20T brake van verandah both ends - *30-38*	60	70
1370/0	**LMS** 29850 grey 12T van - *30-38*	60	70
1370/0	**LMS** 291859 grey van - *?*	60	70
1380/0	**LMS** 17741, 14548 grey cattle wagon - *30-40*	60	70
1353/0	**NE** 130911 green 5-plank - *30-40*	35	40
1361/0	**NE** 140517 grey 20T brake van verandah both ends - *30-34*	80	100
1361/0	**NE** 140517 red-brown 20T brake van verandah both ends - *34-40*	90	100
1371/0	**NE** 138971 grey-green** 12T luggage van - *30-40*	50	60
1390/0	**NE** 54849, 153180 white 8T Refrigerator van - *30-40*	120	140
1400/0	**NE** 451004 brown bogie Brick wagon - *30-40*	80	100
1406/0	**NE** 77823 brown standard Flatrol bogie wagon 12" long *** - *32-40*	650	750
1406/0	**NE** 77823 grey Flatrol M **+** brown **'Callender'** cable drum - *30-40*	850	950
1406/0	**NE** 77823 grey standard 'Flatrol' bogie wagon + brown boiler **'Bassett-Lowke Ltd'** 12" - *32-40*	450	950
1354/0	**GW** 91694 green 5-plank - *30-40*	35	40
1354/0	as above but light grey - *30-40*	35	40
1372/0	**GW** 103873 dark green 12T van - *30-40*	35	40
1362/0	**GW** 35642 grey 20T brake Toad van Exeter - *30-40*	60	100
1401/0	**GW 'United Dairies'** 2007 white milk tanker - *30-40*	480	650
1355/0	**SR** 9871, 10252, 19232 dark green 12T open wagon 6-plank - *30-40*	40	45
1373/0	**SR** 15757, 17741 green van - *30-40*	80	90
1356/0	**'Bassett-Lowke Ltd** London Northampton & Manchester' 6285* green-grey 12T 7-plank - *30-40*	70	90
1402/0	**'Pratts Spirit** '1852, 21774 buff petrol tanker - *30-35*	500	650
1404/0	**'Esso'** 21774 cream petrol tanker (also 1042/0) - *3?-40*	450	700
1404/0	**'Mobiloil Vacuum Oil'** dark green-grey tanker (also 1042/0) - *36-40*	450	700
1406/0	77823 brown bogie well wagon **+** orange+green cable drum and coil **'Enfield Cable Works Ltd. London** - *30-40*	850	950

* 6285 was the telephone number of the Bassett-Lowke shop at 112 high Holborn, London. ** The NE van tinplate printing suffered a production problem resulting in almost all the survivors having a crazed appearance. The number also frequently appears as '13897' as the final '1' is lost in a surface groove. *** The load bed was plain having no tinplate tab slots for the attachment of either the cable drum or the boiler.

W5. Wagon Tarpaulins (1920)

Wagon sheets, made either by Bing or Bassett-Lowke, were available for several pre- and post-grouping companies and would fit any tinplate or wooden 4-wheeled open wagon . Each company's sheet had its own number and initials and RCH diamonds parallel with the long edges. The Bing sheets also had a St Andrew's cross stretching to the corners. They were made of black linen and the printing was in white. Strings, with which to tie the sheet to the wagon's buffers, were sewn into short edges but some early sheets had elasticated ends.

-	**L&NWR** black - *20-27*	10	12
-	**MR** 139197 black by Bing - *20-36*	10	12
-	**MR** 1922 black - *20-36*	10	12
-	**GNR** 17220 black by Bing - *20-36*	10	12
-	**GNR** 1922 black - *20-36*	10	12
-	**L&SWR** 1343 black by Bing - *20-27*	10	12
-	**GWR** 5231 black - *20-36*	10	12
-	**LMS** 5231 black - *?*	10	12

W6. Methylated Spirit Tanker for Live Steam Locomotives (1922)

This was 5.25" long and consisted of a brass tank on a wooden base. It had cast WAG/0 axle guards screwed to the solebars, cast buffers screwed to the buffer beams and standard heavy alloy spoked wheels which were painted black and mounted on splined axles. The tank was secured by wire cables to the end stanchions and the wooden base. The tank carried either water or methylated spirits for operating live steam locomotives. Removing the loose cap from the top, disclosed a spring valve which, when operated, allowed the contents to flow out of the outlet pipe beneath the tank.

1922 'Lowko' methylated spirit tank wagon [W6] (Vectis)

3112/0	**'Lowko Spirit'** red - *22-37*	80	120
?	**'Colas'** black - *?*	80	120

W7. Scale LMS (MR) High Capacity Bogie Wagon (1923)

This wagon, which was 12" long, was the type used by the Midland Railway for transportation of rails, girders and other cumbersome items. It was offered for a short period only. The bogies were cast in white metal and could be bought separately as 509/0. The wagon had low stretchers to hold loads in place.

-	**LMS** grey - *23-24*	80	120

Wooden Goods Vehicles

Bassett-Lowke continued to offer, throughout their existence, a bespoke service for top quality, museum standard, rolling stock. However, just prior to the First World War, the Company introduced a standard range of vehicles made of best quality materials for discerning clients who preferred something rather better than the mass produced tinplate wagons. The clients also preferred models made of the same materials as the prototypes i.e. wooden tops, steel wheels and three link couplings.

The specification of the standard range of goods vehicles changed over the period. Some were plain while others had representations of sides and ends printed on. There may have been several suppliers, such as Mills Bros. and the Leeds Model Company, who produced the bodies to which Bassett-Lowke fitted the wheels, couplings and buffers. The Bassett-Lowke wooden vehicles may be recognised by the WAG/O axle guards or the use of box or pine wood with butt joins (as opposed to combed or dovetail joints). Theirs had a one piece wooden base with the tops and solebars pinned and glued on. Except for roofs, Bassett-Lowke never used plywood.

Three link couplings when fitted were not normally sprung. The coupling shanks were twisted through 90° and pinned to small wooden blocks under the wagon's floor. Other couplings included Bing style hook and long link and Stedman LF/16 single hook and single link. Wheels were generally the period Bassett-Lowke heavy alloy spoked wheels mounted on splined axles.

W8. Wooden Pre-Grouping Wagons - Pre-WW1 (1919)

These were 5" long and had printed and/or painted sides.

3311	**LNWR** grey 7T 4-plank - *19-22*	20	25
3321	**LNWR** grey 10T 5-plank - *19-22*	20	25
3331	**LNWR** grey box van - *19-22*	25	30
3341	**LNWR** grey brake van, Crewe - *19-22*	25	30
3322	**MR** grey 10T 6-plank Loco Coal - *20-22*	20	25
3323	**GN** brown 15T 6-plank - *20-22*	20	25

W9. Wooden Pre-Grouping Wagons - Post-WW1 (1919)

The unlettered wagons could be lettered at the request of the purchaser and at extra cost. These were also available as kits. db = dumb buffers

G501E	**GN** brown 10T 5-plank db - *19*	30	35
G501E	**GW** green 10T 5-plank db - *19*	30	35
G501E	**MR** grey 10T 5-plank db - *19*	30	35
G501E	**GC** 10T 5-plank db - *19*	30	35
G501E	**LNWR** grey 10T 5-plank db - *19*	30	35
G504E	**MR** grey high capacity bogie mineral wagon 504/0 bogies - *19*	45	55
G504E	**NER** grey high capacity bogie mineral wagon 504/0 bogies - *19-22*	45	55
G505E	**NER** 90652 white refrigerator van - *19-22*	45	55
G505E	**LNWR** white refrigerator van - *19-22*	45	55
G505E	**GNR** refrigerator van - *19-22*	45	55
G507E	grey unlettered pair of timber bolster wagons with db - *19-22*	30	35
G510	**North Eastern** 108340 brown high capacity bogie box van - *19-22*	45	55
G511E	**NER** 17827 brown 4-wheel 10T brake van, 2 verandas + duckets - *19-22*	30	35
G513E	**NBR** brown 4-wheel brake van, ducket, no veranda - *19-22*	30	35
G514E	**MR** grey 4-wheel 10T brake van, 1 veranda + 1 platform - *19-22*	30	35
G515E	**MR** M1907 grey 6-wheel 20T brake van, 1 veranda + 1 platform - *19-22*	35	45
G516E	**GW** green 4-wheel 10T brake van, 1 veranda - *19-22*	30	35
G561E	**'Bassett-Lowke Ltd** London & Northampton' 10T 8-plank - *19*	15	20
G561E	grey unlettered 8T open - *21-22*	15	20
G561E	grey unlettered 10T open - *21-22*	15	20
G562E	grey unlettered 10T box van - *21-22*	20	25
G582E	**LNWR** grey 10T box wagon - *19*	30	35
G582E	**MR** grey 10T box wagon - *19*	30	35
G582E	**GN** 10T box wagon - *19*	30	35
G582E	**NBR** 10T box wagon - *19*	30	35
G583E	grey unlettered cattle wagon - *21-22*	35	45
G534E	**GN** brown 4-wheel 10T brake van, 2 verandas - *19*	30	35
G585E	**LNWR** grey 4-wheel 10T brake van, 1 veranda - *19*	30	35
G535E	**GN** brown 6-wheel 20T brake van, 2 verandas - *19*	35	45
G586E	**LNWR** grey 6-wheel 20T brake van, 1 verandah - *19*	35	45

W10. Wooden Scale Prototypical Models (1920)

These were 5" long and similar to those in table W9 but were of a better quality - perhaps having come from a different supplier. They were fitted with cast iron turned wheels and detailed fittings; especially the guards vans. They were forerunners to further series of quality wagons. It seems that none of the models were fitted with brake gear or vee-hangers.

03311/0	**LNWR** 1503? grey 7T open - *20-28*	25	30
03321/0	**LNWR** grey 10T open - *20-28*	25	30
03309/0	**GN** 18335? brown 15T high-sided - *23-26*	25	30
03322/0	**MR** 1311? grey 12T open, Loco Coal - *23-26*	25	30
03331/0	**LNWR** 1911? grey van - *23-26*	30	35
03341/0	**LNWR** 1809? grey brake van, 1 verandah - *20-26*	30	35
-	** open wagons - *27-40*	35	45
-	** open wagons - *27-40*	35	45
-	** brake vans - *27-40*	35	45
-	** high capacity bogie mineral wagons - *27-40*	70	80

1925 Schwepps Summer Cordials wooden wagon [W10] (Vectis)

-	**'Schweppes'** Summer Cordials grey open, Sp Edn (Schweppes Ltd) - *25*	NPG	NPG

** These had liveries painted to order.

W11. Wooden Standard Post-Grouping Wagons (1928)

3327/0	**SR** 3753 brown 12T 7-plank - *28-36*	15	25
3333/0	**SR** 15757 brown 12T van - *28-36*	20	30

1928 wooden SR van [W11] (Vectis)

3344/0	**SR** 11892 brown 20T brake van 2 verandahs - *28-36*	15	25
3352/0	**LMS** grey 10T 5-plank - *30-36*	15	25
3354/0	**GW** green 8T 5-plank - *30-36*	15	25
3353/0	**NE** brown 10T 5-plank - *30-36*	15	25
3370/0	**LMS** grey van - *30-36*	20	30
3371/0	**NE** brown van - *30-36*	20	30
3371/0	**NE** 138971 grey van - *30-36*	30	40
3113/0	**'Colas'** grey black tank no valve and pipe - *30-36*	120	140
3362/0	**GW** green brake van, 7.37" - *30-36*	20	30
3360/0	**LMS** 646 grey 10T brake van, 7.5" long - *30-36*	20	30
3361/0	**NE** 451091 grey 10T ** brake van, 5.5" long - *30-36*	20	30

** Catalogue picture shows '20T'.

W12. Wooden Standard Post-Grouping Wagons (attributed to Milbro) (1937)

These wagons were 5.5" long. They had no trademark showing but were almost certainly made for Bassett-Lowke by Milbro. They had Milbro axle guards screwed to the solebars and cast wheels, turned brass buffers, 3-link unsprung couplings and Milbro style wood construction. The wagons were not normally fitted with brake gear or vee-hangers although these may have been fitted at the customer's request or have been done so retrospectively. The brake vans had footboards.

-	**GW** green 12T 5-plank - *37-40*	35	45
-	**LMS** grey 12T 5-plank - *37-40*	35	45
-	**NE** grey 12T 5-plank - *37-40*	35	45
-	**SR** brown 12T 5-plank - *37-40*	35	45
-	black 20T tube wagon - *37-40*	35	45
-	**LMS** red gunpowder van - *37-40*	60	70
-	**GW** green van - *37-40*	45	60
-	**LMS** 1906 grey van - *37-40*	45	60
-	**NE** grey van - *37-40*	45	60
-	**SR** brown van - *37-40*	45	60
-	**GW** green? Eng. Dept. low-sided - *37-40*	35	45
-	**LMS** grey? Eng. Dept. low-sided - *37-40*	35	45
-	**NE** grey? Eng. Dept. low-sided - *37-40*	35	45
-	**SR** brown? Eng. Dept. low-sided - *37-40*	35	45
-	grey cattle wagon - *37-40*	45	60
-	**LMS** grey 20T 6-wheel brake van 2 verandahs - *37-40*	60	70
-	**LMS** grey 10T 4-wheel brake van 2 verandahs 5.5" long - *37-40*	35	45
-	**NE** grey 10T, brake van, 1 verandah - *37-40*	35	45
-	**GW** 98014 green 10T brake van 2 verandahs - *37-40*	35	45
-	**SR** brown 10T brake van - *37-40*	45	60

Bakelite Wagons

These were made in self-coloured bakelite with standard Leeds Model Company axle guards mounted on separate tinplate double brackets which were tabbed to the floor of the wagon. They had non-locking alloy buffers and sprung 3-link couplings. The wagons were fitted with LMC alloy spoked or 4-hole disc wheels and had super details included on the bakelite moulding. Metal fatigue is a common problem with the buffers and wheels on these wagons and these items have often been replaced. Although dropped from the catalogue in 1940, some remained on sale in Bassett-Lowke's shops as late as 1948. (see also the chapter on the Leeds Model Company - Wagons Tables 13 and 14).

W13. Bakelite Wagons (Leeds for Bassett-Lowke) (1938)

P10	**LMS** brown 12T 7-plank - *38-40*	15	20
P20	**NE** 37042 grey 12T 7-plank - *38-40*	15	20
P30	**GW** grey 12T 7-plank - *38-40*	15	20
P40	**SR** brown 12T 7-plank - *38-40*	20	25
P50	**NE** red 12T 7-plank - *38-40*	20	25
P80	**LMS** 606521 brown 12T van - *38-40*	15	20
P90	**LMS** 606521 brown 12T van, ventilators, brake pipes - *38-48*	20	25
P100	**LMS** maroon 6T fish van, passenger brake - *38-40*	25	30
P110	**NE** grey 12T van - *38-40*	15	20
P120	**NE** grey 12T van, ventilators, brake pipes - *38-48*	20	25
P130	**NE** red 12T fruit van, ventilators, brake pipes - *38-48*	20	25

Post-war Tinplate Wagons

The tinplate wagons in the following three tables used WF/0 8-spoked alloy wheel sets as standard but could be had with the better running WCF/0 8-spoked turned steel wheels at extra cost. From 1957, the vehicles could be had with Tri-ang manufactured synthetic 3-hole disc wheels, at a reduced cost, for 2-rail operation. All these vehicles featured standard, later pattern, Bassett-Lowke black hook and short single link couplings but Bassett-Lowke offered a replacement conversion kit (601/13/0) for scale 3-link couplings which are sometimes found on these wagons. So too are track operated hook and loop remotely controlled automatic couplings.

Tarpaulin covers (or 'sheets') were not available for the open wagons after the war.

W14. Late Tinplate Wagons (1938)

Although pre-war tinplate rolling stock appeared in the early post-war catalogues, none was produced except for the later 0 gauge LMS brown goods series which was introduced in 1938 and continued, albeit with modifications, until 1960. iag = black integral axle guards. sag = black separate axle guards.

1352/0	**LMS** 36721, 3672 ** brown 13T open, brown base, iag - *38-48*	20	30
1352/0	**LMS** 36721, 3672 ** brown 13T open, brown base, sag - *48-50*	20	30
1352/0	LMS 36721, 3672 ** brown 13T open, black base, sag - *50-60*	20	30
1370/0	**LMS** 91375 brown 12T van, brown base, iag - *38-48*	25	45

Post-war LMS van [W14] (Vectis)

1370/0	LMS 91375 brown 12T van, brown base, sag - *48-50*	25	45
1370/0	**LMS** 91375 brown 12T van, black base, sag		

	- *50-60*	25	45
1360/0	**LMS** 730273 brown 20T brake van, brown base, iag - *38-48*	30	55
1360/0	**LMS** 730273 brown 20T brake van, brown base, sag - *48-50*	30	55
1360/0	**LMS** 730273 brown 20T brake van, black base, sag - *50-53*	30	55
1364/0	**BR** B37354 grey 20T brake van, LWB, black base, sag - *51-68*	25	35

** Due to a litho printing error some wagons have the last digit ('1') missing on one or both sides making the running number '3672'.

W15. Post-war Wooden Wagons and Kits (1948)

These wagons were available factory made or as sets of parts, for home assembly and finishing, at approximately half the price of factory made vehicles. The specification included parts made of good quality seasoned wood cut to size with planking scribed as necessary. Included in each kit were WAG/0 axle guards, WO/12 or WO/10 oval or round buffers, 601/15/0 3-link couplings, strapping, WF/0 alloy wheel sets, screws, pins, transfers and instructions. Turned steel wheels (WCF/0) were available at extra cost and synthetic 3-hole disc wheels for 2-rail operation were available from 1957 and reduced the price of the kit by 2/-. Prices are provided in this table for factory made models built from these kits and (at the bottom) any unmade kit with all parts still intact.

-	**LMS** 672149** brown 12T 5-plank - *48-56*	15	20
-	**NE** 36720** grey 12T 5-plank - *48-56*	15	20
-	**GW** green 12T 5-plank - *48-50*	15	20
-	**BR** 837483** grey 12T 5-plank - *50-65*	15	20
-	**BR** grey cattle wagon - *52-60*	20	30
-	**LMS** brown 12T van - *48-56*	25	30
-	**NE** 14972** grey 12T van - *48-56*	25	30
-	**GW** green 12T van - *48-50*	25	30
-	**BR** 108283** grey 12T van - *52-60*	25	30
-	**LMS** brown 20T brake van - *48-56*	25	30
-	**NE** 13758** grey 20T brake van - *48-56*	25	30
-	**GW** green 20T brake van - *48-50*	25	30
-	**BR** 37463** grey 20T brake van - *52-60*	25	30
-	any kit complete - *48-68*	NPG	25

** The numbers given are for known examples, however, these changed over the years and depended on the production batches.

W16. Long Wheelbase Special Load Wagons (1957)

These wagons used the base of the 1364/0 guards van. All bases were black.

Vehicle A	black chained metal plates - *57-65*	30	60
Vehicle B	black + strung and wedged 2 **'Hornby Liverpool Cables'** drums - *57-65*	30	60
Vehicle E	black + chained large metal tube - *57-65*	30	60
Vehicle M	large log chained black - *57-65*	30	60
Vehicle N	black + chained lg square timber - *57-65*	30	60

W17. Standard Wheelbase Special Load Wagons (1957)

These wagons used the base of 1352/0, 1370/0 and 1360/0 standard wagons; all with black bases.

Vehicle C	black + pinned **'Hornby'** insulated meat container - *57-65*	30	60
Vehicle D	black + chained machinery casting (varied) - *57-65*	30	60
Vehicle F	black + chained 12 **'Bassett-Lowke'** wooden sleepers - *57-65*	30	60
Vehicle G	black + chained 4 **'Bassett-Lowke'** loco driving wheels - *57-65*	30	60
Vehicle H	black + strung and wedged **'Hornby Liverpool Cables'** drum - *57-65*	30	60
Vehicle K	black + pinned **'Hornby'** furniture container - *57-65*	30	60
Vehicle L	black + 2 chained ship propellers - *57-65*	30	60

ACCESSORIES

Bassett-Lowke produced quite an extensive range of accessories not least their various series of track which offered the public different standards according to what they could afford. Lineside equipment included stations, goods depots, level crossings, signals and platform personnel and equipment.

SETS

Train sets did not play a big part in the Company's marketing policy but starter sets were available.

Bassett-Lowke
by Corgi & Hornby

HISTORY

Corgi Classics purchased the tools and intellectual assets of Bassett-Lowke in 1996 and decided to introduce a range of 0 gauge models, in 1999, based on earlier Bassett-Lowke designs with the Greenly valve gear. The first was released as a steam driven model but only one steam version was made. After that all new models have had 12v electric mechanisms fitted with smoke generators. All electric steam outline locomotives were able to run in either 2-rail or 3-rail control through a unique switching system. This included an 'off' setting operated by a control rod in the cab. A second control rod operated the smoke unit.

The models were individually made in brass using soldered construction. The plan from the start was to develop each new model, release it in a range of liveries and then move on to a new model. The recommended smallest radius for the locomotives is 3 feet.

With mounting financial worries, due largely to over production in the diecast model industry, late in 2004, Corgi decided to pull out of locomotive production and terminated the employment of their designer and engineer, Len Mills, who transferred to Ace Trains to work on their future locomotives. It was rumoured that the Bassett-Lowke name was available for sale. However, a year later, the Bassett-Lowke range was still alive and moving forward.

There followed an LNER/BR Class A3 and a prototype for the LMS 6202 'Turbomotive' was made and displayed at various venues in 2004. A Great Western 'Castle' class loco was also announced but Len Mills developed this for Ace Trains instead.

In 2006, Corgi Classics turned to ETS, in The Czech Republic, and commissioned some models from them. These started to arrive in 2007 and were made in tinplate using ETS manufacturing and design technology. They had no generic or common features with the earlier locomotives and, moreover, the new models were made to Continental European 1:45 scale rather than British 0 gauge 1:43 scale.

In May 2008, Hornby purchased the Corgi Classics brand, tooling and intellectual assets and with them the Bassett-Lowke business. Initially, Hornby see the link with ETS continuing but are expected to have exciting plans for developing the range.

LOCOMOTIVES

In the cab, each model carries an identity plate with its production number. The locomotives can be switched between 2-rail and 3-rail operation and from 2007 they were advertised as having smoke generators fitted.

Cat No.	Company, Number, Colour, Dates	£	£

Locomotives by Corgi

L1. Peckett 0-4-0ST (2011)

Peckett 0-4-0ST Wenman [L1] (Hornby)

Work on this started under Corgi's management and the project was taken over by Hornby. Models are fitted with smoke generators.

BL99053	**Wenman** red Ltd Edn 250 - *11*	NPG	250
BL99063	**Joseph** green Ltd Edn 250 - *11*	NPG	250

L2. LNER Class J39 0-6-0 (2008)

Branded 'Bassett-Lowke'. Made in tinplate to 1:45 scale. 12-14V. 2-rail /3-rail switch in cab. All are fitted with smoke generators.

99032	**2714** LNER black Ltd Edn 250 - *not made*	NA	NA
99032A	**1532** LNER black Ltd Edn 50 - *09*	350	550
99032B	**1563** LNER black Ltd Edn 50 - *09*	350	550
99032C	**1580** LNER black Ltd Edn 50 - *09*	350	550
99032D	**1586** LNER black Ltd Edn 50 - *09*	350	550
99032E	**1875** LNER black Ltd Edn 50 - *09*	350	550
99031	**64744** BRc black Ltd Edn 130 - *09*	330	490
99031A	**64757** BRc black Ltd Edn 40 - *09*	330	490
99031B	**64781** BRc black Ltd Edn 40 - *09*	330	490
99031C	**64816** BRc black Ltd Edn 40 - *09*	330	490

L3. LMS Stanier 'Mogul' 2-6-0 (2000)

This was steam powered when first released, but it was soon found that the market demanded electic powered locomotives and so steam was soon dropped.

99002	**2945** LMS lined maroon Ltd Edn 750 - *00*	280	460
99001	**42981** BRb black steam powered Ltd Edn 520 - *00*	250	250

L4. SR Maunsell N Class 'Mogul' 2-6-0 (2001)

Most of the initial releases of the SR N Class 'Mogul' locomotives were marred by the wheels being out of gauge at 29mm back-to-back, instead of 28mm and they had a very noisy mechanism. Corgi arranged a 'return to works' programme for a replacement redesigned mechanism and wheels of the correct gauge. Intending purchasers of locomotives from the 2001 batches are strongly advised to ascertain the status of the locomotives mechanism as the upgrade is essential. The Hornby batch of 2009 have enhanced detail, new low resonance gearboxes as standard and are fitted with smoke generators.

SR Class N in Maunsell green livery No.1864 [L4] (Vectis)

99042	**810** SECR Austerity grey Ltd Edn 50 - *09*	580	700
99064	**?** LSWR lined green Ltd Edn 75 - *09*	580	700
99003	**1864** SR lined green Ltd Edn 500 - *01*	220	240
99054	**?** SR Ltd Edn 75 - *09*	580	700
99004	**31407** BRb lined black Ltd Edn 500 - *01*	220	240
99005	**372** CIE lined green Ltd Edn 60 - *01*	330	350

L5. LMS 'Rebuilt Patriot' Class 4-6-0 (2004)

99017	**45527 *Southport*** BRb green Ltd Edn 200 - *04*	430	450
99041	**45534 *E.Tootal Broadhurst*** BRc green Ltd Edn 180 smoke generator - *09*	630	700

L6. LMS 'Rebuilt Royal Scot' Class 4-6-0 (2003)

12-14v electric motor, sprung buffers, lamp irons and lamps, smoke generator

99015	**6162 *Queens Westminster Rifleman*** LMS black Ltd Edn 200 - *04*	480	500
99016	**6100 *Royal Scot*** LMS maroon (as preserved) Ltd Edn 100 - *04*	580	600
99056	**6100 *Royal Scot*** LMS maroon Ltd Edn 100 - *09*	NPG	700
99011	**46100 *Royal Scot*** BRb green Ltd Edn 500 - *03*	350	370
99012	**46102 *Black Watch*** BRb green ex-Thames-Clyde set* Ltd Edn 350 - *04*	480	500

* Sold in a set with Ace Trains C5 crimson and cream coaches.

L7. LMS 'Princess Royal' Class 4-6-2 (2002)

99006	**6201 *Princess Elizabeth*** LMS maroon Ltd Edn 480 - *02*	440	460
99010	**6210 *Lady Patricia*** LMS black Ltd Edn 200 - *03*	480	500

99010	6210 ***Lady Patricia*** LMS black Ltd Edn 200 - *03*	480	500
99014	**46205 *Princess Victoria*** BRa black Ltd Edn 100 - *04*	440	460
99008	**46203 *Princess Margaret Rose*** BRb blue Sp Edn 100 (Much Ado About Toys) - *02*	480	500
99009	**6206 *Princess Marie Louise*** LMS black Ltd Edn 100 - *02*	480	500
99007	**46200 *The Princess Royal*** BRb green Ltd Edn 396 - *02*	480	500
99013	**46208 *Princess Helena Victoria*** BRc maroon Ltd Edn 200 - *04*	480	500

L8. LNER Class A3 4-6-2 (2005)

The LNER/BR A3 series models are fitted with a red fire glow lamp in the firebox. dc = double chimney.

Brass finish Flying Scotsman [L8] (Vectis)

90018	**2751 *Humorist*** SR green* dc Ltd Edn 100 - *05*	550	575
99021	**4472 *Flying Scotsman*** LNER polished brass Ltd Edn 100 - *06*	350	375
99022	**4472 *Flying Scotsman*** LNER green double tender Ltd Edn 400 - *06*	470	490
99023	**4472 *Flying Scotsman*** LNER green Australian Tour Sp Edn (Much Ado) - *06*	480	500
99024	**4472 *Flying Scotsman*** LNER green USA Tour** Sp Edn 100 (Modelzone) - *06*	780	800
99040	**4472 *Flying Fox*** LNER green Ltd Edn 180 - *09*	500	685
90019	**60052 *Prince Palatine*** BRb blue* Sp Edn 50 (Much Ado About Toys) - *05*	580	600
99026	**60103 *Flying Scotsman*** BR green, double chimney, German smoke deflectors, high sided tender Ltd Edn 350 - *07*	NPG	NPG
99024	**60103 *Flying Scotsman*** BRc green, smoke deflectors Ltd Edn 350 - *07*	500	700
99068	**60046 *Diamond Jubilee*** BR green, smoke deflectors Ltd Edn 50 - *09*	550	685
99069	**60048 *Trigo*** BR green, smoke deflectors Ltd Edn 50 - *09*	550	685

* The livery is best described as Maunsell Southern green with Southern lining. Some were returned by dissatisfied customers. ** This has the headlight, cowcatcher, whistle, hooter, red backed nameplates, smoke unit, green cylinders and double tender.

Models by E.T.S.

L9. Class 20 Diesel Bo-Bo (2007)

Branded 'Bassett-Lowke'. Made in tinplate to 1:45 scale. 12-14V. 2-rail /3-rail switch. Directional lights (also changeable to allow nose to nose double heading).

99027	**8001** BRc green + goods, vent and insulated van Ltd Edn train pack 150 - *07*	NA	330
-	above loco on its own - *07*	300	NA
99028	**202227 *Traction*** BRe Railfreight red stripe grey + 3 12T vent vans Ltd Edn train pack 100 - *07*	NA	300
-	above loco on its own - *07*	270	NA

WAGONS

These are all made by ETS of The Czech Republic but branded 'Bassett-Lowke'

Cat No.	Company, Number, Colour, Dates	£	£

W1. 3-plank Wagon (2007)

99037	**'Bassett-Lowke'** 6207 green - *07*	25	32
99060	**'Bassett-Lowke'** ? brown - *09*	18	33
99071	**LMS** 99071? grey - *09*	23	33
99059	**LNER** 990 grey - *09*	23	33
99066	**SR** 99064? dark brown - *09*	23	33
(99034)	**BR** M268922 grey	25	NA
(99034)	**BR** M268923 grey	25	NA
(99034)	**BR** M268924? grey	25	NA
99037	set of 3 above wagons - *07*	NA	95

W2. 7-plank Wagon (2007)

99036	**'Bassett-Lowke'** 6285 green - *07*	27	35
99057	**'Bassett-Lowke'** ? brown - *09*	20	35
99079	**'Firestone'** 99079 dark blue - *09*	30	35
99078	**'DR Llewellyn'** 55 brown - *09*	30	35
99073	**LMS** 99073 grey - *09*	25	35
99072	**LNER** 99072 grey - *09*	25	35
99074	**SR** 99074 dark brown - *09*	25	35
(99033)	**BR** E4659451 grey	25	NA
(99033)	**BR** E698264 grey	25	NA
(99033)	**BR** E4659452 grey	25	NA
99033	set of 3 above wagons - *07*	NA	100

W3. Tank Wagons (2008)

Set of 3 tank wagons [W3] (Hornby)

99038	**'Bassett-Lowke'** 6288? green - *09*	NPG	50
99062	**'Bassett-Lowke'** 6388 brown - *09*	30	50
99065	**'Esso'** 21774 buff - *09*	30	50
99067	**'Pratt's Spirit'** 1852 buff - *09*	30	50
99070	**'United Dairies' GW** 2007 white - *09*	30	50
(99035)	**'National'** ? silver	30	NA
(99035)	**'BP Motor Spirit'** 1449 buff	30	NA
(99035)	**'Shell'** ? red	30	NA
99035	set of 3 above tank wagons - *09*	NA	150

W4. Vans (2007)

99076	**LMS** 99076 grey - *09*	NPG	35
99075	**LNER** 99076 grey - *09*	NPG	35
99077	**SR** 99077 dark brown - *09*	NPG	35
-	**BR** M32385 white 8T goods van	28	NA
-	**BR** maroon ventilated meat van	28	NA
-	**BR** B872056 white 10T Insulmeat van	28	NA
99029	set of above 3 vans - *07*	NA	85
-	**BR** B785753 brown 12T ventilated van	28	NA
-	**BR** B785436 brown 12T ventilated van	28	NA
-	**BR** B785159 brown 12T ventilated van	28	NA
99030	set of above 3 ventilated vans Ltd Edn 150 - *07*	NA	97

W5. 20T Standard Brake Van (2007)

White platform rails and working red rear light run off 2 AAA batteries.

99043	**LNER** 259501 brown - *09*	35	60
99039	**BR** B950490? brown - *09*	35	60

Bond's 0

HISTORY

Bond's are primarily known as a manufacturer of mechanisms, locomotives, rolling stock and track parts as well as being agents for other manufacturer's products. They were established in 1887 as Bond's Ltd but in April 1926 took the name Bond's O'Euston Road Ltd; their address being 254 Euston Road.

They catered principally for the 0 gauge and larger scales but made small quantities of 00 scale from 1925. The pre-war catalogues show a wide selection of model railway items by both British and Continental manufacturers. Materials, castings, tools, lathes, milling machines and boilers were also offered for those interested in model engineering.

Bond's electric motors and gearboxes are highly regarded; in fact, they are often found fitted to other makers' locomotives. Some will have been changed during the life of the engine but others may have been installed when new, as many manufacturers were quite pleased to fulfil extra requirements, such as a Bond's motor, at extra cost. Bond's also made brass framed motor bogies as well as sprung coach bogies.

Following the Second World War, things did not get back to normal until late in 1947. The company, by then, had changed direction, becoming more retail orientated, and during the 1950s their catalogues listed the Hornby Dublo, Tri-ang and Trix ranges as well as a wide selection of parts for not only model railways but also aircraft and boats.

The shop in Euston Road had to be closed in 1973 as the whole site was to be redeveloped and the company moved to Midhurst. Although a retail shop continued, the business now became mostly mail order.

'Bonzone' 0-6-0ST [L1]

Collectors Club

There is no collector's society for Bond's equipment but the Bassett-Lowke Society may be able to help or indicate sources of information (see details under 'Bassett-Lowke').

Repairs

A limited repair service for Bond's mechanisms is available from DM Leakey, 7 Camplin Street, New Cross, London SE14 5QX (tel. 020 7732 6453). Send an SAE with any request. Leakey mechanisms followed similar design principles to Bond's mechanisms and, although no longer made, are equally sought after.

Prices - It is difficult to assess the value of Bond's locomotives as they are not often found for sale. The two prices shown represent the likely range for one in good condition.

New Information - We would welcome information on other locomotives and rolling stock by this manufacturer.

LOCOMOTIVES

Bond's own locomotives were offered in gauges 00, 0 and 1, as well as 2.5" and 3.5" and many were made to special order. Indeed, their catalogues offered to quote for building any type "from the tiny 4mm 00 gauge electric model to a 1.5" scale garden steam locomotive".

Other Gauges - The locomotives listed below were also available in gauge 1 electric and in live steam in gauges 1, 2.5" and 3.5".

Cat No.	Company, Number, Colour, Dates	£	£
L1.	**Peckett Dockland Tank 0-6-0ST (Freelance)**		
	Referred to as the Bonzone, the model was based on Peckett lines and had six balanced, all flanged, wheels. It also had a toolbox with a lid that opened to reveal the winding key. This box varied in position and there were slight variations in the shape of the body. It had a copper top chimney and brass dome and the numbering was progressive. Post-war mechanisms were 12V.		
	1, 2, 3, 4, 6 Bonzone		
-	Brunswick green c/w - *27-56?*	250	350
-	Brunswick green 6-8V DC - *28-56?*	250	350
-	black c/w - *27-56?*	250	350
-	black 6-8V DC - *28-56?*	250	350
-	deep yellow c/w - *28-56?*	250	350
-	deep yellow 6-8V DC - *28-56?*	250	350
-	red-brown - *28-56?*	250	350
	Unnamed		
-	Great Western green - *28-56?*	225	300
-	Southern green - *28-56?*	250	350
-	**6** dark green - *28-56?*	250	350
L2.	**Hunslet Diesel Shunter 0-6-0DS**		
-	**3** black electric - *32-40?*	250	300
-	**3** green electric - *32-40?*	250	300
L3.	**LMS 'Jinty' Type 3F Tank Engine 0-6-0T**		
	Post-war mechanisms were 12V.		
-	**7118** LMS black 6-8V DC electric - *38-60*	300	350

LMS 'Jinty' type 0-6-0T [L3] (Vectis)

Cat No.	Company, Number, Colour, Dates	£	£
L4.	**LNER J39 Goods 0-6-0 (by Vulcan)**		
	This model was made by Harry D'Arcy of Vulcan of Kendal.		
-	**4811** LNER black 12V DC electric - *64-69*	150	250
-	**47260** BR black 12V DC electric - *64-69*	150	250
L5.	**Bond's Special Order Locomotives**		
	The following Bond's locomotives were built to order. Post-war mechanisms were 12V.		
-	LNER **Gresley V1 Class 2-6-2T** black 6-8V DC - *35-c55*	850	1100
-	LMS ex-LNWR **Bowen-Cooke 4-6-2T** 6798 black 6-8V - *35-c55*	350	450
-	as above but red - *35-c55*	350	450
-	LNER **Gresley A3 Class** 4472 *Flying Scotsman* green 6-8V DC - *35-c55*	NPG	NPG
-	LMS **Stanier 4-6-0 Class 5MT** 5020 black 6-8V DC - *35-c55*	750	1300
-	LMS **Stanier 'Princess Royal' Class** maroon 6200 *The Princess Royal* 6-8V - *35-c55*	2100	2300
-	as above but black - *35-c55*	2100	2300
-	GWR **Collett 'King' Class** 6000 *King George V* green 4-6-0 6-8V DC - *35-c55*	2100	2300
-	LMS ex-L&Y **2-4-2T** 1384 black 6-8V DC - *35-c55*	250	350

-	LMS **Stanier 2-6-0** red 6-8V DC - *35-c55*	NPG	NPG
-	as above but black - *35-c55*	NPG	NPG
-	SR **Maunsell LN Class** 850 *Lord Nelson* green 6-8V DC - *35-c55*	NPG	NPG
-	LNER **Worsdell Class N10** black 0-6-2 - *35-c55*	NPG	NPG
-	SR **Urie N15 Class** A767 *Sir Valence* green 6-8V DC - *35-c55*	NPG	NPG
-	GWR **Dean 'City' Class** 3440 *City of Truro* green 4-4-0 6-8V DC - *35-c55*	NPG	NPG
-	LMS **ex-CR 0-4-4T** 15201 black - *?*	NPG	NPG
-	LSWR **0-4-4** 73 green - *?*	NPG	NPG
-	SR **Stroudley Class E1** 0-6-0T - *?*	NPG	NPG

Bond's continued to build models to order in gauges 0 and 1 and, in their catalogues during the 1970s, illustrated an LMS 6247 *City of Liverpool* they had built for a Mr Liverpool.

L6. LMS Main Line Diesel 10001 Co-Co

A small batch was made in 1956.

-	**10000** BR black electric - *65*	3500	4000
-	**10001** BR black electric - *65*	3500	4000

COACHES

In the 1920s Bond's also sold a range of coach bodies of their own manufacture and stocked coaches by Marklin, Bing, Bassett-Lowke, Leeds and others. Those of German origin (especially Marklin) had their identity concealed after the First World War. In the 1930s the company offered their own range of wooden bodied hand painted coaches which were of a good quality. After the Second World War the 0 gauge range stocked by Bond's was limited to Exley's and kits by CCW and Ratio. However, they continued to sell their own coach fittings into the 1960s.

Cat No.	Company, Number, Colour, Dates	£	£

C1. Wooden Coach Bodies

These unpainted wooden bodies were sold without bogies but glazed. They were based on real prototypes and varied in length according to the subject - 15", 16" and 17". Fittings including bogies were available separately.

C8/A	**LMS** 57' corridor 1st - *27-32*	15	20
C8/B	**LMS** 57' corridor 1st/3rd - *27-32*	15	20
C8/C	**LMS** 57' brake 3rd - *27-32*	15	20
C8/D	**LMS** 50' all 3rd - *27-32*	15	20
C8/E	50' kitchen car - *27-32*	15	20
C8/F	**GNR LNER** 60' corridor 1st/3rd - *27-32*	15	20
C8/G	**GNR LNER** 57' corridor brake 3rd - *27-32*	15	20
C8/H	**GNR LNER** 57' 1st/3rd diner - *27-32*	15	20
C8/I	**GWR** 57' corridor 1st/3rd - *27-32*	15	20
C8/J	**GWR** corridor brake 3rd - *27-32*	15	20
C8/K	**GWR** 57' 1st/3rd diner - *27-32*	15	20
C8/L	**GWR** 70' corridor 1st/3rd - *27-32*	15	20
C8/M	**GWR** 70' brake 3rd *-27-32*	15	20
C8/N	**GWR** 70' 1st/3rd diner - *27-32*	15	20
C8/O	**GWR** 57' old type corr 1st/3rd - *27-32*	15	20
C8/P	**GWR** 57' old type brake 3rd - *27-32*	15	20
C8/Q	**Pullman** coach - *27-32*	15	20
C8/R	**Pullman** kitchen - *27-32*	15	20

Ready-Made Coaches

Between 1932 and the outbreak of the Second World War, Bond's advertised 'New Super Detail Coaches' in their catalogues but little detail of the types available was given. They were a range of corridor and suburban coaches and it is assumed that these were built to order in their own workshop. We know that the wooden and hand painted bodies were not all of a standard design but were specific to the companies whose livery they carried and varied in length accordingly. They had glass in the windows, corridor compartments and separate door handles fitted. They also had bogies of special construction, metal wheels, oval brass buffers and corridor coaches had corridor connections. They were not quite so heavy in proportion as the Milbro coaches and sold at a standard price of £1-18-6. The listing below is based on very limited evidence and the editor would welcome further information.

C2. LMS Stock

-	corridor 1st/3rd crimson - *32-40*	120	170
-	corridor all 3rd crimson - *32-40*	120	170
-	corridor brake 3rd crimson - *32-40*	120	170
-	suburban coach crimson - *32-40*	120	170
-	suburban brake crimson - *32-40*	120	170

C3. LNER Stock

Not a lot is known about these coaches

Great Northern Railway coach [C3] (Andrew Woodfield)

-	Gresley corridor 1st/3rd teak - *32-40*	120	170
-	Gresley corridor brake teak - *32-40*	120	170
-	suburban coach teak - *32-40*	120	170
-	suburban brake teak - *32-40*	120	170

C4. GWR Stock

-	corridor 1st/3rd dark brown+cream - *32-40*	120	170
-	corridor brake dark brown+cream - *32-40*	120	170
-	suburban coach dark brown+cream - *32-40*	120	170
-	suburban brake dark brown+cream - *32-40*	120	170

C5. SR Stock

-	corridor coach green - *32-40*	120	170
-	corridor brake end green - *32-40*	120	170
-	suburban coach green - *32-40*	120	170
-	suburban brake green - *32-40*	120	170

WAGONS

These were listed as 'True Scale Model Wagons' and described as 'models of lesser known types of goods stock'. Originally, these were made by a Sheffield company known as the Miniature Reproductions Company (MRCo) and were sold almost exclusively by Bond's between the late '20s and the outbreak of the Second World War. Later introductions may have been made in Bond's workshop.

The majority were made of wood and fitted with sprung 3-link couplings and oval head buffers (3/6 extra). All had turned cast iron wheels and some had metal chassis; the LMS 20 ton coke hopper was all metal. It seems that while a stock of finished wagons was kept in the shop, the models could be finished to the customer's requirements, involving a few days delay, and this included, up to 1931, private owner liveries (1/- extra).

Unusual types include an LNER trestle wagon, LNER pulley wagon, Harwich ferry wagon, NE 40 ton hopper (also all metal) and a bogie well wagon with a length of 15.5 inches (390mm) which had sprung bogies and sold for £1-18-6!

Bond's also sold wagons of other manufacturers.

Cat No.	Company, Number, Colour, Dates	£	£

First Series (MRCo. for Bond's)

W1. Machinery Flat Wagon

-	flat top machinery truck - *28?-31*	25	30
-	ditto with spring buffers/couplings - *28?-31*	25	30

W2. Ballast and Mineral Wagons

-	**LMS** 15T ballast wagon - *26?-40*	25	30
-	as above but two end doors - *26?-40*	25	30
-	**NE** 12T ballast dropside - *26?-40*	25	30
-	**LMS** 12T mineral, door - *26?-40*	25	30
-	Private Owner wagons - *36-40*	30	35

W3. Other Open Wagons

Doors in the following open wagons were usually made to open.

-	**LNER** dropside 3-plank fish truck with		

	Westinghouse pipes - *26?-40*	25	30
-	as above with vacuum pipes - *26?-40*	25	30
-	**GWR** 12T drop-door wagon - *26?-40*	25	30

W4. Bolster Wagons

	NE long single bolster - *28?-33*	25	30
	ditto with spring buffers/couplings - *28?-33*	28	32
-	double bolster timber wagon - *26?-33*	25	30
-	6-wheel double bolster rail and timber wagon - *26?-33*	30	35
-	**LMS** 20T 6-wheel double bolster timber wagon - *26?-40*	30	35
-	ditto with spring buffers/couplings - *28?-33*	32	37

W5. Small Vans

Doors in the following covered vans were usually made to open.

-	**NE** van, 2 doors each side - *26?-40*	25	30
-	as above but ventilated van - *26?-40*	25	30
-	ditto + pipes + torpedo vents - *26?-40*	27	32
-	ditto with dual braking - *26?-40*	27	32
-	refrigerator van with end ladders - *26?-40*	30	35

W6. Early Brake Vans

These were available in different company designs.

-	**NE** short 4-wheel - 26*?-33*	25	30
-	6-wheel - *26?-33*	30	35

W7. GWR Hopper Wagon

-	**GWR** hopper wagon - *28?-31*	60	70

W8. Well Wagons

This was a superb model with sprung bogies and buffers and a removable load.

-	with girder frame - *28?-40*	60	70
-	ditto with brake wheels - *31-40*	60	70
-	ditto with LMS brakes fitted - *31-32*	60	70

W9. Bogie Vans

-	bogie covered van (8 doors) - *32-40*	70	80
-	ditto with vents - *32-40*	70	80
-	ditto with vacuum pipes - *32-40*	70	80
-	ditto with brake gear - *32-40*	70	80

W10. Other Bogie Wagons

Fitted with sprung buffers and couplings.

-	bogie open wagon - *32-40*	60	70
-	bogie bolster wagon - *32-40*	60	70

Second Series

W11. Harwich Ferry Wagon

Doors in the following open wagons and covered vans were usually made to open.

-	grey - *32-40*	70	80

W12. Brake Vans

More recent style with long wheelbase, metal chassis, sprung buffers and couplings and glazed windows.

-	**SR** dark brown with platforms - *32-40*	30	35
-	**LNER** with platforms - *32-40*	27	32
-	**LMS** (modern) - *32-40*	27	32
-	**GWR** 20T - *33-40*	27	32

W13. Refrigerator Vans

Fitted with all metal chassis, ladders, vacuum pipes, sprung buffers and couplings. The LNER and GWR versions had vents at each end.

-	**LMS** - *32-40*	25	30
-	**SR** - *32-40*	25	30
-	**LNER** 139284 white - *32-40*	25	30
-	**GWR** white - *36-40*	25	30

W14. Small Hopper Wagons

Fitted with all metal body and chassis, opening hopper doors, sprung buffers and couplings.

-	**'Roberts & Co.'** - *32-40*	80	90
-	**'City of Birmingham Gas Dept.'** - *32-40*	80	90

W15. Meat Van

Fitted with all metal chassis.

-	**LMS** - *32-40*	25	30

W16. Horse Box

Fitted with all metal chassis.

-	**LMS** - *32-40*	25	30

W17. Fish Vans

Fitted with all metal chassis, ladders, vacuum pipes, sprung buffers and couplings.

-	**LNER** dummy louvres - *32-40*	25	30
-	**LMS** dummy sliding doors - *32-40*	25	30

W18. Cattle Wagon

Correct open plank sides. Dummy swing doors and flap. Fitted with all metal chassis, ladders, vacuum pipes, sprung buffers and couplings.

-	**LMS** - *32-40*	25	30
-	**LNER** - *32-40*	25	30

W19. 1-plank Container Wagons

Fitted with all metal chassis, ladders, vacuum pipes, sprung buffers and couplings.

-	**GWR + GWR** container - *32-40*	35	40
-	**LMS + LMS** open container - *32-40*	35	40
-	**LMS + LMS** closed container - *32-40*	35	40
-	**LNER + LNER** open container - *32-40*	35	40
-	**LNER + LNER** closed contain. - *32-40*	35	40

W20. 40T Bogie Hopper Wagon

All metal with sliding hopper doors. Sprung buffers and couplings.

-	**LNER** 100011 - *32-40*	70	80

W21. 20T Well Wagon

All metal wagon fitted with brake handle wheels. Equalised bogies, ladders, sprung buffers and couplings.

-	**LNER** - *32-40*	70	80
-	girder load - *32-40*	25	30
-	**GWR** - *32-40*	70	80
-	diesel road roller load - *33-40*	25	30

W22. PO Lime Wagon

All metal with sliding roof door.

-	various PO names - *32-40*	35	40

W23. 20T Coke Hopper Wagon

All metal wagon fitted with sprung buffers and couplings.

-	**LMS** grey - *33-40*	70	80

W24. Trestle Wagon

Fitted with sprung buffers and couplings

-	**LNER** 14710 - *33-40*	70	80

W25. Pulley Wagon

Fitted with sprung buffers and couplings

-	**LNER** 46470 + ship's propeller - *33-40*	70	80

W26. Flat Container Wagon

Fitted with sprung buffers and couplings.

-	**GWR** 39015 + meat container - *33-40*	70	80

Midland Railway brake van (Vectis)

Bonds

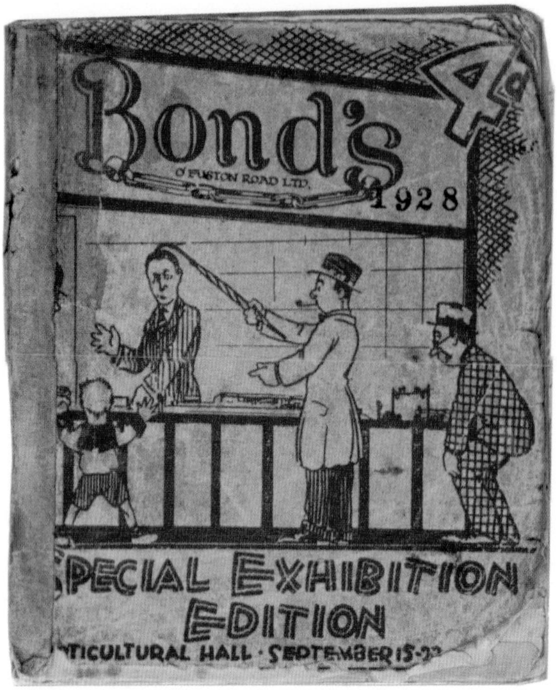

Bond's
O' EUSTON ROAD LTD.
4d
1928
PECIAL EXHIBITION
EDITION
TICULTURAL HALL · SEPTEMBER 15-

BOND'S REMOVAL
1926-7 Issue of Bond's
MODEL PRICE LIST
Bond's
MODEL PRICE LIST 1928
4d
1929-1930 EDITION 4D
1931-1932 EDITION 6d
MODEL AND EXPERIMENTAL ENGINEERING HANDBOOK
1939-1940
1938
1937-1938
1936-7
1934-5
1933-1934
PRICE 6d
WAR EDITION
BOND'S HANDBOOK
1946-1947 EDITION
PRICE 1949
Price 9d
BOND'S O' EUSTON RO
1950 EDITION
1955-1956 EDITION
1957-1958 EDITION
1958-1959 EDITION
1959-1960 EDITION
BOND'S
MODEL HANDBOOK
Price 2/-

Bowman

HISTORY

Although they built locomotives for only 10 years, this firm's products had a major impact on the live steam locomotive market and many enthusiasts are continuing to run these engines.

Geoffrey Bowman Jenkins (born in 1891) took out his first patent in 1919. This was for driving a toy locomotive with elastic. He had also patented a number of ideas for toy steam boats, which he was successfully making in London and in 1923 he was invited to join forces with the well established firm of Hobbies Ltd at Dereham in Norfolk, who traded in materials and tools for keen amateur woodworkers. With Jenkins' ideas and Hobbies machinery and marketing the firm Bowman Models was established.

'Baby Bowman' 0-4-0T [L1] (Vectis)

The powerful single-acting oscillating-cylinder engines were first placed in a series of successful steamboats and then developed onto horizontal stationary engines. In 1925, the first of three non-reversing model railway locomotives was placed on the market, most being powered by two oscillating cylinders. In 1927 a patent was obtained for his design of track and the following year Jenkins exhibited his models at the British Industries Fair. During this, a 4-4-0 locomotive with six coaches behind it clocked up 183 miles. It was refuelled every 40 minutes and the success of this exercise lead directly to Bassett-Lowke developing their Enterprise 4-4-0 model to achieve a similar performance.

The scale of these locomotives was really gauge 1 which allowed for the use of a large boiler and burner (meths fired) but the wheels were built to gauge 0. At this stage, gauge 1 was on the decline so it was advantageous to have models which would run on the more popular 0 gauge track.

Most of the brass parts were made in Birmingham but assembly and finishing was done at Dereham. It was there also that the wooden parts such as sleepers and rolling stock parts were made. Initially the models were packed in wooden boxes but, later, card ones were used. These could be identified by their brown and cream striped finish.

The production of Bowman trains was run down during the early 1930s and had ceased by 1935, when Jenkins started the Jentique furniture making firm and the following year parted company with Hobbies Ltd. The only post-war production of Bowman was stationary and marine engines done at Luton. These were made until about 1950. Jenkins died in 1959. The withdrawal of Jenkins from Hobbies Ltd left a gap which was filled by Geoffrey Malins and this lead to the Mamod range.

Bowman items used to be very cheap but the market has risen over recent years.

Collector's Club

Bowman collectors are catered for by the Bowman Circle who publish a quarterly journal and anyone interested in joining should contact John M. Jones, 9 Field Drive, Shrewsbury, SY4 3LB. Members of the Bowman Circle have provided much of the information given above.

Type 300 small 0-4-0T [L2]

Prices - The two prices shown represent the likely range for one in good condition.

LOCOMOTIVES

The largest locomotive was a 4-4-0 tender engine whilst the other three were 0-4-0 tanks, one being smaller in size and a bit nearer 0 scale. Strictly speaking the wheel arrangements were not as just described, as the locomotives had no coupling rods, only connecting rods to the rear set of wheels.

Although you will go a long way before you will find a real locomotive looking quite like a Bowman, with its long thin cylinders and distinctive safety valve, Bowman locomotives were characterised by their simple design, sound engineering and superb performance.

Power and speed were effectively controlled by blanking off up to three of the burner wicks with burner caps, making the engine quite docile and able to trundle round 2ft curves without a load. Unfortunately the wick caps were often lost and in later years operated on full throttle unless substitute wick caps or plugs were fitted. This gave them a reputation for being too fast and needing plenty of stock behind them to slow them down and keep them on the track.

As evidence of their good performance, a Bowman 4-4-0 tender locomotive hauled six Bowman carriages for 183 actual miles at the British Industries Fair in the late 1920s.

Restored type 265 0-4-0T [L3] (Vectis)

Cat No.	Company, Number, Colour, Dates	£	£
L1.	**Small 0-4-0 Tank Engine ('Baby Bowman')** (Freelance) (1932)		
Single oscillating cylinder on the cab floor driving the rear axle by gearing.			
410	green - *32-34*	175	250
410	black - *32-34*	NPG	NPG
L2.	**Small 0-4-0 Tank Engine** (Freelance) (1927)		
300	**300** LNER green - *27-35*	120	160
300	**300** LMS black - *27-35*	120	160

300	**300** LMS maroon - *27-35*	120	160
30	**30** LMS maroon - *27-35*	120	160

L3. Large 0-4-0 Tank Engine (Freelance) (1927)

Outside cylinders.

265	**265** LNER green - *27-35*	120	170
265	**265** LNER black - *27-35*	120	180
265	**265** LMS maroon - *27-35*	120	160
265	**265** LMS black - *27-35*	120	170

Restored LMS 4-4-0 [L4] (Vectis)

L4. 4-4-0 Tender Locomotive (Freelance) (1927)

The model carried the number on the tender and an oval badge on cabside marked 'Bowman Patent'. On later versions this was worded 'Bowman Models'. These were sold in wooden boxes.

234	**4472** LNER green also numbered **234** + others - *27-35*	150	200
234	**4472** LNER black - *27-35*	NPG	NPG
234	**4073** GWR green also numbered **234**, **4472** + others - *27-35*	250	350
234	**453** SR green also numbered **234**, **4472** + others - *27-35*	200	280
234	**13000** LMS maroon - *27-35*	175	250
234	**13000** LMS black also numbered **234**, **4472** + others - *27-35*	175	250

COACHES

Without doubt the passenger coach was the most attractive model made by Bowman. It was a bogie coach with a heavy wooden base and ends but with nicely lithographed tin sides with opening doors and a pair of large gas cylinders under the floor. No brake coach was made. Like the locomotives, the coach was built to gauge 1 proportions but for 0 gauge track. They are not common and consequently can be more expensive to buy than the locomotives.

Cat No.	Company, Number, Colour, Dates	£	£
C1.	**1st/3rd Composite** (1927)		
551	**LNER** 17172 teak - *27-35*	180	260

GWR coach [C1] (Vectis)

551	**GWR** 10152 dark brown+cream - *27-35*	180	260
551	**LMS** 10153 maroon - *27-35*	180	260

WAGONS

Bowman produced wagons to go with the locomotives and again, although 0 gauge, they were built to gauge 1 proportions. A range of 0 scale wagons was planned but never made. In June 1933 retailers were informed that the wagons were no longer available. The open wagon and brake van had the 'Bowman Models' badge on each end, the tank wagon was badged on the side and the timber wagons carried no badge.

Cat No.	Company, Number, Colour, Dates	£	£
W1.	**Timber Wagon** (1927)		
664	**LMS** grey - *27-35*	30	40
664	**LNER** grey - *27-35*	30	40
W2.	**5-plank Open Wagon** (1927)		
661	**LMS** grey - *27-35*	35	50
661	**LNER** grey - *27-35*	35	50
W3.	**Tank Wagon** (1927)		
663	**'Shell'** red - *27-35*	60	75
W4.	**Brake Van** (1927)		

LNER brake van [W4] (Chris Ellis)

662	**LMS** grey - *27-35*	40	55
662	**LNER** grey - *27-35*	40	55

PACKAGING

A rarely mentioned feature of the Bowman range of models was that many of the locomotives were packed in unpainted wooden boxes. The lid was printed with the Bowman trademark which consisted of 'Bowman Models' in a diamond, with a North American Indian Chief with a bow and arrow. The ends of the boxes were printed with the contents. Later specially printed cardboard boxes were used. The tender was packed in a box of its own.

1929 Bowman catalogue

Dapol 00

Please note that the tables in this section have been renumbered in this edition.

History

David Boyle, of Highfield Birds & Models, who in 1981 had been unsuccessful in a bid to buy the model railway division of Airfix when the Company was being broken up and sold off, founded a company with his wife Pauline called Dapol. This was established to handle a large amount of Airfix stock and spares that he had been able to acquire. Boyle's ambition, all along, was to produce a range of British outline locomotives and rolling stock of a quality in performance and detail that, previously, had only been found in some Continental ranges.

Research and development had already commenced for a L&Y Pug, a GWR County Class and a J94 tank to the extent that plans had been drawn and the tools manufactured.

Milestones

1981 Dapol formed by David and Pauline Boyle.
1983 Dapol market their own wagons and renamed 'Castles'.
1984 first Dapol locos released.
1985 Dapol buy the intellectual assets of the Mainline system from Palitoy and Airfix tooling.
1986 1st catalogue published.
1988 Dapol acquire residue of British Liliput.
1988 2nd catalogue published.
1989 3rd catalogue published.
1993 Dapol buy G&R Wrenn.
1994/5 Dapol move to Llangollen.
1995 fire at Winsford factory.
1995 4th catalogue published.
1999 David Boyle leaves Dapol.
2001 5th catalogue published.
2001 Dapol sell G&R Wrenn Ltd to Mordvale Ltd.
2001 1st new loco for 12 years.
2003 Dapol enter the N gauge market.
2004 Company moves to Chirk.

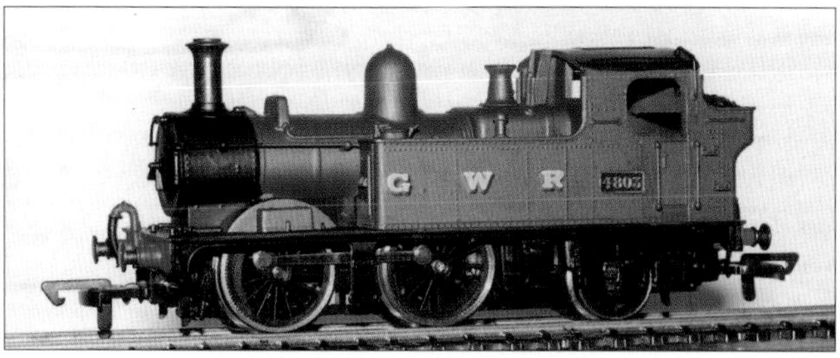

GWR Class 14xx 0-4-2T No.4803 [L3]

When Airfix stocks ran low, Boyle had new moulds made of some of the old Airfix wagons, which went on the market in November 1983. His company also commenced the production of the ex-L&Y 'Pug', which was released the following year, and the Hawksworth 'County' which arrived soon after.

When Palitoy closed down in 1985, David Boyle was finally offered the Airfix models as well as the intellectual assets of Palitoy's Mainline Railways range. There followed a merging of Airfix, Mainline and Dapol products under the Dapol name. In fact, very few Mainline designs were used, except as old stock, as the vast majority of the tools for them belonged to the production company in Hong Kong - Kader.

Dapol next took over the remnants of some of the Trix Trains/ Lilliput (UK) range in the late '80s and these included the tooling for the bodies of the E3000 and 'TransPennine' DMU, the chassis remaining with Liliput in Austria and ending up with Bachmann.

Dapol also bought the tools and intellectual assets of G&R Wrenn in 1992 and some wagons from the Wrenn range joined the Dapol catalogue. Some of these were sold on chassis purchased from Bachmann when the latter turned production over to their Blue Riband range. Dapol also make plastic kits from the former Airfix and Kitmaster tools and have added one or two of their own. At one time they also made kits from the former Tri-ang Model-Land tools.

Stock was stored in various places including Boyle's own home. From time to time, forgotten boxes of obsolete stock emerged and the contents sold, often through Dapol's shop - especially at their Winsford addresses in Cheshire. Some of this stock was never advertised making it difficult to record what and when models were released.

In 1994, Dapol started to move their entire operation to Llangollen, in Wales, where they opened an exhibition called 'Model Railway World' which, at one time, included some of the former Wrenn machines and tools which started life in the Hornby-Dublo production line at the Meccano factory in Liverpool. It was while this move was in progress during 1995 that a severe fire at the Winsford factory destroyed much of the stock and damaged a number of tools.

To raise much needed capital, some of the Dapol and former Airfix tools were offered to Bachmann but, subsequently, were sold to Hornby in 1996. Almost all of these are back in production out in China, having first undergone further improvements. Dapol, however, continued to produce limited runs of some of these models from their stock of parts.

Ex-LMS Class 2P 4-4-0 in early BR black No.40567 [L13]

In April 1999 Dapol Ltd parted company with its founder, David Boyle, and came under the management of Pauline Boyle with George Smith as Director of Corporate Affairs. Later, following the death of Pauline Boyle, George Smith took over direction of the company as Managing Director.

At the 2000 Warley National Model Railway Exhibition, Dapol announced one of their largest projects for several years - the production of a model of the 'Pendolino', the flagship of the Virgin Trains fleet. The model was delivered a year later. At about the same time, having extracted what they wanted from the Wrenn tooling, the company sold the remainder, the archives and intellectual assets of G&R Wrenn Ltd to Mordvale Ltd.

In January 2004 the company moved once more, this time to a new factory complex not far away at Chirk. This gave them the opportunity to dispense with much of the clutter from the past and consolidate on what had become their main products - *00* gauge private owner wagons and a new and serious bid for the N gauge market. In 2005 they started to upgrade the 00 wagon range with new tooling and two years later were announcing two completely new 00 wagons based on designs they were developing in their N gauge range.

By 2006 they had established themselves as a major competitor to Bachmann's Graham Farish range and were now showing that they could compete with them in 00 in the production of quality modern wagons. 2008 saw a return to producing new 00 gauge models.

Confusion - As we have said, this is a very difficult range to record as there was such a mix up of old stock from other manufacturers that was repackaged and new batches made by Dapol from the old tooling. There were also models made from duplicate tooling produced for Dapol in the Far East from samples of models sent out there for copying.

An example of the confusion is Dapol coaches which are ex-Mainline, ex-Airfix or produced by Dapol. Some of the 'Dapol' variety have 'Dapol' printed on the underside. However, several have the Mainline arc with 'Railways' printed below it. The word 'Mainline' has been blanked out and 'Dapol' printed above the arc. To make matters worse, there are two versions of the (now blank) arc. In the case of one, it looks as if the name 'Mainline' has been removed from the mould using a file as there are vertical striations where the word had been. In the case of the other, the arc is totally smooth and appears never to have had any wording on it.

14 ton tank wagon 'Ronuk' [W26[

We have not attempted to separate out these variations in the following listing.

Also beware of strange locomotives with swapped tenders, wrong numbers and even carrying a different name on each side. This seems to be particularly prevalent amongst the Castles and Counties. This suggests that quality control was not a high priority in the early days of Dapol production, especially that done by Dapol themselves. This is a far cry from the standards set today.

Listing - The locos are listed in order of size starting with tank engines followed by tender locos and ending with diesels and multiple units. The coaches are listed with pre-Nationalisation stock first followed by vehicles of later years. Wagons are listed in the order of: flats, open wagons, hoppers, tanks, vans, brake vans and bogie stock.

Dates - We have found little information about when early models first became available or when they were out of production. The dates of early models quoted in the tables below are based on this limited knowledge, coming largely from press advertising and are for guidance only. However, one breakthrough was the discovery of a stock list prepared during the drafting of the 1995 catalogue which included many models no longer being advertised. One of the reasons for this was the haphazard stock control exercised before the present management took over. It resulted in boxes of stock being uncovered and offered for sale long after it had been thought that they were sold out. We even found models included in the 1995 catalogue which had been missing from advertised sales lists for several years and did not return to them. No doubt their inclusion was a statement of intent which Dapol were not able to fulfil largely because of the extra work that came with the acquisition of the Wrenn tools and parts. We therefore express caution in using catalogues as a means of dating and to not take too literally the early dates we have given below. In the case of models made in recent years, a single date is given as it is assumed that a single batch was released. If a further batch was made, a second date has been added.

Ex-LNER Class N2 0-6-2T No.69532 [L11]

Packaging - Items in the following lists shown as being 'ex-Airfix stock' or 'ex-Mainline stock' were, as far as we know, sold in their original packaging.

(A) = ex-Airfix stock
(M) = ex-Mainline stock

Further Reading

There was a series of articles by Graham Smith-Thompson, in Model Railway Enthusiast magazine, profiling the Airfix and Mainline ranges and other systems that later used the tools. There were four parts devoted specifically to Dapol published in the August-November 1999 issues of the magazine.

LOCOMOTIVES

Cat No.	Company, Number, Colour, Dates	£	£

Tank Engines

L1.	**L&Y Class 0F ' Pug' 0-4-0ST** (1984)		
D10	**19** L&Y black - *90-02*	28	38

Lancashire & Yorkshire Railway 0-4-0ST in wartime black with spark arrester [L1]

D1	**11217** LMS black - *84-94*	30	40
D?	**821** WD black, spark arrester fitted to chimney Ltd Edn 100 - *99?*	65	85
D?	**402** black Ltd Edn 100 - *03*	40	60
D2	**51241** BRb black - *84-99*	28	38

The tooling was sold to Hornby in 1996 and the model reintroduced by them.

L2.	**Y1/3 Class Sentinel 100hp 4wT** (2010)		

This is made exclusively for *Model Rail* magazine who own the tooling.

MR-001	**13** GWR plain green - *11*	60	72
L3	**GWR Class 14XX 0-4-2T** (ex-Airfix) (1985)		
D19	**1466** GWR green (A) - *85-95*	20	30
D19	**1420** GWR (button) green, new chassis - *95-02*	22	35
D97	**1459**** GWR black new chassis - *95-02*	25	35
D97	**1466** GWR black new chassis - *95-02*	25	35
D97S1	**4803** GWR green Ltd Edn 100 - *99*	65	90
D96	**1438*** BRb black new chassis - *95-02*	25	35
?	**1401** BR black from the film Titfield Thunderbolt Ltd Edn 100 *** - *02*	50	70

D20	**1466** BRc green lined (A) - *85-95*	22	32

* also shown in catalogue as 1442. ** also shown as black 1456 in 1989 catalogue.
*** This model was claimed by Dapol to be their last limited edition locomotive. The tooling was sold to Hornby in 1996 and the model reintroduced by them.

L4. **LSWR 0289 Beattie Well Tank 2-4-0WT** (2011)

This model has been sponsored by Kernow Models. It will have a 5-pole motor with flywheel, 8-pin DCC socket (with possible proviso for sound chip and speaker), NEM coupling pockets, opening smokebox door and modelled interior, darkened RP25.110 see-through wheel sets with 14.4mm back to back measurements, an accessory pack for 'individualising' the model and Phosphor Bronze self-lubricating axle bushes.

K2051	**30587** BRb black - *11*	NPG	90
K2052	**30586** BRb black - *11*	NPG	90
K2053	**30585** BRc black - *11*	NPG	90

L5. **LSWR Class O2 0-4-4T** (2011)

This model is being produced for Kernow Model Rail Centre and the tooling will be owned by them.

K2101	**24 *Calbourne*** BRb black - *11*	NPG	92
K2102	**16 *Ventnor*** BRc black - *11*	NPG	92
K2103	**30182** BRb black with push-pull equipment - *11*	NPG	92
K2104	**30225** BRc black - *11*	NPG	92

L6. **GWR Class 57XX 0-6-0PT** (ex-Mainline) (1985)

D61	**5768** BRb black (M) - *85*	30	38

L7. **LNER Class J72 0-6-0T** (ex-Mainline) (1985)

D56	***Joem*** North Eastern green (M) - *85-86*	20	28
D54	**581** LNER green (M) - *85-94*	20	28
D55	**68745** BRa black, Ross pop safety valves (M) - *85-94*	20	28
D57	**69001** BRb black enclosed safety valves (M) - *85-86*	18	26

L8. **LBSCR 'Terrier' 0-6-0T** (1988)

D69	**662** LBSC Marsh Umber - *89-95*	35	45
D100	**82 *Boxhill*** LBSC yellow-brown - *89-95*	35	45
D101	**82 *Boxhill*** LBSC yellow-brown, as D100 but Ltd Edn - *99*	50	75

London Brighton & South Coast Railway 'Terrier' tank 0-6-0T in Marsh Umber livery [L8]

D102	**55 *Stepney*** LBSC yellow-brown - *90-98*	50	65
D70	**2635** SR lined green - *89-94*	35	45
D6A	**2655** SR dark green Ltd Edn 100 - *98-99*	75	90
D101S2	**B636** SR black Ltd Edn 100 - *99-00*	75	90
D?	**2647** SR plain black Ltd Edn 100 -*01*	85	130
D101S1	**2659** SR black, wartime 'Sunshine' lettering, Ltd Edn 100 - *97*	75	90
D72	**6** GWR button green - *88-94*	35	45
D101S3	**5 *Portishead*** GWR button green Ltd Edn 100 - *99*	80	95
D71	**32640** BRb lined black - *89-94*	30	40

The tooling was sold to Hornby in 1996 and the model reintroduced by them.

L9. **WD Class J94 'Austerity' 0-6-0ST** (1984)

This model was revolutionary in having sprung buffers.

D7	**WD150 *Warrington*** WD* deep grey - *85-98*	25	40
?	**8049** LNER desert sand livery Ltd Edn 125 - *98-99*	65	85
?	**8054** LNER black Ltd Edn 125 - *98*	65	85
D8B	**68034** BRb black - *86-88*	25	40
D9	**68080** BR black** - *90-96*	22	38
D8A	**68077** BRc black, rectangular windows - *86-87*	25	40
D8C	**68068** BRc black, round windows - *86-89*	25	40

* Under-feeder stoker type chimney, preserved livery ** With extended bunker kit and corrected balance weights. An EM wheel conversion kit was available. The tooling was sold to Hornby in 1996 and the model reintroduced by them.

L10. **GWR Class 66XX 0-6-2T** (ex-Mainline) (1985)

D60	**6697** GWR green (M) - *85-89*	30	35
D59	**6652** BRb black (M) - *85-94, 98*	30	35

L11. **LNER Class N2 0-6-2T** (ex-Airfix) (1985)

D51	**4744** LNER black, red lining (M) - *85-01*	28	38
D53	**9522** LNER lined green (M) - *85-96*	22	30
D52	**69532** BRb black lined (M) - *85-01*	22	30

The tooling was sold to Hornby in 1996 and the model reintroduced by them.

L12. **GWR Class 61XX 2-6-2T** (ex-Airfix) (1985)

D22*	**6110** Great Western green (A) - *85-94*	18	32
D24*	**6169** GWR green (M) - *85-88*	27	35
D21	**6167** BRb lined black (A) - *85-94*	20	32
D23	**6167** BRc lined green (M) - *85-89*	27	35

* Some confusion exists as to which number applies to which loco. The tooling was sold to Hornby in 1996 and the model reintroduced by them.

Tender Engines

L13. **LMS Class 2P 4-4-0** (ex-Mainline) (1985)

Many of the Mainline stock absorbed had only polystyrene trays and had to be put in Dapol boxes to sell.

D15	**635** LMS black, lined red (M) - *85-96*	32	42
D17	**563** LMS lined maroon - *86-96*	30	38
D67	**45** very dark blue SDJR - *88-96*	32	40
D16	**40568** BRb lined black (M) - *85-90*	30	40
D16A	**40567** BRb lined black - *90-93*	30	38
D16B	BRb lined black - *90-93*	NPG	NPG
D16C	**40569** BRb lined black - *90-95*	32	40

The tooling was sold to Hornby in 1996 and the model reintroduced by them.

L14. **GWR Dean Class 2301 0-6-0** (ex-Airfix) (1985)

GWR 'Dean Goods' 0-6-0 No.2515 [L14]

D18A	**2517** Great Western green - *86-98*	25	38
D018S1	**2515** Great Western green, Ltd Edn 100 - *99*	65	90
D18	**2516** GWR green (M) - *85-88*	28	38
D18B	**2518** GWR green - *86-94*	25	38
D18C	**2519** GWR (button) green - *86-94*	25	38
D50	**2538** BRb black (M) - *85-94*	28	38

The tooling was sold to Hornby in 1996 and the model reintroduced by them.

L15. **LMS Class 4F 0-6-0** (ex-Airfix) (1985)

D25	**4454** LMS black (A) - *85-94*	25	30
D25	**4312** LMS black, lined red - *not made*	NA	NA
D98	LMS maroon - *not made*	NA	NA
D99	SDJR blue - *not made*	NA	NA
D26	**44454** black BRb (small or large) (A) - *85-94*	30	40

The tooling was sold to Hornby in 1996 and the model reintroduced by them.

L16. **GWR Class 43XX 2-6-0** (ex-Mainline) (1985)

D48	**5322** Great Western green (M) - *85-90*	32	40
D47	**5328** BRb black (M) - *85-00*	37	45
D49	**4358** BRb lined green (M) - *85-90*	32	40

L17. **GWR Manor Class 4-6-0** (ex-Mainline) (1985)

D44	**7808 *Cookham Manor*** GWR green (button) (M) - *85-94*	32	40
D45	**7819 *Hinton Manor*** GWR green (M) - *85-94*	32	40
D46	**7827 *Lydham Manor*** BRc green (M) - *85-94*	32	40

L18. **GWR Class 4073 'Castle' 4-6-0** (ex-Airfix) (1983)

Some of the stock of Airfix Castles (with tender drive) were renamed and renumbered by

Dapol. Of these, some were sold in their original Airfix boxes while others were put into new Dapol packaging once the expanded polystyrene tray had been trimmed with a large knife!

D30	**4073 *Caerphilly Castle*** Great () Western green (A) - *83-89*	35	50
?	**4080 *Powderham Castle*** Great () Western green (Airfix 54124 renamed by Dapol) - *83-85*	75	100
?	**4078 *Pembroke Castle*** Great () Western green (Airfix 54124 renamed by Dapol) - *83-85*	75	100
?	**4080 *Powderham Castle*** BRb green (Airfix 54125 renamed by Dapol) - *83-85*	75	100
D29	**4079 *Pendennis Castle*** BRb green (A) - *85-94*	35	50
?	**4078 *Pembroke Castle*** BRb green (Airfix 54125 renamed by Dapol) - *83-85*	75	100

L19. GWR Class 4073 'Castle' 4-6-0 (1985)

This model had loco drive and a Hawksworth tender.

D6	**5090 *Neath Abbey*** G()W green - *85-93*	40	50

GWR 'Castle' Class No.5090 Neath Abbey [L19]

D107	**5090 *Isambard Kingdom Brunel*** GW green - *not made*	NA	NA
D5	**4090 *Dorchester Castle*** BRb lined green, optional double chimney - *85-95*	40	50

The tooling was sold to Hornby in 1996 and the model reintroduced by them.

L20. GWR Class 1000 'County' 4-6-0 (1985)

This model had loco drive and a Hawksworth tender. sc = single chimney, dc = double chimney.

D3	**1029 *County of Worcester*** G()W green sc - *85-94*	40	50
D3	**1029 *County of Worcester/County of Stafford*** ** BRb green sc - *?*	NPG	NPG
D3	**1027 ** *County of Worcester*** BRb green & BR cab lining sc, '1029' on bufferbeam - *?*	NPG	NPG
D103	**1011 *County of Chester*** G()W green * - *90-96*	40	50
D?	**1000 *County of Middlesex*** G()W green Ltd Edn 100 - *02*	80	95
D68	**1019 *County of Merioneth*** BRb gloss black - *88-94*	40	50
D4	**1027 *County of Stafford*** BRc green, dc - *85-94*	40	50

* remodelled boiler and firebox, improved finish. The tooling was sold to Hornby in 1996 and the model reintroduced by them. ** This could be a one-off factory error.

L21. LMS 'Royal Scot' 4-6-0 (ex-Mainline) (1985)

D34	**6127 *Old Contemptibles*** LMS maroon (M) - *85-94*	32	40
D35	**46137 *Prince of Wales Volunteers, South Lancashire*** BRb green (M) - *85-94*	32	40

L22. LMS Rebuilt 'Royal Scot' 4-6-0 (ex-Airfix) (1985)

D28	**6103 *Royal Scots Fusilier*** LMS black (A) - *85-94*	25	40
D27	**46100 *Royal Scot*** BRb green (A) - *85-94*	25	40

L23. LMS Rebuilt 'Royal Scot' 4-6-0 (ex-M/line) (1985)

D58	**6100 *Royal Scot*** LMS maroon bell on front, name on smokebox door (M) - *85-96*	30	38
D36	**6115 *Scots Guardsman*** LMS black (M) - *85-94*	30	38
D41	**46115 *Scots Guardsman*** BRc green (M) - *85-93*	35	42

L24. LMS 'Jubilee' 4-6-0 (ex-Mainline) (1985)

FT + Fowler tender. ST = Stanier tender

D37	**5687 *Neptune*** LMS black, ST (M) - *85-94*	30	38
D42	**45700 *Amethyst*** BRb blk, FT (M) - *85-95*	30	38
D43	**45698 *Mars*** BRb green, FT (M) - *85-94*	35	42
D38	**45691 *Orion*** BRc green, ST (M) - *85-98*	35	42

L25. LMS Rebuilt 'Patriot' 4-6-0 (ex-Mainline) (1985)

D39	**45536 *Private W.Wood V.C.*** BRa black (M) - *85-94*	35	42
D40	**45532 *Illustrious*** BRc green (M) - *85-93*	35	42

L26. LNER Class A4 4-6-2 (ex-Trix)

D85	**2512 *Silver Fox*** LNER silver with valances - *not made*	NA	NA
D84	**4468 *Mallard*** LNER blue with valances - *not made*	NA	NA
D86	**60027 *Merlin*** BRc green - *not made*	NA	NA

L27. LNER Class A3 4-6-2 (ex-Trix)

D87	**4472 *Flying Scotsman*** LNER green - *not made*	NA	NA
D88	**60103 *Flying Scotsman*** BRc green - *not made*	NA	NA

L28. LNER Class A2 4-6-2 (ex-Trix)

D89	**525 *A.H.Peppercorn*** LNER green - *not made*	NA	NA
D90	**60532 *Blue Peter*** BRc green - *not made*	NA	NA

D9 & D10 - In 1985, these numbers were originally allocated to two versions of a Beyer-Garratt locomotive due to be released in 1987 but the model did not reach production and D10 was reallocated to the L&Y Pug.

D11 - In 1985 this number was allocated to a WD 2-8-0, also due for release in 1987 but about which no more was heard.

Diesel & Electric Locomotives

L29. Class 21/29 Diesel Bo-Bo (2011)

This model will contain a new 5-pole skew wound 'Supercreep' can motor with brass flywheels, have low friction mechanism with pin point bearings, have a 21-pin DCC board fitted for DCC sound compatibility, have a removable cab, directional lighting, lit headcode boxes, alternate customer fitted headcode characters, metal split-frame, etched steel windscreen wipers, roof grille with fan detail below and NEM coupling sockets.

D1001a	**D?** BRc green small yellow panel - *11*	NPG	NPG

L30. Class 22 Diesel Hydraulic B-B (2011)

The model contains a new 5-pole skew wound 'Supercreep' can motor with brass flywheels, low friction mechanism with pin point bearings, 21-pin DCC board fitted, DCC sound compatible, removable cab, directional lighting, cab lighting, lit headcode boxes, alternate customer fitted headcode characters, metal split-frame chassis, etched steel windscreen wipers and roof fan grille with fan detail below and NEM coupling sockets. sb = splitcode box.

D1000d	**D6319** BRc green small yellow panel sb Ltd Edn 300 - *11*	100	125

CAD picture of the Class 22 in development [L30] (Dapol)

D1000a	**D6324** BRe blue full yell end sb Ltd Edn 300 - *11*	100	125
D1000c	**D6314** BRc green small yellow panel sb Ltd Edn 300 - *11*	100	125
D1000b	**D6326** BRe blue full yell end sb Ltd Edn 300 - *11*	100	125
D1000f	**D6332** BRc green no yellow panel sb Ltd Edn 300 - *11*	100	125
D1000e	**D6327** BRc green small yellow panel sb Ltd Edn 300 - *11*	100	125

L31. Class 31/4 Diesel Co-Co (ex-Airfix) (1985)

D31**	**D5531** BRc green (A) - *85*	15	30
D62	**D5531** BRc green (A) - *88-94*	15	30
D32	**31217** BRe Rft Distribution grey - *not made*	NA	NA
D30	**31226** BReLL Rft plain grey - *not made*	NA	NA
D31	**31247** BReLL Railfreight red stripe grey - *not made*	NA	NA
D61	**31401** BRe blue (A) - *88-94*	15	30
D30**	**31401** BRe blue (A) new bogie - *85*	15	30
D73	BRe Rft Distribution grey - *not made*	NA	NA

** Early code numbers used for D61 and D62. Some of the tools were amongst those bought by Hornby in 1996 but there were insufficient to make a complete model.

L32. Class 41 'Warship' Diesel Hydraulic B-B (2011)

The A1A-A1A 'Warships' were built by the North British Locomotive Co. and introduced to the Western Region in 1958. Only 5 were built and all five are being modelled exclusively for Kernow Model Rail Centre. 750 of each are being made and all will come with numbered certificates.

The models have a 5-pole skew wound can motor and 2 large brass flywheels. They are 21-pin DCC board fitted, DCC sound compatible, have removable painted cab (for crew fitting), directional lighting, cab lighting, heavy metal split frame chassis, low friction mechanism with pinpoint bearings, lit headcode boxes, alternate customer fitted headcode characters, etched steel windscreen wipers, an etched roof fan grille with fan detail below and NEM coupling sockets Both front ends and 2 different side variants to be modelled. mg = mesh grills. hd = headcode discs. hb = headcode boxes.

K2600	**D600 *Active*** BRe blue, full yellow cab fronts, mg, hb - *11*	NPG	130
K2601	**D601 *Ark Royal*** BRc green, green cab fronts, louvres, hd - *11*	NPG	130
K2602	**D602 *Bulldog*** BRc green, small yellow cab front panels, hb, mg - *11*	NPG	130
K2603	**D603 *Conquest*** BRc green, small yellow cab front panels, hd, mg - *11*	NPG	130
K2604	**D604 *Cossack*** BRc green, green cab fronts, hd, mg - *11*	NPG	130

L33. Class 42 'Warship' Diesel Hydraulic B-B (ex-Mainline) (1985)

D66	**D824 *Highflyer*** BRc green (M) - *85-87*	22	30
D65	**827 *Kelly*** BRe blue (M) - *85-89*	20	30
D64	**827 *Kelly*** BRe blue as D65 with diesel sound and klaxon (M) - *85-88*	30	40

L34. LMS 'Twins' Main Line Diesels (2011)

This model is being produced exclusively for Hattons of Liverpool. It will have all-wheel pick-up and drive, sprung buffers, centrally mounted Dapol 5-pole acute skew wound motor, flywheels, separate handrails and wipers, etched see through roof grill and detailed side grills, yellow and red LED lighting, 21 pin DCC socket, full metal chassis, NEM coupling pocket, space for sound decoder, split frame chassis, pinpoint axles, separately fitted roof horns, cab lights and brass worksplate.

10000AP	**10000** LMS black - *11*	NPG	125
10000BP	**10000** BR black - *11*	NPG	125
10000DP	**10000** BR lined green - *11*	NPG	125
10001FP	**10001** BR no insignia black - *11*	NPG	125
10001JP	**10001** BR green + light blue band - *11*	NPG	125

L35. SR Bulleid 1-Co-Co-1 (2012)

Designed by Oliver Bulleid for the Southern Railway, the locomotives did not appear until after Nationalisation. 10201 and 10202 were built at Ashford Works in 1950 with 10203 being built at Brighton Works in 1954. The diesel engine and transmission were supplied by English Electric.Kernow Model Rail Centre has commissioned this model and will own the tooling.

K2701	**10201** BRb black - *12*	NPG	140
K2702	**10202** BRb black - *12*	NPG	140
K2703	**10203** BRb black - *12*	NPG	140

L36. DP2 Co-Co (2011)

This was an experimental machine for a 2nd generation of Type 4 locomotives. It was designed by English Electric and built at their Vulcan Foundry. It used a production 'Deltic' body but it had a totally different equipment inside. In fact, internally, it was closer to the later Class 50s.

The model will have a new 5-pole can motor with heavy large brass flywheels, darkened RP25.110 wheel sets with 14.4mm back to backs and 2mm axles and 26mm over pin points, directional lighting, cab lighting, DCC 21 pin decoder sockets, a large socket for a sealed speaker under etched roof fan grilles and possible fuel tank, separate cab steps etc.

?	**D?** BRc green - *12*	NPG	NPG

L37. Class 56 Diesel Co-Co (ex-Mainline) (1985)

D81	unpainted grey - *89-93*	25	35

Class 56 No.56094 in Railfreight coal livery [L37]

D80	**56001** BRe Construction grey - *89-98*	30	40
D14A	**56064** Railfreight grey - *89-98*	30	40
D14B	**56068** Railfreight grey - *89-98*	30	40
D14	**56075 *West Yorkshire Enterprise*** Railfreight red stripe grey - *85-88*	35	45
D12*	**56077** BRe blue - *?*	30	40
D14	**56077** BRe blue - 94-*95*	25	35
D12	**56079** BRe blue, (M) - *85-98*	25	35
D13	**56086** BReLL blue, (M renumbered) - *85-93*	22	35
D14C	**56090** Railfreight grey - *89-96*	30	40
D104	**56094** Rft Coal Sector grey - *91-95*	30	40

* also shown as D14. The tooling was sold to Hornby in 1996 and the model reintroduced by them.

L38. Class 81 (ex-Trix)

D91	**E3000** BRd electric blue - *not made*	NA	NA
D92	BRe rail blue - *not made*	NA	NA
D93	BRe Executive grey - *not made*	NA	NA

Multiple Units

L39. Class 124 'TransPennine' DMU (ex-Trix) (1994)

These were assembled using mouldings made at Dapol's Winsford factory and fitted with their Sprinter motor bogie with new sideframes clipped on. The units were adapted to take Dapol coach weights to give them extra weight.

D95	**NE51953+NE51954** BRc green 2-car, single motor - *94-95*	75	90
D105	**NE51953+NE51954** BRc green 2-car, 2 motors, 221 were made - *00-01*	80	100
D94	BRe blue 2-car single motor - *not made*	NA	NA

The tools were amongst those bought by Hornby in 1996 but as the model is under scale, it is unlikely that it will be made by them.

L40. Class 150/2 Sprinter (1992)

It was not a very accurate model, particularly the front end and the body side windows, and it was not very reliable. Hornby bought the tooling but because of its reputation are unlikely to reintroduce the model unless it is from new tooling.

D82+ D82A	**150237**(**57237+52237**) BRe Provincial grey + blue 2-car - *92-94*	50	70
D82+ D82A	**150237**(**57237+52237**) BRe Provincial grey + blue improved 2-car - *93-99*	50	70
D108	Centro 2-car - *?*	NA	NA
D109	PTE 2-car - *?*	NA	NA

L41. Class 155 Super Sprinter (1992)

D83+ D83A	**155329**(**57329+52329**) BRe Provincial grey + blue 2-car - *92-94*	50	70
D83+ D83A	**155329**(**57329+52329**) BRe Regional Rlys grey + blue improved 2-car - *93-98*	50	70
D110	**155345**(**57345+52345**) BRe Metro PTE maroon 2-car - *?*	NPG	NPG
D106	BRe Regional Railways grey + blue 2-car - *not made*	NA	NA

The tooling was sold to Hornby in 1996 and the model reintroduced by them.

L42. Class 205 2-H 'Thumper' EMU (2010)

These were to be made by Dapol for Kernow Model Railway Centre but in March 2010 the order was switched to Bachmann.

L43. Class 390 'Pendolino' (2001)

Virgin Trains Class 390 'Pendolino' [L43]

D390-1	**390001 *Virgin Pioneer*** Virgin red+grey 4-car Ltd Edn 2000 - *01-02*	50	80
D390-2	**390002 *Red Revolution*** Virgin red+grey 4-car Ltd Edn 2000 - *01*	50	80
?	**390002 *Red Revolution*** Virgin red+grey motorless power car Sp Edn launch special presentation sleeve Angel Trains - Alstrom - Virgin Trains given to staff involved - *01*	50	90

D390-3	**390006** ***Mission Impossible*** Virgin red+grey 4-car Ltd Edn 200 - *03*	50	80
D390-4	**390007** ***Virgin Lady*** Virgin red+grey 4-car Ltd Edn 200 - *03*	50	80
D390-5	**390010** ***Commonwealth Games 2002*** Virgin red +grey 4-car Ltd Edn 200 - *03*	50	80
D390-6	**390011** ***City of Preston*** Virgin red+grey 4-car Ltd Edn 200 - *03*	50	80
D390-7	**390014** ***City of Manchester*** Virgin red+grey 4-car Ltd Edn 200 - *03*	50	80
-	Virgin red+grey 4-car Ltd Edn named ***Pen y darren*** one side and ***Pendolino***, only one specially commissioned by Virgin Trains for Railfest 2004 - *04*	NPG	NPG

L44. U.S. 4-4-0 (ex-Bachmann/Airfix) (1985)

D33	***Jupiter*** red + silver (A) - *85-94*	25	35

COACHES

For its coaches, Dapol depended principally on old Airfix and Mainline stock and Airfix tooling. Initially they sold the large surpluses of stock they acquired from Airfix and Palitoy but then produced variations of the former Airfix models. These included Mk2D coaches in Executive livery and the 12 wheel LMS diner which was planned by both Airfix and Palitoy but not actually released until Dapol took it over. The coaches were numbered with an 'E' prefix and E41 seems to have been the highest number reached.

(A) = ex-Airfix stock
(M) = ex-Mainline stock

Cat No.	Company, Number, Colour, Dates	£	£

Pre-Nationalisation

C1a. GWR 'Centenary' Coach (ex-Airfix) (1985)

E16	**GWR** 6659 dark brown+cream** (M) - *85-95*	8	14
E20	**BR** W6562W red+cream* - *90-02*	10	16
E20	**BR** W6662W red+cream* - *90-02*	10	16
E18	**BR** W6659W maroon (A) - *85-87*	10	17
E18	**BR** W6661W maroon* - *88-01*	10	16

*Paddington Newport Cardiff and Swansea coach boards. ** 'Cornish Riviera' coach boards. The tooling was sold to Hornby in 1996 and the model reintroduced by them.

C1b. GWR 'Centenary' Brake End (ex-Airfix) (1985)

E17	**GWR** 4575 dark brown+cream** (M+A) - *85-02*	8	14
E21	**BR** W4576W red+cream* - *90-02*	10	16
E19	**BR** W4576W maroon* (A) - *85-02*	10	17

*Paddington Newport Cardiff and Swansea coach boards. ** 'Cornish Riviera' coach boards. The tooling was sold to Hornby in 1996 and the model reintroduced by them.

C2. GWR Suburban B Stock (ex-Airfix) (1985)

E22	**GWR** 6896 dark brown+cream (A/M) - *85-02*	8	14
E23	**BR** W6894W maroon (A) - *85-88*	8	14
E24	**BR** W6447W lined maroon (M) - *85-02*	12	18

The tooling was sold to Hornby in 1996 and the model reintroduced by them.

C3. GWR Auto Trailer (ex-Airfix) (1985)

E25	**GWR** 187 dark brown+cream (M) - *85-98*	12	18
E25	**GWR** 188 dark brown+cream - *?*	12	18
E27	**BR** W176W red+cream (M) - *85-87*	12	18
E27	**BR** W178W red+cream - *88-90*	10	16
E26	**BR** W187W maroon (A) - *85-95*	8	14

The tooling was sold to Hornby in 1996 and the model reintroduced by them.

C4a. LMS Stanier Composite (ex-Airfix) (1985)

E4	**LMS** 3935 maroon (A) - *87*	8	14
E4	**LMS** 3936 maroon - *88-02*	10	16
E6	**BR** M3935M red+cream (A) - *85-86*	8	14
E8	**BR** M3868M maroon (M) - *87*	8	14
E8	**BR** M3868M maroon - *91-02*	10	16

C4b. LMS Stanier Brake End (ex-Airfix) (1985)

E5	**LMS** 5542 maroon (A) - *85-86*	8	14
E5	**LMS** 5545 maroon - *89-92*	10	16
E7	**BR** M5542M red+cream (A) - *85-86*	8	14
E7	**BR** M5542M red+cream - *97-02*	10	16
E9	**BR** M3868M maroon (M) - *85*	12	20
E9	**BR** M5648M maroon - *87-02*	10	16

C5a. LMS 57' Non-Corridor Lav (ex-Airfix) (1985)

E28	**LMS** 19195 maroon (A) - *85-87*	8	14
E28	**LMS** 19191 maroon - *88-02*	10	16
E41	**BR** M16456M red - *02*	10	16
E42	**BR** M16161M red (all 2nd) - *02*	10	16
E30	**BR** M19199M maroon - *88-02*	10	16
E31	**BR** M19195M maroon (A) - *85-92*	10	18
E31	**BR** M16161M maroon - *88-02*	10	16

C5b. LMS 57' Non-Corr Lav Brake (ex-Airfix) (1986)

E29	**LMS** 15185 maroon (A) - *87-?*	8	14
E29	**LMS** 25250 maroon - *95-02*	10	16
E40	**BR** M16370 red - *02*	10	16
E30	**BR** M25250M maroon (A) - *86-91*	10	17
E30	**BR** M16161M maroon - *94-02*	10	16

C6. LMS 12-Wheel Dining Car (ex-Mainline) (1985)

These were boxed in standard Dapol maroon boxes with blank labels and included a spare chassis. This was an LMS Period 2 coach.

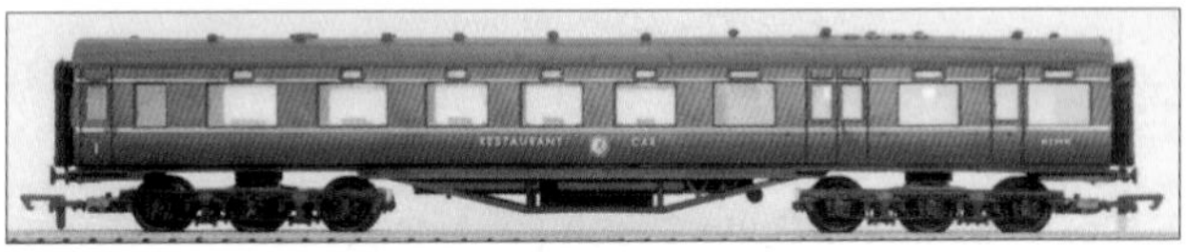

Ex-LMS 12-wheel dining car No.M239M [C6]

E1	**LMS** 10440 * maroon - *87-88*	15	25
E1A	**LMS** 10440 * maroon panelled - *88*	15	25
E1A	**LMS** 238* maroon panelled - *88*	15	25
E3	**BR** 10440 red+cream - *85-86*	20	35
?	**BR** maroon+cream - not made	NA	NA
E2	**BR** M239M maroon - *86-90, 98-99*	15	25
E2A	**BR** M239M maroon - *98-99*	15	25

*The actual coach was renumbered from 10440 to 238 in 1932/33. The tooling was sold to Hornby in 1996 and the model reintroduced by them.

C7. LMS 50' Parcels Van BG (ex-Mainline) (1985)

E37	**LMS** 30965 maroon (M) - *86*	8	12
E35	**BR** red+cream (M) - *86*	15	18
E36	**BR** lined maroon (M) - *86*	15	18
E33	**BR** M31262M blue+grey NFV (M) - *85-02*	10	15
E34	**BR** M31398 blue NFV (M) - *85-01*	10	15

C8. LMS 'Stove R' (2010)

This is the result of a joint project with *Hornby Magazine*. The model is the first Dapol 00 gauge model to feature sprung buffers and it also has small tension lock couplings, fine profile wheels, a finely moulded body, spearately fitted footboards and steps, brass handrails, separate gangway connections and full underframe detail. The chassis features a floating centre axle and pivoting outer axles to allow it to negotiate second radius curves.

LMS 'Stove R' 6-wheel passenger brake van commissioned by Hornby Magazine [C8] (Ian Allan Ltd)

E?	**LMS** ? lined maroon - *10*	NPG	28
E?	**BR** ? red - *10*	NPG	28

E?	**BR** ? maroon - *10*	NPG	28
E?	**BR** ? lined maroon - *10*	NPG	28
E?	**BRe** ? blue - *10*	NPG	28

Post-Nationalisation

C9a. BR Mk1 Corridor Coach (ex-Mainline) (1985)

E38	**BR** S25915 green (M) - *86*	14	17
E39	**BR** M25390 maroon (M) - *86*	10	15
E32	**BR** M1709 blue+grey (M) - *85-88*	9	13

C9b. BR Mk1 Brake End BSK (ex-Mainline) (1985)

E40	**BR** M35040 maroon (M) - *85-87*	10	15

C10a. Mk2d TSO Open Coach (ex-Airfix) (1985)

BR Mk2D 2nd open coach in InterCity livery [C10a]

E11	**BR** E5690 blue+grey (M) - *85-99*	10	20
E14	**BR** ICs E5732 executive grey - *86-02*	10	16

The tooling was sold to Hornby in 1996 and the model reintroduced by them.

C10b. Mk2d BSO Open Brake End (ex-Airfix) (1985)

E12	**BR** E9479 blue+grey (M) - *85-02*	10	14
E15	**BR ICs** E9483 executive grey - *86-02*	12	16

The tooling was sold to Hornby in 1996 and the model reintroduced by them.

C10c. Mk2d FO Open Coach (ex-Airfix) (1985)

E10	**BR** E3170 blue+grey (A) - *85-02*	8	14
E13	**BR ICs** E3207 executive grey - *86-02*	10	16

The tooling was sold to Hornby in 1996 and the model reintroduced by them.

C11. U.S. Passenger Car (ex-Bachmann/Airfix) (1985)

E41	**CPRR** 3 red saloon car with trapdoor in roof (A) - *85-87*	8	14

C12a. 'Pendolino' Standard Class (2003)

Makes coaches AD or AJ for 390-001 and 390-002 and coaches AC, AD or AJ for 390-006, 390-007, 390-*010*, 390-*011* and 390-*014*.

DPC-*01*	**Virgin** with transfers for any set - *03*	12	15

C12b. 'Pendolino' 2nd Class (2003)

Makes coach AF for 390-001 and 390-002.

DPC-*02*	**Virgin** with transfers for 390-001 and 390-002 - *03*	15	20

Coach Gift Sets

These were introduced in 1999 to clear surplus stocks of coaches.

CS1 Mk2D Open Stock (1999)

E100	2 x E10 - *99*	NA	24
E200	2 x E12 - *99*	NA	24
E300	2 x E14 - *99*	NA	24
E400	E13 + E15 - *99*	NA	24
E500	E30 + E31- *01*	NA	24
E600	E40 + E41 - *01*	NA	24
E700	E8 + E9 - *01*	NA	24

WAGONS

Private owner wagons were colourful and model versions of them have become very popular. They have consequently become the principal subject for specially commissioned models and Dapol have commanded this market due to their willingness to supply quite small numbers of each type chosen. This has been possible because they have kept the work close to home and as a semi-cottage industry.

While quite a lot of the models produced are colourful, in reality 53% of private owner wagons were finished in red oxide (red-brown) and 30% in black as these were the two cheapest pigments being based on iron oxide and carbon, respectively. The next most common colour was grey while rare colours were green, dark blue and yellow. The lettering was normally applied with lead based paint and therefore white - again for cheapness.

GWR 'Conflat' No.39029 with 'V.J.Blew' container [W2b] (Dapol)

Former Airfix and Mainline Wagons - Dapol had hoped to acquire the Airfix wagon tooling when Airfix collapsed but it went to Palitoy with much of it being put back into use to produce new Mainline wagons. Instead, Dapol had a series of wagons tooled up for them in Hong Kong. These may have included the 12T tanker, 'Mogo' van, 7-plank wagon, 5-plank wagon, double vent van, SR box van, LMS brake van, GWR Toad, 'Conflat' and container, 12T hopper wagon, the large steel mineral wagon and possibly the PCA V tank. These duplicates were very much like the Airfix and Mainline ones that were copied and it is often difficult to tell them apart. Later, Dapol acquired the Airfix tools but also tooled up at least five new wagons themselves. Further newly tooled and better detailed wagons have recently followed, replacing earlier ones.

The first Dapol wagons were released in 1984 and were numbered with a 'B' prefix. The wagon range was the most prolific of all the ranges produced by Dapol.

Dapol did acquire surplus Airfix stock from Palitoy and later purchased the entire Mainline stock when Palitoy ceased production of it. Some of these were then sold under the Dapol name until the stocks were used up. Dapol also obtained Airfix and Mainline wagon parts and assembled some of the wagons themselves, packaging them as Dapol wagons. No records have come to light to show the origins of these wagons and so a 'B' number can include repackaged Airfix or Mainline stock, models assembled from factory clearance parts, replica parts made by Dapol or a mixture of all these. Thus, the listing here has had to be done on a generic basis but with divisions made in the tabling only where detective work suggests that these should be. Much more research is needed and we would welcome further information on this subject.

Dapol reissued some popular Airfix wagons, often taking the opportunity to change the running number, but the printing on these reissues was sometimes of a poorer quality which helps to identify them. They also reissued some Mainline wagons but using the equivalent Dapol replica or Airfix body but with Mainline artwork.

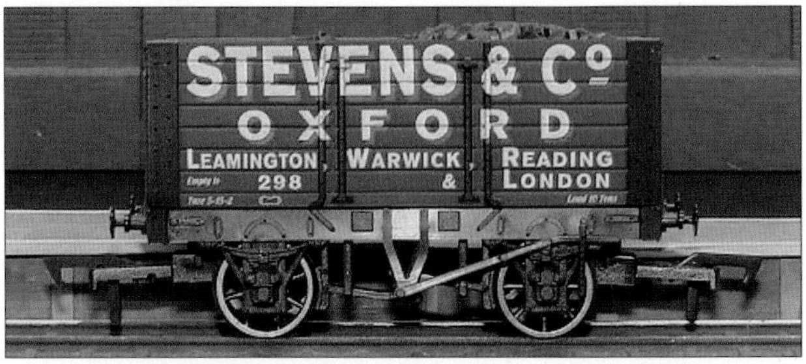

New 9' wheel base 7-plank coal wagon - 'Stevens & Co' [W8] (Dapol)

Former Wrenn Wagons - In 1993, Dapol purchased the Wrenn company and its tooling and, while on this occasion they did not receive any completed stock, they did have all the unassembled parts from which wagons were made up and sold.

From 1997 these were sold in three different categories. Where all Wrenn parts were used they was sold as Wrenn models with a 'WR1' prefix to the catalogue number. If the wagons were made up from Wrenn bodies fitted to a Dapol chassis they were sold as Dapol wagons with a 'WR2' prefix and if new bodies were made from the Wrenn tools they were sold as Dapol models with a 'WR3' prefix. Once original parts were used up the WR1 and WR2 categories disappeared and WR3 wagons were absorbed into the main wagon series and given 'B' prefixes.

Unfortunately, we had no production records when compiling this list and depended to a large extent on catalogues and price lists. Thus, the inclusion of a wagon in the following tables is not evidence that it was actually made. It is merely an indication that Dapol listed it.

When, in 2001, Dapol sold G&R Wrenn Ltd to Mordvale, they retained all but 9 of the former HD/Wrenn wagon body tools including the following: utility van, gunpowder van, Presflo, 5-plank wagon, banana van, mineral wagon, grain wagon, salt van and cattle van.

WRCC Models - Dapol produced wagon bodies for the Wrenn Railways Collectors Club which were supplied in Dapol boxes and with two gold printed labels. The pairs of labels carried a unique number and indicated the size of the run. The idea was that members would fit these special edition bodies to any spare Wrenn chassis they had and if they wished, boxed them in Wrenn boxes to which they affixed the gold label The bodies sold for about £6 each. Later special editions for the club were complete wagons. In all there were ten of these releases by Dapol.

Special Editions - In recent years Dapol have established themselves as the leading manufacturer of special edition wagons commissioned by shops and organisations. These are often produced in numbers no greater than 100 and quickly sell out. Due to the vast number of variations produced, we have not been able to trace every one of them and the absence of one from the tables below is not an indication that the model is rarer than others. We are always interested to learn of ones we have missed and in each case would like to know inscription, colour, running number, production quantity, year of release and who it was made for, etc. - if known.

New Wheels & Chassis - New metal (bush insulated) wheels were introduced in the Summer of 2008. These are very free running, having metal axles with pinpoint bearings. The wheels are 3-hole discs with darkened centres or spoked. A new improved 10ft chassis with narrower couplings in NEM pockets was also introduced during the year.

(A) = ex-Airfix stock
(M) = ex-Mainline stock

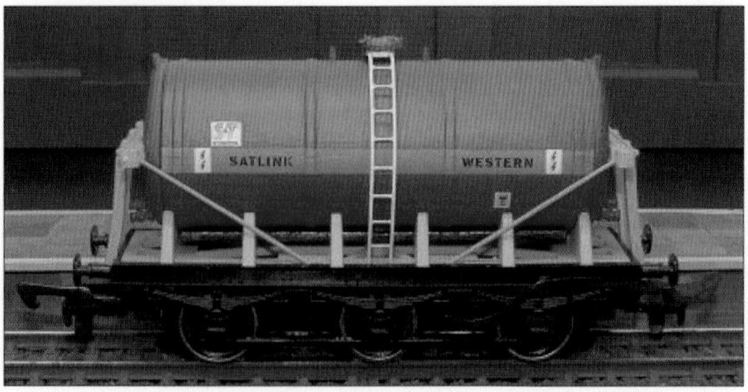

6-wheel milk tank wagon in 'Satlink Western' livery [W29b] (Dapol)

Cat No.	Company, Number, Colour, Dates	£	£

Flat Wagons

W1. 'Lowmac' MS (ex-Airfix) (1985)

The Hornby Dublo 'Lowmac' tool was damaged and not used by Dapol. It was later sold, with others, to Morevale Ltd with the G&R Wrenn Ltd assets.

Cat No.	Company, Number, Colour, Dates	£	£
B57	**BR** dark grey + crate - *89-91*	5	12
B57	**BR** B904662 red brown + crate (A) - *85-86*	8	12
B58	**BR** B904662 red brown + **'Sea Land'** container (A) - *85-86*	10	15

The tooling was sold to Hornby in 1996 and the model reintroduced by them.

W2a. 'Conflat B' (ex-Airfix) (2007)

Cat No.	Company, Number, Colour, Dates	£	£
-	**BR** TDB701783 brown Sp Edn 100 (Alexandra Models) - *07*	9	16
-	**GNR** 277 brown Sp Edn (Leslie McAllister) - *10*	7	9
-	**GNR** 1957 grey Sp Edn (Leslie McAllister) - *10*	7	9

W2b. 'Conflat B' with Container (1986)

Duplicate tools for the wagon and container were made and one set sold to Hornby in 1996, who have produced their own versions of the model.

Cat No.	Company, Number, Colour, Dates	£	£
A4	brown+grey - unfinished - *86-03*	5	6
-	**LB&SCR** 7160 grey + **'Curtiss & Sons'** container pale brown Sp Edn 168 (Wessex Wagons) - *08*	9	12
-	**LB&SCR** 7986 grey + **'White & Co.'** 200 container brown+cream Sp Edn 128 (Wessex Wagons) - *09*	15	19
-	**L&SWR** 32245 + **'White & Co.'** container dark brown Sp Edn (Wessex Wagons) - *09*	10	13
-	**LSWR** 32245 brown + **'White & Co.'** 200 container brown+cream Sp Edn 139 (Wessex Wagons) - *09*	15	19
-	**GNR** 1997 brown + Furniture Removals container No.1 dark blue Sp Edn 129 (Provincial Wagons) *- not made*	NA	NA
-	**GNR** (Ireland) 4287 brown + **GNR** Furniture Removals container No.4 dark blue Sp Edn 136 (Provincial Wagons) - *08*	10	13

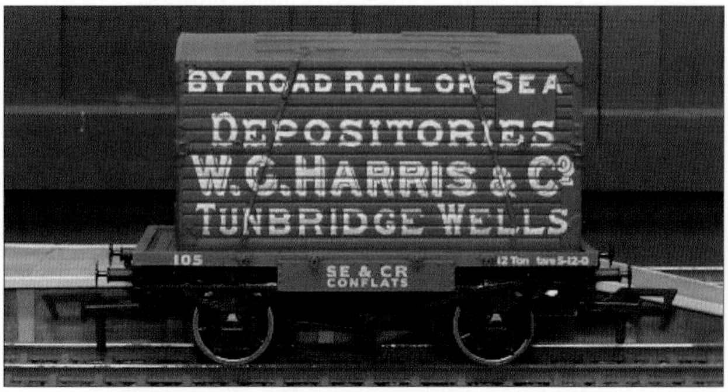

SE&CR 'Conflat' with 'W.C Harris & Co' container [W2b] (Dapol)

Cat No.	Company, Number, Colour, Dates	£	£
-	**SECR** 105 brown + **'W G Harris'** container dark green Sp Edn 1000 (Ballards) - *03*	10	12
-	**SE&CR** 105 grey + **'W G Harris'** container dark green Sp Edn (Ballards) - *09*	7	9
-	**WHR** 5 red-brown + **WHR** 5 container grey Sp Edn 150 (Welsh Highland Railway) - *10*	10	13
B91	**GW** 39324 dark grey + **'C&G Ayers'** container 37 green (M) - *87-92*	8	12
B399	**GW** 39005 dark grey + **'C&G Ayers'** container 37 dark blue (also boxed as B91) - *02-03*	8	10
B119	**GW** 39324 dark grey + **GWR** BK1828 container brown - *88-92*	10	12
B119	**GW** 39005 dark grey + **GWR** container BK1828 dark brown - *95-99*	10	12
B531	**GW** 39005 dark grey + **GWR** container BK1828 dark brown - *03*	7	9
B650	**GW** 39024 grey + **GWR** K1691 dark brown - *06*	7	9
-	**GW** 39005 grey + **'W&A Chapman'** brown container Sp Edn 270 (Wessex Wags) - *05*	10	12
-	**GW** 39005 grey + **'Hawkes & Freeman'** 4 brown container Sp Edn 93 (Buffers) - *10*	9	11

No.11	**GW** 39050 dark grey + **'Jane's'** 50 container cream Sp Edn 97 (W Wales Wagon Works) - *03*	10	12
-	**GW** 39005 grey + **'Llangollen International Musical Eisteddfod'** green container Sp Edn 108 (Llangollen Railway GW Loco Group) - *07*	10	12
-	**GW** 39005 grey + **'Medway Queen'** 37 dark green Sp Edn 80 (Medway Queen PS) - *08*	9	11
-	**GW** 39024 grey + **'New Medway'** 66 green Sp Edn 60 (Medway Queen PS) - *07*	10	12
-	**GW** 39024 grey + **'Lane & Hawkes'** green Sp Edn 180 (Wessex Wagons) - *07*	10	12
-	**GW** 39029 brown + **'VJ Blew'** container 23 dark blue Sp Edn 167 (Wessex Wagons) - *08*	10	12
-	**GW** 39005 grey + **'Peace'** container 2 blue Sp Edn 74 (Burnham & Dist. MRC) - *09*	10	12
-	**GW** 39024 grey + **'F.R.Pruchase'** 3 green Sp Edn 141 (Burnham & District MRC) - *10*	11	14
B162	**LMS** 300478 light grey + **LMS** container K1 maroon - *91-99*	9	11
B544	**LMS** N300478 grey + **LMS** container K1 maroon - *03*	7	9
B120	**NE** 240749 grey + **'J Miles'** container red (A) - *88-89*	8	12
B120	**NE** 240747 grey + **'J Miles'** container red (A) - *88-89*	9	12
B383	**NE** 240748 grey + **'J Miles'** container 3 red - *02-03*	7	9
B121	**NE** 240747 brown + **LNER** container dark blue BK1828 - *88-92*	9	11
B121	**NE** 240749 brown + **LNER** container dark blue BK1828 - *88-92*	9	11
B563	**NE** 240748 grey + **LNER** container BK1828 dark blue - *03*	7	9
-	**NE** 240748 light grey + **'Bolingbroke & Wenley'** container red-brown Sp Edn 243 (Chelmsford & District MRC) - *08*	9	11
B129	**SR** 39115, 39155 dark brown + **SR** container K591 - *94-97*	9	11
B530	**SR** 31955 dark brown + **SR** container K591 green - *not made*	NA	NA
B530	**SR** 31955 dark brown + **SR** container K595 green - *03*	7	9
-	**SR** 31955 dark brown + **'T.Browning & Sons'** white container Sp Edn 145 (E.Kent MRS) - *05*	10	12
-	**SR** 31945 dark brown + **'Colyer & Co.'** maroon Sp Edn 188 (Wessex Wagons) - *06*	10	12
-	**SR** 31927 dark brown + **'Day & Co.'** container cream Sp Edn 280 (Wessex Wagons) - *06*	10	12
-	**SR** 31955 grey + **'Hawkes & Freeman'** 4 brown container Sp Edn 101 (Buffers) - *10*	9	11
-	**SR** 31927 dark brown + **'Medway Queen'** 37 blue Sp Edn 80 (Medway Queen PS) - *08*	10	12
-	**SR** 31927 grey + **'Peace'** container 2 dark blue Sp Edn 63 (Burnham & District MRC) - *09*	10	12
-	**SR** 31875 brown + **'New Medway'** 66 blue Sp Edn 60 (Medway Queen PS) - *07*	11	13
-	**SR** 31875 dark brown + **'JC Nutt'** container green Sp Edn 280 (Wessex Wagons) - *06*	10	12
-	**SR** 31875 dark brown + **'James Sayers'** cream Sp Edn 200 (Wessex Wagons) - *06*	10	12
No.16	**SR** 31947 dark brown + **'Reeves'** brown container Sp Edn 93 (West Wales Wagon Works) - *04*	11	13
-	**SR** 31952 brown + **'Pimm & Son'** brown Sp Edn 108 (West Wales Wagon Works) - *07*	10	12
-	**SR** 39028 dark brown + **SR** container B255 dark brown Sp Edn 1000 (Ballards) - *04*	10	12
B118	**BR** W36507 brown + **'Pickfords'** 1666 container dark blue - *87-89*	9	11
-	**BR** W36507 brown + **'Trago Mills'** container dark brown Sp Edn 250 (Trago Mills) - *06*	10	12
B100	**BR** B735700 red-brown + **BR** furniture container (A) - *86-88*	8	12
-	**BR** B735759 red-brown + **'Beale & Piper'** yellow container Sp Edn 96 (Strathspey Railway) - *06*	11	13
-	**MHR** 02004 dark grey + **'Watercress Line'** container K904 green Sp Edn (Mid Hants Railway) - *04*	10	12
-	**'Reg Stickells'** grey (Conflat only) Sp Edn 100 1st issue (Hythe Models) - *02*	11	13

Planked Goods Wagons

W3a. 1-plank Wagon (ex-Wrenn) (1995)

B241	**'Auto Trader'** 115 red brown - *c95*	12	15
WR1-30	**'Auto Spares'** 115 brown + 4 tyres - *99*	12	20
WR2-29	as above Dapol chassis - *99*	12	15
B240	**LMS** + LMS container - *not made*	NA	NA
B239	**BR** B459325 grey - *c95*	10	15
WR1-31	as above - *99*	10	17

W3b. 1-plank Wagon + Container (ex-Mainline) (1986)

B90	**BR** B450023 red brown + **'Bird's Eye'** BD container (M) - *86*	8	12

W4. 3-plank Open Wagon (ex-Mainline) (1985)

A8	brown - unfinished - *85-89*	6	8
B47	**'Carter'** 172 grey (M) - *85-86*	6	10
B96	'E.**Turner**' 26 cream (M) - *86-87*	6	10
B48	**LMS** 471624 grey - *85-92*	8	10
B24	**LMS** 471194 grey - *?*	8	10
B24	**LMS** 473449 red brown - *85-95*	8	10
B49	**NE** 535962 grey (M) - *85-89*	6	10
B23	**BR** M471363 light grey - *85-89*	8	10
B50	**BR** M473453 red brown, new chassis (M) - *85-87*	6	10

W5. 4-plank Open Wagon (2006)

-	**'Abercriban Quarries'** 57 red + granite load Sp Edn 109 (David Dacey) - *08*	7	9
BE5	**'Arnold Sands'** 803 brown sand load Sp Edn 150 (1E Promotionals) - *07*	7	9
-	**'BCWW'** 159 yellow Sp Edn 165 (Wessex Wagons' - *10*	7	10
-	**'Blue Circle Cement'** 5 yellow Sp Edn 113 (Wessex Wagons) - *09*	7	9
-	**'Blue Circle Cement'** 18 yellow Sp Edn 100 (Wessex Wagons) - *09*	7	9
B665	'The **Bold Venture Lime Co.**' 24 grey - *06-07*	6	8
No.8	'Willm H **Booth**' 701 red-brown Sp Edn 200 (Mid-Suffolk Light Railway) - *08*	7	9
B755	**'BW Co.'** 1100 red - *08*	6	8

4-plank open wagon - 'Cadbury' [W5]

SY2	**'Cadbury Co.'** 10 red Sp Edn 350 (1E Promotionals) - *08*	7	9
-	**'Ceiriog Granite Co.'** 195 dark brown, granite load Sp Edn (Dapol Shop) - *08*	7	9
B743	**'Clee Hill Granite Co.'** 331 light grey - *08*	6	8
-	**'Corris Railway'** 1 light grey + brick load Sp Edn 120 (West Wales Wagon Works) - *09*	7	10
-	**'Corris Railway'** 1 light grey W + sand load Sp Edn 40 (West Wales Wagon Works) - *09*	8	11
E06A	**'Cranmore Granite'** 343 light grey Sp Edn 150 (East Somerset Models)	7	NA
E06B	**'Cranmore Granite'** 347 light grey Sp Edn 150 (East Somerset Models)	7	NA
-	above pair - *07*	NA	16
-	**'Cwmbran Brick Co.** '15 dark brown Sp Edn 109 (David Dacey) - *09*	6	8
-	**'East Downshire Steamship Co.'** 14 grey Sp Edn 110 (Provincial Wagons) - *07*	7	9
-	**'East Downshire Steamship Co.'** (Irish) 2 grey Sp Edn 143 (Provincial Wagons) - *08*	7	9
-	'C&F **Gaen**' 4 black + black tar load Sp Edn 120		

	(West Wales Wagon Works) - *07*	7	9
-	'C&F **Gaen**' 4 black W + black tar load Sp Edn 40 (West Wales Wagon Works) - *07*	7	9
-	**'Holms Sand & Gravel Co.'** 20 black Sp Edn 163 (Wessex Wagons) - *07*	7	9
ANT 031	**'Hoare Brothers'** 60 black Sp Edn 250 (Antics) - *08*	7	9
B682	**'Hudson Bro.'** 10 grey + brick load - *07*	6	8
-	'Richard **Hughes**' 10 red-brown Sp Edn 157 (Wessex Wagons) - *10*	8	10

4-plank wagons 'Foster Yeoman' Nos.130&126 [W5] (Dapol)

E07A	**'Foster Yeoman'** 126 light grey Sp Edn 175 (East Somerset Models) - *08*	7	9
E07B	**'Foster Yeoman'** 130 light grey Sp Edn 175 (East Somerset Models) - *08*	7	9
-	**'Kilsmerdon Colliery'** 342 ? Sp Edn (Wessex Wagons) - *07*	7	9
-	**'Llanharry'** 37 cream W Sp Edn* (Barry & Penarth MRS) - *07*	8	10
-	'E **Marsh**' 1 grey with stone load Sp Edn 146 (West Wales Wagon Works) - *07*	7	9
-	'L **Mcallister**' GN ? Sp Edn (1E Promotionals) - *09*	7	9
-	'**Mendip Granite Works**' 8 buff Sp Edn 167 (Wessex Wagons) - *08*	7	9
-	**Mid Suffolk** 5 light grey Sp Edn 200 (Middy Trading Co.) - *09*	7	9
B718	**'New Cransley Iron & Steel'** 76 grey - *08*	6	8
-	**'T Pearson'** 2 white Sp Edn (St.Albans Signal Box Preservation Trust) - *10*	9	12
-	**'Pentrefelin Slab & Slate Works'** 3 light grey Sp Edn 109 (Llangollen Railway GWR grp) - *07*	7	9
-	**'Penwyllt Silica Works'** 19 grey Sp Edn 103 (David Dacey) - *08*	7	9
B662	**'Pwllheli Granite Co.'** 155 grey - *06-07*	7	9
-	**'Radstock Coal Co.'** 1379 black Sp Edn 244 (Wessex Wagons) - *06*	8	10
-	**'RVR'** 1 grey Sp Edn 108 (K&ESR) - *07*	8	12
B674	**'Stonehouse Brick & Tile'** 10 red - *06-07*	7	9
B736	**'Teign Valley Granite'** 1145 black - *08*	6	8
-	**'Timsbury Collieries'** 118 grey Sp Edn 116 (Wessex Wagons) - *08*	7	9
-	**'Timsbury Collieries'** 126 grey Sp Edn 112 (Wessex Wagons) - *08*	7	9
ANT032	**'The Covertry Ordnance Work'** 2 red-brown Sp Edn 250 (Antic) - *08*	7	9
-	**'The Earl Waldegrave Radstock Collieries'** 563 black Sp Edn 147 (Burnham & District MRC) - *10*	7	9

Great Northern Railway 4-plank wagon [W5]

CMM001	**'Threlkeld Granite'** 103 grey Sp Edn 150 (C&M Models) - *10*	9	11
-	**'Tonfanau Granite Quarries'** 5 plank Sp Edn 83 (West Wales Wagon Works) - *10*	8	11
-	**'Tonfanau Granite Quarries'** 5 plank W Sp Edn 29 (West Wales Wagon Works) - *10*	9	12
-	**'Tonfanau Granite Quarries'** 9 plank Sp Edn 85 (West Wales Wagon Works) - *10*	8	11
-	**'Tonfanau Granite Quarries'** 9 plank W Sp Edn 31 (West Wales Wagon Works) - *10*	9	12
-	**'Toyne Carter & Co.'** 71 grey Sp Edn 164 (Wessex Wagons) - *10*	8	10
B714	**'Weardale'** 805 brown - *07-08*	6	8
-	'F **Wilkinson**' 11 red-brown Sp Edn 130 (Crafty Hobbies) - *07*	7	9
-	**'Writhlington & Kilmersdon Colliery** "K"' 342 black Sp Edn 206 (Wessex Wagons) - *07*	7	9
-	**'Writhlington & Kilmersdon Colliery** "K"' 93 black Sp Edn 204 (Wessex Wagons) - *07*	7	9
-	**'Ynysybwl Pennant Stone'** 12 red-brown Sp Edn 106 (South Wales Coalfields) - *07*	8	10
-	**BCDR** (Belfast & County Down Ralway) 107 dark grey Sp Edn 156 (Provincial Wagons) - *09*	7	9
-	**CM&PD Light Railway** 2 grey Sp Edn 100 (West Wales Wagon Works) - *07*	7	9
B761	**GW** 45505 grey - *09*	7	9
B761A	**GW** 45504 grey with timber load ** - *10*	7	9
-	**GN** 3164 grey Sp Edn 100 (Provincial Wagons) - *07*	7	9
-	**GN** 5558 grey Sp Edn 115 (Provincial Wagons) - *08*	7	9
-	**GN** 3616 grey with timber load Sp Edn 164 (Provincial Wagons) - *09*	8	11
-	**UT** (Ulster Transport) C85 red-brown Sp Edn 150 (Provincial Wagons) - *09*	7	9
-	**WC&PR** grey Sp Edn (Kent & East Sussex Railway) - *08*	8	11

* Short run weathered by Dapol for an eBay retailer. ** Possibly renumbered old stock.

W6. 5-plank Open Wagon 9ft wb (2009)

The new chassis has deeper frames and brakes fitted to one side only.

B838	**'Chipping Norton Co-op'** 10 black - *10*	7	10
B812	**'J James & Co.'** 98 red-brown - *09*	7	10
-	'**Hocknulls**' 1 grey Sp Edn (Wessex Wagons) - *10*	7	10
B767	**'Marshall'** 2 red-brown - *09*	7	10
-	**'FW Pinniger'** 2 black Sp Edn 152 (Burnham & District MRC) - *10*	7	9
B813	'EA **Robinson**' 1905 red-brown - *09*	7	10
B814	'FH **Silvey & Co.**' 196 dark brown - *09*	7	10
B818	**'Stevens & Co.'** 3 red - *09*	7	9
-	**'Taylor & Anderson'** 900 dark green Sp Edn 150 (Wessex Wagons) - *10*	8	10
ANT44	**'Worcester New Co-operative & Industrial Society'** 20 red-brown Sp Edn 140 (Antics) - *10*	8	11

W7a. 5-plank Open Wagon 10ft wb (ex-Airfix) (1984)

This table includes models made from the Airfix tool and from a replica tool produced in China for Dapol. We have no record as to which models were done with which tool.

A2	grey - unfinished - *84-99*	4	6
A001	grey - unfinished - *04-07*	4	6
B160	**'Alloa'** 1124 yellow (A) - *89-?*	6	10
B160	**'Alloa'** 1125 yellow - *?-99*	8	10
B38	**'Arnold'** 156 red brown (A) - *86-87*	6	10
B45	**'BAC'** 4253 red brown (M) - *85-82*	6	10
B46	**'Black Rock'** 46 black (M) - *85-92*	6	10
B268	**'Black Rock'** 46 black - *98-02*	7	9
B515	**'Corporation of Dundee Gas Dept.'** 67 red-brown - *not made (see W7c)*	NA	NA
B39	**'Devizes Sand'** 1 grey (A) - *85-87*	6	10
B41	**'Harts Hill'** 2 brown (A) - *85-92*	6	10
B41	**'Harts Hill'** 2 brown - *95-02*	7	9
B199	**'Higginbotham'** 521 dark brown - *91-92, 95-02*	9	11
B101	'James **Marriott**' 14 brown - *not made*	NA	NA
B183	'James **Marriott**' 14 brown - *91-92, 97-02*	9	11
-	'John **North & Son**' 18 red-brown, Sp Edn 200+ (Geoff Osborn) - *99*	11	13
(3)	**'Old Radnor Lime'** 126 grey Sp Edn 200 (Hereford Model Centre) - *02*	11	13
(5)	**'Old Radnor Co.'** 159 grey Sp Edn 200 (Hereford Model Centre) - *02*	11	13
(04)	**'Old Radnor Co.'** 238 grey Sp Edn 200 (Hereford Model Centre) - *02*	11	13
B40	**'Spencer'** 24 red (A) - *85-89*	6	10
B163	**'Warrener'** 3 green - *94-02*	9	11
B126	**'Webster'** 341 dark brown (M) - ?	6	10

B267	**'Wolverton Mutual Society'** ** 29 grey Sp Edn 500 (Chris Wright) - *88*	11	13

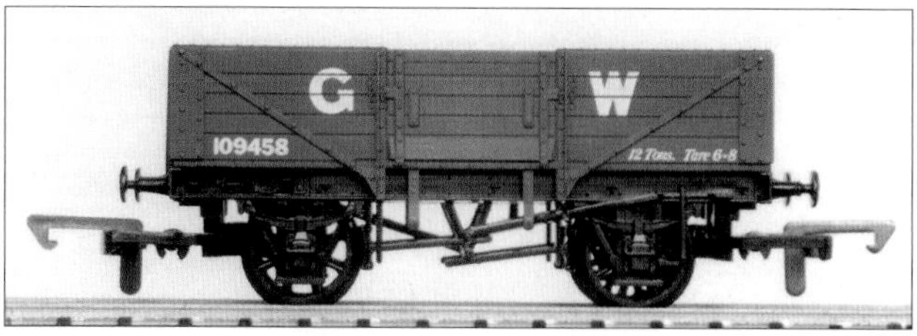

Ex-Airfix 5-plank wagon GWR [W7a]

B18	**GW** (thick) 109458 dark grey (A) - *84-95*	6	10
B18	**GW** (thin) 109459 dark grey (A) - *84-95*	6	10
B3	**LMS** 413833 red brown - *84-97*	6	8
B42	**LMS** 404104 grey (A) - *86-92*	6	10
B42	**LMS** 404105 grey - *95-99*	6	8
B177	**NE** 535962 grey - *89-03*	6	8
B13	**NE** 104021 red brown - *84-?*	6	8
B13	**NE** 214021 red brown - *?-03*	6	8
B179	**SR** 27348 dark brown - *89-99*	6	8
B11	**BR** M407562 light grey (A) - *84-03*	6	10
B11	**BR** M407565 light grey - *84-03*	6	8
B11	**BR** M407580 light grey - *84-03*	6	8
B19	**BR** M411455 red brown - *84-90*	6	8

The tooling was sold to Hornby in 1996 and the model reintroduced by them.

W7b. 5-plank Open Wagon 10ft wb (ex-Mainline) (1985)

B164	**'Ellis & Everard'** 136 red+black (M) - ?	6	10
B67	**'Timpson'** 5 blue grey (M) - *85-92, 97-02*	6	10
B99	**'Wadworths'** 66 black (M) - *86*	6	10
B163	**'Warrener'** 3 - green - (M) - *89-92*	6	10

W7c. 5-plank Open Wagon 10ft wb (ex-HD/Wrenn) (1995)

Almost without exception, the models in this table were sold with a coal (or other) load infill.

A2	grey - unfinished - *02-03*	4	6
-	**'Abram Coal Co.'** 462 red-brown Sp Edn 150 (Astley Green Colliery Museum) - *10*	7	9
-	'C **Addicott & Son'** 30 black Sp Edn 152 (Wessex Wagons) - *05*	9	11
-	**'Affleck F Fyfe'** 1 brown Sp Edn 100 (Strathspey Railway) - *03*	10	12
-	**'Affleck F Fyfe'** 2 brown Sp Edn 100 (Strathspey Railway) - *06*	9	11
-	**'Albion Dockyard'** 9 black Sp Edn 60 (Medway Queen Preservation Society) - *09*	7	9
-	**'Albion Dockyard'** 9 dark green Sp Edn 90 (Medway Queen Preservation Society) - *09*	7	9

Ex-Hornby Dublo/Wrenn 5-plank wagon - 'William Ambrose' [W7c] (Dapol)

B369	**'Alloa'** 1125 cream - *02-03*	8	10
-	'William **Ambrose**' 4 black Sp Edn 191 (Wessex Wagons) - *06*	9	11
No.4	'Wm. **Aplin**' 2 black Sp Edn 120 (West Wales Wagon Works) - *03*	9	11
No.5	'Wm. **Aplin**' 5 black Sp Edn 100 (West Wales Wagon Works) - *03*	9	11
-	**'Arbroath Friendly Coal Soc.'** 295 light grey Sp Edn 500 (Virgin Trains) for Glasgow Show - *03*	9	11
B591	**'Arenig Granite'** 207 red - *04-05*	7	9
-	'EJ **Astin'** 1 brown 102 Sp Edn (Nene Valley Railway) - *09*	7	9
-	**'Atherton'** 911 bright red Sp Edn 100 (Astley Colliery Museum) - *04*	9	11
-	'Octavius **Atkinson & Sons'** 4 red-brown Sp Edn (Starbeck Models) - *08*	7x	9
-	**'Bagg & Sons'** T yellow Sp Edn 150 (Buffers) - *10*	9	11
-	'Thomas **Bailey'** 1 red-brown Sp Edn (Salisbury Model Centre) - *08*	7	9
-	**'Barham Bros. Limited'** 4 grey brick load Sp Edn 148 (Burnham & District MRC) - *09*	7	9
11	'John **Barnett**' 45 dark brown Sp Edn 250 (Hereford Model Centre) - *06*	8	10
B151	**'Barnsley Main'** 350 red - *95*	9	11
WR3-07	**'Barnsley Main'** 350 red - *98-02*	9	12
-	'WH **Bartlet'** E34 red-brown Sp Edn 120 (Wessex Wagons) - *09*	8	10
B155	**'Bassetts'** 77 grey - *95*	10	12
WR3-16	**'Bassetts'** 77 grey - *99-02*	8	12
WR2-23	**'Bassetts'** 77 grey - *99-02*	8	12
-	**'Bath Gas Light & Coke'** 6 light grey Sp Edn 163 (Wessex Wagons) - *06*	8	10
-	**'Bath Gas Light & Coke'** 3 light grey Sp Edn 200 (Wessex Wagons) - *06*	8	10
-	**'Bath Railwaymen's Direct Coal Supply'** 1 grey Sp Edn 200 (Wessex Wagons) - *06*	8	10
-	'Charles & Frank **Beadle'** 28 black Sp Edn 204 (Erith MRC) - *02*	10	12
RM3	'Charles & Frank **Beadle'** 28 grey Sp Edn 275 (1E Promotionals) - *08*	7	9
-	'E **Bedford & Co.'** 34 dark green Sp Edn 163 (Pennine Models) - *08*	7	9
B157	'Amos **Benbow'** 3 grey - *95*	12	14
WR3-*03*	'Amos **Benbow'** 3 grey - *97-02*	11	15
-	**'Bennett & Carter'** 12 grey + sand Sp Edn 1000 (Ballards) - *03*	9	11
-	**'Betteshanger'** * black Sp Edn 100 (Hythe Models) 1st issue - *00*	11	13
-	**'Betteshanger'** * black Sp Edn 119 (Hythe Models) 2nd issue - *01*	10	12
-	**'Betteshanger'** black Sp Edn (Hythe Models) 3rd issue - *02*?	10	12
-	**'Betteshanger'** black Sp Edn (Hythe Models) 4th issue - *02*?	10	12
-	**'Betteshanger'** 7 black Sp Edn 536 (Hythe Models) 5th issue - *03*	9	11
-	**'Betteshanger'** black Sp Edn (Hythe Models) 6th issue - *06*	8	10
-	'VJ **Blew'** 03 black Sp Edn 177 (Wessex Wagons) - *07*	7	9
-	**'Bickershaw'** 555 red-brown Sp Edn 100 (Astley Colliery Museum) - *04*	9	11
-	'AH&S **Bird'** 27 grey Sp Edn 149 (Wessex Wagons) - *06*	8	10
-	'Wm **Black & Sons**' 849 black Sp Edn 220 (Ayr Glass & Glazing) - *03*	9	11
B715	**'Black Rock Quarries'** 49 black - *07-08*	6	8
B387	**'Blake'** 136 red - *02-03*	9	11
#32	**'Blake'** 112 bright red Sp Edn 250 (Hereford Model Shop) - *06*	8	10

5-plank 'Bletchley & District Co-op' [W7c]

-	'John **Bland & Co.**' 7 red-brown Sp Edn 141 (Burnham & District MRC) - *09*	7	9
B575	'H **Blandford & Sons**' 7 light grey - *04*	9	11
BY5	**'Bletchley & District Co-op'** 86 black Sp Edn 250 (1E Promotionals) - *06*	8	10
-	**'Blisworth Tunnel'** 1805-2005 pale blue Sp Edn 200 (Blisworth Bygones) - *05*	8	10
B154	'J **Bly**' black - *95*	12	14
W5000	'J **Bly**' black Sp Edn 250 (Wrenn RCC - WRCC1) - *99*	12	15
-	'John **Board & Co.**' 11 black Sp Edn 208 (Wessex Wagons) - *06*	8	10
-	**'Bobbett'** 7 dark brown Sp Edn 1000 (Ballards) - *09*	9	11
-	**'Bonnell'** 12 red-brown Sp Edn 1000 (Ballards) - *05*	8	10
-	**'Bottrill'** 12 black Sp Edn 100 (Richard Essen/ Wicor Models) - *07*	7	9
-	**'Bowden Bros.'** 16 grey Sp Edn 100 (Henford Halt) - *05*	8	10
BY4	'A **Bramley**' 16 dark brown Sp Edn 250 (1E Promotionals) - *05*	8	10
B152	'A **Bramley**' 6 red-brown - *95*	15	20
-	**'Braysdown Colliery'** 97 black Sp Edn 237 (Wessex Wagons) - *08*	7	9
-	**'Brighton - Corrall & Co.'** 401 red Sp Edn 1000 (Ballards) - *07*	7	9
B150	**'British Soda'** 14 brown - *95*	12	15
WR1-10	as above grey or white load - *99*	12	15
WR2-26	as above, Dapol chassis - *99*	12	15
WR3-02	**'British Soda'** 14 brown - *97-02*	7	11
-	'S **Brookman**' 30 light grey Sp Edn 200 (West & Wales Assn. of MRCs) - *06*	8	10
-	'RJ **Broughton**' 24 grey Sp Edn 100 (Nene Valley Railway) - *08*	7	9
B300	**'Broughton & Plas'** 630 olive green, Ltd Edn 600 - *98-02*	10	12
-	'George **Bryant & Son**' 4 black Sp Edn 100 (Burnham & District MRC) - *08*	7	9
-	**'G Bryant Coal & Coke'** 17 black Sp Edn 90 (Burnham & District MRC) - *08*	7	9
W07	'C H **Burt**' 1 black Sp Edn 150 (1E Promotionals) - *10*	9	11
-	'Walter **Burt**' 2 dark brown Sp Edn 200 (Wessex Wagons) - *06*	8	10
(20)	'W **Butler**' 29 light grey Sp Edn 250 (Hereford Model Shop) - *05*	8	10
-	**'Cam Rys'** grey Sp Edn 120 (Cambrian Railway Society) - *01*	10	15
-	**'Carriage & Wagon Dept - Dover Marine'** 4121 blk Sp Edn 200 (Carriage & Wagons Models) - *08*	7	10
B392	**'Cefn Mawr & Rhosymedre'** 12 red-brown - *02-03*	7	9
-	'AF **Chainey**' 2 dark brown Sp Edn 164 (Wessex Wagons) - *05*	8	10

5-plank - 'Chipping Norton Co-op' [W7c]

-	**'Champion Brothers'** 4 black Sp Edn 200 (Wessex Wagons) - *05*	8	10
No.6	**'Christie & Son'** 103 black Sp Edn 200 (Mid Suffolk Light Railway) - *06*	8	10
-	**'Carter & Co.'** 7 red-brown Sp Edn 195 (Wessex Wagons) - *07*	7	9
-	**'Chichester Coal Co.'** 50 red-brown Sp Edn 149 (Richard Essen) - *11*	7	9
OX2	**'Chipping Norton Co-op'** 9 black Sp Edn 250 (1E Promotionals) - *05*	8	10

-	**'Clarke Sharp & Co.'** 400 black Sp Edn 300 (Ballards) - *10*	9	11
-	**'Clee Hill Granite'** 350 pale grey Sp Edn 95 (Dartmoor Railway) - *03?*	12	15
B658	'The **Cliffe Hill Stone Pavement**' 805 pale blue-grey - *06*	8	10
21	'Edward R **Cole**' 6 red-brown Sp Edn 250 (Hereford Model Shop) - *05*	8	10
-	**'Conduit Colliery'** 124 red-brown Sp Edn 200 (Tutbury Jinny) ex-set of 2 - *02*	10	NA
B149	**'Consolidated Fisheries'** 76 grey - *95*	12	15
WR1-36	as above - *99*	12	15
WR2-02	as above but Dapol chassis - *97-99*	8	12
B515	**'Corporation of Dundee Gas Dept.'** 67 red-brown - *03*	7	9
B515	**'Corporation of Dundee Gas Dept.'** 67 dark brown - *03*	7	9
ANT013	'Alexander **Crane**' 103 brown Sp Edn 250 (Antics Online) - *04*	9	11
-	**'Critchlow & Shepperd'** 3 grey Sp Edn (cotswold Steam Preservation Ltd - *08*	7	9
B161	**'Cranston'** 347 red - *95*	10	15
-	**'Crook & Greenway'** 2 blue Sp Edn 600 (Glouc/ Warks Railway) - *03-04*	9	11
-	**'Crook & Greenway'** 10 dark brown Sp Edn (Glouc/Warks Railway) - *07*	7	9
-	**'Crook & Greenway'** 29 dark green+red - Sp Edn (Cotswold Steam Preservation) - *08*	7	9
-	**'Cudham'** pale grey Sp Edn 500 (*Model Railway Enthusiast* magazine) - *99-00*	10	12
-	**'Cudham'** red brown Sp Edn 500 (*Model Railway Enthusiast* magazine) - *99-00*	10	12
CMM001	**'Cumberland Tarred Slag'** 22 black Sp Edn 150 (C&M Models) - *09*	7	10
B726	**'Cumberland Granite'** 22 black - *08*	6	8
-	**'Dapol 2000'** green Sp Edn (Dapol) - *00*	11	13
-	'EE **Davies & Co.**' 9 black Sp Edn (Dapol Shop) - *08*	6	8
-	**'Dawson Bros.'** 22 black Sp Edn 160 (Wessex Wagons) - *06*	8	10

5-plank - 'Dean Forest Coal Co.' [W7c] (Dapol)

26	**'Dean Forest Coal Co.'** 311 red-brown Sp Edn 250 (Hereford Model shop) - *06*	8	10
NR10	'JI **Dennick**' 123 red-brown Sp Edn 125 (1E Promotionals) - *09*	6	8
RM1	'R **Deveson & Co.**' 8 black Sp Edn 200 (1E Promotionals) - *07*	7	9
-	**'Didcot Railway Centre'** 817200 green Sp Edn 110 (DRC) - *01*	10	12
-	'Albert **Down**' 1 dark brown Sp Edn 150 (Burnham & District MRC) - *10*	9	11
-	**'Dunball Steam Pottery Tile & Brick Company'** 10 brown Sp Edn 141 (Burnham & Dist MRC) - *09*	6	8
-	'EA **Earley**' 105 pale blue Sp Edn 156 (Wessex Wagons) - *10*	8	10
-	**'ECLP'** 1614 red-brown no load Sp Edn (Mevagissey Model Railway) - *02*	10	NA
-	**'ECLP'** 1707 red-brown no load Sp Edn (Mevagissey Model Railway) - *02*	10	NA
-	**'Eglwyseg Quarries Limestone'** 5 yellow Sp Edn 150 (Llangollen Railway Locomotive Group) - *10*	8	10

-	**'English China Clays Lovering Pochin & Co.'** 163 red-brown no load Sp Edn (Mevagissey Model Railway) - *02*	10	NA
-	**'English China Clays Lovering Pochin & Co.'** 318 red-brown no load Sp Edn (Mevagissey Model Railway) - *02*	10	NA
-	'John **Evans**' 4 red-brown Sp Edn 109 (Welshpool & Llanfair Railway) - *07*	7	9
(9)	'W **Evans**' 2 black Sp Edn 250 (Hereford Model Centre) - *05?*	8	10
-	**'Executors of Colonel Hargreaves'** (Burnley Collieries) 262 red-brown Sp Edn 100 (Red Rose Steam Society) - *09*	7	9
-	'GE **Farrant'** 21 brown Sp Edn 550 (Ballards) - *02*	9	11
-	'GE **Farrant'** 20 brown Sp Edn 1000 (Ballards) - *07*	6	8
-	'BF **Faulkner**' 1 dark brown Sp Edn 1000 (Gloucester Warwickshire Railway) - *06*	6	8
-	**'Field & Mackay'** 4 red-brown Sp Edn 103 (SVR Erlestoke Manor Fund) - *09*	6	8
-	'H **Finch & Son'** 16 red-brown Sp Edn 225 (Cotswald Steam Preservation) - *09*	7	9
-	**'Fogwills Seeds'** 98 grey (all grey body) Sp Edn (Wessex Wagons) - *09*	6	8
-	**'Fogwills Seeds'** 98 grey (corner irons in black) Sp Edn (Wessex Wagons) - error - *not released*	NA	NA
E01A	**'Foster Yeoman'** 36 black, stone load Sp Edn 125 (East Somerset Models) - *01*	10	12
E01B	**'Foster Yeoman'** 74 black, stone load Sp Edn 125 (East Somerset Models) - *01*	10	12
E01C	**'Foster Yeoman'** 39 black, stone load Sp Edn 150 (East Somerset Models) - *03*	9	11
E01D	**'Foster Yeoman'** 61 black, stone load Sp Edn 150 (East Somerset Models) - *03*	9	11
-	'Thomas **Fowler'** 3 light grey Sp Edn (Cotswold Steam Preservation Ltd) - *07*	7	9
-	'Thomas **Fowler'** 4 light grey Sp Edn 200 (Cotswold Steam Preservation Ltd) - *09*	7	9
-	'James **Frame**' 30 red Sp Edn 100 (Strathspey) - *04*	9	11
NR1	'H **Fulcher**' 5 brown Sp Edn 250 (1E Promotionals) - *04*	9	11
No.13	'Isaiah **Gadd**' 29 black Sp Edn 155 (WWW/ Loddon Vale Railway Club) - *03*	9	11
NR9	'**Gann & Brown**' 211 red-brown Sp Edn 250 (1E Promotionals) - *09*	6	8
-	**'Garswood Hall Collieries'** 1600 red-brown Sp Edn 100 (Red Rose Steam Society) - *09*	7	9
-	**'General Refractories'** 85 pale cream Sp Edn 200 (TAG Models) - *02*	10	12

5-plank - 'Godden & Rudd' [W7c]

B577	'W.C.**Gethen**' 14 bright red - *04-05*	7	9
BE4	**'Godden & Rudd'** 10 red-brown Sp Edn 250 (1E Promotionals) - *06*	8	10
B301	'J B **Gregory**' 37 red brown , Ltd Edn 600 - *98-02*	10	12
No.27	**'Gresford Colliery'** 631>637 black Sp Edn 129 (West Wales Wagon Works) - *05*	8	10
-	**'Gresford Colliery'** 638 black Sp Edn 129 (West Wales Wagon Works) - *?*	8	10
B378	**'Groby Granite Co.**' 471 grey - *02-03*	8	10
-	'Charles **Gush & Son**' 30 black Sp Edn 150 (Buffers) - *10*	8	11
-	**'Gwili Railway'** 2 pale grey ***** Sp Edn (West Wales Wagon Works) - *07*	7	9
-	**'Gwili Railway'** 2 pale grey W Sp Edn ***** (West Wales Wagon Works) - *07*	7	9
-	'W Stanley **Gwilt'** 17 light grey Sp Edn 115 (Welshpool & Llanfair Railway) - *09*	7	9
-	**'Hamworth Wharf'** 300 black Sp Edn 181 (Wessex Wagons) - *06*	8	10
B156	'S **Harris**' 14 black - *95*	10	15
WR1-53	as above - *99*	10	18
WR1-20	as above - *99*	10	15
ANT012	**'Hathway** 1 grey Sp Edn 250 (Antics Online) - *05*	8	10
-	**'Hatton's'** light grey Sp Edn (Hattons) - *88*	10	15
-	'TG **Hearnden**' 12 red-brown Sp Edn 1000 (Ballards) - *09*	7	9
-	'C. **Heywood & Sons'** 1 black Sp Edn 150 (Burnham & District MRC) - *10*	7	9
WR1-38	**'Higgs'** light grey - *99*	10	15
WR2-04	as above but with a Dapol chassis - *98-99*	8	10

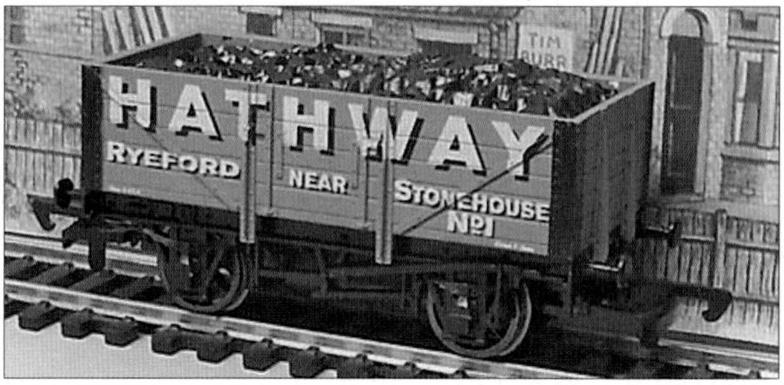

5-plank - 'Hathway' [W7c] (Dapol)

-	'Charles **Hill**' 2 dark brown Sp Edn 150 (Wessex Wagons) - *09*	7	9
-	**'Hingley'** 14 dark brown Sp Edn 100 (Modellers Mecca) - *01*	10	NA
31	'S **Holmes, Kidnalls & Nags Head Collieries**' 317 dk.brown Sp Edn 250 (Hereford Model Shop) - *06*	8	10
B702	**'Hopton-Wood Stone Firms'** 2 grey - *07*	6	8
-	**'Hulton**' 982 red-brown Sp Edn 100 (The Red Rose Steam Society) - *08*	7	9
-	'JH **Hutt & Sons**' 1 red Sp Edn 148 (Wessex Wagons) - *07*	7	9
-	**'Huxford & Co.'** 153 red-brown Sp Edn 320 (Hythe Kent Models + KESR) 2nd issue - *01*	9	11
-	**'Huxford & Co.'** 153 red-brown Sp Edn 664 (Hythe Kent Models + KESR) - *03*	8	10
B347	**'ICI'** L3102 grey blue - *01*	8	10
IP7	**'Ipswich Gas Company'** 1 brown Sp Edn 150 (1E Promotionals) - *10*	7	9
WO6	**'Itters Brick Co.'** 151 red-brown with brick load Sp Edn 200 (1E Promotionals) - *08*	7	9
HMC42	'Basil **Jayne & Co.'** 120 grey Sp Edn 250 (Hereford Model Centre) - *07*	7	9
B569	'Samuel **Jeffries**' 7 red - *04*	7	9
-	**'Jeram & Co.'** 60 red Sp Edn 234 (Wessex Wagons) - *08*	7	9
HMC 46	**'Jones & Co.**' 14 light grey Sp Edn 250 (Hereford Model Centre) - *08*	7	9
HMC 40	**'Jones & Co.**' 20 light grey Sp Edn 250 (Hereford Model Centre) - *07*	7	9
ANT020	'CW **Jones'** 19 grey Sp Edn 250 (Antics) - *07*	7	9
-	'Maurice **Jones'** 40 brown Sp Edn 158 (Wessex Wagons) - *08*	7	9
-	**'Kent & East Sussex Rly'** * grey Sp Edn 1st issue of 215 (Hythe Models + KESR) - *02*	10	12
B656	**'Ketton Cement**' 9 buff - *06*	8	10
-	'WJ **King**' 39 black Sp Edn 200 (Wessex Wagons) - *04*	9	11
-	'WJ **King**' 150 black Sp Edn 127 (Wessex Wagons) - *05*	8	10
-	'WJ **King**' 37 black Sp Edn 150 (Wessex		

	Wagons) - *05*	8	10
-	**'Kingsbury Collieries'** 699 dark green Sp Edn 100 (The UK Model Shop Directory) - *07*	10	12
-	**'Lanemark Coal Co.'** 20 pale grey Sp Edn 110 (Ayr Glass & Glazing) - *04*	9	11

5-plank - 'Llay Hall' [W7c] (Dapol)

ANT021	'Edward **Langford**' 6 grey Sp Edn 250 (Antics) - *07*	7	9
BE7	**'Leighton Buzzard Sand'** 2 red-brown + sand load Sp Edn 150 (1E Promotionals) - *08*	7	9
-	**'Llanfyllin Coal & Lime Co.'** 15 black Sp Edn 112 (Welshpool & Llanfair Rlway) - *05?*	8	10
B305	**'Llay Hall'** 492 black - *98-02*	9	11
-	**'Llay Hall'** 491 black Sp Edn (Dapol Shop) - *08*	6	8
28	'Samuel **Llewellyn**' 9 dark brown Sp Edn 250 (Hereford Model shop) - *06*	8	10
-	'A T **Locke**' 4 red-brown Sp Edn 110 (Astolat MRC) - *03*	10	12
-	'James **Macpherson**' 12 brown Sp Edn 100 (Strathspey Railway) - *03*	10	12
-	'James **Macpherson**' 14 brown Sp Edn 100 (Strathspey Railway) - *04*	10	12
-	**'Manchester Ship Canal'** 1259 black Sp Edn 150 (Astley Green Colliery Museum) - *10*	7	9
-	**'Mapperley'** 72 brown Sp Edn 250 (Tutbury Jinny) ex-set of 2 - *04*	9	11
-	**'Martin'** 25 grey Sp Edn 180 (Wessex Wagons) - *05*	8	10
-	**'May & Hassell'** 4 yellow Sp Edn 157 (Burnham & District MRC) - *10*	7	9
-	'WH&HL **May - Hop Factors'** 10614 SE&CR dark grey Sp Edn 1000 (Ballards) - *05*	7	9

5-plank - 'Mendip Mountain Quarries Co.' [W7c] (Dapol)

E04A	**'Mendip Mountain Quarries'** 342 light grey Sp Edn 150 (East Somerset Models) - *06*	8	10
E04B	**'Mendip Mountain Quarries'** 335 light grey Sp Edn 150 (East Somerset Models) - *06*	8	10
No.1	**'Mid Suffolk'** 16 grey Sp Edn 100 (Mid-Suffolk Light Railway) - *02*	10	12
No.2	**'Mid Suffolk'** 17 grey Sp Edn 200 (Mid-Suffolk Light Railway) - *03*	9	11
No.2	**'Mid Suffolk'** 17 dark brown Sp Edn (Mid-Suffolk Light Railway) - *02*	10	15
B314	'Tom **Milner**' 2 grey - *00-02*	8	10
ANT019	'WW **Milton & Co.**' 19 grey Sp Edn 250 (Antics) - *07*	7	9
B393	'The **Minera Lime Company**' 125 brown - *02-03*	8	10
-	**'Moira Collieries'** 1340 brown Sp Edn 500 (Tutbury Jinny) - *00*	10	12
12	**'Morgan Bros.'** 16 dark brown Sp Edn 250 (Hereford Model Centre) - *05*	8	10
4th	'WE **Morgan**' ? ? Sp Edn (Welshpool & Llanfair Railway) - *07*	7	9
-	'F G **Mullis & Co**.' 31 black Sp Edn 85 (West Wales Wagon Works) - *07*	7	9
-	'F G **Mullis & Co**'. 31 black W Sp Edn 85 (West Wales Wagon Works) - *07*	7	9
OX5	'EW **Nappin**' 1 red Sp Edn 250 (1E Promotionals) - *06*	8	10
-	'Walter E **Neate**' 2 red-brown Sp Edn 150 Wessex Wagons) - *05*	8	10
-	**'Newcastle Main'** 415 grey Sp Edn 500 (G Allison) - *99*	11	13
-	**'Newcastle Main'** 415 brown Sp Edn 12 (G Allison) - *99*	18	20
-	**'New Hem Heath'** 22 grey Sp Edn 100 (Tutbury Jinny) - *07*	7	9
-	**'Norley Coal & Cannel Co.'** 205 mid blue Sp Edn 100 (Red Rose Steam Society) - *08*	7	9
-	**'North Devon Clay Co.'** 114 black Sp Edn (P.McAllister) - *07*	7	9
-	'The **North London Clay Co.**' 114 black Sp Edn (P.McAllister) - *not made*	NA	NA
B313	'W&W **Nunnerley**' 1 grey - *00-02*	8	10
-	'WJ **Oldacre**' 3 black Sp Edn (Gloucester & Warwickshire Railway) - *07*	7	9
-	'J. LL **Peate & Sons**' 1 brown Sp Edn 400 (Welshpool & Llanfair Railway) - *02*	9	11
-	**'PD&SW'** 41 red Sp Edn 191 (Essex Wagons) - *07*	7	9
B595	**'Palmer & Sawdye'** 16 grey - *04-05*	8	10

5-plank - 'Nathaniel Pegg' [W7c] (Dapol)

-	**'Par Harbour'** 3 light grey Sp Edn (World of Model Railways of Mevagissey) - *10*	7	9
-	'Nathaniel **Pegg**' 155 bright red Sp Edn 210 (Hythe Models) 1st issue - *02*	10	12
-	'Nathaniel **Pegg**' 155 bright red Sp Edn 100 (K&ES Railway) 2nd issue - *06*	8	10
B397	**'Penderyn Limestone'** 336 grey + limestone - *02-03*	8	10
-	**'Pepper & Son'** 17 light grey Sp Edn (Amberley Museum) - *10*	8	10
-	'D **Petrie**' 65 red Sp Edn 100 (Strathspey Railway) - *04*	9	11
B586	'The **Phoenix Coal Co.**' 10 black - *04-05*	7	9
25	**'Phoenix Coal Co.**' 50 black Sp Edn 250 (Hereford Model shop) - *06*	8	10
24	**'Phoenix Coal Co.**' 520 black Sp Edn 250 (Hereford Model shop) - *06*	8	10
-	**'Pilch Collard'** * light grey Sp Edn 200 (Hythe Models) 1st issue - *01*	10	12
ANT022	'Wm **Playne & Co.**' 1 brown Sp Edn 250 (Antics Online) - *06*	8	10
-	**'Poppit Sands'** 710 deep cream Sp Edn 121 (WWWW for Teifi Valley Railway) - *02*	10	12
No.7	**'Poppit Sands'** 711 deep cream Sp Edn 100 (WWWW for Teifi Valley Railway) - *03*	9	11
TVR6	**'Poppit Sands'** 712 deep cream Sp Edn 120 (WWWW for Teifi Valley Railway) - *02*	10	12
B307	**'Pounsbury'** 1 green - *00-02*	8	10
-	**'Pothywaen Lime Co.'** 3 grey Sp Edn 108 (Welshpool & Llanfair Railway) - *05?*	8	10

B543	'H **Preston**' 1 dark brown + coal - *03*	7	9
-	'W **Ramsden & Sons**' 139 red-brown Sp Edn 100 (Red Rose Steam Society) - *08*	7	9
-	**'Raunds Co-operative Society'** 14 bright blue Sp Edn 100 (Kitmaster Club) - *04*	9	11
-	'C&J **Read**' 6 grey Sp Edn 142 (Somerset & Dorset Railway Trust) - *08*	7	9
B611	**'Renwick & Wilton'** 107 light grey - *05*	7	9
-	'John **Reynolds'** 5 black, brick load Sp Edn 220 (Wessex Wagons) - *07*	7	9
-	**'Rickett Smith & Co.'** 8501 red-brown Sp Edn 1000 (Ballards) - *07*	7	9
-	**'Ringwood Coal Co.'** (see Thomas Bailey)	-	-
-	'The **Road Supplies & Construction Co.'** red-brown each with different transfer number (1-50) 4 different loads, different text either side Sp Edn 50 (Oliver Leetham) - *04*	9	11
-	same but black and numbered 51-100 - *04*	9	11
-	**'Roberts & Maginnis'** 7 grey Sp Edn 90 (Llangollen Railway GW Loco Group) - *09*	7	9

5-plank - 'Ringwood Coal Co.' [W7c] (Dapol)

-	'EA **Robinson**' 1907 red-brown Sp Edn 1000 (Ballards) - *08*	6	8
-	**'Royal Welsh Whiskey'** 9 dark brown Sp Edn 103 (Llangollen Rly GWR Loco Gp) - *07*	7	9
-	'Edward **Russell**' 140 grey Sp Edn 100 (Modellers Mecca) - *01*	10	NA
B733	'Hannah **Samwel & Co.**' 060 grey - *08*	6	8
-	**'Scatter Rock'** 88 grey Sp Edn 100 (The Model Shop Exeter) - *03*	9	11
6	**'Settle Speakman'** 2143 black Sp Edn 200 (Haslington Models) - *03*	9	11
-	**'Shap Tarred Granite'** black, each with different gold transfer number (1-50) Sp Edn 50 (Oliver Leetham) - *04*	9	11
-	as above but white numbers (101-160) - *04*	9	11
BY9	'A **Sharp**' grey Sp Edn 150 (1E Promotionals) - *08*	7	9
B572	'F.H.**Silvey**' 205 light grey - *04-05*	7	9
B547	'W **Simmonds & Son**' 23 dark brown + coal - *03*	7	9
-	'JE **Smith'** 102 brown Sp Edn 170 (Wessex Wagons) - *10*	8	9
-	'R **Smith & Son**' grey Ltd Edn (West Wales Wagon Works for Corwen Eisteddfodd) - *03*	9	11
-	'John **Snow**' 201 light grey + timber load Sp Edn 204 (Wessex Wagons) - *06*	8	10
-	**'Snowdon'** 48 grey Sp Edn 107 (Hythe Kent Models) - *09*	6	8
-	**'Somerset County Council'** 71 red-brown Sp Edn 139 (Burnham & Dist. MRC) - *10*	7	9
B551	**'Somerset Trading Company'** 56 red + coal - *03*	9	11
BI1	**'South & Gasson'** 105 dark brown, Sp Edn 175 (1E Promotionals) - *09*	7	9
-	**'Spalding'** 52 light grey Sp Edn 200 (Tutbury Jinny) ex-set of 2 - *02*	10	NA
-	**'Stafford Corporation Gas'** 33 red Sp Edn 100 (Trident Trains) - *07*	7	9
WO2	'JG **Stanton**' 22 red-brown Sp Edn 250 (1E Promotionals) - *05*	8	10

5-plank - 'Stephens' [W7c] (Dapol)

No.39	**'Stephens Silica Brick Co.'** 22 brown Sp Edn 109 (West Wales Wagon Works) - *06*	8	10
B632	**'Stevenson'** 10 blue - *05*	7	9
-	**'Stevens & Son'** 1 black Sp Edn (Buffers) - *10*	8	10
-	'H **Stone**' 1 dark green + wood load Sp Edn 113 (Wessex Wagons) - *09*	7	9
-	**'Sussex Brick Co.'** 115 red-brown Sp Edn 90 (Richard Essen) - *09*	7	9
-	**'Swan Lane Collieries'** 42 red-brown Sp Edn 100 (Red Rose Steam Society) - *09*	7	9
-	'James **Taylor**' 19 brown Sp Edn 250 (Cotswold Steam Preservation Ltd) - *03*	9	11
-	'James **Taylor'** 23 brown Sp Edn 250 (Cotswold Steam Preservation Ltd) - *03*	9	11
-	'James **Taylor**' 24 brown Sp Edn 250 (Cotswold Steam Preservation Ltd) - *05*	8	10
-	'James **Taylor**' 25 red-brown Sp Edn (Cotswold Steam Preservation) - *06*	8	10
-	'James **Taylor**' 26 dark brown Sp Edn (Cotswold Steam Preservation) - *08*	7	9
-	**'Tilmanstone Colliery'** 155 grey Sp Edn 200 (Colnel Stephens Railway Enterprises) - *09*	9	13
WTW/ No.21	'William **Thomas'** **** grey Sp Edn 170 (West Wales Wagon Works) - *04*	9	11
-	**'Thomas & Fowler'** 3 light grey Sp Edn 200 (West Wales Wagon Works) - *07*	7	9
-	**'Thomas & Jones'** 2 light grey Sp Edn 160 (West Wales Wagon Works) - *07*	7	9
-	'F **Thorndike**' 2 dark brown Sp Edn 200 (Carriage & Wagon Models) - *09*	7	10
-	**'Tredegar'** 3410 grey Sp Edn (David Dacey) - *10*	8	10
RT200/ No.18	'Richard **Trevithick**' 200 brown Sp Edn 102 (West Wales Wagon Works) - *04*	9	11
-	'John **Toomer & Sons'** 35 red-brown Sp Edn 200 (Froude & Hext) - *08*	7	9
-	'John **Toomer & Sons'** 35 red-brown W Sp Edn 146 (Froude & Hext) - *08*	7	9
-	**'W&J Turner (Wigan Junction Colliery)**' 301 grey Sp Edn 100 (Red Rose Steam Society) - *09*	7	9
BY6	'James **Turney'** 28 red-brown Sp Edn 200 (1E Promotionals) - *06*	8	10
B153	**'Twining'** 95 red-brown - *95*	10	15
WR1-25	as above ochre and no shading - *99*	40	50
B618	**'Twining'** 150 light grey - *05-06*	4	6
-	**'Tyldesley'** 49 grey Sp Edn 100 (The Red Rose Steam Society) - *05*	8	10
B302	**'Vauxhall'** 292 green-grey, Ltd Edn 600 - *98-02*	9	11

5-plank - 'Vectis' [W7c]

-	**'Vectis'** 34 grey Sp Edn 200 (I of W Model Railways) ex-set of 2 - *02*	10	NA
-	**'Vectis Cement Co.'** 68 grey Sp Edn 200 (I of W Model Railways) ex-set of 2 - *02*	10	NA
CA5	'JO **Vinter**' 315 light grey, Sp Edn 175 (1E Promotionals) - *09*	7	9
B303	**'Vron'** 175 black, Ltd Edn 600 - *98-99*	9	11
OX8	**'Wade'** 11 dark brown Sp Edn 150 (1E Promotionals) - *07*	7	9
PE1	'L **Wagstaff**' 22 red Sp Edn 150 (1E Promotionals) - *08*	7	9
-	'John **Wainwright & Co.**' 268 black 418 Sp Edn 418 (Wessex Wagons) - *06*	8	10
B126	**'Webster'** 47 grey - *95*	12	15
WR3-17	**'Webster'** 47 green - *99-02*	5	9
(B522)	'R **Webster**' 303 red-brown - *03*	9	NA
-	**'Weedon Brothers'** 131 grey Sp Edn (Wessex Wagons) - *09*	8	10
-	'George **West**' 4 red-brown Sp Edn (West Wales Wagon Works) - *10*	8	11
-	'George **West**' 4 red-brown W Sp Edn (West Wales Wagon Works) - *10*	8	11
-	**'Western Coal Co.'** 37 grey Sp Edn 193 (Wales & West Assn of MRCs) - *05*	8	10
-	'**WestHoughton**' 240 black Sp Edn 150 (Red Rose Steam Society) - *10*	9	11
B304	**'Westminster'** 74 grey, Ltd Edn 600 - *98-02*	9	11
-	'John S **White & Son**' 31 bright red Sp Edn 160 (Wessex Wagons) - *07*	7	9
OX4	'HO **White**' 16 red-brown Sp Edn 250 (1E Promotionals) - *06*	8	10
B663	'Harry **Whitehouse**' 16 red-brown + sand load - *06*	7	9
SY4	'Harry **Whitehouse**' 15 red-brown + sand load Sp Edn 300 (1E Promotionals) - *10*	9	11
-	'Wm **Whitmore**' 26 red-brown Sp Edn 120 (Wessex Wagons) - *09*	7	9
-	'Wm **Whitmore**' 56 red-brown Sp Edn 120 (Wessex Wagons) - *09*	7	9
-	**'Wigan Coal Corporation'** 126 red-brown Sp Edn 150 (Astley Green Colliery Museum) - *10*	7	9
-	'Amos **Williams**' 1 red Sp Edn 110 (Llangollen Railway GW Loco Group) - *08*	7	9
-	'L **Williams & Son**' 1 ochre, white load Sp Edn 107 (Barry & Penarth MRC) - *03*	9	11
(2)	'Robt. **Williams & Sons**' 9 light grey Sp Edn 250 (Hereford Model Centre) - *02*	10	12
-	**'Wilmer'** 83 grey Sp Edn 160 (Froude & Hext) - *07*	7	9
-	**'Wincanton Coal Gas Co.'** 18 red-brown Sp Edn 150 (S&D Railway Trust) - *08*	7	9
-	**'Wolverton Mutual Society'** 29 grey Sp Edn 500 (Wolverton Railway Works 150th Anniv.) - *97*	10	12
BY7	**'Wolverton Mutual Society'** 29 dark grey Sp Edn 150 (1E Promotionals) - *07*	7	9
-	'S **Woodcock**' 7 grey Sp Edn 85 (West Wales Wagon Works) - *09*	7	10
-	'S **Woodcock**' 7 grey W Sp Edn 46 (West Wales Wagon Works) - *09*	8	11
WD1	**'Woodman Bros.'** 75 red-brown Sp Edn 250 (1E Promotionals) - *05*	8	10
-	'FT **Woolway**' 16 black Sp Edn 100 (The Model Shop, Exeter) ex set - *04*	9	NA
-	'AC **Woolway**' 26 black Sp Edn 100 (The Model Shop, Exeter) ex set - *04*	9	NA
ANTO16	**'Wyken & Craven'** 72 dark brown Sp Edn 250 (Antics Online) - *05*	8	10
B306	**'Wynnstay'** Q551 brown - *00-02*	8	10
	Railway Companies		
-	**CIE** 412d grey Sp Edn (Mark's Models) - *02?*	9	11
-	**CV** 46 grey Sp Edn 90 (Colne Valley Railway) - *07*	8	10
-	**GE** 7748 grey (Chalk marks - 'Prent. Bros 2227') + coal load Sp Edn 62 (Stowmarket Railway Club) - *02*	14	16
-	**GE** 7748 grey (Chalk marks - 'Prent. Bros 2227') + sand load Sp Edn 23 (Stowmarket Railway Club) - *03*	16	18
-	**GE** 7748 grey (Chalk marks - 'Prent. Bros 2227') + packing cases Sp Edn 20 (Stowmarket Railway Club) - *03*	16	18

Great Eastern Railway 5-plank wagon [W7c]

-	**GE** 7748 dark brown (Chalk marks - 'Prent. Bros 2227') Sp Edn 62 (Stowmarket Railway Club) - *03*	12	15
WRCC16	**GW** 109438 dark green Sp Edn 100 (Wrenn Railways Collectors Club) - *08*	12	14
-	**IWC** 117 black Sp Edn 100 (I of W Model Railways) ex-set of 2 - *01*	10	NA
-	**IWC** 68 grey Sp Edn 100 (I of W Model Railways) ex-set of 2 - *01*	10	NA
-	**IWR** 29 brown Sp Edn 200 (I of W Model Railways) ex-set of 2 - *02*	10	NA
-	**LBSCR** - Corrall & Co.' 514 red Sp Edn 1000 (Ballards) - *07*	7	9
B338	**LMS** 404102 light grey - *01-03*	7	9
-	**NE** 600002 blue, Loco Sand Sp Edn 100 (Stowmarket Railway Club) - *03*	8	10
-	**SE&CR** ('WH&HJ May Hop Factors') 10614 grey Sp Edn 1000 (Ballards) - *05*	7	9
-	**SECR** 50899 grey Sp Edn 101 (Blubell Rly) - *09*	7	9
-	**S&DJR** 356 grey Sp Edn 140 (Burnham & District MRC) - *10*	7	9
WRCC17	**SR** 12785 bright green Sp Edn 100 (Wrenn Railways Collectors Club) - *09*	8	10

* These were delivered unnumbered and were individually numbered by Steve Skelton of Hythe (Kent) Models. ** Produced to celebrate the 150th anniversary of Wolverton Railway Works. *** A spelling error and the wagons were sold abroad in sets. **** Individually numbered. ***** issued with a choice of 4 loads - coal, sand, bricks or timber and total of 112 made.

7-Plank Coal Wagons

W8. 7-plank Open Wagon Early 9ft wb (2009)

The new chassis has deeper frames and brakes fitted to one side only.

DAGM03	**'Bognor Coal & Transport Co.'** 3 red-brown Sp Edn 150 (Gaugemaster) - *10*	9	12
B860	**'Bradbury'** 2018 black, misspelt 'Southampton' and model was withdrawn from Sale - *10*	12	14
ANT41	**'Bristol & District Co-operative Society'** 12 black Sp Edn 160 (Antics) - *10*	9	12
ANT40	**'Cainscross & Ebley Co-operative Society'** 1 black Sp Edn 160 (Antics) - *10*	9	12
B810	**'Dickinson Prosser & Cox'** 21 grey - *09*	7	9
B766	'M&W **Glazebrook**' 49 red-brown - *09*	7	9
ANT 42	**'Gloucester Co-operative & Industrial Society '** 47 dark brown Sp Edn 150 (Antics) - *10*	9	12
-	'C. **Heywood & Sons**' 10 black Sp Edn 169 (Burnham & District MRC) - *10*	7	9
B832	**'Kingsbury Collieries'** 700 green - *10*	7	9
DAGM05	'A **Munday**' 6 red-brown W Sp Edn 150 (Gaugemaster) - *11*	9	12
DAGM05	'**Portsmouth Dockyard**' 10 black Sp Edn 155 (Wessex Wagons) - *10*	9	12
B771	**'Small & Son'** 17 grey - *09*	7	9
DAGM08	**'Stalybridge Corporation Gas Department'** 18 red-brown Sp Edn 150 (Gaugemaster) - *11*	10	13
ANT43	**'Stevens & Co.'** 298 dark green Sp Edn 140 (Antics) - *10*	8	11
B842	**'Stockingford Colliery Co.'** 9 grey - *10*	7	9

DAGM07	'R **Taylor & Sons**' 451 red-brown Sp Edn 150 (Gaugemaster) - *11*	10	13s
B821	**'The Arley Colliery'** 27 red - *10*	7	9

New 9ft wheelbase 7-plank wagon - 'C.Heywood & Sons' [W8] (Dapol)

DAGM06	'**The Country Gentlemans Association**' 4 red-brown Sp Edn 150 (Gaugemaster) - *11*	9	11
DAGM04	'**Usher & Sons**' 19 red-brown Sp Edn 150 (Gaugemaster) - *10*	9	11
-	**'Vallance'** 1910 black Sp Edn 152 (Buffers) - *10*	9	11
-	'WA **Vallis'** 31 black Sp Edn 156 (Wessex Wagons) - *10*	7	10
-	**'Wheeler & Gregory'** 324 buff Sp Edn 144 (Wessex Wagons) - *10*	7	10
B772	**'John Yates'** 3 grey - *09*	7	9

W9a. 7-plank Open Wagon 10ft wb (ex-Mainline) (1984)

B171	**'Bass'** 62 grey (M) - *c89*	6	10
B171	**'Bass'** 56 grey - *?*	4	6
B174	**'Cambrian'** 1078 (M) black - *?*	6	10
B174	**'Cambrian'** 107 black - *?*	8	10
B167	**'Colman's'** 35 yellow (M) - *c89*	6	10
B169	**'Courtaulds'** 18 green (M) - *c89*	6	10
B69	**'CWS'** 1941 dark brown (M) - *85-89*	6	10
B173	**'Diamond'** 34 red (M) - *c98*	6	10
B170	**'Emlyn'** 813 grey (M) - *c89*	6	10
B170	**'Emlyn'** 811 grey - *?*	8	10
B80	**'Horlicks'** 1 brown (M) - *85-88*	6	10
B166	'SJ **Moreland'** 1 red+black (M) - *c89*	6	10
B82	**'Parkinson'** 107 dark blue (M) - *85-?*	6	10
B82	**'Parkinson'** 100 dark blue - ?	8	10
B172	**'Patent Nut & Bolt Co.'** 658 dark brown (M) - *c89*	6	10
B70	**'Perfection Soap'** 82 brown (M) - *85-92*	6	10
B168	**'Persil'** 258 dark green (M) - *c89*	6	10
B172	**'Persil'** 258 dark green (M) - *c89*	6	10
B14	**GW** 06515 dark grey (M) - *84-92*	6	10
B81	**NE** 'Loco Coal' HB4333 grey (M) - *85-87*	6	10
B10	**BR** P99347 grey (M) - *84-?*	4	7
B10	**BR** P130288 grey - *?-96*	4	7

Although 'S.J.Moreland', 'Colman's', 'Persil', 'Courtaulds', 'Emlyn', 'Bass', 'Patent Nut & Bolt Co.', 'Diamond' and 'Cambrian' were illustrated in catalogues, we have found no evidence that any of them was sold in Dapol packaging although some were reissued using the Airfix body (see above).

W9b. 7-plank Open Wagon 10ft wb (ex-Airfix) (1985)

This table includes models made from the Airfix tool or from a replica tool produced in China for Dapol. We have no record as to which models were done with which tool but one of the almost identical tools was sold to Hornby in 1996. Almost without exception, the models in this table were sold with a coal (or other) load in-fill.

A3	brown or grey - unfinished - *86-03*	4	6
A002	grey - unfinished - *04-07*	4	6
-	'**Abbott**' 1028 grey Sp Edn (Warley Show) - *03*	12	15
BE2	'James **Abbott**' 20 red Sp Edn 250 (1E Promotionals) - *05*	8	10
-	**'Aberbeeg Colliery'** 569 light grey Sp Edn 90 (South Wales Coalfield) - *04*	10	12
-	**'Abercrave'** 331 red-brown Sp Edn 105 (South Wales Coalfields) - *04*	9	11
-	**'Aberdare Graig Coal'** 2 red-brown Sp Edn 90 (South Wales Coalfields) - *03*	10	12
-	**'Aberdeen MRC 35th Anniv.'** light grey Sp Edn 250 (Aberdeen MRC) - *06*	8	10
-	**'Aberpergwm'** 1 black Sp Edn 110 (Roger Mileman) - *03*	9	11

Former Airfix 7-plank - 'Abingdon-on-Thames Gas' [W9b] (Dapol)

-	**'Abingdon on Thames Gas Dept.'** **** red Sp Edn 104 (West Wales Wagon Works) - *09*	7	9
-	'Ed T **Agius & Co.'** 91 dark brown Sp Edn 252 (Wessex Wagons) - *08*	7	9
-	'Thomas C **Allan**' 3 black Sp Edn 1000 (Ballards) - *05*	7	9
-	**'Amalgamated Anthracite'** 7520 black Sp Edn 108 (South Wales Coalfields) - *07*	7	9
B375	**'Ammanford'** 24 - dark brown - *02-03*	8	10
B375A	**'Ammanford'** 48 - dark brown - *02-03*	8	10
RM4	**'Anderson & Co.'** 4 red-brown Sp Edn 275 (1E Promotionals) - *08*	7	9
TMCD006A	**'Annesley'** 162 brown, Sp Edn 100 (The Model Centre) - *03*	9	11
TMCD006B	**'Annesley'** 173 brown, Sp Edn 100 (The Model Centre) - *03*	9	11
TMCD006C	**'Annesley'** 195 brown, Sp Edn 100 (The Model Centre) - *03*	9	11
-	**'Arnell'** 1 dark brown Sp Edn 100 (Richard Essen/Wicor Models) - *07*	7	9
-	**'Arscott Collieries'** 21 light grey Sp Edn (Shrewsbury Model Centre) - *07*	7	9
B546	**'Asquith & Tompkins'** 21 red - *03*	9	11
-	**'Astley Green Colliery'** 245 red-brown 'M' Sp Edn 100 (Astley Green Mining Museum) - *02*	10	12
-	**'Astley Green Colliery'** 229 red-brown 'M' Sp Edn 100 (Astley Green Mining Museum) - *03*	9	11
-	**'Astley Green Colliery'** 337 red-brown 'M' Sp Edn 100 (Astley Green Mining Museum) - *03*	9	11
-	**'A T (Astley & Tyldesley Collieries Ltd)'** 1473 red-brown Sp Edn (Astley Green Mining Museum) - *07*	7	9
-	**'Atherton'** 1980 red Sp Edn 100 (The Red Rose Steam Society) - *09*	8	10
-	**'Atkinson & Prickett'** 1518 red-brown Sp Edn (D.Hewins) - *03?*	9	11
-	**'Atkinson & Prickett'** P238288 red-brown (overprinted BR 1516) Sp Edn (D.Hewins) - *03?*	9	11
CA3	**'Austin & Co.'** 602 red-brown Sp Edn 200 (1E Promotionals) - *06*	8	10
-	**'Avan Hill'** 128 black Sp Edn (Jenny's) - *03?*	9	11
-	**'Babbington Colliery'** 80 black Sp Edn 100 (Paul Freer) - *03*	9	11
RM5	'AG **Bailey**' red-brown Sp Edn 250 (1E Promotionals) - *09*	7	9
-	'AG **Bailey**' * brown Sp Edn 200 (Hythe Models Kent) - *04*	9	11
-	'E **Baily & Son**' 15 black Sp Edn 178 (Wessex Wagons) - *08*	7	9
-	**'Baird's & Dalmellington'** 550 red-brown Sp Edn 92 (Ayr Glass & Glazing) - *04*	9	11

7-plank - 'Baker & Kemick' [W9b] (Dapol)

No.36	**'Baker & Kernick'** 410 black Sp Edn 151 (West Wales Wagon Works) - *05*	8	10
57	'IW **Baldwin & Co.**' 22 dark brown Sp Edn 250 (Hereford Model Centre) - *09*	6	8
-	**'Baldwin Locomotive Fund'** ? ? Sp Edn (Welsh Highland Railway) - *?*	8	10
PBR13	**'Baldwins'** 132 black Sp Edn 250 (Pontypool & Blaenavon Railway) - *05*	8	10
-	'Robert **Balfour**' 161 red-brown Sp Edn 190 (Crafty Hobbies) - *06*	8	10
-	'C **Ball**' 1 Sp Edn (Wessex Wagons) - not made	NA	NA
OX7	'C **Ball**' 1 red Sp Edn 150 (1E Promotionals) - *07*	7	9
-	**'Baltic Saw Mills'** 10 red brown Sp Edn 330 (Ballards) - *01*	10	12
B603	'CT **Bamfurlong & Mains**' 1482 red - *04-05*	8	10
-	**'Banbury Gas Co.'** 200 black Sp Edn 110 (West Wales Wagon Works) - *09*	7	9
-	**'Banbury Gas Co.'** 200 black W Sp Edn 40 (West Wales Wagon Works) - *09*	7	9
-	'Ed **Bannister**' 1500 light grey Sp Edn 100 (D Hewins) - *00*	11	13
SWL11	**'Barrow'** 623 red Sp Edn 120 (Midlander) - *01*	10	12
-	**'Barrow Hill'** 1870 brown Sp Edn 94 (Barrow Hill Ltd) - *06*	8	10
-	**'Barrow Hill'** 1998 brown Sp Edn 209 (Barrow Hill Engine Shed Society) - *06*	8	10
-	**'Barrow Hill'** 2008 dark brown Sp Edn 2008 (Barrow Hill Engine Shed Society) - *08*	7	9
-	**'Barrow of Barnsley'** cream Sp Edn 117 (Modellers Mecca) - *02*	10	12
SWL28	**'Barrow Barnsley'** cream Sp Edn (Midlander) - *03*	9	11
-	**'Barry Coal Coy.'** 14 black Sp Edn 116 (Barry & Penarth MRC) - *04*	9	11
-	**'Barry Rhondda'** 148 black, Sp Edn 130 (South Wales Coalfields) - *03*	9	11
-	'WH **Bartlett**' E34 bright red Sp Edn 100 (The Model Shop Exeter) - *03*	9	11
B171	**'Bass'** 56 light grey - *90-02*	8	10
-	**'Bass'** 56 light grey, Sp Edn 200 (Tutbury Jinny) ex 2-wagon pack - *02*	10	NA
-	**'Bass'** 32 light grey, Sp Edn 200 (Tutbury Jinny) - *09*	7	9
-	**'Bassil King & Co.'** 6 grey Sp Edn 209 (Wessex Wagons) - *05*	8	10
TMCD005A	'Archd **Bathgate & Sons**' 201 red, Sp Edn 100 (The Model Centre) - *03*	9	11
TMCD005B	'Archd **Bathgate & Sons**' 205 red, Sp Edn 100 (The Model Centre) - *03*	9	11
TMCD005C	'Archd **Bathgate & Sons**' 211 red, Sp Edn 100 (The Model Centre) - *03*	9	11
B574	'S.J.**Baverstock**' 51 black - *04*	9	11
No.9	'Charles **Bazzard & Son**' 192 black Sp Edn 151 (West Wales Wagon Works) - *03, 05*	8	10
-	**'Bear's Beer'** ? ? Sp Edn (*Model Rail* magazine) - *05*	8	10
B519	**'Beaumont'** 665 red-brown - *03*	7	9
IP6	**'Beaumont & Co.'** 665 red-brown Sp Edn 150 (1E Promotionals) - *09*	7	9

7-plank - 'Beili - Glas' [W9b] (Dapol)

-	**'Beeby & Son'** 1735 red-brown Sp Edn 99 (Nene Valley Railway) - *08*	7	9
-	**'Beili-Glas'** 25 black Sp Edn 92 (D.Dacey) - *06*	8	10
-	**'Berry Hill Collieries'** 1505 red-brown Sp Edn 100 (Trident Trains) - *06*	8	10
-	**'Berry Hill Collieries'** 1505 red-brown Sp Edn 150 (Tutbury Jinny) - *08*	7	9
B524	**'Berthlwyd'** 966 black - *03*	7	9
NR3	**'Bessey & Palmer'** 743 grey Sp Edn 250 (1E Promotionals) - *05*	8	10
-	'T **Beynon & Co.**' 3 black Sp Edn 100 (David Dacey) - *08*	7	9
-	**'Bickershaw'** 970 red-brown Sp Edn 100 (The Red Rose Steam Society) - *08*	7	9
-	**'Bickershaw'** 960 red Sp Edn 100 (The Red Rose Steam Society) - *09*	8	10
-	**'Bideford 150'** 1855 grey Sp Edn 100 (P.McAllister) - *05*	8	10
-	**'Billingsley'** 17 dark brown Sp Edn 150 (Foot Plate) - *05*	8	10
-	'John T **Bingham & Co.**' 10 black Sp Edn 1000 (Ballards) - *03*	8	10
7	**'Birchenwood Colliery'** 53 red-brown Sp Edn 200 (Haslington Models) - *05*	8	10
-	'Wm **Black & Sons**' 800 black Sp Edn 200 (Ayr Glass) - *made?*	NPG	NPG
B377A	**'Black Park'** Ruabon 329 brown	8	NA
B377B	**'Black Park'** Chirk 2021 red-brown	8	NA
B377	above 2 wagons in a twin pack - *02-03*	NA	18
No.17	**'Blackwell'** 1836 red brown Sp Edn 130 (Midlander) - *01*	10	12
No.24	**'Blackwell'** 1298 red-brown Sp Edn 115 (Midlander) - *02*	10	12
PBR4	**'Blaenavon'** 1530 grey Sp Edn 150 (Pontypool & Blaenavon Railway) - *03*	9	11
PBR8	**'Blaenavon'** 1472 pale grey Sp Edn 200 (Pontypool & Blaenavon Railway) - *04*	9	11
PBR11	**'Blaenavon'** 1378 grey Sp Edn 300 (Pontypool & Blaenavon Railway) - *05*	8	10
-	**'Blaen-Cae-Gurwen Colliery Co.'** 61 dark brown Sp Edn 98 (D Dacey) - *06*	9	11
-	**'Blaendare Co.'** 254 grey + brick load Sp Edn 100 (David Dacey) - *08*	7	9
-	**'Blaen-Graigola'** 29 red Sp Edn 94 (South Wales Coalfields) - *03*	10	12
-	'The **Blaenmawr Colliery**' 163 black Sp Edn 106 (D Dacey) - *05*	8	10
-	**'Blaina Colliery Co.'** 1004 black Sp Edn 106 (D Dacey) - *05*	8	10
B521	**'Blidworth'** 2323 grey - *03*	7	9
No.12	**'Bliss Tweed Mills'** 6 green Sp Edn 159 (Banbury MR Show + West Wales Wagon Works) - *03*	9	11
B316	**'Blue Circle'** 173 yellow - *00-03*	7	9
B693	'Joseph **Boam**' 510 red-brown - *07-08*	7	9
-	'Wm **Body & Sons**' deep green Sp Edn (Colonel Stephens Railway Enterprise) - *09*	10	13
-	'FJ **Bonner & Mason & Toogood**' 1 light grey Sp Edn 208 (Wessex Wagons) - *06*	8	10
-	**'Bonvilles Court Coal Coy.'** 13 grey Sp Edn 114 (West Wales Wagon Works) - *09*	7	10
-	**'Bonvilles Court Coal Coy.'** 13 grey W Sp Edn 50 (West Wales Wagon Works) - *09*	8	11
B322	'John G **Boreland & Peat**' 317 pale grey - *01-02*	8	10
B680	**'Bourne Fisher & Co.'** 21 brown - *06-07*	7	9
B680	**'Bourne Fisher & Co.'** 21 red-brown W - *08*	6	8
38	**'Bowson'** 1334 red-brown Sp Edn 250 (Hereford Model Centre) - *06*	8	10
-	**'Bradford & Sons'** 1 brown Sp Edn 100 (Buffers) - *03*	9	11
-	**'Bradford & Sons'** 2 brown Sp Edn 100 (Buffers) - *03*	9	11

7-plank - 'Bradford & Sons' [W9b] (Dapol)

-	**'Bradford & Sons'** 4 brown Sp Edn (Buffers) - *04*	9	11
-	**'Bradford & Sons'** 5 brown Sp Edn (Buffers) - *05*	8	10
-	**'Bradford Colliery Co.'** 249 red-brown Sp Edn 100 (The Red Rose Steam Society) - *08*	7	9
BY11	**'Bramley & Son'** 5 dark brown Sp Edn 175 (1E Promotionals) - *09*	7	9
-	**'Breeze'** 23 dark blue Sp Edn 100 (Shrewsbury Model Centre) - *08*	7	9
B94	**'Brentnall & Cleland'** 3000 blk (M) - *86-02*	6	10
-	**'BC Bridgewater Collieries'** 1870 black Sp Edn 100 (Astley Green Mining Museum) - *09*	7	9
B323	**'Brightmore'** 113 grey - *01-02*	8	10
-	'G **Briyer Ash**' 1110 black Sp Edn 100 (Buffers) - *04*	9	11
B175	**'Broadoak'** 460 brown (A) - *89-?*	6	10
B175	**'Broadoak'** 406 brown - *?-01*	8	10
-	'Isambard Kingdom **Brunel**' 37 green Sp Edn 120 (West Wales Wagon Works) - *05*	10	12
-	**'Brynn Hall'** 748 red-brown Sp Edn (Astley Green Mining Museum) 100 - *07*	7	9
-	**'Brynhenllys'** 337 black Sp Edn 100 (D Dacey) - *06*	8	10
-	**'BT'** (Bridgewater Trustees) 837 black Sp Edn 183 (Red Rose Steam Society) - *04*	9	11
39	**'Budd & Company'** 3175 black Sp Edn 250 (Hereford Model Centre) - *06*	8	10
B566	**'Bullcroft'** 288 bright red - *04*	7	9
LB3	**'Burnyeat, Brown & Co.'** 335 black Sp Edn 100 (Lord & Butler Model Railways) ex double pack. - *02*	10	NA
-	**'Burton-on-Trent Co-op'** 11 brown Sp Edn 250 (Tutbury Jinny) - *01*	10	12
-	'FW **Butcher**' 3 dull green Sp Edn 1000 (Ballards) - *02*	7	9
ANT008	**'Bute'** 115 black Sp Edn 250 (Antics) - *04*	9	11
-	'TF **Butler**' ? ? Sp Edn 275 (Crafty Hobbies) - *05*	8	10
ANT028	'T **Butt & Sons**' 2 black Sp Edn 250 (Antics) - *07*	7	9
ANT028A	'T **Butt & Sons**' 29 black Sp Edn 250 (Antics) - *08*	7	9
No.1	**'Butterley'** 2322 red brown Sp Edn 102 (Midlander) - *00*	11	13
SWL14	**'Butterley'** 01702 dark grey Sp Edn 105 (Midlander) - *01*	10	12
No.2	**'Butterley'** 5513 grey Sp Edn 130 (Midlander) - *01*	10	12
No.25	**'Caerbryn Colliery'** 219 black Sp Edn 220 (West Wales Wagon Works) - *04*	9	11
-	**'Caerphilly Coal Co.'** red-brown Sp Edn 107 (David Dacey) - *07*	7	9
B638	**'Cain'** 3 black - *05*	7	9
CA2	**'Cambridge Gas Co.'** 19 black Sp Edn 250 (1E Promotionals) - *05*	8	10
B174	**'Cambrian'** 107 black - *89-02*	10	12
ANT005	**'Cambrian Standard'** 1923 cream Sp Edn 100 (Antics) - *04*	9	11
-	**'Came & Storey'** 8 black Sp Edn 150 (Burnham & District MRC) - *08*	7	9
E02A	**'Camerton Collieries'** 175 black Sp Edn 125 (E. Somerset Models)	10	NA
E02B	**'Camerton Collieries'** 199 black Sp Edn 125 (E.Somerset Models)	10	NA
-	Above 2 wagons were sold only together as a pair in a double box, 125 sets sold - *02*	NA	15
-	**'Camerton Collieries'** 169 black Sp Edn 115 (Wessex Wagons) - *05*	8	10
-	**'Cannock & Leacroft Colliery'** 4129 brown Sp Edn 200 (Tutbury Jinny) ex set of 2 - *04*	9	NA
-	**'Cannock Rugeley'** 648 grey+red Sp Edn 200 (Tutbury Jinny) ex-set of 2 - *01*	10	NA
-	**'Cannock & Rugeley'** 465 red Sp Edn 200 (Tutbury Jinny) ex-set of 2 - *04*	9	NA
51	**'Cannop'** 27 black Sp Edn 300 (Hereford Model Centre) - *09*	6	8
-	**'Cardiff Navigation'** 256 black Sp Edn 110 (South Wales Coalfields) - *04*	9	11
No.17	**'Cardigan Mercantile Co.'** various numbers carried black Sp Edn 175 (West Wales Wagon Works) - *04*	9	11
-	**'Cardigan Mercantile Co.'** 900 [2] black, 4 different loads, Sp Edn 150 (West Wales Wagon Works) - *10*	9	11
-	**'Cardox'** (see Wolstanton Cardox)	-	-
B122	**'Carlton'** 4372 black (A) - *?*	6	10
B550	**'Carpenter & Son'** 4 red-brown - *03-05*	7	9
-	**'Carpenter & Sons'** 27 red-brown Sp Edn 135 (P.McAllister) - *06*	8	10

7-plank - 'Cefn-Y-Bryn' [W9b] (Dapol)

-	**'Carterhatch Brick & Tile Co.'** 2 dark brown Sp Edn 100 (Peter Paye) - *06*	8	10
-	**'Cefn-Y-Bryn'** 76 dark brown Sp Edn 110 (D Dacey) - *06*	8	10
-	**'Chadwick & Smith'** 2 red-brown Sp Edn 100 (Colwyn Model Railway Club) - *04*	9	11
-	**'Chadwick & Smith'** 5 red-brown Sp Edn 100 (Colwyn Model Railway Club) - *04*	9	11
B360	**'Charles Roberts'** 1910 red-brown - *01-02*	8	10
B319	**'Chatterley-Whitfield'** 1822 grey - *00-02*	8	10
-	**'Chatterley-Whitfield'** 1822 pale grey, re-run of B319 Sp Edn 100 (Trident Trains) - *06?*	8	10
-	**'Chislet'** * 440 black Sp Edn 520 (Hythe Models) 1st issue - *01*	9	11
-	**'Chislet'** * black Sp Edn (Hythe Models) - *05*	8	10
SWL20	**'City of Birmingham'** 1747 black Sp Edn 140 (Midlander) - *01*	10	12
-	**'City of Liverpool'** 800 grey Sp Edn 128 (West Wales Wagon Works) - *07*	7	9
-	**'City of Liverpool'** 800 grey W Sp Edn 46 (West Wales Wagon Works) - *07*	9	11
-	'Thos. J **Clarke**' 603 brown Sp Edn 210 (Wessex Wagons) - *05*	8	10
SWL3	**'Claycross'** 1254 red brown Sp Edn 140 (Midlander) - *00*	11	13
B101	'S J **Claye**' 825 red-brown - *86-99*	9	11
-	'S J **Claye**' 825 red-brown Sp Edn (Railway & Barter Shop) - *08*	7	9
RTR4	**'Clement's Tump'** 2 black Sp Edn 250 (RD Whyborn) - *96?*	12	14
-	**'Clevedon Gas Company'** 21 light grey Sp Edn		

	200 (Wessex Wagons) - *05*	8	10
-	**'Clevedon Gas Company'** 21 red Sp Edn (Col. Stevens Railway Enterprise) - *08*	7	10
-	**'Clifton & Kersley'** 2224 bright red Sp Edn 337 (Red Rose Steam Soc.) - *03*	9	11
-	**'Clifton & Kersley'** 2250 red-brown Sp Edn 150 (Astley Green Colliery Museum) - *10*	8	10
-	**'Clifton Colliery'** 2121 red Sp Edn 110 (Paul Freer) - *03*	9	12
-	**'Clutton (The Earl of Warwick's Collieries)'** 533 black Sp Edn 120 (Burnham & District MRC) - *09*	7	9
-	**'Clyde Shipping Co.'** green? Sp Edn (Ayr Glass & Glazing) - *not made*	NA	NA
B181	**'Coal Agencies'** 42 black - *89-02*	8	10
-	**'Coales'** 8 pale grey Sp Edn 150 (1E Promotionals) - *10*	8	10
-	'Geo J **Cockerell & Co.**' 5375 red-brown Sp Edn 1000 (Ballards) - *08*	7	9
RTR2	**'Coleford Red Ash'** 6 black Sp Edn 250 (RD Whyborn) - *94?*	12	14
-	as above but red (error)	NPG	NPG
52	**'Coleford Red Ash'** 6 black Sp Edn 250 (Hereford Model Centre) - *09*	6	8
-	'**Colhurst Symons & Co.**' 7 light grey Sp Edn (Burnham & District MRC) - *09*	6	8
-	'R **Coller & Sons**' 55 red-brown Sp Edn 151 (Nene Valley Railway) - *10*	7	9
-	'C **Collett & Sons**' 5 brown Sp Edn 75 (West Wales Wagon Works) - *08*	7	9
-	'C **Collett & Sons**' 5 brown W Sp Edn 25 (West Wales Wagon Works) - *08*	7	9
-	'C **Collett & Sons**' 6 green Sp Edn (Bourton-on-the-Water Model Railway) - *04*	9	11
-	'C **Collett & Sons'** 7 brown Sp Edn 80 (West Wales Wagon Works) - *08*	7	9
-	'C **Collett & Sons'** 7 brown W Sp Edn 24 (West Wales Wagon Works) - *08*	7	9

7-plank - 'D.Colley' [W9b] (Dapol)

33	'D **Colley**' 49 bright red Sp Edn 250 (Hereford Model Centre) - *06*	8	10
RM2	'JT **Collins & Sons'** 35 black Sp Edn 200 (1E Promotionals) - *07*	7	9
B384	**'Collins Green**' 417 brown - *02-03*	8	10
B167	**'Colman's'** 35 yellow - *91-99*	9	11
-	**'Colthurst, Symons and Co.'** 7 light grey Sp Edn 160 (Burnham & District MRC) - *09*	6	8
-	**'Coltness Kinghill Colliery**' 349 orange-red Sp Edn 200 (Model Rail Scotland) - *08*	9	12
-	**'Cooke & Nuttall'** 11 red Sp Edn 100 (Trains & Diecast) - *06*	8	10
-	**'Co-operative Society - Twerton'** 1 maroon Sp Edn 182 (Wessex Wagons) - *08*	7	9
-	**'Co-operative Society - Trowbridge'** 1 maroon Sp Edn 187 (Wessex Wagons) - *08*	7	9
WO1	**'Coote & Warren'** 2176 dark brown Sp Edn 250 (1E Promotionals) - *05*	8	10
-	**'Cope & Baker'** 4 dark brown Sp Edn 250 (Hereford Model Centre) - *05*	8	10
-	**Corrall & Co.'** 1341 grey-green Sp Edn 100 (Richard Essen) - *09*	7	9

7-plank - 'Cope & Baker' [W9b] (Dapol)

B186	**'Cory Bros.'** 9644 black - *91-02*	8	10
-	'W **Counsell & Co.'** 7 black Sp Edn 171 (Wessex Wagons) - *05*	8	10
B169	**'Courtaulds'** 18 green - *90-01*	8	10
SWL19	**'Coventry Collieries'** The Warwickshire Coal Co 334 black Sp Edn 143 (Midlander) - *01*	10	12
-	**'Coventry Collieries'** 1404 black Sp Edn (Castle Trains) - *made?*	NPG	NPG
2nd	**'Coventry Collieries'** 1436 black Sp Edn 150 (Castle Trains) - *07*	7	9
-	'Wm **Coward & Co.'** 4 dark green Sp Edn 109 (Llangollen Railway GWR Loco Group) - *08*	7	9
ANT006	'Alexander **Crane**' 102 brown Sp Edn 100 (Antics) - *04*	9	11
-	**'Crane & Company'** 107 bright red Sp Edn 185 (Wales & West Assn MRCs) - *04*	9	11
-	**'Crawshay Bros.'** 1120 black Sp Edn 107 (South Wales Coalfields) - *03*	9	11
PRB14	**'Crawshay's'** 15 cream Sp Edn 250 (Pontypool & Blaenavon Railway) - *06*	8	10
-	**'Cribbwr Fawr Collieries'** 468 red Sp Edn 112 (South Wales Coalfields) - *03*	9	11
-	**'Crippins Arley Coal'** 1048 red Sp Edn 100 (Astley Green Mining Museum) - *09*	7	9
ANT011	**'Critchlow & Sheppard'** 15 red-brown Sp Edn 250 (Antics) - *05*	8	10
-	'W C**rocker**' 40 red-brown 40th Anniversary Sp Edn 220 (Hampton Court MRS) - *03*	9	11
B536	**'Crosfields' Perfection Soap'** 84 red - *03*	10	12
PBR10	**'Crumlin Valley Collieries'** 15 black Sp Edn 300 (Pontypool & Blaenavon RS) - *05*	8	10
-	**'Crynant Colliery'** 332 grey+red Sp Edn 171 (West Wales Wagon Works) - *08*	7	9
-	**'Crynant Colliery'** 335 grey+red Sp Edn 191 (West Wales Wagon Works) - *08*	7	9
-	**'Crynant Colliery'** 332 grey+red W Sp Edn 37 (West Wales Wagon Works) - *08*	9	11
-	**'Crynant Colliery'** 335 grey+red W Sp Edn 36 (West Wales Wagon Works) - *08*	9	11
-	**'Crystalate'** 1262 bright yellow Sp Edn 1000 (Ballards) - *04*	8	10
-	**'Cwmaman'** 541 black, Sp Edn 130 (South Wales Coalfields) - *03*	9	11
-	**'Cwmteg'** 152 black Sp Edn 99 (South Wales Coalfields) - *04*	9	11
PBR2	**'Cwmtillery'** 2537 black Sp Edn 100 (Pontypool & Blaenavon Railway) - *03*	9	11
-	**'Cynon'** 221 black Sp Edn 90 (Jenny's) - *04*	10	12
-	**'Dalmellington Iron Co.'** 351 bright red Sp Edn 350 (Ayrshire Railway Pres Group) - *01*	10	12
B178	**'Dapol'** black Sp Edn (Dapol) - *c89*	10	15
RTR5	**'Darkhill & Elwood'** 50 black Sp Edn (RD Whyborn) - *97?*	12	14
B324	**'Darton'** 145 red - *01-02*	8	10
-	**'Davies Brothers'** 60 black Sp Edn 110 (Barry & Penarth MRC) - *04*	9	11
BY2	'FJ **Davis**' 1 green+yellow Sp Edn 250 (1E Promotionals) - *04*	9	11

-	'JL **Davies**' 125 red Sp Edn 79 (West Wales Wagon Works) - *07*	9	11

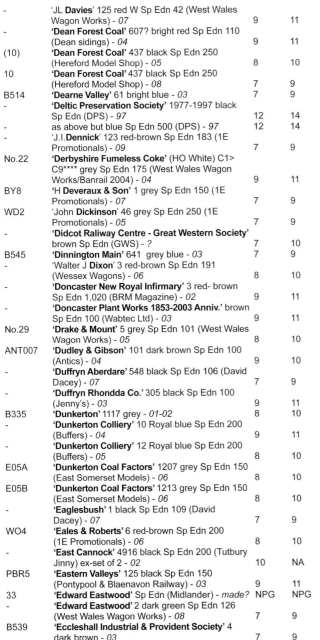

7-plank - 'F.J. Davis' [W9b]

-	'JL **Davies**' 125 red W Sp Edn 42 (West Wales Wagon Works) - *07*	9	11
-	**'Dean Forest Coal'** 607? bright red Sp Edn 110 (Dean sidings) - *04*	9	11
(10)	**'Dean Forest Coal'** 437 black Sp Edn 250 (Hereford Model Shop) - *05*	8	10
10	**'Dean Forest Coal'** 437 black Sp Edn 250 (Hereford Model Shop) - *08*	7	9
B514	**'Dearne Valley'** 61 bright blue - *03*	7	9
-	**'Deltic Preservation Society'** 1977-1997 black Sp Edn (DPS) - *97*	12	14
-	as above but blue Sp Edn 500 (DPS) - *97*	12	14
-	'J.I.**Dennick**' 123 red-brown Sp Edn 183 (1E Promotionals) - *09*	7	9
No.22	**'Derbyshire Fumeless Coke'** (HO White) C1> C9**** grey Sp Edn 175 (West Wales Wagon Works/Banrail 2004) - *04*	9	11
BY8	'H **Deveraux & Son**' 1 grey Sp Edn 150 (1E Promotionals) - *07*	7	9
WD2	'John **Dickinson**' 46 grey Sp Edn 250 (1E Promotionals) - *05*	7	9
-	**'Didcot Railway Centre - Great Western Society'** brown Sp Edn (GWS) - *?*	7	10
B545	**'Dinnington Main'** 641 grey blue - *03*	7	9
-	'Walter J **Dixon**' 3 red-brown Sp Edn 191 (Wessex Wagons) - *06*	8	10
-	**'Doncaster New Royal Infirmary'** 3 red- brown Sp Edn 1,020 (BRM Magazine) - *02*	9	11
-	**'Doncaster Plant Works 1853-2003 Anniv.'** brown Sp Edn 100 (Wabtec Ltd) - *03*	9	11
No.29	**'Drake & Mount'** 5 grey Sp Edn 101 (West Wales Wagon Works) - *05*	8	10
ANT007	**'Dudley & Gibson'** 101 dark brown Sp Edn 100 (Antics) - *04*	9	10
-	**'Duffryn Aberdare'** 548 black Sp Edn 106 (David Dacey) - *07*	7	9
-	**'Duffryn Rhondda Co.'** 305 black Sp Edn 100 (Jenny's) - *03*	9	11
B335	**'Dunkerton'** 1117 grey - *01-02*	8	10
-	**'Dunkerton Colliery'** 10 Royal blue Sp Edn 200 (Buffers) - *04*	9	11
-	**'Dunkerton Colliery'** 12 Royal blue Sp Edn 200 (Buffers) - *05*	8	10
E05A	**'Dunkerton Coal Factors'** 1207 grey Sp Edn 150 (East Somerset Models) - *06*	8	10
E05B	**'Dunkerton Coal Factors'** 1213 grey Sp Edn 150 (East Somerset Models) - *06*	8	10
-	**'Eaglesbush'** 1 black Sp Edn 109 (David Dacey) - *07*	7	9
WO4	**'Eales & Roberts'** 6 red-brown Sp Edn 200 (1E Promotionals) - *06*	8	10
-	**'East Cannock'** 4916 black Sp Edn 200 (Tutbury Jinny) ex-set of 2 - *02*	10	NA
PBR5	**'Eastern Valleys'** 125 black Sp Edn 150 (Pontypool & Blaenavon Railway) - *03*	9	11
33	**'Edward Eastwood'** Sp Edn (Midlander) - *made?*	NPG	NPG
-	**'Edward Eastwood'** 2 dark green Sp Edn 126 (West Wales Wagon Works) - *08*	7	9
B539	**'Eccleshall Industrial & Provident Society'** 4 dark brown - *03*	7	9

-	**'Economic Coal Co.'** 3 red-brown Sp Edn (Footplate Models) - *07*	7	9
-	**'ED'** 675 red brown Sp Edn 100 (Modellers Mecca) - *01*	10	NA

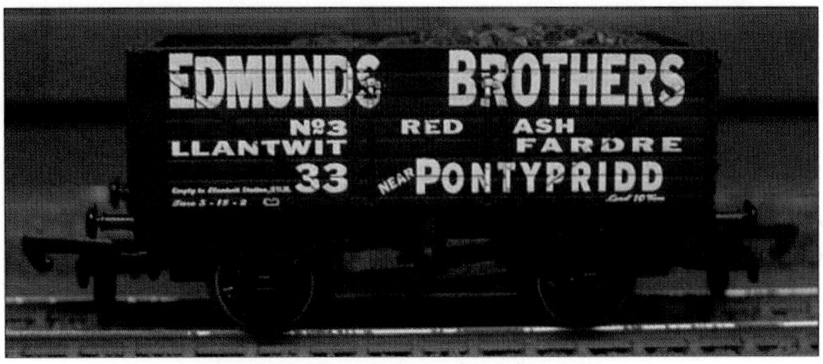

7-plank - 'Edmunds Brothers' [W9b] (Dapol)

-	**'Edmunds Brothers'** 33 black Sp Edn 94 (D Dacey) - *06*	8	10
TMCD008A	'WH **Edwards**' 10 red-brown Sp Edn (TMC) - *04*	9	11
TMCD008B	'WH **Edwards**' 18 red-brown Sp Edn (TMC) - *04*	9	11
TMCD008C	'WH **Edwards**' 25 red-brown Sp Edn (TMC) - *04*	9	11
-	**'O Edwards & Son'** 148 pale brown Sp Edn 300 (Hythe Models) - *01*	10	12
-	**'Eifionyd Farmers Association'** 17 grey Sp Edn 117 (West Wales Wagon Works) - *06*	8	10
RTR6	**'Elders Steam Navigation'** 466 black Sp Edn 250 (RD Whyborn) - *98?*	12	14
-	'G&G **Ellis**' * blue Sp Edn 100 (Hythe Models 30th Anniversary) - *02*	10	12
SWL12	**'Elsecar'** 771 bright red Sp Edn 130 (Midlander) - *01*	10	12
CA1	**'Ely Gas Co.'** 4 brown-red Sp Edn 250 (1E Promotionals) - *04*	9	11
B170	**'Emlyn'** 811 olive green - *90-02*	8	10
ANT004	**'Empire'** 1673 black Sp Edn 250 (Antics) - *04*	9	11
BY1	'JH & E **Essen**' 4 dark brown Sp Edn 250 (E1 Promotionals) - *04*	9	11
B192	'Wm **Evans**' 174 black - *90-02*	8	10
B320	**'Evans & Bevan'** 386 grey - *01-02*	8	10
HMC 41	**'Evans & Jones'** 4 mid grey Sp Edn 250 (Hereford Model Centre) - *07*	7	9
-	**'Evans, Adlard & Co.'** No.1 black Sp Edn 200 (Glos & Warks Railway) - *00*	11	13
-	'W **Evans**' 2 Sp Edn (Antics) - *03*	9	11
-	'Samuel **Evers**' 34 dark grey Sp Edn 200 (Modellers Mecca) ex set - *02*	10	NA
-	**'Eveson'** 343 red-brown Sp Edn 140 (Midlander) - *03*	9	11
-	**'Ewens Brothers'** 1 red Sp Edn 180 (Wessex Wagons) - *09*	8	10
-	'W **Fairclough**' 32 brown-red Sp Edn 219 (Toys2Save) - *04*	9	11
-	'W **Fairclough**' 28 brown-red Sp Edn 200 (Toys2Save) - *04*	9	11
-	**'Fairweather & Son'** 37 red-brown Sp Edn 124 (Nene Valley Railway) - *07*	7	9
-	'Allan **Feaver**' 10 red-brown Sp Edn 100 (Henfold Halt) - *04*	9	11
No.35	**'Felinfoel Brewery'** **** black Sp Edn 160 (WW Wagon Works) - *05*	8	10
-	**'Fernhill'** 670 black Sp Edn 105 (D Dacey) - *05*	8	10
-	**'Firbeck Main Colliery'** 751 red-brown Sp Edn 100 (Richard Essen) - *08*	7	9
B723	**'Flower & Sons'** 1 grey - *08*	6	8
-	'A **Flowers & Co.**' 16 red-brown Sp Edn 200 (Wessex Wagons) - *06*	8	10
No.5	**'Fosdick'** 251 red-brown Sp Edn 220 (The Middy Trading Company) - *05*	8	10

7-plank - 'John Fowler' [W9b] (Dapol)

25	'**Fountain & Burnley**' 104 red brown Sp Edn 120 (Midlander) - *02*	10	12
35	'John **Fowler**' 125 grey Sp Edn 250 (Hereford Model Shop) - *06*	8	10
NR9	'W **Fowler**' 301 red-brown Sp Edn 225 (1E Promotionals) - *09*	7	9
-	**'Fox'** 458 black Sp Edn 200 (Tutbury Jinny) ex set of 2 - *04*	9	NA
-	**'Foxfield Colliery'** 2 red Sp Edn 250 (Alsager Toys & Models) - *02*	10	12
-	'**Foxfield**' 101 red-brown Sp Edn (Nostalgic Memories of Trentham) - *10*	7	9
-	**'Foxfield'** 538 red-brown Sp Edn 100 (Nostalgic Memories of Trentham) - *07*	7	9
BE8	'Henry **Francis**' 7 red Sp Edn 275 (1E Promotionals) - *09*	7	9
BE3	**'Franklin'** 203 black Sp Edn 250 (1E Promotionals) - *05*	8	10
No.34	'JU **Freeman'** 3 black Sp Edn 120 (West Wales Wagon Works/Banrail 2005) - *06*	8	10
-	'TR **Freeman & Sons'** 5 grey Sp Edn 214 (Wessex Wagons) - *05*	8	10
-	**'Galashiels Gas Light Co.'** 249 black Sp Edn 150 (1E Promotionals) - *10*	7	9
01, 04	**'Gann & Brown'** * grey-blue Sp Edn 323 (Hythe Kent Models) 1st issue - *01*	10	12
-	**'Gann & Brown'** 211 red-brown Sp Edn 150 (1E Promotionals) - *09*	7	9
NR5	**'Gardner'** 306 red Sp Edn 250 (1E Promotionals) - *06*	8	10
-	'KG&NA **Gay'** 73226 black Sp Edn 158 (Wessex Wagons) - *09*	8	10
-	**'GCG'** 269 black Sp Edn 105 (South Wales Coalfields) - *08*	7	9
B581	**'Gedling'** 2598 bright red - *04*	7	9
-	**'Gellyonen Collieries'** 510 pale grey Sp Edn 99 (South Wales Coalfields) - *03*	9	11
-	**'Gilwen'** 532 dark red Sp Edn 92 (South Wales Coalfields) - *03*	9	11
HMC 44	**'Gittings & Sons'** 4 mid grey Sp Edn 250 (Hereford Model Centre) - *07*	7	9
-	**'Glan-Garnant'** 292 black Sp Edn 141 (West Wales Wagon Works) - *09*	7	9
-	**'Glan-Garnant'** 292 black W Sp Edn 70 (West Wales Wagon Works) - *09*	7	9
-	**'Glascote'** 255 pale grey Sp Edn 200 (Tutbury Jinny) - *04*	9	11
-	**'Glasgow Iron & Steel Co.'** 952 grey Sp Edn 100 (Model Rail Scotland) - *07*	12	20
-	**'Glenavon'** 1063 black Sp Edn (Jenny's) - *04*	9	11
B43	**'Gloucester Gas Light'** 51 black (A) - *85-88*	6	10
BRM/0046	**'Gloucester Gas Light Company'** 37 black Sp Edn 500 (BRM Magazine) - *05*	8	10
BRM/0048	**'Gloucester Gas Light Company'** 51 black Sp Edn 500 (BRM magazine) - *05*	8	10
-	**'Glyncoed'** 162 dark brown, Sp Edn 130 (South Wales Coalfields) - *03*	9	11
-	**'Glyncorrwg Collieries'** 276 black Sp Edn 79 (Jenny's) - *02*	10	12

-	**'Glyncorrwg Colliery'** 535 black Sp Edn (Jenny's) - *05*	8	10
B359	**'Glynea & Castle'** 191 brown - *01-02*	8	10
No.15	**'Goldthorpe'** 2744 red-brown Sp Edn 122 (Midlander) - *01*	10	12
-	**'Goodland'** 30 black Sp Edn 250 (Wessex Wagons) - *05*	8	10
-	'WT **Goolden & Co.'** (uniquely numbered with transfers 1-77) dark red, 5 different loads used Sp Edn 77 (Oliver Leetham) - *03*	10	12
B541	**'Gortac'** 29 yellow - *03*	7	9
-	**'Granville'** 227 grey Sp Edn 200 (Tutbury Jinny) ex-set of 2 - *02*	10	NA
23	**'Grassmoor'** 940 black Sp Edn 115 (Midlander) - *02*	10	12
-	**'Great Grimsby Coal Salt'** 1180 black Sp Edn 100 (D Hewins) - *00*	11	13
-	**'Great Treverbyn'** 48 red-brown no load Sp Edn (Railtronics) ex-set - *01*	10	NA
-	**'Great Treverbyn'** 48 red-brown + chalk Sp Edn (Railtronics) ex-set - *01-02*	10	NA
-	**'Great Western Society'** green Sp Edn (GWS) - *?*	10	15
-	**'Great Western Society'** 1 red-brown Sp Edn (GWS) - *?*	10	15
-	**'Great Western Colliery Co.'** 650 black Sp Edn 95 (D Dacey) - *05*	8	10
-	'Victor **Grey'** 54 bright red, Sp Edn 130 (South Wales Coalfields) - *03*	9	11
36	'James **Griffin'** 5 grey Sp Edn 250 (Hereford Model Shop) - *06*	8	10

7-plank - 'Grumbly Gas Works' [W9b] (Dapol)

-	'AE **Griffiths'** 35 light grey, choice of 5 loads*** Sp Edn 96 (O Leedham) - *03*	10	12
-	**'Grist'** - *(see 'Matthew Grist')*	-	-
-	**'Grumbly Gas Works'** 1 grey Sp Edn 116 (West Wales Wagon Works) - *08*	7	9
-	**'Guest, Keen & Nettlefolds'** 0747 black, Sp Edn 151 (South Wales Coalfields) - *03*	9	11
-	'SP **Gunn & Sons'** 1 bright red Sp Edn (Dartmoor Railway) - *04*	9	11
NA1	'SP **Gunn & Sons'** 1 bright red Sp Edn 150 (1E Promotionals) - *09*	9	11
-	**'Gwili Railway'** 1 pale grey+red Sp Edn 120 (West Wales Wagon Works) - *06*	8	10
PBR7	**'Hafodyrynys'** 729 brown Sp Edn 300 (Pontypool & Blaenavon Railway Soc.) - *05*	8	10
B44	**'Hales Fuels'** 241 grey (A) - *85-88*	6	10
-	**'Hall & Co.'** 161 red LBSC Sp Edn (Antics) - *09*	8	10
-	**'Hall & Co.'** 161 red-brown Sp Edn 1000 (Ballards) - *09*	8	10
SWL7	**'Hall's Collieries'** 1401 black Sp Edn 132 (Midlander) - *01*	10	12
B182	**'Halls Swadlincote'** 711 brown - *89,95*	9	11
-	'FJ **Hall'** 65 brown Sp Edn 200 (Tutbury Jinny) ex set of 2 - *04*	9	NA
-	'Herbert **Hall'** 111 maroon Sp Edn 200 (Modellers Mecca) ex-set - *02*	10	NA
-	**'Halstead Co-operative Society'** 11 red-brown Sp Edn 85 (Colne Valley Railway) - *07*	8	10
-	'Edwin **Hammond'** 1 black Sp Edn 101 (D Dacey) - *05*	8	10
-	**'Hampson & Co.'** dark brown Sp Edn 108 (Richard Hampson) - *04*	9	11
B535	'Fred **Hardisty'** 2 red-brown - *03*	7	9

-	**'Harecastle'** 55 brown Sp Edn 200 (Tutbury Jinny) - *03*	9	11
ANT003	**'Harris & Co.'** 21 black Sp Edn 100 (Antics) ex-set of 2 with 'Matthew Grist' - *03*	9	NA
B334	**'Hartnell'** 22 black - *01-03*	7	9
-	**'Hartnell & Son'** 23 black Sp Edn 183 (Wessex Wagons) - *08*	7	9
-	**'Harwood Rake'** 20 black Sp Edn 106 (D Dacey) - *05*	8	10
-	**'Hatton's'** brown Sp Edn (Hattons) - *?*	8	10
-	**'Haverhill UDC'** 4 red-brown Sp Edn 98 (Colne Valley Railway) - *09*	6	8
-	T A **Hawkins'** 271 red brown Sp Edn 200 (Tutbury Jinny) ex-set of 2 - *01*	10	NA

7-plank - 'Heath' [W9b]

-	**'Haydock'** 561 black Sp Edn 100 (Trains & Diecast) - *04*	9	11
IP1	**'Heath'** 20 grey Sp Edn 250 (1E Promotionals) - *04*	9	11
-	'Samuel **Heath Jnr.'** 8 black Sp Edn 200 (Haslington Models) - *made?*	NPG	NPG
8	'Samuel **Heath Jnr.'** 24 black Sp Edn 200 (Haslington Models) - *06*	8	10
B542	'John **Heaton'** 101 grey - *03*	7	9
B200	**'Hendy Merthyr'** 1862 brown - *91-92*	9	11
ANT017	'Henry **Heaven'** 1 dark brown Sp Edn 250 (Antics) - *05*	8	10
-	**'Helston Gas Company'** 10 black Sp Edn (Kernow MRCentre) ex-set of 2 - *03*	9	NA
-	**'Helston Gas Company'** 20 black Sp Edn (Kernow MRCentre) ex-set of 2 - *04*	9	NA
-	**'Helston Gas Company'** 30 black Sp Edn (Kernow MRCentre) ex-set of 2 - *03*	9	NA
-	**'Helston Gas Company'** 40 black Sp Edn (Kernow MRCentre) ex-set of 2 - *04*	9	NA
-	**'Helston Gas Company'** 50 black Sp Edn (Kernow MRCentre) - *05*	8	10
-	**'Hempsted'** 37 black Sp Edn 500 (BRM) - *05*	8	10
34	**'Hereford Corporation Gas Works'** 7 grey Sp Edn 250 (Hereford Model Shop) - *06*	8	10
-	**'Hertingfordbury'** 1 buff Sp Edn 100 (Great Eastern Railway Society) - *03*	9	11
B367	**'Hickleton'** 3166 brown - *02-03*	7	9
-	**'The High Brooms'** red Sp Edn 300 (Ballards) - *01*	10	12
-	**'The High Brooms'** 12 red Sp Edn 1000 (Ballards) - *05*	7	9
B176	**'Highley Mining'** 425 brown (A) - *89-?*	6	10
B176	**'Highley Mining'** 245 brown - *?-02*	8	10
-	**'Highley Mining Co.'** 246 red-brown Sp Edn 100 (Severn Valley Railway) - *05?*	8	10
-	**'Highley Mining Co.'** 247 brown Sp Edn 100 (Severn Valley Railway) - *06*	8	10
-	**'Hills Bros.'** 3 red-brown Sp Edn 1000 (Ballards) - *07*	6	8
-	**'Hind, Chesterfield'** blue Sp Edn (Geoff Osbourne's Railway & Model Shop) - *06*	12	15
-	'A **Hinxman & Co.'** 75 grey Sp Edn 176 (Wessex Wagons) - *08*	8	10
-	**'HM Office of Works'** 172 grey Sp Edn 160 (Wessex Wagons) - *10*	7	10
B555	**'Hockaday & Co.'** 4 black - *03*	7	9
30	'John **Hollins'** 6 black Sp Edn 250 (Hereford Model shop) - *06*	8	10

-	**'Holly Bank'** 62 brown Sp Edn 200 (Modellers Mecca) ex set - *02*	10	NA
-	**'Holly Bank'** 62 brown Sp Edn 100 (Tutbury Jinny) - *04*	9	NA
-	**'Hood & Son'** 2 green Sp Edn (Salisbury Model Centre) - *08*	7	9
-	**'Hood & Son'** 3 dark green Sp Edn 162 (Salisbury Model Centre) - *07*	7	9
-	**'Hook Anthracite'** 602 black Sp Edn 175 (West Wales Wagon Works) - *07*	7	9
-	**'Horlicks'** 2 red Sp Edn 128 (West Wales Wagon Works) - *08*	7	9
-	**'Horlicks'** 2 red W Sp Edn 45 (West Wales Wagon Works) - *08*	7	9
-	**'Horwich Industrial Co-operative Society Ltd.'** 12 red-brown Sp Edn 100 (Trains & Diecast) - *09*	7	9
SWL27	**'Houghton Main'** 2029 red-brown Sp Edn 120 (The Midlander) - *03*	9	11
-	**'Howes Models'** 1 blue Sp Edn 110 (Howes Models) - *02*	10	12

7-plank - 'H.P. Sauce Works' [W9b]

SY1	**'HP Sauce Works'** 1 red-brown Sp Edn 350 (1E Promotionals/Warley Show 2007) - *07*	7	9
No.1	'Wm **Hubbard'** 30 black, Sp Edn 294 (Teifi Valley Railway) - *02*	10	12
-	'Wm **Hubbard'** 200 black Sp Edn 100 (West Wales Wagon Works) - *07*	7	9
B190	**'Huddersfield Co-op'** 14 black - *90*	9	11
ANT027	'AP **Hudson'** 21 red Sp Edn 250 (Antics) - *07*	7	9
-	**'Hulton Colliery Co.'** 164 black Sp Edn 150 (Red Rose Steam Society) - *10*	9	11
B557	**'Humber'** 100 red - *03*	7	9
-	**'Hunstanton Models'** brown Sp Edn 150 (Hunstanton Model Shop) - *04*	9	11
No.46	**'Hunt Edmunds & Co.'** 8 light grey Sp Edn 166 (West Wales Wagon Works) - *06*	8	10
-	**'Hunting & Co.'** 61 red-brown Sp Edn (Nene Valley Railway) - *09*	7	9
No.28	**'Huntley & Palmers'** **** black Sp Edn 147 (West Wales Wagon Works) - *05*	8	10
-	'CJ **Hyslop'** 12 red-brown Sp Edn 110 (West Wales Wagon Works) - *07*	7	9
B380	**'Ilkeston & Heanor Water Board'** 14 blue-grey - *02-03*	7	9
-	**'International Colliery'** French Anthrecite 400 red-brown Sp Edn 100 (South Wales Coalfield) - *04*	9	11
-	**'Ipswich Co-operative Society'** 115 red Sp Edn 99 (Old Wagon Works) - *04*	9	11
-	**'Itshide'** 265 black Sp Edn 1000 (Ballards) - *03*	8	10
PBR6	**'James & Emanuel'** 189 black Sp Edn 170 (Pontypool & Blaenavon RS) - *04*	9	11
WD4	**'Jeayes Kasner & Co.'** 121 red-brown Sp Edn 150 (1E Promotionals) - *07*	7	9
-	'GE **Jenkins** - Master Engineer' light blue Sp Edn 100 (Tywyn & District MRC) - *08*	7	9
No.24	'T **Jenkerson & Sons'** 274 black Sp Edn 189 (West Wales Wagon Works) - *04*	9	11
-	'Ann **Jones'** 4 black Sp Edn 150 (Llangollen Railway GW Loco Group) - *09*	7	10
B89	'David **Jones'** 650 red brown (M) - *86*	6	10
B89	'David **Jones**' 650 red brown - *95-02*	8	10
-	'David **Jones'** Llandyssul 5 black Sp Edn 129 (West Wales Wagon Works) - *06*	8	10
-	'David **Jones**' Pencader 1 black Sp Edn 121		

	(West Wales Wagon Works) - *06*	8	10
NR11	'H **Jones**' 1 grey Sp Edn 150 (1E Promotionals) - *10*	7	9
-	**'Jury Brick Co.'** 4 black Sp Edn 100 (Richard Essen) - *08*	7	9
B623	'Sir John LL **Kaye Bart**.' 9 blue - *05*	7	9
-	'John **Kerkin**' 1 grey Sp Edn 125 (West Wales Wagon Works) - *10*	8	11
-	'John **Kerkin**' 1 grey W Sp Edn 29 (West Wales Wagon Works) - *10*	8	11
NR4	'ET **Ketteringham**' 30 red-brown Sp Edn 250 (1E Promotionals) - *05*	8	10
-	**'Kilmersdon Colliery'** 22 green Sp Edn (Buffers) - *04*	8	10
-	**'Kilmersdon Colliery'** 24 green Sp Edn 100 (Buffers) - *04*	9	11
-	**'Kilmersdon Colliery'** 26 Sp Edn (Buffers) - *04*	9	11
-	**'K&K (A.Knowles)'** 360 red-brown Sp Edn 100 (Red Rose Steam Society) - *05*	8	10

7-plank - 'Kinneil' [W9b] (Dapol)

B589	**'Kinneil'** 118 red-brown - *04-05*	7	9
-	**'Kinneil'** 189 red-brown Sp Edn (Scottish Railway Preservation Society) - *08*	7	9
-	**'Kirkby-in-Furness Co-operative Society'** 4 light grey Sp Edn 159 (Crafty Hobbies) - *08*	7	9
-	**'Kirkland & Perkins'** 18 bright red Sp Edn 370 (Peak Rail) - *04*	9	11
-	**'Lachlan Grant'** 1 buff Sp Edn 100 (Strathspey Railway) - *03*	9	12
-	**'Lachlan Grant'** 2 beige Sp Edn 100 (Strathspey Railway) - *06*	8	12
-	**'Lachlan Grant'** 3 beige Sp Edn 100 (Strathspey Railway) - *06*	8	12
-	**'Lamb Brewery'** 1 brown Sp Edn 150 (Wessex Wagons) - *05-06*	8	10
-	**'Lamdin & Sons'** 11 red-brown Sp Edn 160 (Wessex Wagons) - *09*	8	10
PBR3	'John **Lancaster & Co.**' 1063 black Sp Edn 100 (Pontypool & Blaenavon Railway) - *03*	9	11
-	'SV **Lancey**' 20 Royal blue Sp Edn 145 (Wessex Wagons) - *07*	7	9
B390	**'Lawley'** 391 grey - *02-03*	7	9
-	**'Lawrence & Co.'** 12 black Sp Edn 167 (Wessex Wagons) - *08*	7	9
-	**'Leadbeter'** 105 light grey Sp Edn 103 (Barry & Penarth MRC) - *04*	9	11

7-plank - 'Leek & Moorlands' [W9b] (Dapol)

22	**'Leadbeter'** 211 bright red Sp Edn 250 (Hereford Model Centre) - *05*	8	10
-	**'Leadbeter'** 211 bright red Sp Edn 500 (The Pontypool & Blaenavon Railway) - *08*	7	9
-	**'Leek & Moorlands'** 175 grey Sp Edn (Tutbury Jinny) ex-set of 2 - *05*	8	NA
-	**'Leek & Moorlands'** 175 cream Sp Edn 92 (Tutbury Jinny) - *?*	NPG	NPG
-	**'Leek & Moorlands'** 167 cream Sp Edn (Tutbury Jinny) - *09*	7	9
B374	**'Lewis'** 0196 black - *02-03*	7	9
B374A	**'Lewis'** 0199 black - *02-03*	7	9
-	**'Lewis'** Merthyr' 955 black Sp Edn 103 (David Dacey) - *07*	7	9
LB3	**'Lewis'** Merthyr Navigation' 768 black Sp Edn 100 (Lord & Butler Model Railways) ex double pack - *02*	10	NA
-	**'Lightmoor'** 263 grey, Sp Edn 200+ (Geoff Osborn) - *99*	12	14
ANT019	'RA **Lister**' 1 dark brown Sp Edn 250 (Antics) - *07+08*	7	9
-	**'Llanbradach'** 252 black Sp Edn 100 (D Dacey) - *05*	8	10
-	**'Llantrisant Railwaymen's Coal Association'** 1 red-brown Sp Edn 110 (South Wales Coalfields) - *04*	9	11
-	'Samuel **Llewellyn**' 122 grey, Sp Edn 179 (South Wales Coalfields) - *03*	9	11
-	'Samuel **Llewellyn Carw**' 58 red-brown Sp Edn 100 (South Wales Coalfields) - *07*	7	9
-	**'Locket's Merthyr'** 362 black Sp Edn 150 (D.Dacey) - *10*	7	9
BE1	'Wm **Lockhart**' 63 black Sp Edn 250 (1E Promotionals) - *04*	9	11
No.16	'Henry **Lodge**' 214 bright red Sp Edn 159 (Midlander) - *01*	10	12
-	'Frank **Lomas**' 4 pale grey Sp Edn 520 (Peak Rail Stock Fund) - *04*	9	11
TMCD007A	**'Longbottom & Co.'** 703 red, Sp Edn 100 (The Model Centre) - *03*	9	11
TMCD007B	**'Longbottom & Co.'** 716 red, Sp Edn 100 (The Model Centre) - *03*	9	11
TMCD007C	**'Longbottom & Co.'** 728 red, Sp Edn 100 (The Model Centre) - *03*	9	11
-	'S **Loney & Co**.' 51 grey Sp Edn 200 (Wessex Wagons) - *05*	8	10
IP3	**'Lowestoft Coaling Co.'** 4567 dark red Sp Edn 250 (1E Promotionals) - *06*	8	10
-	**'Lydney Coal Co.'** 9 grey Sp Edn (Dean Sidings) - *03*	9	11
56	**'Lydney Coal Co.'** 9 grey Sp Edn 250 (Hereford Model Shop) - *09*	7	9
-	'John **Lysaght's**' 1471 black 40th Anniversary Sp Edn 100 (Scunthorpe District MRS) - *03*	9	11
B525	**'Macclesfield'** 10 red-brown - *03*	7	9
B570	**'Macclesfield Co-op'** 41 brown - *04*	7	9
-	**'Main Colliery Co.'** 568 black, Sp Edn 110 (D Dacey) - *04*	9	11
-	'The **Mains Coal & Cannal Co.**' 475 grey Sp Edn 200 (Buffers) - *04*	9	11
B677	**'Maltby Main'** 298 red W - *06-07*	6	8
TMCD004A	**'Manchester Collieries'** 8692 brown, Sp Edn 100 (The Model Centre) - *03*	9	11
TMCD004B	**'Manchester Collieries'** 8743 brown, Sp Edn 100 (The Model Centre) - *03*	9	11
TMCD004C	**'Manchester Collieries'** 8785 brown, Sp Edn 100 (The Model Centre) - *03*	9	11
-	**'Mansfield Bros.'** Sp Edn (Dean Sidings) - *made?*	NPG	NPG
-	'Rowland **Manthorpe & Co.**' Sp Edn 162 (Middy Trading Company) - *10*	7	9
B394	**'Manton'** 891 brown - *02-03*	7	9
3rd	**'Manton'** 6502 red-brown Sp Edn 200 (Castle Trains) - *07*	7	9
22	**'Manvers Main'** 3044 red brown Sp Edn (Midlander) - *02*	10	12
-	**'Manx Tails'** brown, Dapol for show Ltd Edn (also WWWW) - *03*	9	11

B362	**'Marlborough Gas Co.'** 4 black - *01-02*	8	10
OX6	'James **Marriott'** 91 black Sp Edn 200 (1E Promotionals) - *06*	8	10
-	**'Marshall Bros.'** 7 black Sp Edn (?) - *06*	8	10
-	**'Martin Bros.'** 26 brown no load Sp Edn (Mevagissy Model Railways) ex-set - *01*	10	NA
-	**'Martin Bros.'** 26 brown + chalk Sp Edn (Mevagissy Model Railways) ex-set - *02*	10	NA
(ANT003)	**'Matthew Grist'** 2 grey Sp Edn 100 (Antics) ex-set of 2 - *03*	9	NA
(ANT014)	**'Matthew Grist'** 2 grey Sp Edn 250 (Antics) - *05*	8	10
-	**'MC'** (Manchester Collieries) 10743 black Sp Edn 150 (Astley Green Colliery Museum) - *10*	7	9
-	'W **McMichael & Co.'** 5 red-brown Sp Edn 120 (Nene Valley Railway) - *07*	7	9
SWL8	**'Measham'** 1305 black Sp Edn 123 (Midlander) - *01*	10	12
-	**'Medway Coal Co.'** 17 black Sp Edn 1000 (Ballards) - *06*	7	9
-	'Charles **Meehan & Son'** **** black, Sp Edn 160 (West Wales Wagon Works) - *06*	8	10
-	'The **Mains Coal & Canal Co**.' 475 grey Sp Edn 200 (Buffers) - *?*	8	10
-	**'Mein, Wooding & C**o.' 250 black Sp Edn 120 (Barry & Penarth MRC) - *03*	9	11
No.7	**'Mellonie'** 244 grey Sp Edn 214 (Middy Trading Company) - *07*	7	9
No.20	'Elizabeth **Meredith Jones**' 1>9 red-brown Sp Edn 160 (W Wales Wagon Works) - *04*	9	11
-	**'Mid-Hants Rly'** green Sp Edn 110 (Mid-Hants Railway) - *03?*	9	11
4	**'Midland Coal, Coke & Iron'** 5004 red Sp Edn 200 (Haslington Models) - *02*	10	12
-	**'Midland Coal, Coke & Iron'** 2234 red-brown Sp Edn 200 (Tutbury Jinny) ex-set of 2 - *04*	9	NA
ANT001	''W **Miles'** 5 black Sp Edn 100 (Antics) - *03*	9	11
ANT?	''Wm **Miles'** 4 brown Ltd Edn 100 (Antics) - *09*	9	11
DAGM002	''Wm **Miles'** 4 brown Ltd Edn 160 (Gaugemaster) - *09*	8	10
B351	**'Miller & Lilley'** 66 black - *01-03*	7	9
-	**'Ministry of Munitions'** 5141 red Sp Edn 113 (West Wales Wagons Works) - *10*	8	11
-	**'Ministry of Munitions'** 5141 red W Sp Edn 45 (West Wales Wagons Works) - *10*	9	12
ANT026	'WW **Milton & Co.'** 6 grey Sp Edn 250 (Antics) - *07*	7	9
ANT026a	'WW **Milton & Co.'** 6 dark brown Sp Edn 250 (Antics) - *07*	7	9

7-plank - 'Moger & Co.' [W9b] (Dapol)

ANT015	'T **Mitchell**' 1902 black Sp Edn 250 (Antics) - *05*	8	10
-	**'Moger & Co.'** 576 red-brown Sp Edn 1000 (Ballards) - *08*	7	9
-	**'Moira'** 467 red brown Sp Edn 500 (Tutbury Jinny) - *00*	11	13
-	**'Moira'** 267 red-brown Sp Edn 200 (Tutbury Jinny) - *00*	11	13
B599	**'Mold Collieries'** 258 blue grey - *04-05*	7	9
-	**'Mold Collieries'** 258 grey (this is B599 factory over sprayed with light grey wash with a large 'P' and **'P12963'** Sp Edn 34 (Wirral Models) - *08*	15	20
-	**'Monk Bar'** deep blue 40th Anniversary Sp Edn (Monk Bar Model Shop) - *03*	9	11
(18)	**'Monmouth Steam Saw Mills'** 1 light grey Sp Edn 250 (Hereford Model Centre) - *05*	8	10
(16)	**'Monmouth Steam Saw Mills'** 7 black Sp Edn 250 (Hereford Model Shop) - *05*	8	10
(17)	**'Monmouth Steam Saw Mills'** 13 grey Sp Edn 250 (Hereford Model Centre) - *06*	8	10
(15)	**'Monmouth Steam Saw Mills'** 18 grey Sp Edn 250 (Hereford Model Shop) - *05*	8	10
-	**Moors Valley Railway** 2006 red Sp Edn 247 (Moors Valley Railway) - *06*	8	10
(14)	**'Morgan Bros.'** 14 light grey Sp Edn 250 (Hereford Model Centre) - *05*	8	10

7-plank - 'D.E. Morgan' [W9b] (Dapol)

23	**'Morgan Bros.'** 2 grey Sp Edn 250 (Hereford Model Centre) - *06*	8	10
(13)	**'Morgan Bros.'** 6 dark grey Sp Edn 250 (Hereford Model Centre) - *05*	8	10
-	**'Morgan Lloyd Williams'** 1072 grey Sp Edn 111 (Albatross Models) - *07*	7	9
-	'DE **Morgan**' 29 dark green with sand load Sp Edn (Albatross Models) - *08*	7	9
54	'EP&RL **Morgan**' 154 red-brown Sp Edn 250 (Hereford Model Shop) - *09*	6	8
-	**'Morris Bros.'** 22 red-brown Sp Edn 104 (West Wales Wagon Works) - *09*	6	8
-	**'Morris Bros.'** 22 red-brown W Sp Edn 30 (West Wales Wagon Works) - *09*	6	8
CA4	'Wm **Morris'** 100 black Sp Edn 175 (1E Promotionals) - *08*	7	9
(8)	**'Morris & Holloway'** 4 grey Sp Edn 250 (Hereford Model Centre) - *05*	8	10
-	**'Mortimore'** red-brown 56 Sp Edn 187 (Wessex Wagons) - *06*	8	10
-	**'Mottramwood'** 2021 red-brown Sp Edn (Midlander) - *03*	9	11
No.4	**'Moy'** 4194 red-brown Sp Edn 200 (Mid Suffolk Light Railway) - *04*	9	11
B553	'A **Munday**' 6 red-brown - *03*	7	9
No.35	**'Mwrwg Vale Colliery'** 26 black Sp Edn 124 (West Wales Wagon Works) - *06*	8	10
-	**'Mynydd Maen Colliery'** 105 light grey Sp Edn 110 (South Wales Coalfields) - *04*	9	11
-	**'Napier & Co.'** 25 black Sp Edn 110 (Roger Mileman) - *04*	9	11
-	**'Naval Colliery'** 540 black Sp Edn 108 (D Dacey) - *05*	8	10
-	**'NCB - Bowes'** 406 red-brown Sp Edn 100 (Bowes Railway) - *03+08*	7	9
-	**'Neath Abbey'** 15 black Sp Edn 101 (David Dacey) - *04*	9	11
-	**'Neath Merthyr Colliery'** 259 red-brown Sp Edn 107 (D Dacey) - *05*	8	10
SWL6	**'Netherseal'** 881 red brown Sp Edn 109 (Midlander) - *01*	10	12
No.32	**'New Cross Hands Colliery'** 390>399 *** grey Sp Edn 143 (WW Wagon Works) - *05*	8	10
No.9	**'New CwmGorse Colliery'** *** brown Sp Edn 160 (West Wales Wagon Works) - *03*	9	11
-	**'New Hey Industrial Co-operative'** 21 yellow Sp Edn 100 (Paul Devlin) - *04*	9	12
-	**'New Medway'** 19 red-brown Sp Edn 100 (Medway Queen) - *03, 04*	9	11
-	**'New Medway'** 19 black Sp Edn 100 (Medway Queen) - *03, 04*	9	11
-	**'New Medway'** 19 green Sp Edn 30 (Medway Queen) - *04*	12	14

-	**'New Medway'** 24 black Sp Edn 65 (Medway Queen) - *04*	11	13
-	**'New Medway'** 24 brown Sp Edn 65 (Medway Queen) - *04*	11	13
-	**'New Medway'** 24 green Sp Edn 30 (Medway Queen) - *04*	12	14
-	**'Newport & Abercarn'** 3 black Sp Edn 100 (David Dacey) - *08*	7	9
E03A	**'New Rock'** 207 black Sp Edn 150 (East Somerset Models) ex-set - *04*	9	11
E03B	**'New Rock'** 212 black Sp Edn 150 (East Somerset Models) ex-set - *04-05*	9	11
-	'FJ **Newton'** 37 grey Sp Edn 200 (Modellers Mecca) ex set - *02*	10	NA
B363	**'Nicholsons'** 1 black - *01-02*	8	10
HMC 60	**'Norchard'** 801 grey Sp Edn 250 (Hereford Model Centre) - *10*	6	8
B265	**'Normans Super Warehouse'** brown - *97-98*	9	11
B395	**'Norstand'** 376 maroon - *02-03*	7	9
-	**'North Cornwall'** 3 brown no load Sp Edn (Mevagissy Model Railways) ex-set - *01*	10	NA
-	**'North Cornwall'** 3 brown + chalk Sp Edn (Mevagissy Model Railways) ex-set - *02*	10	NA
-	**'North End'** 42 black Sp Edn 104 (D Dacey) - *05*	8	10
-	**'North & Rose'** 19 brown no load Sp Edn (Mevagissy Model Railways) ex-set - *00*	11	NA
-	**'North & Rose'** 19 brown + chalk Sp Edn (Mevagissy Model Railways) ex-set - *01*	10	NA
-	**North Norfolk Railway** brown Sp Edn (NNR) - ?	8	10
-	**'North Rhondda'** 21 very dark brown Sp Edn 110 (Jenny's) - *04*	9	11
37	**'Northern United'** 220 black Sp Edn 250 (Hereford Model Centre) - *06*	8	10
	'North's Navigation Collieries' 7 maroon Sp Edn 220 (MIB models) - *04*	9	15
-	**'Norton & Biddulph'** 3237 black Sp Edn 200 (Haslington Models) - *02*	10	15
-	**'Norton & Biddulph'** 3237 black Sp Edn 100 (Trident Trains) - *07*	7	9
No.3	**'Norton & Co.'** 176 black Sp Edn 213 (W.Wales Wagon Works) - *02-03*	9	11
NR7	**'Norwich Co-operative Society'** 16 red-brown Sp Edn 200 (1E Promotionals) - *08*	7	9
-	**'Notts & Derby'** 3601 black Sp Edn 195 (Sherwood Models) - *03*	9	11
-	**'Nottingham Corporation Gas'** 169 black Sp Edn 200 (Sherwood Models) - *02*	10	12
-	**'Novis & Son'** 1 bright red Sp Edn 1000 (Ballards) - *02-07*	6	8
TMCD009	**'NRM'** 2004 maroon Sp Edn 200 (TMC) - *04*	9	11
TMCD012	**'NRM'** Keep Scotsman Steaming black Sp Edn 4472 (TMC) - *05*	8	10

7-plank - 'NYMR' [W9b] (Dapol)

-	**NYMR** 454491 grey Sp Edn (North Yorkshire Moors Railway) - *01*	10	12
-	**NYMR** 454491 grey Sp Edn (North Yorkshire Moors Railway) letters small - *03*	9	11
-	**NYMR** 454491 grey Sp Edn (North Yorkshire Moors Railway) letters larger - *05*	8	10
5	'James **Oakes & Co**.' 772 black Sp Edn 200 (Haslington Models) - *02*	10	12
B331	**'Old Silkstone'** 2401 bright red - *01-02*	8	10
B565	**'Oldham Corporation Gas'** 019 red-brown - *03*	7	9
B558	**'Old Roundwood Collieries'** 312 red-brown - *03*	7	9
-	**'Orrell Colliery'** 443 bright red Sp Edn 100 (Red Rose Steam Society) - *05*	8	10
(ANT024)	**'Osman Trevor Powell'** 57 black Sp Edn 250 (Antics) - *05*	8	10
No.2	'GD **Owen'** 16 red-brown Sp Edn 400 ** (West Wales Wagon Works) - *02, 03*	9	11
-	**'Palmer & Sons'** 7 black Sp Edn 120 (West Wales Wagon Works) - *07*	7	9
RTR3	**'Parc-y-Bryn'** 58 black Sp Edn 250 (RD Whyborn) - *95?*	12	14
-	**'Parkhall & Foxfield'** 1143 red-brown Sp Edn 170 (West Wales Wagon Works) - *10*	9	11
-	**'Parkhouse Colliery'** 2993 brown Sp Edn 200 (Haslington Models) - *01*	10	12
B82	**'Parkinson'** 100 dark blue - *?-99*	9	11
-	**'Parkyn & Peters'** 35 red no load Sp Edn (Mevagissy Model Railways) ex-set - *00*	11	NA
-	**'Parkyn & Peters'** 35 red + chalk Sp Edn (Mevagissy Model Railways) ex-set - *01*	10	NA
-	**'Pates & Co.'** 18 bright red Sp Edn 200 (Cotswold Steam Preservation) - *08*	7	9
-	**'Pates & Co.'** 22 bright red Sp Edn 250 (Cotswold Steam Preservation) - *04*	9	11
-	**'Pates & Co.'** 24 bright red Sp Edn 200 (Cotswold Steam Preservation) - *05*	8	10
(19)	**'Payne & Son'** 2 bright red Sp Edn 250 (Hereford Model Centre) - *05*	8	10

7-plank - 'PD' (Powell Duffryn) [W9b] (Dapol)

WD3	'F **Payne'** 14 red-brown Sp Edn 250 (1E Promotionals) - *06*	8	10
-	**'PD'** (Powell Duffryn)1853 grey Sp Edn 205 (Bristol 2008 Model Railway Exhibition) - *08*	7	9
-	**'Peacock Bros. & Harris'** 6 brown Sp Edn 1000 (Ballards) - *04*	7	9
OX9	'AT **Pearse'** 7 maroon Sp Edn 200 (1E Promotionals) - *08*	7	9
-	**'Pemberton & Co.'** 25 dark brown Sp Edn 100 (Osbornes Models) - *05*	8	10
RM8	**'Pemberton & Co.'** 25 dark brown Sp Edn 150 (1E Promotionals) - *09*	8	10
-	**'Penlan Colliery'** 114 black Sp Edn (West Wales Wagon Works) - *07*	7	9
-	**'Penlan Colliery'** 114 black W Sp Edn (West Wales Wagon Works) - *07*	7	9
-	**'Penlan Colliery'** 117 black Sp Edn (West Wales Wagon Works) - *07*	7	9
-	**'Penlan Colliery'** 117 black W Sp Edn (West Wales Wagon Works) - *07*	7	9
-	**'Pennington Mining Co.'** 17 green Sp Edn 114 (Crafty Hobbies) - *09*	7	10
-	'Thos S **Penny'** 1 red-brown Sp Edn 180 (Wessex Wagons) - *05*	8	10
SWL9	**'Pentrich'** 1674 black Sp Edn 127 (Midlander) - *01*	10	12
-	'John **Perry'** 13 red-brown Sp Edn 345 (East Kent MRS) - *02*	10	12
-	**'Peterborough Coal & Coke Co.'** 143288 red-brown Sp Edn 750 (Osbornes) - *99*	10	12
-	**'Peterboro Coal Co.'** 404 black Sp Edn 95 (Nene Valley Railway) - *09*	6	8
-	**'Peterborough Co-op Society'** 138 grey Sp Edn 96 (Nene Valley Railway) - *08*	7	9

No.6	'SJ **Phillips**' 7 black Sp Edn 250 (West Wales Wagon Works) - *02*	10	12
B325	**'Phorpes Bricks'** 988 black - *01-02*	8	10
-	**'Pilch Collard'** 41 pale grey Sp Edn 170 (East Kent MRS) - *06*	8	10
No.18	**'Pilsley'** 4437 red brown Sp Edn 120 (Midlander) - *01*	10	12
IP5	'W **Pipe**' 20 black Sp Edn 200 (1E Promotionals) - *08*	7	9
-	**'Platelayers'** 2002 black Sp Edn 125 (Great British Train Show, Ontario) - *02*	10	12
ANT002	**'Plymouth Coal'** 309 black Sp Edn 250 (Antics) - *03*	9	11
-	**'Pochin'** 114 grey no load Sp Edn (Mevagissy Model Railways) ex-set - *00*	11	NA
-	**'Pochin'** 114 grey + chalk Sp Edn (Mevagissy Model Railways) ex-set - *01*	10	NA
B321	**'Polmaise'** A260 red-brown - *01-02*	8	10
-	**'Ponthenry Colliery Co.'** 143 brown Sp Edn 111 (Voyles) - *07*	7	9
-	**'Porter & Son'** 62 brown Sp Edn 85 (West Wales Wagon Works) - *10*	8	11
-	**'Porter & Son'** 62 brown W Sp Edn 62 (West Wales Wagon Works) - *10*	9	12
-	**'Porter & Son'** 121 grey Sp Edn 85 (West Wales Wagon Works) - *10*	8	11
-	**'Porter & Son'** 121 grey W Sp Edn 28 (West Wales Wagon Works) - *10*	9	12
-	**'The Port Talbot Steel Co.'** 20 dark red Sp Edn 110 (D Dacey) - *06*	8	10
B571	'J **Potts**' 531 blue - *04*	7	9

7-plank - 'Pountney & Co.' [W9b] (Dapol)

-	**'Pountney & Co.'** 2 black Sp Edn 130 (West Wales Wagon Works) - *08*	7	9
-	**'Powell, Gwinnell & Co.'** 191 black Sp Edn 1000 (Cotswold Steam Preservation Society) - *02*	9	11
-	**'Powell, Gwinnell & Co.'** 1121 black Sp Edn 200 (Cotswold Steam Preserv'n Soc.) - *05*	8	10
-	**'Primrose'** 489 black, Sp Edn 110 (South Wales Coalfields) - *03*	9	11
26	**'Prince of Wales Collieries'** 554 dark red Sp Edn 118 (Midlander) - *02*	10	12
55	**'Princess Royal Colliery Co.'** 301 red-brown Sp Edn 250 (Hereford model Shop) - *09*	6	8
-	'FW **Pinniger**' 2 black Sp Edn 200 (Geoff Osbourne's Railway & Model Shop) - *?*	12	15
HMC45	'James **Probert**' 5 black Sp Edn 250 (Hereford Model Centre) - *07*	7	9
PBR9	'Vernon **Pryce**' 7 red Sp Edn 250 (Pontypool & Blaenavon RS) - *05*	8	10
(ANT023)	**'Purified Flock & Bedding Co.'** 20 black Sp Edn 250 (Antics) - *05*	8	10
-	**'Pwllbach'** 279 dark brown Sp Edn 139 (D.Dacey) - *09*	7	9
-	**'Pryce Hughes'** 2 grey Sp Edn 141 (Llangollen Railway GW Loco Group) - *10*	7	10
-	**'Railway Enthusiasts Club'** grey Sp Edn 91 (Cove Models) - *04*	9	12
BY3	**'Rance & Reading'** 5 bright red Sp Edn 250 (1E Promotionals) - *05*	8	12
WD6	'Theodore **Ransome**' 18 reddy-pink Sp Edn 150 (1E Promotionals) - *09*	7	9
-	**'Raven Anthracite Collieries'** 313 maroon Sp Edn 100 (D Dacey) - *05*	8	10
-	**'Raunds Cooperative Society'** 2 bright blue Sp Edn 97 (Kitmaster Club) - *04*	9	12
-	**'G Rawlings & Sons'** 1 black Sp Edn 171 (Wessex Wagons) - *08*	7	9
-	'John **Read**' 1913 red Sp Edn 140 (Wessex Wagons) - *06*	8	10
B332	**'Redgrave'** 1386 grey - *01-02*	8	10
SWL4	**'Renishaw Park Collieries'** 379 red-brown Sp Edn 118 (Midlander) - *01*	10	12
B699	**'Renwick & Wilton'** 124 black - *07*	6	8
B552	**'Renwick, Wilton & Co.'** 521 brown - *03*	7	9
-	**'Renwick Wilton & Dobson'** 1020 black - *made?*	NPG	NPG
B333	**'Rhymney'** 1927 grey - *01-02*	8	10
-	'AET **Richards**' 2 black Sp Edn 110 (D Dacey) - *06*	8	10
-	'W **Rickman & Sons**' 8 red-brown Sp Edn 206 (Wessex Wagons) - *07*	7	9
-	**'Ripponden Industrial Society'** 10 black Sp Edn 250 (Sutcliff's Model Shop?) - *?*	8	10

7-plank - 'Rock Veins' [W9b] (Dapol)

B540	**'Rix & Groom'** 21 red - *03*	7	9
-	**'RNCF'** 15 grey Sp Edn 160 (Wessex Wagons) - *10*	7	10
-	'DA **Roberts**' 1 grey Sp Edn (?) - *?*	6	8
-	**'Rock Colliery'** 153 red-brown Sp Edn 143 (D. Dacey) - *10*	7	9
-	**'Rock Veins'** 61 red-brown Sp Edn 96 (South Wales Coalfields) - *05*	8	10
-	'John **Rogers & Son**' 3 light grey Sp Edn 250 (Antics) - *09*	7	9
-	'James **Roscoe & Sons**' 130 red-brown Sp Edn 100 (Red Rose Steam Society) - *08*	7	9
-	**'Rose Richards'** 114 black Sp Edn 100 (Richard Essen) - *08*	7	9
-	**'Rowe Camborne'** 14 red-brown Sp Edn 97 (Kernow MR Centre) - *05*	8	10
IP4	**'Rowland Manthorpe Co.'** 1400 red-brown Sp Edn 150 (1E Promotionals) - *07*	7	9
-	**'Rowland Manthorpe & Co.'** 20 red-brown Sp Edn 182 (Mid-Suffolk Light Railway) - *10*	7	10
-	'W **Sanders & Son**' 1 dark grey Ltd Edn (Wessex Wagons) - *09*	7	9
-	**'St Leger'** 225th Anniversary 86451 grey Peco extension planks supplied Sp Edn 225 (Oliver Leetham) - *01*	10	12
-	'Thomas Rees **Saunders**' 6? black Sp Edn 115 (West Wales Wagon Works) - *08*	7	9
-	'Thomas Rees **Saunders**' 6? black W Sp Edn 40 (West Wales Wagon Works) - *08*	9	11
-	'W **Saunders & Son**' 1 black Sp Edn 142 (Wessex Wagons) - *09*	8	10
-	'John **Scowercroft**' 1380 grey Sp Edn 100 (Red Rose Steam Society) - *08*	7	9
-	'J **Settle**' 25 grey Sp Edn 170 (Alsager Railway Association) - *04*	9	11
ANT037	**'Severn Valley Gas Corporation'** 105 grey Sp Edn 140 (Antics) - *09*	9	12
B361	**'Sharlston'** 1420 brown - *01-02*	8	10
B318	**'Sheepbridge'** 6091 red-brown - *00-02*	8	10
-	**'Sheffield & Eccleshall Co-op Soc.'** 13 maroon Sp Edn 100 (TAG Models) - *02*	10	12
B710	**'Sherwood'** 6089 maroon W - *07-08*	6	8
SWL13	**'Shipley'** 1254 red brown Sp Edn 130 (Midlander) - *01*	10	12
-	**'Siddons & Sons'** 12 red-brown Sp Edn 137 (Nene Valley Railway) - *10*	7	9

-	**'Silverdale Co.'** 175 red-brown Sp Edn (Tutbury Jinny) ex-set of 2 - *05*	8	NA
-	**'Silverhills Models & Toys'** crimson 25th Anniv. Sp Edn (Silverhill Models) - *04*	9	11
-	**'Sleight'** P201194 grey Sp Edn 50 (D Hewins) - *02*	12	14
-	**'Sleight'** P201083 grey Sp Edn 50 (D Hewins) - *02*	12	14
B594	**'Small & Son'** 17 black - *04-05*	7	9
-	**'Small & Son'** 17 black (this is B594 factory over sprayed with light grey wash with a large letter 'P' in centre and 'P12957' Sp Edn 34 (Wirral Models) - *08*	15	20
ANT030	'Alfred J **Smith'** 260 red-brown Sp Edn 250 (Antics) - *08*	7	9
-	'AW **Smith & Son**' 8 black Sp Edn 223 (Wessex Wagons) - *07*	7	9
-	'GH **Smith & Son (Fuel)**' 24 black Sp Edn 1000 (Ballards) - *02*	8	10

7-plank - 'James Smith' [W9b] (Dapol)

B520	'HG **Smith**' 24 red-brown - *03*	9	11
(ANT010)	'James **Smith**' 819 grey Sp Edn 250 (Antics) - *05*	8	10
SWL5	**'Sneyd'** 1414 red brown Sp Edn 104 (Midlander) - *01*	10	12
-	**'Snowdown'** * grey Sp Edn 300 (Hythe Models) 3rd issue - *00*	11	13
NR2	'P **Softley**' 11 grey Sp Edn 250 (1E Promotionals) - *04*	9	11
BI 1	**'South & Gasson'** 105 dark brown, Ltd Edn 225 (1E Promotionals) - *09*	7	9
-	**'South Ayrshire Collieries'** 68 red brown Sp 110 (Ayr Glass & Glazing) - *04*	9	11
-	**'South Crofty Mine'** 26 blue Sp Edn 110 (Blewetts of Hayle) - *02*	10	12
(6)	**'South Herefordshire'** 4 brown Sp Edn 250 (Hereford Model Centre) - *05*	8	10
-	**'South Leicester'** 2120 red Sp Edn 200 (Tutbury Jinny) ex-set of 2 - *02*	10	NA
B576	**'South Wales'** 20 grey - *04-05*	7	9
-	**'Southwold MRE'** blue-grey Sp Edn 500 (Southwold MRC) - *03*	9	11
SWL30	**'South Yorkshire Chemical Works'** 330 red-brown Sp Edn 140 (Midlander) - *03*	9	11
-	'John **Speakman & Sons**' 426 grey Sp Edn 100 (The Red Rose Steam Society) - *05*	8	10
-	**'Speech House'** Sp Edn 250 (RD Whyborn) - *93?*	12	14
27	**'Speech House Collieries'** 101 black Sp Edn 250 (Hereford Model Shop) - *06*	8	10
58	**'Speech House Collieries'** 102 black Sp Edn 250 (Hereford Model Centre) - *09*	6	8
59	**'Speech House Collieries'** 103 black Sp Edn 250 (Hereford Model Centre) - *09*	6	8
RTR1	**'Stafford Coal & Iron Co.'** 903 red-brown Sp Edn (Tutbury Jinny) ex-set of 2 - *05*	8	NA
B162	**'Stalybridge Corporation'** 15 brown (A) - *04*	6	10
B165	**'Stalybridge Corporation'** 18 brown (A) - *04*	6	10
-	**'Standard Merthyr'** 626 black Sp Edn 101 (David Dacey) - *04*	9	11
-	**'Stanton'** 9958 red-brown Sp Edn (Albatross Models) - *08*	7	9
-	**'Stanton'** 9988 red-brown Sp Edn (Railway & Barter Shop) - *08*	7	9
B617	**'Staveley'** 4994 black - *05*	7	9
-	**'Steamtown'** black Sp Edn (Steamtown Museum Shop) - *?*	8	10
B396	**'Steam Trawlers Coal & Trading Co.'** 71 brown - *02-03*	7	9
-	'IL **Stent**' 3 black Sp Edn 100 (Richard Essen) - *08*	7	9
ANT025	'John **Stephens, Son & Co**.' 26 black Sp Edn 250 (Antics) - *06*	8	10
OX1	**'Stevens & Co.'** 31 bright red Sp Edn 250 (1E Promotionals) - *04*	9	11
-	**'Stevens & Son'** 1 black Sp Edn 140 (Buffers) - *10*	8	10
-	**'Stewart Coal Co.'** 2320 brown Sp Edn 107 - *?*	8	10
CA6	'FD **Stigwood & Sons**' 2 black Sp Edn 150 (1E Promotionals) - *10*	7	9
-	**'Stirrup & Pye'** 848 black Sp Edn 150 (The Hobby Goblin) - *10*	7	9
-	**'Stuart Coal Coy.'** 85? dark brown Sp Edn 107 (Barry & Penarth MRC) - *03*	9	11
-	'GS **Sturgeon**' 465 black Sp Edn 330 (Ballards) - *01*	10	12
-	**'Sully & Co.'** 596 black Sp Edn 186 (Wessex Wagons) - *05*	8	10
B370	**'Summers'** 69 black - *02-03*	7	9
-	'Edward **Sutcliffe**' 75 red-brown Sp Edn 124 (West Wales Wagon Works) - *10*	8	11
-	'Edward **Sutcliffe**' 75 red-brown W Sp Edn 38 (West Wales Wagon Works) - *10*	9	12
ANT039	**'Sutton'** 48 red-brown Sp Edn 170 (Antics) - *09*	9	12
-	**'Sutton Heath Collieries'** 1186 grey Sp Edn 100 (Astley Green Mining Museum) - *09*	7	9
B195	**'Sutton Manor'** 1075 light grey - *90,95-02*	8	10
-	**'Sutton Manor'** 1480 grey Sp Edn 100 (The Red Rose Steam Society) - *09*	8	10
-	**'Swansea Navigation'** 247 black Sp Edn 100 (David Dacey) - *03*	9	11

7-plank - 'H S. Syrus' [W9b] (Dapol)

SWL10	**'Swanwick'** 551 bright red Sp Edn 137 (Midlander) - *01*	10	12
-	**'Symes'** 21 black Sp Edn (?) - *09*	8	10
-	'H **Syrus**' 1 pale grey Sp Edn 1000 (Ballards) - *05*	7	19
-	**'Talk-O'Th Hill Colliery'** 5 red-brown Sp Edn (Tutbury Jinny) ex-set of 2 - *05*	8	NA
No.40	'GW **Talbot**' 703 brown Sp Edn 141 (West Wales Wagon Works) - *06*	8	10
-	'AF **Tapp & Son**' 5 red-brown Sp Edn 192 (Wessex Wagons) - *05*	8	10
NR8	**'Tassell'** 107 red-brown Sp Edn 200 (1E Promotionals) - *08*	7	9
-	'A **Taunt**' 3 blue Sp Edn 190 (Hythe Models) 1st issue - *04*	9	11
B529	'C H **Taylor**' 3 grey - *03*	7	9
B368	'R.**Taylor**' 451 red-brown - *02-03*	7	9

B604	'S.**Taylor,** Firth' 731 red - *04-05*	7	9
TVR1	**'Teifi Valley'** 1 dark green Sp Edn 108 (TVR) - *00*	11	13
TVR2	**'Teifi Valley'** 285 black Sp Edn 121 (TVR) - *01*	10	12
TVR3	**'Teifi Valley'** 28 black Sp Edn 97 (TVR) - *01*	10	12
No.8	**'Teifi Valley'** 20 green Sp Edn 91 (West Wales Wagon Works) - *03*	9	11
-	**'Ten Commandments'** bright red Sp Edn 100 (Ten Commandments) - *02*	10	12
No.14	**'Thomas Thomas'** various numbers black + filled with builders materials Sp Edn 200 (West Wales Wagon Works) - *04*	9	11
B708	'William **Thomas**' 1 black - *07-08*	6	8
-	'William **Thomas & Co.**' 1 black Sp Edn 167 (Wessex Wagons) - *05*	8	10
BY10	**'Thomas & Green'** 10 red-brown Sp Edn 150 (1E Promotionals) - *08*	8	10
-	**'Thomas, Rees Sanders'** 6 black Sp Edn 115 (West Wales Wagon Works) - *08*	7	9
B103	**'Thrutchley'** 2212 red - *86-92, 96-02*	8	10
-	**'Tilmanstone'** * red-brown Sp Edn 100 (Hythe Kent Models) - *00*	11	13
-	**'Tilmanstone'** * dark brown Sp Edn 200 (Hythe Kent Models) - *00*	11	13
-	**'Tilmanstone'** *dark brown Sp Edn 310 (Hythe Kent Models) - *00*	11	13
-	**'Tilmanstone'** * dark brown Sp Edn 514 (Hythe Kent Models) - *00*	11	13
B371	'John J **Tims**' 413 brown - *02-03*	7	9
-	**'Timsbury Colliery'** 14 red Sp Edn 200 (Buffers) - *04*	9	11
-	**'Timsbury Colliery'** 15 red Sp Edn 200 (Buffers) - *05*	8	10
PBR1	**'Tirpentwys'** 121 black Sp Edn 100 (Pontypool & Blaenavon Railway) - *02*	10	12
PBR15	**'Tirpentwys'** 457 black Sp Edn 250 (Pontypool & Blaenavon Railway Society) - *08*	7	9
-	'**Ton Hir Colliery**' 217 black Sp Edn 117 (D Dacey) - *04*	9	11
-	**'Ton Phillip Rhondda'** 277 black Sp Edn 102 (David Dacey) - *05*	8	10
-	'R **Toomers & Co.**' **** black Sp Edn 87 (West Wales Wagon Works) - *07*	10	12
-	'R **Toomers & Co.**' black W Sp Edn 86 (West Wales Wagon Works) - *07*	10	12

7-plank - 'Treoch Granite' [W9b] (Dapol)

-	**'Travis Perkins'** dark green Sp Edn 155 (Travis Perkins) - *06*	8	10
-	**'Tredegar'** 3410 grey Sp Edn 140 (D.Dacey) - *10*	7	9
-	**'Treoch Granite Co.'** blue-grey Sp Edn 120 (Model Rail) - *06*	8	10
-	**'Trimsaram Anthracite'** 295 dark blue Sp Edn 96 (David Dacey) - *08*	7	9
-	**'Tunbridge Wells Co-operative Society'** 1 red-brown Sp Edn 1000 (Ballards) - *04*	9	11
OX3	'B **Turner**' 20 red-brown Sp Edn 250 (1E Promotionals) - *05*	8	10
B587	'E.**Turner & Sons**' 25 cream - *04*	7	9
53	'E.**Turner & Sons**' 25 cream Sp Edn 250 (Hereford model Shop) - *09*	6	8
-	**'Tyldesley Coal Co.'** 289 red-brown Sp Edn 100 (Astley Green Mining Museum) - *07*	7	9
-	**'Tyldesley Coal Co.'** 598 red-brown Sp Edn 150 (Astley Green Mining Museum) - *10*	8	10
-	**'Tynygraig'** 28 black Sp Edn 108 (D Dacey) - *06*	8	10
43	**'Underwood & Co.'** 100 red Sp Edn 250 (Hereford Model Centre) - *07*	7	9
B516	**'United Collieries'** 1505 black - *03*	7	9
B516	**'United Collieries'** 1505 dark grey - *03*	10	15
-	**'Vale of Glamorgan'** Sp Edn (Vale of Glamorgan Railway) - *05*	8	10
-	**'Vancey'** 20 ? Sp Edn (Wessex Wagons) - *07*	8	10
-	**'V&S Morfa Colliery'** 142 black Sp Edn 165 (D.Darcy) - *10*	7	9
-	**'Varteg Collieries'** 312 black, Sp Edn 130 (D Dacey) - *03*	9	11
-	**'Victoria Coal - Wales' Best Productions'** 10 grey Sp Edn 102 (David Dacey) - *06*	8	10
No.33	'W **Vincent & Co.**' **** red Sp Edn 160 (W Wales Wagon Works/Shirehampton MR Show) - *06*	8	10
PBR12	'John **Vipond**' 814 brown Sp Edn 280 (Pontypool & Bleanavon Railway Society) - *05*	8	10
-	'John **Vipond**' 877 dark brown Sp Edn 101 (South Wales Coalfields) - *03*	9	11
RM8	**'FW Wacher'** 6 black Sp Edn 275 (1E Promotionals) - *09*	7	9

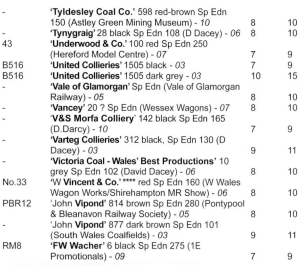

7-plank - 'Wales Best Productions' [W9b] (Dapol)

ANT018	**'Walker & Rogers'** 3 bright red Sp Edn 250 (Antics) - *05*	8	10
1st	'John **Walker**' 2 black Sp Edn 150 (Castle Trains) - *07*	7	9
-	**'Ward & Son'** 14 red-brown Sp Edn 1000 (Ballards) - *02*	8	10
ANT009	'ET **Ward** 4 black Sp Edn 100 (Antics) - *04*	9	11
-	**'Warwick Coal'** ? ? Sp Edn (The Midlander) - *02*	10	12
TMCD003A	**'Waterloo"** 853 black, Sp Edn 100 (The Model Centre) - *03*	9	11
TMCD003B	**'Waterloo'** 932 black, Sp Edn 100 (The Model Centre) - *03*	9	11
TMCD003C	**'Waterloo'** 949 black, Sp Edn 100 (The Model Centre) - *03*	9	11
SWL21	**'Wath Main'** 1875 red brown Sp Edn 159 (Midlander) - *02*	10	12
-	'William **Watkeys**' 465 dark brown Sp Edn 107 (Voyles) - *07*	7	9
B608	**'Webbs' Coals'** 86 black - *04-05*	7	9
(B522)	'R **Webster & Sons**' 302 maroon - *03*	7	NA
-	**'Wellingborough'** 29 grey Sp Edn 128 (Kitmaster Collectors Club) - *06*	8	10
-	**'West Goonbarrow'** 28 grey no load Sp Edn (Mevagissy Model Railways) - *01*	10	12
-	**'West Goonbarrow'** 28 grey + chalk Sp Edn (Mevagissy Model Railways) ex-set - *02*	10	NA
-	**'West of England'** 126 light grey no load Sp Edn (Mevagissy Model Railways) ex-set - *00*	11	NA
-	**'West of England'** 126 light grey + chalk Sp Edn (Mevagissy Model Railways) ex-set - *01*	10	NA
-	**'WLC West Leigh Collieries'** 868 red Sp Edn 100 (Astley Green Mining Museum) - *09*	7	9
-	**'West Wales Wagon Works'** 60 ? Sp Edn (West Wales Wagon Works) - *07*	10	12
B596	**'Western Valleys'** 670 dark brown - *04-05*	7	9
-	**'Wetmore'** 27 dark red Sp Edn 183 (Assoc. of Model Railway Clubs Wales & West England) - *07*	7	9
SWL29	**'Wharncliffe Woodmoor'** 1540 red-brown Sp Edn (Midlander) - *02*	7	9

7-plank - 'Richard White' [W9b] (Dapol)

B614	**'White & Beeny'** 17 black - *05*	7	9
ANT035	'Richard **White & Sons'** 109 light blue Sp Edn 250 (Antics) - *08*	7	10
-	**'Whitehaven'** 11 light grey Sp Edn 180 (Crafty Hobbies) - *10*	8	11
-	**'White Moss'** 174 red Sp Edn (Red Rose Steam Society) - *09*	6	8
-	**'White, Winchester & Eastley'** ? ? Sp Edn (Wessex Wagons) - *07*	10	12
B649	**'Whitwood'** 1583 grey+red - *06*	7	9
-	**'Whitstable Shipping'** 21 black Sp Edn 330 (East Kent MRS) - *01*	10	12
-	**'Whitstable Shipping'** 22 brown Sp Edn 110 (East Kent MRS) - *02*	10	12
-	**'Whitstable Shipping'** 24 grey Sp Edn 130 (East Kent MRS) - *03*	9	11
-	**'Whitstable Shipping'** 21 black Sp Edn (1E Promotionals) - *08*	7	9
RM7	**'Whitstable Shipping Co.'** 21 black Sp Edn 275 (1E Promotionals) - *09*	7	9
No.45	**'Whitwill Cole & Co.'** **** black Sp Edn 176 (West Wales Wagon Works) - *06*	8	10
B649	**'Whitwood'** 1583 pale grey - *?*	8	10
-	**'Whitwick Colliery'** 1046 black Sp Edn 200 (Tutbury Jinny) ex-set of 2 - *02*	10	NA
B598	**'Wigan Coal & Iron'** A147 grey - *04-05*	7	9
-	**'Wigan Coal & Iron'** A147 grey (this is B598 factory over sprayed with light grey wash with a large 'P' and 'P12959' Sp Edn 34 (Wirral Models) - *08*	15	20
WO3	**'Wiggins'** 276 black Sp Edn 250 (1E Promotionals) - *06*	8	10
-	**'Wilkin Coal Company'** 291 black Sp Edn 160 (Wessex Wagons) - *10*	7	9
-	'Joseph **Williams & Son'** 134 red-brown Sp Edn 106 (Welshpool & Llanfair Railway) - *09*	7	9
-	'Robert **Williams'** ? ? Sp Edn (Hereford Model Centre) - *07?*	8	10
-	'TL **Williams'** 29 red Sp Edn 120 (Barry & Penarth MRC) - *03*	9	11
(1)	'WT **Williams'** 6 brown Sp Edn 500 (Hereford Model Centre) - *01*	10	12
-	**'Williams, Foster & Co.'** 203 dark grey Sp Edn 106 (South Wales Coalfields) - *04*	9	11

7-plank - 'Williams' [W9b]

WO5	**'Williams'** 13 brown Sp Edn 200 (1E Promotionals) - *07*	7	9
-	**'Willmer & Son'** 3069 red-brown Sp Edn 100 (Wicor Models) ex-set of 2 - *07*	7	NA
-	**'Willmer & Son'** 3073 red-brown Sp Edn 100 (Wicor Models) ex-set of 2 - *07*	7	NA
-	**'Wimberry'** 2 black Sp Edn (Dean Sidings) - *03*	9	11
-	**'Winchcombe Coal Co.'** 12 grey Sp Edn 1000 (Glous & Wark Railway) - *98*	10	12
-	**'Winchcombe Coal Co.'** 10 grey Sp Edn 1000 (Glous & Wark Railway) - *00*	9	11
-	**'Winchcombe Coal Co.'** 7 grey Sp Edn (Gloustershire & Warwickshire Railway) - *03?*	9	11
-	**'Windsor'** 1584 black Sp Edn 124 (South Wales Coalfield) - *04*	9	11
-	**'Winstanley Collieries'** 592 grey Sp Edn 90 (Red Rose Steam Society) - *08*	8	10
-	**'WM'** (White Moss Colliery) 174 red-brown Sp Edn 100 (Red Rose Steam Society) - *09*	7	9
-	**'Wolstanton Cardox Mined Coals'** 601 grey Sp Edn 100 (Trident Trains) - *07*	7	9
-	**'Woolcombers'** 15 red-brown Sp Edn 72 (West Wales Wagon Works) - *09*	6	8
-	**'Woolcombers'** 15 red-brown W Sp Edn 30 (West Wales Wagon Works) - *09*	6	8
-	'Tom **Wright'** 19 red-brown Sp Edn 500 (Peak Rail Stock Fund) - *03*	9	11
B554	**'Wright's'** 14 brown - *03*	7	9
-	**'Writhlington Colliery'** 160 dark grey Sp Edn 200 (Buffers) - *04*	9	11
-	**'Writhlington Colliery'** 140 dark grey Sp Edn (Buffers) - *05*	8	10
-	**'Writhlington Colliery'** 144 dark grey Sp Edn (Buffers) - *not made*	NA	NA
29	'John **Yates'** 3 grey Sp Edn 250 (Hereford Model shop) - *06*	8	10
-	**'Yeovil Gas Works'** 24 dark brown Sp Edn 200 (Buffers) - *04*	9	11
-	**'Yeovil Gas Works'** 25 dark brown Sp Edn 200 (Buffers) - *04*	9	11
-	**'Yeovil Railway Centre'** black Sp Edn 200 (Buffers) - *04*	9	11
-	**'Ynisgynon'** 160 black Sp Edn 90 (South Wales Coalfields) - *05*	8	10
-	**'Ystradgynlais & Yniscedwyn'** 779 black Sp Edn 100 (W Wales Wagon Wks) - *not made*	NA	NA
	Railway Companies		
-	**G&KERy** 67 mid grey Sp Edn 200 (Toys2Save) - *03*	9	11
-	**G&SW** (Ayr Glass & Glazing) - *not made*	NA	NA
No.3	**GE** 5043 grey Sp Edn 200 (Mid-Suffolk Light Railway) - *03*	9	11
-	**GN** 39850 brown Sp Edn 92 (Old Wagon Works) - *03*	9	11
B14	**GW** (thick) 06515 dark grey - *95-01?*	8	10
B14	**GW** (thin) 29019 dark grey - *95-01?*	8	10
B348	**GW** 06512 grey - *01-09*	6	8
B348A	**GW** 06577 grey [1] - *10*	6	8
-	**GW** 45,51,64,451,645,864,6451,8645 and 86851 dark grey part hand painted from St Ledger wagon + Peco extensions horse wagon Sp Edn 33 (Oliver Leetham) - *04*	12	15
B6	**LMS** 609525 red brown - *84-92*	9	11
B337	**LMS** 602504 light grey - *01-05*	8	10
B111	**LMS** 602604 grey - *89-?*	6	10
B111	**LMS** 602508 grey - *?-99*	8	10
B758	**LMS** 302511 grey - *09*	6	8
B758A	**LMS** 502078 grey [1] - *10*	6	8
-	**LWR** LW114 grey Sp Edn 100 (Leadhills & Wanlochhead Railway) - *03*	9	11
B12	**NE** 171519 grey - *84-89*	9	11
B356	**NE Loco** HB4333 grey - *01-02*	8	10
-	**NE Loco Coal** 454941 dark grey Sp Edn 100 (Grantham Railway Society) - *08*	7	9
	SECR various numbers dark grey part hand painted from above + Peco extension, sheep wagon Sp Edn 20 (Oliver Leetham) - *04*	12	15
	SER various numbers dark grey part hand painted ex-St Ledger + Peco extension, sheep wagon Sp Edn 40 (Oliver Leetham) - *04*	12	15

These 3 wagons were standard issues of which there were large stocks. 34 of each were lightly sprayed grey in the factory and then over printed with a large letter 'P' and a new ex-private owner number for a customer in the Wirrel.

B205	**SR** 37427 dark brown - *94-95*	9	11
B328	**SR** 37423 dark brown - *01-07*	7	9
4	**WHR** 60 grey Sp Edn (Welsh Highland Rly) - *08*	7	9
B568	**BR** P238864 grey - *04-09*	6	8
B568A	**BR** P238832 grey [1] - *10*	6	8
B10	**BR** P130288 grey (M) - *84-96*	9	11
-	**CIE** 412d grey Sp Edn (Mark's Models) - *02?*	9	11

* These were delivered unnumbered and were individually numbered by Steve Skelton of Hythe (Kent) Models. ** 200 were sold as solo models and the other 200 came in wagon sets. *** The 5 loads are Dapol coal, real coal, crushed brick rubble, limestone and crystaline salt. Just 96 of each load were made. **** These were individually numbered by West Wales Wagon Works. ***** 3 alternative numbers. . [1] Possibly renumbered unsold stock. [2] produced to commemorate the 900th Anniversary of the town of Cardigan. The actual wagon carried the number "900" - the original had the number "18". Also, available with sand, bricks, planks or coal load.

Larger Coal & Cole Wagons

W10a. 8-plank Open Wagon with 9' Chassis (2010)

This model has the 9ft wheelbase timber chassis. W = weathered.

-	**'Sheffield & Eccleshall'** 12 red Sp Edn 140 (Antics) - *10*	9	12

W10b. 8-plank Open Wagon with 10' Chassis (2006)

W = weathered.

-	**'Aberthaw & Bristol Channel'** 39 red-brown Sp Edn 98 (David Dacey) - *08*	7	9
B863	'**Banks**' 351 light grey - *10*	9	11
B681	'HC**Bull & Co**.' 103 brown - *06-07*	6	8
CR1	'JT **Buxton & Sons'** 1930 red-brown Sp Edn 200 (1E Promotionals) - *08*	7	9
B696	**'Chatterley-Whitfield'** 4055 grey - *07*	6	8
SY3	**'City of Birmingham Gas Dept.**' 1225 red-brown Sp Edn 300 (1E Promotionals Warley Charity link) - *10*	7	9
-	**'Colliery Supply Co.'** 7 red-brown Sp Edn 306 (Wessex Wagons) - *08*	7	9
-	'Hiram **Cox**' 10 beige Sp Edn 245 (Wessex Wagons) - *08*	7	9
-	**'Cramer & Sons'** 23 black Sp Edn 258 (Wessex Wagons) - *08*	7	9
BE6	'John **Facer & Son'** 120 maroon Sp Edn 150 (1E Promotionals) - *07*	7	9
B840	**'Hatfield Main'** 1213 red-brown - *10*	7	9
-	'RW **Hearn & Son'** 105 red-brown, brick load, Sp Edn 276 (Wessex Wagons) - *07*	7	9

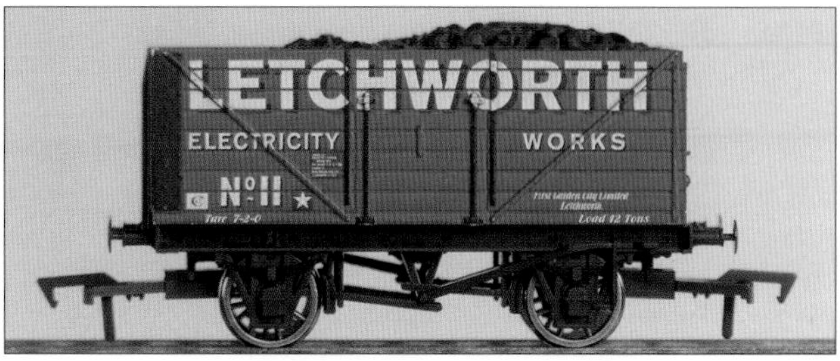

8-plank - 'Letchworth Electricity Works' [W10b]

BE9	'B **Laporte**' 55 black, white Barite load, Sp Edn 150 (1E Promotionals) - *10*	7	9
B730	**'LC'** (Littleton Collieries) 151 black - *08*	6	8
WD5	**'Letchworth Electricity Works'** 11 red-brown Sp Edn 150 (1E Promotionals) - *08*	7	9
-	**'Measham Collieries'** 1308 black Sp Edn (Tutbury Jinny) - *08*	7	9
-	**'Minehead Gas Light & Coke Co.'** 73 light grey Sp Edn 325 (Wessex Wagons) - *09*	7	9
B705	**'Osborne & Son'** 11 grey W - *07*	6	8
-	'WT **Parkes'** 19 dark brown Sp Edn 195 (Wessex Wagons) - *07*	7	9
B825	**'Partington Steel & Iron Co.'** 184 grey - *10*	7	9
-	**'Porter & Son'** * brown Sp Edn (West Wales Wagon Works) - *10*	7	9
-	**'Porter & Son'** * brown W Sp Edn (West Wales Wagon Works) - *10*	7	9
-	**'Porter & Son'** * grey Sp Edn (West Wales Wagon Works) - *10*	7	9
-	**'Porter & Son'** * grey W Sp Edn (West Wales Wagon Works) - *10*	7	9
-	**'Pugh & Co.'** 380 red-brown Sp Edn 1000 (Ballards) - *08*	7	9
-	**'Railway Employees Coal Club - St Albans City'** 3 black Sp Edn 85 (St Albans Signal Box Preservation Trust) - *08*	7	9
-	**'Railway Employees Coal Club - St Albans City'** 3 black W Sp Edn 25 (St Albans Signal Box Preservation Trust) - *08*	8	10
-	**'Railway Employees Coal Club - St Albans City'** 2 black Sp Edn (St Albans Signal Box Preservation Trust) - *10*	9	12
NR6	'B **Raywood & Son'** 1933 black Sp Edn 150 (1E Promotionals) - *07*	7	9
B669	**'Royal Leamington Spa'** 24 brown - *06-07*	6	8
-	**'Shelton Iron Steel & Coal'** 2298 red Sp Edn 100 (Trident Trains) - *07*	7	9
B671	**'Smith Parkinson & Cole'** 5009 black - *06-07*	6	8
B820	**'South Wales & Cannock Chase Coal & Coke Co.'** 977 light grey - *10*	7	9
-	**'Tenterden Brewery Co.'** 148 red-brown Sp Edn (Col. Stephens Railway Enterprise) - *08*	8	10
B675	**'Thorncliffe Izal'** 2915 black - *06-07*	6	8
-	**'Westbury Iron Works'** 51 dark brown Sp Edn 236 (Wessex Wagons) - *07*	7	9
-	'TW **Woolford'** 1908 grey Sp Edn 182 (Wessex Wagons) - *08*	7	9

* Various numbers applied by West Wales Wagon Works.

W11. 9-plank Coke Wagon (ex-Mainline) (c1989)

B152	**'Baldwin'** 2030 black (M) - *c89*	6	10
B148	**'Bedwas'** 621 light grey (M) - *c89*	6	10
B154	**'Carpenter'** 28 red (M) - *c89*	6	10
B156	**'CCC'** 105 dark red (M) - *c89*	6	10
B150	**'Coalite'** 552 dark brown new chassis (M) - *c89*	6	10
B71	**'Dinnington'** 254 red brown (M) - *85-89*	6	10
B151	**'MOY'** 1851 red brown (M) - *c89*	6	10
B153	'Arthur H **Stabler**' 21 grey (M) - *c89*	6	10
B149	**'TCD'** 171 dark brown (M) - *c89*	6	10

B155	**'TWW'** 1746 brown (M) - *c89*	6	10

Although a number of other coke wagons were illustrated in catalogues we have found no evidence that any were sold in Dapol packaging.

W12a. NE 20T 9-plank Mineral Wagon (ex-Airfix) (1985)

A9	brown or grey - unfinished - *85-02*	4	6
B54	**'Charringtons'** 257 brown (M) - *85-88*	7	11
B55	**'Gas Light & Coke'** 794 grey (M) - *85-88*	7	11
B114	**NE** 31273 grey (A) - *?*	7	11
B266	**NE** 31285 grey ex-set B402 - *97-02*	6	8
B115	**BR** E10995, E30995 grey (A) - *86-?*	7	11
B115	**BR** E30996 grey - *?- 02*	6	8

The tools were sold to Hornby in 1996 and the model reintroduced by them.

W12b. NE 20T 9-plank Mineral Wagon (2005)

This model was one of four new wagons tooled up in 2005.

B864	**'Baldwin'** 4602 black - *10*	9	12
B661	**'Bedwas Coke'** 331 brown - *06*	7	9
B641	**'Charringtons'** 259 red-brown - *05-06*	7	9
B689	**'Co-operative Society Ltd - Dovercourt Bay'** red-brown - *07*	7	9
B637	**'The Gas Light & Coke Co.'** 766 pale grey - *05*	7	9
S1153	**'Geoscenics Natural Scenic Products'** dark green, coal in-fill + bag of natural stone Sp Edn 100* (Geoscenics) - *07*	8	10
ANT 036	**'Gloucester'** black Sp Edn 250 (Antics) - *07*	7	9
-	**'Harrogate Gas Co.'** 14 black Sp Edn 94 (Starbeck Models) - *08*	7	9
No.38	**'Isambard Kingdom Brunel'** 1806 green Sp Edn 120 (West Wales Wagon Works) - *06*	8	10
B670	**'Lowell Baldwin'** 4301 black - *not made*	NA	NA
B670	**'Lowell Baldwin'** 4601 black - *06*	7	9
TVR4	**'Teifi Valley'** 25 dark green Sp Edn 140 (TVR /West Wales Wagon Works) - *08*	7	9
B651	**'Welingborough Gas Light Company'** 5 grey - *06*	7	9
B631	**BR** E30994 grey - *05-09*	6	8
B631A	**BR** E30910 grey - *10*	7	9

* Actually 117 made but 17 retained by shop.

Steel Open Wagons

W13. 'Grampus' Ballast Wagon (2008)

The wagon has self-centering couplings in NEM pockets and steel buffers. Wagons are supplied with a granite load. The original chassis had grease type axleboxes but in 2009 Dapol introduced a chassis with roller bearing axleboxes. The new moulding has shorter and slimmer buffers, a vacuum cylinder underneath and steel bar across the chassis to the brake handles. The brake handles are also different.

B742	**'Taunton Concrete Works'** DB986428 dark green - *08*	10	13
B742A	**'Taunton Concrete Works'** DB986700 dark green - *10*	10	13
B734	**BR** DB990488 black Grampus - *08*	10	13
B734/1	**BR** DB988395 black Grampus * Sp Edn 250 (Hattons) - *09*	10	13
B734/5	**BR** DB988393 black Grampus * Sp Edn 275 (Hattons) - *09*	9	12
B734/2	**BR** DB988395 black W Grampus * Sp Edn 250 (Hattons) - *09*	10	13
B734/6W	**BR** DB988393 black W Grampus * Sp Edn 360 (Hattons) - *09*	9	12
B734/3	**BR** DB990173 olive green Grampus * Sp Edn 250 (Hattons) - *09*	10	12
B734/4	**BR** DB990173 olive green W Grampus * Sp Edn 250 (Hattons) - *09*	10	12
B822a	**BR** Eng. DB990644 brown - *10*	10	13
B822b	**BR** Eng. DB990646 brown - *10*	10	13
B836a	**BR** Eng. DB990648 brown W - *10*	10	14
B836b	**BR** Eng. DB990641 brown W - *10*	10	14
B749a	**BR** Eng. DB988456 grey+yellow - *09*	10	13
B749b	**BR** Eng. DB991640 grey+yellow - *09*	10	13
B749c	**BR** Eng. DB991571 grey+yellow - *09*	10	13
B749d	**BR** Eng. DB991500 grey+yellow - *09*	10	13
B749e	**BR** Eng. DB988546 grey+yellow - *09*	10	13
B749f	**BR** Eng. DB991487 grey+yellow - *09*	10	13
B749g	**BR** Eng. DB988237 grey+yellow - *09*	10	13
B749h	**BR** Eng. DB991747 grey+yellow - *09*	10	13
B756a	**BR** Eng. DB988458 grey+yellow W - *09*	10	13
B756b	**BR** Eng. DB991643 grey+yellow W - *09*	10	13
B836a	**BR** Eng. ? red-brown W - *10*	10	14
B836b	**BR** Eng. ? red-brown W - *10*	10	14

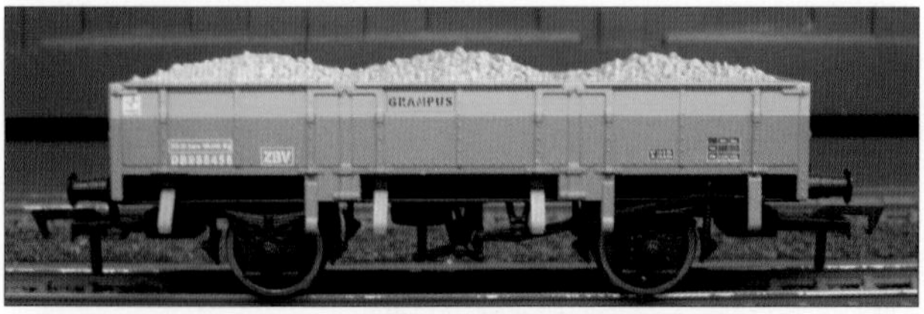

'Grampus' ballast wagon with load [W13] (Dapol)

* New roller bearing chassis.

W14. YCV 'Turbot' Ballast Wagon (2011)

-	**ER** Eng. ? grey+yellow - *11*	NPG	NPG
-	**ER** Eng. ? grey+yellow - *11*	NPG	NPG
-	**ER** Eng. ? grey+yellow - *11*	NPG	NPG
-	**ER** Eng. ? grey+yellow - *11*	NPG	NPG
-	**EWS**. ? maroon - *11*	NPG	NPG
-	**EWS**. ? maroon - *11*	NPG	NPG
-	**EWS**. ? maroon - *11*	NPG	NPG
-	**EWS**. ? maroon - *11*	NPG	NPG

W15. 13T Steel Sided Wagon (1995)

The former Hornby Dublo steel wagon body tool was lost and so Dapol had a copy made.

B237	**'BAC'** 4253 red brown - *c95*	10	15
WR1-26	as above - *?*	10	15
WR3-06	as above - *98-02*	10	15
TMCD011	**NRM** 2004 maroon Sp Edn 200 (TMC) - *04*	12	18
B236	**'NTG'** B486863 buff - *c95*	10	15
WR1-19	as above - *99*	10	15
WR2-17	as above Dapol chassis - *99*	10	12
TVM/ No.19	**TVR** Extension Project Department 120>129 grey Sp Edn 170 (W Wales WW) - *04*	12	18
B238	**BR** B466865 brown - *c95*	10	15
WR1-50	as above - *99*	10	15
WR2-32	**BR** B468865 red-brown + coal 12T - *99*	10	12
B354	**BR** Soda Ash B745543 grey + grey load - *01-02*	8	10
B358	**BR** B490563 grey + coal - *01-03*	8	10
B559	**BR** B489177 red-brown Sand - *03*	7	9
B691	**BR** B480202 red-brown - *07*	6	8
B826	**BR** B478605 red-brown - *10*	7	9

W16a. 16T Steel Mineral Wagon (ex-Mainline) (1985)

B28	**'ICI'** 776 dark blue (M) - *86*	6	10
WR2-10	**'Shell'** silver - *01*	8	10
B27	**BR** B118301 grey (M) - *86*	6	10
B73	**BR** B595150 red brown + coal (M) - *85-87*	6	10

W16b. 16T Steel Mineral Wagon (ex-HD/Wrenn) (1995)

W = weathered

B655	**'Atkinson & Prickett'** 1609 grey - *06*	7	9
B843	**'Atkinson & Prickett'** 1611 grey - *10*	7	9
B229	**'Esso'** silver - *c95*	15	18
WR1-14	as above - *99*	15	20
WR2-31	as above but with a Dapol chassis	NPG	NPG
B346	**'ICI'** 268 blue-grey + coal - *01*	8	10
B728	**'ICI'** 268 blue-green - *08*	6	8

16 ton steel mineral wagon produced for the Train Collectors Society [W16b] (Dapol)

B364	**'NCB'** 30 pale grey + coal - *01-02*	8	10
-	'A **Oakes**' 100 years white Sp Edn 100 (A. Oakes) - *04*	9	11
B90	**'Park Ward'** 7 brown - *c95*	10	15
WR1-15	as above - *99*	10	18
B230	**'Shell'** silver - *c95*	9	11
WR2-10	as above - *98-99*	10	12
PR4	**'TCS'** light grey, Sp Edn 175 (Train Collectors Society/1E Promotionals) - *09*	7	9
-	**'Virgin & Dapol'** 'Pendolino' red Sp Edn 500 Virgin Trains) - *01*	25	30
-	**'Virgin & Dapol'** 'Pendolino' white Sp Edn 100 (Dapol for dealers) - *01*	35	40
B228	**GW** 110265 dark grey - *c95*	10	15
B350	**GW** 'Loco' 18810 grey + coal - *01-05*	8	10
B27	**BR** B54884 grey - *c95*	9	11
WR2-11	as above - *98-99*	8	10
B73	**BR** B54884 brown - *c95*	10	15
WR2-06	as above - *98-99*	10	20
B352	**BR** B54882 grey + coal - *01*	8	10
B353	**BR** B54884 brown + coal - *01*	8	10
WR2-11	as above - *01*	10	12
B398	**BR** 105530 grey Coal - *02*	8	10
B398A	**BR** 105534 grey Coal - *02*	8	10
B523	**BR** B480215 red-brown + coal - *03*	7	9
B686	**BR** B480623 brown - *07-09*	6	8
B701	**BR** B550220 brown (1st batch - door stripe at wrong end) - *07*	6	8
B701	**BR** B550220 brown (2nd batch - door stripe correct) - *07-09*	6	8
B706	**BR** M620248 grey W - *07-09*	6	8
B748	**BR** M620638 brown W - *09*	6	8
WR1-43	? ? ? - ?	NPG	NPG

W17a. 20T Steel Mineral Wagon (ex-Airfix) (1984)

A5	brown - unfinished - *84-99*	5	7
B51	**'Avon Tyres'** 1 black (M) - *85-92, 97-99*	7	10
B53	**'Blaenavon'** 2441 red brown (M) - *85-94*	7	10
B53	**'Blaenavon'** 2441 red brown - *97-02*	8	10
B52	**'Glenhafod'** 2277 black (M) - *85-92*	7	10
B83	**'PJ&JP'** 3619 black (M) - *85-02*	7	10
B95	**'SC'** 25503 dark grey (M) - *86-87*	7	11
B95	**'SC'** 25503 light grey-green - *c95*	8	10
B56	**'Stewart & Lloyds'** 3506 grey (M) - *85-89*	7	11
B25	**GW Loco** 83516 grey (A) - *85-92, 97-98*	7	11
B25	**GW Loco** 83517 grey - *?*	7	9
B8	**BR** P339371K grey (A) - *84-89*	7	11
B8	**BR** P339377K grey (brown inside) - *89?*	7	9
B8	**BR** P339377K dark grey - *89?*	7	9

The tooling was sold to Hornby in 1996 and the model reintroduced by them. * Variously numbered with transfers between 120 and 129.

W17b. 20T Steel Mineral Wagon (2006)

-	**'AAC Anthracite'** (Amalgamated Anthracite)T300 black Sp Edn 101 (David Dacey) - *09*	6	8
B727	**'Bolsover'** 6490 red-brown - *08*	6	8
B727b	**'Bolsover'** 6390 red-brown W - *08*	6	8
B735	**'Cilely'** 12 black - *08*	6	8
-	**'Ebbw Vale'** 17103 black Sp Edn 112 (David Dacey) - *08*	7	9
-	**'Emlyn Anthracite'** 5000 grey Sp Edn 106 (South Wales Coalfields) - *07*	7	9
B861	'**Emlyn Anthracite**' 2000 grey - *10*	7	9

20 ton steel mineral wagon 'Nene Valley Railway' [W17b] (Dapol)]

B698	**'Glenhafod'** 2277 black - *07*	6	8
B685	**'Gloucester Corporation'** 3 grey - *07*	6	8
-	**'NVR'** 272 grey Sp Edn (Nene Valley Railway) - *10*	7	9
B694	**'SC'** 25506 olive green - *07-08*	6	8
-	**'Scatter Rock Macadams'** 9 blue-grey, stone load, Sp Edn 267 (Wessex Wagons) - *07*	7	9
B659	**'Stevens'** 1001 red - *06*	7	9
B703	'Richard **Thomas**' 23301 black - *07*	6	8
B672	**'West Midlands Joint Electricity Authority'** 16 black - *06*	6	8
B834	**'West Midlands Joint Electricity Authority'** 18 black - *10*	6	8
B712	**GW** 33152 dark grey - *07-09*	6	8
B712A	**GW** 33225 dark grey ** - *10*	7	9
B664	**GW** 33156 dark grey Loco - *06-07*	7	9
B770	**GW** 33156 dark grey Loco - *09*	7	9
B823	**GW** 33159 black - *10*	7	9
-	**GW** (Ebbw Vale) 10972 * grey Sp Edn 97 (West Wales Wagon Works) - *08*	6	8
-	**GW** (Ebbw Vale) 10995 * grey Sp Edn 118 (West Wales Wagon Works) - *08*	6	8
E08	**'GW 'Fredk. Bendle'** 63066 dark grey Sp Edn 150 (East Somerset Models) - *10*	8	11
B679	**BR** B315748 grey Coal 21 - *06-09*	6	8
B679A	**BR** B315739 light grey Coal 21 ** - *10*	7	9

* These should have been 6 figure numbers and, although transfers for a 6th digit were produced to correct them, there was insufficient room and the wagons were sold with the incorrect numbers as manufactured. ** These appear to be renumbered old stock.

Hopper & Dry Powder Wagons

W18a. 24T Ore Hopper Wagon (ex-Mainline) (1985)

B97	**'BISC'** 776 dark grey Iron Ore (M) - *86-88, 91-02*	7	10
B142	**'Cadbury Bournville'** 156 blue (M) - *91-02*	7	10
B143	**'Clay Cross'** 72 red brown (M) - *?*	7	11
B68	**'Hoare Bros.'** 101 black (M) - *85-02*	7	10
B139	**'Sheepbridge'** 8251 red brown - *91-02*	7	9
B72	**BR** Sand B436398 grey + sand (M) - *85*	8	12
B72	**BR** Sand B437319 grey + sand - *91-02*	8	10
B140	**BR** B435975 red brown (M) - *?*	7	11
B141	**BR** B435475 grey Ore Hop (M) - *91-02*	7	10

W18b. 12T Ore Hopper Wagon (2005)

This model was one of four new wagons tooled up in 2005.

B713	**'Bell Brothers'** 1 black - *07-08*	7	9
B639	**'Clay Cross Iron Ore Co.'** ? red brown - *05-06*	7	9
B707	**'DL (Cleveland)'** A224 red-brown - *07-08*	7	9
B628	**'Hoare Bros.'** 102 black - *05*	8	10
B828	**'Hoare Bros.'** 105 black - *10*	7	9
B633	**'Millom Iron Works'** 261 red-brown - *05*	8	10
B690	**'Millom Iron Works'** 271 red-brown - *07*	8	10
B643	**BR** B433472 light grey Ore Hop - *05-08*	7	9
B833	**BR** B433472 light grey Ore Hop - *10*	7	9
B645	**BR** B437316 light grey Sand - *06*	8	10

W19a. NE 21T Hopper Wagon (ex-Airfix) (1984)

There is confusion between this former Airfix model and the former Wrenn hopper and listing here is divided between the two according to catalogue illustrations - some models may be in both lists. After acquisition of the Wrenn tooling in 1993, it seemed that, for a while, these models replaced the former Airfix ones. Three years later, in 1996, the Airfix tools were sold to Hornby, but it is known that a stock of mouldings was made from some tools before Dapol parted with them. Five years later, in 2001, the former Wrenn hopper wagon tooling was sold to the re-established G&R Wrenn company. According to catalogue illustrations, an Airfix style hopper reappeared in several versions around 2004. These may have used mouldings previously stored and, if so, this stock seems to have run out in 2007, after which the model was dropped from the catalogue. Of course, Dapol could have retooled the model based on the Airfix version, or maybe they had duplicate tooling that was not sold to Hornby. However, neither of these would explain the disappearance of the model in 2007.

A1	grey - unfinished - *84-99*	5	7
A003	grey - unfinished - *04-07*	5	7
BHW/ No.26	**'Blaenavon'** 2051, 2053, 2055 (40 made), 2061 * grey Sp Edn 40 (West Wales Wagon Works) - *05*	8	10
B668	**'Borough of Bedford Electricity'** 42 black - *06*	6	8
B201	**'British Gas'** 142 dark grey - *c95*	5	7
B579	**'British Gas'** 142 red-brown - *04-06*	7	9
B201	**'British Steel'** 28 brown - *98-99*	8	10

B602	**'British Steel'** 26 red-brown - *04-05*	7	9
B692	**'Cadbury Bournville'** 156 pale blue - *07*	7	9
B113	**'Charringtons'** B421814K grey+red (M) - *89-92*	7	13
B113	**'Charringtons'** B461818K grey+red - *89-92*	9	11
B646	**'Charringtons'** B441834K grey+red - *06*	7	9
-	**'Geoscenics Natural Scenic Products'** 345875 dark green, coal in-fill + bag of natural stone Sp Edn 97 (Geoscenics) - *07*	8	10
B124	**'House Coal Concentration'** B429816K red brown (M) - *89-94*	7	13
B676	**'House Coal Concentration'** 429911 brown - *06-07*	7	9
B59	'Norman **Jackson**' 10 black (M) *85-?*	9	13
B59	'Norman **Jackson**' 10 black - *?-99*	8	10
-	**'Locomotion'** B345872 orange-brown Sp Edn (NRM Shildon) - *07*	8	10
-	**'Meldon Quarry'** 291 brown, white ore load Sp Edn 110 - *03?*	20	25
-	**'Meldon Quarry'** 291 brown, no load Sp Edn 100 (Dartmoor Railway) - *04*	10	15
-	**MHR** S2007 grey Sp Edn 90 (Mid Hants Railway) - *07*	7	9
B60	**'MOT'** 1324 black (M) - *85-94*	7	13
B588	**'MOT'** 1328 black - *04-05*	7	9
B606	**'NCB'** 128 dark grey - *04-06*	7	9
B657	'The **Northampton Electric Light & Power Co.**' 80 brown - *06*	7	9
-	**North Norfolk Railway** grey Sp Edn 250 (NNR) - *?*	8	10
B622	**'Simpson'** 72 grey - *05*	7	9
B610	**'Sykes'** 10 pale grey - *05*	7	9
-	**'Trago Mills Shopping Centre'** grey Sp Edn 250 (Trago Mills) - *?*	8	10
-	**'Trago Mills Shopping Centre'** black Sp Edn 250 (Trago Mills) - *?*	8	10
-	**TVLR** B345921 cream Sp Edn 110 (Tanat Valley Light Railway Co.) - *07*	8	10
B203	'G **Weaver Transport**' 152 brown - *94-00*	8	10
B616	'G **Weaver**' 154 brown - *05*	7	9
B592	**NE** 193264 pale grey - *04-05*	7	9
B112	**NE** 193258 grey (M) - *88-99*	7	11
B1	**BR** E289595K light grey (A) - *84-88*	7	13
B1	**BR** E289592K light grey - *89-94*	9	11
B1	**BR** E289593K light grey - *89-94*	9	11
B128	**BR** - ? - red brown - *?*	NPG	NPG
B201	**BR** B??6398 grey - *?*	NPG	NPG
B585	**BR** E289595K grey - *04-06*	7	9

The tooling was sold to Hornby in 1996 and the model reintroduced by them. * various numbers applied with transfers.

W19b. 21T Hopper Wagon (ex-HD/Wrenn) (c1995)

B202	**'British Gas'** 142 dark grey - *c95*	15	25
WR1-44	as above - *99*	15	30
B187	**'Hoveringham'** red brown - *c95*	10	15
WR1-09	as above - *99*	10	15
WR1-08	**'NCB'** black - *c99*	20	45
B189	**'Sykes'** 7 light grey - *c95*	10	15
WR1-23	as above - *99*	10	45
B188	**'Tarmac'** M82 beige - *c95*	10	15
WR1-07	as above - *98-99*	10	15
WR1-48	**BR** B413021 dark grey - *99*	15	30

W20. HBA/HEA Hopper Wagon (1991)

This wagon was designed and tooled by Dapol.

B158	**BR** 360634 red brown HBA - *91-02*	8	10
B159	**BR** 360394 red+grey Railfreight HEA - *91-01*	8	10
B159	**BR** 361874 red+grey Railfreight HEA - *?*	8	10

The tooling was sold to Hornby in 1996 and the model reintroduced by them.

W21. 20T Grain Hopper Wagon (ex-HD/Wrenn) (1995)

-	**'Bass'** 3 blue Sp Edn (Tutbury Jinny) - *08*	7	10
-	**'Bass'** 11 blue Sp Edn ex-set	10	NA
B252	**'Bass Charrington'** 24 maroon - *c95*	10	15
WR1-42	as above - *99*	10	35
B548	**'Bass Charrington'** 9 brick red - *03*	7	9
B254	**'Kelloggs'** B885040 grey - *c95*	10	15
B255	**'Quaker Oats'** red brown - *c95*	10	15
B517	**'SGD'** 18 grey - *03*	7	9
B517	**'SGD'** 18 pale grey - *03*	10	12

20 ton grain hopper wagon - 'Worthington' [W21]

B765	**'SGD'** 16 grey - *09*	8	10
-	**'Worthington'** 8 bright green Sp Edn ex-set	10	NA
-	**'Worthington'** 8 and 'Bass' 3 as a Sp Edn set (Tutbury Jinny) - *06*	NA	20
-	**'Worthington'** 2 green Sp Edn (Tutbury Jinny) - *08*	7	10
B503	**GW** grey 'Grano' - *02-09*	6	8
B503A	**GW** grey 'Grano' (smaller GW and newer couplings) * - *10*	7	9
B528	**GW** 42315 grey 'Grano' - *03-05*	6	8
B534	**LMS** 701314 grey Bulk Grain - *03*	6	8
B562	**LMS** 710351 red-brown Bulk Grain - *03-05*	6	8
B251	**BR** B885040 light grey - *c95*	10	15
WR1-49	as above - *99*	10	15
B502	**BR** B885044 grey - *02-09*	6	8
B502A	**BR** B885364 - grey - *02-05*	6	8
B502A	**BR** B885302 - grey * - *10*	7	9

* These appear to be resprayed and freprinted old stock.

W22a. Ore Wagon (ex-Wrenn) (c1995)

B593	**'BISC Iron Ore'** 398 dark grey - *04-05*	6	8
B243	'Wm.**Carter**' 7 black - *c95*	10	15
WR1-41	as above - *99*	10	17
B249	**'Clay Cross'** black - *c95*	50	60
WR1-24	**'Hinchley'** blue - *99*	10	18
B605	**'NCB'** 69 grey - *05-06*	6	8
B607	**'Sheepbridge'** 2149 Coal & Iron brown - *04-05*	6	8
B250	**'Southdown'** 17 blue - *c95*	15	18

W22b. 'Presflo' Cement Wagon (ex-HD/Wrenn) (c1995)

'Presflo' - 'Blue Circle Cement' [W22b] (unknown)

B600	**'ARC'** AR12640 yellow - *04-06*	7	9
B242	**'Blue Circle'** grey - *c95*	10	15

B578	**'Blue Circle Cement'** grey - *04-06*	7	9
B683	**'Blue Circle'** yellow - *07-09*	6	8
-	**'Brierfield'** dark green Sp Edn 90 (St Luke's MRC) - *08*	7	9
B248	**'Bulk Cement'** 52 orange - *c95*	10	15
B720	**'Bulk Cement'** 32 brown - *08*	6	8
B246	**'Cerebos Salt'** orange - *c95*	15	18
B582	**'Cerebos Salt'** red - *04-05*	7	9
-	**'Hattons of Liverpool'** red - *05*	7	9
B725	**'ICI Bulk Salt'** green - *08*	6	8
PR3	**'Milton Keynes Model Railway Society 40th'** 40 brown Sp Edn 110 (1E Promotionals) - *09*	6	8
-	**'Model Rail Scotland'** pale grey Sp Edn (Model Rail Scotland) - *06*	7	9
B615	**'Pozzoianic'** 41094 brown - *05*	7	9
B609	**'Readymix Concrete'** 66 grey - *05*	7	9
B247	**'RMC'** 68 grey - *c95*	30	35
B620	**'Rugby Cement'** brown - *05*	7	9
-	**Sittingbourne & Kemsley Light Railway** 100 grey Sp Edn 92 (S&KLR) - *05*	8	10
B739	**'Slate Powder'** 4888189* dark grey - *08*	6	8
B244	**'Tunnel Bulk'** grey - *c95*	10	15
B601	**'Tunnel Cement'** grey - *04-06*	7	9
B621	**'Bulk Tunnel Cement'** grey - *05-07*	7	9
-	**'Virgin Trains'** Warley 2004 red - *04*	7	9
B245	**BR** 'Presflo' 72 brown - *c95*	10	15
B763	**BR** 'Presflo' 75 brown - *09*	6	8

* Incorrectly numbered - it should have been B888189. The box label has the same error printed.

W22c. 'Presflo' Silo Wagon (2009)

B763	**'Presflo'** 75 brown - *09*	8	10
B763	**'Presflo'** 75 brown W Sp Edn (Hattons) - *09*	8	10

W23. 'Prestwin' Silo Wagon *(ex-HD/Wrenn)* (c1995)

B191	**'Fisons'** B873000 brown - *c95*	10	15
B190	**BR** B873000 brown - *c95*	10	15

W24. PCA 'Presflo' V Tank (1995)

Identical to the Lima PCA. This could have been one of the duplicate wagons tooled up in China for Dapol.

B197	**'Albright & Wilson'** PR10126 greeny-blue - *95-03*	7	9
B198	**'APCM'** 9344 very pale grey - *95-03*	7	9
B196	**'BOC'** 1066 very pale grey - *95-03*	7	9

The tooling was sold to Hornby in 1996 and the model reintroduced by them.

Tank Wagons

W25. Rectangular Tank (2008)

B751	**'ACC'** 436 black - *09*	9	12
B816	**'The Burnden Tar Oil Co.'** black Sp Edn (Trains & Diecast) - *10*	8	10
B738	'Wm **Butler & Co.'** 64 black - *08*	8	10
B816	'RS **Clare & Co.'** 12 grey - *09*	9	12
ANT038	'TH **Harvey Chemical Works'** 7 black Sp Edn 150 (Antics) - *09*	11	14
B731	**'Imperial Chemical Industries'** 50 grey - *08*	8	10
B731A	**'Imperial Chemical Industries'** 60 grey - *10*	9	12
-	**'Model Rail Scotland'** black Sp Edn (Model Rail Scotland) - *09*	8	10
-	**'Railton & Son'** 3 red+grey Sp Edn 200 (AMRCWWE) - *09*	9	12

Rectangular tank wagon - 'Scottish Fish Oil' [W25] (Dapol)

B835	**'Rimer Bros'** 5 grey - *10*	9	12
-	**'Scottish Fish Oil & Guano & Co,'** 3 red-brown Sp Edn (Harburn Hobbies) - *10*	9	12
B744	**'Smith & Forrest'** 2 red - *08*	8	10
B815	**'Smith & Forrest'** 2 red W - *09*	9	12
B865	**'South Eastern Tar Distillers'** R9 black - *10*	9	12
-	**'South Eastern Tar Distillers'** 45 blue Sp Edn 191 (East Kent MRS) - *10*	10	14
B775	**'Walkers'** 25 blue - *09*	9	12
B757	**'Yorkshire & Lincolnshire Tar Distillation Co.'** 6 black - *09*	9	12

W26. 12T Tank Wagon (ex-Mainline) (1985)

This tank was later made by Dapol from tools, almost identical to the Mainline version, which were made in China for Dapol and are now owned by Hornby. Both ex-Mainline and Dapol made versions are included here.

B136	**'Benzole By-Products'** 1 buff - *91-99*	10	12
B131	**'BP'** 5049 grey - *91-97*	10	12
B133	**'Crossfield'** 49 green grey - *91-02*	10	12
B134	**'Esso'** 3066 silver white spirit - *91-95*	10	12
B137	**'ICI'** 895 dark blue - *91-99*	10	12
B132	**'National Benzol'** 731 silver - *91-95*	10	12
B138	**'Ronuk'** 38 blue - *91-02*	9	11
B130	**'Royal Daylight'** 1534 black (M) - *91-02*	8	12

12 ton tank wagon - 'Benzol & By-products' [W26]

B135	**'Shell'** 4492 silver - *91-95*	10	12
B86	**'Shell Electrical Oils'** SM2202 brown (M) - *86*	8	14
B86	**'Shell Electrical Oils'** SM2202 v.dark grey - *90-02*	9	11
B32	**'United Molasses'** 128 red brown (M) - *85-86*	10	14
B32	**'United Molasses'** 128 red brown larger letters - *91-02*	8	11
B87	**LMS Creosote** 304592 grey (M) - *86*	8	14
B87	**LMS Creosote** 304592? grey - *90-02*	9	11

The tooling was sold to Hornby in 1996 and the model reintroduced by them.

W27. 12T Tank Wagon (2004)

B583	**'Anglo Persian Oil Co.'** 1595 red brown - *04*	8	10
B597	**'Barrow'** 4 bright red - *04*	8	10
-	**'Esso'** silver Sp Edn 50 (Llangollen Railway Preservation Society) - *made?*	NPG	NPG
-	**'Express Dairy'** 041348 silver + additional brass ladders Sp Edn 200 (Buffers) - *04*	10	12
-	**'Express Dairy'** 744 silver Sp Edn 40 (West Wales Wagon Works) - *?*	12	14
-	**'Fothergill Brothers'** 2 bright red Sp Edn 100 (The Model Shop, Exeter) - *04*	10	12
-	**'Pendle Forest MRS'** yellow Sp Edn 92 (Pendle Forest MRS) - *04*	11	13
-	'John **Samper Dairy'** 1 white Sp Edn 186 (East Kent MRS) - *04*	10	12
-	**'Tunbridge Wells Gas, Light & Coke, Tar'** 34 black Sp Edn 400 (Ballards) - *04*	9	11
No.23	**'United Dairies'** 636 white, print blue Sp Edn 135 (West Wales Wagon Works) - *04*	8	10
-	**'United Dairies'** 041882 white + additional ladders, print blk Sp Edn 200 (Buffers) - *04*	8	10
B590	**'United Molasses'** 13 maroon - *04*	8	10

12 ton tank wagon - 'The Yorkshire & Lincolnshire Tar Distillation Co.' [W27]

B580	**'Yorkshire & Lincolnshire Tar Distillation Co.'** 4 red - *04*	8	10

W28. 20T Tank Wagon (ex-Airfix) (1985)

A13	unfinished - *98*	5	7
B85	**'Crosfield'** 15 dark green (M) - *86*	8	14
B85	**'Crosfield'** 15 green and no number on ends of tank - *97-99*	10	12
B29	**'ICI'** 499 dark blue (M) - *85-?*	8	14
B29	**'ICI'** 400 dark blue - *?-87*	10	12
B107	**'Newcastle & Gateshead'** 18 black also ex set B404 - *87-88, 96-99*	10	12
B106	**'Rainford Tar Prods.'** 1 black - *87-88*	10	12
B106	**'Rainford Tar Prods.'** 1 brown - *97-99*	9	11
B20	**'Shell'** 2373 buff (A) - *?*	8	14
B21	**'Shell BP'** 3967 black (A) - *?*	8	12
B116	**'United Molasses'** 86 red brown - *88-89*	10	12

The tooling was sold to Hornby in 1996 and the model reintroduced by them.

W29a. 6-wheel Tank Wagon (ex-HD/Wrenn) (c1995)

B214	**'Co-op'** 172 white - *c95*	40	45
B220	**'Double Diamond'** red brown - *c95*	20	25
B215	**'Express Dairies'** 50 blue - *c95*	25	30
B222	**'Guinness'** silver - *c95*	20	25
B218	**'Milk Marketing Board'** blue - *c95*	20	25
B217	**'St Ivel Gold'** white - *c95*	50	55
B221	**'Skol Lager'** red brown - *c95*	20	25
B219	**'UD'** white also W4657P - *c95*	15	20
B216	**'Unigate'** 220 white - *c95*	50	55

W29b. 6-wheel Tank Wagon (2005)

This model was one of four new wagons tooled up in 2005 and believed to be based on an LMS design. In 2009 new wheels were being fitted.

B673	**'Alpin & Barrett'** brown - *06*	11	13
-	**'Boat of Garten Dairy'** 7 silver Sp Edn 200 (Strathspey Railway Co. Ltd) - *07*	13	15
-	**'Boat of Garten Dairy'** 7 silver W Sp Edn 100 (Strathspey Railway Co. Ltd) - *07*	13	15
-	**'British Vinegars'** T10 red Sp Edn 135 (Buffers) - *09*	10	13
-	**'British Vinegars'** T12 red Sp Edn 140 (Buffers) - *10*	9	12
-	**'Classic Trains - 10th Anniversary'** dark blue Sp Edn 150 (Classic Trains, Models & Buses) - *08*	13	15
-	**'Coates Cider'** 2 white Sp Edn 169 (Burnham & District MRC) - *10*	10	13
B654	**'Co-op Milk'** 169 white - *06*	10	13
B841	**'Co-operative Wholesale Society'** (Pure New Milk) red - *10*	10	13
-	**'Culm Valley Dairy Company'** 19 silver Sp Edn 162 (Wessex Wagons) - *10*	10	13
B678	**'CWS'** green - *06-07*	10	13
B634	**'Express Dairy'** dark blue - *05-06*	10	13
B667	**'Express Dairy'** 45 dark blue - *06*	10	13
B732	**'Express Dairy'** dark blue - *08*	10	13
B697	**'Express Dairy'** silver - *07-09*	9	11
-	**'Express Dairy'** I white Sp Edn 180 (Burnham & District MRC) - *10*	10	13
-	**'Felin Foel Brewery'** dark green Sp Edn 154 (Voyles) - *10*	11	14
-	**'Glenbogle Dairy'** buff Sp Edn 100 (Strathspey Rly Co Ltd) - *06*	12	14
-	**'Glenbogle Dairy'** buff W Sp Edn 100 (Strathspey Rly Co Ltd) - *07*	12	14
B640	**'IMS'** 23 light blue - *05-06*	10	13
B660	**'Independent Milk Supplies'** brown - *06*	10	13
B741	**'Independent Milk Supplies'** red-brown - *08*	10	13
B648	**'Milk Marketing Board'** dark blue - *06*	10	13
B817	**'Milk Marketing Board'** dark blue - *09*	9	11
B719	**'MMB'** 113 dark blue - *08*	10	13
-	**'MMB'** dark grey Sp Edn 100 (Barry & Penarth Rly) - *06*	10	13

6-wheeled milk tank wagon - 'Nestles' [W29b] (Dapol)

-	**'National Smelting Company'** 295 grey Sp Edn 300 (Burnham & District MRC) - *10*	10	13
-	**'Nestles'** blue Sp Edn 177 (Burnham & District MRC) - *10*	10	13
-	**'Newcastle Emlyn'** black Sp Edn (West Wales Wagon Works) - *06*	12	14
-	**'Royal Arsenal Co-op Society'** - Pure New Milk bright red Sp Edn 186 (Wessex Wagons) - *06*	12	15
-	**'Royal Arsenal Co-op Society'** - Pure New Milk bright red W Sp Edn 260 (Wessex Wagons) - *06*	14	20
-	**'Satlink Western'** red+yellow Sp Edn (Model Rail Magazine) - *08*	10	13
-	**'Scottish Cables Limited'** T1 black Sp Edn 150 (Buffers) - *09*	9	12
-	**'Sheppy's Cider'** 7 light brown Sp Edn 275 (Burnham & District MRC) - *10*	10	13
-	**'Taunton Cider'** 11 cream Sp Edn 260 (Wessex Wagons) - *07*	15	18
-	**'The Cheddar Valley Dairy Co.'** 3 cream Sp Edn 196 (Burnham & District MRC) - *10*	10	13
B709	**'United Creameries'** 70351 219 silver - *07-08*	10	13
SBB3	**'United Creameries'** 70351 219 silver W Sp Edn 300 (Signal Box) - *09*	10	12
B629	**'United Dairies'** white - *05-07*	10	13
-	**'United Dairies'** silver Sp Edn 133 +118 (Barry & Penarth MRC) - *05, 09*	10	13
B629S	**'United Dairies'** 107 white W Sp Edn 300 (Signal Box) - *07*	10	13
B687	**'United Dairies'** SR white - *07*	10	13
B759	**'United Dairies'** white heavily weathered - *09*	9	11
-	**'United Dairies'** - Wilts' 25 cream Sp Edn 150 (Burnham & District MRC) - *10*	9	11
B762	**'UD'** white - *09*	9	11
-	**'Wensleydale Creamery'** * cream Sp Edn 212 (Wensleydale Creamery/WWWW) - *08*	20	30
B644	**'West Park Dairy Co.'** 2 brown - *05-06*	10	13
B831	**'West Park Dairy Company'** 175 brown - *10*	9	11
-	**'Whiteways Cider Co,'** 17 cream Sp Edn 146 (Wessex Wagons) - *10*	10	14
-	**'Wilts. United Dairies'** 21 cream Sp Edn 131 (Burnham & Dist. MRC) - *09*	10	12
-	**'Whitstable Bitumen'** 5 red-brown Sp Edn 188 (East Kent MRS) - *08*	10	11
2	**WHR Ltd** 2 black Sp Edn 192 (Welsh Highland Railway) - *05*	10	14
No.37	plain black Sp Edn 150 (West Wales Wagon Works) - *06*	10	13
-	**BR(WR) Drinking Water** 105 brown Sp Edn 233 (Wessex Wagons) - *07*	14	19
SBB2**	**BR Diluted Antifreeze** silver with blue band Sp		

	Edn 300 (Signal Box) - *09*	8	11

* Various numbers on ends of tank. Those with numbers less than 200 were sold by WWWW and those with 200 or more were sold by the creamery who received 100 wagons in all (in two batches of 50). ** Box marked 'S882' in error.

Lime & Salt Wagons

W30. Lime Wagon (2005)

This model was one of four new wagons tooled up in 2005. It is also referred to as a 'salt' wagon by Dapol.

B653	'Richard **Briggs & Sons'** 187 red - *06*	7	9
B819	'Richard **Briggs & Sons'** 189 red-brown - *10*	7	9
-	'George **Brown & Sons'** 1 grey Sp Edn 98 (SVR Erlestoke Manor Fund) - *09*	6	8
B630	**'Crawshay Brothers'** 138 pale yellow - *05*	7	9
B837	**'Crawshay Brothers'** 134 cream - *10*	7	8
-	**'Evercreech Lime & Stone Co.'** 6 light grey Sp Edn 137 (Burnham & District MRC) - *09*	8	10
-	**'Glan-Yr-Afon'** 11 cream Sp Edn 103 (David Dacey) - *08*	7	9
-	**Gwili Railway** 30 grey St Edn 160 (West Wales Wagon Works) - *07*	7	9
No.31	**'Llywernog Silver-Lead Mining Co.'** Cardiganshire * grey Sp Edn 160 (WWWW) - *05*	8	10
B717	**'The Minera Lime Co.'** 125 brown - *07-08*	6	8
-	**'North Devon Clay Co.'** 107 grey Sp Edn 126 (Wessex Wagons) - *09*	8	10
B624	**'Peak Lime Co.'** 45 grey - *05-07*	7	9
B624	**'Peak Lime Co.'** 45 grey W - *05-07*	7	9
B830	**'Peak Lime Co.'** 48 grey - *10*	6	8
B619	**'Porthywaen Lime Co.'** pale grey - *05*	7	9
B626	**'SLB'** 527 pale grey - *05-06*	7	9

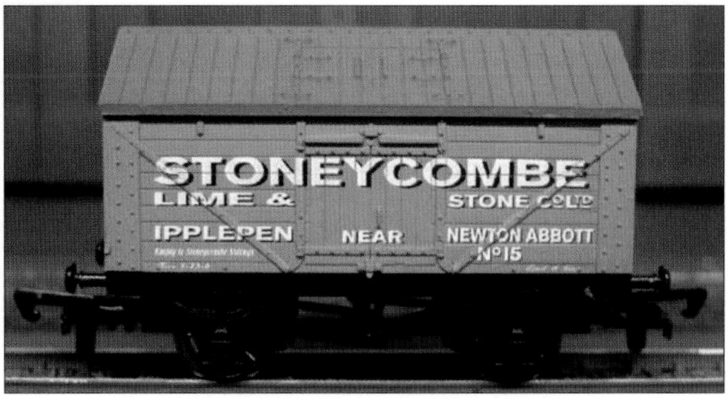

Lime wagon - 'Stoneycombe' [W30] (Dapol)

-	**'Statfold'** 21 dark green Sp Edn (Statfold Barn Railway) - *09?*	12	15
-	**'Stoneycombe'** 15* grey Sp Edn 150 (Wessex Wagons) - *05*	8	10
-	'D **Thomas & Son'** 10 buff with white roof Sp Edn 90 (David Dacey) - *03*	9	11
B684	'D **Thomas & Son'** 10 grey - *07*	7	9
-	**'Tollemache'** 1000 black Sp Edn 90 (South Wales Coalfields) - *08*	7	9
B729	**'Whitecliff Lime Co.'** 6 buff - *08*	6	8

* various numbers carried.

W31. Salt Van (ex-HD/Wrenn) (c1995)

Originally sold as 'WR3' stock it was absorbed from the Wrenn range when G&R Wrenn was sold to Mordvale in 2001.

1	**'AMETIA Eurotrack'** yellow Sp Edn 100 (Solent Model Railway Group) - *04*	10	12
-	**'Aspect'** grey Sp Edn 250 (?) - *?*	7	10
1	**'Baldwin Locomotive Works'** 590 red Sp Edn (Welsh Highland Railway) - *05*	8	10
-	**BC Rly** 24 grey Ltd Edn 100 (Bishops Castle Railway) - *07*	7	9
B?	'The **Bovey Pottery Company'** 5 black Sp Edn 307 (Wessex Wagons) - *07*	7	9
-	'George **Brown**' 1 grey Sp Edn 100 (Modellers Mecca) - *01*	10	NA
-	'George **Brown & Sons'** 1 grey Sp Edn (Erlestoke Manor Fund) - *09*	6	8
B308	**'Chance & Hunt'** 333, 33 maroon - *00-02*	8	10
-	**'Chance & Hunt'** 100 brown Sp Edn 100 (A Oakes) - *05*	8	10
B223	'Jas. **Colman'** 15 pale green - *c95*	10	15
S238	**'Dapol'** 20th Anniversary 2003 silver Ltd Edn 200 - *03*	16	20
B225	**'DCL'** 87 grey - *c95*	10	15
WR3-04	**'DCL'** 87 grey - *98-02*	8	10
-	**'ICI Fleetwood Salt'** 12 maroon Sp Edn 232 (Toys2Save) - *04*	9	11
-	**'ICI Fleetwood Salt'** 14 maroon Sp Edn 250 (Toys2Save) - *04*	9	11
-	**G&KERy** 15 dark grey Sp Edn 110 (Toys2Save) - *03*	9	11
B224	**'ICI Bulk Salt'** 25 grey - *c95*	30	35
WR3-*05*	**'ICI Bulk Salt'** 25 grey - *98-02*	10	12
W5101	**'ICI Salt'** 25 white (body only) Sp Edn 70* (Wrenn RCC - WRCC5) - *01*	10	12
-	**'Llanharry Limestone & Gravel Coy'** 33 crm Sp Edn 109 (Barry & Penarth MRC) - *03*	9	11
-	**'Llanharry Limestone & Gravel Coy'** 37 crm Sp Edn 100 (Barry & Penarth MRC) - *04*	9	11
No.15	**'Llywernog Silver-Lead Mining Co.'** 12 Ceredigon grey Sp Edn 160 (W Wales W W) - *04*	9	11
-	**'New Explosives Co.'** 10 black Sp Edn 100 (Stowmarket MRC) - *02*	10	12
TMCD010	**'NRM'** 2004 maroon Sp Edn 200 (TMC) - *04*	9	11
TMC-D013	**'NRM'** Keep Scotsman Steaming black Sp Edn (TMC) - *05*	9	11
(No.2)	'GD **Owen'** 12 red-brown Sp Edn ** 400 (West Wales Wagon Works) - *02-03*	9	11

Salt wagon - 'G.D. Owen' [W31]

-	**'Pepper & Son'** 10 light grey Sp Edn (Amberley Museum) - *10*	8	10
-	**'Salt Union'** 639 dark red Sp Edn 78 (West Wales Wagon Works) - *08*	7	9
-	**'Salt Union'** 639 dark red W Sp Edn 56 (West Wales Wagon Works) - *08*	7	9
B226	**'Saxa Salt'** 248 lemon yellow - *c95*	10	15
B226	**'Saxa Salt'** 248 yellow - *00-01*	8	10
B505	**'Saxa Salt'** 248 yellow - *02-03*	7	9
B612	**'Saxa Salt'** 242 yellow - *05*	7	9
B612b	**'Saxa Salt'** 235 yellow - *made?*	6	8
B612b	**'Saxa Salt'** 247 yellow - *07-09*	6	8
WR3-*01*	**'Saxa Salt'** 248 yellow - *97-91*	10	12
W4665	**'Saxa Salt'** 25 white (body only) Sp Edn 70* (WrennRCC - WRCC4) - *01*	20	30
B366	**'Shaka Salt'** 119 blue - *02-03*	7	9
B811	**'Snowdrift Salt'** 309 green - *09*	8	10
-	**'South Wales Portland Cement & Lime Co.'** 115 grey Sp Edn 120 (Barry & Penarth MRC) - *03*	9	11
-	**'South Wales Portland Cement & Lime Co.'** 110 grey Sp Edn 150 (Barry & Penarth MRC) - *03*	9	11
-	**'St Matthews School'** Tuck Shop Supplies 8 yellow Sp Edn 100 (St Matthews) - *04*	9	11
B635	**'Stafford Salt Works'** C,25 red - *05*	7	9
B647	**'Star Salt'** 108 red - *06*	7	9
B647b	**'Star Salt'** 11274 red - *07*	6	8
B309	**'Stubbs Salt'** 37 orange-red - *00-02*	8	10
-	'D **Thomas Lime'** 10 pink/stone Sp Edn 90		

	(David Dacey) - *03*	9	11
B827	**'Union Salt.'** 2169 grey - *10*	7	9
-	**'Virgin Trains'** Warley 2004 white+red Sp Edn 500 (Virgin Trains) - *04*	9	11

* 125 of each body were produced but only about 70 of each were usable due to faults with the others. These were returned to the factory. ** 200 were sold as solo models and the other 200 came in wagon sets.

Vans

W32. BR GPV Gunpowder Van (ex-HD/Wrenn) (c1995)

This is a steel low sided van. Originally sold as 'WR3' stock, it was absorbed into the Dapol range when G&R Wrenn was sold to Mordvale in 2001. While the prototype of this model was the BR Standard gunpowder van it has been used to represent a GW Iron Mink van. Several of these were either owned by, or carried the livery of, the Associated Portland Cement Company, whose brands included 'Blue Circle', 'Ferrocrete' and 'Sandtex'.

-	**'Arnold & Hancock'** 3 brown Sp Edn 150 (Wessex Wagons) - *05*	8	10
-	**'Axminster Carpets'** B895006 light grey Sp Edn 150 (Buffers Model Railways) - *03*	9	11
-	**'Axminster Carpets'** B895006 white Sp Edn (Buffers Model Railways) - *05*	8	10
-	**'Bear's Beers'** - purple Sp Edn 100 (Model Rail) - *05*	8	10
B750	**'Blue Circle'** 173 yellow - *09*	6	8
B315	**'Blue Circle'** 177 yellow - *00-03*	7	9
-	'John **Board & Co.'** 12 cream Sp Edn 153 (Burnham & District MRC) - *09*	8	10
W5200	**'Brock's Fireworks'** B887008 black Sp Edn 100 (Wrenn Collectors Club - WRCC8) - *02*	20	30
WRCC14	**'Brock's Fireworks'** B887008 bright green Sp Edn 100 (Wrenn Collectors Club) - *04*	10	14
B209	**'BSA'** B887002 brown - *c95*	10	15
-	'Joe Miller **Buggleskelly'** 1937 red-brown Sp Edn 107 (Aslan Associates) - *07*	7	9
B372	**Cambrian Railways** 139 black - *02-05*	7	9
-	**'Cotton Powder Co.'** var. nos. brown Sp Edn 310 (Hythe Models) - *02*	10	12
-	**'Cotton Powder Co.'** 2 brown Sp Edn 1,000 (Ballards) - *08*	7	9
B556	**'Elterwater Gunpowder'** 11 light grey - *03-05*	7	9
B311	**'Ferrocrete'** 167 -yellow - *00-03*	7	9
B688	**'Ferrocrete'** 262 yellow - *07*	6	8
B513	**'2002 Golden Jubilee'** 1952 purple - *02*	8	10
B513	**'2002 Golden Jubilee'** 1952 blue - *02*	8	10
WCC10	**'Golden Anniversary'** gold Sp Edn 150 (Wrenn Collectors Club) - *03*	10	14
TVR5	**'Jubilee'** 1952 blue, Union Jack Sp Edn 110 (Teifi Valley Railway) * - *01*	10	12
TVR4	**'Jiwbili'** 2002 white, Welsh flag Sp Edn 111 (Teifi Valley Railway) * - *01*	10	12
-	above two wagons in a set (50 sets made in addition to the above numbers) - *01*	NA	22
-	**'Marley Tile Co.'** 7 dark green Sp Edn 1000 (Ballards) - *05*	7	9

Gunpowder van - 'Ministry of Munitions' [W32] (Dapol)

-	**'Mevagissey Model Railways'** 1 royal blue Sp Edn (Mevaguissey Models) - *?*	10	12
-	**'Minitry of Munitions'** red-brown 4159 Sp Edn 200 (Wessex Wagons) - *06*	8	10
-	**'Morgan Lloyd Williams'** 388 dark brown Sp Edn (Albatross Models) - *09*	8	10
-	'A **Oaks'** 100 Years white Sp Edn 100 - *05*	8	10
-	**'Platelayers'** dark grey Sp Edn 125 (The Great British Train Show 2004) - *04*	9	11
-	**'R&D Models 1977-2002'** dark green Sp Edn 100 (R&D Models) - *02*	10	12
-	**'Rialtronics'** Sp Edn (Railtronics) - *?*	8	10
B652	**'ROF'** M12 grey, red cross - *06*	7	9
-	**'Royal Leamington Spa'** DB887499 brown Enparts van Sp Edn 200 (Classic Train & Motor Bus) - *02*	10	12
-	**'Royal Leamington Spa'** DB887499 faded blue Enparts van Sp Edn 50 (Classic Train & Motor Bus) - *04*	9	11
B365	**'Rugby'** 13 black - *02-03*	7	9
B760	**'Rugby'** 13 black - *09*	6	8
-	**'Simonds Brewery'** 16 dark red Sp Edn 218 (Wessex Wagons) - *06*	8	10
B573	**'Spillers Flour'** 175 white - *04*	7	9
B824	**'Spillers Flour'** 179 white - *10*	7	9
-	**'Square Wheels'** yellow Sp Edn100 (Square Wheels) - *03*	9	12
B210	**'Standard Fireworks'** B887002 brown - *c95*	12	15
W4313P	**'Standard Fireworks'** B887007 light blue Sp Edn 100 (Wrenn Collectors Club - WRCC7) - *02*	20	30
WRCC13	**'Standard Fireworks'** B887007 bright red Sp Edn 100 (Wrenn Collectors Club) - *04*	20	30
-	**Talyllyn Railway** Sp Edn (Talyllyn Railway) - *05*	8	10
-	**'Taunton Cider Co'**. 17 cream Sp Edn 275 (Wessex Wagons) - *06*	8	10
-	**'TMC'** blue Sp Edn 180 (The Model Centre) - *03*	9	11

Gunpowder van - 'Taunton Cider' [W32] (Dapol)

-	**'Trains, Models & Hobbies'** white Sp Edn 108 (TM&H) - *01*	10	12
	Railway Companies		
B310	**LNWR** light grey - *00-02*	8	10
B518	**NB** 12 bright red gunpowder van - *03*	7	9
B518	**NB** 12 maroon gunpowder van - *03*	7	10
B330	**LSWR** 1379 red - *01-03*	7	9
B207	**GW** W105780 black red X - *c95*	12	15
WR1-52	as above - *99*	12	15
WR2-*01*	as above (Dapol chassis) - *99*	8	10
B312	**GW** 37985 dark grey - *00-05*	7	9
-	**GWR** Salvage 47305 light blue Iron Mink Sp Edn 250 (Lord & Butler) - *03?*	9	11
B336	**LMS** 299031 light grey - *01-03*	6	8
B355	**NE** grey - *01-02*	6	8
B560	**NE** 71418 bright red gunpowder van - *03-05*	6	8
B329	**SR** 61204 brown - *01-07*	6	8
B722	**SR** GPV(Improvised) 59061 black - *08*	6	8
B349	**BR** W105780 black, red cross - *01-09*	6	8
B349A	**BR** W105743 black, red cross ** - *10*	7	9
B208	**BR** B887002 red brown - *c95*	10	15
B510	**BR** B887002 red brown - *02*	8	10
WR3-15	**BR** B887002 red brown - *99-01*	9	11
B510	**BR** B887002 red-brown - *02-03*	7	9
B700	**BR** M701058 brown - *07-09*	6	8
B700A	**BR** M701048 brown ** - *10*	7	9
-	**BR** B887029 black (trencher train) Sp Edn 100 (Alexandra Models) - *07*	7	9

* See also boxed wagon sets (below). ** Possibly renumbered old stock.

W33. LMS Cattle Wagon (ex-Mainline) (1986)

B157	**BR** M12093 red brown - *86*	9	11

W34. 8T Cattle Wagon (ex-HD/Wrenn) (c1995)

From 2007, these were fitted with a new chassis.

-	**CV** 140 grey Sp Edn 92 (Colne Valley Railway) - *08*	8	10
-	**K&ESR** 13 light grey Sp Edn 200 (Col. Stephens Rly Enterprise KESR) - *06*	8	10
-	**LBSC** 7479 dark grey Sp Edn 1000 (Ballards) - *06*	8	10
-	**Mid Hants Railway** S2006 brown Ale Wagon Sp Edn 101 (Mid Hants Railway) - *06*	8	10
-	**NYMR** B894178 grey Sp Edn (NYMR) - *07*	7	9
-	**TR** 2004 dark grey Sp Edn (Talyllyn Railway) - *04*	9	11
-	**TVR** 115 black Sp Edn 85 (West Wales Wagon Works) - *10*	7	9
-	**TVR** 115 black W Sp Edn 24 (West Wales Wagon Works) - *10*	7	9
-	**TVR** 175 black Sp Edn 105 (West Wales Wagon Works) - *10*	7	9
-	**TVR** 175 black W Sp Edn 21 (West Wales Wagon Works) - *10*	7	9
B58	**GW** 103240 grey - *c95*	10	15
WR1-*03*	as above - *97-99*	10	25
B500	**GW** 13813 dark grey - *02-09*	6	8
B500A	**GW** 13818 dark grey * - *10*	7	9
B549	**GW** 38659 grey Ale Wagon - *03-09*	6	8
B549A	**GW** 38618 grey Ale Wagon * - *10*	7	9
B504W	**GW** 38231 grey W Ltd Edn 250 - *10*	6	8
-	**SR** 53172 dark brown Sp Edn 1000 (Ballards) - *05*	7	9
B47	**BR** B893344 red-brown - *c95*	10	15
WR1-04	as above - *98-99*	10	15
B501	**BR** B893380 red brown - *02-09*	6	8
B501	**BR** B893344 red brown - *02-06*	7	9
B501A	**BR** B893369 red brown - *02-03*	7	9
B501A	**BR** B893373 red brown * - *10*	7	9

CIE cattle wagon [W34] (Dapol)

-	**BR** 'Bass' W102208 brown Ale Wagon Sp Edn 200 (Tutbury Jinny) - *06*	8	10
-	**BR** 'Bass' W102200 brown Ale Wagon Sp Edn 200 (Tutbury Jinny) - *09*	8	10
-	**CIE** 510 pale grey Sp Edn (Marks Models) - *04, 06*	8	10
-	**SLNC** (Sligo, Leitrim & Northern Counties Railway) 158 grey Sp Edn 143 (Provincial Wagons) - *08*	8	10
-	**SLNC** 110 grey Sp Edn (West Wales Wagon Works) - *10*	8	11

* Possibly rebumbered old stock.

W35. 8T Y10 GWR Fruit Van (ex-Wrenn) (c1995)

This was the Hornby Dublo cattle wagon converted by Wrenn to a fruit van and represents one of 130 so converted by the GWR in 1939.

-	**'Felin Foel Brewery'** 1 dark grey Sp Edn 124 (Voyles) - *08*	9	11
-	'George **Gale & Co.'** 6 dark green Sp Edn 228 (Wessex Wagons) - *10*	9	11
B212	**GW** 38200 grey - *c95*	NPG	NPG
B504	**GW** 38231 grey - *02-09*	6	8
B504A	**GW** 38218 grey - *02-05*	7	9
B504A	**GW** 38228 grey * - *10*	7	9
B211	**BR** B872181 grey - *c95*	15	18
WR1-33	as above - *99*	15	75
B213	**BR** B872181 brown - *c95*	10	15
WR1-32	as above - *99*	10	20
B584	**BR** B833341 brown Mex - *04-09*	6	8
B584A	**BR** B833340 brown Mex * - *10*	7	9
-	**BR** W106133 red-brown Evesham Sp Edn 300 (Classic Train & Motor Bus) - *03*	9	11
-	**BR** W106147 brown, Sp Edn 100 (Classic Train & Motor Bus) - *05*	8	10

* Possibly rebumbered old stock.

W36a. BR Passenger Fruit Van (ex-HD/Wrenn) (1998)

This is a standard GWR design with a long wheelbase, some of which were built by BR.

WR1-*05*	**BR** W28720 blue - *98-99*	10	22
WR1-51	**BR** B517112 grey - *99*	30	60

W36b. BR Passenger 'Fruit D' Van (2008)

This uses the slightly adapted body from the above but with a new well detailed chassis.

GWR Passenger 'Fruit D' van [W36b]

B746	**GWR** (large) 2877 dark brown - *08*	12	15
B746A	**GWR** (large) 2882 dark brown * - *10*	12	15
B737	**GWR** (button) 2881 dark brown - *08*	12	15
B737A	**GWR** (button) 2878 dark brown * - *10*	12	15
B737W	**GWR** (button) 2878 dark brown W * Sp Edn 300 (Hattons) - *10*	12	15
B745	**BR** W2919 maroon - *08*	12	15
B745A	**BR** W2010 maroon * - *10*	12	15
B745W	**GWR** (button) W2010 maroon W * Sp Edn 300 (Hattons) - *10*	12	15
B753	**BRe** W38129 Rail blue - *09*	12	15
B753A	**BRe** W38103 Rail blue * - *10*	12	15
SBB5	**BRe** W38129 Rail blue W (with chalk marks on both sides) Sp Edn 300 (Signal Box) - *09*	14	17

* Possibly renumbered old stock.

W37. GWR 12T Goods Fruit Van (ex-Mainline) (1989)

This van is of standard length and has louvered panels along the top of each side, either side of the doors.

B261	**'Fyffes'** 1437 yellow - *?*	NPG	NPG
B81	**GW** 134149 grey - *89-03*	7	9
B98	**BR** W134251 brown - Fruit - *91-02*	8	10
B261	**BR** grey - *c95*	NPG	NPG

W38. 12T Banana Van (ex-HD/Wrenn) (c1995)

This van has no plank effect on the sides and no protruding vents in the ends. The ends are corrugated. Originally sold as 'WR3' stock it was absorbed from the Wrenn range when G&R Wrenn was sold to Mordvale in 2001.

-	'JS **Fry & Sons'** 59741 white Sp Edn 145 (Wessex Wagons) - *08*	8	10
-	'JS **Fry & Sons'** 105870 white Sp Edn 130 (Wessex Wagons) - *08*	8	10
-	**'Stogumber Brewery'** 19 cream Sp Edn 280 (Wessex Wagons) - *07*	7	9
B263	**'Tropical Fruit Co.'** M40 grey - *?*	10	15
B716	**'Tropical Fruit Co.'** M40 grey - *07-08*	6	8
WR1-54	as above - *99*	10	15
WR2-*08*	as above Dapol chassis - *98-99*	8	10
B862	**'Tropical Fruit Co.'** M45 grey - *10*	7	9
-	**'Whiteways Cyder Co.'** 31 cream Sp Edn 174 (Wessex Wagons) - *08*	8	10
B182	**BR 'Jaffa'** B881902 grey - *c95*	NPG	NPG
B379	**BR 'Jaffa'** B881902 grey - *02-03*	7	9
W5105	**BR 'Jaffa'** B881867 orange Sp Edn 100 (Wrenn Collectors Club - WRCC6) - *02*	20	30
WRCC9	**BR 'Jaffa'** B881867 lemon yellow Sp Edn 100 (Wrenn Collectors Club) - *02*	20	30

B180	**BR 'Fyffes'** B881687 brown - *89-90*	10	15
B381	**BR 'Fyffes'** B881620 brown - *02-03*	7	9
B381	**BR 'Fyffes'** B881967 brown - *02-03*	7	9
B721	**BR 'Fyffes'** B881804 brown - *08*	6	8
B264	**BR 'Fyffes'** B881867 yellow (also B263) - *c95*	12	15
WR1-27	as above - *99*	12	15
B511	**BR 'Fyffes'** 881902 yellow - *02-03*	7	9
WR3-18	**BR 'Fyffes'** 881902 yellow - *00-01*	8	10
B754	**BR 'Fyffes'** B861846 yellow - *09*	7	9
B204	**BR 'Geest'** B881902 grey - *94-95*	10	15
WR1-28	as above - *99*	10	50
B512	**BR 'Geest'** B881967 grey - *02*	8	10
WR3-19	**BR 'Geest'** B881967 grey - *00-01*	8	10
W5007A	**BR 'Geest'** B881902 black (body only) SP Edn 135 (Wrenn RCC - WRCC2) - *00*	20	30
W5007A	**BR 'Geest'** B881902 dark grey (body only) SP Edn 115 (Wrenn RCC - WRCC3) - *00*	20	30
B561	**BR 'Geest'** B881632 brown - *04-05*	7	9
	Railway Companies		
B178	**BR** B881902 brown Banana - *?*	10	15
WR1-18	**BR** B881902 brown - *99*	10	35
B345	**BR** B881902 brown Banana - *01-09*	6	8
B345	**BR** B881632 brown Banana - *01-06*	7	9
B345A	**BR** B881900 brown Banana * - *09*	7	9
B561	**BR** B882117 brown Geest - *03*	7	9
B711	**BR** B882128 brown Geest - *07-08*	6	8
B373	**BR** B784879 brown - *02-03*	7	9
B373A	**BR** B784870 brown - *02-03*	7	9
B385	**BR** B753479 grey - *not made*	NA	NA
B385	**BR** B753498 grey - *02-03*	7	9
B385A	**BR** B753487 grey - *02-03*	7	9
-	**CIE** 2017 brown Sp Edn (Marks Models) - *08*	7	9
-	**CIE** 2017 brown W Sp Edn (Marks Models) - *08*	7	9
-	**GN** (Irish) 2229 grey Sp Edn 155 (Provincial Wagons) - *08*	7	9

Great Northern Railway banana van [W38] (Dapol)

B357	**NE** 158677 light grey - *01-03*	7	9
B326	**SR** 41596 dark brown, dark grey roof - *01-02*	8	10
B326	**SR** 41594 dark brown, light grey roof (box marked 'Ventilated Van') - *01-06*	7	9
B326	**SR** 41535? dark brown - *07*	7	9

* Possibly renumbered old stock.

W39. GWR 12T 'Mogo' Van (ex-Mainline) (1991)

This van has sides like the Mainline ventilated van but has end doors. It was made from duplicate tools which Hornby later bought.

B147	**'Shepherd Neame'** 3 cream (M) - *?*	7	11
B146	**GW** 126342 grey Mogo - *91-03*	7	9
B145	**BR** W105682 red-brown Mogo - *91-03*	7	9

W40a. LMS 12T Single Vent Sliding Door Van (ex-Mainline) (1984)

On the model the doors slide or fixed.

B7	**LMS** 511476 grey doors slide (M) - *84-99*	7	11

W40b. LMS 12T Planked Single Vent Van (ex-Airfix) (1984)

On the model the doors are part of a single body moulding and so do not slide unlike those on the Mainline model above.

A6	grey unfinished - *84-03*	4	6
-	**'Anglo Swiss Condensed Milk Co.'** 23 cream Sp Edn 181 (Burnham & District MRC) - *10*	8	10
-	**'Bass'** 15 grey Sp Edn 200 (The Tutbury Jinny) - *10*	8	10
-	**'Bass'** 16 olive green Sp Edn (Tutbury Jinny) - *?*	10	12
-	**'Bass'** 17 olive green Sp Edn 200 (Tutbury Jinny) ex-set of 2 (with Bass 7-plank) - *02*	10	NA
-	**'Bass'** 19 olive grey Sp Edn (Tutbury Jinny) - *08*	7	9
-	**'Bass'** 23 olive green, Sp Edn 200 (Tutbury Jinny) ex-set of 2 - *02*	10	NA
-	**'Bass'** 24 grey, Sp Edn 200 (Tutbury Jinny) ex-set of 2 - *05*	8	NA
-	**'Bass'** 28 grey Sp Edn 200 (Tutbury Jinny) ex-set of 2 (with Worthington 88) - *05*	8	NA
-	**'Bass'** 29 light grey, Sp Edn 200 (Tutbury Jinny) ex-set of 2 - *03*	9	NA
PR2	**'BBRUA'** 25th Anniversary maroon Sp Edn 250 (1E Promotionals) - *05*	8	10
PR1	**'Bletchley TMD 40th Anniversary'** white Sp Edn 250 (1E Promotionals) - *05*	8	10
-	**'BPCM'** 143 pinkish-brown Sp Edn 229 (Wessex Wagons) - *06*	8	10
-	'**Brickwoods Brewery**' 29 dark brown Sp Edn 191 (Wessex Wagons) - *08*	7	10
-	'The **Charlton Brewery**' 22 green Sp Edn (Burnham & District MRC) - *10*	9	11
-	'**Burts of Ventner**' 1 cream Sp Edn (Wessex Wagons) - *10*	7	10
-	**'Devenish Weymouth Ales'** 34 green Sp Edn 210 (Wessex Wagons) - *09*	9	11
-	'The **Duchess of Devonshire Dairy Co.**' 15 cream Sp Edn (Burnham & District MRC) - *10*	9	11
-	'The **Eclipse Peat Co.**' 23 dark brown Sp Edn 153 (Burnham & District MRC) - *09*	8	10
B64	**'English Eggs'** 506150 dark blue (A) - *85-87*	9	14
B376	**'English Eggs'** deep blue - *02-03*	7	9
-	**'English Eggs'** (Westmoreland) dark blue Sp Edn (Trident Trains) - *06*	8	10
-	'Wm **Furze & Sons**' 23 cream Sp Edn 217 (Wessex Wagons) - *10*	7	10
-	**'Gibbs, Mew & Co.'** 3 dark blue Sp Edn 178 (Wessex Wagons) - *08*	7	10
-	**'Great Western Society'** dark brown Sp Edn (GWS) - *06*	8	10
-	**'Grey & Church St Breweries'** 1 cream Sp Edn 190 (Wessex Wagons) - *07*	7	9
-	**'Grey & Church St Breweries'** 2 cream Sp Edn 152 (Wessex Wagons) - *05*	8	10
-	**'Hall & Woodhouse'** 5 green Sp Edn 197 (Wessex Wagons) - *06*	8	10

Ex-LMS ventilated van - 'Holts Brewery Co.' [W40b] (Dapol)

-	**'Harveys of Hayle'** 81802 brown Sp Edn 100 (Blewetts of Hayle) - *04*	9	11
-	**'Heavitree Brewery'** 131 red-brown Sp Edn 230 (Wessex Wagons) - *10*	9	11
-	**'Holts Brewery Co.'** 4 buff Sp Edn 140 (Burnham & District MRC) - *09*	8	10
10B161	**'Huntley & Palmer'** 566327 green (A) - *?*	9	12
B65	**'ICI Salt'** 2300 maroon doors fixed (M) - *85-95*	8	12
-	**'Kelsey'** dark brown Sp Edn 300 (Ballards) - *10*	8	11
-	'W&H **Marriage & Sons**' 2007 light grey Sp Edn		

	315 (Chelmsford & Dist MRC) - *07*	7	10
B66	**'Nestle's Milk'** 531179 blue (A) - *85-87*	8	12
-	**'Oakhill Brewery Co.'** 14 green Sp Edn 240 (Burnham & District MRC) - *10*	9	11
-	**'Otter Brewery'** 3 cream Sp Edn 190 (Buffers) - *10*	8	11
-	**'Otter Brewery'** 4 light blue Sp Edn 204 (Buffers) -*10*	8	11
B62	**'Persil'** 547921 green (A) - *85-92*	8	12
-	**'Petter & Sons Anchor Brewery'** 5 light blue Sp Edn 195 (Buffers) - *10*	8	11
-	'JW **Phipp & Sons'** 43 light grey Sp Edn 300 (Wessex Wagons) - *08*	7	9
-	**'Queenborough Cement Co.'** 10 cream Sp Edn 1000 (Ballards) - *09*	8	10
-	**'Saltley Depot Commemoration'** 150 years DM5 14921 black, Sp Edn 180 (Classic Train & Motor Bus) - *04*	9	11
-	**'SMR War Department'** 30 light grey Sp Edn 100 (Shrewsbury Model Centre) - *08*	7	9
-	**'Starkey, Knight & Ford'** 3 buff Sp Edn 250 (Wessex Wagons) - *07*	7	9
-	**SVR 40th Anniv.** white Sp Edn (SVR Wolverhampton Branch) - *07*	7	9
B61	**'Tizer'** 561772 yellow (A) - *85-88*	8	12

Ex-LMS van - 'Trago Mills' [W40b] (Paul Harman)

-	**'Trago Mills'** yellow Sp Edn 250 (Trago Mills) - *89*	12	14
-	same but blue Sp Edn 250 - *89*	12	14
-	same but green Sp Edn 250 - *89*	12	14
-	same but red Sp Edn 5000 - *89*	12	14
-	same but brown Sp Edn 250 - *89*	20	24
-	**TVLR** M632154 cream Sp Edn 96 (Tanat Valley Light Railway Co.) - *07*	7	10
-	**UT** (Ulster Transport Authority) 2478 red-brown Sp Edn 152 (Provincial Wagons) - *08*	7	9
-	**'Wilts United Daries'** 3 cream Sp Edn 136 (Burnham & Dist MRC) - *09*	7	9
-	**'Wilts United Dairies'** 4 cream Sp Edn 160 (Burnham & District MRC) - *10*	8	10
-	**'Worthington'** 3 brown, Sp Edn 200 (Tutbury Jinny) ex-set of 2 - *03*	9	NA
-	**'Worthington'** 8 brown Sp Edn 200 (The Tutbury Jinny) - *10*	8	10
-	**'Worthington'** 30 brown Sp Edn (Tutbury Jinny) - *08*	7	9
-	**'Worthington'** 33 brown, Sp Edn 200 (Tutbury Jinny) ex-set of 2 - *05*	8	NA
-	**'Worthington'** 88 brown Sp Edn 200 (Tutbury Jinny) ex-set of 2 (with Bass 28) - *05*	8	NA
No.30	**LMS** 282093 brown LMS Salvage Campaign, Sp Edn 119 (West Wales Wagon Works) - *05*	8	10
B4	**LMS** 520212 brown - *?*	8	10
B7	**LMS** 501086 grey - *84-85*	8	10
B7	**LMS** 508587 grey (M) - *88-99*	8	12
B9	**LMS** 511840 red brown - *84-88*	8	10
B382	**LMS** 508587 light grey - *02-03*	7	9
B382A	**LMS** 508579 light grey - *02-03*	7	9
B839	**LMS** 511235 grey, Egg Van - *10*	7	9
B829	**LMS** 511239 grey, Fruit Van - *10*	7	9
B526	**LMS** 511240 grey, Egg Van - *03*	7	9
B527	**LMS** 511246 grey, Fruit Van - *03*	7	9
B567	**LMS** 611846 brown - *04-05*	7	9
B752	**LMS** 538864 grey - *09*	6	8
B22	**BR** M501085 light grey - *84-87*	8	10
B63	**BR** B753722, B751707 red brown (M) - *85-92*	8	12
B386	**BR** M283328 grey - *02-07*	7	9
B386A	**BR** M283331 grey - *02-03*	7	9
B764	**BR** M183317 grey - *09*	6	8

* These were delivered unnumbered and were individually numbered by Steve Skelton of Hythe (Kent) Models.

W41a. 12T Planked Single Vent Van (ex-HD/Wrenn) (1993)

This van is very like the Dapol single vent planked van but has no bolt protruding downwards from the point where the doors join.

A11	grey - unfinished - *02-03*	4	6
A004	grey - unfinished - *04-07*	4	6
-	**'Anglo Bavarian Brewery'** 12 dark blue Sp Edn 275 (Wessex Wagons) - *07*	7	10
WRCC11	**'Camerons'** B757051 white Sp Edn 100 (Wrenn Collectors Club) - *03*	10	12
B613	**'Carricks'** 181 grey - *05*	7	9
TMCD001	**'CLA Game Fair'** green Sp Edn 137 (TMC) - *03*	9	11
-	**'Dee Valley Eggs'** 1 brown Sp Edn 111 (Llangollen Railway) - *08*	7	9
-	**'Fremlin Bros.'** 1 white, grey roof Sp Edn 1000 (Ballards) - *02*	9	11
-	**'Fremlin Bros.'** 2 white Sp Edn 1000 (Ballards) - *09*	8	11

Former Hornby Dublo ventilated van - 'HM Dockyard Portsmouth' [W41a] (Dapol)

-	**'HM Dockyard Portsmouth'** 11 blue Sp Edn 162 (Wessex Wagons) - *09*	9	11
-	**'Holts Brewery Co.'** 4 buff Sp Edn 140 (Burnham & District MRC) - *10*	8	10
B317	**'ICI Salt'** 2653 red - *00-02*	8	10
-	**'Mevagissey Model Railway'** 20061 dark red Sp Edn (Mevagissey Models) - *06*	8	10
-	**'MHR'** S2009 light grey Sp Edn 96 (Mid Hants Railway) - *09*	7	9
-	**Nene Valley Railway** 402 grey Sp Edn (Nene Valley Railway) - *09*	7	9
-	'John **Norton & Son'** 9* dark green Sp Edn 194 (Hythe Kent Models) 1st issue - *01*	10	12
-	**'The Norton Mills Company'** 6 dark green Sp Edn 160 (Burnham & District MRC) - *10*	8	10
-	**NYMR** NE133971 dark grey Sp Edn 200 (North Yorkshire Moors Rly) - *01, 04, 05*	8	10
-	**'Palmers Brewery'** 4 blue Sp Edn 200 (Buffers) - *10*	9	11
WRCC12	**'Rebellion Beer Co. 1993 The Marlow Brewery'** white Sp Edn 100 (Wrenn Collectors Club) - *03*	30	45
WR2-*03*	**'Robertson's'** B757051 brown - *98-99*	10	15
-	**'Rother Valley Brewery'** 49225 dark green Sp Edn 198 (Hythe Kent Models) - *02*	10	12
-	**'Rother Valley Brewery'** 49225 dark green Sp Edn 113 (Hythe Kent Models) - *03*	9	11
-	**'Royal Navy Stores'** * dark blue Sp Edn 200 (Hythe Kent Models) - *04-07*	7	9
-	**'Shepherd Neame'** 3 cream Sp Edn 400 (East Kent MRS) - *02*	9	11
-	**'The Cheddar Valley Dairy Co.'** 11 cream Sp Edn (Burnham & District MRC) - *10*	9	11

Ventilated van - 'Vickerys' Pure Cider' [W41a] (Dapol)

-	'SNSO' 419 navy blue Sp Edn 240 (Wessex Wagons) - *10*	9	11
TMCD002	**'TMC 5th Anniversary'** blue Sp Edn 173 (The Model Centre) - *03*	9	11
-	**'Vickery's Pure Cider'** 5 buff Sp Edn 147 (Burnham & District MRC) - *09*	8	10
-	**'Wensleydale Creamery'** 1984 cream Sp Edn 85 (West Wales Wagon Works) - *09*	7	10
-	**'Wensleydale Creamery'** 1984 cream W Sp Edn 84 (West Wales Wagon Works) - *09*	8	11
-	**'Wensleydale Creamery'** 1989 cream Sp Edn 85 (West Wales Wagon Works) - *09*	7	10
-	**'Wensleydale Creamery'** 1989 cream W Sp Edn 84 (West Wales Wagon Works) - *09*	8	11
-	**'Wensleydale Creamery'** 1992 cream Sp Edn 85 (West Wales Wagon Works) - *09*	7	10
-	**'Wensleydale Creamery'** 1992 cream W Sp Edn 83 (West Wales Wagon Works) - *09*	8	11
-	**'Wensleydale Creamery'** 1997 cream Sp Edn 87 (West Wales Wagon Works) - *09*	7	10
-	**'Wensleydale Creamery'** 1997 cream W Sp Edn 80 (West Wales Wagon Works) - *09*	8	11
	Railway Companies		
-	**IWCR** 297 light grey Sp Edn 175 (Wessex Wagons) - *08*	7	9
-	**S&DJR** 756 grey road van Sp Edn 207 (Wessex Wagons) - *09*	9	11
-	**GW** 2356 dark brown Fruit Sp Edn 150 (West Wales Wagon Works - *07*	7	9
B532	**GW** 95444 grey Steam Banana - *03*	7	9
B339	**LMS** 511840 light grey - *01-02*	8	10
B339	**LMS** 59673 red - *?*	10	12
WR1-39	as above - *99*	10	15
WR2-*05*	as above but Dapol chassis - *98-99*	9	11
B235	**SR** 41596 dark brown - *c95*	10	15
WR1-61	as above - *99*	10	15
WR2-*09*	as above Dapol chassis - *98-99*	8	10
WR1-35	**BR** 57 brown - *99*	25	30
WR1-22	**BR** B545523 brown - *99*	10	35
WR1-34	**BR** W145207 grey - *99*	25	30
B16	**BR** M501085 grey - *84-92*	9	11
B389	**BR** B753889 grey - *02-03*	7	9
B389A	**BR** B753896 grey - *02-03*	7	9
B391	**BR** B760561 brown - *02-03*	7	9
B391A	**BR** B760579 brown - *02-05*	7	9
-	**CIE** 315 pale grey W Sp Edn (Mark's Models) - *02*	10	12

* These were individually numbered by Hythe Models.

W41b. 12T Planked Single Vent Van (1988)

This wagon was designed and tooled by Dapol. It has one vent each end and has angled braces on the doors. The corner irons are also tapered and it differs from the HD/Wrenn vent van in having a bolt protruding downwards from the point where the doors join. The tool was later sold to Hornby.

A11	? - unfinished - *98-99*	4	6
B109	**BR** B760563 red brown - *88-99*	8	10
B110	**BR** B753894 grey - *89-96*	9	11

W41c. BR 12T Plywood Single Vent Van (1986)

This wagon was designed and tooled by Dapol. It has no plank effect on the sides but has vents in the ends. It also has a raised data panel near the bottom left hand corner of the sides.

A10	brown or grey - unfinished - *95-03*	4	6
-	**'Cathcart Railway Exhib.'** 1968-1992 brown Sp Edn 265 (Cathcart MRS) - *92*	12	14
-	**'Crewe Heritage Centre'** grey Sp Edn (Crewe Centre Models) - *?*	10	15
-	**North Norfolk Railway** brown Sp Edn (NNR) - *?*	8	10
B102	**BR** B784873 red brown, also ex set B404 - *86-99*	8	10
B108	**BR** B753498 grey - *89-96*	9	11

W41d. GWR 12T Planked Double Vent Van (ex-Mainline) (1984)

This van has two vents at each end and no angled braces on the doors. Duplicate tools were made in China. One set was sold to Hornby in 1996 and the model reintroduced by them.

B144	**GW** 123507 grey - *91-03*	7	9
B4	**LMS** 521202 red brown - *84-88*	9	11
B92	**BR** W141826 red brown (M?) - *86, 91-02*	8	10
B93	**BR** W133971 grey (M?) - *86-02*	8	10

W42a. SR 12T Double Vent Box Van (ex-Airfix) (1984)

This van has an elliptically curved roof, the sharpest curves being just above the sides. For B17, two sizes of 'SR' may be found. It is thought that the tooling was sold to Hornby in 1996.

A7	grey - brown roof, unfinished - *84-02*	4	6
B15	**GW** 144888 dark grey - *84-95*	9	11
B16	**SR** 44433 grey - *84-92*	9	11
B16	**SR** 44434 grey - *?*	9	11
B17	**SR** 273843 dark brown - *84-?*	9	11
B17	**SR** 44393 dark brown - *?-94*	9	11
B327	**SR** 273840 dark brown - *01-02*	8	10
B16	**BR** S44434 grey - *84-92*	9	11

W42b. SR 12T Double Vent Box Van (2005)

This van was retooled in 2005.

-	**'Baldwins'** * dark brown Sp Edn 114 (West Wales Wagon Works) - *08*	7	9
-	**'Bryant & Son'** 1 red-brown Sp Edn 193 (Buffers) - *10*	8	11
-	'Alfred **Day**' 273836 dark blue Sp Edn (Colonel Stephens Railway Enterprise) - *09*	10	13
-	**'Dover Packet Yard - Stores'** 2 grey Sp Edn 150 (Carriage & Wagon Models) - *10*	8	12
-	**'Eldridge, Pope & Co.'** 48345 green Sp Edn 250 (Wessex Wagons) - *07*	7	9
-	**'Express Dairy Co. English Eggs'** (Devonshire) 48323 blue-grey Sp Edn 230 (Wessex Wagons) - *06*	8	10
-	**'Express Dary Co. English Eggs'** (Fine Cheeses) 49345 blue-grey Sp Edn 302 (Wessex Wagons) - *07*	7	10
-	**'Express Dary Co. - English Eggs (Devonshire)'** 49168 dk.blue Sp Edn 180 (Wessex Wagons) - *08*	8	10

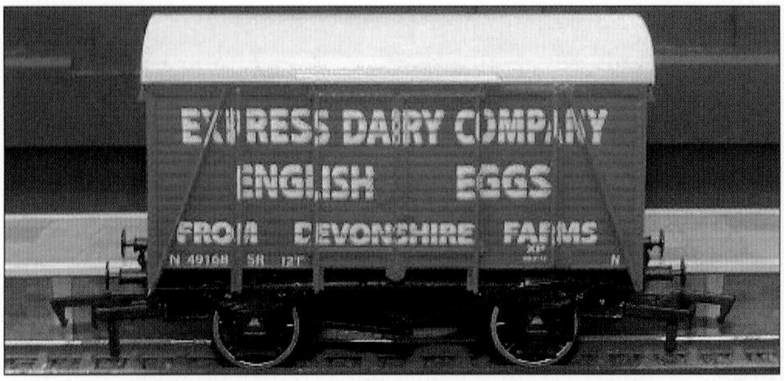

Ex-SR ventilated van - 'Express Dairy Co. English Eggs' [W42b]

-	'RH&J **Follett**' 2 red-brown Sp Edn 149 (Buffers) - *09*	8	11
-	'RH&J **Follett**' 4 red-brown Sp Edn 213 (Buffers) - *10*	8	11
-	'John **Groves & Son**' 3 pale brown Sp Edn 200 (Buffers) - *10*	8	11

-	**'JS & JL Hilder'** 273849 red-brown Sp Edn (Col. Stephens Railway Enterprises) - *10*	8	11
-	**'Mitchell Toms & Co.'** 3 green Sp Edn 230 (Wessex Wagons) - *07*	7	9
-	**Moors Valley Railway** 2009 red maintenance van Sp Edn 232 (Moors Valley Railway) - *09*	8	10
-	**'New Medway'** 40 blue-grey Sp Edn 95 (Medway Queen Preservation Society) - *07*	7	9
-	**'New Medway'** 53 blue-grey Sp Edn 90 (Medway Queen Preservation Society) - *07*	7	9
-	**'Oysters from Whitstable'** EKMRS07 pale blue Sp Edn 171 (East Kent MRS) - *07*	7	9
-	**'Oysters from Whitstable'** 10 dark green Sp Edn 182 (East Kent MRS) - *10*	8	10
-	**'Pride of Sussex'** bright green Sp Edn 185 (Kent & East Sussex Railway) - *07*	7	9
-	**'Rother Valley Brewery'** bright green Sp Edn 200 (Col. Stephens Railway Enterprises KESR) - *06*	7	9
-	'**Seccotine**' blue with orange roof Sp Edn 150 (McDiamid) - *10*	9	11
-	**'Shepherd Neame & Co.'** 1 cream Sp Edn 236 (East Kent MRS) - *09*	7	9

Ex-SR ventilated van - 'Vallance Brewery Co.' [W42b] (Dapol)

-	**'Strong & Co.'** 7 dark blue Sp Edn 240 (Wessex Wagons) - *07*	7	9
-	**'Vallance Brewery Co.'** 1 dark green Sp Edn 143 (Buffers) - *09*	8	11
	Railway Companies		
3	**WHR** 20 grey Sp Edn (Welsh Highland Rly) - *08*	7	9
B636	**GW** 144859 grey - *05-09*	6	8
B636A	**GW** 144852 grey ** - *10*	7	9
B642	**LMS** 611819 brown - *05-09*	6	8
B627	**SR** 273849 brown - *05-09*	6	8
B627A	**SR** 273830 brown ** - *10*	7	9
-	**SR** 46946 dark brown Fish Sp Edn 1000 (Ballards) - *07*	6	8
-	**SR** 'Fish Traffic Only' 46940 dark brown Sp Edn (Ballaeds) - *10*	8	10
B625	**BR** B753848 grey - *05-07*	6	8

*various running numbers. ** Possibly renumbered old stock.

W43. BR CCT Utility Van (ex-HD/Wrenn) (2001)

-	**Mid Hants Railway** S2005 green Sp Edn (Mid Hants Railway) - *05*	10	14
B341	**SR** S2279S green - *01-09*	10	12
B388	**BR** S2380S green - *02-09*	10	12
B342	**BR** M527071 red - *01-05*	10	12
B342	**BR** M527042 red - *01-09*	10	12
B340	**BR** S2514S blue - *01-03*	10	12
SBB4	**BR** S25148 blue W Sp Edn 300 (Signal Box) - *09*	14	17

W44. BR 10T Quadruple Vent Meat Van (1985)

This wagon was designed and tooled by Dapol and the body tool later sold to Hornby.

A14	red - unfinished - *98-03*	3	5
B102	**LMS** 173127 brown - *?*	10	12
B26	**BR** B870074 red also ex-set B402 - *85-99*	8	10
B180	**BR** B670006 red brown - *89-90*	9	11

W45. GWR 12T 'Mica B' Van (ex-HD/Wrenn) (c1995)

B234	**'Birds Eye'** 312 blue - *c95*	10	15
WR2-07	**'Eskimo'** W59850 white - *98-99*	9	11
WR1-12	**'Young's'** 78 white - *99*	10	15
WR1-13	W59850 plain green - *99*	25	35
B233	**GW** 59828 white 'Mica B' - *c95*	10	15
B231	**BR** 150721 grey 'Insulmeat' - *c95*	NPG	NPG
B232	**BR** W145207 white 'Mica B' - *c95*	15	18

W46. BR 'Blue Spot' Van (ex-HD/Wrenn) (c1995)

Originally sold as 'WR3' stock it was absorbed from the Wrenn range when G&R Wrenn was sold to Mordvale in 2001.

WR3-12	**'Findus'** E87232 white - *00-02*	8	10
B257	**'North Sea Fish'** E67840 blue - *c95*	10	15
B509	**'North Sea Fish'** E87642 white - *02-03*	7	9
WR3-11	**'North Sea Fish'** E87642 white - *00-01*	8	10
B258	**'Ross'** white - *c95*	10	15
WR3-13	**'Ross'** E87234 white - *00-02*	8	10
-	**'Virgin Trains'** red + silver Sp Edn 500 (Virgin for Crewe Open Day) - *03*	9	11
-	**'York Model Railway'** 2002 light blue Sp Edn 100 (YMR) - *02*	10	12
-	as above but numbered 2003 - *03*	9	11
-	as above but numbered 2004 - *04*	9	11
B256	**BR** E87231 white 'Insulfish' - *c95*	10	12
B507	**BR** E87234 white Blue Spot - *02-03, 07-09*	6	8
WR3-*09*	**BR** E87232 white Blue Spot - *99-01*	8	10
-	**BR(SR)** * white LNER design 'Insulfish' Sp Edn 61 (Oliver Leetham) - *05*	8	10
B538	**BR** E87488 light blue 'Insulvan' - *03*	7	9
-	**BR** E87464 ice blue with black lettering Sp Edn 70 (O.Leetham) - *02*	11	13
-	**BR** E87464 ice blue with white lettering Sp Edn 70 (O.Leetham) - *02*	11	13
B259	**BRe** E87003 blue Red Star - *c95*	15	18
B508	**BRe** E87160 blue Red Star - *02*	8	10
WR3-10	**BRe** E87537 blue Red Star - *99-01*	8	10
WR3-10	**BRe** E87160 blue Red Star - *99-01*	8	10
B262	**BRe** E87003 blue Exp. Parcels - *c95*	15	18
B506	**BRe** E87160 blue Exp. Parcels - *02*	8	10
WR3-*08*	**BRe** E87537 blue Exp. Parcels - *99-01*	8	10
B533	**BRe** E88005 blue Exp Parcels NRV - *03-05*	7	9
-	**BR** 041317 blue Express Parcels Sp Edn 110 (Alexandra Models) - *07*	9	12
SBB6	**BRe** E88005 blue W Express Parcels Sp Edn 300 (Signal Box) - *09*	8	11
B537	**BR** E75575 brown 'Van Fit' - *03*	7	9
B564	**BR** DE75575 brown 'Van Fit' ballast cleaner van - *03-05*	7	9
B260	**BRe** E67840 beige BRT - *c95*	10	15
WR1-*06*	as above - *98-99*	10	20
WR3-14	**BRe** E87539 ochre BRT - *00-02*	8	10
-	**BRe** ADB975419 red Barrowhill Depot Tool Van Sp Edn 90 (O.Leetham) - *01*	11	13
B704	**BRe** ADB975424 red (Barrowhill Depot MPD tool van) - *07-08*	6	8
-	**BR** ADB975418 yellow (Shirebrook Depot) Sp Edn 120 (O.Leetham) - *01*	11	13

Ex-'Blue Spot' packing van [W46] (Dapol)

B695	**BR** ADB975436 yellow (Shirebrook Depot packing van) - *07*	6	8
-	**BR** M87793 red-brown RBV barrier wagon Sp Edn 93 (O.Leetham) - *02*	11	13

-	9 of above had unique numbers ** applied by Oliver Leetham - *04?*	10	12
-	3 of above but solebars and bufferbeams brown + brake handle white Sp Edn - *04?*	13	15
-	**BRe** ADE75415 rail blue boiler van Sp Edn 59 (Oliver Leetham) - *05*	9	11
-	**BR** ADB975329 red ZQV Frodingham tool van Sp Edn 134 (Oliver Leetham) - *05*	8	10
B773	**BR** ADB975324 red with black+yellow wasp stripes on the ends ZQV Frodingham Packing Van - *09*	8	10
-	**BR** ADB975350 yellow Immingham tool van Sp Edn 107 (O.Leetham) - *05*	8	10
B769	**BR** ADB975356 yellow Immingham tool van - *09*	8	10
-	**BR** ADW87706 yellow (Shirebrook Depot) tool van Sp Edn 91 (Oliver Leetham) - *05*	8	10

* Each wagon had a different running number in the E75xxx series. The first four digits were put on by Dapol and the rest by Oliver Leetham. ** These were M87707/34/52/59/63/75/76/77/90 also shown on modified certificates.

Brake Vans

W47a. GWR 20T 'Toad' Brake Van (ex-Airfix) (1985)

B104	**GW** 56835 grey Rhymney - *87-88*	9	11
B105	**GW** 114925 grey Saltney - *86-92, 98-99*	8	10
B117	**GW** 68796 dark grey Park Royal - *88-89*	9	11
B33	**BR** 114926 grey (A) also - *85-02*	8	12

The tooling was sold to Hornby in 1996 and the model reintroduced by them.

W47b. GWR 20T Brake Van (ex-Mainline) (1985)

B34	**BR** W68855 light grey (M) - *85-99*	8	12
B35	**BR** W68816 red brown (M) - *?*	8	12

W48a. LMS 20T Brake Van (ex-HD/Wrenn) (1984)

B2	**LMS** 730670 red-brown - *84-97*	10	12
B2	**LMS** 730973 red-brown - *84-97*	10	12
WR1-46	as above - *99*	10	15

W48b. LMS 20T Brake Van (ex-Airfix) (1984)

B123	**LMS** 730097 grey (A) - *92-95*	4	8
B5	**BR** M730836 grey - *84-86*	9	11
B5	**BR** M? grey - *97-98*	9	11
B127	**BR** B950016 brown + yellow (A) - *92-95*	8	13
B185	**BR** M732148 red-brown - *94-95*	9	11

The tooling was sold to Hornby in 1996 and the model reintroduced by them.

W49a. Short Brake Van (ex-Mainline) (1985)

B37	**NE** 182030 - red-brown - *85-89*	9	11
B31	**BR** E168064 grey (M) - *85-88*	8	12

W49b. BR Short Brake Van (ex-HD/Wrenn) (c1995)

This had a diecast chassis.

B31	**NE** 128105 grey - *c95*	10	18
WR1-*02*	as above - *97-99*	10	18

W50a. LNER/Standard Brake Van (ex-Mainline) (1985)

B30	**BR** B951480 dark brown (M) - *85-88*	8	12
B36	**BR** B950880 grey (M) - *85-87*	8	12

W50b. LNER/Standard Brake Van (ex-HD/Wrenn) (c1995)

This had a diecast chassis.

B206	**SR** 32831 dark brown - *c95*	10	18
WR1-*01*	as above - *97-99*	10	18
B30	**BR** B950350 red-brown - *c95*	10	18
B36	**BR** B932103 grey - *c95*	15	20
WR1-47	as above - *99*	15	40

Bogie Flat & Container Wagons

W51. FEA Spine Wagon (2008)

A French built design with a low floor for high capacity containers and swap-bodies. Containers are available separately. Sold in pairs and with a close-coupling system and a diecast deck for a low centre of gravity. Only 250 of each pair of numbers are produced and each comes with a bag of add-on detail. Comes with a pack of add-ons.

-	**Fastline Freight** ? + ? grey Sp Edn (Rail Express Modeller) - *09*	20	25
B853	**Freightliner** 640101 + 640102 green FEA-B - *10*	16	20
B854	**Freightliner** 640103 + 640104 green FEA-B - *10*	16	20
B724a	**Freightliner** 640121 + 640122 green - *08*	16	20
B724b	as above numbered 640209 + 640210 - *08*	16	20
B724c	**Freightliner** 640213 + 640214 green - *09*	16	20
B724d	as above numbered 640353 + 640354 - *09*	16	20
B724e	as above numbered 640235 + 640236 - *09*	16	20
B724f	as above numbered 640221 + 640222 - *09*	16	20
B724m	**Freightliner** 640709 + 640710 dark green - *09*	20	25
B724n	as above but numbered 640499 + 640500 - *09*	20	25
-	**Freightliner** 640351 + 640352 olive green W Sp Edn 250 (Trainlines of Derby) - *08*	18	23
B740a	**GBRf** 640603 + 640604 dark blue - *08*	16	20
B740b	as above numbered 640619 + 640620 - *08*	16	20
B740c	as above numbered 640619 + 640620 - *08*	16	20
B740d	as above numbered 640601 + 640602 - *08*	16	20

W52. FIA 'Megafret' Wagon (2010)

This has a diecast body and NEM coupling pockets with self-centering couplings.

FEA-B 'Spine' wagon [W52] (Dapol)

B782a	**Crawshay Brothers** 33 68 4943 079 light blue - *10*	20	25
B782b	as above numbered 33 68 4943 083 light blue - *11*	20	25
B782c	as above numbered 33 68 4943 059 light blue - *11*	20	25
B782d	as above numbered 33 68 4943 091 light blue - *11*	20	25
-	**EWS**33 70 4938 ? ? ? W Sp Edn 250 (Trainlines of Derby) - *10*	NPG	NPG
B782e	33 68 4943 094 black W Sp Edn (the Dapol shop) - *10*	22	28
B782f	33 68 4943 088 black W Sp Edn (the Dapol shop) - *10*	22	28

W53. KTA/KQA 'Pocket' Wagon (2010)

The model features close coupling, NEM coupling sockets, profile wheels, weighted for correct running and etched steel details. It is one of the few 'missing link' modern image intermodal wagons and carries a 40' container.

B779a	**Tiphook Rail** 84 70 4907 019 9 blue - *10*	20	25
B779b	as above numbered 84 70 4907 015 5 - *10*	20	25
B779c	as above numbered 84 70 4907 070 3 - *10*	20	25
B779d	as above numbered 84 70 4907 017 4 - *10*	20	25
K8001	**Tiphook** ? blue W - *10*	20	25
K8002	**Tiphook** ? blue W - *10*	20	25
K8003	**Tiphook** ? blue W - *10*	20	25
K8004	**Tiphook** ? blue W - *10*	20	25

W54a. 20ft Containers (2009)

Opening doors and fully compatible with existing 'Intermodal' wagons.

-	**'EWL'** EWLU230196 light blue	4	NA
-	**'Hanjin'** HJCU829660 blue	4	NA
-	**'MSC'** MSCU222133 buff	4	NA
-	**'Triton'** TTNU150118 brown	4	NA
B776a	above 4 containers - *09*	NA	18
-	**'China Shipping'** CCLU237754 green	4	NA
-	NPCU700741 brown	4	NA
-	**'Hanjin'** HJCU829620 blue	4	NA
-	**'Water Front'** WFCL1247165	4	NA
B776b	above 4 containers - *09*	NA	18
-	**'MSC'** GLDU505229[2] red-brown	4	NA
-	**'Triton'** TRIU398477 brown	4	NA
B776c	above 2 containers - *10*	NA	9

W54b. 40ft Containers (2009)

Opening doors and fully compatible with existing 'intermodal' wagons.

-	(no name) APZU431656 blue	4	NA
-	**'Evergreen'** EMCU127934 green	4	NA
-	**'Tiphook'** TPHU577349 dark brown	4	NA
-	**'UASC'** UACU807238 green	4	NA
B775a	above 4 containers - *09*	NA	20

40ft containers [W54b]

-	**'Genstar'** GSTU836120-1 red-brown	4	NA
-	**'Hanjin'** HJCU755528 blue	4	NA
-	**'Italia'** IMTU109833-0 blue	4	NA
-	**'MSC'** MSCU422133 cream	4	NA
B775b	above 4 containers - *09*	NA	20
-	**'MSC'** MSCU484614 cream	4	NA
-	**'TEX'** TGHU438578[3] red-brown	4	NA
B775c	above 2 containers - *10*	NA	10

W54c. 45ft Curtain-sided Containers (2009)

?	**?** ? - *09*	NPG	NPG

W54d. 45ft 'Hi Cube' Containers (2010)

9.5ft high containers.

B896a	**'CMA & CGM'** red-brown FSCU638511[0] + **'GTS'** dark blue MUCU002308[0] - *10*	NA	11
B896b	**'ECS'** maroon ECBU462709[7] + **'Deanside'** blue DSCU000762[-] twin pack - *10*	NA	11
(B857a)	**'Stobart'** 2 dark blue containers TESU450099[5] + TESU450124[5] - *10*	NA	12
(B857b)	**'Stobart'** 2 dark blue containers TESU450057[3] + TESU 450083[0] - *10*	NA	12

W54e. 40ft 'Hi Cube' Containers (2009)

Opening doors and fully compatible with existing 'Intermodal' wagons. Door latching bars packed unattached.

-	**'Cosco'** CBHU822817[5] grey	4	NA
-	**'Florens'** FSCU912374[6] red-brown	4	NA
-	**'MSC'** MSCU994560[0] buff	4	NA
-	unbranded TRLU707834[8] red-brown	4	NA
B780	above 4 containers - *09*	NA	19

W55. GWR 'Macaw H' Bogie Bolster (ex-Airfix) (1986)

Short wagon.

A12	grey - unfinished - *98-99*	5	7
B88	**BR** W107364 grey - *86-92*	8	10

The tooling was sold to Hornby in 1996 and the model reintroduced by them.

W56. GWR 'Macaw B' Bogie Bolster (ex-Mainline) (1985)

Long wagon.

B125	**GW** 107291 dark grey Macaw B, (MS?) - *90-92*	8	10
B125	**GW** 123507 dark grey Macaw B, - *?*	8	10
B75	**BR** W84921 grey + girder (M) - *85-87*	8	12

W57. BBA Bogie Steel Wagon (2011)

Built between 1973 and 1981 by BREL at Ashford, these are bolster wagons with end walls. They are modelled with a removable steel coil load.

B858a	**Railfreight** 910414 black - *11*	NPG	NPG
-	**Railfreight** ? black W Sp Edn (Hattons) - *11*	NPG	NPG

W58. GWR Crocodile H Well Wagon (ex-Mainline) (1985)

B74	**GW** 41973 dark grey Crocodile H + marine boiler (M) - *85-88*	10	14

Bogie Open Wagons

W59. JNA Network Rail 'Falcon' Ballast Wagon (2010)

These wagons are used on engineering work throughout the rail network.

B855a	**N-R** NLU29003 bright yellow - *10*	16	20
B855b	as above numbered NLU29012 - *10*	16	20
B855c	as above numbered NLU29047 - *10*	16	20
B855d	as above numbered NLU29064 - *10*	16	20

Network Rail JNA 'Falcon' ballast wagon [W59] (Dapol)

B855e	**N-R** ? bright yellow W Sp Edn 250 (Hattons) - *10*	16	20
B855f	as above numbered ? - *10*	16	20
B855g	as above numbered ? - *10*	16	20
B855h	as above numbered ? - *10*	16	20

W60. IOA-E Network Rail Bogie Box Wagon (2010)

A wagon employed to carry ballast to virtual quarry sites.

B856a	**N-R** 3170 5992 002 3 bright yellow - *10*	16	20
B856b	as above numbered 3170 5992 014 8 - *10*	16	20
B856c	as above numbered 3170 5992 021 3 - *10*	16	20
B856d	as above numbered 3170 5992 016 2 - *10*	16	20

Network Rail IOA bogie box wagon [W60] (Dapol)

B856e	**N-R** ? bright yellow W Sp Edn 250 (Hattons) - *10*	16	10
B856f	as above numbered ? - *10*	16	10
B856g	as above numbered ? - *10*	16	10
B856h	as above numbered ? - *10*	16	10

W61. MLA Bogie Low-Sided Open Ballast Wagon (2011)

These were built in 2008 by Wagony Swidnica in Poland.

B854b	**EWS** 503505 maroon - *11*	NPG	NPG
?	as above numbered ? - *11*	NPG	NPG
?	as above numbered ? - *11*	NPG	NPG
?	as above numbered ? - *11*	NPG	NPG
?	**EWS** ? maroon W Sp Edn (Hattons) - *11*	NPG	NPG
B854c	**N-R** 503097 yellow - *11*	NPG	NPG
?	as above numbered ? - *11*	NPG	NPG
?	as above numbered ? - *11*	NPG	NPG
?	as above numbered ? - *11*	NPG	NPG
?	**N-R** ? yellow W Sp Edn (Hattons) - *11*	NPG	NPG
B854a	**GBRf Metronet** 503103 yellow - *11*	NPG	NPG
?	as above numbered ? - *11*	NPG	NPG
?	as above numbered ? - *11*	NPG	NPG
?	as above numbered ? - *11*	NPG	NPG
?	**GBRf Metronet** ? yellow W Sp Edn (Hattons) - *11*	NPG	NPG

W62. MRA Bogie Side-Tippler Wagon (2011)

These were built between 2003 and 2004 by Astro Vagoane of Arad, Romania and operate in permanent sets of five wagons. Dapol supply them in sets of five.

B859b	**Railtrack** ? blue+beige set of 5 wagons - *11*	NPG	125
?	**Railtrack** ? blue+beige W set of 5 wagons Sp Edn (Hattons) - *11*	NPG	125
B859a	**N-R** ? yellow set of 5 wagons - *11*	NPG	125
?	**N-R** ? yellow W set of 5 wagons Sp Edn (Hattons) - *11*	NPG	125

W63. EWS MBA 102t 'Megabox' (High-sided) (2009)

Self-centering coupling system, available with buffers suitable for the relevant prototype and removable ballast load. The real wagons entered service with EWS in 1999 and were used for aggregates, slag and scrap metal and have been used for coal, wood and spoil.

300 were built and run in semi-permanent sets of five, consisting of two 'outers' with buffers at one end and three 'inners' without buffers..

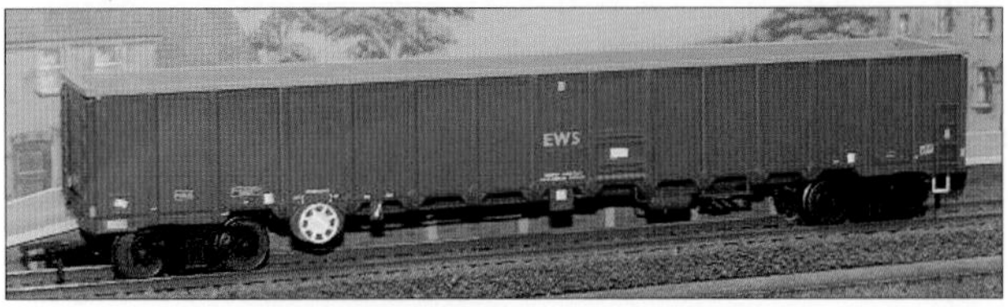

EWS MBA 'Megabox' wagon [W63] (Dapol)

B777A	**EWS** 500003 maroon - *09*	15	20
B777B	as above numbered 500017 - *09*	15	20
B777C	as above numbered 500045 - *09*	15	20
B777D	as above numbered 500098 - *09*	15	20
B777E	**EWS** 500112 maroon Sp Edn 200 (Hattons) - *09*	15	19
B777H	**EWS** 500199 maroon - *09*	15	20
B777F	**EWS** 500234 maroon W Sp Edn 250 (Trainlines of Derby) - *09*	17	22
B777G	**EWS** 500238 maroon W Sp Edn 250 (Trainlines of Derby) - *09*	17	22

W64. EWS MCA 'Megabox' (Low-sided) (2009)

Self-centering coupling system, available with buffers suitable for the relevant prototype and removable ballast load. 100 of the MBAs were later cut down in height to give easier access and to restrict load maximums

EWS MCA 'Megabox' wagon [W64] (Dapol)

B778F	**EWS** 500153 maroon W Sp Edn 250 (Trainlines of Derby) - *09*	20	23
B778G	**EWS** 500161 maroon W Sp Edn 250 (Trainlines of Derby) - *09*	20	23
B778A	**EWS** 500207 maroon - *09*	15	20
B778B	as above numbered 500213 - *09*	15	20
B778C	as above numbered 500221 - *09*	15	20
B778D	as above numbered 500229 - *09*	15	20
B778E	**EWS** 500231 maroon Sp Edn 200 (Hattons) - *09*	15	19
B778H	**EWS** 500240 maroon - *09*	14	18

W65. MJA Freightliner Heavy Haul Box Twin (2011)

Commissioned by Hattons for their exclusive use. The bogie box wagons run permanently coupled in pairs with buffers on the outer ends. Introduced in 2006, they are used to carry stone to sites were there is no hopper unloading facility.

?	**Freightliner Heavy Haul** ? green - *11*	NPG	NPG
?	**Freightliner Heavy Haul** ? white - *11*	NPG	NPG

Bogie Hopper & Dry Powder Wagons

W66. HIA Freightliner Heavy Haul Hopper (2011)

Commissioned by Hattons for their exclusive use. Freightliner Heavy Haul acquired a fleet of HIAs in 2005-6 for bulk limestone, sand and aggregate traffic.

?	**Freightliner Heavy Haul** ? grey - *11*	NPG	NPG

W67. PBA Tiger China Clay Covered Hoppers (2010)

Built by Fauvet Girel in1982 for Tiger Rail Leasing and English China Clays International. Etched handrails, steps and walkways and fitted with NEM pockets for couplings. Tooling belonging to Kernow Model Rail Centre.

SB002a	**'ECC International'** TRL11600 white Sp Edn (Kernow MRC) - *10*	20	27
SB002b	as above numbered TRL11602 - *10*	20	27
SB002c	as above numbered TRL11605 - *10*	20	27
SB002d	as above numbered TRL11609 - *10*	20	27
SB002e	**'ECC International'** TRL11626 white W Sp Edn (Kernow MRC) - *10*	23	30
SB002f	as above numbered TRL11628 - *10*	23	30
SB002g	as above numbered TRL11629 - *10*	23	30
SB002h	as above numbered TRL11631 - *10*	23	30

W68. JIA NACCO China Clay Covered Hoppers (2010)

Built by Fauvet Girel in1982 for Tiger Rail Leasing and English China Clays International. Etched handrails, steps and walkways and fitted with NEM pockets for couplings. Tooling belonging to Kernow Model Rail Centre.

SB001a	**'Imerys'** (33) 70 0894 020-3 light blue Sp Edn (Kernow MRC) - *10*	22	29
SB001b	as above numbered 33 70 0894 000-5 - *10*	22	29
SB001c	as above numbered 33 70 0894 001-3 - *10*	22	29
SB001d	as above numbered 33 70 0894 002-1 - *10*	22	29
SB001e	**'Imerys'** 33 70 0894 003-9 light blue W Sp Edn (Kernow MRC) - *10*	23	30
SB001f	as above numbered 33 70 0894 004-7 - *10*	23	30
SB001g	as above numbered 33 70 0894 005-4 - *10*	23	30
SB001h	as above numbered 33 70 0894 006-2 - *10*	23	30

W69. 'Silver Bullet' China Clay Tank Wagon (2010)

Widely seen chromed bodied V-tank used for the transportation of clay from Cornwall to Scotland. NEM pockets and darkened profiled wheels

B076a	**'ECC'** 33 87 789 8 046-0 NACCO chrome - *not made*	NA	NA
B076b	as above numbered 33 87 789 8 047-8 - *10*	NPG	NPG
B076c	as above numbered 33 87 789 8 057-7 - *10*	NPG	NPG
B076d	as above numbered 33 87 789 8 062-7 - *10*	NPG	NPG

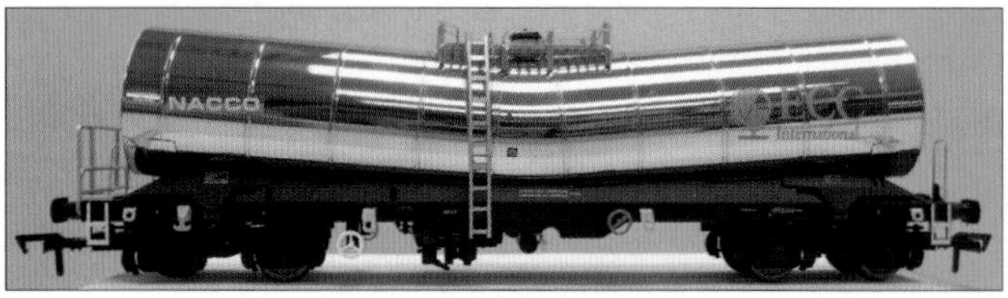

'Silver Bullet' china clay tank wagon [W69] (Dapol)

B850a	**'ECC'** 33 87 789 8 102-4 NACCO chrome - *10*	22	27
B850b	as above numbered 33 87 789 8 066-? - *10*	22	27
B850c	as above numbered 33 87 789 8 147-? - *10*	22	27
B850d	as above numbered 33 87 789 8 076-? - *10*	22	27
B850e	**'ECC'** 33 87 789 8 093-5 Sp Edn 250 (Hattons) - *10*	22	27
B850f	as above numbered 33 87 789 8 055-3 - *10*	22	27
B850g	as above numbered 33 87 789 8 100-0 - *10*	22	27
B850h	as above numbered 33 87 789 8 105-5 - *10*	22	27
B850o	**'ECC'** 33 87 789 8 054-7 chrome NRCCO Sp Edn (Kernow MRC) - *10*	24	29
B850p	as above numbered 33 87 789 8 057-0 - *10*	24	29
B850q	**'ECC'** 33 87 789 8 042-2 brown W NRCCO Sp Edn (Kernow MRC) - *10*	24	29
B850r	as above numbered 33 87 789 8 041-4 - *10*	24	29
B850s	as above numbered 33 80 789 8 091-1 - *10*	25	33
B850t	as above numbered 33 80 789 8 087-4 - *10*	25	33
B850u	as above numbered 33 80 789 8 083-6 - *10*	25	33
B850v	as above numbered 33 80 789 8 080-5 - *10*	25	33
B850w	**'ECC'** 33 87 789 8 063 brown W NRCCO Sp Edn (Kernow MRC) - *10*	24	29
B850x	as above numbered 33 87 789 8 064-? - *10*	24	29
B850y	as above numbered 33 87 789 8 061-? - *10*	24	29
B850z	as above numbered 33 87 789 8 060-? - *10*	24	29

Other Bogie Wagons

W70. Telescopic Steel Hood Wagon (2009)

A modern air-braked wagon used for the protected transportation of steel coil. 4 drums of steel coil supplied with each wagon. Only 250 of each number produced.

B747e	**'Tiphook Rail'** 089 9 024-0 blue - *09*	21	25
B747f	**'Tiphook Rail'** 089 9 037-0 blue - *09*	21	25

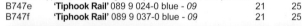

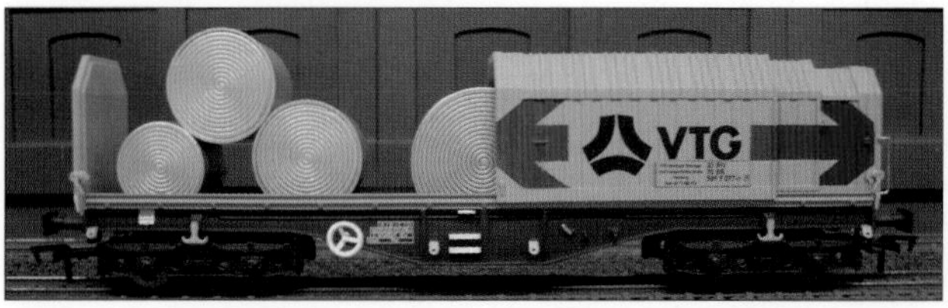

VGT Ferrywagon telescopic hood steel wagon [W70] (Dapol)

B747g	**'Tiphook Rail'** 089 9 042-0 blue - *09*	21	25
B747h	**'Tiphook Rail'** 089 9 066-0 blue - *09*	21	25
-	**'Tiphook Rail'** 089 9 046-3 blue W Sp Edn 300 (Trainlines of Derby) - *09*	22	27
B747a	**'VTG Ferrywagon'** 589 9 087-6 silver+blue - *09*	21	25
B747b	**'VTG Ferrywagon'** 589 9 082-7 silver+blue - *09*	21	25
B747c	**'VTG Ferrywagon'** 589 9 077-7 silver+blue - *09*	21	25
B747d	**'VTG Ferrywagon'** 589 9 076-9 silver+blue - *09*	21	25
-	**'VTG Ferrywagon'** 474 6 442-9 silver W Sp Edn 250 (Trainlines of Derby) - *09*	22	27

W71. GWR 'Siphon G' Bogie Milk Van (ex-Airfix) (1985)

B77	**GW** 1478 brown (A) - ?	10	14
B78	**BR** W1478 maroon (A) - *85*	10	14
B78	**BR** W1457 maroon (M) - *85-86*	10	15
B78	**BR** W1452 maroon - *88-01*	10	15

The tooling was sold to Hornby in 1996 and the model reintroduced by them.

W72. GWR 'Siphon H' Bogie Milk Van (ex-Airfix) (1985)

B76	**GW** 1435 brown - *85*	9	14
B76	**GW** 1437 brown (M) - *85-86*	10	15
B76	**GW** 1437 brown - *90-01*	10	15
B262	**GW** 1437 brown - ?	NPG	NPG
B79	**BR** W1429 maroon (A) - *85-86*	10	14
B79	**BR** W1429 maroon - *88-02*	10	15

The tooling was sold to Hornby in 1996 and the model reintroduced by them.

W73. U.S. Caboose (ex-Bachmann/Airfix) (1985)

B84	**Union Pacific** yellow - (A) - *85-88*	4	6

Packs of Wagons

In 1999, Dapol offered a range of wagon packs in an attempt to move some of the more stagnant items in their stock. They also had rather a large number of the GWR and BR Class 14XX locos and used up some of these in 'loco and wagon' packs which contained one of three versions of the loco, a BR liveried toad brake van and two other wagons.

P1. Wagon Packs (1999)

B400	**BR** 'Toad', -plank **'B&C'**, **BR** plywood van, **BR** 9-plank mineral - *99-02*	NA	25
B401	**BR** 'Toad', 7-plank **'Thrutchley'**, 10T **BR** meat, 20T Rainford Tar brown - *99-02*	NA	25
B402	**BR** 'Toad', 7-plank **'Coal Agencies'**, 10T **BR** meat, **NE** 9-plank mineral - *99-02*	NA	25
B403	**BR** 'Toad', 7-plank **'Broadoak'**, 10T **BR** meat, 20T **Joseph Crosfield** - *99-02*	NA	25
B404	**BR** 'Toad', **BR** plywood van, 7-plank **'Emlyn'**, 20T **Newcastle Gas** - *99-02*	NA	25
B405	**BR** 'Toad', 7-plank **Emlyn**, **BR** plywood van, **BR + NE** 9-plank minerals - *99-02*	NA	25
B409s	4 Welsh wagon set - *01-02*	NA	25
B522	**'Webster'** brown twin pack 7-plank 302 + 5-plank 303 - *03*	NA	18
-	5-plank **'Spalding Colliery'** 52 light grey + 7-plank **'Granville'** 227 grey Sp Edn 200 (Tutbury Jinny) - *02*	NA	18
-	set of 4 - 7-plank **'Edward Russell'** 140 grey + 5-plank **'N Hingley & Sons'** 14 brown + 7-plank 'ED' 14 red-brown + salt wagon **'George Brown & Sons'** 1 grey Sp Edn 100 (Modellers Mecca) - *01*	NA	22
-	2 x 7-planks **'Whitwick Colliery'** 1046 black + ' **South Leicester'** 2120 red-brown Sp Edn 200 Tutbury Jinny) - *02*	NA	18
-	7-plank **'East Cannock'** 4916 black + 5-plank **'Conduit Colliery'** 124 brown Sp Edn 200 (Tutbury Jinny) - *02-04*	NA	18
-	2 x 7-planks **'Cannock Rugeley'** 248 grey + **'Hawkins'** 271 red-brown Sp Edn 200 (Tutbury Jinny) - *02*	NA	18
-	4 x 7-planks **'Herbert Hall'** 111 brown + **'FJ Newton'** 37 grey + **'Holly Bank'** 62 brown + **'Samuel Evers'** 34 grey Sp Edn 200 (Modellers Mecca) - *02*	NA	22
-	4 x 7-planks **'North & Rose'** 9 brown + **'Parkyn & Peters'** 35 red + **'Pochin'** 114 grey + **'West of England'** 126 light grey Sp Edn (Mevagissy Models) - *00-01*	NA	35
-	4 x 7-planks **'Great Treverbyn'** 48 red-brown + **'Martin Bros.'** 28 brown + **'North Cornwall'** 3 brown + **'West Goonbarrow'** 28 grey Sp Edn (Mevagissy Models) - *01-02*	NA	35
-	2 wagons - **'Camerton Collieries'** 175+199 black + coal Sp Edn 125 (East Somerset Models) - *02*	NA	18
-	7-plank **'GD Owen'** 16 dark red + salt van **'GD Owen'** 12 Sp Edn 200 (West Wales Wagon Works) - *02-03*	NA	18
-	2 x Mink vans **'Jubilee'** 1952 + **'Jiwbili'** 2002 Sp Edn 50 (Teifi Valley Railway) - *01*	NA	18
-	2 x 5-planks **IWC** 117 + 68 grey Sp Edn 100 (I of W Model Railways) - *01*	NA	18
-	2 x 5-planks IWR 29 brown + **'Vectis Cement Co.'** 34 grey Sp Edn 200 (I of W Model Railways) - *02*	NA	28
-	2 x 7-planks **'Lewis, Merthyr Navigation'** 768 black + **'Burnyeat, Brown & Co.'** 335 black Sp Edn 100 (Lord & Butler Model Railways) - *02*	NA	18
-	4 x 5-planks **'English China Clays Lovering Pochin & Co.'** 318 + 163, **'ECLP'** 1614 + 1707 Sp Edn (Mevagissey Model Railway) - *02*	NA	30
-	7-plank **'Bass'** 56 grey + vent van **'Bass'** 23 grey Sp Edn 188 (Tutbury Jinny) - *02*	NA	18
-	7-plank **'Bass'** 56 grey + vent van **'Bass'** 17 grey Sp Edn 200 (Tutbury Jinny) - *02*	NA	18
-	2 LMS style vent vans * **'Worthington'** 3 brown + **'Bass'** 29 grey Sp Edn 200 (Tutbury Jinny) - *03*	NA	18
-	2 LMS style vent vans * **'Worthington'** 33 brown + **'Bass'** 24 grey Sp Edn 200 (Tutbury Jinny) - *05*	NA	18
ANT003	7-plank **'Harris & Co.'** 21 black + 7-plank **'Mathew Grist'** 2 grey Sp Edn 250 (Antics) - *03-05*	NA	18
-	2 x 7-planks **'FJ Hall'** 65 red-brown + '**Cannock & Leacroft Colliery'** 4129 red-brown Sp Edn 200 (Tutbury Jinny) - *04*	NA	18
-	5-plank '**Mapperley'** 72 and 7-plank **Fox** 458 black Sp Edn 200 (Tutbury Jinny) - *04*	NA	18
-	**'FT Woolway'** 16 black '**AC Woolway'** 26 black Sp Edn 100 (The Model Shop, Exeter) - *04*	NA	18
-	**'New Rock'** 207 + 212 black Sp Edn 150 (East Somerset Models) - *04*	NA	18
-	**'Cannock & Rugeley'** 7-plank + '**Midland Coal'** 7-plank Sp Edn 150 (Tutbury Jinny) - *05*	NA	18
-	2 x 7-plank **'Helston Gas Company'** 10 + 30 black Sp Edn (Kernow MRC) - *03*	NA	18
-	**'Helston Gas Company'** 20 + 40 black Sp Edn (Kernow MRC) - *04*	NA	18
-	2 x 7-plank **'Leek & Moorlands'** grey + **'Silverdale Co.'** brown Sp Edn 175 (Tutbury Jinny) - *05*	NA	18
-	2 x 7-plank **'Stafford Coal & Iron'** 903 brown + **'Talk-O'Th Hill Colliery'** 5 brown Sp Edn (Tutbury Jinny) - *05*	NA	18

P2. Loco + Wagon Gift Sets (1999)

B406	**GWR** 14xx + toad + 2 wagons - *99-02*	NA	50
B407	as above but shirt button - *99-02*	NA	50
B408	as above but BR black tank - *99-02*	NA	50

SETS

Dapol sets went under the prefix 'F' in their catalogue numbering scheme and tended to be made up with surplus stock, including Airfix, Mainline and Dapol models (often mixed) in order to use up stock. In selling sets, like other companies, Dapol found it difficult to compete with Hornby whose name was familiar to first-time buyers. In 1983 there were just three sets but these rose to ten by 1987. While a few were added as more were dropped, the sets were not pushed very hard from this time on and were soon dropped from the advertising. If they did not sell well they are likely to become collectable in the future and prices are only now beginning to rise as Dapol becomes more collectable. Do not be surprised if you get offered little more than the value of their contents, for one. If this is the case, the best advice is to hang on to them and hope that their value will rise.

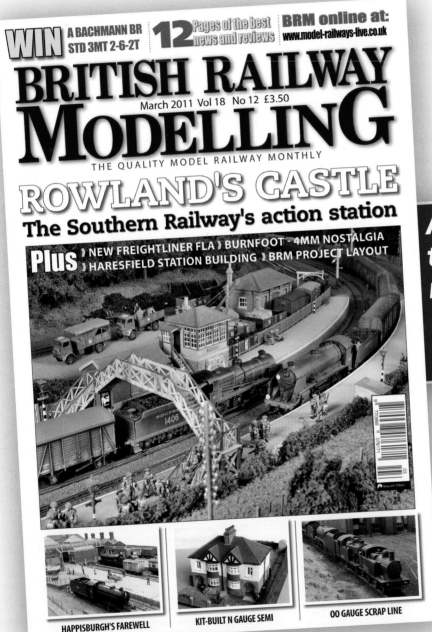

Dapol N

Please note that the tables in this section have been renumbered in this edition and Ixion models have been removed to a chapter of their own.

HISTORY

Developed in great secrecy, Dapol N gauge (1:148) was launched in 2003 at the Warley National Model Railway Exhibition at the National Exhibition Centre in Birmingham and was the talk of the show.

Initially, the subjects chosen had all been ones previously made in 00 gauge by Airfix and Hornby Dublo/Wrenn and subsequently produced by Dapol after their acquisition of the Airfix and Wrenn tooling. Tooling is done in China and the mechanisms bought in. Indeed, it is believed that the motors come from the same company that supplies Bachmann for their Graham Farish models. No more than a 1,000 of each standard release are produced and in some cases a lot less.

LOCOMOTIVES

Early locos had bright metal wheels but following suggestions from their customers Dapol had all metalwork darkened in subsequent batches. From April 2005, only 500 of each diesel locomotive were made.

Cat No.	Company, Number, Colour, Dates	£	£

Tank Engines

L1. GWR Class 14XX 0-4-2T (2004)

When first released, the model had bright metal wheels but later these were darkened.

ND-017	**1403** GWR green - *05*	38	45

GWR Class 14xx 0-4-2T [L1]

ND-001	**1425** GWR green - *04*	38	45
ND-080-1	**1466** GWR green ex-set - *08*	38	NA
ND-080-3	**1467** GWR green + autocoach - *09*	NPG	NPG
ND-009	**1472** GWR green - *05*	38	45
ND-004	**1420** GWR (button) green - *04*	38	45
ND-010	**1433** GWR (button) green - *05*	38	45
ND-080-4	**4865** GWR (button) green + autocoach - *09*	NPG	NPG
ND-080-2	**4866** GWR (button) green ex-set - *08*	38	NA
ND-104a	**1414** BRb black - *09*	NPG	NPG
ND-104b	**1438** BRb black - *09*	NPG	NPG
ND-002	**1458** BR black - *04*	38	45
ND-003	**1466** BR lined green - *04*	38	45
ND-016	**1462** BR green - *05*	38	45

L2. SR Class M7 0-4-4T (2005)

NEM coupling pockets and Dapol chain/shackle interchangeable decorative fitting. Extra fine in-cab detail. Following criticism, the dome was restyled and the chimney shortened. Batches after May 2006 should have these modifications.

ND-057	**245** LSWR light green - *07*	50	65
ND-046	SR plain Maunsell green - *not made*	NA	NA
ND-046	**676** SR malachite green * - *06*	50	65
ND-026	**37** SR lined Maunsell green - *05*	50	65
ND-058	**30241** BRa green - *07*	50	65
ND-025	**30031** BRb lined black - *05*	50	65
ND-045	**30128** BRc lined black * - *06*	50	65

* Reshaped dome, shortened chimney and added weight under coal load.

L3. SR Class A1 'Terrier' 0-6-0T (2009)

Stroudley's famous suburban passenger tank with NEM coupling pockets, profiled wheels 40:1 gearing and add-on accessories. Because of the model's small size, an extra small motor had to be found and it is believed that the one in use is a development of a motor used in mobile phones.

LBSCR 'Terrier' tank 0-6-0T in Stroudley livery [L3] (Dapol)

ND-100j	**53 *Ashtead*** LBSCR orange-brown - *10*	52	65
ND-100k	**54 *Waddon*** LBSCR orange-brown - *11*	NPG	NPG
ND-100b	**55 *Stepney*** LBSCR orange-brown - *09*	50	62
ND-100m	**62 *Martello*** LBSCR orange-brown - *11*	NPG	NPG
ND-100a	**82 *Boxhill*** LBSCR orange-brown - *09*	50	62
ND-100h	**84 *Crowborough*** LBSCR orange-brown - *10*	52	65
ND-100i	**DS377 Brighton Works** - LBSCR orange-brown Ltd Edn 250 - *09*	NPG	NPG
DAGM01	**32635 Brighton Works** - LBSCR orange-brown Sp Edn 250 (Gaugemaster) - *09*	52	65
-	**5 *Portland*** GWR green Sp Edn 250 (Osborn's Models) - *09*	NPG	NPG
ND-100f	**8 *Freshwater*** SR lined green - *09*	50	62
ND-100c	**2662** SR black - *09*	NPG	65
ND-100e	**32640** BRb lined black - *09*	50	62
ND-100n	**32677** BRb lined black - *11*	NPG	NPG
ND-100d	**32667** BRc lined black - *made?*	NPG	NPG
ND-100d	**32642** BRc lined black - *09*	50	62
ND-100g	**32646** BRc lined black - *09*	50	62
ND-100p	**32646** BRc lined black - *11*	NPG	NPG

L4a. GWR Class 45XX 2-6-2T (2005)

Churchward designed tank dating from 1906 with straight tanks. The model has much detail including brake rigging beneath the chassis, whistles, rivet detail, glazed cab and tank top fittings.

ND-014	**4523** Great Western green - *05*	50	65
ND-020	**4567** GWR (button) green - *05*	50	65
ND-023	**4527** GWR green - *05*	50	65
ND-024	**4571** BRa plain black - *05*	50	65
ND-013	**4580** BRb unlined green - *05*	50	65
ND-013	**4570** BRb unlined green - *05*	50	65
ND-019	**4554** BRb plain black - *05*	50	65
ND-035	**4565** BRc lined green - *05*	50	65

L4b. GWR Class 4575 2-6-2T (2006)

Collett modified 45XX tank dating from 1927. They had larger side tanks with sloping tops. The model has much detail including brake rigging beneath the chassis, whistles, rivet detail, glazed cab and tank top fittings.

GWR Class 45xx 2-6-2T [L4b]

ND-047	**5531** GWR green - *06*	50	65
ND-059	**5529** GWR (button) green - *06*	50	65
ND-048a	**5511** BRb plain black Ltd Edn 100 - *06*	50	65
ND-048b	**5521** BRb plain black Ltd Edn 100 - *06*	50	65
ND-048c	**5532** BRb plain black Ltd Edn 100 - *06*	50	65
ND-048d	**5539** BRb plain black Ltd Edn 100 - *06*	50	65
ND-048e	**5542** BRb plain black Ltd Edn 100 - *06*	50	65
ND-048f	**5572** BRb plain black Ltd Edn 100 - *06*	50	65
ND-048g	**5574** BRb plain black Ltd Edn 100 - *06*	50	65
ND-048	**5576** BRb plain black - *not made*	NA	NA
ND-060	**5552** BRc lined green - *not made*	NA	NA
ND-060a	**5522** BRc lined green Ltd Edn 100 - *06*	50	65
ND-060b	**5524** BRc lined green Ltd Edn 100 - *06*	50	65
ND-060c	**5530** BRc lined green Ltd Edn 100 - *06*	50	65
ND-105	**5532** BRc lined green - *09*	NPG	NPG
ND-106	**5538** BRc lined green - *09*	NPG	NPG
ND-060d	**5541** BRc lined green Ltd Edn 100 - *06*	50	65
ND-060e	**5552** BRc lined green Ltd Edn 100 - *06*	50	65
ND-060f	**5553** BRc lined green Ltd Edn 100 - *06*	50	65
ND-060g	**5573** BRc lined green Ltd Edn 100 - *06*	50	65

L5. LMS Ivatt 2MT 2-6-2T (2006)

Both push-pull and non-push-pull versions of the tank are being developed. NEM pockets fitted and supplied with optional buckeye and decorative chain & shackle couplings. Limited to 500 of each number.

ND-062a	**1200** LMS plain black - *06*	NPG	NPG
ND-062b	**1205** LMS plain black - *06*	NPG	NPG
ND-064a	**41225** BRb lined black push-pull - *08*	NPG	NPG
ND-064b	**41265** BRb lined black push-pull - *not made*	NA	NA
ND-064b	**41271** BRb lined black push-pull - *08*	NPG	NPG
ND-064a	**41285** BRb lined black push-pull - *not made*	NA	NA
ND-061b	**41312** BRc lined black - *06*	NPG	NPG
ND-061a	**41234** BRc lined black - *06*	NPG	NPG

Tender Locomotives

L6. SR Class Q1 0-6-0 (2007)

Tender powered with loco drive through a drive shaft between tender and loco. DCC ready. See-through wheels on loco and tender, wire handrails, removable coal load, all-axle pick-up and headcode discs supplied. Only 250 of each made.

ND-092a	**C11** SR black - *08*	70	90
ND-092b	**C16** SR black - *08*	70	90
ND-092c	**C21** SR black - *08*	70	90
ND-092d	**C28** SR black - *08*	70	90
ND-076a	**33030** BRb black - *07*	70	90
ND-076b	**33040** BRb black - *07*	70	90
ND-075a	**33004** BRc black - *07*	70	90
ND-075b	**33009** BRc black - *07*	70	90
ND-094	**33002** BRc black - *08*	70	90

L8. Class B1 4-6-0 (2010)

Platinum range with super creep motor, 30:1 gearing, DCC ready and NEM pockets. Alternate coupling bar (loco to tender) and drive shaft for closer coupling, spring power transfer from engine to tender, traction tyres, square axle ends for perfect quartering, RP25.72 wheel sets, tungsten locomotive body weight and owner fitted front foot steps. Accessory pack with spare parts.

ND-120c	**1230** LNER light green - *10*	NPG	NPG
ND-120d	**1234** LNER light green - *10*	NPG	NPG
ND-120g	**1252** LNER light green - *11*	NPG	NPG
ND-120h	**1225** LNER light green - *11*	NPG	NPG
ND-120b	**61097** BRb black - *10*	NPG	NPG
ND-120f	**61363** BRb lined black - *11*	NPG	NPG
ND-120a	**61099** BRc black - *10*	NPG	NPG
ND-120e	**61406** BRb lined black - *11*	NPG	NPG

L9. Class B17 'Footballer' 4-6-0 (2008)

Platinum range with super creep motor, 40:1 gearing, DCC ready and NEM pockets.

LNER Class B17 No.2857 Doncaster Rovers [L9]

ND-079a	**2850** ***Grimsby Town*** LNER light green - *09*	80	100
(ND-079c)	**2854** ***Sunderland*** LNER light green – *not made*	NA	NA
(ND-079d)	**2869** ***Barnsley*** LNER light green - *10*	80	100
(ND-079-1)	**2857** ***Doncaster Rovers*** LNER light green - *08*	NPG	NA
ND-079f	**2863** ***Everton*** LNER light green - *11*	80	100
ND-079e	**61655** ***Middlesbrough*** BRb green - *11*	80	100
ND-079a	**61660** ***Hull City*** BRc green - *09*	80	100
(ND-079-2)	**61652** ***Darlington*** BRc green - *08*	80	NA
(ND-079-3)	**61665** ***Leicester City*** BRc green ex train pack - *not made*	NA	NA
(ND-079c)	**61647** ***Helmingham Hall*** BRc green - *10*	85	102

L10. BR 'Britannia' 4-6-2 (2010)

BR Standard express loco with super creep skew wound 5 pole motor, 30:1 gearing for quieter mechanism, 6-pin 'DCC ready', see through darkened wheels, , tractions tyres on each rear driver, squared off axle ends to allow for perfect quartering, NEM coupling pockets and add-on accessories, water scoop moulded, close coupling between cab and tender. An accessory pack includes air pipes, coupling chains, 'knuckle couplers' and 2 replacement traction tyres.

ND-095a	**70000** ***Britannia*** BR green - *10*	90	110
ND-095b	**70013** ***Oliver Cromwell*** BRb green - *11*	90	110
ND-?	**70014** ***Iron Duke*** BRb green + Golden Arrow insignia Sp Edn (Osborn Models) - *10*	100	120
ND-095c	**70038** ***Robin Hood*** BRb green - *10*	90	110
ND-095d	**70050** ***Firth of Clyde*** BR green - *10*	90	110
ND-095e	**70004** ***William Shakespeare*** BR green - *10*	90	110
ND-095f	**70030** ***William Wordsworth*** BRc green - *11*	90	110
ND-095g	**70022** ***Tornado*** BRc green - *11*	90	110
ND-095h	**70048** ***The Territorial Army*** BR green - *10*	90	110

L11. GWR Class 38xx 2-8-0 (2011)

Platinum range with super creep motor, 40:1 gearing, 6-pin DCC ready and NEM pockets. etched brass number plates.

ND-???	**?** GWR green - *?*	NPG	NPG
ND-???	**?** BR green - *?*	NPG	NPG
ND-???	**?** BR black - *?*	NPG	NPG

L12 BR Class 9F 2-10-0 (2008)

Platinum range with 5-pole skew-wound motor, DCC ready, NEM 651 socket, tender powered, 16 wheel pickups, RP25 see-through wheels, 10 wheels driving. sc + single chimney. dc = double chimney.

ND-090j	**92001** BRb black BR1G tender dc - *09*	85	105
ND-090b	**92002** BRb black BR1G tender sc - *08*	85	105
ND-090f	**92100** BRb black BR1G tender sc - *08*	85	105
ND-090k	**92233** BRb black BR1G tender dc - *09*	85	105
ND-090r	**92052** BRb black BR1B tender - 11	NPG	NPG
ND-090s	**92082** BRc black BR1B tender - *11*	NPG	NPG
ND-090p	**92088** BRc black BR1B tender - *11*	NPG	NPG
ND-090m	**92133** BRb black W - *10*	NPG	NPG
ND-090d	**92247** BRb black BR1G tender dc - *08*	85	105
ND-090a	**92008** BRc black BR1G tender sc - *08*	85	105
ND-090e	**92050** BRc black BR1G tender sc - *08*	85	105
ND-090g	**92208** BRc black BR1G tender dc - *08*	85	105

Class 9F No.92220 Evening Star [L12]

ND-090i	**92220** ***Evening Star*** BRc black dc - *08*	85	105
ND-090c	**92226** BRc black BR1G tender dc - *08*	85	105
ND-090q	**92226** BRc black BR1G tender - *11*	NPG	NPG
ND-090h	**92231** BRc black BR1G tender dc - *08*	85	105
ND-92203	**92203** ***Black Prince*** BRc black BR1G tender dc *Sp Edn 150 (TMC) - *09*	85	110

* Etched brass nameplates and headboards for both 'Pines Express' and 'The David Shepherd Wildlife Foundation'. David Shepherd signed each box sleeve.

Diesel & Electric Locomotives

L13. Class 03 Drewry Shunter

Planned for 2006 but dropped after Bachmann announced their plan to introduce one.

L14. Class 04 Drewry Shunter
Planned for 2006 but dropped after Bachmann announced their plan to introduce one.

L15. Class 22 Diesel Electric Bo-Bo (2011)
Proposed.

L16. Class 26 Diesel Electric Bo-Bo (2011)
Both 26/1 and 26/2 versions planned. Round or ova\al buffers, as appropriate, and other batch detail differences. Platinum range with super creep motor, 40:1 gearing, 6-pin DCC ready and NEM pockets.

ND-145b	**D5301** BRc green - *11*	NPG	NPG
ND-145a	**26015** BRe blue - *11*	NPG	NPG
ND-145c	**26038** BRe Railfreight 'red stripe' grey - *11*	NPG	NPG
ND-145d	**26027** BRe Rft Coal grey - *11*	NPG	NPG

L17. Class 35 'Hymek' (2008)
5-pole skew wound motor, DCC ready (NEM 651), wire handrails, yellow-glow marker lights, air-pipes and snowploughs to add. Limited Editions to 250.

ND-084r	**D7001** BRe blue, yellow ends, non-powered - *11*	NPG	NPG
ND-084q	**D7005** BRe blue, yellow ends - *11*	NPG	NPG
ND-084b	**D7008** BRc green - *08*	75	95
ND-084d	**D7011** BRe blue - *08*	75	95
ND-084z	**D7017** BRe green, no yellow panels, Sp Edn 150 (Kernow Model Centre) - *08*	75	95
ND-084f	**D7018** BRe green Sp Edn 150 (Kernow Model Centre) - *08*	75	95
ND-084c	**D7023** BRc green, yellow ends - *08*	75	95
ND-084y	**D7036** BRe chromatic blue, small yellow panels Sp Edn 150 (Kernow Model Cente) - *08*	75	95
ND-084m	**D7042** BRc 2-tone green non-powered - *11*	NPG	NPG
ND-084z	**D7048** BRe green W + 5 'NCB' mineral wagons Sp Edn (Dapol Club) - *09*	NA	100
(ND-084z)	above loco only - *09*	75	NA
ND-084j	**D7057** BRc 2-tone green, half yellow ends - *10*	NPG	NPG
ND-084a	**D7066** BRc green - *08*	75	95
ND-084n	**D7071** BRc 2-tone green non-powered - *11*	NPG	NPG
ND-084h	**D7083** BRc 2-tone green, half yellow ends - *10*	NPG	NPG
ND-084p	**D7084** BRc 2-tone green - *11*	NPG	NPG
ND-084g	**D7093** BRe green Sp Edn 150 (Kernow Model Centre) - *08*	75	95
(ND-084e)	**D7099** BRe blue W ex-pack - *08*	75	NA
ND-084e	above with 6x6-wheel milk tanks - *08*	NA	125

L18. Class 43 InterCity 125 Power Car 4-6-0 (2010)
Platinum range with super creep motor, 40:1 gearing, 6-pin DCC ready and NEM pockets. Exhaust differences.

ND-111a	**43006+43007** InterCity blue+grey - *10*	NPG	NPG
ND-111b	**43120+43114** ICs Executive grey - *10*	NPG	NPG

CAD illustration of the Class 43 diesel [L18] (Dapol)

ND-111c	**43098+43102** Virgin red+black - *10*	NPG	NPG
ND-122a	**253024** (**43048+?+?+43049**) IC125 blue+grey -*10*	NPG	NPG
ND-122b	**43194+43118** (+2 Mk3 coaches) ICs grey - *10*	NPG	NPG
ND-122c	**253029** (**43056+?+?+43057**) IC125 grey - *10*	NPG	NPG
ND-122d	**43008+43092** (+2 Mk3 coaches Virgin red+black - *10*	NPG	NPG
ND-122e	**43123+43084** (+2 Mk3 coaches) Grand Central black - *11*	NPG	NPG
ND-122f	**43171+43168** (+2 Mk3 coaches) First Great Western purple - *11*	NPG	NPG
ND-122g	**43303+43207** (+2 Mk3 coaches) Cross Country grey - *11*	NPG	NPG

L19. Class 56 Diesel (Romanian) (2009/10)
Platinum range with super creep motor, 40:1 gearing, 6-pin DCC ready and NEM pockets.

ND-???	**56026** BR blue - *11*	NPG	NPG
ND-???	**56019** Rft red stripe - *11*	NPG	NPG
ND-???	**56013** Rft Coal grey - *11*	NPG	NPG

L20. Class 58 Diesel (2009)
Platinum range with super creep motor with flywheel, low friction mechanism, 6-pin DCC ready NEM pockets and directional lighting, plus extras to fit.

ND-103a	**58012** Railfreight 'red stripe', grey - *10*	85	105
ND-103f	**58017** Railfreight triple grey coal - *11*	NPG	NPG
ND-103e	**58021** Mainline blue - *11*	NPG	NPG
ND-103b	**58023** Railfreight 'red stripe', grey - *10*	85	105
ND-103g	**58027** Mainline triple grey - *11*	NPG	NPG
ND-103d	**58037** EWS maroon+yellow - *09*	85	105
ND-103c	**58042** BRe triple grey Coal Sector - *09*	85	105
ND-103h	**58044** triple grey - *11*	NPG	NPG
ND-?	**58**? ACTS dark blue+yellow Sp Edn 100 (Modelbahn Union) - *10*	NPG	NPG

L21a. Class 66 Diesel (2005)
Working white lights in direction of travel, working red lights at rear, day and night settings, separate metal handrails, individual wipers, skew-wound twin flywheel motor, NEM socket couplings ('Rapido' or 'Buck-eye'), decorative couplings, cab interior detail, split and insulated chassis and etched roof detail. After the first 8 EWS models, the light cluster on the cab fronts was modified. Also, the detail on the model was improved with smaller lamp irons, reshaped cab front lifting plates, weathered bodyside grilles, white handrails and factory fitted etched nameplates. A more powerful motor was introduced for the Freightliner locomotives in 2006. High detailed bogies from mid 2007. 2009 models retooled to take the NEM 651 6-pin socket for DCC control and weathered oxidised chrome exhaust.

	EWS Maroon		
ND-027	**66008** Ltd Edn 250 - *05*	65	80
ND-028	**66014** Ltd Edn 250 - *05*	65	80
ND-144a	**66017** non-powered - *11*	NPG	NPG
ND-029	**66050** Ltd Edn 250 - *05*	65	80
ND-030	**66072** Ltd Edn 250 - *05*	65	80
ND-065a	**66081** Ltd Edn 250 no motor or lights - *07*	25	30
ND-065b	**66106** Ltd Edn 250 no motor or lights - *07*	25	30
ND-108b	**66111** maroon+yell W Sp Edn 500 (Hattons) - *09*	55	65
ND-031	**66121** Ltd Edn 250 - *05*	65	80
ND-032	**66155** Ltd Edn 250 - *05*	65	80
ND-144b	**66173** non-powered - *11*	NPG	NPG
ND-108	**66181** - *09*	55	65
ND-033	**66204** Ltd Edn 250 - *05*	65	80
ND-109	**66222** Ltd Edn 250 - *09*	55	65
ND-034	**66225** Ltd Edn 250 - *05*	65	80
	EWSi Maroon		
ND-066b	**66022** new EWS-i livery - *07*	65	70
ND-066a	**66215** new EWS-i livery - *07*	65	70
	DB Schenker Red		
ND-110	**66152** - *09*	55	65
	Freightliner Green		
ND-144c	**66512** non-powered - *11*	NPG	NPG
ND-144d	**66524** non-powered - *11*	NPG	NPG
ND-049	**66539** Ltd Edn 250 - *not made*	NA	NA
ND-049	**66540** ***Ruby*** 40th Anniversary model - *06*	65	80
ND-050	**66545** Ltd Edn 250 - *06*	65	80
ND-051	**66554** 40th Anniversary Ltd Edn 250 - *06*	65	80
ND-052	**66566** Ltd Edn 250 - *06*	65	80
ND-053	**66578** 40th Anniversary Ltd Edn 250 - *06*	65	80
ND-054	**66581** Ltd Edn 250 - *06*	65	80
ND-055	**66610** 40th Anniversary Ltd Edn 250 - *06*	65	80
ND-056	**66613** Ltd Edn 250 - *06*	65	80
	GBRf Blue		
ND-037	**66702** ***Blue Lightning*** Ltd Edn 250 - *06*	65	80

GBRf Class 66 No.66702 Blue Lightning [L21a] (Dapol)

ND-038	**66703** ***Doncaster Spa*** Ltd Edn 250 - *06*	65	80
ND-039	**66705** ***Golden Jubilee'*** Ltd Edn 250 - *06*	65	80
ND-040	**66706** ***Nene Valley*** Ltd Edn 250 - *06*	65	80
ND-041	**66709** ***Medite*** Ltd Edn 250 - *06*	65	80
ND-042	**66713** ***Forest City*** Ltd Edn 250 - *06*	65	80
ND-043	**66714** ***Cromer Lifeboat*** Ltd Edn 250 - *06*	65	80
ND-044	**66716** ***Willesden Traincare*** Ltd Edn 250 - *06*	65	80
-	**66841** Colas Rail orange+yellow	65	NA
-	**66842** Colas Rail orange+yellow non-powered	25	NA
ND-126	above two models in twin pack - *10*	NA	100

* Revised group standard light cluster.

L21b. Class 66 Low Emission Diesel (2007)

Specification for these low emission Class 66 models include new ultra high detail bogie frames and piping, fully re-tooled body with 3rd door, altered cab side windows, 'DCC ready' 'plug and play' board and NEM coupler sockets.

ND-125	**66305** Fastline grey DC6 - *10*	65	84
ND-067	**66411** ***Eddie the Engine*** DRS/Stobart Rail blue Ltd Edn 250 - *07*	65	80
ND-?	as above non-powered - *08*	NPG	NPG
ND-069a	**66413** DRS dark blue Ltd Edn 250 - *07*	65	80
ND-069b	**66417** DRS dark blue Ltd Edn 250 - *07*	65	80
ND-085a	**66585** Freightliner green non-powered - *08*	25	30
ND-077	**66594** ***Spirit of Kyoto*** Freightliner green Ltd Edn 250 - *07*	65	80
ND-068	**66623** Freightliner/'Bardon Aggregates' blue - *07*	65	80
ND-085b	**66718** GBRf/Metronet blue, non-powered - *07*	25	30
ND-078a	**66719** ***Metro-Land*** GBRf/Metronet blue - *07*	65	80
ND-078b	**66720** ***Metronet Pathfinder*** GBRf/Metronet - *07*	65	80
ND-074a	**66723** First/GBRf blue Ltd Edn 250 - *07*	65	80
ND-102	**66725** ***Sunderland*** First GBR blue DC6 'Footballer' nameplate, Sp Edn 500 (Dapol 25th Anniversary) - *08*	45	50
ND-074b	**66727** First/GBRf blue Ltd Edn 250 - *07*	65	80

L22. Class 67 (2009)

Premium range model with new high-torque 5-pole Dapol motor, DCC ready, NEM 651 socket, NEM coupling pockets with choice of couplings, directional lighting, RP25 darkened wheels, cab front cables & hoses, etched see through grilles and etched nameplates.

ND-101m	**67001** EWS maroon non-powered - *11*	NPG	NPG
ND-101h	**67002** EWS maroon+yellow - *11*	NPG	NPG
ND-101k	**67005** EWS purple non-powered - *11*	NPG	NPG
ND-101a	**67006** ***Royal Sovereign*** Royal Train purple - *09*	80	95
ND-101e	**67008** EWS maroon+yellow - *10*	80	95
ND-101b	**67009** EWS maroon+yellow - *09*	80	85
ND-101?	**67010** Wrexham & Shropshire greys + Mk3 DVT Ltd Edn (W&S) train pack - *09*	NA	115
ND-101d	**67012** Wrexham & Shropshire grey+silver + 2x Mk3s + Mk3 DVT train pack - *not made*	NA	NA
-	**67012** ***A Shropshire Lad*** Wrexham & Shropshire grey+silver, non-powered Sp Edn (W&SR) - *09*	15	20
ND-101d	**67013** Wrexham & Shropshire grey+silver + 2 x Mk3s + Mk3 DVT train pack - *09*	NA	100
(ND-101d)	above loco on its own - *09*	85	NA
ND-101f	**67024** EWS maroon+yellow - *10*	80	95
ND-101g	**67026** EWS maroon+yellow non-powered - *10*	80	95
ND-101c	**67027** ***Rising Star*** EWS maroon+yellow - *09*	80	95
ND-101-1	**67029** ***Royal Diamond*** EWS silver + DVT 82146 - *09*	NA	115
ND-101j	**67030** EWS maroon+yellow - 11	NPG	NPG

L23. Class 73 ED Electro-Diesel (2004)

With constant brightness directional lights and illuminated headcode panels which light in the direction of travel. Powered by the Mabuchi self-lubricating 5-pole Macro-motor driving all 4 axles via twin flywheels, in a diecast chassis. Flush glazing, cab interiors, air horns and high level jumper cables. Early examples have over long couplings making close-coupling difficult. This was later changed in 2005 with 73138. From 2007, this model has been 'DCC ready'.

SBD1	**E6003** BRc green (73/0) half yellow panels Sp Edn 300 (Signal Box) DCC - *07*	65	75
ND-999	**E6005** BRe blue (73/0) Sp Edn 92 (Dapol Club) DCC - *08*	70	80
?	**E6007** BRe blue Sp Edn 100 (Nsprays) - *06*	NPG	90
ND-036d	**E6033** BRe blue - *06*	60	75
SBDN3	**73002** BRe blue non-powered Sp Edn 300 (Signal Box) - *09*	22	28
SBDN2	**73005** ***Mid-Hants Watercress*** Line BR blue Sp Edn 300 (Signal Box), etched nameplates - *09*	55	68
ND-011A	**73101** ***Brighton Evening Argus*** Pullman livery - *05*	60	75

Class 73 electro-diesel No.79101 The Royal Alex in Pullman livery [L23] (David Wild)

ND-011B	**73101** ***The Royal Alex*** Pullman livery - *05*	60	75
ND-036b	**73108** BRe blue - *06*	60	75
ND-006	**73109** ***Battle of Britain 50th Anniversary*** NSE bright blue (South West) - *04*	60	75
ND-022b	**73110** BR 'Dutch' grey+yellow - *05*	60	75
ND-036c	**73111** BRe blue - *06*	60	75
ND-021a	**73114** ***Stewarts Lane*** Mainline - *05*	60	75
ND-022a	**73119** ***Kentish Mercury*** BR Dutch grey+ yellow - *05*	60	75
ND-005	**73128** EW&S maroon - *04*	60	75
ND-012a	**73129** ***City of Winchester*** NSE bright blue - *05*	60	75
ND-005	**73131** EW&S maroon - *not made*	NA	NA
ND-021b	**73133** Mainline blue - *05*	60	75
ND-007	**73134** ***Woking Homes 1885-1985*** InterCity Executive grey* - *04*	60	75
ND-012b	**73136** ***Kent Youth Music*** NSE bright blue - *not made*	NA	NA
ND-012b	**73136** NSE bright blue - *05*	60	75
ND-008	**73138** BReLL blue - *05*	60	75
ND-036a	**73142** ***Broadlands*** BRe blue, light grey roof - *06*	60	75
ND-071	**73202** ***Dave Berry*** Gatwick Express grey - *07*	60	75
ND-070a	**73204** ***Janice*** GBRf blue+yellow DCC + non-powered **73205** ***Jeanette*** - *07*	NA	100
ND-070b	**73206** ***Lisa*** GBRf blue+yellow DCC + non-powered **73209** ***Alison*** - *07*	NA	100
ND-072	**73211** Gatwick Express grey - *07*	60	75
-	**73212+73213** Railtrack Sp Edn 100 (N-thusiast Resprays) - *06*	NA	180
-	**73212** Railtrack non-powered ex- above Sp Edn pair - *06*	50	NA
-	**73213** Railtrack powered ex- above Sp Edn pair - *06*	80	NA
ND-008a	(unnumbered) BReLL blue + transfer sheet - *04*	55	75

* May also be available with a wrong coloured roof.

L24. Class 86 Electric (2009)

Announced at the 2008 N Gauge Society AGM. Platinum range model with super creep motor, , low-friction mechanism, flywheels, DCC ready, directional lighting and NEM pockets for couplings. Plastic catenary will be produced.

ND-099?	**86204** ***City of Carlisle*** BRe blue Sp Edn 125 (C+M Models) - *09*	85	105
ND-099b	**86213** Intercity grey - *09*	85	105
ND-099f	**86213** Freightliner grey + 3 Freightliner 'Spine' wagons train pack - *09*	NA	NPG
ND-099g	**86219** Intercity grey + 2 x MK3 + Mk3 DVT train pack - *09*	NA	NPG
ND-099a	**86229** Virgin Trains red+black - *09*	85	105
ND-099?	**86241** ***Glenffidich*** BRe blue Sp Edn 125 (C+M Models) - *09*	85	105
ND-099p	**86241** Royal Mail red+grey - *10*	85	105
ND-099e	**86259** Virgin Trains red+black + 2 x MK3 + Mk3 DVT train pack - *09- 09*	NA	NPG

Freightliner Class 86 electric locomotive No.86621 [L24] (Dapol)

ND-099n	**86261** EWS maroon+yellow - *10*	85	105
ND-099m	**86401 *Northampton Town*** NSE blue - *10*	85	105
ND-099k	**86415** BR Railfreight Distribution triple grey - *10*	85	105
ND-099d	**86425** RES red+dark grey - *09*	NPG	NPG
ND-099c	**86621** Freightliner green - *09*	85	105

L25. Class 92 Electric (2010)

Work had started on this at the time of going to press. 'DCC Ready'.

ND-???	**92???** Railfreight Distribution grey - *10*	NPG	NPG
ND-???	**92???** triple grey unbranded - *10*	NPG	NPG
ND-???	**92???** EWS maroon+yellow - *10*	NPG	NPG
ND-???	**92???** DBS red - *10*	NPG	NPG

Multiple Units

L26. Class 121 'Bubble Car' (2011)

Class 122 also planned at a later date. 'Super creep' 5-pole motor, low friction mechanism, flywheels, 'DCC ready', NEM coupler pockets, alternate exhausts, light bar ready, directional lighting, RP25.72 darkened wheel sets and an accessory pack containing air pipes, coupling chain etc.

ND-118b	**55021** BR green small yellow panel powered - *11*	NPG	NPG
ND-118d	**55022** Network SouthEast bright blue powered - *11*	NPG	NPG
ND-119b	**55023** BR green small yell panel non-powered - *11*	NPG	NPG
ND-118c	**55024** BR blue powered - *11*	NPG	NPG
ND-118a	**55027** BR green with whiskers powered - *11*	NPG	NPG
ND-119d	**55028** Network SouthEast blue non-powered - *11*	NPG	NPG
ND-119c	**55029** BR blue non-powered - *11*	NPG	NPG
ND-119a	**55032** BR green with whiskers non-powered - *11*	NPG	NPG

L27. Class142 'Pacer' DMU (2011)

Directional lighting, 'DCC ready', under floor 'super creep' motor, and corridor connections. Pickup from all wheels and a working 'Scharfenburg' couplers to allow compatibility with the class 153 and 156 models.

ND-116e	**142021** Tyne & Wear PTE powered - *11*	NPG	NPG
ND-116c	**142025** Northern Spirit light blue powered - *11*	NPG	NPG
ND-117a	**142026** Northern Rail purple non-powered - *11*	NPG	NPG
ND-117c	**142050** Northern Spirit light blue powered - *11*	NPG	NPG
ND-116a	**142065** Northern Rail purple powered - *11*	NPG	NPG
ND-117d	**142069** Arriva Trains Wales lt. blue non-powered - *11*	NPG	NPG
ND-117b	**142077** Regional Railways blue non-powered - *11*	NPG	NPG
ND-116b	**142081** Regional Railways blue powered - *11*	NPG	NPG
ND-116d	**142085** Arriva Trains Wales lt. blue powered - *11*	NPG	NPG

L28. Class150/2 2-Car 'Sprinter' DMU

Planned for 2006 but dropped after Bachmann announced their plan to introduce one.

L29. Class153 Single-car 'Super Sprinter' DU (2009)

DCC and light bar ready and have 2 on/off switches on the underside. Working directional lights. Light bar connection in the roof.

ND-114a	**153302** East Midlands blue powered - *09*	NPG	107
ND-115d	**153307** Northern Rail pur+violet non-pow'd - *11*	NPG	NPG
ND-114f	**153320** Arriva Trains Wales lt.blue powered - *10*	NPG	NPG
ND-115a	**153321** East Midlands blue non-powered - *09*	NPG	NPG
ND-145b	**153328** Regional Railways non-powered - *10*	NPG	NPG
ND-114d	**153332** Northern Rail purple+violet powered - *11*	NPG	NPG
ND-114c	**153333** Central Trains green powered - *09*	NPG	107

East Midlands Trains Class 153 'Super Sprinter' railcar [L29] (Dapol)

ND-114e	**153334** London Midland grey+green powered - *09*	NPG	107
ND-114g	**153360** Northern Spirit powered - *11*	NPG	NPG
ND-144b	**153377** Regional Railways powered - *10*	NPG	NPG
ND-115c	**153383** Central Trains green non-powered - *09*	NPG	NPG
ND-114Z	**153329** 'St Ives Bay Belle' light blue Sp Edn 150 (Kernow MRC) DC6 - *10*	100	120

L30. Class 156 2-car 'Super Sprinter' DMU (2009)

Premium range with new high-torque 5-pole Dapol under floor motor, DCC ready (6-pin), NEM 651 socket, below floor mechanism, close coupling, light switch, NEM coupling pockets with working BSI couplings on outer ends, directional lighting, RP25 darkened wheels, seats painted to match livery.

ND-112b	**156404** Regional Railways blue powered - *11*	NPG	NPG
ND-113c	**156409** Regional Railways blue non-powered - *10*	NPG	NPG
ND-113b	**156411** Regional Railways blue non-powered - *11*	NPG	NPG
ND-082a	**156418** Regional Railways 2-car - *09*	85	102
ND-096a	**156418** Central Trains green 2-car - *09*	85	104
ND-112c	**156419** Nat. Express East Anglia powered - *10*	NPG	NPG
ND-096b	**156422** Central Trains green non-powered - *09*	35	39
ND-083b	**156435** Strathclyde PT non-powered - *09*	35	39
ND-098b	**156438** Arriva North Western non-powered - *09*	35	39
ND-081a	**156440** First Northern Rail purple+violet 2-car - *09*	85	105
ND-113a	**156444** Northern Rail pur+violet non-powered - *11*	NPG	NPG
ND-082b	**156448** Regional Railways non-powered - *09*	35	39
ND-112a	**156468** Northern Rail purple+violet powered - *11*	NPG	NPG
ND-spec1	**156484** Northern Rail Settle & Carlisle - *09*	95	122
ND-098a	**156489** Arriva North Western 2-car - *09*	85	104
ND-081b	**156492** First Northern Rail purple+violet non-powered - *09*	35	39
ND-097b	**156502** Strathclyde PT non-powered - *09*	35	39
ND-097a	**156504** Strathclyde PT 2-car - *09*	85	104
ND-083a	**156506** Strathclyde PT 2-car - *09*	85	102
ND-0?	**156???** Northern Transpennine blue+green 2-car - *09*	85	105
ND-0?	**156???** Northern Transpennine blue+green non-powered - *09*	35	39
ND-???	**156???** East Midlands blue powered - *09*	85	105
ND-???	**156???** East Midlands blue non-powered - *09*	35	39

L31. Class 220 'Voyager' 4-car DMU (2006)

DCC ready with 6-pin sockets fitted and ready for digital sound chip, directional lights, close coupled and etched metal nameplates. Sprung pantographs.

ND-063c	**220002 *Forth Voyager* (60302+60202+ 60702+60402)** Virgin red+silver Ltd Edn 250 - *07*	NA	NPG
ND-063a	**220004 *Cumbrian Voyager* (60304+60204 +60704+60404)** Virgin red+silver Ltd Edn 250 - *06*	NA	140
ND-063b	**220007 *Thames Voyager* (60307+60207+ 60707+60407)** Virgin red+silver Ltd Edn 250 - *06*	NA	140
ND-063g	**220016 *Midland Voyager*** Virgin **(60316+ 60216+60716+60416)** red+silver Ltd Edn 250 - *07*	130	150
ND-063h	**220019 *Mersey Voyager* (60319+60219+ 60719+60419)** Virgin red+silver Sp Edn 250 (Hattons) - *07*	NA	150
ND-063e	**220023 *Mancunian Voyager* (60323+60223+ 60723+60423)** Virgin red+silver Ltd Edn 250 - *07*	NA	150
ND-063z	**220029 *Vyajer Kernewek/Cornish Voyager* (60329+60229+60729+60429)** Sp Edn 150 (Kernow Models) - *07*	NA	150
ND-063d	**220032 *Grampian Voyager* (60332+60232 +607232+60432)** Virgin red+silver Ltd Edn 250 - *07*	NA	NPG
ND-063f	**220034 *Yorkshire Voyager* (60334+60234 +60734+60434)** Virgin red+silver Ltd Edn 250 - *07*	NA	NPG

L32. Class 221 'Super Voyager' 4-car DMU (2007)

DCC ready with 6-pin sockets fitted and ready for digital sound chip, working lights, close coupled, new frictionless chassis and etched metal nameplates. The additional coach is available separately. 4-car sets. Individual extra car available.

ND-073a	**221109 *Marco Polo* (60359+60759+ 60959+ 60459)** Virgin red+silver - *07*	85	105
ND-073b	**221110 *James Cook* (60360+60760+ 60960+ 60460)** Virgin red+silver - *07*	85	105
ND-087a	**221120 (60470+60970+60770+60370)** X Country - *08*	85	119
ND-121a	**221128** X Country non-powered car - *10*	NPG	NPG
ND-073c	**221130 *Michael Palin* (60380+60780+ 60980+ 90480)** Virgin red+silver - *07*	85	105
ND-121a	**221134** X Country non-powered car - *10*	NPG	NPG
ND-087b	**221135 (60485+60985+60785+60385)** X Country - *08*	85	119
ND-073d	**221144 *Prince Madoc* (60394+60794+ 60994+ 60494)** Virgin red+silver - *07*	85	105

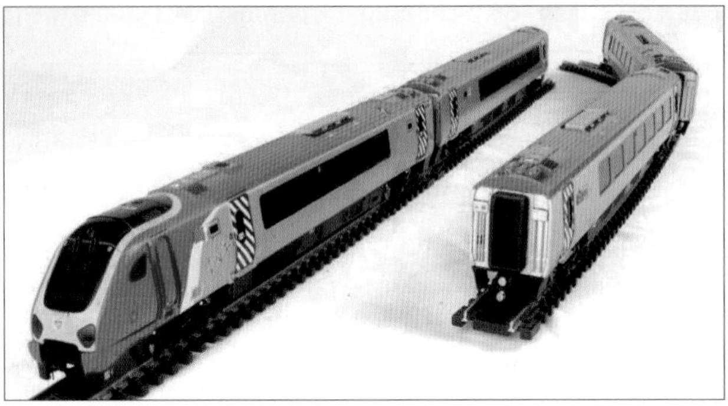

Virgin Trains Class 221 'Super Voyager' No 221109 Marco Polo [L32] (Hattons)

ND-073f	**221122 *Doctor Who* (60372+60772+ 60972+ 60472)** Virgin red+silver non-motorised Sp Edn (Dapol 25th Anniversary) - *08*	45	50

L33. Class 390 'Pendolino' EMU

Train pack with extra coaches available solo.

ND-???	?	NPG	NPG

COACHES

All Dapol coaches have highly detailed interiors and are produced with a range of running numbers. The Collett main line coaches are of a late '30s design.

Cat No.	Company, Number, Colour, Dates	£	£

GWR Stock

C1. GWR Suburban B Set Coach (2003)

B Set coaches were brake ends which were always used in pairs.

NC-007	**GWR** 6736 brown+cream - *03*	8	12
NC-008	**GWR** 6738 brown+cream - *03*	8	12
NC-023*	**GWR** 6736 brown+cream - *05*	8	12
NC-024*	**GWR** 6738 brown+cream - *05*	8	12
NC-005	**BR** W6907W maroon - *03*	8	12
NC-006	**BR** W6970W maroon - *03*	8	12

* These differ from NC-007 and NC-008 in having revised bogies.

C2. GWR Autocoach (2004)

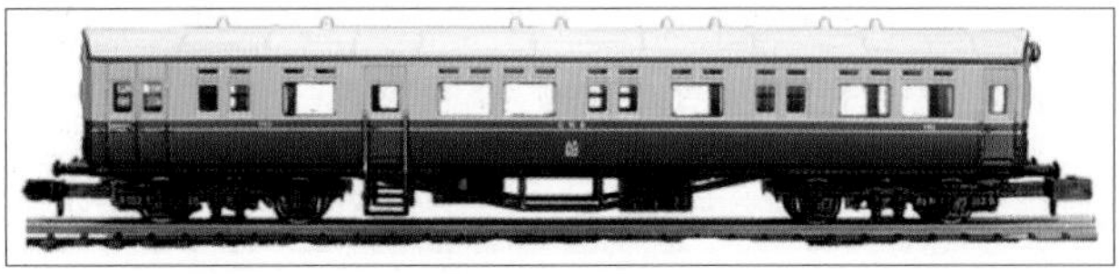

GWR auto coach [C2] (Dapol)

NC-009	**GWR** 187 dark brown+cream - *04*	8	12
ND-080-1	**GWR** 187 dark brown+cream *ex-set- 08*	8	NA
NC-012	**GWR** 189 dark brown+cream - *04*	8	12
ND-080-2	**GWR** (button) 190 dark brown+cream *ex-set- 08*	8	NA
NC-019	**GWR** 191 dark brown+cream - *05*	8	12
NC-013	**GWR** 193 dark brown+cream - *05*	8	12
NC-025	**GWR** 195 dark brown+cream - *not made*	NA	NA
NC-047a	**GWR** 190 dark brown+cream * - *09*	8	10
NC-047b	**GWR** 187 dark brown+cream * - *09*	8	10
NC-011	**BR** W192W red+cream - *04*	8	12
NC-018	**BR** W194W red+cream - *05*	8	12
NC-026	**BR** W190W red+cream - *06*	8	12
NC-010	**BR** W196W maroon with lining - *04*	8	12
NC-014	**BR** W188W maroon - *05*	8	12
NC-025	**BR** W195W maroon - *06*	8	12
SBCN1	**BR** RTC Test Car 1 red+blue Sp Edn 300 (The Signal Box) - *09*	12	16

* sold in card-headed plastic bags instead of the usual plastic boxes.

C3. GWR Collett Stock

From 2009 these were ready for fitting a lighting bar in the roof. (lb = light bar ready.)

C3a. GWR Collett Brake End (2005)

NC-017a	**GWR** 6485 dark brown+cream - *06*	14	18
NC-017b	**GWR** 6543 dark brown+cream - *06*	14	18
NC-035	**GWR** (button) 6487 dark brown+cream - *07*	14	18
NC-042	**GWR** (button) 6486 lb dark brown+cream - *09*	NPG	NPG
NC-057a	**GWR** (button) 6552 lb dark brown+cream - *09*	16	20
NC-057b	**GWR** crest 6603 lb dark brown+cream - *09*	16	20
NC-057c	**GWR** crest 6543 lb dark brown+cream - *10*	16	20
NC-022a	**BR** W6355 red+cream - *06*	14	18
NC-022b	**BR** W6562 red+cream - *06*	14	18
NC-029a	**BR** W6562 maroon - *06*	14	18
NC-029b	**BR** W6605 maroon - *06*	14	18

C3b. GWR Collett Composite (2005)

NC-015a	**GWR** 7050 dark brown+cream - *06*	14	18
NC-015b	**GWR** 7021 dark brown+cream - *06*	14	18
NC-034	**GWR** (button) 7321 dark brown+cream - *07*	14	18
NC-041	**GWR** (button) 7052 lb dark brown+cream - *09*	NPG	NPG
NC-056a	**GWR** (button) 7029 lb dark brown+cream - *09*	16	20
NC-056b	**GWR** crest 7045 lb dark brown+cream - *09*	16	20
NC-056c	**GWR** crest 7059 lb dark brown+cream - *10*	16	20
NC-020a	**BR** W7038 red+cream - *06*	14	18
NC-020b	**BR** W7014 red+cream - *06*	14	18
NC-027a	**BR** W7019 maroon - *06*	14	18
NC-027b	**BR** W7034 maroon - *06*	14	18

C3c. GWR Collett All 3rd/2nd (2005)

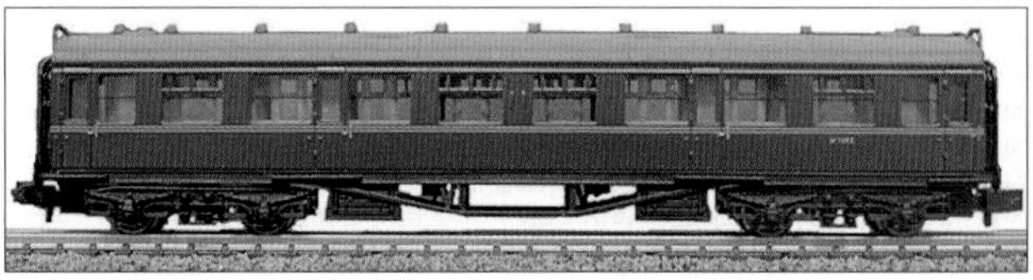

Ex-GWR Collett all-3rd coach [C3c] (Dapol)

NC-016a	**GWR** 1086 dark brown+cream - *06*	14	18
NC-016b	**GWR** 1146 dark brown+cream - *06*	14	18
NC-036	**GWR** (button) 1080 dark brown+cream - *07*	14	18
NC-043	**GWR** (button) 1084 lb dark brown+cream - *09*	16	20
NC-058a	**GWR** (button) 1089 lb dark brown+cream - *09*	16	20
NC-058b	**GWR** crest 1063 lb dark brown+cream - *09*	16	20
NC-058c	**GWR** crest 1112 lb dark brown+cream - 10	16	20
NC-021b	**BR** W1116 red+cream - *06*	14	18
NC-028a	**BR** W1092 maroon - *06*	14	18
NC-028b	**BR** W1138 maroon - *06*	14	18

LMS Stock

The LMS Stanier passenger stock originally planned for 2006 was dropped after Bachmann announced their plan to introduce them.

C4a. LMS 6-wheeled 'Stove R' (2009)

This model is produced exclusively for the N Gauge Society for sale to its members.

-	**LMS** ? maroon - *09*	14	18
-	**BR** ? red - *09*	14	18
-	**BR** ? red+cream - *09*	14	18
-	**BR** ? maroon - *09*	NPG	NPG
-	**BR** ? blue - *09*	14	18
-	**BR** Departmental ? red - *09*	14	18

LNER Stock

C5. LNER Gresley Stock

These were produced with new high definition tools and feature a new close coupling system. They are fitted with NEM pockets for couplings and come with optional buckeye close couplings. Only 750 of each unit were made per running number.

C5a. LNER Gresley Corridor 3rd/2nd (2006)

ND-079-1	**LNER** 364 teak - *08*	20	NA
NC-046	**LNER** 384 teak - *not made*	NA	NA
NC-045a	**LNER** 384 teak - *09*	NPG	NPG

LNER teak all-3rd class coach [C5a]

NC-045b	**LNER** ? teak - *09*	NPG	NPG
NC-045c	**LNER** ? teak - *09*	NPG	NPG
NC-045d	**LNER** ? teak - *09*	NPG	NPG
ND-079-2	**BR** E12101E red+cream - *07*	20	NA
ND-0?	**BR** E12279E red+cream - *09*	NPG	NPG
ND-060a	**BR** E12285E red+cream - *09*	NPG	NPG
ND-060b	**BR** E12691E red+cream - *09*	NPG	NPG
ND-060c	**BR** E?E red+cream - *10*	16	20
ND-060d	**BR** E12614E red+cream - *10*	16	20
NC-031c	**BR** E12002E maroon - *06*	20	25
NC-031d	**BR** E12071E maroon - *06*	20	25
NC-031a	**BR** E12279E maroon - *06*	20	25
NC-031b	**BR** E12704E maroon - *06*	20	25

C5b. LNER Gresley Corridor 1st (2006)

ND-079-1	**LNER** 31879 teak - *08*	20	NA
NC-044	**LNER** 31878 teak - *09*	NPG	NPG
NC-0??	**LNER** ? teak - *09*	NPG	NPG
NC-0??	**LNER** ? teak - *09*	NPG	NPG
ND-0?	**BR** E11028E red+cream - *not made*	NA	NA
ND-0?	**BR** E11020E red+cream - *08*	20	NA
ND-059a	**BR** E11023E red+cream - *09*	NPG	NPG
ND-059b	**BR** E12028E red+cream - *09*	NPG	NPG
ND-059c	**BR** E?E red+cream - *10*	16	20
ND-059d	**BR** E11027E red+cream - *10*	16	20
NC-030b	**BR** E11020E maroon - *06*	20	25
NC-030a	**BR** E11023E maroon - *06*	20	25

C5c. LNER Gresley Brake Composite (2006)

ND-079-1	**LNER** 32558 teak - *08*	20	NA
NC-045	**LNER** 32556 teak - *09*	NPG	NPG
ND-079-2	**BR** E10097E red+cream - *not made*	NA	NA
ND-079-2	**BR** E10077E red+cream - *08*	20	NA
NC-032a	**BR** E10077E maroon - *06*	20	25
NC-032b	**BR** E10080E maroon - *06*	20	25

C5d. LNER Gresley Buffet Car (2006)

NC-046a	**LNER** ? teak - *09*	NPG	NPG
NC-046b	**LNER** ? teak - *09*	NPG	NPG
ND-061a	**BR** E9126E red+cream - *09*	NPG	NPG
ND-061b	**BR** E9128E red+cream - *09*	NPG	NPG
ND-061c	**BR** E?E red+cream - *10*	16	20
ND-061d	**BR** E10112E red+cream - *10*	16	20
NC-033	**BR** E9132E maroon - *06*	20	25

C5e. LNER Gresley Sleeping Car

Proposed.

SR Stock

C6. SR Maunsell Stock

Proposed but now dropped.

BR Stock

C7a. Mk3 TF First Open (2009)

NEM couplings, 'light bar ready'.

NC-037e	**BR** ? blue with buffers - *not made*	NA	NA
NC-037f	**BR** ? blue - *not made*	NA	NA
NC-050c	**BR** M11064 blue+grey with buffers - *09*	16	20
NC-051c	**BR** W41136 blue+grey - *09*	16	20
NC-051?	**BR** W41137 blue+grey - *09*	16	20
NC-069a	**BR** M11081 blue+grey with buffers - *10*	16	20
NC-069b	**BR** M11077 blue+grey with buffers - *10*	16	20
NC-037c	**Intercit**y ? grey with buffers - *not made*	NA	NA

BR Mk3 all-1st coach [C7a]

NC-037d	**Intercity** ? grey - *not made*	NA	NA
NC-050b	**Intercity** 11031 grey with buffers - *09*	16	20
NC-051b	**Intercity** ? grey - *09*	16	20
NC-037a	**Virgin** ? red+black with buffers - *not made*	NA	NA
NC-037b	**Virgin** ? red+black - *not made*	NA	NA
NC-050a	**Virgin** 11017 red+black with buffers - *09*	16	20
NC-051a	**Virgin** 41100 red+black - *09*	16	20
(NC-067)	**Virgin** 11007 red+silver ex-Virgin Relief pack - *10*	16	NA
(NC-067)	**Virgin** 11018 red+silver ex-Virgin Relief pack - *10*	16	NA
(NC-067)	**Virgin** 11048 red+silver ex-Virgin Relief pack - *10*	16	NA

C7b. Mk3 TS Tourist Standard Open (2009)

NEM couplings, 'light bar ready'.

NC-038e	**BR** ? blue with buffers - *not made*	NA	NA
NC-038f	**BR** ? blue - *not made*	NA	NA
NC-052c	**BR** 12043 blue+grey with buffers - *09*	16	20
NC-053c	**BR** W42252 blue+grey - *09*	16	20
NC-053?	**BR** W42251 blue+grey - *09*	16	20
NC-053f	**BR** W42280 blue+grey - *09*	16	20
NC-053?	**BR** W42279 blue+grey - *09*	16	20
NC-068a	**BR** M12119 blue+grey with buffers - *10*	16	20
NC-068b	**BR** M12095 blue+grey with buffers - *10*	16	20
NC-068c	**BR** M12063 blue+grey with buffers - *10*	16	20
NC-068d	**BR** M12068 blue+grey with buffers - *10*	16	20
NC-038c	**Intercity** ? grey with buffers - *not made*	NA	NA
NC-038d	**Intercity** ? grey - *not made*	NA	NA
NC-052b	**Intercity** 12079 grey with buffers - *09*	16	20
NC-053b	**Intercity** 42101 grey - *09*	16	20
NC-038a	**Virgin** ? red+black with buffers - *not made*	NA	NA
NC-038b	**Virgin** ? red+black - *not made*	NA	NA
NC-052a	**Virgin** 12085 red+black with buffers - *09*	16	20
NC-053a	**Virgin** 42235 red+black - *09*	16	20
NC-066a	**Virgin** Charter Relief 12011 red+silver - *10*	16	NA
NC-066b	**Virgin** Charter Relief 12078 red+silver - *10*	16	NA
NC-066c	**Virgin** Charter Relief 12133 red+silver - *10*	16	NA
(ND-101d)	**Wrexham & Shropshire** ? greys with buffers ex-train pack - *09*	NPG	NA

C7c. Mk3 Buffet Car RFM (2010)

NEM couplings, 'light bar ready'. Currently in production.

NC-039e	**BR** ? blue with buffers - *10*	NPG	NPG
NC-039f	**BR** ? blue - *10*	NPG	NPG
NC-039c	**Intercity** ? grey with buffers - *10*	NPG	NPG
NC-039d	**Intercity** ? grey - *10*	NPG	NPG
NC-039a	**Virgin** ? red+black with buffers - *10*	NPG	NPG
NC-039b	**Virgin** ? red+black - *10*	NPG	NPG
(ND-101d)	**Wrexham & Shropshire** ? greys with buffers ex-train pack - *10*	NPG	NA

C7d. Mk3 TGS (2010)

Currently in production.

NC-?	**BR** ? blue - *10*	NPG	NPG
NC-?	**Intercity** ? grey - *10*	NPG	NPG
NC-?	**Virgin** ? red+black - *10*	NPG	NPG

C8. Mk3b DVT (2009)

DCC ready (NEM 651 socket) NEM coupling pockets with choice of couplings, directional lighting, RP25 darkened wheels.

Vrgin Trains DVT and Mk1 coaches [C8]

ND-089c	**Intercity** 82116 grey - *09*	20	25

ND-089d	**Intercity** 82132 grey - *09*	20	25
ND-089a	**Virgin** 82106 red+black - *09*	20	25
ND-089b	**Virgin** 82125 red+black - *09*	20	25
NC-067	**Virgin** Charter Relief 82126 red+silver + 3 Mk3 FOs DC6 - *10*	60	75
(ND-101-1)	**Wrexham & Shropshire** 82146 greys with buffers ex-train pack - *09*	23	NA

C9. 'Super Voyager' Car (2007)

Supplied with a sheet of transfers.

ND-073e	un-numbered **Virgin** silver+red - *07*	12	15
ND-087c	**X Country** un-numbered silver+black+red - *08*	12	15

WAGONS

Cat No.	Company, Number, Colour, Dates	£	£

Planked Wagons

W1. 3-plank Wagon

Proposed.

W2. 7-plank Open Wagon (end door) (2005)

W = weathered.

-	**'Abingdon on Thames Gas Dept.'** red Sp Edn (West Wales Wagon Works) - *09*	6	8
-	**'Abingdon on Thames Gas Dept.'** red W Sp Edn (West Wales Wagon Works) - *09*	6	8
-	**'Ace of Clubs Brewery'** brown Sp Edn 100 (Modelbahn Union) ex-Sept - *08*	6	NA
-	**'Ackton Hall Colliery'** 25 black Sp Edn (Pennine Wagons) - *08*	6	9
-	**'Albion Brewery'** 12 blue Sp Edn 100 (Modelbahn Union) ex-Sept - *08*	6	NA
-	**'Albion Brewery'** 10 black Sp Edn (Medway Queen Preservation Society) - *10*	6	8
-	**'Arscott'** 21 light grey Sp Edn (Midland Model Products) - *08*	5	7
-	'MC **Ashwin & Son'** 24 red Sp Edn (Stephen Braund) - *07*	5	7
N004	**'Baker & Kernick'** 410 black Sp Edn 110 (West Wales Wagon Works) - *05*	5	8
-	'C **Ball'** 1 red Sp Edn (Osbourn Models) - *06*	6	9
-	**'Baltic Sawmills'** 10 red-brown Sp Edn 100 (Ballards) - *05*	5	7
-	**'Bennett & Carter'** 12 light grey with sand load Sp Edn 100 (Ballards) - *07*	6	9
-	**'Billingsley'** 17 brown Sp Edn (DMB Footplate) - *06*	5	7

7-plank - 'Billingsley' [W2] (Dapol)

-	'John T **Bingham'** 10 black Sp Edn (Ballards) - *07*	5	8
-	'Fredrick **Biss'** 3 grey 200 Sp Edn (Bristol East MRC) - *06*	5	8
-	**'Black Rock Quarries'** 17 black Sp Edn (Osborn's Models) - *09*	5	NA
N003	**'Bliss Tweed Mills'** 6 green Sp Edn 150 (West Wales Wagon Works) - *05*	5	8
NB-020	**'Blue Circle'** 173 yellow - *05*	5	7
NB-071	**'Bourne Fisher'** 21 red Ltd Edn 250 - *08*	5	8
-	**'Britannic'** 1346 black Sp Edn (Lord & Butler) - *07*	5	8
-	**'Burton-on-Trent Co-op'** 11 maroon Sp Edn 150 (Tutbury) - *05*	5	7
-	'FW **Butcher'** 3 green Sp Edn 100 (Ballards) - *05*	5	8
-	**'Bute'** 115 black Sp Edn (Lord & Butler) - *07*	5	8
NB-034	**'Bute Merthyr'** 325 black - *06*	5	7
-	'TF **Butler'** 129 red Sp Edn (Craft Hobbies) - *10*	6	8
-	'T **Butt & Son'** 3 black Sp Edn (Antics) - *07*	6	8
-	**'Caerbryn Colliery'** 219 black Sp Edn (West Wales Wagon Works) - *07*	5	7
-	**'Caerbryn Colliery'** 219 black W Sp Edn (West Wales Wagon Works) - *08*	5	7
-	'R **Carder & Co.'** 5 brown Sp Edn (Pennine Models) - *07*	6	9
-	**'Cardigan Mercantile Co.'** black Sp Edn (West Wales Wagon Works) - *09*	5	8
PW001	**'CFC' (Chapman Fletcher & Cawood)** 980 black Sp Edn 96 (Pennine Wagons) - *05*	6	8
-	**'Clevedon Gas Works'** 21 grey Sp Edn (Osborn's Models) - *09*	5	NA
-	'Jabez **Cole'** 17 black Sp Edn (Frizinghall) - *10*	6	8
-	**'Corrall & Co.'** 401 brown Sp Edn (Ballards) - *07*	6	8
-	**'Corrall & Co.'** 514 brown Sp Edn (Ballards) - *09*	7	9
-	**'Crane & Co.'** 107 red Sp Edn 195 (Bristol East MRC) - *05*	6	8
-	'Alexander **Crane'** 102 brown Sp Edn (Antics) - *06*	6	8
-	**'Coventry Collieries'** 1404 black Sp Edn (Castle Trains) - *07*	6	8
CCN-N	**'Crynant Colliery'** Sp Edn (West Wales Wagon Works) - *not made*	NA	NA
-	**'Crystalate'** 1262 yellow Sp Edn 100 (Ballards) - *07*	5	8
-	**'Dapol Club'** 1 purple Sp Edn (Dapol) - *07*	5	8
-	**'Dapol Club Open Days'** grey Sp Edn (Dapol) - *07*	5	8
NB-057	**'Dinnington Main'** 641 dark blue - *07*	6	8
-	**'Economic Coal Co.'** 3 red Sp Edn (DMB Footplate Models) - *07*	6	8
-	'BF **Falkner'** 1 brown Sp Edn (Gloucester & Warwickshire Railway) - *06*	6	9

7-plank - 'Fear Bros.' [W2] (Dapol)

-	'G E **Farrant'** 21 brown Sp Edn 100 (Ballards) - *05*	6	8
-	**'Fear Bros.'** 41 red-brown Sp Edn 84 (West Wales Wagon Works) - *06*	5	7
-	'JU **Freeman'** 3 black Sp Edn 69 (West Wales Wagon Works) - *08*	6	8
-	'JU **Freeman'** 3 black W Sp Edn 29 (West Wales Wagon Works) - *08*	7	9
-	'Isaiah **Gadd'** 29 Sp Edn (West Wales Wagon Works) - *07?*	5	7
BRM/N47	**'Gloucester Gas Light Company'** 37 black Sp Edn 500 (*BRM* Magazine) - *05*	6	8
BRM/N49	**'Gloucester Gas Light Company'** 51 black Sp Edn 500 (BRM Magazine) - *05*	6	8
N006	**'Gresford Colliery'** 638 black Sp Edn 129 (West Wales Wagon Works) - *06*	5	8
-	**Gwili Railway** 1 grey+red Sp Edn (West Wales Wagon Works) - *07*	5	8
-	**'Hall & Co.'** 499 red-brown Sp Edn (E Surrey		

	N Gauge Group) - *07*	5	8
-	**'Hall & Co.'** 597 red-brown Sp Edn (E Surrey N Gauge Group) - *07*	5	8
NB-025	**'Hartnell & Son'** 22 black - *05*	5	7
-	**'Hempsted'** 37 black Sp Edn 500 (BRM) - *not made*	NA	NA
	'Helston Gas Company' 10 black Sp Edn (Kernow Models) - *06*	6	NA
-	**'Helston Gas Company'** 30 black Sp Edn (Kernow Models) - *06*	6	NA
NB-001K	above two models	NA	15
-	'The **High Brooms Brick & Tile Co.'** maroon Sp Edn (Ballards) - *05*	6	8
-	**'Highley Mining'** 246 brown Sp Edn (Severn Valley Railway) - *06*	5	7
-	**'HillsBros'** 3 red-brown Sp Edn (Ballards) - *09*	5	7
-	**'Hind & Fisher'** 2007 brown Sp Edn (West Wales Wagon Works) - *07*	5	7
-	**'Hood & Sons'** 3 green Sp Edn (Salisbury Model Centre) - *07*	5	7
-	**'Hood & Sons'** 2 green Sp Edn (Salisbury Model Centre) - *07*	5	7
-	**'Horlicks'** 2 red Sp Edn 80 (West Wales Wagon Works) - *08*	5	7
-	**'Horlicks'** 2 red W Sp Edn 20 (West Wales Wagon Works) - *08*	6	8
-	'AP **Hudson'** 21 red-brown Sp Edn (Antics) - *07*	5	7
HPR-N	**'Huntley & Palmer'** 21 black Sp Edn 100 (West Wales Wagon Works) - *05*	5	7
-	'Samuel **Jeffries'** 14 red Sp Edn (Antics) - *06*	6	8

7-plank - 'Mid-Suffolk' [W2]

PW003	**'Lancashire Foundry Coke Co.'** 322 grey Sp Edn 96 (Pennine Wagons) - *05*	6	8
-	'SV **Lancey'** 20 blue Sp Edn 112 (Stephen Braund) - *07*	6	8
?	**'Leamington Priors Gas Co.'** 10 red - *10*	6	8
?	**'Leamington Priors Gas Co.'** 10 red W - *10*	6	8
-	**'Lewis Merthyr Navigation'** 768 black Sp Edn (Lord & Butler) - *06*	5	7
-	'RA **Lister'** 1 brown Sp Edn (Antics) - *07*	6	8
(NB1S)	**'Llay Main'** 588 black from set of 2 - *06*	6	9
(NB1S)	**'Llay Main'** 591 black from set of 2 - *06*	6	9
NB-073	**'Maltby Main'** 195 red-brown Ltd Edn 250 - *08*	5	8
NB-071	**'Maltby Main'** 298 yellow-brown - *08*	5	7
-	**'Medway Coal'** 17 black Sp Edn (Ballards) - *08*	5	8
-	**Mid Hants Rly** black Sp Edn (Mid-Hants Railway) - *05*	5	7
-	**Mid Suffolk** 25 grey Sp Edn (Middy Trading Company) - *09*	5	7
NB-021	**'Miller & Lilley'** 66 black - *05*	5	7
-	'WW **Milton & Co.'** 6 brown Sp Edn (Antics) - *07*	5	8
-	'WW **Milton & Co.'** 6 grey Sp Edn (Antics) - *07*	5	8
-	**Ministry of Munitions** ? black? Sp Edn 150? (West Wales Wagon Works) - *10*	6	8
(NB1S)	**'Mwrwg-Vale'** 26 black Sp Edn (West Wales Wagon Works) - *06*	6	9
-	**'New Cross Hands Collieries'** 392 grey Sp Edn 100 (West Wales Wagon Works) - *05*	5	7
NCG-N	**'New Cwmgorse'** 42 brown Sp Edn 100 (West Wales Wagon Works) - *05*	5	7
-	**'New Medway Steam Packet Co.'** 24 green Sp Edn 109 (Medway Queen PS) - *06*	6	8
GOC-N/N005	'G D **Owen'** 16 red-brown Sp Edn 93 (West Wales Wagon Works) - *05*	5	8
-	**'Peacock Bros. & Harris'** 6 red-brown Sp Edn (Ballards) - *08*	6	9
-	**'Pemberton & Co'** 25 brown Sp Edn 100 (Osborne Models) - *06*	6	9
-	**'Pilkington Brothers Ltd'** 1489 red with sand load Sp Edn 115 (Mill Lane Sidings) - *08*	6	9
-	**'Pilkington Brothers Ltd** '1489 red W with sand load Sp Edn 20 (W Wales Wagon Works) - *08*	6	9
-	**'Renwick & Wilton'** 1020 black Sp Edn 100 (Osborne Models) - *05*	5	7
-	**'Ringwood Coal - Thomas Bailey'** ? ? Sp Edn (Salisbury Model Centre) - *08*	6	9
-	'Issac **Roberts'** 19 black Sp Edn (W Wales Wagon Works) - *?*	6	9
-	'Issac **Roberts'** 19 black W Sp Edn (W Wales Wagon Works) - *08*	6	9
-	**'Seddon's Salt'** 224 red-brown Sp Edn (Pennine Wagons) - *06*	6	9
Ant09	**'Sheffield & Eccleshall Co-op'** ?? Sp Edn (Antics) - *08*	6	9
Ant?	**'Sheffield & Eccleshall Co-op'** 12 red Sp Edn (Antics) - *10*	7	9

7-plank - 'Skinner' [W2] (Stephen Braund)

-	'J **Shepherd'** 3 grey Sp Edn (Salisbury Model Centre) - *08*	6	9
-	'J **Skinner'** 8 green+red	8	NA
-	'S **Skinner'** 1 green+red	8	NA
-	above 2 wagons Sp Edn 107 (Stephen Braund) - *07*	NA	18
Ant08	'Alfred J **Smith'** ? red Sp Edn (Antics) - *08*	7	9
-	'GH **Smith & Son'** 24 black Sp Edn 100 (Ballards) - *06*	5	8
NB-019	**'Somerset Trading'** 58 red - *05*	5	7
NB-058	**'South Wales'** 20 grey - *07*	6	8
-	'GS **Sturgeon'** 465 black Sp Edn 100 (Ballards) - *08*	5	8
-	'H **Syrus'** 1 light grey Sp Edn 100 (Ballards) - *08*	6	9
-	'Edward **Sutcliffe'** 75 brown Sp Edn 167 (West Wales Wagon Works) - *10*	6	8
-	'Edward **Sutcliffe'** 75 brown W Sp Edn (West Wales Wagon Works) - *10*	6	8
NB-024	**'Taylor'** 3 grey - *05*	5	7
-	**'Tilmanstone Colliery'** 120 brown Sp Edn 100 (Hythe Kent Models) - *05*	5	7
-	**'Thomas Thomas'** 1 black Sp Edn (West Wales Wagon Works) - *07*	6	8
-	**'Thomas Thomas'** 1 black W Sp Edn (West Wales Wagon Works) - *08*	7	9
-	**'Tunbridge Wells Co-op'** 1 red-brown Sp Edn 100 (Ballards) - *06*	5	8
-	**'Vincent'** 31 red Sp Edn (West Wales Wagon Works - *08*		
-	'John **Walker'** 2 black Sp Edn (Castle Trains) - *07*	6	8
-	**'Walker & Rogers'** ? bright red? Sp Edn (Castle Trains) - *08*	6	8
-	**'Warwick Gas Light Co.'** ? ? Sp Edn (Castle Trains) - *made?*	NPG	NPG
?	**'Warwick Gas Light Co.'** 6 grey - *10*	6	8
?	**'Warwick Gas Light Co.'** 6 grey W - *10*	6	8

-	**'Wetmore'** 27 red 100 Sp Edn (Bristol East MRC) - *08*	6	8
-	'Richard **White & Sons'** 109 light blue Sp Edn 250 (Antics) - *08*	7	9
NB-072	**'Whitwood'** 1583 grey+red Ltd Edn 250 - *08*	5	7
NB-026	**'Wigan Coal'** A147 grey - *05*	5	7
-	**'Winchcombe Coal Co.'** 7 grey Sp Edn (Gloucester & Warwickshire Railway) - *05*	5	7
-	**'Woolcombers'** 15 red-brown Sp Edn (West Wales Wagon Works) - *09*	5	7
-	**'Woolcombers'** 15 red-brown W Sp Edn (West Wales Wagon Works) - *09*	5	7

W3a. 8-Plank Wagon 9' Wheelbase (2010)

It has internal detail, high definition body and chassis moulding, darkened RP25.72 wheels, turned brass buffers, NEM coupler boxes, separately applied brake rigging and lever. The models are produced for Dapol by Helixon in China.

FMR-N1	'Jabez **Cole'** 151 black Sp Edn (FMR) - *10*	5	7

8-plank - 'Littleton Collieries' [W3a] (Dapol)

NB-095a	**'Coltorp'** 123 black - *09*	5	7
NB-094a	**'Gas Company Pennistone'** 7 red - *10*	5	7
NB-085a	**'Hatfield Main'** 1213 brown - *09*	5	7
NB-083a	**'LC'** (Littleton Collieries) 151 black - *10*	5	7
NB-091a	**'Leamington Spa'** 24 red - *10*	5	7
NB-?	**'Northern'** ? ? - *09*	5	7
NB-084a	**'Partington Steel & Iron Co.'** 184 brown - *10*	5	7
NB-092a	**'SPC'** 5009 black - *10*	5	7
NB-096a	**'Stewarts & Lloyds'** 6301 grey - *10*	5	7
NB-093a	**'Thorncliffe Izal'**? black - *10*	5	7
NB-?	**'Welsh Midland'** ? ? - *09*	5	7

W3b. 8-Plank Coke Wagon 9' Wheelbase

It has high definition body and chassis moulding, including internal detail, darkened RP25.72 wheels, turned brass buffers, NEM coupler boxes, separately applied brake rigging, brake lever and coke extension boards. The models are produced for Dapol by Helixon in China.

-	-	NPG	NPG

Steel & Hopper Wagons

W4. 'Sea Urchin' Engineers Wagon

Proposed.

W5. BR 20T Steel Mineral Wagon (2006)

500 of each number were made. W= weathered

NC-060a	**'Blaenavon'** 2438 brown - *07*	8	10
NC-060b	**'Blaenavon'** 2441 brown - *07*	8	10
NC-060c	**'Blaenavon'** 2449 brown - *07*	8	10
NC-060d	**'Blaenavon'** 2450 brown - *07*	8	10
-	**'Cicely'** 23 black Sp Edn (West Wales Wagon Works) - *07*	8	10
-	**'Cicely'** 23 black W Sp Edn (West Wales Wagon Works) - *08*	9	11
-	**GW 'Ebbw Vale Steel Works'** 109728 grey Sp Edn (West Wales Wagon Works) - *08*	8	10
-	**GW 'Ebbw Vale Steel Works'** 109728 grey W Sp Edn (West Wales Wagon Works) - *08*	9	11
(ND-084Z)	**'NCB'** 128 grey? Sp End (Dapol Club) - *09*	NPG	NPG
(ND-084Z)	**'NCB'** 135 grey? Sp End (Dapol Club) - *09*	NPG	NPG
(ND-084Z)	**'NCB'** 136 grey? Sp End (Dapol Club) - *09*	NPG	NPG
(ND-084Z)	**'NCB'** 154 grey? Sp End (Dapol Club) - *09*	NPG	NPG
(ND-084Z)	**'NCB'** 198 grey? Sp End (Dapol Club) - *09*	NPG	NPG

20 ton steel mineral wagon - 'PJ&JP' [W5] (Dapol)

-	**'New Medway Steam Packet Co.'** 37 green Sp Edn (Medway Queen Preservation Society) - *08*	8	10
-	**'New Medway Steam Packet Co.'** 37 black Sp Edn (Medway Queen Preservation Society) - *08*	8	10
NC-041a	**'PJ&JP'** 3619 black - *06*	8	10
NC-041b	**'PJ&JP'** 3621 black - *06*	8	10
NC-059a	**GWR** 33156 grey - *07*	8	10
NC-059b	**GWR** 33147 grey - *07*	8	10
NC-059c	**GWR** 33153 grey - *07*	8	10
NC-059d	**GWR** 33162 grey - *07*	8	10
NC-040a	**BR** P339377K grey - *06*	8	10
NC-040b	**BR** P339354K grey - *06*	8	10
NC-040c	**BR** P339391K grey - *06*	8	10
NC-040d	**BR** P339324K grey - *06*	8	10

W6. BR 21T Hopper Wagon (2006)

500 of each number were made.

NC-046a	**'British Steel'** 26 brown - *07*	8	10
NC-046b	**'British Steel'** 22 brown - *07*	8	10
NC-047a	**'House Coal'** B421943 brown - *07*	8	10
NC-047b	**'House Coal'** B421957 brown - *07*	8	10
NC-0?	**'Locomotion'** B429897 brown - *07*	8	10
NC-039a	**'NCB'** 128 grey - *06*	8	10
NC-039b	**'NCB'** 198 grey - *06*	8	10
NC-039c	**'NCB'** 136 grey - *06*	8	10
NC-039d	**'NCB'** 154 grey - *06*	8	10
-	**Mid Hants Railway** ? Sp Edn (Mid-Hants Railway) - *05*	8	10
-	**MHR** 52007 grey Sp Edn (Mid-Hants Railway) - *07*	8	10
-	**'Pilkington Brothers'** 1973 red Sp Edn 112 (Mill Lane Sidings) - *09*	7	8
NC-038a	**BR** E289595K grey - *06*	8	10
NC-038b	**BR** E307163K grey - *06*	8	10
NC-038c	**BR** B414050? grey - *06*	8	10
NC-038d	**BR** B414038? grey - *06*	8	10

W7. 'Dogfish' Hopper Wagon (2005)

Unless otherwise stated, 500 of each running number were made. The brown wagons are sprayed to appear rusty with parts of the lettering missing and all 10 wagons are different and so too are the two sides of each wagon. Five of the 10 black hoppers have Scottish ESC markings.

BR 'Dogfish' hopper wagon [W7] (Dapol)

NB-029a	**BR** DB993315 grey - *05*	8	10
NB-029b	**BR** DB993037 grey - *05*	8	10

NB-029c	**BR** DB993024 grey - *05*	8	10
NB-029d	**BR** DB993111 grey - *05*	8	10
NB-029e	**BR** DB993318 grey - *05*	8	10
NB-029f	**BR** DB993177 grey - *05*	8	10
NB-029g	**BR** DB992924 grey - *05*	8	10
NB-029h	**BR** DB992938 grey - *05*	8	10
NB-029j	**BR** DB992944 grey - *05*	8	10
NB-029k	**BR** DB992902 grey - *05*	8	10
NB-030a	**BR** DB993292 black - *06*	8	10
NB-030b	**BR** DB993149 black - *06*	8	10
NB-030c	**BR** DB993307 black - *06*	8	10
NB-030d	**BR** DB993188 black - *06*	8	10
NB-030e	**BR** DB993019 black - *06*	8	10
NB-030f	**BR** DB993021 black - *06*	8	10
NB-030g	**BR** DB992873 black - *06*	8	10
NB-030h	**BR** DB992859 black - *06*	8	10
NB-030j	**BR** DB992898 black - *06*	8	10
NB-030k	**BR** DB993058 black - *06*	8	10
NB-033a	**BR** DB993311 brown - *06*	8	10
NB-033b	**BR** DB993367 brown - *06*	8	10
NB-033c	**BR** DB993380 brown - *06*	8	10
NB-033d	**BR** DB993203 brown - *not made*	NA	NA
NB-033d	**BR** DB983098 brown - *06*	8	10
NB-033e	**BR** DB993309 brown - *not made*	NA	NA
NB-033e	**BR** DB983309 brown - *06*	8	10
NB-033f	**BR** DB993457 brown - *06*	8	10
NB-033g	**BR** DB993470 brown - *06*	8	10
NB-033h	**BR** DB993401 brown - *06*	8	10
NB-033j	**BR** DB993422 brown - *06*	8	10
NB-033k	**BR** DB993450 brown - *06*	8	10
NB-070a	**BR** DB983587 grey+yellow Ltd Edn 250 - *08*	8	11
NB-070b	**BR** DB982958 grey+yellow Ltd Edn 250 - *08*	8	11
NB-070c	**BR** DB982961 grey+yellow Ltd Edn 250 - *08*	8	11
NB-070d	**BR** DB983314 grey+yellow Ltd Edn 250 - *08*	8	11
NB-070e	**BR** DB983556 grey+yellow - *10*	8	11
NB-070f	**BR** DB993312 grey+yellow - *10*	8	11
NB-070g	**BR** DB992902 grey+yellow - *10*	8	11
NB-070h	**BR** DB992972 grey+yellow - *10*	8	11

W8. LMS/GWR Bulk Grain Hopper Wagon (2006)

500 of each number were made.

Grain hopper wagon - 'Bass Charrington' [W8] (Dapol)

NB-037a	**'Bass Charington'** 24 brown - *07*	8	10
NB-037b	**'Bass Charington'** 28 brown - *07*	8	10
NB-037c	**'Bass Charington'** 32 brown - *07*	8	10
NB-037d	**'Bass Charington'** 36 brown - *07*	8	10
?	**'Dapol'** 2 purple - *08*	5	6
NB-042a	**GWR** 42302 grey - *07*	8	10
NB-042b	**GWR** 42303 grey - *07*	8	10
NB-042c	**GWR** 42316 grey - *07*	8	10
NB-042d	**GWR** 42318 grey - *07*	8	10
NB-043a	**LMS** 701351 brown - *06*	8	10
NB-043b	**LMS** 701347 brown - *06*	8	10
NB-043c	**LMS** 701359 brown - *06*	8	10
NB-043d	**LMS** 701362 brown - *06*	8	10
NB-036a	**BR** B885364 grey - *06*	8	10
NB-036b	**BR** B885280 grey - *06*	8	10
NB-036c	**BR** B885040 grey - *06*	8	10
NB-036d	**BR** B885143 grey - *06*	8	10
NB-037a	**BR** ? brown - *not made*	NA	NA
NB-037b	**BR** ? brown - *not made*	NA	NA

Tank Wagons

W9. 6-wheel Milk Tank Wagon (2005)

500 of each running number are made.

NB-044	**'Co-op Milk'** 169 white - *07*	10	13
NB-032	**'CWS'** T44 green - *06*	10	13
NB-028	**'Express Dairy'** blue - *05*	10	13
NB-053	**'Express Dairy'** 45 light blue - *07*	10	13
NB-054	**'IMS'** 23 blue - *07*	10	13
NB-031	**'Independent Milk Supplies'** red - *06*	10	13
NB-045	**'Milk Marketing Board'** blue - *07*	10	13
NB-056	**'Pure New Milk'** Co-op London red - *07*	10	13
NB-?	**'Satlink Western'** red+yellow Ltd Edn 250 - *not made **	NA	NA
NB-050	**'United Creameries'** 219 silver - *07*	10	13
NB-?	**'Unigate Creameries'** 220 silver W Sp (Dapol Club) - *07*	12	14
(ND-084e)	**'Unigate Creameries'** 182, 191, 196, 207, 225, 238 silver W 6 wagons ex-set - *made?*	NPG	NPG

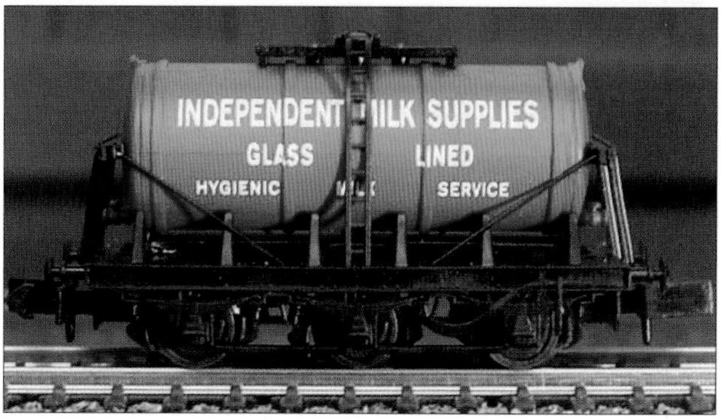

6-wheel milk tank wagon - 'Independent Milk Supplies' [W9] (Dapol)

(ND-084e)	**'Unigate Creameries'** 2992, 2995 silver W 6 wagons ex-set - *08*	10	NA
NB-027	**'United Dairies'** white - *05*	10	13
NBS-002	**'United Dairies'** white W (red lettering) Sp Edn 500 (Hattons) - *10*	10	12

* Too few orders were received.

Vans

W10. GWR GPV Gunpowder Van (2004)

NB-035	**'Blue Circle'** 177 yellow - *06*	4	6
-	**'Cotton Powder Co.'** 2 brown Sp Edn (Ballards) - *09*	4	6
-	**'Dapol'** 2 purple * - *08*	10	NA

Ex-gunpowder van - 'Blue Circle Cement' [W10] (Dapol)

NB-006	**'Elterwater Gunpowder Co.'** 11 light grey - *04*	4	6
NB-018	**'Ferrocrete'** 167 yellow - *05*	4	6
-	**'Fremlin Bros.'** 1 white Sp Edn 100 (Ballards) - *06*	6	8
-	**'Marley Tiles'** 7 green Sp Edn 100 (Ballards) - *09*	6	8
-	**'New Medway Steam Packet Co.'** 53 blue Sp Edn 108 (Medway Queen PS) - *07*	6	8
-	**'Palmers Brewery'** 4 pale blue Sp Edn 200 (Buffers) - *10*	8	10
-	**'Queensborough Cement Co.'** 10 white Sp Edn (Ballards) - *10*	8	10
-	**'ROF'** M12 light grey Sp Edn (Dapol Club) - *10*	8	10
-	**'Seddon Salt'** 66 red-brown Sp Edn (Pennine Wagons) - *06*	5	8
MU34000	**'Willow Brewery'** ? ? Sp Edn (Modelbatin Union) - *10*	NPG	NPG
NB-005	**LNWR** light grey - *04*	4	6
NB-010	**NB** red - *04*	4	6
NB-009	**NB** red - *not made*	NA	NA
-	**GNR** 1899 cream Sp Edn (Going Loco) - *10*	7	9
NB-017	**LSWR** 1379 - *05*	4	6
NB-010	**LSWR** 1379 - *not made*	NA	NA
NB-001	**GWR** 37985 grey - *04*	4	6
NB-012	**GWR** W105753 black with red cross - *04*	4	6
PW002	**GWR 'Salvage Save For Victory'** 47305 pale blue Sp Edn (Pennine Wagons) - *06*	5	8
-	**GWR** 175 black with red cross Sp Edn 99 (Country Rolling Stock) - *10*	7	9
-	**GWR** 175 black W with red cross Sp Edn 50 (Country Rolling Stock) - *10*	8	10
-	**GWR** 35374 grey Sand Van Sp Edn 100 (Country Rolling Stock) - *10*	7	9
-	**GWR** 35374 grey W Sand Van Sp Edn 50 (Country Rolling Stock) - *10*	8	10
NB-011	**NE** grey - *04*	4	6
NB-009	**SR** S61204 dark brown - *04*	4	6
NB-002	**BR** B887002 brown - *04*	4	6

* A few of these were produced by visitors to the trade open days in October 2008 and may well appear on the market.

W11. LNER 'Blue Spot' Van (2007)

250 of each running number are made.

NB-051a	**BR** E87234 white - *07*	4	6
NB-051b	**BR** E87228 white - *07*	4	6
NB-051c	**BR** E87002 white - *07*	4	6
NB-051d	**BR** E87329 white - *07*	4	6
NB-051e	**BR** E87221 white - *10*	4	6
NB-051f	**BR** E87009 white - *10*	4	6
NB-051g	**BR** E87242 white - *10*	4	6
NB-051h	**BR** E87324 white - *10*	4	6
NB-068a	**BR** E88005 blue - *08*	4	6
NB-068b	**BR** E88001 blue - *08*	4	6
NB-052a	**BR** ADB975436 yellow - *07*	4	6
NB-052b	**BR** ADB975402 yellow - *07*	4	6
NB-069a	**BR** ADB974524 red - *08*	4	6
NB-069b	**BR** ADB975417 red - *08*	4	6
(ND-079-3)	**BR** E? white ex-train pack - *not made*	NA	NA

W12. SR CCT Utility Van (2004)

Original body.

SR CCT van [W12] (Dapol)

NB-016	**SR** S2279S Malachite green - *05*	8	12
NB-023	**SR** S2283S Malachite green - *05*	8	12
NB-003	**BR** S2380S green - *04*	8	12
NB-007	**BR** S2385S green - *04*	8	12
NB-013	**BR** S2394S green - *05*	8	12
NB-022	**BR** S2396S green - *05*	8	12
NB-015	**BR** S2388S green - *05*	8	12
NB-004	**BR** M527042 * maroon - *04*	8	12
NB-014	**BR** M527467 maroon - *05*	8	12
NB-008	**BR** S2514S blue - *04*	8	12

* The running number on the box was shown as M527402.

W12b. SR CCT Utility Van (New Body) (2010)

With flush blazing, profiled wheels, NEM coupling pockets and close coupling.

NB-080a	**SR** ? Malachite green - *10*	NPG	NPG
NB-080b	**BR** ? maroon - *10*	NPG	NPG
NB-080c	**BR** ? blue - *10*	NPG	NPG
NB-080d	**BR** ? Engineer's red - *10*	NPG	NPG

Bogie Wagons

W13a. FEA 'Megafret' Intermodal Wagon (2008)

A French built design with a low floor for high capacity containers and swap-bodies. Containers are available separately. Sold in pairs and with a close-coupling system and a diecast deck for a low centre of gravity.

NB-067	basic 'Megafret' wagon - *08*	20	25
NB-076a	33 68 490 9 796-7P - *not made*	NA	NA
NB-076a	33 68 494 3 073-9P - *08*	20	25
NB-076b	33 68 490 9 915-3 - *not made*	NA	NA
NB-076b	33 68 490 9 351-1P - *08*	20	25
NB-076c	33 68 490 9 889-0 - *not made*	NA	NA
NB-076c	33 68 490 9 985-6P - *08*	20	25
NB-076d	33 68 490 9 360-2P - *not made*	NA	NA
NB-076d	33 68 494 6 263-5P - *08*	20	25
NB-076e	33 68 490 9 361-5P - *09*	20	25
NB-076f	33 68 490 9 351-1P - *09*	20	25
NB-076W	33 68 490 9 918-4P ? W - *10*	20	25

W13b. 45' Containers for FEA (2008)

Inscribed 'Less CO2'. curtain = curtain sided container.

NB-077b	**'Arei Van Donge'** blue - *08*	4	NA
NB-077a	**'Deanside International'** blue + 'GTS' blue- *08*	4	NA
NB-077c	**'GTS'** blue - *08*	4	NA

45ft containers for FEA 'Megafret' Intermodal wagons [W13b] (Dapol)

NB-077g	**'K-Line'** red - *09*	4	NA
NB-077d	**'MOL'** green - *09*	4	NA
NB-067k	**'Tesco/Stobart'** Stobart 57 blue, curtain - *10*	4	5
NB-067m	**'Tesco/Stobart'** Stobart 83 blue, curtain - *10*	4	5
NB-067n	**'Tesco/Stobart'** Stobart 99 blue, curtain - *10*	4	5
NB-067p	**'Tesco/Stobart'** Stobart 124 blue, curtain - *10*	4	5
NB-067b	**'Tesco/Stobart'** Stobart 06 blue - *08*	4	5
NB-067c	**'Tesco/Stobart'** Stobart 10 blue - *08*	4	5
NB-067d	**'Tesco/Stobart'** Stobart 17 blue - *08*	4	5
NB-067e	**'Tesco/Stobart'** Stobart 21 blue - *08*	4	5

NB-067f	**'Tesco/Stobart'** Stobart 01 blue - *08*	4	5
NB-067g	**'Tesco/Stobart'** Stobart 07 blue - *08*	4	5
NB-067h	**'Tesco/Stobart'** Stobart 16 blue - *08*	4	5
NB-067j	**'Tesco/Stobart'** Stobart 26 blue - *08*	4	5
NB-077e	**'Triton'** orange - *09*	4	NA
NB-077f	unmarked blue - *09*	4	NA

W14a. FEA-B 'Spine' 2-Car Container Wagons (2008)

Sold in pairs and each wagon will take 1 x 40' and 1 x 20' container.

NB-062a	**Freightliner** 640121 + 640122 green - *07*	16	20
NB-062b	**Freightliner** 640209 + 640210 green - *07*	16	20
NB-062e	**Freightliner** 640212 + 640213 green - *08*	16	20
NB-062f	**Freightliner** 640352 + 640353 green - *08*	16	20
NB-062g	**Freightliner** 640303 + 640304 green - *08*	16	20
NB-062h	**Freightliner** 640353 + 640354 green - *08*	16	20
NB-062i	**Freightliner** 640499 + 640500 green - *09*	16	20
NB-062j	**Freightliner** 640327 + 640328 green - *09*	16	20
NB-062c	**GBRf** 640603 + 640604 blue - *07*	16	20
NB-062d	**GBRf** 640603 + 640604 blue - *not made*	NA	NA
NB-062d	**GBRf** 640619 + 640620 blue - *07*	6	20
NB-062k	**GBRf** 640601 + 640602 blue - *10*	6	20
NB-062m	**GBRf** 640621 + 640622 blue - *10*	6	20

W14b. 40' Containers (2008)

These 8" high containers are for the 'Spine' wagon and sold in packs of one 40' and one 20' container with liveries and mix changing.

(NB-063)	**'American Lines'** white - *08*	5	NA
(NB-063)	**'China Worldwide'** blue - *08*	5	NA
(NB-063)	**'Globestar'** brown - *08*	5	NA
(NB-063)	**'Hanjin'** blue - *08*	5	NA
(NB-063)	**'Italia'** blue - *08*	5	NA
(NB-063)	**'MSC'** buff - *08*	5	NA
(NB-063)	**'Trans Asia'** green - *08*	5	NA
(NB-063)	**'Triton'** brown - *08*	5	NA

W14c. 20' Containers (2008)

These 8" high containers are for the 'Spine' wagon and sold in packs of one 40' and one 20' container with liveries and mix changing.

(NB-063)	**'Cosco'** grey - *08*	NPG	NA
(NB-063)	**'Eurofreight'** green - *08*	NPG	NA
(NB-063)	**'Hamburg Lines'** black - *08*	NPG	NPG
(NB-063)	**'MSC'** buff - *08*	NPG	NA
(NB-063)	**'Nordic'** dark brown - *08*	NPG	NPG
(NB-063)	**'Zim'** orange-brown - *08*	NPG	NA
?	? red - *08*	NPG	NPG
(NB-063)	unbranded brown - *08*	NPG	NPG

W14d. 40' 'High Cube' Containers (2009)

Opening doors and fully compatible with existing 'Intermodal' wagons.

(NB-077)	**'Cosco'** ? grey - *09*	NPG	NPG
(NB-077)	**'Florens'** ? brown - *09*	NPG	NPG
(NB-077)	**'MSC'** ? buff - *09*	NPG	NPG
(NB-077)	unbranded ? brown - *09*	NPG	NPG

W15. KQA 'Pocket' Wagon (2009)

The model will feature close coupling, NEM coupling sockets, profile wheels, weighted for correct running and etched steel details. It is one of the few 'missing link' modern image 'Intermodal' wagons.

?	**? ? ?** - *09*	NPG	NPG

W16. EWS MBA 'Monsterbox' (2009)

NEM coupling pockets along with alternate couplers and darkened profile wheels. Also available with buffers suitable for the relevant prototype and removable ballast load.

?	**EWS** ? maroon - *not made*	NA	NA

W17. EWS MCA/MDA 'Mini-Monsterbox' (2009)

NEM coupling pockets along with alternate couplers and darkened profile wheels. Also available with buffers suitable for the relevant prototype and removable ballast load.

?	**EWS** ? maroon - *not made*	NA	NA

W18. MJA Freightliner Heavy Haul Box Twin (2010)

The bogie box wagons run permanently coupled in pairs with buffers on the outer ends. Introduced in 2006, they are used to carry stone to sites were there is no hopper unloading facility.

?	**Freightliner Heavy Haul** ? green - *10*	NPG	NPG
?	**Freightliner Heavy Haul** ? white - *10*	NPG	NPG

W19. SR Seacow Bogie Ballast Hopper

Planned for 2006 but dropped after Bachmann announced their plan to introduce one.

W20. HIA Freightliner Heavyy Haul Hopper (2010)

Freightliner Heavy Haul acquired a fleet of HIAs in 2005-6 for bulk limestone, sand and aggregate traffic.

NB?	**Freightliner Heavy Haul** ? green - *10*	NPG	NPG

W21. PBA Tiger China Clay Covered Hoppers (2010)

Built by Fauvet Girel in1982 for Tiger Rail Leasing and English China Clays International. Etched handrails, steps and walkways and fitted with NEM pockets for couplings.

NB?	**'ECC International'** TRL116? white *10*	20	27
NB?	as above but numbered TRL116? - *10*	20	27
NB?	as above but numbered TRL116? - *10*	20	27
NB?	as above but numbered TRL116? - *10*	20	27
NB?	**'ECC International'** TRL116? white W - *10*	23	30
NB?	as above but numbered TRL116? - *10*	23	30
NB?	as above but numbered TRL116? - *10*	23	30
NB?	as above but numbered TRL116? - *10*	23	30

W22. JIA NACCO China Clay Covered Hoppers (2010)

Built by Fauvet Girel in1982 for Tiger Rail Leasing and English China Clays International. Etched handrails, steps and walkways and fitted with NEM pockets for couplings.

NB?	**'Imerys'** 33 70 089 4 ? blue - *10*	22	29
NB?	as above but numbered 33 70 089 4 ? - *10*	22	29
NB?	as above but numbered 33 70 089 4 ? - *10*	22	29
NB?	as above but numbered 33 70 089 4 ? - *10*	22	29
NB?	**'Imerys'** 33 70 0894 ? blue W - *10*	23	30
NB?	as above but numbered 33 70 089 4 ? - *10*	23	30
NB?	as above but numbered 33 70 089 4 ? - *10*	23	30
NB?	as above but numbered 33 70 089 4 ? - *10*	23	30

W23. ICA NACCO 'Silver Bullet' Tank Wagon (2010)

Widely seen chromed bodied V-tank. NEM pockets and darkened profiled wheels.

-	**'ECC'** 33 87 789 8 101-2 chrome Sp Edn 250 (Hattons) - *10*	20	25
-	as above numbered 33 87 789 8 088-3 - *10*	20	25
-	as above numbered 33 87 789 8 071-2 - *10*	20	25
-	as above numbered 33 87 789 8 044-5 - *10*	20	25
NB-076a	**'ECC'** 33 70 789 8 046-0 chrome - *made?*	20	25
NB-076b	as above numbered 33 70 789 8 047-8 - *made?*	20	25
NB-076c	as above numbered 33 70 789 8 057-7 - *made?*	20	25
NB-076d	as above numbered 33 70 789 8 062-7 - *made?*	20	25
NB-074e	**'ECC'** rust brown W 33 70 789 8 060-6 - *10*	20	25
NB-074f	as above numbered 33 87 789 8 063-5 - *10*	20	25
NB-074g	as above numbered 33 87 789 8 064-5 - *10*	20	25
NB-074h	as above numbered 33 87 789 8 061-6 - *10*	20	25

English China Clays NACCO weathered ICA 'Silver Bullet' tank wagon [W23] (Dapol)

NB-074a	**'ECC'** chrome W 33 70 789 0 102 - *10*	NPG	NPG
NB-074b	as above but numbered 33 70 789 8 066 - *10*	NPG	NPG
NB-074c	as above but numbered 33 70 789 8 047 - *10*	NPG	NPG
NB-074d	as above but numbered 33 70 789 8 046 - *10*	NPG	NPG

W24. Telescopic Hood Steel Wagon (2007)

Features sliding panels and a close coupling system, NEM pockets, optional buckeye couplings, opening rear panel. 500 made of each number.

NB-061a	**'VTG'** 589 9 087 6 silver+blue - *07*	15	20
NB-061b	**'VTG'** 589 9 082 7 silver+blue - *07*	15	20
NB-061c	**'VTG'** 589 9 077 7 silver+blue - *07*	15	20
NB-061d	**'VTG** 589 9 076 9 silver+blue - *07*	15	20
NB-075a	**'VTG'** 589 9 068 silver+blue - *07*	15	20
NB-075b	**'VTG'** 589 9 078 silver+blue - *07*	15	20
NB-075c	**'VTG'** 589 9 055 silver+blue - *07*	15	20

NB-075d	**'VTG'** 589 9 057 silver+blue - *07*	15	20
NB-075e	**'VTG'** 589 9 068 silver+blue - *10*	15	20

Tiphook Rail telescopic hood steel carriers [W20] (Dapol)

NB-075f	**'VTG'** 589 9 078 silver+blue - *10*	15	20
NB-075g	**'VTG'** 589 9 055 silver+blue - *10*	15	20
NB-075h	**'VTG'** 589 9 057 silver+blue - *10*	15	20
NB-066a	**'Tiphook Rail'** 338 0 4667 017 blue - *not made*	NA	NA
NB-066b	**'Tiphook Rail'** 338 0 4667 023 blue - *not made*	NA	NA
NB-066c	**'Tiphook Rail'** 338 0 4667 028 blue - *not made*	NA	NA
NB-066d	**'Tiphook Rail'** 338 0 4667 046 blue - *not made*	NA	NA
NB-066a	**'Tiphook Rail'** 337 0 0899 024 blue - *08*	15	20
NB-066b	**'Tiphook Rail'** 337 0 0899 037 blue - *08*	15	20
NB-066c	**'Tiphook Rail'** 337 0 0899 042 blue - *08*	15	20
NB-066d	**'Tiphook Rail'** 337 0 0899 066 blue - *08*	15	20

W25. GWR 'Siphon G' Bogie Milk Van (2003)

From 2010 these featured restyled bogies, progile wheels and NEM coupling pockets.

?	**'Dapol Nthusiasts Club'** No.4 yellow Sp Edn (Dapol Club) - *10*	NPG	NPG
NB-002	**GWR** 1443 dark brown - *03-06*	8	12
NC-002b	**GWR** 1448 dark brown - *04*	8	12
NB-081a	**GWR** 1447 dark brown - *10*	8	12
NB-081b	**GWR** 1451 dark brown - *10*	8	12
NB-001	**BR** W1449 maroon - *03*	8	12
NB-081c	**BR** W1445 maroon ? - *10*	8	12
NB-081d	**BR** W1457 maroon ? - *10*	8	12

W26. GWR 'Siphon H' Bogie Milk Van (2003)

From 2010 these featured restyled bogies, progile wheels and NEM coupling pockets.

NB-004	**GWR** 1435 dark brown - *03*	8	12
NC-004b	**GWR** 1432 dark brown - *04*	8	12
NB-082a	**GWR** 1424 dark brown - *10*	8	12
NB-082b	**GWR** 1430 dark brown - *10*	8	12
NB-003	**BR** W1431 maroon - *03*	8	12
NB-082c	**BR** 1428 maroon ? - *10*	8	12
NB-082d	**BR** 1434 maroon ? - *10*	8	12

W27. IWA Bogie Ferry Van (2006)

500 units per running number were made. Close-coupling system, NEM pockets, optional buckeye couplings.

'GE Rail Services'

NB-048a	279 7 604-6 silver+ blue - *06*	12	18
NB-048b	279 7 671-5 silver+ blue - *06*	12	18
NB-048c	279 7 607-5 silver+ blue - *06*	12	18
NB-048d	279 7 617-6 silver+ blue - *06*	12	18

'Blue Circle Cement' IWA bogie ferry van [W23] (Hattons)

'CargoWaggon'

NB-049a	279 7 589-9p grey - *07*	12	18
NB-049b	279 7 632-7p grey - *07*	12	18
NB-049c	279 7 650-9p grey - *07*	12	18
NB-049d	279 7 663-2p grey - *07*	12	18
NB-065a	279 7 619-4p grey - *08*	12	18
NB-065b	279 7 661-6p grey - *08*	12	18
NB-065c	279 7 710-2p grey - *08*	12	18
NB-065d	279 7 716-4p grey - *08*	12	18

'Blue Circle'

NB-055a	2797 611-9p yellow+blue - *07*	12	18
NB-055b	2797 613-9p yellow+blue - *07*	12	18
NB-055c	2797 649-9p yellow+blue - *07*	12	18
NB-055d	2797 683-9p yellow+blue - *07*	12	18
NSPEC2	2797 669-9p yellow+blue W Sp Edn (Dapol Club) - *07*	12	18
-	**'Taunton Cider'** 2797-664-9p beige Sp Edn 750 (N Gauge Society) - *07*	12	16
-	**'CargoWaggon'** 2797-664-0p slate blue Sp Edn 750 (N Gauge Society) - *07*	12	16

W28. BEA Bogie 'Plate E'

Proposed.

Darstaed & Vintage Trains

Trains-de-Luxe

HISTORY

The Darstaed brand was established in 1966 by Marcel Darphin of Zug, Switzerland, to reproduce accurate replicas of the famous pre-war 40cm Marklin coaches. Actual fabrication was by the Swiss firm of Twerenbold. No locomotives were produced. Today, these Darstaed examples are very keenly sought after in auction rooms world-wide. In 1993 Andries Grabowsky, a Dutch national and award winning modeller, bought the name and tooling from M. Darphin with the object of continuing and expanding the range.

During the period 1995 to 2008 Mr Grabowsky was the manufacturing arm of the entire ACE range, a story well recorded elsewhere.

Vintage Trains LNER 0-6-0 No.8245 (Darstaed)

In 2008 the two companies decided to part and in late 2008 Darstaed launched its first British product, the LNER J19 tender locomotive in 5 different liveries, under the Vintage Trains label. The first item to be issued under the Darstaed name was a classic pre-war Pullman coach to honour the 40th Anniversary of the Hornby Railway Collectors Association (HRCA), celebrated in July 2009. Since then the range has expanded rapidly to include the 3 versions of the Brighton Belle (2009), 9 of the fondly remembered Pullman trains that ran in the UK from the 1930s to the1970s (2009), a first run of 10 advertising vans (2009) and the first sets of an extensive range of Edwardian suburban coaches (2010).

LOCOMOTIVES

Steam Locomotives

L1. Caledonian Railway 'Single' 4-2-2 (2011)

These were made exclusively for Wynford Classics.

130101	**123** CR light blue – *11*	NPG	NPG
130102	**123** CR dark blue – *11*	NPG	NPG
130103	**123** CR black - *11*	NPG	NPG

L2. 2-6-2T Freelance Tank Engine (2010)

A generic design, modified to include the key features of each railway company represented. All carry full lining and crest where suitable. 20v dc new mechanism. Working lamps, on/off switch in cab. 3R only.

120201	**316** LNWR black - *10*	NPG	325
120401	**950** CR blue - *10*	NPG	325
121001	**64** GER blue – *10*	NPG	325

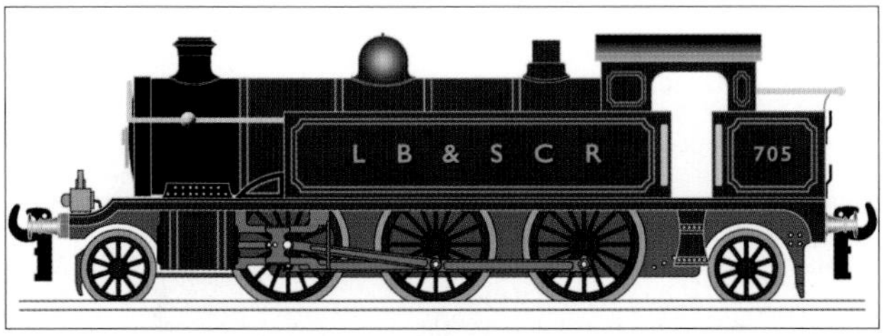

LBSCR 2-6-2T No.705 in Marsh Umber livery [L2] (Darstaed)

120601	**753** SECR dark green - *10*	NPG	325
120101	**705** LBSCR Marsh umber - *10*	NPG	325
120701	**516** LSWR green - *10*	NPG	325
120301	**8118** GWR green - *10*	NPG	325
120501	**58** LMS maroon - *10*	NPG	325
120502	**6939** LMS black with black wheels - *10*	NPG	325
120503	**6939** LMS black with red wheels - *10*	NPG	325
120901	**4515** LNER black with black wheels - *10*	NPG	325
120901	**4515** LNER black with red wheels - *10*	NPG	325
120801	**2712** SR olive - *10*	NPG	325
120802	**429** SR black with black wheels - *10*	NPG	325
120803	**429** SR black with red wheels - *10*	NPG	325
120901	**2009** BRc green - *10*	NPG	325
120902	**5577** BRb black - *10*	NPG	325

L3. 4-6-2 Class A1 Peppercorn Pacific (2011)

This model is produced and marketed exclusively by agreement with the A1 Trust, the owners of new build A1 locomotive. The model is in 3-rail only.

115001	**60163 *Tornado*** grey - *11*	NPG	850
115002	**60163 *Tornado*** BR apple green - *11*	NPG	850
115003	**60163 *Tornado*** BR green - *11*	NPG	850
110101	various (see below) - *11*	NPG	850

110101 offers customers a choice of names from **60113 *Great Northern*** to **60162 *Saint Johnstoun***

EMU Sets

L4. The Brighton Belle (2009)

These are 5-coach units based on the prototype sets numbered 3051-3 which ran between Victoria and Brighton from 1934 to 1972. They are in the Umber and cream livery inspired by the pre-war Leeds Model Company (LMC), with support of the Leeds Stedman Trust. Each car is 35cm long, fully fitted inside with LED table lamps, white or grey roofs with accurately modelled detail, illuminated indicator board, insulated wheel sets, working rear light. 3-rail (but 2-rail conversion available in 2010). The power car has a 24V DC motor with an on/off switch underneath. They are suitable for 2ft curves and are fitted with push/pull couplings between cars and drop link couplings at the ends.

	Brighton Belle Set 3051		
213009	***Car No.88*** 3rd parlour driving *car*	90	NA
213002	***Doris*** 1st kitchen	90	NA
213002	***Hazel*** 1st kitchen	90	NA
213007	***Car No.86*** 3rd parlour	90	NA
213009	***Car No.89*** 3rd driving trailer	90	NA
219951	above set of 5 - *09*	NA	495
	Brighton Belle Set 3052		
213109	***Car No.90*** 3rd parlour driving car	90	NA
213102	***Vera*** 1st kitchen	90	NA
213102	***Audrey*** 1st kitchen	90	NA
213107	***Car No.87*** 3rd parlour	90	NA
219909	***Car No.91*** 3rd driving trailer	90	NA
213152	above set of 5 - *09*	495	495
	Brighton Belle Set 3053		
213920	***Car No.92*** 3rd parlour driving car	90	NA
213202	***Mona*** 1st kitchen	90	NA
213202	***Gwen*** 1st kitchen	90	NA
213207	***Car No.85*** 3rd parlour	90	NA
213209	***Car No.93*** 3rd driving trailer	90	NA
219953	above set of 5 - *09*	NA	495

COACHES

Pullman Cars

These are in the Umber and cream livery with lit table lamps, sprung bogies, working rear light and there is a choice of Pewter grey or Ivory white roofs. Spare sets of roofs and alternative roof indicator boards are available to order. Electrical connection between the cars is by Marklin style jumper leads. Early sets were issued with drop link couplings and without lampshades. Later sets had L-shaped, variable distance, couplings fitted between cars and also had red lampshades. There are working rear lamps on brake cars. Variable couplings and lampshades are available to order for retro fitting to the early sets.

Some Pullman singles may have been available, subject to agents' availability and these are valued at £90 each when new.

C1a. Pullman Parlour Car (2009)

Sold solo, this car is 35cms long.

310101	***Michaela*** 1st parlour car Sp Edn 250 (HRCA 40th Anniversary) - *09*	NPG	NPG

C1b. Sets of Pullman Cars of Mixed Types (2009)

These have been sold in sets of five cars, specific to a specified loco hauled Pullman express train, as indicated. All cars are 35cms long.

Golden Arrow

310212	***Cecelia*** 1st kitchen car	75	NA
310201	***Lydia*** 1st kitchen car	75	NA
310102	***Onyx*** 1st parlour car	75	NA
310702	***Car No.194*** 3rd parlour car	75	NA
310301	***Montana*** 1st brake parlour car	75	NA
319901	above set of 5 - *09*	NA	395

Yorkshire Pullman

310202	***Belinda*** 1st kitchen car	75	NA
310801	***Car No.171*** 3rd kitchen car	75	NA
310103	***Sheila*** 1st parlour car	75	NA
310701	***Car No.64*** 3rd parlour car	75	NA
310902	***Car No.248*** 3rd brake parlour car	75	NA
319902	above set of 5 - *09*	NA	395

Pullman 1st class kitchen car Aurelia [C1b] (Darstaed)

The Queen of Scots

310203	***Joan*** 1st kitchen car	75	NA
310204	***Aurelia*** 1st kitchen car	75	NA
310104	***Zena*** 1st parlour car	75	NA
310702	***Car No.194*** 3rd parlour car	75	NA
310901	***Car No.77*** 3rd brake parlour car	75	NA
319903	above set of 5 - *09*	NA	395

Torbay Pullman/Bournemouth Belle

310205	***Loraine*** 1st kitchen car	75	NA
310105	***Eunice*** 1st parlour car	75	NA
310206	***Evadne*** 1st kitchen car	75	NA
310106	***Juana*** 1st parlour car	75	NA
310302	***Juno*** 1st brake parlour car	75	NA
319904	above set of 5 - *09*	NA	395

Supplied with both sets of coachboards

Tees-Tyne Pullman

310207	***Aries*** 1st kitchen car	75	NA
310505	***Car No.303*** 2nd kitchen car	75	NA
310107	***Ursula*** 1st parlour car	75	NA
310402	***Car No.66*** 2nd parlour car	75	NA
310605	***Car No.82*** 2nd brake parlour car	75	NA
319905	above set of 5 - *09*	NA	395

Devon Belle

310208	***Fingall*** 1st kitchen car	75	NA
310108	***Minerva*** 1st parlour car	75	NA
310501	***Car No.32*** 2nd kitchen car	75	NA
310401	***Car No.35*** 2nd parlour car	75	NA
310602	***Car No.65*** 2nd brake parlour car	75	NA
319906	above set of 5 - *09*	NA	395

South Wales Pullman

310209	***Chloria*** 1st kitchen car	75	NA
310504	***Car No.171*** 2nd kitchen car	75	NA
310102	***Onyx*** 1st parlour car	75	NA
310404	***Car No.84*** 2nd parlour car	75	NA
310603	***Car No.67*** 2nd brake parlour car	75	NA
319907	above set of 5 - *09*	NA	395

Cunarder

310210	***Rosamund*** 1st kitchen car	75	NA
310211	***Argus*** 1st kitchen car	75	NA
310109	***Agatha*** 1st parlour car	75	NA
310403	***Car No.74*** 2nd parlour car	75	NA
310604	***Car No.69*** 2nd brake parlour car	75	NA
319908	above set of 5 - *09*	NA	395

Thanet Belle/Kentish Belle

310213	***Maid of Kent*** 1st kitchen car	75	NA
310303	***Isles of Thanet*** 1st parlour car	75	NA
310502	***Car No.132*** 2nd kitchen car	75	NA
310503	***Car No.133*** 2nd kitchen car	75	NA
310601	***Car No.16*** 2nd brake parlour car	75	NA
319909	above set of 5 - *10*	NA	395

C1c. Pullman Bar Cars (2010)

311001	***The Trianon Bar*** (Golden Arrow) - *10*	75	89
311002	***The Hadrian Bar*** (Tees-Tyne) - *10*	75	89
311003	***Daffodil Bar*** (South Wales) - *10*	75	89
311004	***The New Century Bar*** (Golden Arrow) - *10*	75	89

Vintage Suburban Stock

C2. 35cm Non-Corridor Sets (2010)

These are non-corridor suburban sets. Originally introduced in the Edwardian era, many of them lasted well into BR days.

Only the SR and BR sets list a sixth coach, a composite, which is available only unboxed. There should have also been a CR composite coach but the printing of this failed. All standard 5-coach sets come in a large carrying box containing 2 identical 3-coach set boxes. One of these 3-coach boxes contains a brake end (with power pick-up and end lamp), a third class and a first class coach. The other 3-coach box contains a brake end (without pick-up and lamp), another third class coach and an empty space. This means that a further coach can be added and also dealers can split a 5-coach set into a 3-coach and a 2-coach set for selling seperately. The power pick-up bogie and rear lamp are available on their own for upgrading brake ends without them. The composite coach, where one exists, is designed to fit in the empty space. The suggested value of 3 cars, if sold separately is £210 and that for 2 cars is £140 (or £150 with power pick-up and a rear lamp). The extra composite coach is valued at £70. The pick-up/lamp unit on its own is valued at £20.

The models have sprung bogies, sole bar detail, interior compartment detail (including pictures on the walls above the seats) and ceiling lighting, glazed windows, rear lamp on brakes (rl), some with glazed lit clerestory roofs (c). In all 20 liveries are planned.

LNWR

320301	**1059** 1st purple-brown+white	55	NA
320302	**875** 3rd purple-brown+white	55	NA
320303	**912** 3rd purple-brown+white	55	NA
320304	**958**, **967** brake 3rd purple-brown+white	55	NA
320305	**967**, **958** brake 3rd purple-brown+white, rl	55	NA
329903	set of 5 coaches limited run of only 34 sets - *10*	NA	295

CR

320501	**571** 1st purple lake+white	55	NA
320502	**136** composite purple lake+white - *not made*	NA	NA
320503	**135** 3rd purple lake+white	55	NA
320504	**541** 3rd purple lake+white	55	NA
320505	**754**, **678** brake 3rd purple lake+white	55	NA
320506	**678**, **754** brake 3rd purple lake+white, rl	55	NA
320507	**127** brake composite purple lake+white	55	NA
329905	set of 5 coaches - *10*	NA	295

GER

321201	**84** 1st teak	55	NA
321202	**93** 3rd teak	55	NA
321203	**206** 3rd teak	55	NA
321204	**542**, **207** brake 3rd teak	55	NA
321205	**207**, **542** brake 3rd teak, rl	55	NA
329912	set of 5 coaches - *10*	NA	295

SECR

320801	**3028** 1st maroon	55	NA
320802	**758** 3rd maroon	55	NA
320803	**3824** 3rd maroon	55	NA
320804	**3571**, **803** brake 3rd maroon	55	NA
320805	**803**, **3571** brake 3rd maroon	55	NA
329908	set of 5 coaches - *10*	NA	295

LBSCR

320201	**610** 1st brown+cream	55	NA

320202	**540** 3rd brown+cream	55	NA
320203	**556** 3rd brown+cream	55	NA
320204	**85**, **205** brake 3rd brown+cream	55	NA
320205	**205**, **85** brake 3rd brown+cream, rl	55	NA
329902	set of 5 coaches - *10*	NA	295
	LSWR		
320901	**504** 1st salmon+brown	55	NA
320902	**205** 3rd salmon+brown	55	NA
320903	**372** 3rd salmon+brown	55	NA
320904	**302**, **275** brake 3rd salmon+brown, rl	55	NA
320905	**275**, **302** brake 3rd salmon+brown	55	NA
329909	set of 5 coaches Ltd Edn of 34 sets - *10*	NA	295
	GWR		
320401	**1059**1st brown+cream, c	55	NA
320402	**856** 3rd brown+cream, c	55	NA
320403	**987** 3rd brown+cream, c	55	NA
320404	**1952**, **1942** brake 3rd brown+cream, c	55	NA
320405	**1942**, **1952** brake 3rd brown+cream, c, rl	55	NA
329904	set of 5 coaches - *10*	NA	295
	LMS		
320601	**5049** 1st maroon, c	55	NA
320602	**2501** 3rd maroon, c	55	NA
320603	**7125** 3rd maroon, c	55	NA
320604	**2142** brake composite maroon, c	55	NA
320605	**1904** brake 3rd maroon, c, rl	55	NA
329906	above set of 5 - *10*	NA	295
	LMS		
320701	**3330** (a) composite maroon	55	NA
320702	**2502** (a) 3rd maroon	55	NA
320703	**7126** (a) 3rd maroon	55	NA
320704	**1904** (a) brake 3rd maroon	55	NA
320705	**2142** (a) brake composite maroon, rl	55	NA
329907	above set of 5 - *10*	NA	295
	LNER		

Vintage suburban LNER brake 3rd [C2] (Darstaed)

320101	**573** 1st teak, c	55	NA
320102	**459** 3rd teak, c	55	NA
320103	**945** 3rd teak, c	55	NA
320104	**354, 395** brake 3rd teak, c	55	NA
320105	**395**, **354** brake 3rd teak, c, rl	55	NA
329901	set of 5 coaches - *10*	NA	295
	SR		
321001	**461** 1st olive green	55	NA
321002	**2046** 3rd olive green	55	NA
321003	**1025** 3rd olive green	55	NA
321004	**384** composite olive green	55	69
321005	**825**, **705** brake 3rd olive green	55	NA
321006	**705**, **825** brake 3rd olive green, rl	55	NA
329910	set of 5 coaches - *10*	NA	295
	BR		
321101	**M41005** composite maroon	55	NA
321102	**M41012** composite maroon	55	NA
321103	**M42568** 3rd maroon	55	NA
321104	**M46105** composite maroon	55	69
321105	**M42312**, **M46852** brake 3rd maroon	55	NA
321106	**M46852**, **M42312** brake 3rd maroon, rl	55	NA
329910	set of 5 coaches - *10*	NA	295

WAGONS

W1. Pre-Grouping Advertising Vans (2009)

This first series of 10 advertising vans was inspired by some of the small enamelled advertising signs made and marketed by Bassett-Lowke and others during the period before the Grouping, i.e. 1905 to 1923. Each van carries a livery and return station based on the location of the factory, firm or products advertised on each van. The weight of each van 500 gms or 1.1lbs. The vans have a cast plank effect roof, detailed brake gear and sprung buffers. Each design contains the artist's hidden logo, as with Cuneo paintings, and each is a limited edition of 500.

Early SECR van - 'Wright's Coal Tar Soap' [W1] (Darstaed)

410109	**'Bass'** 91201 MR - *09*	40	45
410104	**'Burgoyne's Australian Wines'** 4255 GE - *09*	40	45
410105	**'Henry Murton's Waterproofers'** 501735 NE - *09*	40	45
410101	**'Melrose's Tea'** 1408 CR - *09*	40	45
410107	**'Rocket Lubricating Oil'** 7429 GE - *09*	40	45
410103	**'Rowntree's Elect Cocoa'** 3217 NE - *09*	40	45
410110	**'Spratt's Dog Food'** 1087 SECR - *09*	40	45
410108	**'The Captain Magazine'** 8384 GW - *09*	40	45
410106	**'Wood Milne Rubber Heels'** 6008 LNWR - *09*	40	45
410102	**'Wright's Coal Tar Soap'** 27741 SECR - *09*	40	45

VINTAGE TRAINS

HISTORY

Vintage Trains, previously known as ACE Trains Co. Ltd., was the manufacturer of the ACE range from its inception in 1995 until 2008, when the two companies parted. As a result, Vintage was left with an amount of stock and parts which will be re-issued from time to time.

LOCOMOTIVES

VL1. LNER Class J19 0-6-0 (2008)

010109	**8145** LNER green extra cab lining - *10*	300	345
010101	**8245** LNER green - *08* *	300	345
010110	**8262** LNER green extra cab lining - *10*	300	345
010102	**8281** LNER green - *08* *	300	345
010103	**8141** LNER lined black - *08* *	300	345
010104	**64649** BRa black - *08*	250	299
010105	**64670** BRb black - *08*	250	299
010106	NZR black - *09*	300	345
010107	SAR black - *09*	300	345
010108	NSWGR green – *09*	300	345

WAGONS

VW1. Milk Tanker (2010)

This was a limited run of 340 examples, with cream lettering on a blue background.

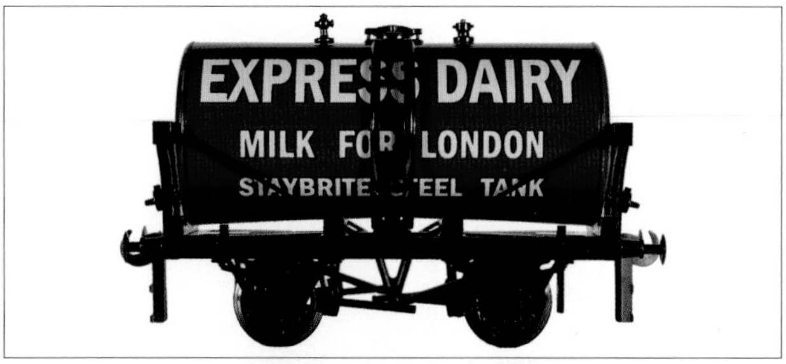

Vintage Trains milk tank wagon - 'Express Dairies' [VW1] (Darstaed)

040101	**'Express Dairies'** blue – *10*	30	35
046001	Set of 3 of the above wagon - *10*	NA	99

VW2. 20T Guards Van (2010)

This is a 4-wheel tinplate vehicle, working rear lamp, internal light, ducket and sprung buffers.

040201	**LNER** 178717 brown - *10*	32	39
040202	**BR** E178717 brown - *10*	32	39

Exley 0

HISTORY

This firm is primarily known for its coaching stock in 00 and 0 gauge and was founded at Bradford by Edward Exley in 1923 but did not become a limited company until 1947. Initially the products were locomotives, in live steam, clockwork and electrically powered, in gauges 0 and 1, which were made to order.

By the 1930s, 0 gauge coaches had joined the range of products, and both locos and coaches were available 'off the shelf' as well as to order. During this period the company started supplying Bassett-Lowke with models, including the range of 0 gauge coaches which the latter company sold as their 'scale range'! It should be remembered that this was in the days before current consumer legislation, and as we have seen elsewhere in this catalogue, Bassett-Lowke bought in much of their range of products from other manufacturers and sold them through their catalogues under their own name. At the same time a business relationship was formed with J S Beeson, Mills Bros., Leeds Model Company and others, with much cross-fertilisation of products between the parties involved.

In the later 1930s, partly as a result of Vivien Boyd-Carpenter having joined the company, high quality 00 coaching stock was added to feed a growing market in this new scale.

During the Second World War, work turned to the war effort and scale model ships for naval recognition use were made. With the return of peace, the company retooled in 1945 to produce their railway models again. The underframes and bogies of the early post war coaches were improved from those of the pre-war era, and around 1950 the tooling for the coach bodies was also upgraded to the style most commonly found today.

Edward Exley Ltd also produced industrial models to commissioned orders, which included charabancs, industrial installations, large diesel engines, etc., and continued to supply Bassett-Lowke with 'scale' coaches.

In the early post war years the sales department was in Worksop, Nottinghamshire, with Boyd-Carpenter running this part of the business, although the works were still in Bradford. By 1952, however, Edward Exley (Sales) Ltd had moved to Baslow in Derbyshire and Edward Exley had resigned as a director of the sales company in July 1955 after a disagreement. Indeed, it seems that the directors were continually changing due to boardroom squabbles. Edward continued to manage the works in Bradford and the Edward Exley (sales) Ltd catalogue carried the statement 'This company is not now a manufacturing undertaking'. Lists of coaches in 00 and 0 scale were issued by the factory but these were headed 'Exley of Bradford'.

An interesting link is worth mentioning here. Both before and after the Second World War, there was close association between Exley and Mills Bros. Indeed, Frank Mills was, for some time in the '50s, a director of Edward Exley Ltd. and the two companies were known to build for each other. This can cause some confusion for collectors and historians.

Locomotives had continued to be available after the war, mainly to order, including a number of highly detailed and large scale display models for companies such as Hudswell Clarke, Ruston & Hornsby and British Railways. But, in the late 1950s Edward Exley sold the loco construction part of the business to Stanley Beeson, who had made locos for a number of Exley clients. Coaches were listed until 1962, when there was a terrible fire on 24th June which destroyed the Bradford premises and most of the tools. At this point Edward Exley decided to retire. A note in the 1962-63 catalogue, reporting the fire, indicated the company's intention to rebuild the factory but it seems that this did not happen.

In 1962 Edward Exley Ltd took over Mills Bros. stock and the Milbro name and became the sole suppliers of Milbro products which are covered elsewhere in this book.

The company at Baslow continued to offer coaches but discontinued the 00 gauge range as the manufacturing facility was lost in the fire. The 7mm models were listed as available until the death of Boyd-Carpenter in January 1995, but were being made to order by outside workers. It has to be said that quality of the coaches made after 1962, once a hallmark of the company name, was variable, and to the purist no true Exleys were made after the destruction of the Bradford factory.

After the death of Boyd-Carpenter in 1995, Edward Exley Ltd ceased trading at Baslow, and all the shares and remnants of the company were purchased by Quentin and Tricia Lucas from Fife. In the latter half of the 1990s they rebuilt the company, trading in original Exley models, carrying out restorations, and selling modern finescale 0 gauge kits, models and components. Quentin specialised in the 0 gauge Exley market, and Tricia in 00. They were a familiar sight at model railway exhibitions and at selected Train Fairs and Auctions, and operated a mail order service too. In January 1999 they moved the business to near Berwick-upon-Tweed, and not long after this wound up the company when they retired.

In August 2004, Edward Exley Limited was sold by Quentin and Tricia Lucas to Richard Gordon-Brown and Joe Brown. Work began on developing a new range of ready-to-run 0 gauge coaching stock.

Dates - Only post-war coaches are listed here at present as more research is required on pre-war production. Approximate dates of availability (for guidance only) are given in the tables and none are given after the factory burnt down in 1962.

North British Railway 0-6-0 No 848 [L3]

LOCOMOTIVES

The majority of the Exley locomotives were hand-built, true to prototype and made to order. In the early days of the company many of them were built by Edward himself, as this was his first love in the business, but by the 1930s many were built by employees in the factory, and by other contemporary builders such as Mills Bros. and Stanley Beeson. As a result of almost no records being kept, exact production details have been impossible to obtain.

Pre-war, the Exley catalogue listed the following locos as available in both 0 gauge and gauge 1: 'Royal Scot', LNER A3, LMS 'Compound', LNWR *Hardwicke*, LNER N2, LMS 'Prince of Wales', LNER 10000, LMS 'Princess Royal', GNR 'Single', GWR 'King', Caledonian 4-6-0, SR 'Lord Nelson', GWR 2-6-2T, GWR 'Castle' and a freelance steam 0-4-0 saddle tank. All of these were listed as stock items, and others were advertised as built to order.

Post-war catalogues show an LNER *Flying Scotsman*, a Southern 4-6-0 'Lord Nelson', a Southern 'Schools' Class, a 36XX Class GWR 2-4-2T and a number of overseas locomotives for special purposes. Further known products were a NBR J35 and an LMS 2-6-4T. Catalogue illustrations post-war were usually of locos that had been supplied to customers, rather than an indication of what may be available from stock. As mentioned above, the locomotive building part of the Bradford business was sold to Stanley Beeson in the late 1950s.

Prices - It is difficult to assess the value of Exley locomotives as they are not often found for sale, nor are they easy to identify. They are very well crafted models with nicely finished detail but they rarely carry the makers mark and when buying, one relies more on the provenance. The price for an Exley locomotive model is entirely dependent upon this as well as originality, condition, and the price the buyer and seller are prepared to negotiate. Naturally locos identified positively as 'Beeson for Exley' attract premium prices. The two prices shown represent the likely range for one in good condition.

Cat No.	Company, Number, Colour, Dates	£	£

L1a. 0-4-0DS (Freelance)

This model had a square bonnet and radiator.

Freelance LNER 0-4-0 diesel shunter No.717 [L1a]

?	**LMS** black - *?*	150	200
?	**LNER** 717 green - *?*	150	200
?	private owner livery - *?*	150	200

L1b. 0-4-0ST (Freelance)

This model had the same body as the above diesel shunter but different fittings to make it look like a steam engine and with outside cylinders.

?	**'Newman Bros.'** orange - *?*	100	150

L2. Southern EMU (Exley for Bassett-Lowke)

These were sold as 2-car sets with 12V DC Bassett-Lowke motor bogies and B-L coach bogies. Although made for Bassett-Lowke, they were also sold by Exley. The motor and trailer cars of the Portsmouth set were 3rd class centre corridor brake ends suitably modified, and many were sold with normal SR corridor coaches in the middle, to create the image of the prototype train. A similar suburban set was made from two suburban coaches in the same way, again often with additional non corridor coaches added. The suburban set is much rarer than the Portsmouth set. Prices quoted should be adjusted where additional coaches have been added to the basic 2-car sets.

SR suburban EMU No.3074 [L2]

?	**LMS*** 9020+9020 maroon all 3rd - *c55*	1600	2200
?	**Southern** green 3080 (11157+11171) Portsmouth 2-car set - *53-60?*	1100	1500
?	**Southern** green 3064, 3074 (3990+?), 2186 (11161+?) 2-car suburban set - *53-60?*	1300	1700

* A very small number of the corridor EMUs were turned out to special order in LMS livery (thought to be less than 10 sets). This was entirely a fictional subject and did not represent any known LMS prototype EMU but, nevertheless, makes a fine looking set.

L3. Miscellaneous Locomotives

MTO = made to order

?	0-6-0ST (freelance) private owner - *?*	150	200
-	**GNR** Stirling 'Single' 4-2-2 No.1 MTO - *?*	2000	3500
?	**NBR** 848 0-6-0 Class J35 dark blue - *?*	400	600
-	**LNWR** 2-4-0 *Hardwick* MTO - *?*	2000	3500
?	**GWR** 4-6-0 'King' Class green - *?*	850	1300
?	**LMS** 4-4-0 'Compound' 1126 red - *?*	400	600
-	**LMS** 'Patriot' 4-6-0 5504 *Royal Signals* maroon MTO - *30-50*	NPG	NPG
?	**LMS** 2-6-4T black - *?*	500	700
?	**LMS** 0-8-0 9500 black MTO - *?*	500	700
?	**GCR/LNER** Class 04/05 'ROD' 2-8-0 5012, 5412 black - *30-50*	670	750
-	**LNER** A4 4498 *Sir Nigel Gresley* blue 3-rail 12V DC, brass, MTO - *57*	2600	4300
-	**LNER** A1 2573 *Harvester* green 3-rail 12V DC, brass, MTO - *57*	2700	4300
-	**LNER** A1 4472 *Flying Scotsman* green MTO - *?*	2500	4000
-	**LNER** Sentinel steam railcar *Fair Maid* green +cream - *?*	NPG	NPG
-	**SR** 'Schools' Class 923 *Bradfield* green - *?*	2000	3500
-	Portsmouth 2-car EMU set 331+313 green - *?*	650	750

COACHES

Exley coaches were made from aluminium using a wrap-round technique so that roof, sides and solebars were one. This was attached to a wooden floor which during the pre- and early post-war period sat high inside the coach body, but from about 1950 sat just above solebar level.

Pre-war, the ends were an alloy casting showing the end planking detail, which was bowed if it was so on the prototype. They incorporated a cast lug which screwed to the underside of the floor. From around 1950, using a heavier alloy, the end castings were changed to a more modern pattern which was based on the LMS Stanier coach end. These were retained by copper wires cast into the end at solebar level. The heavier cast ends, with integral buffers also became plastic in the late 1950s.

The windows were glass, held in place by spring clips and should not be taken apart - unless by someone experienced in doing so.

Before the war, battery boxes were usually blocks of wood with little or no underframe detail. Post-war, pressed metal battery boxes were introduced, initially with an open bottom and an indication of truss rodding. Bogies were mounted on a central spigot bolted through the wooden floor.

These construction methods were modified with the introduction of the K5 and K6 series of the '50s. There has been much speculation about the significance of K5 and K6 but, suffice to say, the principal difference between them is that K5 and earlier coaches have the window ventilators painted onto the glass, whereas K6, and the plastic range, have window ventilators stamped out from the metal of the coach side. However, this is not an infallible rule, as many K5 coaches have stamped metal vents! K6 coaches, and K5 metal vents, do attract a price premium over those with painted vents. The K5 and K6 series also had different bogies but we have not distinguished between them here.

SR restaurant car (Vectis)

Apart from modified bogie fittings with the advent of the split pin, the underframes became more detailed and were an all metal construction. The bodies were lowered on the bogies so that no daylight showed underneath and material for the interiors changed in the late 1950s so that they now had coloured seats in metal. The final modification to the coaches themselves was the utilisation of plastic for coach ends, bogies and parts of the underframe, and they now carried the 'BFD EXLEY MODDEX' trade mark.

A variety of bogies have been used with Exley coaches over the years. Pre-war the Exley bogie had pressed steel and cast side frames. They had a central spigot socket and wire bracing and the axle ends were suspended on spring steel wire. Exley coaches sold by Bassett-Lowke were fitted with their range of bogies.

Post-war, Exley bogies developed to the familiar 'V' shaped central stretcher for split pin attachment. These had cast side frames and wire end stretchers, but still with spring steel wire support to the axle ends. Again, coaches sold by Bassett-Lowke were fitted with their post-war compensated bogie. Today, post-war coaches appearing on the market are about evenly divided between the two bogie types, and this has no effect upon value.

Quite a variety of coaches were made in the liveries of the 'Big Four' railway companies and latterly in the crimson & cream and maroon BR colour schemes; although BR coaches generally are far less common. Available to special order were coaches for the pre-grouping companies and freelance concerns. The rare availability on the market of these specials makes it impossible to provide a realistic price guide for them, however, good to excellent examples have changed hands recently at prices between £500 and £1200 each, depending upon the livery they carried and their rarity.

The coaches made before 1940 tend to be more accurate to the prototype whereas after the introduction of the K5 series, which were largely based upon the LMS Stanier profile, it became a matter of changing livery, rainstrips and window positions.

Exley coaches are always impressive, run well and, in their day, were the leaders in their field. More recently, hand-built scale coaches have overtaken Exleys for the finescale enthusiast, but they still have a major following amongst operators, as well as among collectors.

GWR Royal Mail coach No.6384 [C13] (Vectis)

Numbers - It seems that a very large range of running numbers were used on each coach type and it is near impossible to find two identical coaches identically numbered.

Prices - We cannot give a price guide to all the types of coach made but we have given an indication of value, of coaches manufactured after the 2nd World War. The values given refer to coaches in good to excellent condition. Those in poor, altered and well used condition are worth much less.

We apologise for the incompleteness of this section but much more research is required - and help with this is needed.

Cat No.	Company, Number, Colour, Dates	£	£
C1.	**Suburban 6-Wheel Coaches 31'**		
-	**GWR** all 3rd dark brown+cream - *54?*	250	350
-	**GWR** brake 3rd dark brown+cream - *54?*	250	350

LMS 6-wheeled brake 3rd [C1]

Cat No.	Company, Number, Colour, Dates	£	£
-	**GWR** 1st/3rd dark brown+cream - *54?*	250	350
-	**LMS** all 3rd maroon - *54?*	250	350
-	**LMS** 271 brake 3rd maroon - *54?*	250	350
-	**LMS** 1st/3rd maroon - *54?*	250	350
-	**LMS** Brake Stove R maroon - *54?*	300	400
-	**LNER** 222 all 3rd teak - *54?*	250	350
-	**LNER** brake 3rd teak - *54?*	250	350
-	**LNER** 223 1st/3rd teak - *54?*	250	350
-	**SR** all 3rd green - *54?*	250	500
-	**SR** brake 3rd green - *54?*	250	500
-	**SR** 1st/3rd green - *54?*	250	500
C2.	**Suburban Brake 3rd 50'**		
-	**GWR** 5111, 6661 dark brown+cream - *50?-62*	250	350
-	**LMS** 2681, 2721, 18777, 20078, 23322 maroon - *50?-62*	200	250
-	**LNER** 3330 brown - *53?-62*	300	375
-	**SR** 3805, 3807, 4442 green - *50?-62*	400	650
-	**BR** maroon - *59?-62*	NPG	NPG
C3.	**Suburban Brake 1st/3rd 50'**		
-	**LMS** 478 maroon - *50?-62*	250	350
C4.	**Suburban 1st/3rd 50'**		

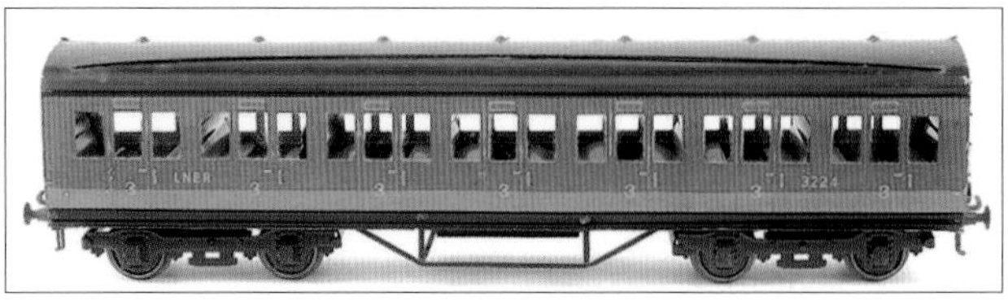

LNER suburban 1st/3rd composite No.3224 [C4] (Vectis)

Cat No.	Company, Number, Colour, Dates	£	£
-	**GWR** 1071, 2315, 3232, 3555, 8017 dark brown+cream - *50?-62*	200	250
-	**LMS** 1620, 2420, 19992 maroon - *50?-62*	200	250
-	**LNER** 223, 3224 brown - *53?-62*	300	375
-	**SR** 7632 green - *50?-62*	400	650
-	**BR** maroon - *59?-62*	NPG	NPG
C5.	**Suburban Full 3rd 50'**		
-	**GWR** 443 dark brown+cream - *50?-62*	250	350
-	**LMS** 10033, 12225, 19161, 20011, 21537 maroon - *50?-62*	200	250
-	**LNER** brown - *53?-62*	300	375
-	**SR** 1999 green - *50?-62*	400	650
-	**BR** maroon - *59?-62*	NPG	NPG
C6.	**Suburban Full 1st 50'**		
-	**LMS** 10002 maroon - *?*	250	300
C7.	**Restaurant Car Kitchen 1st 57'**		
-	**LMS** 31, 33, 45, 4203, 5081 maroon - *50?-62*	200	250
-	**SR** 6011, 6577 green - *50?-62*	450	900
-	**BR** red+cream - *61?-62*	500	600
C8.	**Restaurant Car Kitchen 1st 69'**		
-	**LMS** 20, 41?, 66 maroon - *?*	NPG	NPG
C9.	**Restaurant Car 1st/3rd Kitchen 57'**		
-	**GWR** 3280, 4721, 5005 choc+cream - *50?-62*	300	375
-	**LMS** 16 maroon - *50?-62*	300	375
C10	**Queen Mary Restaurant Car**		
-	**GWR** 9112 choc+cream - *?*	300	375
C11.	**Kitchen Car 50'**		
-	**GWR** 2060 dark brown+cream - *50?-62*	325	400
-	**LMS** 364, 30088 ,31221, 37771, 30075, 41115 maroon - *50?-62*	200	250
-	**BR** 30075 red+cream - *61?-62*	400	500
C12.	**Buffet Car** (with bar and pantry)		
-	**LMS** maroon - *50?-62*	300	400

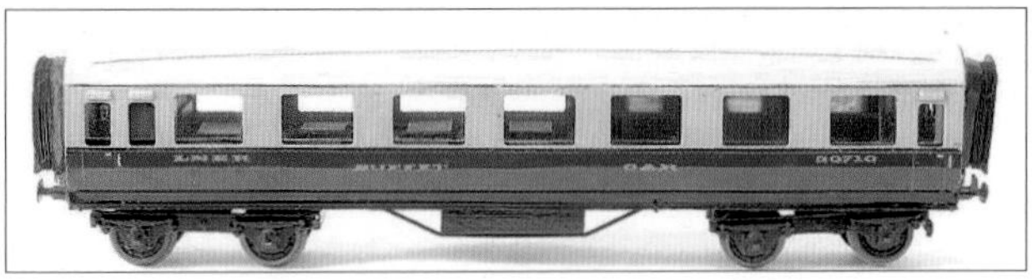

LNER tourist buffer car No.30710 [C12] (Vectis)

-	**LNER** 21601, 21602, 21603, 21607, 30710 green+cream - *50?-62*	200	250
-	**SR** 1250, 1254, 1259 green - *50?-62*	450	900
-	**BR** maroon - *59?-62*	NPG	NPG

C13. Travelling Post Office 57'

-	**GWR** 818?, 910?, 6384 dark brown+cream - *50?-62*	370	525
-	**LMS** 20007, 30220?, 30234 maroon - *50?-62*	200	250
-	**LNER** 808, 988 brown - *57?-62*	800	1000
-	**BR** red+cream - *58?*	500	575
-	**BR** maroon - *59?-62*	NPG	NPG

C14. Ocean Mails Van 57'

-	**GWR** 1110, 1111, 1196?, 1199 dark brown+cream - *50?-62*	400	475
-	**BR** maroon - *59?-62*	NPG	NPG

C15. Parcels Train Brake Van 57'

-	**GWR** 151, 6295 dark brown+cream - *50?-62*	300	350
-	**BR** maroon - *59?-62*	NPG	NPG

C16. Non-Gangwayed Full Brake 50'

-	**GWR** 200, 202 dark brown+cream - *50?-62*	250	325
-	**LMS** maroon - *50?-62*	250	300
-	**LNER** 303, 101 brown - *53?-62*	250	350
-	**SR** 113, 441 green - *53?-62*	350	650
-	**BR** crimson+cream - *58?-59?*	350	400
-	**BR** maroon - *59?-62*	NPG	NPG

C17. Parcels Train Non-Gangwayed 50'

-	**GWR** 6196 dark brown+cream - *57?-62*	300	350
-	**LMS** 31322 maroon - *50?-62*	250	300
-	**LNER** brown - *59?-62*	250	350
-	**SR** green - *50?-62*	350	650

C18. Corridor Full Brake 57'

-	**GWR** 202, 224,1120, 16 dark brown+cream - *50?-62*	325	350
-	**BR** maroon - *59?-62*	NPG	NPG

C19. Corridor Full Brake 50'

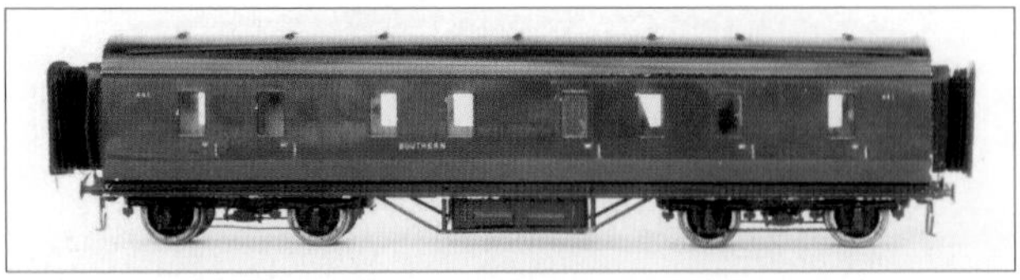

SR full brake No.441 [C19]

-	**LMS** 25, 31181, 31187, 31321 maroon - *50?-62*	200	250
-	**LNER** brown - *53?-62*	300	250
-	**SR** 441 green - *50?-62*	350	650
-	**BR** red+cream - *58?*	375	450
-	**BR** maroon - *59?-62*	NPG	NPG

C20. Side Corridor 3rd Brake End 57'

-	**GWR** 1900, 2220, 2720, 5518?, 7207, 10707 dark brown+cream - *50?-62*	200	250
-	**LMS** 888, 2288, 3000, 6266, 6464, 6656, 6661, 6668, 6888, 8723, 67777 maroon - *50?-62*	200	250
-	**LNER** 1553 brown - *53?-62*	350	300
-	**SR** 4447 green - *50?-62*	375	650
-	**BR** S4410 red+cream - *57?-58?*	425	500

BR side corridor brake 3rd [C20]

-	**BR** maroon - *59?-62*	350	400

C21. Side Corridor 1st Brake

-	**LMS** 888, 1221 maroon - *?*	250	300

C22. Side Corridor Full 3rd 57'

-	**GWR** 212, 2220, 3000, 5120, 6444, 6604, 6626, 8027, 8083, 8107, 9132, 9991 dark brown+cream - *50?-62*	200	250
-	**LMS** 1592, 2001,121, 2222, 2288, 2344, 2555, 3546, 4563, 6345, 7001, maroon - *50?-62*	200	250
-	**LNER** 8000, 8107, 8882 brown - *53?-62*	350	400
-	**SR** 5480?, 6055?, 8000, 8400, 8673, 8881, 8883, 8888 green - *50?-62*	200	250
-	**BR** M2210, M2211M, M2221 red+cream - *57?-58?*	425	500
-	**BR** maroon - *59?-62*	350	400

C23. Side Corridor Full 1st 57'

-	**GWR** 720, 1071, 4200 dark brown+cream - *50?-62*	250	300

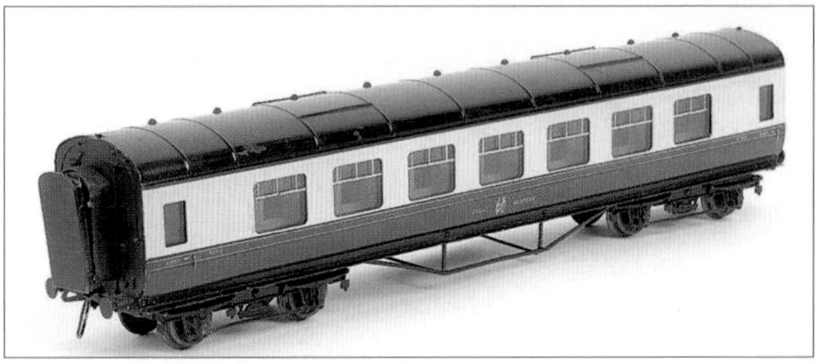

GWR all-1st side corridor coach [C23] (Vectis)

-	**LMS** 6727, 8001, 8035, 8037, 8333, 8777 maroon - *50?-62*	200	250
-	**LNER** 8004, 8001 brown - *53?-62*	350	380
-	**SR** 8103, 8531, 8771 green - *50?-62*	375	650
-	**BR** red+cream - *57?-58?*	475	550
-	**BR** maroon - 59?-62	350	400

C24. Side Corridor 1st/3rd Composite 57'

-	**GWR** 2255, 4722, 8892, 8989, 9555 dark brown +cream - *50?-62*	200	250
-	**LMS** 1111?, 1119, 3032, 3113, 3232, 4044, 4224, 4440, 10774, 22707 maroon - *50?-62*	200	250
-	**LNER** 7207 brown - *?*	250	350
-	**BR** M3322W red+cream - *59?-62*	250	350

C25. Corridor Brake Composite 1st/3rd

-	**LMS** 3760 maroon - *?*	200	250

C26. Centre Corridor 3rd Brake End 57'

-	**LMS** 9955, 26141 maroon - *50?-62*	200	250
-	**LNER** green+cream *-53?-62*	475	550
-	**SR** green - *50?-62*	700	650
-	**BR** M11721M red+cream *-58?*	525	600
-	**BR** maroon - *59?-62*	350	400

C27. Centre Corridor 1st Brake End 57'

-	**LMS** 3032, 8811 maroon - *50?-62*	200	250

C28.	**Centre Corridor Full 3rd 57'**		
-	**GWR** 2033?, 6000 dark brown+cream - *50?-62*	300	380
-	**LMS** 1114?, 4424, 6616, 6667, 6777, 9000, 9200 maroon - *50?-62*	200	250
-	**LNER** 45001 green+cream - *53?-62*	475	550
-	**SR** 6611 green - *50?-62*	400	680
-	**BR** red+cream - *58?*	525	600
-	**BR** maroon - *59?-62*	350	400
C29.	**Centre Corridor Full 1st 57'**		
-	**LMS** 7778maroon - *50?-62*	200	250
-	**BR** maroon - *59?-62*	NPG	NPG
C30.	**Sleeping Car 1st/3rd 57'**		
-	**LMS** 250? maroon 57' -*50?-62*	250	350
-	**BR** M660 red+cream - *59?-62*	375	450
C31.	**Sleeping Car 1st/3rd 69'**		

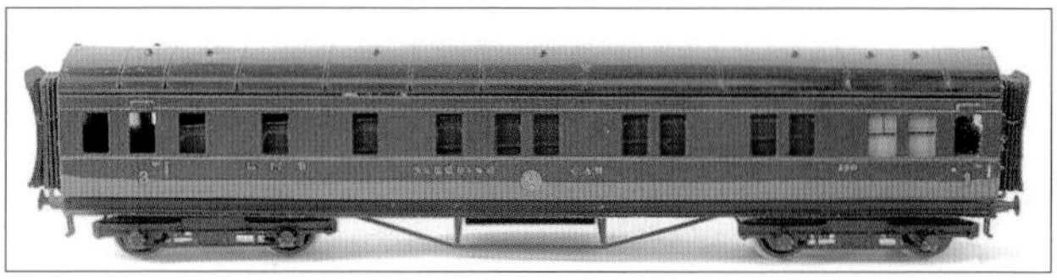

LMS 1st/3rd sleeping car [C31] (Vectis)

-	**LMS** 2?0, 737, 744, 3425 maroon 69' - *60?-62*	200	250
C32.	**Sleeping Car Full 1st**		
-	**GWR** 6560? dark brown+cream - *50?-62*	375	620
-	**LNER** 6461 brown - *57?-62*	350	430
-	**LNER** 6463 brown - *57?-62*	300	350
-	**BR** maroon - *59?-62*	NPG	NPG
C33.	**Sleeping Car Full 3rd**		
-	**GWR** 9040 dark brown+cream - *50?-62*	375	450
-	**LNER** brown - *57?-62*	350	425
-	**BR** maroon - *59?-62*	NPG	NPG
C34.	**LMS Engineer's Inspection Saloon 50'**		
-	**LMS** maroon - *57?-62*	400	450
-	**BR** maroon - *59?-62*	NPG	NPG

Other coaches in pre-grouping and private liveries were available to order.

K5 Series Coaches

C35.	**LMS Side Corridor Composite**		
-	**BR** M3030M, M3040M, M3044M red+cream - *?*	500	650
C36.	**LMS Side Corridor All-3rd**		
-	**BR** M3040M red+cream - *?*	400	500
C37.	**LMS Side Corridor Brake 3rd**		
-	**BR** M6432M red+cream - *?*	450	600
C38.	**LMS Side Corridor Brake Composite**		
-	**BR** M3344M red+cream - ?	400	600

Hornby T9 model on the Waterloo-Guilford line in 1938 - from computer artwork by Robbie McGavin

Exley 00

HISTORY

For a history of Edward Exley Ltd, see the Exley 0 gauge chapter.

In the later 1930s (1938 is assumed for our purpose), partly as a result of Vivien Boyd-Carpenter having joined the company, high quality 00 coaching stock was added to feed a growing market in this new scale.

It is assumed that the post-war Standard coaches were a revival of the pre-war range. All changed in December 1956 when Exley brought out their cheaper Zenith and Popular ranges. Major wholesalers such as W&H promptly dropped the Standard models and, by the end of 1957, were offering only the Zenith range. 00 coach production continued until the Exley works was burnt down in 1962.

LOCOMOTIVES

While we always think of coaches when the name Exley is mentioned, they also marketed a few locomotives as well. In many cases the majority of pre-war 00 gauge locomotives were made for Exley by Holtzappfel and later by Cimco. These included a 'Duchess' and a' Royal Scot'. Little is known about these but those that are, are listed here.

Cat No.	Company, Number, Colour, Dates	£	£

GWR 4-4-0 County of Devon [L1]

L1.	**Steam Locomotives** (by Cimco)		
-	**3835 *County of Devon*** GWR 4-4-0 'County' Class green - *51*	60	80
-	**1127** LNER 2-6-0 black - *52*	60	80
-	**4016 *Knight of the Golden Fleece*** GWR 4-6-0 'Star' Class green - *51*	60	80
-	**6100 *Royal Scot*** LMS 4-6-0 maroon - *37?*	60	80
-	**6230 *Duchess of Buccleuch*** LMS 4-6-2 maroon - *37*	60	80
L2.	**DMUs**		
-	**M58642+M59286+M58242** BR green Leyland 3-car DMU - *59*	120	150

L3. EMUs

2-car sets consisting of a centre-corridor 3rd class motor car and trailer car - both 57' vehicles. The powered car was fitted with a Romford flywheel motor bogie 12v DC and available in 2-rail, outer third rail and inner third rail versions.

LMS EMU [L3]

-	? (?+?) SR green main line set- *38*	100	120
-	**3083** (11128+11113) SR green main line set - *55*	100	120
-	? (11150+?) LMS maroon main line set- *56*	100	120
-	**2614?** (5374+?) Great()Western brown+ cream main line set - *56*	100	120
-	? (?+?) SR green suburban set - *38*	100	120

COACHES

These had correct ventilators on the roof and doors, correct type bogies, roof gutters, accumulator boxes, tie rods, window rails, rain strips, compartment partitions and seats, a new type of corridor connection, glass in the windows, oval non-locking buffers and gold lacquered door and commode handles. They had brass wheels on steel axles and every coach was differently numbered and was appropriately lined and lettered.

Production ceased during the war and it seems that the LMS and SR ranges were the first to reappear in 1947. These were followed by the GWR range and then LNER in 1951

They also underwent structural changes and cheaper 'Zephyr' and 'Popular' ranges were available from December 1956 (see below), which gradually replaced the Standard coaches in the late 1950s.

From the early 1950s, coaches could be supplied to special order in MR, LNWR, SE&CR, LB&SCR, L&SWR, CR, NBR, HR, G&SWR and LMSR (NCC) livery.

Cat No.	Company, Number, Colour, Dates	£	£

Pre-Grouping Coaches

C1. LNWR 57' Stock

These were also available in LMS livery on request. This stock had elliptical roofs.

-	side corridor full 3rd brown+white - *59*	35	60
-	side corridor full 1st brown+white - *59*	35	60
-	side corridor 3rd brake brown+white - *59*	35	60
-	sleeping car brown+white - *62*	NPG	NPG
-	dining car brown+white - *62*	NPG	NPG
C2.	**MR 34' Bain 4-wheel Clerestory Stock**		
-	non-corridor full 3rd maroon - *60*	30	50
-	non-corridor full 1st maroon - *60*	30	50
-	non-corridor 3rd brake maroon - *60*	30	50
-	full brake maroon - *60*	30	50

MR 3rd class clerestory coach (Vectis)

C3.	**MR 54' Bain Clerestory Suburban Stock**		
-	non-corridor full 3rd maroon - *59*	30	50
-	non-corridor full 1st maroon - *59*	30	50
-	non-corridor 3rd brake maroon - *59*	30	50
C4.	**MR 54' Clerestory Corridor Stock**		
-	MR full brake maroon - *60*	30	50
-	LMS full brake maroon - *60*	30	50

C5. MR 54' Reid Suburban Stock

This stock had elliptical roofs.

-	non-corridor full 3rd maroon - *59*	30	50
-	non-corridor full 1st maroon - *59*	30	50
-	non-corridor 3rd brake maroon - *59*	30	50
C6.	**MR 57' Clerestory Stock**		
-	side corridor full 3rd maroon - *59*	30	50
-	side corridor full 1st maroon - *59*	30	50
-	side corridor 3rd brake maroon - *59*	30	50

C7. MR 65' Clerestory Stock

These were fitted with 6-wheel bogies.

-	**MR** dining carriage maroon - *59*	30	50
	LMS dining carriage maroon - *59*	30	50

Pre-war Coaches

C8. Pullmans

It would seem that the Pullman cars did not return after the war.

-	Ist class brown+cream - *38*	30	50
-	3rd class brown+cream - *38*	30	50
-	brake 3rd brown+cream - *38*	30	50

C9. GWR 50' Suburban Stock

Brown+Cream

-	suburban non-corridor - *38*	22	35
-	suburban non-corridor brake end - *38*	22	35
-	suburban brake - *38*	22	35

C10. GWR 57' Stock

Brown+Cream

-	'Ocean Mails' - *38*	25	40
-	side corridor bow end - *38*	20	30

GWR suburban coaches (Vectis)

-	side corridor brake bow end - *38*	20	30
-	side corridor straight end - *38*	20	30
-	side corridor brake straight end - *38*	20	30
-	corridor full brake bow ended - *38*	20	30
-	restaurant car - *38*	22	35
-	sleeping car 3rd 8-wheel - *38*	22	35
-	sleeping car 1st 12-wheel - *38*	25	40
-	buffet car - *38*	25	40

C11. GWR 60' Stock

-	sleeping car 1st brown+cream - *38*	30	50

C12. GWR 65' Stock

-	*Queen Mary* Pullman car brown+cream - *38*	30	50

C13. GWR 70' Stock

-	side corridor brown+cream - *38*	25	40
-	side corridor brake end brown+cream - *38*	25	40

C14. LMS 42' Stock

-	motor car van maroon - *38*	20	30

C15. LMS 50' Stock

Maroon

-	50 non-gangwayed full brake - *38*	22	35
-	kitchen car - *38*	25	40
-	non-corridor compartment coach - *38*	20	30
-	non-corridor compartment brake end - *38*	20	30
-	luggage van - *38*	22	35

C16. LMS 54' Stock

LMS inspectors saloon (Vectis)

-	side corridor maroon - *38*	20	30
-	Side corridor brake end maroon - *38*	20	30
-	Dynamometer car maroon - *38*	25	40

C17. LMS 60' Stock

Maroon

-	centre vestibule low waisted - *38*	20	30
-	centre vestibule low waisted brake end - *38*	20	30
-	centre corridor - *38*	20	30
-	dining car low waisted 8-wheel - *38*	22	35
-	dining car low waisted 12-wheel - *38*	25	40
-	side corridor low waisted - *38*	20	30
-	side corridor low waisted brake end - *38*	20	30
-	mail stowage van - *38*	25	40
-	sleeping car 1st 12-wheel - *38*	25	40
-	sleeping car 3rd 8-wheel - *38*	22	35

C18. LMS Coronation Stock

-	60' side corridor - *38*	35	60
-	60' side corridor brake end - *38*	35	60
-	60' centre vestibule - *38*	35	60
-	65' centre vestibule - *38*	35	60
-	50' kitchen car - *38*	35	60

C19. LMS Articulated Stock

-	twin excursion set maroon - *38*	65	100

C20. LNER 50' Suburban Teak Stock

-	suburban non-corridor - *38*	22	35
-	suburban non-corridor brake end - *38*	22	35

C21. LNER 54' Stock

-	side corridor bow end drop roof teak - *38*	22	35
-	side corridor bow end drop roof brake end teak - *38*	22	35
-	luggage van and brake teak - *38*	22	35
-	buffet car cream+green - 38	25	40

C22. LNER 60' Teak Stock

-	side corridor bow end - *38*	22	35
-	side corridor brake bow end - *38*	22	35
-	restaurant car - *38*	22	35
-	sleeping car - *38*	25	40

C23. LNER Silver Link Stock

-	coach silver - *38*	40	65
-	brake end silver - *38*	40	65

C24. LNER Articulated Stock

East Coast 1st/3rd composite (Vectis)

-	triple buffet green+cream - *38*	80	130
-	twin extention set green+cream - *38*	70	110

C25. SR 50' Stock

-	suburban non-corridor green - *38*	28	45
-	suburban non-corridor brake end green - *38*	28	45
-	luggage van green - *38*	28	45

C26. SR 54' Stock

-	side corridor green - *38*	28	45
-	1616 side corridor brake end green - *38*	28	45

C27. SR 57' Stock

-	1258? buffet car green - *38*	28	45

C28. SR 60' Stock

-	side corridor high window green - *38*	28	45
-	side corridor high window brake green - *38*	28	45
-	dining car 8-wheel green - *38*	28	45
-	dining car 12-wheel green - *38*	30	50

Post-War Standard Coaches

After the Second World War the coaches were sold without bogies and wheels, which you bought separately and fixed to the wooden floor of the coach. Single link couplings were normal but Exley would fit other types if you preferred. All had interior fittings except for the sleeping cars, full brakes, parcels vans, TPOs and GWR Ocean Mails. Seats were now metal and coloured blue for 1st class and maroon for 3rd class. The 60' coaches had disappeared by 1957.

C29. 32' 4-wheel Van

Wheels ready fitted.

-	**GWR** brown+cream - *53*	30	45
-	**LMS** maroon - *53*	30	45
-	**LNER** teak - *53*	30	45
-	**SR** green - *53*	30	45

C30. 32' 4-wheel Suburban Stock

Wheels ready fitted.

-	**GWR** brake 3rd brown+cream - *53*	30	45
-	**LMS** brake 3rd maroon - *53*	30	45
-	**LNER** brake 3rd teak - *53*	30	45
-	**SR** brake 3rd green - *53*	30	45
-	**GWR** composite brown+cream - *53*	30	45
-	**LMS** composite maroon - *53*	30	45
-	**LNER** composite teak - *53*	30	45
-	**SR** composite green - *53*	30	45
-	**GWR** full 3rd brown+cream - *53*	30	45
-	**LMS** full 3rd maroon - *53*	30	45
-	**LNER** full 3rd teak - *53*	30	45
-	**SR** full 3rd green - *53*	30	45

C31. 34' 6-wheel Corridor Full Brake

Wheels ready fitted.

-	**GWR** brown+cream - *53*	30	45

LMS 6-wheeled composite coach (Alan Farrow)

-	**LMS** maroon - *53*	30	45
-	**LNER** teak - *53*	30	45
-	**SR** green - *53*	30	45

C32. 34' 6-wheel Suburban Stock

Wheels ready fitted.

-	**GWR** brake 3rd brown+cream - *53*	30	45
-	**LMS** brake 3rd maroon - *53*	30	45
-	**LNER** brake 3rd teak - *53*	30	45
-	**SR** brake 3rd green - *53*	30	45
-	**GWR** composite brown+cream - *53*	30	45
-	**LMS** composite maroon - *53*	30	45
-	**LNER** composite teak - *53*	30	45
-	**SR** composite green - *53*	30	45
-	**GWR** full 3rd brown+cream - *53*	30	45
-	**LMS** full 3rd maroon - *53*	30	45
-	**LNER** full 3rd teak - *53*	30	45
-	**SR** full 3rd green - *53*	30	45

C33. GWR 50' Suburban Stock

-	composite brown+cream - *49*	22	35
-	full 3rd brown+cream - *49*	22	35
-	brake 3rd brown+cream - *49*	22	35
-	full brake brown+cream - *49*	25	40
-	parcel van brown+cream - *49*	25	40

C34. GWR 57' Main Line Stock

-	'Ocean Mails' brown+cream - *50*	25	40
-	parcels train brake van brown+cream - *50*	25	40
-	corridor full brake brown+cream - *49*	20	30
-	side corridor brake 3rd brown+cream - *49*	20	30
-	side corridor full 3rd brown+cream - *49*	20	30
-	side corridor composite brown+cream - *49*	20	30
-	side corridor full 1st brown+cream - *50*	20	30
-	sleeping car 3rd brown+cream - *51*	22	35
-	sleeping car 1st brown+cream - *51*	22	35

C35. GWR Special Vehicles

-	centre corridor full 3rd brown+cream - *51*	20	30
-	restaurant 1st/3rd kitchen brown+cream - *51*	22	35
-	traveling post office 57' brown+cream - *53*	25	40

C36. LMS Suburban 50' Stock

-	composite maroon - *47*	20	30
-	full 3rd maroon - *47*	20	30
-	full 1st maroon - *47*	20	30

BR maroon brake 2nd & LMS brake 3rd (Vectis)

-	brake 3rd maroon - *47*	20	30
-	brake 1st maroon - *47*	20	30
-	brake composite maroon - *47*	20	30
-	full brake maroon - *47*	22	35
-	parcel van maroon - *49*	22	35

C37. LMS Main Line Stock

-	corridor full brake maroon 50' - *47*	20	30
-	side corridor brake 3rd 57' maroon - *47*	20	30
-	side corridor brake 1st 57' maroon - *47*	20	30
-	side corridor full 3rd 57' maroon - *47*	20	30
-	side corridor full 1st 57' maroon - *47*	20	30
-	side corridor brake 1st/3rd 57' maroon - *47*	20	30
-	kitchen car 50' maroon - *51*	22	35
-	composite sleeping car 57' maroon - *51*	22	35

C38. LMS Special Vehicles

-	centre corridor brake 3rd maroon - *50*	20	30
-	centre corridor full 3rd maroon - *50*	20	30
-	centre corridor full 1st maroon - *50*	20	30
-	restaurant kitchen 1st 57' maroon * - *57*	25	40
-	dining car/kitchen 1st maroon - *50*	22	35
-	dining /kitchen 3rd maroon - *50*	22	35
-	buffet car *57' maroon* - *53*	22	35
-	traveling post office 57' maroon - *51*	25	40
-	Engineers' inspection saloon maroon - *57*	30	50

* This car should have 6-wheeled bogies but may be fitted with 4-wheel ones.

C39. LNER Suburban 50' Stock

-	full 3rd teak - *51*	20	30
-	composite teak - *51*	20	30
-	brake 3rd teak - *51*	20	30
-	full brake teak - *51*	22	35
-	parcel van teak - *51*	22	35

C40. LNER Main Line Stock

-	corridor full brake 50' teak - *53*	20	30
-	side corridor brake 3rd 57' teak - *53*	20	30
-	side corridor full 3rd 57' teak - *53*	20	30

-	side corridor full 1st 57' teak - *53*	20	30
-	sleeping car 3rd 57' teak - *53*	22	35
-	sleeping car 1st 57' teak - *53*	22	35

C41. LNER Special Vehicles

-	buffet car 57' green+cream - *53*	22	35
-	centre corridor full 3rd green+cream - *54*	20	30
-	centre corridor brake 3rd green+cream - *54*	20	30
-	traveling post office 57' teak - *54*	25	40

C42. SR Suburban 50' Stock

-	full 3rd green - *47*	25	40
-	full 1st green - *47*	25	40
-	composite green - *47*	25	40

Highland Railway coaches (Vectis)

-	brake 3rd green - *47*	25	40
-	full brake green - *47*	25	40
-	parcel van green - *47*	25	40

C43. SR Main Line Stock

-	corridor full brake 50' green - *47*	25	40
-	side corridor full 3rd 57' green - *47*	25	40
-	side corridor composite 57' green - *47*	25	40
-	side corridor full 1st 57' green - *53*	25	40
-	side corridor brake 3rd 57' green - *47*	25	40

C44. SR 57' Special Vehicles

-	centre corridor full 3rd green - *51*	25	40
-	centre corridor full 1st green - *53*	25	40
-	centre corridor brake 3rd green - *53*	25	40
-	dining car/kitchen 1st green - *51*	28	45
-	buffet car green - *53*	28	45
-	restaurant kitchen 1st maroon * - *57*	30	50

* This car should have 6-wheeled bogies but may be fitted with 4-wheel ones.

C45. BR 57' Stock

-	side corridor brake 3rd crimson+cream - *?*	30	50
-	side corridor full 3rd crimson+cream - *?*	30	50
-	side corridor full 1st crimson+cream- *?*	30	50

'Zephyr' (Type A) Coaches

These were available from December 1956. The mainline stock was 57' long and suburban stock was 50' in length. Unlike the Standard range of coaches, these were all sold complete with 2-rail bogies and wheels or as complete, ready-painted, kits. They had single link couplings but would take a Peco coupling and they were fitted with full interiors. The coaches could be supplied fully lit.

C46. GWR 34' 6-wheel Stock

-	suburban brake 3rd brown+cream - *60*	25	35
-	suburban full 3rd brown+cream - *60*	25	35
-	suburban full 1st brown+cream - *60*	25	35

C47. GWR 34' 6-wheel Clerestory Stock

-	suburban brake 3rd brown+cream - *60*	25	35
-	suburban full 3rd brown+cream - *60*	25	35
-	suburban full 1st brown+cream - *60*	25	35
-	corridor full brake brown+cream - *60*	25	35

C48. GWR 50' Stock

-	suburban brake 3rd brown+cream - *56*	20	30
-	suburban full 3rd brown+cream - *56*	20	30
-	suburban full 1st brown+cream - *56*	20	30
-	non-gangwayed full brake brown+cream - *60*	20	30
-	non-gangwayed parcels van brn+cream - *60*	20	30

GWR all-1st side corridor coach (Vectis)

C49. GWR 54' Suburban Stock

Wagon roofs.

-	suburban brake 3rd brown+cream - *61*	20	30
-	suburban full 3rd brown+cream - *61*	20	30
-	suburban full 1st brown+cream - *61*	20	30

C50. GWR 57' Stock

-	corridor full brake brown+cream - *56*	18	28
-	non-gangwayed full brake brown+cream - *56*	20	30
-	side corridor brake 3rd brown+cream - *56*	18	28
-	side corridor full 3rd brown+cream - *56*	18	28
-	side corridor full 1st brown+cream - *56*	18	28
-	centre corridor brake 3rd brown+cream - *56*	18	28
-	centre corridor full 3rd brown+cream - *56*	18	28
-	centre corridor full 1st brown+cream - *56*	18	28
-	composite sleeping car brown+cream - *56*	20	30
-	restaurant kitchen 1st/3rd brn+cream - *56*	20	30
-	Ocean Mails van brown+cream - *60*	22	35
-	traveling post office brown+cream - *60*	25	40

C51. LMS 34' 6-wheel Stock

-	suburban brake 3rd maroon - *60*	25	35
-	suburban full 3rd maroon - *60*	25	35
-	suburban full 1st maroon - *60*	25	35

C52. LMS 34' Clerestory Stock

-	suburban brake 3rd maroon - *60*	25	35
-	suburban full 3rd maroon - *60*	25	35
-	suburban full 1st maroon - *60*	25	35
-	corridor full brake maroon - *60*	25	35

C53. LMS 50' Stock

-	kitchen car maroon - *56*	20	30
-	suburban brake 3rd maroon - *56*	20	30
-	suburban full 3rd maroon - *56*	20	30
-	suburban full 1st maroon - *56*	20	30
-	corridor full brake maroon - *56*	20	30
-	non-gangwayed full brake maroon - *60*	20	30
-	Engineers' inspection saloon maroon - *60*	25	40
-	non-gangwayed parcels van maroon - *60*	22	35

C54. LMS 54' Suburban Stock

Wagon roofs.

-	suburban brake 3rd maroon - *61*	20	30
-	suburban full 3rd maroon - *61*	20	30
-	suburban full 1st maroon - *61*	20	30

C55. LMS 57' Stock

Highland Railway coaches (Vectis)

-	non-gangwayed full brake maroon - *56*	18	28
-	side corridor brake 3rd maroon - *56*	18	28
-	side corridor full 3rd maroon - *56*	18	28
-	side corridor full 1st maroon - *56*	18	28

-	centre corridor brake 3rd maroon - *56*	18	28
-	centre corridor full 3rd maroon - *56*	18	28
-	centre corridor full 1st maroon - *56*	18	28
-	composite sleeping car maroon - *56*	20	30
-	restaurant kitchen 1st maroon - *56*	20	30
-	buffet car maroon - *56*	20	30
-	traveling post office maroon - *60*	22	35

C56. LMS 68/69' Stock

-	12-wheel restaurant car maroon - *60*	25	40
-	12-wheel sleeping car maroon - *60*	25	40

C57. LNER 50' Stock

-	suburban brake 3rd teak - *56*	20	30
-	suburban full 3rd teak - *56*	20	30
-	suburban full 1st teak - *56*	20	30
-	corridor full brake teak - *56*	20	30
-	non-gangwayed full brake teak - *60*	20	30
-	non-gangwayed parcels van teak - *60*	20	30

C58. LNER 57' Stock

-	non-gangwayed full brake teak - *56*	18	28
-	side corridor brake 3rd teak - *56*	18	28
-	side corridor full 3rd teak - *56*	18	28
-	side corridor full 1st teak - *56*	18	28
-	centre corridor brake 3rd teak - *56*	18	28
-	centre corridor full 3rd teak - *56*	18	28
-	centre corridor full 1st teak - *56*	18	28
-	composite sleeping car teak - *56*	20	30
-	restaurant kitchen 1st teak - *56*	20	30
-	buffet car teak - *56*	20	30
-	traveling post office teak - *60*	22	35

C59. SR 34' 6-wheel Stock

-	suburban brake 3rd green - *60*	28	40
-	suburban full 3rd green - *60*	28	40
-	suburban full 1st green - *60*	28	40

C60. SR 50' Stock

-	suburban brake 3rd green - *56*	22	35
-	suburban full 3rd green - *56*	22	35

LNWR 3rd class coach (Vectis)

-	suburban full 1st green - *56*	22	35
-	corridor full brake green - *56*	22	35
-	non-gangwayed full brake green - *60*	22	35
-	non-gangwayed parcels van green - *60*	22	35

C61. SR 54' Suburban Stock

Wagon roofs.

-	suburban brake 3rd green - *61*	22	35
-	suburban full 3rd green - *61*	22	35
-	suburban full 1st green - *61*	22	35

C62. SR 57' Stock

-	non-gangwayed full brake green - *56*	20	30
-	side corridor brake 3rd green - *56*	20	30
-	side corridor full 3rd green - *56*	20	30
-	side corridor full 1st green - *56*	20	30
-	centre corridor brake 3rd green - *56*	20	30
-	centre corridor full 3rd green - *56*	20	30
-	centre corridor full 1st green - *56*	20	30
-	restaurant kitchen 1st green - *56*	22	35

C63. BR 50' Stock

-	kitchen car - *56*	22	35
-	suburban brake 3rd - *56*	22	35
-	suburban full 3rd - *56*	22	35
-	suburban full 1st - *56*	22	35
-	corridor full brake green - *60*	22	35
-	non-gangwayed full brake - *60*	22	35
-	non-gangwayed parcels van - *60*	22	35

C64. BR 57' Stock

-	corridor full brake - *56*	22	35
-	non-gangwayed full brake - *56*	22	35
-	side corridor brake 3rd - *56*	22	35
-	side corridor full 3rd - *56*	22	35
-	side corridor full 1st - *56*	22	35
-	centre corridor brake 3rd - *56*	22	35
-	centre corridor full 3rd - *56*	22	35
-	centre corridor full 1st - *56*	22	35
-	composite sleeping car - *56*	25	40
-	restaurant kitchen 1st - *56*	25	40
-	buffet car - *56*	25	40

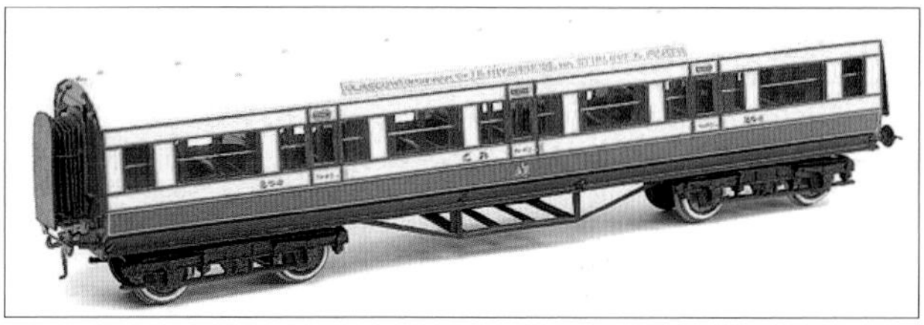

Caledonian Railway 3rd class coach (Vectis)

-	Ocean Mails van - *60*	28	45
-	traveling post office - *60*	28	45
-	Engineers' inspection saloon - *60*	30	50

C65. BR 68/69' Stock

-	12-wheel restaurant car maroon - *60*	28	45
-	12-wheel sleeping car maroon - *60*	28	45

'Popular' (Type B) Coaches

The 'Popular' (also called 'B Type') range was 50' for all stock and was also available from December 1956. These were also sold complete with 2-rail bogies and wheels or as complete, ready-painted, kits. They also had single link couplings and would take a Peco coupling. They were fitted with full interiors. This was obviously and attempt to break into the Hornby Dublo and Tri-ang market with coaches that were fine on tight curves and were not too expensive.

C66. GWR 50' Stock

-	corridor full brake brown+cream - *56*	20	30
-	non-gangwayed full brake brown+cream - *56*	20	30
-	side corridor brake 3rd brown+cream - *56*	20	30
-	side corridor full 3rd brown+cream - *56*	20	30
-	side corridor full 1st brown+cream - *56*	20	30
-	centre corridor brake 3rd brown+cream - *56*	20	30
-	centre corridor full 3rd brown+cream - *56*	20	30
-	centre corridor full 1st brown+cream - *56*	20	30
-	composite sleeping car brown+cream - *56*	22	35
-	restaurant car brown+cream - *56*	22	35
-	suburban brake 3rd brown+cream - *56*	22	35
-	suburban full 3rd brown+cream - *56*	22	35
-	suburban full 1st brown+cream - *56*	22	35

C67. LMS 50' Stock

-	corridor full brake maroon - *56*	20	30
-	non-gangwayed full brake maroon - *56*	20	30
-	side corridor brake 3rd maroon - *56*	20	30
-	side corridor full 3rd maroon - *56*	20	30
-	side corridor full 1st maroon - *56*	20	30
-	centre corridor brake 3rd maroon - *56*	20	30
-	centre corridor full 3rd maroon - *56*	20	30
-	centre corridor full 1st maroon - *56*	20	30

-	composite sleeping car maroon - *56*	22	35
-	restaurant car maroon - *56*	22	35
-	buffet car maroon - *56*	22	35
-	kitchen car maroon - *56*	22	35
-	suburban brake 3rd maroon - *56*	22	35
-	suburban full 3rd maroon - *56*	22	35
-	suburban full 1st maroon - *56*	22	35

C68. LNER 50' Stock

-	corridor full brake teak - *56*	20	30
-	non-gangwayed full brake teak - *56*	20	30
-	side corridor brake 3rd teak - *56*	20	30
-	side corridor full 3rd teak - *56*	20	30
-	side corridor full 1st teak - *56*	20	30
-	centre corridor brake 3rd teak - *56*	20	30
-	centre corridor full 3rd teak - *56*	20	30
-	centre corridor full 1st teak - *56*	20	30
-	composite sleeping car teak - *56*	22	35
-	restaurant car teak - *56*	22	35
-	buffet car teak - *56*	22	35
-	suburban brake 3rd teak - *56*	22	35
-	suburban full 3rd teak - *56*	22	35
-	suburban full 1st teak - *56*	22	35

C69. SR 50' Stock

-	corridor full brake green - *56*	22	35
-	non-gangwayed full brake green - *56*	22	35
-	side corridor brake 3rd green - *56*	22	35
-	side corridor full 3rd green - *56*	22	35
-	side corridor full 1st green - *56*	22	35
-	centre corridor brake 3rd green - *56*	22	35
-	centre corridor full 3rd green - *56*	22	35
-	centre corridor full 1st green - *56*	22	35
-	composite sleeping car green - *56*	25	40
-	restaurant car green - *56*	25	40
-	suburban brake 3rd green - *56*	25	40
-	suburban full 3rd green - *56*	25	40
-	suburban full 1st green - *56*	25	40

BR (ER) corridor 3rd (Alan Farrow)

C70. BR 50' Stock

-	corridor full brake - *56*	22	35
-	non-gangwayed full brake - *56*	22	35
-	side corridor brake 3rd - *56*	22	35
-	side corridor full 3rd - *56*	22	35
-	side corridor full 1st - *56*	22	35
-	centre corridor brake 3rd - *56*	22	35
-	centre corridor full 3rd - *56*	22	35
-	centre corridor full 1st - *56*	22	35
-	composite sleeping car - *56*	25	40
-	restaurant car - *56*	25	40
-	buffet car - *56*	25	40
-	kitchen car - *56*	25	40
-	suburban brake 3rd - *56*	25	40
-	suburban full 3rd - *56*	25	40
-	suburban full 1st - *56*	25	40

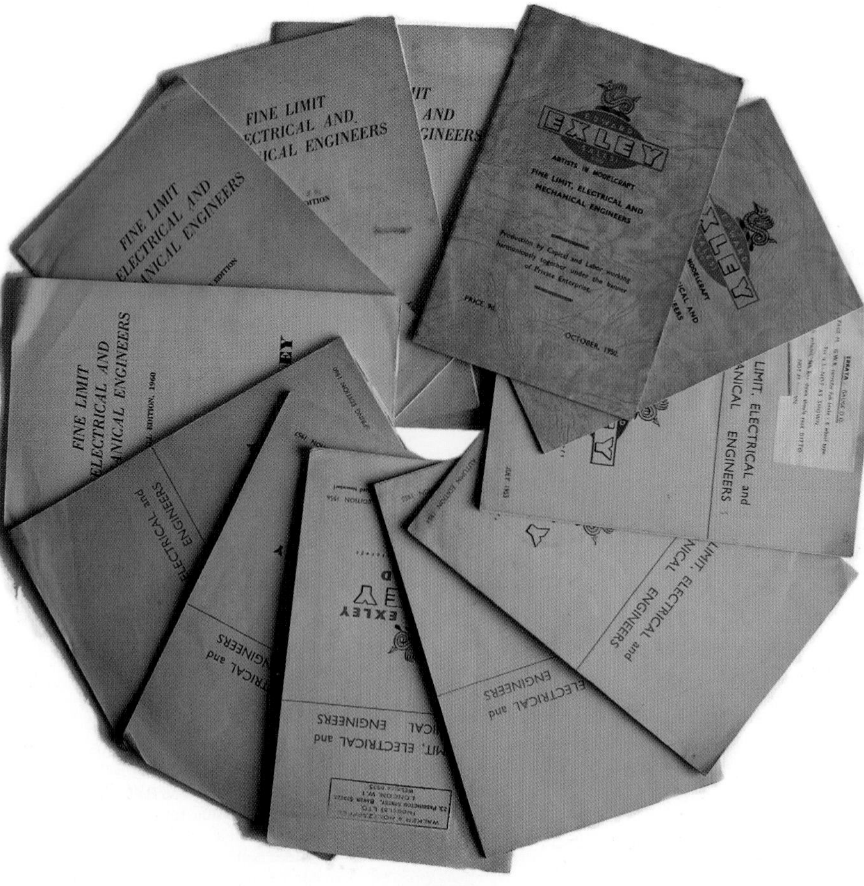

Fleischmann H0 (British)

HISTORY

Fleischmann was founded in 1887 and acquired the German company, Doll, in 1938. They first made trains under the Fleischmann name in 1949, starting with 0 gauge and adding H0 to their range of products in 1952.

Class 42 'Warship' diesel [L1] (Fleischmann)

The German model manufacturer decided to attempt a break into the UK market in 1977 and produced a model of a Warship diesel locomotive and three Bulleid coaches. This was a strange combination but apparently they could have been seen together when they ran the out of Waterloo in the mid 1960s.

Unfortunately, Fleischmann produced their models in H0 scale and not the slightly larger British 00 scale. As a result of this, the models did not sell well in Britain but in both liveries, and with their original catalogue numbers, they have remained in the Fleischmann catalogue and were still being advertised in the 2000/2001 German edition and on the Fleischmann website until recently.

The only evidence we have seen that further batches were made is that there was a second design of mechanism, taken from their V200 and used in the 'Warship' model. This would have required a redesigned chassis and underframe in the 1980s.

The locos and coaches were available separately and were not available in a set.

Class 42 'Warship' diesel [L1] (Fleischmann)

Included in the boxes of both locomotives were three alternative headboards. These were for the 'Torbay Express', 'Cornish Riviera Express' and 'The Mayflower'.

An H0 scale 'West Country' locomotive was also planned in 1977. This was to have been *Blackmore Vale* but, with sales of the 'Warship' being so poor, the project was abandoned. The Bulleid coaches were produced to go with this model had it gone ahead.

LOCOMOTIVES

Cat No.	Company, Number, Colour, Dates	£	£
L1.	**Class 42 'Warship' Diesel-Hydraulic B-B**		
4247	**D818 *Glory*** BRe blue - *77-04*	50	110
4246	**D821 *Greyhound*** BRc green - *77-04*	50	110
L2.	**'West Country' 4-6-2**		
-	***Blackmore Vale*** green - *not made*	NA	NA

Headboards supplied with 'Warship' diesel (Fleischmann)

COACHES

These were based on BR built stock preserved on the Bluebell Railway in Sussex. The models had snap-in corridor end boards and a sheet of rub-down transfers representing 'set' numbers.

Cat No.	Company, Number, Colour, Dates	£	£
C1a.	**Bulleid 1st/3rd Composite**		
5146	**BR** S5751S green - *77-01?*	10	25
C1b.	**Bulleid Corridor 3rd**		
5147	**BR** S130S green - *77-01?*	10	25
C1c.	**Bulleid Open Brake 3rd**		
5148	**BR** S4279 green - *77-01?*	10	25

Bulleid coaches (Fleischmann)

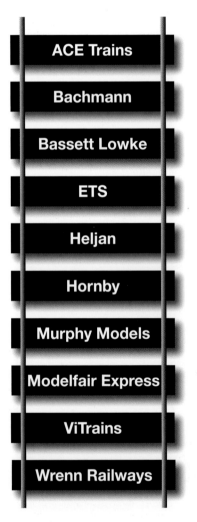

Graham Farish 00

HISTORY

The Company was founded by Thomas Graham Farish in 1919, at the end of the Great War, with a view to cashing in on the new interest in radio. In those days, if you wanted a wireless, you built your own and there was, therefore, a market for radio components. Remember, this was six years before the BBC came into being. Marconi, the radio pioneer, was a personal friend of Graham Farish.

The business was initially in Catford but in 1922 it moved to Masons Hill in Bromley, Kent. At its peak, the company was producing over 35,000 radio components per day. The boom lasted for about fifteen years, before competition from off-the-shelf radio sets took away much of their business. The company gradually turned over to other products, such as electric fires, of which over 8,000,000 were made and it is interesting to note that two of the company's senior managers were Donal Morphy and Charles Richards who later left to form Morphy-Richards. The company developed the first successful submarine aerial and were one of the first to use the early type of plastic known as Bakelite.

'GP5' loco based on an LMS 'Black 5' [L5]

During the Second World War they made hand grenades, shell and land mine casings, electronic equipment and an important sideline was 'Snap Vacuum Closures'. These consisted of a tinned lid, a rubber sealing ring and a reusable clip and they were used for sealing glass jars for storing preserved fruit. These were particularly useful during the war and over 1,000,000,000 were made! Other items manufactured up to 1949 included water pumps for ornamental fountains, underwater lights, lightning conductors for buildings, metal flower baskets and, in 1949, the Plantoid plant food pellets! Much sought after today are 60 or more figures that were made in 1953 to celebrate the Coronation.

With peace had come the need to look for new products for the company's fourteen toolmakers and four hundred production workers, not to mention the diecasting and other machines that had grown in number during the war. The steel and chromium needed for electric fire production were in short supply but alloy for casting and the new plastics were available. Like others, Graham Farish saw the potential of the model railway market and in particular they saw a need for a 2-rail electric system and good quality 2-rail flexible track. Here were products which required the available materials, the design and electrical skills within the company and which were labour intensive - in other words, ideal for Graham Farish to tackle.

In 1948 Graham Farish announced their proposed 'Scale Model Railroads' and demonstrated their new 'Formo' flexible track on a massive layout at the 1948 British Industries Fair at Earls Court. This type of track was a first in the British market and track production became a very big part of the company's output in those early days and right through the 1960s, when 'Formoway' was one of the best on the market. It was said that 60 miles of track was sold by them each year and at one stage the company was manufacturing 13 types of point.

The GP5 train sets of 1949, with their 'Black 5' locomotives, were Britain's first 2-rail ready-to-run 00 model railways. They came in four versions - goods or passenger (with 4-wheel coaches) and with or without track and the set's contents were available separately the following year together with transfers for the rolling stock.

No sooner had the company started train set production, than it was hit by material shortages due to the Korean War. It is also possible that some staff were directed back onto war work. The GWR 'Prairie', when it arrived in March 1952, was initially available only as a kit and a 3-rail version of the kit was also proposed. The body casting for the 'Prairie' was contracted out to Universal Engineering of Nottingham and it is possible that other early work was contracted out.

The GP5 loco was also followed by a Bulleid 'Pacific', a GWR 'King' and a New York 'Hudson' 4-6-4. Early wagons were diecast, the first series of five being released in 1949 but had gone by March 1951. They were replaced by three low-sided or flat wagons in 1952. Perhaps the best remembered item of early rolling stock was the cellulose acetate bodied Pullman car which distorted with age to give it a double bow to the roof. These were particularly attractive models and remained firm favourites over the years. It was claimed that over 100,000 of them were made in the early '50s. There were also bogie suburban coaches and the first Brookdale building kits arrived in 1951 and West's metal figures in 1952.

By the summer of 1953, stocks in shops were not moving and everywhere prices were being slashed. At the factory, production of 2-rail models was halted and, in November, a 3-rail train set with an oval of track was released onto the market. After being the first in the market with a 2-rail system, this move has surprised historians for many years but, with difficulty in selling the 00 system, Graham Farish had turned to what other companies such as Meccano Ltd and Trix were successfully selling - 3-rail! It should be born in mind that Tri-ang Railways, with their successful 2-rail system, had been launched only a year before and it was too early to see the impact of this.

The new 3-rail system was sold under the 'Formo' name, rather than that of Graham Farish, possibly because they were successfully selling their track under that name and hoped that success would rub off. Literature was published carrying the name 'Formo Ltd' but with the Bromley address. The range consisted of a Southern 0-6-0 Q Class loco, some wagons and tinplate track which looked rather like that made at the time by Marklin. The loco and rolling stock were available separately or in a boxed set. The wagons were from the same moulds as the earlier Graham Farish 2-rail vehicles but had diecast non-insulated wheels and the name 'Formo' cast into the underside of the chassis. The 3-rail system did not sell and was quickly dropped but not before there had been some preparations made to release the 'King' and 'Merchant Navy' in 3-rail forms. One could see that the 'Merchant Navy' would have been of interest to Hornby Dublo modellers, had it gone into production.

7-plank wagon 'Joseph Ellis & Sons' [W14]

Possibly the Company had hoped to develop the 2-rail system further but the poor motor design made the stocks they were holding difficult to sell. In 1958 Graham Farish disposed of their remaining complete and unmade stock through one of their subsidiaries, Hutchinson Roe of Bromley, who sold the models and parts cheaply to the public. The 'Formo' set for example was offered at £2.17.6 instead of £5.12.3. They also invited orders for Pullman coaches they could assemble from parts in stock. It seems that S. French & Sons Ltd. of Tolworth had bought a lot of the remaining stock by the following year and offered it to the public. Hutchinson Roe & Co. had the same address (Masons Hill, Bromley) as Graham Farish Ltd. Indeed, the latter had no fewer than ten subsidiaries in 1951 including Formo Products Ltd, Grafar Products Ltd and West & Short Ltd, who made the platform accessories.

After a break of eight years, and having cleared the factory of the old stock, the return to serious 00 modelling for Graham Farish came in 1961 with the release of the 'Prairie' tank with a much improved motor and chassis and a new Pannier tank. The revised range also included the first series of four plastic wagons and the Pullman cars, now in rigid polystyrene. Suburban and mainline coach kits were also available in the 1960s and mail and baggage coaches were also planned. By now the company was selling a much improved quality Formoway track which had a moulded plastic sleeper web and a good range of points.

In 1964, Graham Farish moved to a former armaments factory at Holton Heath in Dorset, not far from Poole. Here a number of factory units were developed. Throughout the 1960s the Company published their handbook which both contained modelling tips and promoted their products. A 21st Anniversary edition of this was published in 1969 to celebrate the 21 years Farish had been involved in the model railway industry. At this time Peter Graham Farish was Sales Director and Dudley Dimmock (who had previously been associated with Bassett-Lowke) was General Manager of the Models Division.

In 1970, Graham Farish launched their N gauge system and a range of nicely printed 00 rolling stock followed in 1973. However, in 1975, it was decided to phase out production of 00 models after Peter Graham Farish had visited the Brighton Toy Fair and learned of the plans by both Airfix and Palitoy to enter the 00 gauge market. It was decided that the 00 market was about to be flooded and that Graham Farish would do better to concentrate all its efforts on N gauge. The last 00 model to be made at Holton Heath was a special edition van in 1980. 00 stock was no longer advertised after 1981.

Tom Graham Farish's son Gordon, who was a naval architect, had established the Romney Boats business in 1959 and this occupied one of the factory units at Holton Heath. When Tom retired in 1973, Gordon disposed of the boat business and joined his brother Peter in running Graham Farish Ltd. Gordon retired first and moved to South Africa and Peter Graham Farish continued with the business on his own. Wishing to retire, himself, in the summer of 2000, Peter sold Graham Farish Ltd to Bachmann Industries Europe Ltd. Today, the Graham Farish name is solely associated with their dominant N gauge system which is described elsewhere in this book.

Twin vent van 'Gibbs SR' [W17]

***'Metal Fatigue'* -** Like some other manufacturers, Graham Farish had problems with diecast components due to impurities in the alloy used. Chassis are especially prone to mazak disintegration which results in the 'growth' of parts. This can result in the distortion of the chassis or body and breakage of small components. The problem cannot be cured but if not evident now may well never occur. It may be restricted to, say, a pony truck which can be replaced. It is advisable to check carefully for any evidence of this problem: our guide values assume that the item is in good sound condition with no trace of 'fatigue'.

Further Reading

To date we are unaware of any books published on the Graham Farish system but there have been a number of magazine articles including a series by Dennis Lovett in *TCS News*.

Dates - we have found little evidence of when models first became available and particularly when they were out of production. Those quoted in the tables below are based on this limited knowledge, coming largely from catalogues and press advertising, and are for guidance only.

Listing - The models are now arranged in the order adopted elsewhere in this book.

Couplings - These were like a cross between the early type IIb Tri-ang couplings and their later tension-lock type which were adopted as the British standard after 1965. Consequently Graham Farish models will couple to most British post 1965 makes.

LOCOMOTIVES

The first locomotive, an LMS 'Black 5', was initially available only in train sets. As a scale model it was not bad for the time, even if mechanically poor and lacking a good finish - not helped by the embossed cabside numbers. It had a diecast body but the tender body was a plastic moulding. It was claimed that it was designed to BRMSB standards and it has been suggested that some components were war surplus.

The tender drive motor unit of this model, as well as in the Bulleid, 'King' and 'Hudson' locomotives, was revolutionary. It consisted of an enclosed permanent magnet rotor with two coils of wire both above and below which, in turn, were connected to two contact blades which oscillated via the rotor shaft between four electrical contacts. These were connected to the two electrical plunger pick ups situated below the tender side frames. Two pieces of steel rod were situated either side of the coils which, in theory, returned the rotor to its starting point. The drive from the tender in later models was via a spring drive and centrifugal clutch to reduction gears and by pinion shaft to the locomotive's driving wheels.

***3-Rail Operation* -** The 3-rail Q Class 0-6-0 had a 5-pole conventional design motor with easily replaceable brushes. It was said at the time to be similar to the Pittman DC.60 motor. It had a 30:1 reduction worm set with a single-start square thread steel worm running in a 15mm diameter brass wheel. The model also had plunger type power collectors.

Evidence that later models of the 'King', Bulleid 'Pacific' and 'Prairie' tank were being prepared for 3-rail operation comes in the form of later models having the gear bracket extended backwards, ending in a vertical cylindrical boss bored to accept a pickup plunger similar to those on tenders. Some tender base plates also carry a marking which would be where the power supply wire would pass. However, there is no evidence of these models actually being sold fitted for 3-rail operation.

***Later Mechanisms* -** The 5-pole motor used in the later 'Prairie' and Pannier tanks was developed in 1957 and was very like the Tri-ang X04 in design. It employed Alcomax magnets, a drum commutator, bronze bearings and carbon brushes. The chassis had plated, see-through, wheels, Tufnol worms for quiet running and phosphor bronze power collectors There was a choice of scale (BRMSB standards) or universal wheels. The bodies were diecast and fitted with nickel handrails, connecting rods and crossheads.

Cat No.	Company, Number, Colour, Dates	£	£

L1. GWR Class 94xx Pannier Tank 0-6-0 (1961)
This was an excellent model with a choice of scale or universal wheels. The early mechanism used for this model had an open frame motor, whereas later models had a modified chassis with a can motor and finer wheels. The subject was also chosen early

on for the N gauge range.

BE1W	**9410** GWR green - *61-79*	25	40
-	GWR green no number - *?*	30	45

Ex-GWR Class 94xx 0-6-0ST [L1]

BE1BR	**9410** BRb black - *75-79*	40	60

L2. GWR Class 81xx 'Prairie' Tank 2-6-2 (1951)

This started life as a kit and was initially a poor performer, possibly because the metal body shell interfered with eddy currents, from the unorthodox motor, restricting the available power. Due to this, few of the early '50s models have survived in working order and on many the cast drive gearbox suffers from metal fatigue. The 1960s model, fitted with a conventional motor, was a good performer and a nice looking model, especially with scale wheels. 1950s models had plunger pickups but the 1960s models had wipers on the wheels.

-	**8103** black kit - *51-53*	NA	60
-	**8103** green kit - *51-53*	NA	60
-	**8103** kit - *51-53*	NA	60
-	**8103** BRb black - *52-53*	40	65
-	**8103** GWR green - *52-53*	30	55
-	**8105** Great Western green new motor and chassis - *61-71*	30	55
-	**8105** BR grn new motor and chassis - *61-71*	30	55

L3. SR Class Q 0-6-0 (1953)

This was the only 3-rail locomotive made by Graham Farish and was strongly built to withstand heavy use and performed well. It had a 5-pole conventional motor and a diecast mazak body for loco and tender. Power collection was with plungers on the centre rail and, in effect, it offered Dublo operators a fourth locomotive to run. The name 'Formo' was cast into the smokebox and the cabsides.

-	**Formo** BRb black - *53*	80	NA
-	**Formo** BRb green - *53*	125	NA
-	**Formo** BRb black rear splashers extended to cab - *53*	100	NA

L4. GWR 'King' Class 4-6-0 (1951)

Mechanically this model was similar to the Bulleid 'Pacific'. The safety valve cover was strange in having only the top half with a copper finish. All models, irrespective of the name they carried, had '6000' cast into the cab sides. Some suffer from 'metal fatigue' to the gearbox casting. 3-rail versions also exist which have a plunger pickup beneath the tender.

-	**6000 *King Charles*** Great () Western green - *51-53*	70	120

GWR King Class No.6000 King John [L4]

-	**6000 *King Charles*** BRb blue - *51-53*	80	140
-	**6000 *King John*** Great () Western green - *51-53*	70	120
-	**6000 *King John*** BRb blue - *51-53*	80	140
-	**6000 *King Henry V*** Great () Western green - *51-53*	70	120
-	**6000 *King Henry* V** BRb blue - *51-53*	80	140
-	**6000 *King George V*** Great () Western green + bell - *51-53*	70	120
-	**6000 *King George V*** BRb blue + bell - *51-53*	80	140
-	**6000 *King George V*** Great () Western green no bell - 51-53	70	120
-	**6000 *King George V*** BRb blue no bell - *51-53*	80	140
-	**6000** BRb green - *?*	NPG	NPG
-	**6000** BRb black - *?*	NPG	NPG
-	**6000** kit - *?*	NPG	NPG

L5. LMS 'GP5' Class 5MT ('Black 5') 4-6-0 (1949)

Known by Graham Farish as the 'GP5', the locomotive was propelled by a tender-mounted motor driven as described above. It had strangely designed central drivers with thicker rims and traction tyres and also had poor representation of valve gear. Power was collected from the track by a single sprung pickup each side. On the numberless first batch, the valve gear top pin was secured in a hole in part of the footplate casting and the cab floor brace plate was initially too thin to carry the chassis and subsequently snapped within a few months. This problem was overcome by strengthening the brace and, at the same time, the cabside number 44753 was cast into the body shell and the valve positioning hole became a slot. The chassis was also modified regarding its fixing to the cab floor and one of the pinions driving the wheels was deleted. The incorrect number '44753' belonged to a member of the class fitted with Caprotti valve gear and yet a more suitable number '44758' was used in illustrations.

-	**44753** BRb black thin cab floor brace plate - *49*	35	60
-	BRb black unpainted numbers - *49-51*	30	50

L6. SR Bulleid 'Pacific' 4-6-2 (1950)

The same model was passed-off as a 'West Country', 'Battle of Britain' and a 'Merchant Navy' Class although in real life the first two should have been smaller. Mechanically, the model was originally similar to the GP5 but a revised version of the model soon followed which was completely different, both mechanically and in its body casting. Some models suffer from 'metal fatigue' to the gearbox casting. You could have any Bulleid 'Pacific' finished as a Golden Arrow locomotive for an extra 5/-. 3-rail versions of the Bulleid 'Pacific' were also made. These had a central plunger pickup on the underside of the tender.

Ex-SR West Country Class No.34101 Exeter [L6] (Vectis)

-	**21C25 *Brocklebank Line*** SR green - *50-53*	90	170
-	**21C103 *Plymouth*** SR green - *50-53*	100	180
-	**21C90 *Sir Eustace Missenden*** SR green - *50-53*	80	170
-	**21C90 *Sir Eustace Missenden*** SR green Golden Arrow** + flags - *50-53*	140	220
-	**34090 *Sir Eustace Missenden*** BRb green 'Golden Arrow' + flags - *50-53*	150	250
-	**34090 *Sir Eustace Missenden*** BRb blue ** 'Golden Arrow' + flags - *50-53*	150	250
-	as above but numbered 34090 with BRb decals	NPG	NPG
-	**35017 *Belgian Marine*** SR green 'Golden Arrow' + flags - *?*	NPG	NPG
-	**35017 *Belgian Marine*** BRb blue - *50-53*	100	200
-	**35027 *Port Line*** BRb blue - *50-53*	100	200
-	**35027 *Port Line*** BRb green 'Golden Arrow' + flags - *50-53*	150	250
-	**34101 *Exeter*** BRb blue * - *50-53*	100	200
-	kit - *?*	NPG	NPG

* None of the 'West Country' Class were painted blue and the number should have been '34001'. This was just one of several numbering errors which included models with SR numbers that were built post Nationalisation. ** It is understood that one of these was presented by Graham Farish to O V Bulleid when he left the Southern/BR.

L7. New York Central 'Hudson' 4-6-4 (H0) (1952)

This model was noted for its scale wheels, Baker's valve gear detail and considerable body detail. Unlike its predecessors, the model had power collection from the tender wheels and axles. It was sold in a wooden box with a sliding lid.

-	**5405** New York Central black - *52-53*	120	200
-	**5405** New York Central black with 5-pole motor - *54*	130	240

COACHES

Coaches came in three phases - 1950s, 1960s and 1970s. In the early 1950s there were heavy plastic bodied 4-wheel and bogie suburbans, Pullman cars and a coach for the New York Central 'Hudson'. The suburban bogie coaches survived as kits into the 1960 phase when main line coach kits arrived and improved versions of the Pullman cars were introduced. The final phase came in the 1970s when the coaches were produced as ready-to-run models in a lighter all-plastic form and with tampo printed liveries.

The coaches in the final stage had plug-fit reversible bogies. One end had a Farish version of the hook and bar coupling while the other end would take a Tri-ang coupling unit and there was a centre hole which would take a Peco or Dublo coupling.

Cat No.	Company, Number, Colour, Dates	£	£

C1. 4-wheel Suburban Stock (1949)

These coaches were 6" long and made for only a few months. They had a bakelite body, tin roof and metal sideframes.

-	**BR** red 1st - *49*	35	45
-	**BR** red 3rd - *49*	35	45
-	**BR** red composite - *49*	35	45
-	**BR** red 3rd luggage - *49*	35	45

C2a. Pullmans (Early) (1950)

After some time, these developed a strange double bow to the roof. This has been caused by the use of cellulose acetate for the plastic mouldings and the vehicle having a solid diecast chassis and floor unit which, due to 'metal fatigue', has grown in length over the years, distorting the plastic roof in the process. The prices below recognise that Pullmans in perfect condition are virtually unheard of and, if found, would sell for quite a bit more. Pullmans made before late 1952 had no printed surround to the name board. The Golden Arrow (GA) versions have 'Golden Arrow' at one end and 'Fleche D'Or' at the other. Early Pullman cars were issued ready named and had the name rubber-stamped on the end of the box. A little later they were issued unnamed but with a sheet of name transfers (as was also the case later when the Pullmans were reissued- table C2b).

-	***Iolanthe*** dark brown+cream - *50-53*	25	40
-	***Lydia*** dark brown+cream - *50-53*	25	40
-	***Minerva*** dark brown+cream - *50-53*	25	40
-	***Pauline*** dark brown+cream - *50-53*	25	40
-	***Phyllis*** dark brown+cream - *50-53*	25	40
-	***Iolanthe*** dark brown+cream GA - *51-53*	30	50
-	***Lydia*** dark brown+cream GA - *51-53*	30	50
-	***Minerva*** dark brown+cream GA - *51-53*	30	50
-	***Pauline*** dark brown+cream GA - *51-53*	30	50
-	***Phyllis*** dark brown+cream GA - *51-53*	30	50
-	**Wagon Lits** blue - *51-53*	30	50
-	**Pullman** TC No.94 dark brown+cream - *52-53*	25	40

C2b. Pullmans (Later) (1962)

The early 1960's version is type C2a with solid metal bogie casting and three part plastic wheels with a more stable polystyrene body. These are obviously employing the same production techniques as the third series wagons. The box was blue and yellow non-window type. The saloons came with blank nameboards and a choice of names as transfers.

B64	dark brown+cream 1st parlour - *62-?*	20	40
B65	TC No.94 dk.brown+cream brake end - *62-?*	20	40

The choice of names was: *Alice, Belinda, Fingall, Gladys, Ibis, Iolanthe, Joan, Lydia, Minerva, Niobe, Penelope, Phyllis* and *Rosamunde*. The choice of numbers for the brake car was: No. 27, No. 36, No. 54, No. 55, No. 62, No. 63, No. 67, No. 68, No. 69, No. 70, No. 71, No. 72, No. 77, No. 78, No. 79, No. 80, No. 81 and No. 82.

C2c. Pullmans (Final)

These had plastic bogies, steel pinpoint axles, plastic wheels and came in transparent window box.

B64	dark brown+cream 1st parlour - *?-75*	20	40
B65	TC No.94 dark brown+cream brake end - *?-75*	20	40

C3. Stainless Steel Stock (H0) (1952)

These had plastic bodies and the same metal bogies as the tender of the 'Hudson' loco in table L7. These are very rarely found in perfect condition and this is recognised in the prices suggested below.

-	**New York Central** 3029 silver - *52-53*	30	40
-	**Chesapeake & Ohio** 3029 blue+cream - *not made* *	NA	NA

* This was due to be released late in 1952 and a pre-production model was painted up and featured in adverts; however, they were not released.

C4a. Bogie Non-Corridor Suburban Coach (1952)

These were similar in appearance to the 4-wheel coaches but were twice as long. They were probably based on an LMS design and were well-detailed models, complete with seats, compartment partitions and fittings in relief - all part of the basic body moulding. They had a metal roof and floor and most had 'LMS', 'Southern', '1st', '3rd' etc. heat printed onto their sides. Early ones had a riveted fixing for Pullman type bogies while later ones (and the kits) had a nut and bolt attachment and smaller, improved, bogies. They were made in large quantities and collectors should be aware that many have received subsequent alterations by their owners.

1952 LMS suburban all-3rd [C4a]

-	**LMS** maroon 1st - *52-53*	10	18
-	**LMS** maroon 3rd - *52-53*	10	18
-	**LMS** maroon composite - *52-53*	10	18
-	**SR** green 1st - *52-53*	10	18
-	**SR** green 3rd - *52-53*	10	18
-	**SR** green composite - *52-53*	10	18
-	**BR** red 1st - *52-53*	10	18
-	**BR** red 3rd - *52-53*	10	18
-	**BR** red composite - *52-53*	10	18

C4b. Bogie Non-Corridor Suburban Brake End (1953)

See header notes for C4a

-	**LMS** maroon brake 3rd - *53*	10	18
-	**SR** green brake 3rd - *53*	10	18
-	**BR** red brake 3rd - *53*	12	20

C5a. Suburban Kits (1963?)

These kits used the original suburban coach one-piece body moulding, steel floor and diecast under-gear but had a lighter tinplate roof and bogies simplified for home construction.

A40*	black composite kit - *63?-74*	NA	20
A41*	black brake end kit - *63?-74*	NA	20

C5b. Main Line Kits (1970?)

Although substantially similar to the C5a kits (above), they used a new body moulding which was fractionally longer and with different window spacing.

A42	black composite kit - *70?-74*	NA	20
A43	black brake end kit - *70?-74*	NA	20

C6a. Bogie Non-Corridor Suburban Composite (1975)

These were outwardly similar to the earlier coaches (table C4 above) but were of a much lighter construction with all plastic parts. They were reduced in height and weight by removal of the solebar and the use of a new design of plug-in solebar/bogie mounting and side truss/battery box. They also had a plastic roof, reversible bogies and were issued in the liveries of the big four and BR. dl = detailed livery. Catalogue numbers changed and both are provided. 'Shirt button' type logos on GWR Coaches.

10601	**LMS** 16385 maroon (also BR60M) - *75-81*	10	18
10602	**LNER** ? teak (also BR60N) - *77-81*	10	18
BR60W	**GWR** ? brown+cream, simple livery - *75-77*	10	18
10604	**GWR** 7053 brown+cream, dl (also BR60W) - *77-81*	10	18
10603	**SR** ? green (also BR60S) - *75-81*	10	18
10605	**BR** ? red (also BR60) - *77-81*	10	18

C6b. Bogie Non-Corridor Suburban Brake End (1975)

See heading notes for C6a. Catalogue numbers changed and both are provided. 'Shirt button' type logos on GWR Coaches.

10611	**LMS** 20485 maroon (also BR61M) - *75-81*	10	18
10612	**LNER** ? teak (also BR61N) - *76-81*	10	18

BR61W	**GWR** 7294 brown+cream simple livery - *75-77*	10	18
10614	**GWR** 7294 brown+cream detailed livery (BR61W) - *77-81*	10	18
10613	**SR** 2697 green (also BR61S) - *75-81*	10	18
10615	**BR** ? red (also BR61) - *77-81*	12	20

C7a. Main Line Composite (1975)

These were almost identical to the suburban stock in table C6a above but one side showed the larger corridor. 'Shirt button' type logos on GWR Coaches.

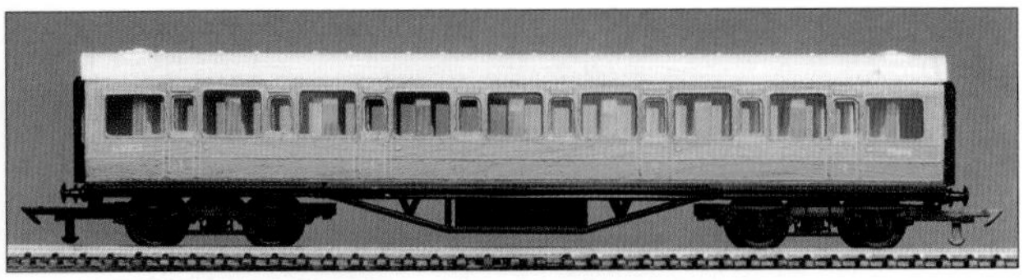

LNER teak 1st/3rd composite coach [C7a]

10621	**LMS** ? maroon (also BR62M) - *75-81*	10	18
10622	**LNER** 75674 teak (also BR62N) - *76-81*	10	18
BR62W	**GWR** ? brown+cream, simple livery - *75-77*	10	18
10624	**GWR** (button) 7053 brown+cream, dl (also BR62W) - *77-81*	10	18
10624	**GWR** (button) 9003 brown+cream, dl (also BR62W) - *77-81*	10	18
10623	**SR** 1787 olive green (also BR62S) - *75-81*	10	18

C7b. Main Line Brake (1975)

These were almost identical to the suburban stock in table C6b above but one side showed the larger corridor windows. dl = detailed livery. Catalogue numbers changed and both are provided. 'Shirt button' type logos on GWR Coaches.

10631	**LMS** ? maroon (also BR63M) - *75-81*	10	18
10632	**LNER** ? teak (also BR63N) - *76-81*	10	18
BR63W	**GWR** ? brown+cream simple livery - *75-77*	10	18
10634	**GWR** 7094 brown+cream dl (BR63W) - *77-81*	10	18
10631	**SR** 2763 or 2783 olive green (BR63S) - *75-81*	10	18

WAGONS

The first series of wagons was released with the couplings in their original nickel-silver condition. Apart from being overscale they were rather obtrusive and within a few months were painted black prior to assembly. A second series of diecast wagons arrived in 1952 but a year later, production had ceased. Besides coupling and body colour variations, all early rolling stock could have either plain plastic or nickel-silver rimmed plastic wheels.

Although some publicity material showed wagons and vans with markings implying the existence of a fruit van, refrigerated van, insulated van, fish van and wagons with company lettering, it is understood that only the eight plain unmarked wagons and vans listed in tables W1 to W8 below were released.

A third series of wagons came with the revival of the system in 1961 and these had plastic bodies on diecast chassis and came non-printed but with transfers you could apply. The final series started in the 1970s and was quite extensive. The wagons were all plastic except for the couplings and had factory finished liveries.

Cat No.	Company, Number, Colour, Dates	£	£

1st Series Wagons (Diecast)

All except the brake van had a realistic looking brake lever each side and the separate underframe on the surviving examples sometimes suffers from metal fatigue.

W1. 5-plank Wagon (1949)

-	light grey - *49-51*	4	10
-	dark grey - *49-51*	4	10
-	light brown - *49-51*	4	10
-	dark brown - *49-51*	4	10
-	red brown - *49-51*	4	10

W2. 7-plank Wagon (1949)

-	light grey - *49-51*	4	10
-	dark grey - *49-51*	4	10

1st series 5-plank wagon [W1]

-	light brown - *49-51*	4	10
-	dark brown - *49-51*	4	10
-	red brown - *49-51*	4	10

W3. Steel Mineral Wagon (1949)

-	light grey - *49-51*	4	10
-	dark grey - *49-51*	4	10
-	light brown - *49-51*	4	10
-	dark brown - *49-51*	4	10
-	red brown - *49-51*	4	10

W4. Goods Van (1949)

-	red brown, grey roof - *49-51*	5	10
-	light grey, white or cream roof - *49-51*	5	10
-	grey, white or cream roof - *49-51*	5	10
-	'Formo'* - *53*	6	12

*This has 'Formo' cast into box on the underside of the body which is of a slightly different construction, the dummy underframe now being incorporated in the body moulding with separate coupling and axle carrier unit at one end.

W5. Brake Van (1949)

-	red brown - *49-51*	4	10
-	black - *?*	NPG	NPG
-	'Formo'* brown - *53*	5	10

*This was the same as the Formo wagon described above in table W4.

2nd Series Wagons (Diecast)

These followed in 1951, 1952 or 1953 and were produced in lower numbers with the result that they are harder to find. They had a tinplate floor, no handbrake gear and were very prone to metal fatigue.

W6. Match Truck (1952)

A plain flat wagon.

-	brown - *52-53*	8	NA
-	dark brown - *52-53*	8	NA
-	light grey - *52-53*	8	NA

W7. 3-plank Wagon (1952)

Announced and illustrated in the first catalogue but not made until the 2nd series.

-	brown - *52-53*	8	NA
-	dark brown - *52-53*	8	NA
-	light grey - *52-53*	8	NA

W8. Bolster Wagon (1952)

Similar to the match truck (table W6) but with a single bolster cast into the body. Also provided with two pins and a chain.

-	brown - *52-53*	8	NA
-	dark brown - *52-53*	8	NA
-	light grey - *52-53*	8	NA

3rd Series Wagons (Plastic)

The first plastic wagons were fairly short lived. They had non-printed self-coloured polystyrene bodies and were not unlike Trackmaster or early Tri-ang wagons in appearance. Transfer sheets were available allowing the purchaser to apply the finish of one of the big four companies but not BR. Some of the bodies were later used in the 4th series of wagons (below in tables W13-W18). They had a two-part diecast chassis which had been chemically blackened and which had four vertical locating pins for the body (again like Trackmaster or Tri-ang). Unnecessarily they had open axleboxes which rather spoilt the appearance. The chassis may be identified by a small 'GF' on the back of the solebar. The wagons were sold in a roll of corrugated paper and a thin printed outer paper wrapper.

3rd series tarpulin wagon [W9]

W9. Tarpaulin Wagon (1962)

This was a 7-plank wagon with a wire tarpaulin rail.

-	grey - *62-64*	8	12
-	red brown - *62-64*	8	12

W10. Steel Mineral Wagon (1962)

-	grey - *62-64*	8	12
-	red brown - *62-64*	8	12

W11. Fast Goods Van (1962)

-	grey - *62-64*	8	12
-	red brown - *62-64*	8	12

W12. Brake Van (1962)

-	grey - *62-64*	8	12
-	red brown - *62-64*	8	12

4th Series Wagons (Plastic)

This series was of all plastic construction. Early examples had the axles in clips which were part of the floor moulding but later ones had the axles held by the side frames. Vans and brake vans may be found either with excessive roof heights or with later corrected ones. This time they were released from the factory already decorated but, again, no BR liveries.

W13. 5-plank Wagon (1974)

Catalogue numbers changed and both are provided.

12001	**LMS** 165417 grey (also B20M) - *74-81*	5	8
12002	**NE** red brown (also B20N) - *74-81*	5	8
12003	**SR** dark brown (also B20S) - *74-81*	5	8
12004	**GW** 15082 dark grey (also B20W) - *74-81*	5	8
12011	**'D.Pitt'** 2 grey - *79-81*	5	8
12012	**'Spiers'** 513 yellow-orange - *79-81*	5	8
12013	**'Snow'** black - *76-81*	5	8
-	**'Sharp'** grey Sp Edn (Neal's Toys) - *80-81*	8	12

W14. 7-plank wagon (1973)

Catalogue numbers changed and both are provided.

12101	**LMS** 312154 brown (also B21M) - *73-81*	5	8
12102	**NE** 131457 red brown (also B21N) - *73-81*	5	8
12103	**SR** 5079 dark brown (also B21S) - *73-81*	5	8
12104	**GW** 102784 dark grey (also B21W) - *73-81*	5	8
12111	**'Frost'** 31 black (also B21/1) - *75-80*	5	8
12112	**'Pritchard'** 26 green (also B21/2) - *75-81*	5	8
12113	**'Bullcroft'** 9471 red (also B21/3) - *75-81*	5	8
12114	**'Joseph Ellis'** 150? red brown (also B21/4) - *75-80*	5	8
12115	**'South Leicester'** 373 red brown (also B21/5) - *75-80*	5	8
12116	**'Wood'** 1410 yellow (also B21/6) - *75-81*	5	8
12122	**'Sleight'** 79 grey - *79-81*	5	8
12123	**'Powell Gwinnell'** 111 black - *79-81*	5	8
12124	**'Ocean'** 918 black - *79-81*	5	8

4th series 7-plank wagon 'J.R.Wood & Co' [W14]

12125	**'Ormiston'** 54 blue - *made?*	NPG	NPG
12126	**'Staveley'** 8716 black - *79-81*	5	8

W15. 16T Steel Mineral Wagon (1973)

Catalogue numbers changed and both are provided.

12201	**LMS** 616014 red brown (also B22M) - *73-81*	5	8
12204	**GW** 110134 dark grey (also B22W) - *73-81*	5	8
12211	**'SC'** 07217 grey - *79-81*	5	8

W16a. Single Vent Van (tall) (1973)

Catalogue numbers changed and both are provided. There were two body forms as the original was too tall and a shorter version replaced it. The tall version had an extra plank above the door. at present it is assumed that the change of body occurred in 1975 and a split has been made accordingly . If, however, the 1974 models should be in W16b we would like to hear about it.

12301	**LMS** 7701 grey (also B23M) - *73-81*	4	6
12302	**NE** 186547 red brown (also B23N) - *73-81*	4	6

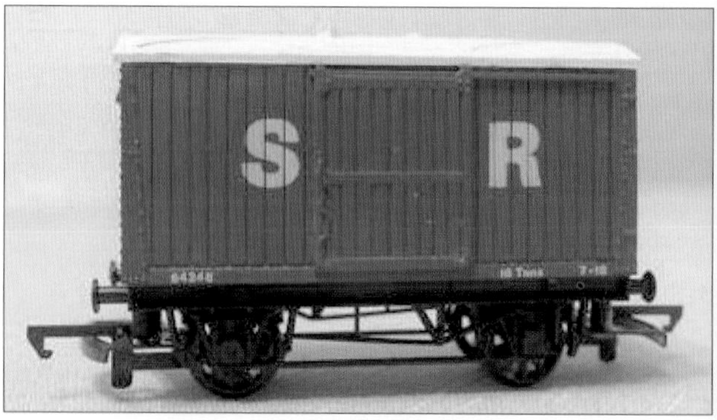

SR single vent van [W16a]

12303	**SR** 50567 dark brown (also B23S) - *73-81*	4	6
12311	**'Bass'** 14 grey (also B23/1) - *74-81*	4	6
12312	**'Worthington'** 5 dark brown (also B23/2) - *74-81*	4	6

W16b. Single Vent Van (short) (1975)

Catalogue numbers changed and both are provided. There were two body forms -see above.

12304	**GW** 95253 dark grey (also B23W) - *75-81*	5	8
12304	**GW** 95677 dark grey (also B23W) - *75-81*	5	8
12313	**'Knorr'** white (also B23/3) - *75-81*	5	8
12314	**'Terrys'** dark brown (also B23/4) - *75-81*	5	8
12315	**'Zoflora'** green (also B23/5) - *75-80*	5	8
12316	**'Fyffes'** yellow (also B23/6) - *75-80*	5	8
B23/7?	**'Railmail'** yellow Sp Edn - *77*	5	8
-	**'Beatties'** black Sp Edn - *80*	5	8

W17. Twin Vent Van (1974)

Catalogue numbers changed and both are provided.

12401	**LMS** 7126 grey (also B24M) - *74-81*	5	8
12403	**SR** 64346 dark brown (also B24S) - *74-81*	5	8
12404	**GW** 95253 dark grey (also B24W) - *74-81*	5	8
12411	**'Sportsman'** white - *77-80*	5	8
12412	**'Gibbs SR'** blue - *77-80*	5	8
12413	**'John West'** green+pink - *77-80*	5	8
-	**'Beatties'** black Sp Edn - *80*	5	8

W18. Short Brake Van (1973)

Catalogue numbers changed and both are provided.

13021	**LMS** 159132 grey (also B31M) - *73-80*	5	8
13022	**NE** 157691 red brown (B31N) - *73-80*	5	8
13023	**SR** 158732 dark brown (B31S) - *73-80*	5	8

ACCESSORIES

Various model railway ancillary items were released between 1949 and 1952 which included a series of three building kits. These were:

Brookdale passenger station
Brookdale goods depot and signal cabin
'Red Roofs' and 'Timbers' (villas)

Each kit included a full set of building papers and supplementary sheets consisting of brick papers, doors and windows etc. and all that was required to complete each kit was balsa wood and glue.

Up until 1950, only a battery control unit was available but the introduction of the new controller/transformer finished in chromium plate and black stove enamel made operating the railway more practical. It had a reverse lever and a four position speed lever which, although it gave much better overall control of running trains, slow running was still a problem. This was overcome by the 'fingertip controller' which used in conjunction with the transformer/controller unit made engine movements and especially shunting more practical.

West & Short Ltd made a range of diecast accessories that were exclusively marketed by Graham Farish. The range included railway personnel, passengers, a railway horse wagon, platform seats, a range of signals, street lamps and a goods depot crane. These were sold in brightly illustrated card boxes. The Graham Farish connection was printed on the packaging and this adds to the value of these.

By the late '60s, the company was selling printed card shop fronts, plastic tunnel mouths and moulded station roofs. There were also six sets of building papers. These later accessories in original packaging are of interest to collectors.

SETS

The first four sets all contained the GP5 LMS 'Black 5' locomotive. The choice was between six wagons or three 4-wheeled coaches and these combinations were available with or without track. Of these the goods set with track is the most common and sells for £80-£120. It seems that very few passenger sets were made and hardly any of the sets released without track have survived.

In 1953, a hard to find 3-rail set was sold under the name 'Formo' and this contained the Q Class 0-6-0 locomotive, 7-plank wagon, steel mineral wagon, van, brake van and an oval of tinplate track. In very good condition this would be expected to sell at between £120 and £150.

The Bachmann model of an Ivatt 4MT from computer artwork by Robbie McGavin

Graham Farish OO and a Gaiety tank (Vectis)

Graham Farish N

HISTORY

The history of the Graham Farish company has been covered elsewhere in this book (see 'Graham Farish 00') and we pick up the story in 1970.

What had previously been referred to as 000 gauge (being approximately half the size of 00) was renamed 'N' gauge in the early 1960s. By 1970 there were already Continental N gauge systems catering for the British market but these were a sideline to larger ranges for customers in Continental Europe and America. All were sold through British companies (Lima/Wrenn, Minitrix/Trix Trains and Rivarossi/Peco). All too often they involved compromises, including those of scale and use of common parts not strictly correct in a British setting.

Dating Models from their Packaging
71-73 alphanumeric numbering and blue and yellow packaging.
73-77 now called 'Grafar'.
78 all figure catalogue numbers used and return to 'Graham Farish' name. Gold on black packaging using a clear plastic tube with rigid plastic ends.
79-80 black card window boxes used.
81-92 the same but colour scheme now yellow on black.
93-00 the same but an additional yellow stripe on the box.

The Gaffer and coach [L2]

What was needed was a complete N gauge system made specifically for the British Market. Graham Farish recognised this need and the opportunity it provided them with, at a time when they were struggling to maintain a toehold in the British 00 market. There had been the pioneering Lone Star in the late '50s and early '60s but this did not provide the quality that serious modellers were seeking, especially the N Gauge Society which had been founded in 1967, the Society setting standards for Graham Farish to work to.

By now, the company were based at Holton Heath near Poole in Dorset and their main product at the time was 'Formoway' track which was a principle competitor for Peco track. The public heard little of the company's N gauge plans until its advertisement appeared in the model railway press in the autumn of 1970. Initially, 32 wagons and a Pannier tank were planned but many other accessories were proposed including an N gauge handbook.

The Pannier tank was released early in 1971 and the GER Holden 0-6-0 tank and some 4-wheel coaches followed in time for Christmas. Early wagons and coaches came non-printed but there were dry transfers (made by Letraset) available to detail them. Suburban bogie and main line coaches followed in 1972, but by September that year the non-printed wagons and coaches were being supplanted by so called 'Superstock' which left the factory with a paint finish and ready printed by the silicone pad method. The first wagons in private owner liveries quickly followed but were initially available only in mixed sets of three.

The range of locomotives and rolling stock quickly expanded and included diesel and electric locomotives in the liveries of the privatised companies and modern rolling stock to go with them. An interesting innovation was the range of 'Magnum' layouts which were large printed cards which included a set design onto which you could lay your track. A large range of N gauge card buildings was also available in their 'Scenecraft' series. Five buildings in the archives have been found which never went into production - one was a terminus station building! Some special limited runs for industrial companies were also produced to be used as promotional aids.

In the summer of 2000, Peter Graham Farish took a well deserved retirement and sold Graham Farish Ltd to Bachmann Industries Europe Ltd. Production was transferred to China and work now started on upgrading the range. The resulting models are listed separately.

Catalogue Numbers - The numbering system changed two or three times in the early days, causing confusion, but settled down to a simple four-figure number in 1978. It is therefore likely that models released before 1978 may be found with differing catalogue numbers although the box content remains the same.

The four digit system worked on the basis that the last digit referred to the variation. This worked well for up to 9 variations but after this letters of the alphabet were used or, alternatively, the numbering continued into five digits for '10', '11' etc. Near the end, an 'FA' prefix was being used and some boxes had a 'FA' number on a printed yellow label one end of the box and a cut out sticker with a Bachmann number on the other end. These were amongst the last models made at Holton Heath.

LNER Class A3 Flying Scotsman [L18]

Variations meant livery changes and not changes in names and running numbers. Thus a given catalogue number could be applied to models with different names and numbers so long as the livery was the same.

An additional '0' was sometimes added in front of three figure numbers to bring them up to four digits. Here we have tended to leave out the surplus '0'.

Couplings - The European standard N gauge coupling was adopted from the start and this was altered towards the end of 1972. Initially these were sprung but, in order to avoid paying a license fee for use of the design which was owned by Arnold, the springs were dropped after a while, the sprung coupling returning in 1981.

Graham Farish by Bachmann

Following their purchase of Graham Farish Ltd in 2000, Bachmann released a list of planned locomotives as follows:
Class 4P 'Compound' 4-4-0 41147 black BRb lined
'Castle' Class 4-6-0 7033 *Hartlebury Castle* green BRb (transfer no.14411)
'Duchess' Class 4-6-2 46255 *City of Hereford* blue BRb
Class A3 4-6-2 60051 *Blink Bonny* green BRc double chimney
Class A3 4-6-2 60080 *Dick Turpin* blue BRb
Class A4 4-6-2 60017 *Silver Fox* blue BRb
Class 8F 2-8-0 3107 black LNER (number on buffer beam)
Class 8F 2-8-0 48045 black BRc with Fowler tender
Class 20 Bo-Bo 20312 blue DRS yellow ends
Class 20 Bo-Bo D8163 green BRc small yellow ends
Class 25 Bo-Bo 25322 *Tamworth Castle* green BRc 2-tone
Class 31 diesel A1A-A1A 31601 *Bletchley Park* black Fragonset
Class 33 Bo-Bo 33109 *Captain Bill Smith RN* blue BRe, yellow ends
Class 37 Co-Co 37609 blue DRS, yellow ends
Class 37 Co-Co 37428 *Great Scottish* maroon EWS LMS type livery
Class 40 1-Co-Co-1 D306 *Atlantic Conveyor* green BRc half yellow ends
Class 43 43047+43058 jade Midland Mainline 3-car
Class 43 43096+43109 navy GNER 3-car
Class 47 Co-Co 47708 *Waverley* black Fragonset
Class 50 Co-Co 50017 maroon VSOE Northern Pullman (LMS 'Royal Scot' type livery)
Class 57 Co-Co 57011 *Freightliner Challenger* green

Class 158 DMU 1525 Northern Spirit 3-car
Class 158 DMU 1550 Central Trains 2-car
Class 158 DMU 1551 dark blue First North Western 2-car
Class 159 DMU 1526 Southwest Trains 3-car

Many of these models, and some refinished rolling stock, were produced at the Holton Heath works using parts available. Some went out with four figure catalogue numbers hand-written on a cut out gummed label while others were given Bachmann six figure numbers printed onto gummed labels using a computer. We understand from Bachmann that, with so much going on at the time when British production was wound down, no comprehensive record of these batches was kept. The question of what was produced during the closing days will make an interesting study and models made during this period are going to be the most sought after by collectors in years to come. This includes some locomotives with blackened rims on the driving wheels which Bachmann requested. Unfortunately the bogie and tender wheels remained in their former bright metal condition.

Bachmann discovered that much work would have to be done to the existing tooling to upgrade the models to a standard expected of their company and so work started on this. At the same time, development of new models started, albeit at a slower pace. All new and improved models are made in China and these started to appear during late 2001.

Large general purpose 0-6-0T LNER [L3]

As far as this guide is concerned we have included in this section all those models that were made at Holton Heath including a few sold under the Bachmann numbering system. Any models made in China will appear in the next section - **'Graham Farish by Bachmann'**.

LOCOMOTIVES

Except for Class 94XX Pannier tanks made in 1971, the locomotives had a split chassis design. The combined motor and chassis unit was used from 1978 with the 'Prairie' tank being the first model to use it. The locomotives had 3-pole motors until March 1984, after which, 5-pole motors were fitted to all Graham Farish locomotives.

During the period 1996-97, there was an unsuccessful experiment with unpainted locomotives.

Cat No.	Company, Number, Colour, Dates	£	£

L1. **Standard Tank 0-6-0T** (Freelance) (1975)

This was made from the former Holden tank tooling which was altered for the purpose. It consequently looked very like a J69 but with slight structural changes.

NE3M	**583** LMS lined maroon - *75-76*	25	40
NE3S	**187** Southern lined green - *75-76*	25	40

L2. **Promotional Tank 0-6-0T** (Freelance) (1989)

This was a cheap to produce, non-powered model.

-	'**The Shredded Wheat Company**' black non powered - *89-99*	25	NA
-	**No1** ***The Gaffer 1994*** bright red powered ex-8530 set - *94*	25	NA

L3. **General Purpose Tank 0-6-0T** (Freelance) (1978)

This replaced the Standard tank as the 'all things to all men' model in the range and was larger than its predecessor.

NE7M	**16389** LMS lined maroon - *78*	25	40
1701	**16389** LMS lined maroon- *78-00*	25	40
1706	**7313** LMS black - *78-00*	25	40
NE7N	**2801** LNER lined green - *78*	25	40
1702	**2801** LNER lined green - *78-00*	25	40
-	**2801** LNER blue ex set 85311 - *?*	30	NA
NE7S	**2579** Southern lined green - *78*	25	40
1703	**2579** Southern lined green - *78-00*	25	40
NE7BR	**47313** BRb lined black - *78*	25	40
1705	**47313** BRb lined black - *78-00*	25	40

L4. **GWR 94XX Class Pannier Tank 0-6-0PT** (1971)

This was based on a Hawksworth design and early models had a Mabuchi can motor fitted a cast metal chassis. From 1972, a split chassis design was used.

NE1	GWR green * - *71*	30	45
NE1GN	GWR green * - *72-74*	30	45
NE1W	GWR green * - *75-77*	30	45
1104	**9405** GWR green - *78-00*	35	50
NE1BK	BRb black * - *72-74*	30	45
NE1BR	BRb black * - *75-77*	30	45
1105	**9401** BRb black - *78-00*	35	50

* These models were supplied unnumbered and with a sheet of transfers with the following numbers: 8427, 9400, 9406, 9410, 9426, 9427.

L5a. **GWR 57XX Class Pannier Tank 0-6-0PT** (1995)

This is identical to L5b but has a Churchward cab.

Ex-GWR Class 57xx in early BR black livery [L5a]

1114	**5768** Great Western green - *95-00*	35	50
111A	**L99** London Transport maroon Ltd Edn 500 (red label) - *96*	55	77
1115	**7777** BRb black - *95-00*	35	50

L5b. **GWR 8750 Class Pannier Tank 0-6-0PT** (1996)

This is identical to L5a but has a Collett cab.

1124	**6752** GWR green - *96-00*	35	50
1124	**8751** GWR green - *96-00*	35	50
1125	**4782** BRc black - *96-00*	35	50
1125	**4672** BRc black - *96-00*	35	50

L6. **LMS 3F Class 'Jinty' 0-6-0T** (1996)

1731	**7277** LMS black - *96-00*	35	50
1731A	? LMS black - *99-00*	35	50
1735	**47394** BRb black - *96-00*	35	50

L7. **LNER Holden J69 Class Tank 0-6-0T** (1972)

The body tool was altered in 1975 to provide a standard tank that could be passed off in various liveries (see L1).

NE2BL	**372** GER lined blue - *72-74*	30	45
NE2E	**372** GER lined blue - *75*	30	45
NE2GN	**1672** LNER lined green - *72-74*	30	45
NE2NE	**1672** LNER lined green - *75*	30	45
NE2BK	? BRb lined black - *72-74*	30	45
NE2BR	? BRb lined black - *75*	30	45

L8. **WD/LNER J94 Class 0-6-0ST** (1986)

1016	**68079** BRb black - *86-00*	35	50
1017	**61** NCB blue, red rods - *86-00*	35	50
(8540)	**07** ***Robert*** Industrial green ex-sets - *86-00*	35	50
?	**196** LMR blue ex-set 8531 - *99-00*	35	50
101A	**NS8811** Dutch dull green - *96*	40	50
101B	**NS8826** Dutch dull green - *96*	40	50

L9. GWR 61XX/81XX Class 'Prairie' Tank 2-6-2T (1977)

The 81XXs were rebuilds of the 61XXs and had smaller wheels but there is no difference to be seen on the models.

1603	**6104** GWR (button) green - *00*	35	50
1604	**3112** GWR lined green - *77-00*	35	50
NE6W	**8106** GWR green - *78*	35	50
1604	**8106** GWR green - *78-00*	35	50
16012	**6104** GWR (button) green - *00*	35	50
?	**6105** BRb unlined green - *84*	40	60
16011	**6135** BRb lined green - *00*	NPG	NPG
16011	**6127** BRb lined green - *00*	35	50
0661	**6113** BRb lined black - *?*	35	50
NE6BR	**8100** BRc lined green - *78*	35	50
1605	**8100** BRc lined green - *78-00*	35	50
1605	**6115** BRc lined green - *77-00*	35	50
1606	**8102** BRc lined black - *79-00*	40	55

L10. BR Standard Class 4 Tank 2-6-4T (1991)

1655	**80064** BRb lined black - *91-00*	40	55
1656	**80079** BRc lined black- *91-00*	40	55

L11. LMS 4P Class 'Compound' 4-4-0 (1980)

SDJR 'Compound' 4-4-0 [L11]

1207	**67** SDJR dark blue - *82-90*	65	80
1217	**375** Caledonian Railway blue - *81-90*	60	75
1201	**1111** LMS lined maroon - *80-00*	40	55
1206	**1118** LMS black - *80-00*	40	55
1205	**40938** BRb lined black - *80-00*	40	55
12011	? BRc black - *00*	40	55

L12. LMS 4F Class 0-6-0 (1993)

1841	**4232** LMS black - *93-00*	40	55
1841	**4269** LMS black - *93-00*	40	55
-	**4210**? LMS black ex-set 8524 - *98-99*	45	NA
1845	**44370** BRc black - *93-00*	40	55

L13. LMS 5F Class 'Crab' 2-6-0 (1993)

1851	**2715** LMS lined black - *93-00*	40	55
185A	**13071** LMS maroon Ltd Edn 500 (red label) - *94*	45	60
1855	**42806** BRb black - *93-00*	40	55
18511	? BRc black - *00*	45	60

L14. GWR 'Hall' Class 4-6-0 (1975)

NE4W	**6998** ***Burton Agnes Hall***** Great () Western green - *75-77*	50	65
1404	**6998** ***Burton Agnes Hall***** Great () Western green - *78-80*	50	65
1404	**6960** ***Raveningham Hall*** Great () Western green - *80-00*	50	65
NE4BR	**7915** ***Mere Hall*** BRb black - *75-77*	50	65
1405	**7915** ***Mere Hall*** BRb black - *78-00*	50	65
140A	**6994** ***Baggrave Hall*** BRc green Sp.Edn (silver label) - *99-00*	60	80
14011	**5955** ***Garth Hall*** BRc green - *00*	NPG	NPG

** an unfortunate choice as *Burton Agnes Hall* was built in 1949 and so did not receive GWR livery until it was preserved.

L15a. GWR 'Castle' Class 4-6-0 (1982)

1444	**7029** ***Clun Castle*** Great () Western green - *82-00*	55	70

Ex-GWR Castle Class No.7029 Clun Castle [L15a]

1446	**5042** ***Winchester Castle*** Great () Western green - *83-00*	55	70
14411	**7033** ***Hartlebury Castle*** BRb green - *00*	60	80
1447	**5037** ***Monmouth Castle*** BR grn - *83-00*	55	70
1442	**5014** ***Goodrich Castle*** BRc green - *99-00*	55	70
1445	**4082** ***Windsor Castle*** BRc green - *82-85*	55	70
1446	**7029** ***Clun Castle*** BRc green - *?*	55	70

L15b. GWR 'King' Class 4-6-0 (2000)

This was the same model as the Castle but had a King Class front bogie specially tooled for it.

1414	**6023** ***King Edward II*** GWR button green - *00*	60	80
1415	**6023** ***King John*** BRb green - *00*	60	80

L16. LMS 'Black 5' 4-6-0 (1978)

1806	**4806** LMS lined maroon - *81-89*	55	70
1806	**5041** LMS lined maroon - *81-89*	55	70
1801	**5041** LMS black - *78-00*	55	70
18011	**5303** LMS lined black - *00*	60	80
18012	**44896** BRb lined black - *00*	60	80
1805	**44911** BRc lined black - *79-00*	55	70
1805	**44923** BRc lined black - *78-00*	55	70
1805	**45296** BRc lined black - *78-00*	55	70

L17. LMS 'Duchess' Class 4-6-2 (1982)

1811	**6242** ***City of Glasgow*** LMS black - *82-00*	60	75
1811	**6255** ***City of Hereford*** LMS black - *83-00*	60	75
18111	**46255** ***City of Hereford*** BR blue - *00*	65	80
1817	**46221** ***Queen Elizabeth*** BRb blue - *82-90*	60	75
1814	**46244** ***King George VI*** BRc green - *82-00*	60	75
1815	**46247** ***City of Liverpool*** BRc maroon Sp Edn (silver label) - *00*	65	80
1816	**46229** ***Duchess of Hamilton*** BRc maroon - *82-00*	60	75

L18. LNER A3 Class 4-6-2 (1987)

Gsd = German smoke deflectors.

1822	**4472** ***Flying Scotsman*** LNER light green - *87-00*	60	75
18211	**60080** ***Dick Turpin*** BRb blue - *00*	65	80
1827	**60052** ***Prince Palatine*** BRc green, Gsd - *87-?*	60	75
1827	**60052** ***Prince Palatine*** BRb green, Gsd - *?-00*	60	75
1825	**60103** ***Flying Scotsman*** BRc green *-87-00*	60	75
18212	**60051** ***Blink Bonny*** BRc green Gsd - *00*	65	80

L19. LNER A4 Class 4-6-2 (1999)

1862	**4498** ***Sir Nigel Gresley*** LNER blue as preserved - *99-00*	60	75
18611	**60017** ***Silver Fox*** BRb blue - *00*	60	75
1865	**60025** ***Falcon*** BRc green - *99-00*	60	75
1865	**60003** ***Andrew K McCosh*** BRc green + 'The Capitals Ltd' headboard ex-set - *00*	65	NA
1865	**60003** ***Andrew K McCosh*** BRc green - *00*	60	95

L20. SR Streamlined Bulleid 'Pacific' 4-6-2 (1977)

This model was passed off as both a light and a heavy Bulleid Pacific. The body tool was damaged and later replaced by an improved one. This version has the two cab windows each side the same size.

NE5S	**21C17** ***Belgian Marine*** SR green - *77*	60	75

SR Merchant Navy Class No.21C1 Channel Packet [L20]

1503	**21C17** ***Belgian Marine*** SR green - *78-92*	60	75
NE5SR	**21C1** ***Channel Packet*** SR green - *77*	60	75
1503	**21C1** ***Channel Packet*** SR green - *78-80*	60	75
NE5GA	**21C1** ***Channel Packet*** SR green, Golden Arrow Ltd Edn - *77*	70	85
1513	**21C1** ***Channel Packet*** SR green, Golden Arrow Ltd Edn - *85*	70	85
NE5BR	**34066** ***Spitfire*** BRb green - *77*	60	75

1505	**34066 *Spitfire*** BRb green - *78-92*	60	75
1507	**35001 *Channel Packet*** BRb blue - *80-92*	60	75

L21. SR Streamlined Bulleid 'Pacific' 4-6-2 (2000)

Following damage to the original body tool, this second version was tooled up. This version has the two cab windows, each side, of different sizes.

1525	**34065 *Hurricane*** BRb green - *00*	65	80
1523	**21C4 *Cunard White Star Line*** SR green - *00*	65	80

L22. BR Rebuilt Bulleid 'Pacific' 4-6-2 (1997)

1513	**35028 *Clan Line*** BRc green - *97-00*	60	75
1515	**34089 *602 Squadron*** BRc green - *97-00*	60	75
151A	**34012 *Launceston*** BRc green Sp Edn (silver label) - *99-00*	65	80
-	**35027 *Port Line*** BRc green ex set 8526 - *00*	65	NA

L23. LMS 8F Class 2-8-0 (1986)

1901	**8177** LMS black - *86-00*	55	70
1902	**3537** LNER black - *87*	55	70
19011	**3107** LNER black - *00*	60	75
1905	**48476** BRc black - *86-00*	55	70
1905	**48331** BRc black - *86-00*	55	70
19012	**48473** BRc black - *00*	60	75

L24. Class 08 Diesel Shunter 0-6-0 (1979)

1003	**54** Southern black - *79-80*	40	55
1001	**7130** LMS black - *79-85*	30	45

Class 08 diesel sunter No.1 Thomas [L24]

1005	**D4019** BRc red rods green - *79-00*	35	50
1007	**08113** BRe blue, yellow rods - *79-00*	35	50
1007	**08493** BRe blue, yellow rods - *79-00*	35	50
1006	**08500 *Thomas 1*** BR red York Wagon Repair Depot - *91-99*	35	50
1008	**08834** BRe Rft Distribution grey - *91-00*	35	50
100G	**08921** EWS maroon+yellow Sp Edn (silver label) - *99*	40	55
100F	**08957** EWS maroon+yellow Sp Edn (silver label) - *99*	40	55
1001	**523** NS (Dutch Railways) grey+yellow - *84*	NPG	NPG
1001	**610** NS (Dutch Railways) grey+yellow - *84*	NPG	NPG
1001	**622** NS (Dutch Railways) grey+yellow - *84*	NPG	NPG
1001	**644** NS (Dutch Railways) grey+yellow - *84*	NPG	NPG
1001	**657** NS (Dutch Railways) grey+yellow - *84*	NPG	NPG

L25. Class 20 Diesel Bo-Bo (1982)

8204	**D8144** BRc green, yellow ends - *82-00*	40	55
8205	**20142** BRe blue - *82-00*	40	55
8205	**20139** BRe blue - *82-00*	40	55
8205	**20215** BRe blue - *made?*	NPG	NPG
8208	**20137** BRe Rft red stripe, grey - *91*	45	60
8208	**20215** BRe Rft red stripe, grey Sp Edn - *91-93*	45	60
82011	? BRc green half ends Sp Edn - *00*	45	60
82012	? DRS blue Sp Edn - *00*	45	60

L26. Class 25 Diesel Bo-Bo (1983)

8304	**D7645** BRc 2-tone green - *83-00*	40	55
83011	**D7672** BRe blue - *00*	45	60
8305	**25288** BRe blue - *83-00*	40	55
8305	**25326** BRe blue - *83-00*	40	55

L27. Class 31 Diesel A1A-A1A (1995)

8064	**D5558** BRc green - *95-00*	45	60
8065	**31140** BRe blue - *95-00*	45	60
8066	**31205** BR Railfreight red stripe grey - *00*	50	65
8067	**31421 *Wigan Pier*** Regional Railways blue+grey - *95-00*	45	60

EWS Class 31 diesel [L27]

806B	**31466** EWS maroon+yellow Sp Edn (silver Label) - *99*	45	60
806A	**31552** BRe Civil Engineering grey+ yellow Sp Edn (silver label) - *97*	50	65
8011	**31601 *Bletchley Park Station X*** Fragonset - *00*	50	65

L28. Class 33 Diesel Bo-Bo (1987)

83111	**D6525 *Captain Bill Smith RNR*** BRe blue (also 371-125) - *00*	45	60
8314	**D6572** BRc green - *87-00*	45	60
8315	**33012** BRe blue - *87-00*	45	60
8312	**33025 *Sultan*** BRe Civil Engineering grey+ yellow Sp Edn (silver label) - *96*	50	65
831A	**33030** EWS maroon Sp Edn (silver label) - *99*	50	65
8315	**33035** BRe blue - *87-00*	45	60
8316	**33056 *The Burma Star*** BRe Rft Construction grey - *90-00*	45	60
8317	**33205** BRe Railfreight Distribution grey - *90-00*	50	65

L29. Class 37 Diesel Co-Co (1981)

There are two main variants - the original split-headcode body and a refurbished centre-headcode version. The split-box one was not particularly good. The tumblehome was rather overdone and it sat too high. Early versions had Class 47 side-frames. The later, refurbished, bodyshell was much better and captured the look of the prototype.

8014	**D6736** BRc green split head code - *81-88*	45	60
8015	**37035** BRe blue split head code - *81-98*	45	60
803D	**37055 *Rail Celebrity*** Mainline blue Sp Edn (silver label) - *97*	50	65
803E	**37408 *Loch Rannoch*** EWS maroon+yellow Sp Edn - *99*	50	65
8035	**37408 *Loch Rannoch*** BReLL blue - *00*	50	65
8036	**37696** BRe Rft Coal grey Canton motifs - *99-00*	45	60
8036	**37699** BRe Rft Coal grey Canton motifs - *90-98*	45	60
8037	**37887** BRe Rft Petroleum grey Ripple Lane motifs - *90-00*	45	60
8038	**37906** BRe Rft Metals grey Canton motifs - *90-00*	45	60
80311	? DRS blue - *00*	50	65
80312	? Great Scottish LMS maroon - *00*	50	65

L30. Class 40 Diesel 1-Co-Co-1 (1986)

BR Class 40 diesel [L30]

8115	**D348** BRc green - *86-00*	50	65
8116	**40015 *Aquitania*** BRe blue - *86-99*	50	65
8114	**40106 *Atlantic Conveyor*** BRc green, yellow nose Sp Edn - *86-88*	50	65
81111	**40106/D306 *Atlantic Conveyor*** BRc green - *00*	50	65
8117	**40145** BRe blue - *86-99*	50	65

L31. Class 43 'HST' (1981)

Early power bogies were unsatisfactory and a new centrally mounted motor was introduced in 1984.

8122	**43185 *Great Western* + 41007+ 43031** FGW green+ivory 3-car - *99-00*	55	70
8165	BRe blue+grey driving car only - *84-00*	35	50

0735	BRe blue+grey dummy driving car only - *84-00*	10	14
8166	BRe I-C Executive grey driving car only - *84-00*	35	50
0736	BRe I-C Executive grey dummy driving car only - *84-00*	10	14
81211	Midland Mainline green 3-car - *00*	70	85
81212	GNER navy 3-car - *00*	70	85
8125	**253007(W43015+W41015+W43014)** *BRe I-C blue+grey 3-car - *81-98*	55	70
8125	**253007(W43015+W42263+W43014)** BRe I-C blue+grey 3-car - *81-98*	55	70
8126	**W43014+?+W43014** BRe I-C Executive grey 3-car - *83-90*	55	70
8127	**43170+42219+43171** ICs grey 3-car - *90-00*	60	75
8127	**43080+42219+43081** ICs grey 3-car - *90-00*	60	75
8128	**43062+42108+43084 *County of Derbyshire*** Virgin red 3-car - *99-00*	60	75
8126	**43129+W42023+43130** BRe I-C Executive grey 3-car - *83-90*	55	70
8126	**43129+W41015+43130** BRe I-C Executive grey 3-car - *83-90*	55	70

* both end cars powered.

L32. Class 47 Diesel Co-Co (1981)

8004	**D1662 *Isambard Kingdom Brunel*** BRc 2-tone green code 1B28 - *81-00*	45	60
-	**D1943 *Chris Green*** Virgin red Ltd Edn - *00*	70	80
8023	**47125** Rft Distribution grey tunnel & Tinsley motifs - *95-00*	45	60
8008	**47231 *The Silcock Express*** BRe Railfreight Distribution grey Tinsley motif - *88-99*	45	60
8008	**47378** BRe Railfreight grey (test batch only) - *88?*	80	95
8005	**47455** BRe blue - *81-99*	45	60
8027	**47479 *Track 29*** BRe Parcels red+dark grey - *91-98*	45	60
8026	**47487** BRe InterCity Exec. grey - *88-92*	45	60
8018	**47582 *County of Norfolk*** BRe Network SouthEast bright blue - *89-92*	45	60
8007	**47583 *County of Hertfordshire*** BReLL blue - *82-99*	45	60
8025	**47594** BRe RES red Crewe Diesel motif - *92-00*	45	60
8024	**47598** BRe NSE bright blue - *91-99*	45	60
80212	**47701 *Waverley*** Fragonset - *00*	50	65
8001	**47708 *Waverley*** BRe ScotRail grey - *88-99*	45	60
8022	**47710 *Lady Godiva*** Waterman Railways black Sp Edn (silver label) - *96*	50	65
8006	**47712 *Lady Diana Spencer*** BReLL blue Ltd Edn - *81*	55	NA
802C	**47744** EWS maroon+yellow Sp Edn (silver label) - *98*	50	65
80211	**47747 *Graham Farish*** Virgin red Sp Edn - *00*	50	65
8002	**47813 *SS Great Britain*** First Great Western green - *99-00*	45	60
800A	**47814 *Totnes Castle*** Virgin red - *99-00*	50	65
801A	**47817** Porterbrook purple+white Ltd Edn 500 (red label) - *98-99*	55	70
8028	**47834 *Fire Fly*** ICs grey - *91-00*	45	60

L33. Class 50 Diesel Co-Co (1983)

8408	**50002 *Superb*** NSE blue - *90-00*	45	60
8404	**50003 *Temeraire*** BReLL blue - *83-88, 00*	50	65
8406	**50007 *Sir Edward Elgar*** BRe green GWR style - *84-99*	45	60
84011	**50017 *Royal Oak*** LMS maroon - *00*	45	60
8405	**50024 *Vanguard*** BReLL blue - *83-99*	45	60

L34. Class 52 'Western' Diesel Hydraulic (1985)

8424	**D1002 *Western Explorer*** BRc green - *made?*	NPG	NPG
8424	**D1036 *Western Emperor*** BRc green - *85-88*	45	65
8426	**D1062 *Western Courier*** BRc maroon - *85-99*	45	65
8426	**D1065 *Western Consort*** BR maroon - *99-00*	45	65
8425	**D1070 *Western Gauntlet*** BRe blue - *85-88*	45	65

L35. Class 55 'Deltic' Co-Co (1984)

814A	**9016 *Gordon Highlander*** Porterbrook purple +white Ltd Edn 500 (red label) - *00*	50	65
8414	**D9021 *Argyll & Sutherland Highlander*** BRc 2-tone green - *84-00*	45	60
8416	**55009 *Alcydion*** BRe blue, white window surrounds - *84-88, 00*	45	60
8414	**55013 *Royal Scots Grey*** BRe blue - *made?*	NPG	NPG
8415	**55013 *Black Watch*** BRe blue - *84-99*	45	60

Porterbrook Class 55 diesel Gordon Highlander [L35]

L36. Class 56 Diesel Co-Co (1993)

805D	**56055** LoadHaul black+orange Sp Edn (silver label) - *97*	50	65
805E	**56057 *British Fuels*** EW&S maroon Sp Edn (silver label) - *97*	50	65

EW&S Class 56 No.56057 British Fuels [L36]

8056	**56059** BRe Railfreight Construction grey - *93-00*	45	60
8055	**56076** BRe blue - *93-00*	45	60
8057	**56092** BRe Rft Coal grey Toton motifs - *93-00*	45	60

L37. Class 57 Diesel Co-Co (1999)

Same model as Class 47 (above)

804A	**57001 *Freightliner Pioneer*** green Freightliner Sp Edn (silver label) - *99*	45	60
80411	**57011 *Freightliner Challenger*** Freightliner green - *00*	50	65

L38. Class 87 Electric (1998)

8837	**87001 *Royal Scot*** ICs grey - *99-00*	50	65
8838	**87009 *City of Birmingham*** Virgin red - *98-00*	50	65
8835	**87101 *Stephenson*** BRe blue - *99-00*	50	65

L39. Class 90 Electric (1995)

882A	**90013 *The Law Society*** Virgin red Sp Edn - *99-00*	55	70
8827	**90015 *BBC North West*** ICs grey - *95-00*	50	65
8825	**90019 *Penny Black*** RES red - *95-00*	50	65
8828	**90022 *Freightconnection*** BRe Railfreight Distribution grey - *95-00*	50	65

L40. Class 91 Electric (1990)

8807	**91004** ICs grey - *90-00*	50	65
8807	**91005** ICs grey - *90-00*	50	65
8807	**91007** ICs grey - *90-00*	50	65

L41a. Class 101 DMU (1982)

BR Green

8133	**W50304+W50329** BRc half yellow panel 2-car - *82-00*	50	65
8143	**W50304+W59122+W50329** BRc half yellow panel 3-car - *82-00*	55	70
8143	**M50313+M59124+M56055** BRc 3-car powered or non-powered - *00?*	55	70
8153	BRc half yellow panel driving car only - *85-00*	35	50
8133	**M50313+M56055** BRc half yellow panel 2-car - *82-00*	50	65
-	**M50331** BRc driving car only - *?*	NPG	NPG

BR Blue+Grey

8135	**M50303+M50330** BRe 2-car - *82-00*	50	65
8145	**M50303+M59130+M50330** BRe 3-car - *82-00*	55	70
8135	**51437+54218** BRe 2-car - *82-00*	50	65
?	**53751+59128+51437** BRe 3-car - *?*	55	70
8145	**51437+59130+54218** BRe 3-car - *?*	50	65
8155	BRe driving car only - *85-00*	35	50
-	**59218** BRe driving car only - *?*	NPG	NPG

	BR Blue		
8136	**M50330+M50303** BRe 2-car - *82-00*	50	65
8146	**M50330+M59130+M50303** BRe 3-car - *82-00*	55	70
?	**M50330+M59130+M50303** BRe 3-car non-powered - *?*	40	50
8156	BRe driving car only - *85-00*	35	50
	BR White+Blue		
8137	**E56063+E50202** BRe 2-car - *82-88*	50	65
8147	**E56063+E59070+E50202** BRe 3-car - *82-88*	55	70
8157	BRe driving car only - *85-00*	35	50
	Regional Liveries		
8148	**L832 (51226+59570+51499)** NSE bright blue 3-car - *91-00*	55	70
814A	**101304(51224+59090+53241)** Strathclyde PTE orange Ltd Edn 500 (red label) - *92*	60	75
8131	**101653(54358+51426)** Regional Railways blue+white 2-car - *91-00*	50	65
?	**101653(54358+51426)** Regional Railways blue+white 2-car non-powered - *92-00*	50	65

L41b. Class 101 Driving Car (non-powered) (DTC) (1985)

0903	**BR** green - *85-?*	10	14
0905	**BR** blue+grey - *85-?*	10	14
0906	**BR** blue - *85-?*	10	14
0907	**BR** white+blue - *85-?*	10	14

L41c. Class 101 Driving Car (non-powered) (DMC) (1985)

0923	**BR** green - *85-?*	10	14
0925	**BR** blue+grey - *85-?*	10	14
0926	**BR** blue - *85-?*	10	14
0927	**BR** white+blue - *85-?*	10	14

L42. Class 158 DMU (1992)

8707	**158865 (52860+57860)** Regional Railways blue+white - *92-00*	55	70
0887	as above non-powered - *92-00*	55	70
8707	**158860 (52865+57865)** Regional Railways blue+white - *92-00*	55	70
8707	as above non-powered - *92-00*	55	70
?	Thai Rail blue+white (export only) - *92-00*	70	100

L43. Class 159 DMU (1994)

8748	**159007 (52879+58724+57879)** NSE bright blue 3-car - *94-00*	55	70

L44. AEC Diesel Railcar (1985)

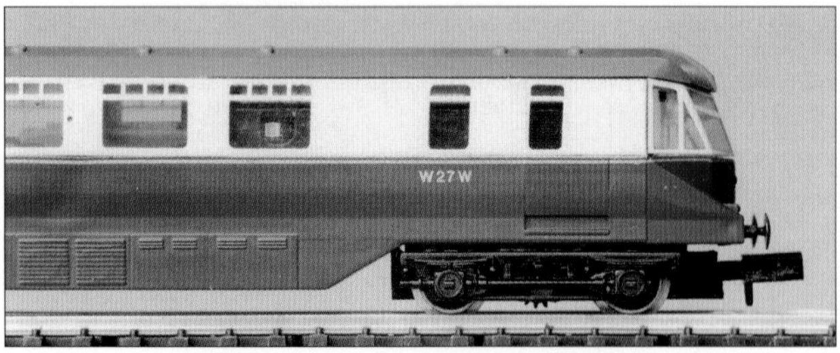

BR ex-GWR AEC diesel railcar No.W27W [L44]

8174	**No.19** GWR button brown+cream - *85-00*	45	60
8175	**W24W** BRc green - *made?*	NPG	NPG
8176	**W27W** BR red+cream - *85-88*	45	60
8175	**W28W** BRc green - *86-88*	45	60

COACHES

The first coaches were 4-wheeled ones, like those initially released in 1949 for the old 00 gauge system. The first announcement of bogie coaches came early in 1972 and by the end of the year, the full range was available in painted and tampo printed finish as the 'Superstock' range.

The GF MK1s were originally produced with the windows on a printed strip inserted into the body-side and this allowed virtually any type to be modelled. At some point in the 1980s, they were revised to feature a totally clear body shell with the entire livery printed on.

Cat No.	Company, Number, Colour, Dates	£	£

C1a. 4-wheeled Coach (Freelance) (1971)

These appear to have been based on a Great Northern Railway design.

NR50T2	light brown 2nd - *71-72*	5	9
NR50T3	light brown 3rd - *71-72*	5	9
NR50M2	maroon 2nd - *71-73*	5	9
NR50M3	maroon 3rd - *71-73*	5	9
NR50G2	green 2nd - *71-73*	5	9
NR50G3	green 3rd - *71-73*	5	9
NR50B2	brown 2nd - *71-73*	5	9
NR50B3	brown 3rd - *71-73*	5	9
NR50/3	teak 3rd - *72-73*	5	9
668	**CR** maroon+white 3rd - *81-88*	10	12
667	**S&DJR** 18 dark blue 3rd - *81-88*	10	12
NR66W	**GWR** dark brown+cream 3rd - *78*	7	9
664	**GWR** dark brown+cream 3rd - *78-88*	7	9
NR66M	**LMS** maroon 3rd - *78*	7	9
661	**LMS** maroon 3rd - *78-88*	7	9
NR66N	**LNER** 3567 teak 3rd - *78*	7	9
662	**LNER** 3567 teak 3rd - *78-88*	7	9
NR66S	**SR** 5303 green 3rd - *78*	7	9
663	**SR** 5303 green 3rd - *78-88*	7	9
-	**'The Shredded Wheat Co.'** yellow 3rd * - *89*	5	8
-	**'Poole No1'** dk.blue, yellow stripe ex set 8350 * - *94-99*	7	9

* These coaches were specially made for train sets (8350) and had a new chassis with non-universal couplings consisting of a hook one end and an oval loop the other. The couplings on the Shredded Wheat coaches had a small circular loop.

C1b. 4-wheeled Brake (Freelance) (1971)

These appear to have been based on a Great Northern Railway design.

NR51T	light brown - *71-73*	5	9
NR51M	maroon - *71-73*	5	9
NR51G	green - *71-73*	5	9
NR51B	brown - *71-73*	5	9
NR51/1	teak - *72-73*	5	9
678	**CR** dk.red+white - *81-88*	10	12
677	**S&DJR** 14 dark blue - *81-88*	10	12
NR67W	**GWR** 253 dark brown+cream - *78*	7	9
674	**GWR** 253 dark brown+cream - *78-88*	7	9
NR67M	**LMS** 376 maroon - *78*	7	9
671	**LMS** 376 maroon - *78-88*	7	9
NR67N	**LNER** 7894 teak - *78*	7	9
672	**LNER** 7894 teak - *78-88*	7	9
NR67S	**SR** 3725 green - *78*	7	9
673	**SR** 3725 green - *78-88*	7	9
-	**'The Shredded Wheat Co.'** * yellow - *89*	5	8

* These coaches were specially made for train sets and had a new chassis with non-universal couplings consisting of a hook one end and a loop the other.

C2a. 57' Suburban Composite (Freelance) (1972)

GWR suburban coach [C2a]

608	**CR** maroon+white panelled - *81-?*	9	12
NR60W	**GWR** 7053 dark brown+cream - *72-78*	6	8
604	**GWR** 273, 7053 dark brown+cream - *78-80*	6	8
604	**GWR** 269, 270 dark brown+cream lined - *79-00*	6	8
NR60M	**LMS** 7094 maroon - *72-78*	6	8
601	**LMS** 7094 maroon - *78-79*	6	8
606	**LMS** 16093 maroon panelled - *82-00*	6	8
NR60N	**LNER** 52347 teak - *76-78*	6	8
602	**LNER** 52347 teak - *78-00*	6	8
NR60S	**SR** 7253 green - *72-78*	6	8
603	**SR** 7253 green - *78-00*	6	8
NR60BR	**BR** M6743 red - *78*	6	8
605	**BR** M6743 red - *78-00*	6	8

C2b. 57' Suburban Brake End (Freelance) (1972)

618	**CR** maroon+white panelled - *81-?*	9	12
NR61W	**GWR** 7294 dark brown+cream - *72-78*	6	8
614	**GWR** 7294 dark brown+cream - *78-80*	6	8
614	**GWR** 849, 854 dark brown+cream lined - *79-00*	6	8
NR61M	**LMS** 3762 maroon - *72-78*	6	8
611	**LMS** 3762 maroon - *78-79?*	6	8
616	**LMS** 20354 red panelled - *82-00*	6	8
NR61N	**LNER** 34789 teak - *76-78*	6	8
612	**LNER** 34789 teak - *78-00*	6	8
NR61S	**SR** 2597 green - *72-78*	6	8
613	**SR** 2597 green - *78-00*	6	8
NR61S	**SR** 2697 green - *72-78*	6	8
NR61BR	**BR** M2570 red - *78*	6	8
615	**BR** M2570 red - *78-00*	6	8

C3a. 57' Main Line Composite (Freelance) (1972)

NR62W	**GWR** 2387? dark brown+cream - *made?*	NPG	NPG
NR62W	**GWR** 9003 dark.brown+cream unlined - *72-78*	6	8
624	**GWR** 2387? dark brown+cream - *78-80*	6	8
624	**GWR** 709 dark brown+cream lined - *79-00*	6	8
NR62M	**LMS** 9485 maroon - *72-78*	6	8
621	**LMS** 9485 maroon - *78-81*	6	8
626	**LMS** 6143? maroon panelled - *82-00*	6	8
NR62N	**LNER** 75674 teak - *76-78*	6	8
622	**LNER** 75674 teak - *78-00*	6	8
NR62S	**SR**1707? green - *72-78*	6	8
623	**SR**1707? green - *78-00*	6	8
NR62BR	**BR** M5801 red+cream - *76-78*	6	8
625	**BR** M5801 red+cream - *78-80*	6	8

C3b. 57' Main Line Brake End (Freelance) (1972)

NR63W	**GWR** 2778? dark brown+cream - *made?*	NPG	NPG
NR63W	**GWR** 7094 dark brown+cream unlined - *72-78*	6	8
634	**GWR** 2778? dark brown+cream - *78-79*	6	8
634	**GWR** 276 dark brown+cream lined - *79-00*	6	8
NR63M	**LMS** 9854 maroon - *72-78*	6	8
631	**LMS** 9854 maroon - *78-81*	6	8
636	**LMS** 6587 maroon panelled - *82-00*	6	8
NR63N	**LNER** 45623 teak - *76-78*	6	8
632	**LNER** 45623 teak - *78-00*	6	8
NR63S	**SR** 2763 green - *72-78*	6	8
633	**SR** 2763 green - *78-00*	6	8
NR63BR	**BR** M5911 red+cream - *76-78*	6	8
635	**BR** M5911 red+cream - *78-80*	6	8

C4a. Pullman 1st Dining Car (1977)

The Pullman Cars were supplied with a choice of transfers.

NR64	**Pullman** brown+cream unnamed - *77-78*	7	9
646	**Pullman** brown+cream unnamed - *78-00*	7	9
646	**Pullman** *Coral* brown+cream - *99?*	7	9
646	**Pullman** *Barbara* brown+cream- *99-00*	7	9
646	**Pullman** *Agatha* brown+cream ex-set - *99*	7	NA
0647	**Wagon Lits** blue - *80*	50	70

C4b. Pullman 3rd Brake (1977)

The Pullman Cars were supplied with a choice of transfers.

Pullman brake end Irene [C4b]

NR65	**Pullman** brown+cream unnamed - *77-78*	7	9
656	**Pullman** brown+cream unnamed - *78-00*	7	9
656	**Pullman** *Irene* brown+cream - *99-00*	7	9
656	**Pullman** *Fortune* brown+cream x-set - *99*	7	NA
0657	**Wagon Lits** blue (labelled 'baggage car') - *80*	30	50

C5a. BR Mk1 Corridor 2nd (SK) (1981)

068B	**BR** W25238 red+cream - *99-00*	6	8
068C	**BR** M25168 red+cream Sp Edn - *99-00*	6	8
686	**BR** W24335, W24753 maroon+cream - *82-00*	6	8
683	**BR** S24316 green - *81-00*	6	8
068A	**BR** S24319 green Sp Edn - *99-00*	6	8
684	**BR** W24167 dark brown+cream - *81-00*	6	8
681	**BR** M24583, M24824, M25250 maroon - *81-00*	6	8
685	**BR** E24772 blue+grey - *81-00*	6	8

C5b. BR Mk1 Brake End (BCK) (1981)

696	**BR** W24753 red+cream - *made?*	NA	NA
069A	**BR** M21237 red+cream Sp Edn - *99-00*	6	9
069C	**BR** M25238 red+cream Sp Edn - *99-00*	6	9
696	**BR** W21021 maroon+cream - *82-00*	6	9
693	**BR** S21179 green - *81-00*	6	9
694	**BR** W21023, W21072 dark brown+cream - *81-00*	6	9
691	**BR** M21033, M21236 maroon - *81-00*	6	9
695	**BR** E21008 blue+grey - *81-00*	6	9

C5c. BR Mk1 Buffet (RMB) (1983)

BR (SR) Mk1 buffet car [C5c]

753	**BR** S1873, S1849 green - *83-00*	6	9
753	**BR** W1822 green - *83-00*	6	9
754	**BR** W1822 dark brown+cream - *83-00*	6	9
751	**BR** M1825 M1859 maroon - *83-00*	6	9
755	**BR** E1834 blue+grey - *83-00*	6	9

C6. BR Mk1 Full Brake (BG) (1984)

775	**BR** W80657 red+cream - *84-00*	7	9
775	**BR** W80657 maroon+cream - *84-00*	7	9
773	**BR** S81542, S81292 green - *84-00*	7	9
771	**BR** M80723 maroon - *84-00*	7	9
776	**BR** E81125 blue+grey - *made?*	NPG	NPG
776	**BR** E81231 blue+grey - *84-00*	7	9
778	**BR 'Express Parcels'** E81125 blue+grey - *84-00*	7	9
777	**BR Newspapers** packing van NCV M80826, M80650, E81231 blue - *84-00*	7	9
774	**BR I-C Exec** 92046, 92075 grey - *88-00*	7	9
772	**BR Scot Rail** 92047, 92086 grey (blue stripe) - *88-00*	7	9
787	**'Post Office Parcels'** 92212, 92233 red NEX - *91-00*	7	9

C7. BR Mk1 57ft GUV (1991)

4101	**BR** M86105 maroon - *93-00*	7	9
4105	**BR** 93356 blue NKV - *91-00*	7	9
4106	**BR RES** 93999 red+black NQX - *91-00*	7	9
4107	**Post Office** 93263 red NJX - *91-00*	7	9

C8. Post Office Sorting (POS) (1991)

797	**'Post Office'** 80387 NSX red - *91-00*	7	9

C9a. BR Mk2e Tourist 2nd Open (TSO) (1984)

805	**BR I-C** M5775 blue+grey - *made?*	NPG	NPG
805	**BR I-C** M5776 blue+grey - *84-00*	7	9
806	**BR I-C** 5749 executive grey - *not made*	NA	NA
806	**BR I-C** 5628 executive grey - *88-89*	8	10
807	**BR ICs** 5628 executive grey - *made?*	NPG	NPG
807	**BR ICs** 5756 executive grey - *90-00*	7	9
FA0806	**BR ICs** 5749 executive grey - *00*	9	12
801	**BR ScotRail** 5653, 5662 grey (blue stripe) - *88-00*	7	9
808	**BR NSE** 5523, 5525 bright blue - *88-00*	7	9
802	**BRe Reg Rlys** 5505, blue+white - *96-00*	9	12
802	**BRe Reg Rlys**, 5520 blue+white - *made?*	NPG	NPG
804	**Virgin** 5903 red - *99-00*	9	12

C9b. BR Mk2d 1st Open (TFO) (1984)

815	**BR I-C** M3199 blue+grey - *84-00*	10	12
816	**BR I-C Executive** 3191, 3202 grey - *88-89*	8	10
817	**BR ICs** 3177 grey - *90-00*	10	12
811	**BR ScotRail** 3248 , 3265 grey (blue stripe) - *88-00*	10	12

818	**BR NSE** 13443, 13514, 13525 blue - *88-00*	10	12
818	**BR NSE** 5523 (error) blue - *?*	12	15
818	**BR NSE** 5525 (error) blue - *?*	12	15
812	**BRe Regional Railways** blue+white - *not made*	NA	NA
814	**Virgin** 3278 red - *99-00*	9	12

Virgin Trains Mk2E brake 2nd open [C9c]

C9c. BR Mk2 Brake 2nd Open (BSO) (1999)

080A	**Virgin** 9521 red Sp Edn - *99*	9	12

C9d. BR Mk2 Refreshment 1st Open (RFO) (1999)

081A	**Virgin** 1200 red - *99*	8	10

C10a. BR Mk3 Open Trailer Second (TS) (1981)

705	**BR I-C** W42023, W42263 blue+grey - *81-00*	6	8
706	**BR I-C** W42023 grey - *83-89*	6	8
706	**BR ICs** 42253 grey - *83-89*	6	8
707	**BR ICs** 42219 grey - *90-00*	6	8
701	**BR ScotRail** 12023, 12026 grey (blue stripe) - *88-00*	6	8
-	**Virgin** 42108 red ex-pack - *99-00*	8	NA
708	**Virgin** 42109 red - *99-00*	8	10
070A	**GWT** 42079 [c] green+ivory Sp Edn - *99*	8	10
702	**GWT** 42080 [b] green+ivory - *99-00*	8	10

C10b. BR Mk3 Open Trailer First (TF) (1981)

725	**BR I-C** W41015, W41128 blue+grey - *81-00*	6	8
726	**BR I-C** W41015, 41121 grey - *83-89*	6	8
726	**BR I-C** W41025 grey - *89-90*	6	8
727	**BR ICs** 41108 grey - *90-00*	6	8
728	**Virgin** 41165 red - *99-00*	8	10
070A	**GWT** 41007 [h] green - *made?*	NPG	NPG
722	**GWT** 41007 green - *99-00*	8	10

C10c. BR Mk3 Trailer Guard 2nd (TGS) (1990)

767	**BR IC** 44079 grey+black - *90-00*	6	8
768	**Virgin** 44076 red - *made?*	NPG	NPG
768	**Virgin** 44087 red - *99-00*	8	10

C10d. BR Mk3 Trailer Rest. Unclassified (TRUB) (1982)

745	**BR I-C** W40301, W40325 blue+grey - *82-00*	6	8
746	**BR I-C** W40301 executive grey - *83-90*	6	8
FA0746	**BR I-C** W40301 executive grey - *00*	6	8

C10e. BR Mk3 Trailer Rest. 1st (TRFB) (1990)

747	**BR ICs** 40715 grey+black - *90-00*	6	8

C10f. BR Mk3 Trailer Rest. 2nd (TRSB) (1999)

748	**Virgin** 40401 red - *99-00*	8	10

C10g. BR Mk3a Sleeper (SLEP) (1982)

765	**BR I-C** 10536, 10623 blue+grey - *82-99*	7	9

C11a. BR Mk 4 Open First (FO) (1990)

827	**BR ICs** 11209 grey - *90-00*	7	9

C11b. BR Mk4 Tourist Second Open (TSO) (1990)

837	**BR ICs** 12406 grey - *90-00*	7	9

C11c. BR Mk4 Standard Open End (TSEO) (1990)

857	**BR ICs** 12203 grey - *90-00*	7	9

C11d. BR Mk4 Restaurant/Buffet (RFM) (1990)

847	**BR ICs** 10300 grey+black - *90-00*	7	9

C12. BR Mk4 Driving Van Trailer (DVT) (1991)

867	**BR ICs** 82204 grey+black - *91-00*	9	12

C13. BR Class 101 Centre Car (TS) (1985)

0913	**BR** W59122 green - *85-?*	10	14
0915	**BR** blue+grey - *85-?*	10	14
0916	**BR** blue - *85-?*	10	14
0917	**BR** white+blue - *85-?*	10	14
0918	**BR NSE** bright blue - *88-?*	10	14

WAGONS

The wagons first started to appear at the end of September 1970 and were then added to month by month. Initially these were non-printed, but a sheet of rub-on transfers, sufficient for 32 wagons, was also available in black or white. From the start, the wagon chassis was also available on its own. It was not long before wagons were leaving the factory in a range of colourful private owner liveries, thanks to the introduction of silicone pad printing. Some of the private owner wagons were initially released only in mixed sets of three but some of these were later available individually.

Cat No.	Company, Number, Colour, Dates	£	£
W1.	**Match Truck** (1970)		
NR4	non-printed (transfers) red brown - *70*	3	5
W2.	**Long Flat and Container** (1988)		
4005	**'OOCL'** container - *88-?*	4	6
4005	**'Dart'** container - *88-?*	4	6
4005	**'CP Ships'** container - *88-?*	4	6
4005	**'Merzario'** container - *88-?*	4	6
W3.	**Container** (1970)		
NR2	non-printed (transfers) brown - *70*	5	7
NR2	non-printed (transfers) grey - *70*	5	7
W4.	**3-plank Wagon** (1970)		
NR17	non-printed (transfers) light grey - *70-71*	3	5
NR17	non-printed (transfers) maroon - *70-71*	3	5
W5.	**5-plank wagon** (1970)		
ex3 = from a 3 wagon set			
NG8	non-printed (transfers) grey - *70-72*	3	5
NG6	non-printed (transfers) brown - *70-72*	3	5
NG6	non-printed (transfers) grey - *70-72*	3	5
NG9	non-printed (transfers) red-brown - *70-72*	3	5
NG10	non-printed (transfers) brown - *70-72*	3	5
2011	**'Pitt'** 2 grey ex3 - *73-00*	3	NA
2012	**'Spiers'** 513 yellow ex3 - *78-00*	3	NA
2013	**'Snow'** black+red ex3 - *78-00*	3	NA
2004	**GW** 15074 dark grey - *78-00*	3	5
NR20M	**LMS** 166187 light grey - *72-78*	3	5
2001	**LMS** 166187 light grey - *78-00*	3	5
NR20M	**LMS** 165417 light grey - *72-78*	3	5
2001	**LMS** 165417 light grey - *78-00*	3	5
NR20N	**NE** 600047 red-brown - *72-78*	3	5
2002	**NE** 600047 red-brown - *78-00*	3	5
NR20S	**SR** 5087 dark brown - *72-78*	3	5
2003	**SR** 5087 dark brown - *78-00*	3	5
2005	**BR** B475908 dark grey - *87-?*	3	NA
W6.	**Sheet Rail Wagon** (1970)		
NR9	non-printed (transfers) red-brown - *made?*	NPG	NPG
W7.	**6-plank wagon** (1970)		
ex3 = from a 3 wagon set			
NR7	non-printed (transfers) brown - *70-72*	3	5
NR7	non-printed (transfers) grey - *70-72*	3	5
NG11	non-printed (transfers) grey - *70-72*	3	5
NG12	non-printed (transfers) red-brown - *70-72*	3	5
NG13	non-printed (transfers) brown - *70-72*	3	5
2128	**'Alloa'** yellow - *86-?*	3	5
2141	**'Barrow Barnsley'** 720 cream - *?*	3	5
-	**'British Railway Modelling'** 2000 - *00-01*	3	5
NR21/3	**'Bullcroft'** 9471 red - *75-78*	3	5
2113	**'Bullcroft'** 9471 red - *78-00*	3	5
NR21/10	**Cam Rys** grey ex3 - *75-78*	3	NA
2120	**Cam Rys** grey ex3 - *78-?*	3	NA

2137	**'Carlton Main'** 5014 red - *99-00*	3	5
2132	**'Courtaulds'** 19 green - *86-?*	3	5
2147	**'Dinnington Main'** blue - *99-00*	3	5
NR21/10	**'Dombey'** No.77 green ex3 - *75-78*	3	NA
2121	**'Dombey'** No.77 green ex3 - *78-?*	3	NA
NR21/9	**'Dutton Massey'** 313 dark grey ex3 - *75-78*	3	NA
2119	**'Dutton Massey'** 313 dark grey ex3 - *78-?*	3	NA
2127	**'Earl of Rosslyns'** No.353 brn - *78-?*	3	5
2129	**'Ebbw Vale'** 6158 black - *86-?*	3	5
2114	**'Ellis'** - *not released*	NA	NA
NR21/5	**'Frost'** 31 black - *75-78*	3	5

6-plank wagon - 'Gray' [W7]

2111	**'Frost'** 31 black - *78-?*	3	5
2138	**'Fulton'** 795 black - *99-00*	3	5
2131	**'General Refractories'** 97 yellow - *86-01*	3	5
2139	**'Geo. Mills'** 15 black - *99-00*	3	5
2140	**'Gray Brothers.'** 52 caramel - *?*	3	5
?	'JK **Harrison'** 134 red - *made?*	NPG	NPG
?	'Wm **Harrison'** 2227 grey - *?*	3	5
2130	**'Harrods'** 64 brown - *86-?*	3	5
2149	**'Ilkeston & Heanor Water Board'** 17 blue - *99-00*	3	5
NR21/9	**'Lebon'** 328 white ex3 - *75-78*	3	NA
2118	**'Lebon'** 328 white ex3 - *78-?*	3	NA
NR23/2	**'Ocean'** 918 black ex3 - *78*	3	NA
2124	**'Ocean'** 918 black ex3 - *78-00*	3	NA
NR21/12	**'Ormiston'** 34 navy blue ex3 - *78*	3	NA
2125	**'Ormiston'** 34 navy blue ex3 - *78-?*	3	NA
NR21/2	**'Parker & Probert'** 80 brown - *75-78*	3	5
2117	**'Parker & Probert'** 80 brown - *78-00*	3	5
NR21/11	**'Powell Gwinnell'** black ex3 - *75-78*	3	NA
2123	**'Powell Gwinnell'** black ex3 - *78-?*	3	NA
2133	**'Prince of Wales'** 1857 lt.grey - *?*	3	5
2134	**'Princess Royal'** 4608 red-brown - *?*	3	5
NR21/4	**'Pritchard'** 26 black - *75-78*	3	5
2112	**'Pritchard'** 26 black - *78-00*	3	5
2146	**'Renishaw'** 917 brown - *99-00*	3	5
2136	**'Richard Thomas'** 6871 black - *99-00*	3	5
NR21/11	**'Sleight'** 79 grey ex3 - *75-78*	3	NA
2122	**'Sleight'** 79 grey ex3 - *78-?*	3	NA
NR21/6	**'South Leicester'** 373 red brown - *75-78*	3	5
2115	**'South Leicester'** 373 red brown - *78-?*	3	5
NR21/12	**'Staveley'** black ex3 - *78*	3	NA
2126	**'Staveley'** black ex3 - *78-?*	3	NA
NR21/1	'JR**Wood'** 1410 yellow - *75-78*	3	5
2116	'JR**Wood'** 1410 yellow - *78-00*	3	5
NR21W	**GW** 102784 dark grey - *72-78*	3	5
2104	**GW** 102784 dark grey - *78-00*	3	5
NR21M	**LMS** 313154 red-brown - *72-78*	3	5
2101	**LMS** 313154 red-brown - *78-00*	3	5
NR21N	**NE** 131457 red-brown - *72-78*	3	5
2102	**NE** 131457 red-brown - *78-00*	3	5
NR21S	**SR** 5079 dark brown - *72-78*	3	5
2103	**SR** 5079 dark brown - *78-00*	3	5
2105	**BR** B785911 brown - *87-?*	3	5

EWS OAA open wagon [W8]

W8. OAA/OBA Long Open Wagon (1988)

3806	**BRe** 100054 brown Open AB - *88-?*	6	8
3805	**BR Railfreight** 100033 grey+red OAA - *88-?*	6	8
3807	**EWS** 200831 maroon OAB - *98-?*	6	8

W9. Steel Mineral Wagon (1970)

An all-welded version was modelled, with top hinged doors at sides and ends.

NR8	non-printed (transfers) light grey - *70-71*	3	5
NR8	non-printed (transfers) red-brown - *70-71*	3	5
2211	**'SC'** 07217 dark grey - *79-?*	3	5
NR22W	**GW** 110134 dark grey - *72-78*	3	5
2204	**GW** 110134 dark grey - *78-00*	3	5
NR22M	**LMS** 616014 red-brown - *72-78*	3	5
2201	**LMS** 616014 red-brown - *78-00*	3	5
2205	**BR** B565010 dark grey MCO - *88-?*	3	5

W10. 'Presflo' Open Hopper Wagons (1982)

3411	**'BISC'** 395 very dark grey - *82-00*	3	5
3412	**'NCB'** 57 dark grey - *82-00*	3	5
3413	**'Sheepbridge'** light brown - *82-00*	3	5
3414	**'Tarmac'** 91 fawn - *82-00*	3	5

W11. 'Presflo' Closed Hopper Wagon (1982)

'Presflo' - 'Cerebos Salt' [W11]

3511	**'ARC'** AR12649 yellow - *82-00*	4	6
3512	**'Blue Circle Cement'** yellow - *82-00*	4	6
3513	**'Cerebos Salt'** red - *82-00*	4	6
3514	**'Tunnel Bulk Cement'** grey - *82-00*	4	6
3505	**BR** brown CSA - *88-?*	4	6

W12. MEA, HEA, HSA (2001)

The components for this wagon were made in Poole but assembled by Bachmann staff in Barwell following the end of production at the Holton Heath factory on 23 December 2000.

373-502	**BR** 360075 brown HSA - *01**	NPG	7
373-501	**Railfreight** Coal 360601 grey - *01*	NPG	7
373-500	**EWS** 361328 maroon - *01*	NPG	7

* Later model from China with this number has different layout of data panels.

W13. PGA Aggregate Hopper Wagon (1993)

4411	**'ARC'** ARC14284 sand - *93-?*	5	7
4413	**'ECC Quarries'** PR14368 blue - *99-00*	5	7
4414	**'Tilbury'** TRL14612 white+brown - *99-00*	5	7
4412	**'Yeoman'** PR14435 grey+blue - *93-?*	5	7

W14. PGA 38T Covered Hopper Wagon (1993)

4511	**'British Industrial Sand'** BIS7842 white PAA - *93-?*	5	7
4512	**'Tullis Russell'** BS7842 blue - *not made*	NA	NA
4512	**'Tullis Russell'** TRL12806 blue - *93-?*	5	7

W15. Sand, Salt & Lime Wagon (1981)

?	**'Dunlow Lime'** brown - *80-?*	4	6
2913	**'Dunlow Lime'** black? - *81-?*	4	6
2911	**NE** Sand grey - *81-?*	4	6
2912	**'Saxa Salt'** yellow - *81-?*	4	6
2914	**'South Wales Lime'** white - *81-?*	4	6

W16. PCA 'Presflo' Tanker (1993)

4213	**'Castle Cement** ' RLS10319 grey - *99-00*	5	7
4212	**'Cerestar'** PR10017 white - *93-00*	5	7
4214	**'ICI'** Mond PR10120 white - *99-00*	5	7
4211	**'Rugby Cement'** PR10041 grey - *93-00*	5	7

W17. PCA Bulk Powder V Tanker (1993)

4311	**'Albright & Wilson'** PR10133 blue - *93-00*	5	7
4315	**'Ketton Cement'** PR9466 yellow - *99-00*	5	7
4314	**'Lever Bros.'** TRL10527 purple - *99-00*	5	7
4312	**'Tiger'** TRL9473 yellow - *93-00*	5	7
4313	**BR** 9150 grey - *not made*	NA	NA
4313	**BR** 9226 grey - *99-00*	5	7
4313	**BR** APCM9150 grey - *99-00*	5	7

W18. Tar Wagon (1970)

Rectangular tank wagon Shell BP [W18]

NR15	non-printed (transfers) black - *70*	NPG	NPG
2811	**'Burnden'** black - *81-?*	4	6
2812	'R S **Clare'** 19 black - *81-?*	4	6
2814	**'Esso'** black - *81-?*	4	6
2813	**'Shell BP'** black - *81-00*	4	6

W19. Cattle Van (1970)

NR13	non-printed (transfers) dark grey - *70-72*	4	6
NR26W	**GW** 106325 dark grey - *72-78*	4	6
2604	**GW** 106325 dark grey - *78-00*	4	6
?	**GW** 10632 dark grey - *?*	6	8
NR26M	**LMS** 22719 green-grey - *72-78*	4	6
2601	**LMS** 22719 green-grey - *78-00*	4	6
2601	**LMS** red-brown - *78-00*	4	6
NR26S	**SR** 53710 dark brown - *72-78*	4	6
2603	**SR** 53710 dark brown - *78-00*	4	6

W20. Horse Box (1970)

This model was based on a horse box on the London, Tilbury & Southend Railway and had a 10' chassis and glazed windows. The chimney on the roof was omitted.

NR14	non-printed (transfers) pale blue - *70-72*	3	5
NG30	non-printed (transfers) red brown - *71-72*	3	5
NG30B	non-printed (tfs) pale blue - *71-72*	3	5
NG30G	non-printed (transfers) green - *71-72*	3	5
NG30F	non-printed (transfers) fawn - *71-72*	3	5
2711	**'Sir George Widgeon'** 2 brown - *78-00*	3	5

W21. LNER Fish Van (1970)

NG12	non-printed (transfers) red - *70-72*	4	6
NG26	non-printed (transfers) red - *70-72*	4	6
NG27	non-printed (transfers) white - *71-72*	4	6
NR25N	**NE** 27456 brown - *72-78*	4	6
2502	**NE** 27456 brown - *78-00*	4	6

W22. 12T Single Vent Van (1970)

ex3 = from a 3 wagon set

NR10	non-printed (transfers) brown - *70-72*	4	6
NG10	non-printed (transfers) grey - *70-72*	4	6
2318	**'Allsops'** 4 ivory - *78-00*	3	5
2311	**'Bass'** 14 light grey - *78-00*	3	6
2317	**'Fremlin Bros.'** 1 white - *78-00*	3	5
2316	**'Fyffes'** yellow - *78-00*	3	NA
2313	**'Knorr'** white - *78-00*	3	5
?	**'Rail Mail'** green - *?*	4	6
?	**'Rail Mail'** buff - *?*	4	6
2314	**'Terrys'** brown - *78-?*	3	5
2312	**'Worthington'** 5 dark brown - *78-00*	3	6
2315	**'Zoflora'** green - *78-?*	3	5
NR23W	**GW** 45677 dark grey - *72-78*	4	6
2304	**GW** 45677 dark grey - *78-00*	4	6
NR23M	**LMS** 7701 grey Refrigerator - *72-78*	4	6
2301	**LMS** 7701 grey Refrigerator - *78-00*	4	6
2301	**LMS** red-brown - *78-00*	4	6
NR23N	**NE** 186547 red brown - *72-78*	4	6
2302	**NE** 186547 red brown - *78-00*	4	6
NR23S	**SR** 50567 dark brown - *72-78*	4	6
2303	**SR** 50567 dark brown - *78-00*	4	6
2305	**BR** E568011 brown - *88-?*	3	5

W23. 12T Twin Vent Van (1970)

NR11	non-printed (transfers) brown - *70-72*	3	5
NR11	non-printed (transfers) grey - *70-72*	3	5
NR?	non-printed (transfers) black - *70-72*	4	6
NG24	non-printed (transfers) grey - *70-72*	3	5
NG24	non-printed (transfers) red brn - *70-72*	3	5
2411	**'Anglo Sportsman'** white - *79-00*	3	5
2412	**'Gibbs SR'** navy - *79-01*	3	5
2413	**'John West'** green+red - *79-00*	3	5
NR24W	**GW** 95253 dark grey - *72-78*	3	5
2404	**GW** 95253 dark grey - *78-00*	3	5
NR24M	**LMS** 7126 dark grey - *72-78*	3	5
2401	**LMS** 7126 dark grey - *78-00*	3	5
2401	**LMS** red-brown - *78-00*	3	5
NR24S	**SR** 52953 dark brown - *72-78*	3	5
2403	**SR** 52953 dark brown - *78-00*	3	5

W24. VAB/VBA Long Van (1988)

BR VBA van [W24]

3906	**BRe** 200163 brown VAB - *88-?*	6	8
3905	**BR Rft** 200631 red+grey VBA - *88-?*	6	8
3907	**EWS** 200631 maroon VBA - *99-00*	6	8

W25. GWR Brake Van (1971)

NR16	non-painted (transfers) grey - *71-72*	4	6
NR13DG	non-painted brown - *71-72*	4	6
NR31	**GW** 114926 mid.grey* Plymouth - *72-78*	4	6
3104	**GW** 114926 dark grey* Plymouth - *78-00*	4	6
3105	**BR** 114920, 114926 grey** - *82-00*	4	6

* white and light grey roof variations. ** with or without handrails painted white.

W26. LBSC Brake Van (1978)

3001	**LMS** red-brown - *79-00*	4	6
3003	**SR** 55657 grey - *79-00*	4	6
3003	**SR** brown - *78-00*	4	6
3106	**BR** M734658 brown - *88-?*	4	6

W27. Freightliner Flats with Containers (1983)

3605	**'OOCL'** + **'OCL'** + **'Freightliner'*** - *83-?*	6	8
3616	**'Ford'** + **'Danzas'**** - *83-?*	6	8
3609	printed 20' containers - *83-?*	6	8
3619	printed 30' containers - *83-?*	6	8
3639	non-printed 20' containers - *83-?*	6	8
3639	non-printed 30' containers - *83-?*	6	8

* Other container combinations include Dart, Zanussi and Hapag-Lloyd. **Other containers used include ACL, Ford, OOCL and a 30' Freightliner.

W28. Bogie Sulphate Wagon (1978)

3211	**GWR** 54004 dark grey Loco Coal - *79-00*	4	6

3212	**NE** 163542 brown Brick - *79-83?*	4	6
NR32N	**NE** red-brown - *78*	4	6
3202	**NE** red-brown - *78*	4	6

BR bogie Sulphate wagon [W28]

NR32BR	**BR** grey - *78*	4	6
3205	**BR** E164857 brown - *79-00*	4	6
3205	**BR** E164857 grey - *79-00*	4	6

W29. TEA Bogie Tank Wagons (1983)

3708	**'BP'** BPO87566 green - *91-?*	8	10
3707	**'BP'** BPO87464 green Sp Edn - *91-?*	8	10
3703	**'Esso'** silver - *83-?*	6	8
3704	**'Esso'** black - *83-?*	6	8
3702	**'Shell BP'** grey - *83-?*	6	8
3705	**'Shell BP'** black - *83-?*	6	8
3701	**'Texaco'** red - *83-?*	6	8
3706	**'Total'** red - *83-?*	6	8

W30. LNER Bogie Van (1978)

3302	**NE** 102496 red-brown York - *78-00*	5	7

W31. Set of Three Wagons (1975)

NR21/7	**'Wood', 'Parker & Probert', 'Bullcroft'** - *75-?*	NA	20
NR21/8	**'Pritchard', 'Frost', 'South Leicester'** - *75-?*	NA	20
NR21/9	**'Lebon', 'Worthington', 'Dutton Massey'** - *75-?*	NA	20
NR21/10	**'Dombey', 'Snow', 'Cam Rys'** - *75-?*	NA	20
NR21/11	**'Sleight', 'Pitt', 'Powell Gwinell'** - *75-?*	NA	20
NR21/12	**'Ormiston', 'Rosslyn', 'Staveley'** - *78-?*	NA	20
NR23/1	**'Fyffes', 'Bass', 'Spiers'** - *75-?*	NA	20
NR23/2	**'Sir G Widgeon', 'Ocean', 'Fremlins'** - *78-?*	NA	20
NR23/3	**'Knorr', 'Terrys', 'Zoflora'** - *78-?*	NA	20
2999	6 PO wagons + vans - *83-?*	NA	30
3799	assorted bogie tankers - *83?*	NA	25

ACCESSORIES

The 'Liveway' track was released at the same time that the first wagons appeared in the autumn of 1970 and the first lineside feature, a pair of tunnel mouths, arrived in May 1971. The Snap power unit was on sale early in 1972.

SETS

The first four train sets arrived in time for Christmas 1971 and consisted of passenger and freight versions with either of the tank engines.

Two Bachmann Class 7Fs on the S+D from computer artwork by Robbie McGavin

Graham Farish N gauge

Class J94 0-6-0ST

Ex LMS 'Jinty' 0-6-0T

Ex GWR class 61xx 2-6-2T

Ex-SR Class BB - Tangmere

Class 40 diesel 1 co-co1

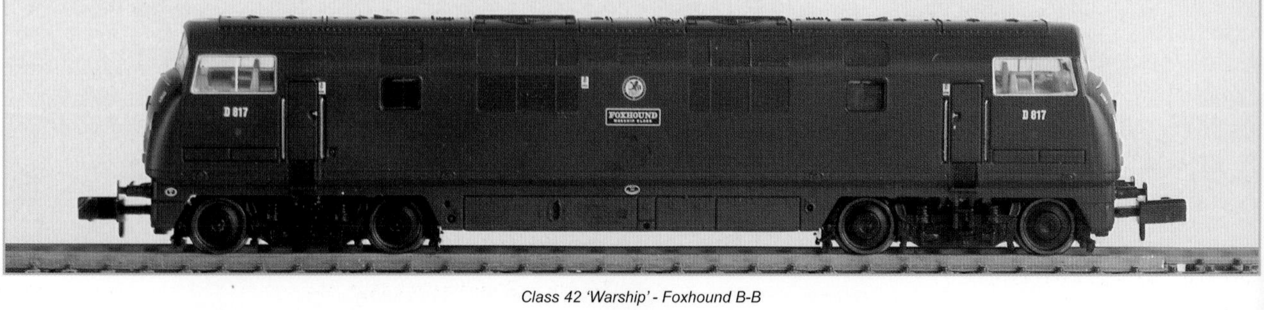

Class 42 'Warship' - Foxhound B-B

Graham Farish
by Bachmann

Please note that some table numbers in this chapter have been altered to include new models in appropriate places.

HISTORY

In the summer of 2000, Peter Graham Farish sold Graham Farish Ltd to Bachmann Industries Europe Ltd. While, for a time, retaining the Holton Heath premises as the Graham Farish headquarters, production was transferred to China and work started on upgrading the range. It had been planned to carry on making the inherited range, gradually updating it but, as adaptations had to be made before the tooling from Poole could be used on the modern machines in Hong Kong, it was decided that the models should be upgraded individually before any products were released.

Bachmann had announced an extensive range of new versions of existing models at the time of the take-over, but only a few of these materialised at the time, those made in the UK being included in the previous section of this catalogue. Pre-production models of the forthcoming range from China were exhibited at the 2002 British International Toy & Hobby Fair in London. As a result of the transfer of production to China and the need to upgrade tooling, there was a gap in the market as shelves in model shops were emptied of remaining Graham Farish stock. A lot of the original brass tooling was found to be badly worn and a process of replacement with steel tools was begun.

Ex-LMS 'Black 5' 4-6-0 No.45157 Gordon Highlander [L18b] (Bachmann)

The first models from Hong Kong started to arrive in the second half of 2001, when a few wagons and improved HSTs reached the shops. Early in 2002 we also learnt that work had started on a completely new steam model - an LNER Class V2 for release in 2004.

Retooling of the chassis was the priority in order to improve mechanisms and performance. This involved a reassessment of every model in the range and nothing was reintroduced until it met the standards that Bachmann demanded.

To date, improvements have been made to wheels, motors and valve gear and just about every locomotive has had a new chassis block produced. Initially, the bodies were all original and originate from Poole tooling. The V2 was the last Poole tooled locomotive. Since then tooling of all new models (and reintroductions) has been carried out by Kader in China.

Some models, such as the 4-4-0s, will not be reintroduced as the tooling is no longer fit for use.

Heritage Range - From 2005, a number of models, based on subjects in the National Collection, were released by Bachmann in a new 'Heritage Range'.

Dates - Wherever possible the year that the model was released is given. In some cases the date quoted is the year that Bachmann planned to release it (i.e. when it appeared in the catalogue), with no confirmation as to whether it was delivered on time. Models were sometimes one or even two years late in arriving. We will correct dates as information becomes available.

Weathering - To save space, weathered models are coded in the text with a 'W' after the colour.

Blue Riband - During 2008, the Blue Riband logo (B) started to appear on some of the new items in the catalogue. This denoted Bachmann's premium range of models. These are designed and manufactured to a higher specification which includes, where appropriate, the use of NEM and DCC standards.

Collectors Club - The Bachmann Collectors Club (BCC) includes Graham Farish in its coverage. Members receive a quarterly magazine and further information about this may be obtained by writing to the Club at Bachmann Europe plc, Moat Way, Barwell, Leicestershire LE9 8EY.

LOCOMOTIVES

Riddles Class 4MT 2-6-0 No.76069 [L13]

DCC - Since 2007, some locomotives have been released ready to receive a DCC chip ('DCC ready'). This means that they have a blanked-off socket into which a standard chip may be plugged.

DC6 -This indicates that the loco has fitted the standard N gauge 6-pin decoder socket ready to receive a decoder, after removing the blanking-off plate.

DC/PCB - Some locomotives have provision for fitting decoders by soldering to a factory fitted PCB (printed circuit board). These are identified by the 'DC/PCB'

Cat No.	Company, Number, Colour, Dates	£	£

<u>*Tank Engines*</u>

L1. General Purpose 0-6-0T (Freelance) (2003)

This was the 'all things to all men' model in the original Graham Farish range and was reintroduced for a cheap train set.

(370-025)	**268** Southern green ex-set - *03*	20	NA

L2a. GWR 57xx Class Pannier Tank 0-6-0PT (2002)

371-900	**5710** GWR (button) green *-02*	35	45
371-902	**8700** GWR (button) green - *02*	32	40
371-906	**5786** GWR green - *07*	40	55
371-900	**7702** GWR green - *02*	35	45
371-905	**7713** GWR green - *06*	35	48
371-901	**8763** BRb lined black - *02*	35	45
371-907	**6724** BRb black - *08*	40	55
371-903	**5796** BRb plain black - *02, 05*	32	40
371-904	**7739** BRb plain black - *06*	35	48
371-901	**5775** BRc lined black - *02*	35	45

L2b. GWR 8750 Pannier Tank 0-6-0PT (2002)

371-930	**3715** GWR green - *06*	35	48
371-931	**4612** GWR green - *07*	40	55
371-931A	**4606** GWR green - *10*	40	57
371-928	**9643** GWR green - *02*	32	40
371-925	**8763** BR lined black - *02*	35	45
371-927	**4672** BRc plain black - *02, 05*	32	40
371-929	**9753** BRc plain black - *06*	35	48
371-932	**8759** BRc plain black - *08*	40	55

L3. GWR 94xx Pannier Tank 0-6-0PT (2002)

371-951	**9401** GWR green - *02*	35	45
371-954	**9402** GWR green - *08*	40	55
371-954A	**9405** GWR green - *10*	40	57
371-953	**9409** GWR green - *03, 06*	35	48
371-950	**8424** BRb plain black - *02*	35	45
371-952	**9436** BRc plain black - *03*	35	48

L4. LMS 3F Class 'Jinty' 0-6-0T (2004)

(370-025A)	**7309** LMS plain maroon ex-set - *10*	25	NA

Ex-LMS 3F 'Jinty' 0-6-0T No.47332 [L4]

372-205	**47332** BRb plain black W - *07*	32	50
372-201	**47483** BRb plain black - *04*	32	40
372-203	**47593** BRb plain black W - *05*	35	48
(370-076)	**47594** BRb plain black ex-set - *05?*	35	NA
372-206	**47231** BRb plain black W - *09*	35	48
372-200	**47338** BRc plain black - *04*	32	40
372-202	**47514** BRc plain black - *05*	35	46
372-204	**47629** BRc plain black - *07*	35	48

L5. WD J94 Class 0-6-0ST (2003)

372-500	**8051** LNER black - *?*	45	60
372-501	**68006** BRb plain black * - *03*	35	41
372-501	**68079** BRb plain black - *03*	35	42
372-501	**68006** BRc plain black - *not made*	NA	NA
372-501	**68012** BRc plain black - *not made*	NA	NA
372-502	**68030** BRc plain black - *06*	35	41
(370-050)	**68040** BRc plain black ex-set - *03*	35	NA
372-503	**68071** BRc plain black - *07*	35	42
372-504	**68059** BRc plain black - *09*	40	50

* Has been found in a box numbered for 68012.

L6. GWR 61xx 'Prairie' Tank 2-6-2T (2003)

371-978	**6116** Great Western green W - *03*	35	45
371-976	**6104** GWR (button) green - *03*	40	48
371-981	**6110** GWR green - *07*	50	67
371-981A	**6114** GWR green - *10*	50	67
371-979	**6169** GWR green - *06*	42	57
371-975	**6135** BRb lined green - *03*	40	48
371-980	**6100** BRb plain black - *06*	42	57
371-977	**5153** BRc lined green - *03*	35	45
(370-075)	**5136** BRc lined green ex-set - *03*	40	NA

L7. BR 3MT 'Standard' Tank 2-6-2T (B) (2010)

'DCC ready'.

372-325	**82016** BRb lined black DC6 - *10*	60	77
372-326	**82005** BRc lined green DC6 - *10*	60	77
372-327	**82028** BRc lined black DC6 - *10*	60	77

L8. BR 4MT 'Standard' Tank 2-6-4T (2004)

Riddles Class 4MT 2-6-4T No.80048 [L8]

372-526	**80032** BRb lined black - *04*	45	55
372-528	**80036** BRb lined black - *05*	55	68
372-530	**80136** BRb lined black W - *not made*	NA	NA
372-530	**80048** BRb lined black W DC6 - *07*	60	76
372-525	**80097** BRc lined black - *04*	45	55
372-527	**80038** BRc lined black W - *05*	55	71
372-529	**80130** BRc lined black - *07*	60	76
372-531	**80086** BRc lined black - *10*	60	76

Tender Engines

L9. LMS Fowler 4F Class 0-6-0 (2003)

372-050	**44018** BRb plain black - *04*	50	65
(370-175)	**44143** BRb black ex-Freight set - *03*	45	NA
372-052	**44027** BRb plain black - *08*	60	75
372-051	**44388** BRc plain black - *04*	50	65
372-053	**44422** BRc plain black - *08*	60	75

L10. LMS Fowler 4P 'Compound' 4-4-0

372-100	**41157** BRc lined black - *not made*	NA	NA

The tooling was found to be in a poor state and abandoned.

L11. Midland 'Crab' 2-6-0 (2004)

Fowler tender.

372-226	**13098** LMS maroon - *04*	65	80
372-227	**42765** BRb lined black - *09*	70	90
372-225	**42932** BRc lined black - *04*	65	80

L12. LMS Ivatt 2MT 2-6-0 (B) (2009)

'DCC ready'.

372-627	**6404** LMS black DC6 - *09*	65	82
372-626	**46440** BRb lined black DC6 - *09*	65	82
372-625	**46521** BRc green DC6 - *09*	65	82

L13. BR Riddles 4MT 2-6-0 (B) (2010)

'DCC ready'.

372-650	**76053** BRb lined black BR1B tender DC6 - *10*	75	96
372-651	**76069** BRc lined black BR1B tender DC6 - *10*	75	96
372-652	**76020** BRb lined black BR2 tender DC6 - *10*	75	96

L14. LNER V2 Class 2-6-2 (2004)

First of a new range of high quality N gauge steam outline models. Has both a single flywheel with damper and a flywheel equivalent Maschima can motor.

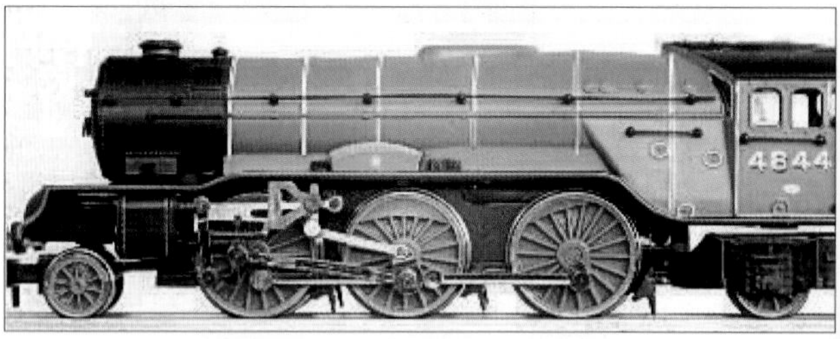

LNER Class V2 2-6-2 No.4844 Coldstreamer [L14]

372-602	**4844 *Coldstreamer*** LNER green - *05*	75	92
372-601	**60807** BRb lined black - *04*	75	92
372-600	**60800 *Green Arrow*** BRc green* - *04*	75	92

* Issued as Heritage Range model.

L15. GWR 49xx 'Hall' Class 4-6-0 (2003)

372-001	**4970 *Sketty Hall*** Great () Western green - *03*	50	65
372-002	**4965 *Rood Ashton Hall*** Great () Western green - *08*	60	80
372-001	**4931 *Banbury Hall*** GWR green - *not made*	NA	NA
372-000	**5955 *Garth Hall*** BRc green - *03*	50	65
372-003	**4979 *Wootton Hall*** BRc green - *08*	60	80

L16. GWR 'Castle' Class 4-6-0 (2003)

372-025	**7033 *Hartlebury Castle*** BRb green single chimney - *03*	55	70
372-026	**4080 *Powderham Castle*** BRc green double chimney - *03*	55	70
(370-150)	**7004 *Eastnor Castle*** BRc green double chimney ex-Bristolian set - *03*	50	NA

L17. GWR 'King' Class 4-6-0 (2003)

372-550	**6021 *King Richard II*** BRb blue - *03*	55	70
372-551	**6008 *King James II*** BRc green double chimney - *03*	55	70

L18a. LMS 'Black 5' 4-6-0 (2004)

Stanier tender.

372-125	**5305** LMS lined black - *04*	65	82

372-126	**44896** BRb lined black - *04*	65	82
(370-102)	**45360** BRb lined black ex-set - *07*	65	NA
372-127	**45231** BRc lined black* - *08*	70	92

* 40 Years of Steam release.

L18b. LMS 'Black 5' 4-6-0 (B) (2010)

A newly designed high quality model to replace the original Graham Farish one of 1989. Stanier tender.

372-135	**5060** LMS lined black DC6 - *10*	85	105
372-137	**45110** BRc lined black DC6 - *10*	85	105
372-137K	**45157 *The Glasgow Highlander*** BRc lined black Sp Edn (BCC) DC6 - *10*	85	105
372-136	**45216** BRb lined black DC6 - *10*	85	105

L19. LMS 'Jubilee' 4-6-0 (B) (2007)

'DCC ready'. St = Stanier 4000g tender. Ft = Fowler tender.

372-477	**5558 *Kashmir*** LMS maroon St - *not made*	NA	NA
372-477	**5563 *Australia*** LMS maroon Ft - *not made*	NA	NA
372-477	**5682 *Trafalgar*** LMS maroon St DC6 - *07*	75	96
372-476	**45568 *Western Australia*** BRb green Ft - *not made*	NA	NA
372-476	**45611 *Hong Kong*** BRb green St DC6 - *07*	80	100
372-476A	**45643 *Rodney*** BRb green St DC6 - *07*	80	100
372-475	**45593 *Kolhapur*** BRc green St - *not made*	NA	NA
372-475	**45699 *Galatea*** BRc green St DC6 - *07*	75	96
372-478	**45698 *Mars*** BRc green St DC6 - *10*	80	102

L20. LMS 'Royal Scot' 4-6-0 (B) (2008)

'DCC ready'. St = Stanier 4000g tender. Ft = Fowler tender.

Ex-LMS 'Rebuilt Royal Scot' No.46159 The Royal Air Force [L20]

372-577	**6115 *Scots Guardsman*** LMS black St - *09*	80	100
372-576	**46106 *Gordon Highlander*** BRb green St* - *09*	80	100
372-575	**46159 *The Royal Air Force*** BRc green St - *08*	80	100

* This has 'Britannia' style smoke deflectors.

L20A. LNER Class B1 4-6-0 (B) (2010)

The locomotive has been developed over the last two years by Bachmann Europe and builds on the success of the recently introduced Blue Riband locomotives. The B1 includes the successful Farish tender drive unit and has a 6-pin DCC decoder socket. The model has an all new body design, with options for welded or flush riveted smoke box detail as well as variations, including door radius, steps and lamp brackets. The tender and locomotive are fitted with separate handrail details and the loco has a fully detailed cab interior including seats for both driver and fireman and a hinged drop plate between locomotive and tender. Other details include a steam generator, AWS battery box and air cylinders. The tender has original or revised coal compartments and a reversible coal load.

The locomotive has see through spoked driving and bogie wheels with alternative scale bogie wheels for display use only. The detailing pack supplied with each model includes a dummy screw link coupling, cylinder drain pipes, front footplate steps, vacuum pipes and spare tender wheels with and without traction tyres. Etched nameplates are included where appropriate.

A detailed service diagram and instructions are provided with each model whilst a downloadable PDF file will be available from Bachmann's website at www.bachmann.co.uk

372-075	**1000 *Springbok*** LNER light green - *10*	90	110
372-076	**61139** BRb lined black - *10*	90	110
372-077	**61251 *Oliver Bury*** BRc lined black - *10*	90	110
372-078	**61321** BRc lined black W - *10*	90	110

L21. LMS 'Duchess' Class 4-6-2 (2003)

Double chimney.

372-176	**6234 *Duchess of Abercorn*** LMS maroon, no smoke deflectors - *03*	70	80
372-180	**6233 *Duchess of Sutherland*** LMS maroon - *06*	70	86
372-175	**46255 *City of Hereford*** BRb blue - *03*	60	70
(370-100)	**46245 *City of London*** BRb green ex-Royal Scot set - *03*	60	NA
372-179	**46248 *City of Leeds*** BRb green - *06*	70	86
(370-135)	**46221 *Queen Elizabeth*** BRb green ex-set - *02*	70	NA
372-177	**46252 *City of Leicester*** BRc green - *04*	55	70
372-178	**46229 *Duchess of Hamilton*** BRc maroon - *04*	55	75

L22. LNER A3 Class 4-6-2 (2003)

gsd = German smoke deflectors. GN = GNR type tender. dc = double chimney

LNER Class A3 No.4472 Flying Scotsman [L22] (Hattons)

372-379	**4472 *Flying Scotsman*** LNER green gsd dc as preserved* - *05*	75	88
372-376	**60080 *Dick Turpin*** BRb blue - *made?*	NPG	NPG
372-377	**60066 *Merry Hampton*** BRb green GN - *03*	75	92
372-378	**60103 *Flying Scotsman*** BRc green gsd corridor tender - *03*	55	75
372-375	**60051 *Blink Bonny*** BRc green dc - *made?*	NPG	NPG
372-380	**60065 *Knight of the Thistle*** BRc green dc - *07?*	75	89

* Issued as Heritage Range model.

L23. LNER A4 Class 4-6-2 (2003)

No valances. Corridor tender.

372-351A	**22 *Mallard*** LNER blue with plaque* - *04*	65	90
372-354	**60033 *Seagull*** BRb blue - *06*	75	90
372-350	**60017 *Silver Fox*** BRb blue - *made?*	NPG	NPG
372-351	**60022 *Mallard*** BRb express blue - *03*	65	80
(370-101)	**60017 *Silver Fox*** BRc green ex-set - *05*	60	NA
372-355	**60017 *Silver Fox*** BRc green - *07*	75	92
372-352	**60009 *Union of South Africa*** BRc green - *03*	60	75
372-353	**60027 *Merlin*** BRc green - *04*	75	90

* Also issued as Heritage Range model.

L24. SR Unrebuilt WC/BB Class 4-6-2 (2004)

372-275	**21C101 *Exeter*** SR malachite green - *04*	70	87
372-277	**34051 *Winston Churchill*** BRb green - *04*	70	87
372-276	**34064 *Fighter Command*** BRc green rebuilt tender - *04*	70	87
372-277	**34067 *Tangmere*** BRc green - *10*	70	93

L25. BR Rebuilt MN Class 4-6-2 (2003)

372-301	**35024 *East Asiatic Co.*** BRb blue - *not made*	NA	NA
372-301	**35005 *Canadian Pacific*** * BRb blue - *04*	70	87
372-300	**35018 *British India Line*** BRb green - *04*	70	87
(370-225)	**35022 *Holland America Line*** BRc green ex-'Atlantic Coast Express' set - *03*	65	NA
372-302	**35028 *Clan Line*** BRc green - *09*	70	90

* This model carries different colour number plates on each side.

L26. LMS 8F/06 Class 2-8-0 (2004)

Ft = Fowler tender. St = Stanier tender.

372-150	**3107** LNER plain black St - *04*	65	85
372-152	**48709** BRb plain black St - *06*	65	84
372-151	**48045** BRc plain black Ft - *04*	65	84
372-153	**48773** BRc plain black* W St - *08*	75	94

* 40 Years of Steam release.

L27. BR 9F 2-10-0 (B)

This had been planned for 2009, but in July 2010 it was announced that Bachmann had decided to no proceed with this model for the time being.

372-426	**92002** BRb black DC6 - *not made*	NA	NA
372-427	**92205** BRc black W DC6 - *not made*	NA	NA
372-425	**92220 *Evening Star*** BRc green* DC6 - *not made*	NA	NA

* Issued as Heritage Range model.

Diesel Locomotives

L28. Class 03 Diesel Shunter 0-6-0 (B) (2011)

371-060	**D2011** BRec green - *11*	40	57
371-061	**D2388** BRc green wasp stripes - *11*	40	57
371-062	**03066** BRe blue wasp stripes - *11*	40	57

L29. Class 04 Diesel Shunter 0-6-0 (2007)

371-052	**11217** BRb black - *09*	40	54
371-050B	**D2228** BRc green wasp stripes - *10*	40	56
371-051A	**D2239** BRe blue wasp stripes - *10*	40	54
371-050	**D2246** BRc green wasp stripes - *07*	35	43
371-051	**D2258** BRe blue wasp stripes - *07*	35	43
371-050A	**D2264** BRc green wasp stripes - *08*	40	54
371-050	**D2280** BRc green - *not made*	NA	NA
371-051	**D2294** BRe blue - *not made*	NA	NA

L30a. Class 08 Diesel Shunter 0-6-0 (2002)

Original tooling with inside frames.

371-008	**13029** BRb black - *04*	28	35
371-003	**13365** BRc green - *03*	28	35
371-009?	**D3032** BRc green - *?*	28	35
371-009	**D3336** BRc green - *06*	28	35
371-001	**D3729** BRc green - *02*	30	38
371-003A	**D4192** BRc green W - *04*	28	35
371-006	**08585** Freightliner green - *03*	28	35
371-004	**08623** BRe blue - *02*	28	35
371-007	**08645** BRe Departmental grey - *not made*	NA	NA
371-007	**08648** BRe Departmental grey - *03*	28	35
371-000	**08653** Railfreight Distribution grey - *02*	30	38
371-004A	**08748** BRe blue - *04*	28	35
371-005	**08800** ICs dark grey+white - *03*	28	35
371-002	**08921** EWS maroon - *not made*	NA	NA
371-002	**08933** EWS maroon - *02*	30	38
371-018	**08585** Freightliner green - *10*	40	59

L30b. Class 08 Diesel Shunter 0-6-0 (2008)

New tooling with outside frames and much detail.

371-018	**08585** Freightliner green - *10*	42	58
371-017	**08653** Rft Distribution triple grey - *08*	42	57
371-015	**08748** BRc blue - *08*	42	57
371-015A	**08763** BRc blue - *10*	42	58
371-016	**08921** EWS maroon+yellow - *08*	42	57

L31. Class 14 Diesel Shunter 0-6-0 (B) (2010)

Class 14 'Teddy Bear' 0-6-0DS No.D9523 [L31]

372-951	**D9523** BRc green W - *10*	50	65
372-950	**D9555** BRc green with wasp stripes- *10*	50	65
372-952	**14029** BRe blue as perserved - *10*	50	65

L32. Class 20 Diesel Bo-Bo (2004)

New crisper finish compared with Graham Farish original model.

371-026	**D8134** BRc green with code boxes - *04*	50	65
371-026	**D8163** BRc green - *not made*	NA	NA
371-028	**D8307** BRe blue W - *09*	50	65
371-027	**20227** BR Railfreight grey (red stripe) - *04*	50	65
371-025	**20312** DRS blue - *not made*	NA	NA
371-025	**20906** DRS blue - *04*	50	65

L33. Class 24 Diesel Bo-Bo (B) (2010)

Fitted with a 6-pin DCC decoder socket and has working bi-directional lights with working headcode discs. Two chassis variations with solebar, sandbox and battery box options. Fitted with NEM coupling pockets and detailed cab interior.

372-976	**D5013** BRc green - *10*	65	80
372-977	**D5038** BRc 2-tone green - *10*	65	80
372-975	**24035** BRe blue - *10*	65	80
372-975Z	**97201** RTC Sp Edn 504 (ModelZone) - *10*	65	80

L34. Class 25 Diesel Bo-Bo (B) (2003)

371-075	**D5237** BRc 2-tone green - *04*	48	63
371-077	**D7646** BRc 2-tone green - *09*	48	63
371-078	**D7649** BRc 2-tone green W 25/2 - *10*	48	63
371-076	**D7667** BRe blue W 25/3 - *04*	55	69
(370-200)	**25322** BRe blue, yellow cabs, silver roof, ex-Diesel Freight set - *03*	55	NA

L35. Class 31 Diesel Co-Co (2004)

Upgraded mechanism, twin flywheel 5-pole skew wound motor.

371-?	**5500** BR - *not made*	NA	NA
371-104	**D5672** BRc green - *10*	65	79
(370-202)	**31135** BRe grey+yellow ex-set - *07*	55	NA
371-102	**31285** Railfreight red stripe grey - *06*	55	69
371-101	**31410** BR Regional Rlys blue+grey - *04*	55	69
371-101	**31421** BR Regional Railways - *not made*	NA	NA
371-103	**31430** ***Sister Dora*** BRe blue - *07*	58	72
371-100	**31601** ***Bletchley Park*** Fragonset black - *04*	55	64

L36. Class 33 Diesel Bo-Bo (2004)

Upgraded mechanism, twin flywheel 5-pole skew wound motor.

DRS Class 33 Minimodal No.33025 [L36] (Bachmann)

371-128	**D6577** BRc green - *06*	50	65
(370-201)	**33002** ***Sea King*** BRe Engineers yellow+grey ex-set - *05*	45	NA
371-130	as above - *07*	48	67
371-126	**33021** ***Eastleigh*** BRe Fragonset red BRe logo + Eastleigh motif - *04*	45	58
371-125K	**33025** DRS Minimodal blue Sp Edn 504 (BCC) - *06*	50	63
371-129	**33028** BRe blue - *06*	50	65
371-127	**33035** ***Spitfire*** NSE blue Eastleigh motif - *04*	45	58
371-125	**33109** ***Captain Bill Smith RNR*** BR blue - *not made*	NA	NA

L37a. Class 37 Diesel Co-Co (2003)

Upgraded mechanism, twin flywheel 5-pole skew wound motor. sh = split headcodes. 'DCC ready'.

371-156	**D6607** ***Ben Cruachan*** BRc green Eastfield motif - *03*	50	65
371-?	**D6700** (NRM Rail 200) - *not made*	NA	NA
371-159	**37412** ***Driver John Elliott*** Transrail triple grey 37/4 - *06*	58	74
371-155	**37417** ***Highland Region*** BReLL blue Inverness motif 37/4 - *03*	58	74
371-153	**37419** EW&S maroon+yellow - *03*	50	65
371-151	**37428** ***Loch Long/Loch Awe*** EWS Great Scottish dark maroon - *03*	50	65
371-152	BRe Dutch grey+yellow - *not made*	NA	NA
371-154	**37429** ***Eisteddfod Genedlaethol*** Regional Railways blue+grey - *03*	50	65
371-160	**37431** ***Bullidae*** IC grey+white 37/4 - *07*	60	78
371-150	**37609** DRS blue - *not made*	NA	NA
371-158	**37671** ***Tre Pol and Pen*** Railfreight Distribution triple grey - *05*	58	74
(370-251)	**37672** ***Freight Transport Association*** Railfreight Distribution triple grey ex-set - *07*	58	74
371-161	**37672** Transrail triple grey 37/6 - *09*	60	81
371-157	**37678** BReLL Railfreight red stripe grey - *05*	55	74

L37b. Class 37 Diesel Co-Co (B) (2008)

New model with better detail, twin flywheel 5-pole skew wound motor. sh = split headcodes. 'DCC ready'.

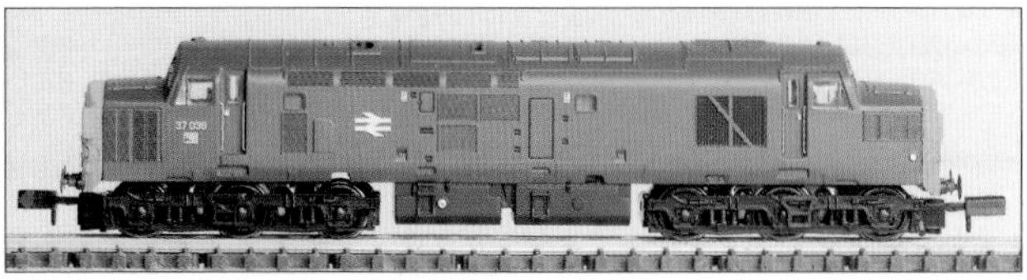

Class 37/0 No.37038 [L37b]

371-451	**D6707** BRc green sh 37/0 DC6 - *08*	65	80
371-451A	**D6707** BRc green sh 37/0 DC6 - *10*	65	82
371-453	**D6826** BRc green 37/0 DC6 - *08*	65	80
371-450	**37038** BRe blue sh 37/0 DC6 - *08*	65	80
371-452	**37238** BRe blue 37/0 DC6 - *08*	65	80

L37c. Class 37 'Cut-nose' Diesel Co-Co (B) (2009)

New model with body cut-away below the cab fronts, twin flywheel 5-pole skew wound motor. sh = split headcodes. 'DCC ready'.

371-466	**37035** BR Civil Eng. grey+yellow 37/0 DC6 - *09*	75	93
371-467	**37239** ***The Coal Merchants' Association of Scotland*** BR Rft Coal grey 37/0 DC6 - *09*	75	93
371-465	**37254** BRe blue 37/0 DC6 - *09*	75	93

L38. Class 40 Diesel 1-Co-Co-1 (2004)

Upgraded mechanism, twin flywheel 5-pole skew wound motor.

371-?	**D200** - *not made*	NA	NA
371-175	**D306** ***Atlantic Conveyor*** BRc green - *04*	60	70
371-177	**D351** BRc green - *06*	60	75
371-177A	**D382** BRc green - *10*	65	84
371-176	**40051** BRe blue - *not made*	NA	NA
371-176	**40052** BRe blue - *04*	60	70
371-178A	**40150** BRe blue - *10*	65	84
371-178	**40192** BRe blue - *06*	65	80

L39. Class 42 Diesel Hydraulic B-B (B) (2008)

These have basically the same mechanism as the new Class 37, twin flywheel 5-pole skew wound motor, working illuminated headcode boxes, detailed cab interior, vac and air pipes for bufferbeams.

371-601	**D804** ***Avenger*** BRe blue DC6 - *made?*	NPG	NPG
371-602	**D814** ***Dragon*** BRc green DC6 - *08*	60	79
371-603	**D815** ***Druid*** BRc maroon yellow front DC6 - *08*	70	90
371-600	**D817** ***Foxhound*** BRc maroon DC6 - *08*	60	79
371-602A	**D819*** ***Goliath*** BRc green DC6 - *10*	70	90
371-601	**D822** ***Hercules*** BRe blue DC6 - *08*	60	79
371-600A	**D823** ***Hermes*** BRc maroon DC6 - *10*	70	90
371-601A	**D827** ***Kelly*** BRe blue DC6 - *10*	70	90
371-603A	**D829** ***Magpie*** BRc maroon DC6 - *10*	70	90

* D814 on the box.

L40. Class 43 HST InterCity 125 (2001)

371-481	**43006+42503+43096** Cross Country grey+ purple 3-car - *not made*	NA	NA
371-475	**43047+42157+43058** ***Midland Pride*** MML green+cream 3-car - *01*	70	90
371-475A	***Midland Pride*** MML green+cream 3-car - *not made*	NA	NA
371-476	**43096+42064+43109** GNER navy blue 3-car - *01*	70	90
371-477	**43004+TS+43025** FGW purple - *not made*	NA	NA
371-477	**43029+42072+43031** FGW purple - *02*	70	90
371-475A	**43056+42112+43178** Midland Mainline blue+grey - *07*	80	101
371-478	**43089+42127+43091** Virgin red+black WCML - *02*	70	90
371-478	**43084+TS+43161** Virgin red+black WCML - *not made*	NA	NA
371-478	**?+?+?** GNER navy blue 3-car - *not made*	NA	NA
371-478A	***Virgin Challenger*** silver+red 3-car - *not made**	NA	NA
371-480	**43096** ***Stirling Castle*****+42058+43006** ***Kingdom of Fife*** GNER Mallard navy blue - *07*	70	90
371-479	**43098+42074+43107** BR ICs grey 3-car - *03*	80	101
371-475A	**43166** Midland Mainline blue+grey - *not made*	NA	NA
371-481	**43221+42377+43378** Cross Country grey+ purple 3-car - *09*	80	101

* Virgin Trains did not go ahead with their Challenger refurbishment HSTs due to changes made by the SRA. A prototype model was produced but not put into production.

L41. Class 44 Diesel Co-Co (B) (2006)

371-201	**D1** ***Scafell Pike*** BRc green - *06*	65	77
371-202	**D7** ***Ingleborough*** BRc green - *10*	68	83
371-200	**44008** ***Penyghent*** BRe blue - *06*	65	80

L42. Class 45 Diesel Co-Co (B) (2006)

Upgraded mechanism, twin flywheel 5-pole skew wound motor.

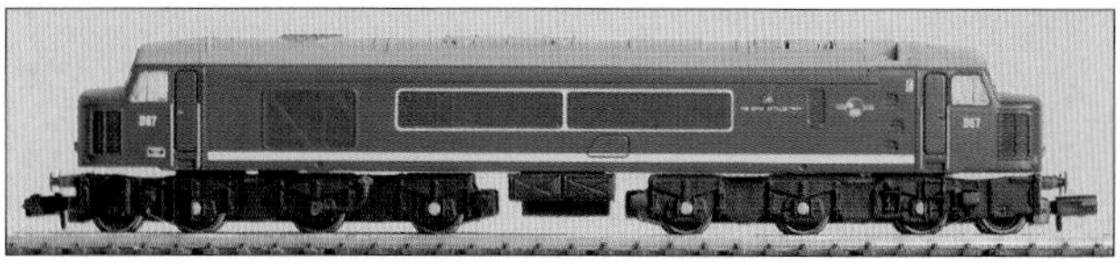

Class 45 No.D67 The Royal Artileryman [L42]

371-575A	**D55** ***Royal Signals*** BRc green - *10*	68	83
371-575	**D67** ***The Royal Artilleryman*** BRc green - *06*	65	77
371-576	**45114** BRe blue, grey roof - *06*	65	77

L43. Class 46 Diesel Co-Co (B) (2006)

Upgraded mechanism, twin flywheel 5-pole skew wound motor.

371-585	**D163** ***Leicestershire and Derbyshire Yeomanry*** BRc green - *06*	65	80
371-586	**46053** BRe blue - *06*	65	80

L44a. Class 47 Diesel Co-Co (2002)

Upgraded mechanism, twin flywheel 5-pole skew wound motor.

371-231	**D1505** BRc 2-tone green W 47/4 - *04*	58	78
371-229	**47150** Freightliner green - *02*	55	65
371-232	**47237** DRS dark blue - *06*	58	75
(370-250)	**47306** ***The Sapper*** Railfreight Distribution triple grey ex-sets (*also 370-252*) - *05, 09*	60	NA
371-233	as above - *07*	60	76
371-230	**47635** ***The Lass O'Ballochmyle*** BReLL blue Highland motif 47/4 - *04*	58	75
371-227	**47701** ***Waverley*** Fragonset black - *02*	50	60
(370-125)	**47734** ***Crewe Diesel Depot*** RES red+black ex-Royal Mail set - *05*	60	NA
371-225	**47747** ***Graham Farish*** Virgin red - *not made*	NA	NA
371-225K	**47805** ***Pride of Toton*** Virgin red Sp Edn 500 (BCC) - *04*	60	74
371-226	**47832** ***Tamar*** FGW green - *02*	58	75

L44b. Class 47 Diesel Co-Co (B) (2008)

New model with easy to remove body and 'DCC ready'.

371-825	**D1500** BRc 2-tone green small yellow panel DC6 - *08*	70	89
371-826	**1764** BRc 2-tone green, yellow cab front DC6 - *08*	70	89
371-827	**47035** BRe blue DC6 - *08*	70	89
371-828	**47404** ***Hadrian*** BRe blue DC6 - *08*	70	89

L44c. Class 47 Refurbished Diesel Co-Co (B) (2010)

New model of the 1980s refurbished 'intermediate' Class 47s. With easy to remove body and 'DCC ready'.

372-242	**47474** ***Sir Rowland Hill*** BRe Parcels red+dark grey DC6 - *10*	70	95
372-240	**47535** ***University of Leicester*** BRe blue DC6 - *10*	70	95
372-241	**47612** ***Titan*** BRe InterCity grey DC6 - *10*	70	95

L45. Class 50 Diesel Co-Co (2003)

Upgraded mechanism, twin flywheel 5-pole skew wound motor.

Class 50 No.50037 Illustrious [L45]

371-251	**50004** ***St Vincent*** BReLL blue - *03*	55	65
371-250	**50017** LMS maroon+gold - *03*	55	65
371-253A	**50033** ***Glorious*** BRe blue - *10*	65	81
371-253	**50037** ***Illustrious*** BRe blue - *06*	65	79
371-252	**50149** ***Defiance*** Rft General triple grey - *05*	58	74

L46. Class 52 'Western' Diesel Hydraulic Co-Co (2004)

This has a new mechanism and crisper well detailed finish than Graham Farish version.

371-402	**D1013** ***Western Ranger*** BRe blue - *06*	60	75
371-400	**D1023** ***Western Fusilier*** BRc maroon* - *04*	60	75
371-401	**D1030** ***Western Musketeer*** BRe Swindon chromatic blue - *04*	60	70
371-403	**D1035** ***Western Yeoman*** BRc green - *10*	65	82

* Also issued as Heritage Range model.

L47a. DP1 Prototype Deltic Diesel Co-Co (B) (2010)

The model has a powerful six axle drive chassis with twin flywheels, bi-directional lighting, recesses fan detail with etched grills, wire handrails, metal buffers, detailed cab interiors and a 6-pin decoder socket for DCC users. This is believed to have been the first time in Britain a laser scan of an actual locomotive was used for an N gauge model.

(370-275)	***Deltic*** Nanking blue as first built ex-'The Merseyside Express' set - *10*	80	NA
372-920	***Deltic*** Nanking blue as preserved at the NRM - *10*	80	99

L47b. Class 55 'Deltic' Co-Co Diesel (2003)

Upgraded mechanism, twin flywheel 5-pole skew wound motor.

371-275	**D9000** ***Royal Scots Grey*** BRc 2-tone green - *03*	58	68
371-277	**55002** ***The King's Own Yorkshire Light Infantry*** BRc 2-tone green* - *05*	58	74
371-276	**55006** ***The Fife & Forfar Yeomanry*** BRe blue - *03*	58	68
371-278	**55008** ***The Green Howards*** BRe blue - *09*	65	81

* Issued as Heritage Range model.

L48. Class 56 Diesel Co-Co (2003)

Upgraded mechanism, twin flywheel 5-pole skew wound motor.

371-301	**56074** ***Killingley Colliery*** LoadHaul black +orange W - *03*	58	77
371-300	**56105** EW&S maroon+yellow - *03*	55	65

L49a. Class 57 Diesel Co-Co (2002)

This used the old Graham Farish Class 47 body

371-228	**57011** ***Freightliner Challenger*** Freightliner green - *02*	55	65

L49b. Class 57 Diesel Co-Co (B) (2007)

Retooled as an accurate model of a Class 57. 'DCC Ready'

371-651	**57003** ***Freightliner Evolution*** Freightliner green DC/PCB - *07*	70	84
371-654	**57011** DRS (compass) dark blue DC/PCB - *08*	70	84
371-650	**57301** ***Scott Tracy*** Virgin grey+red DC/PCB - *07*	70	84
371-653	**57601** Porterbrook purple+silver - *07*	60	78
371-652	**57602** ***Restormel Castle*** FGW green DC/PCB - *07*	70	84

L50. Class 60 Diesel Co-Co (B) (2007)

Upgraded mechanism, twin flywheel 5-pole skew wound motor. 'DCC Ready' Supplied with front end attachments to fit.

371-350K	**60006** ***Scunthorpe Ironmaster*** British Steel light blue Sp Edn 504 (BCC) - *07*	62	78

Mainline Class 60 No.60078 [L50]

371-350	**60052** ***Glofa Twr/Tower Colliery*** EWS maroon+yellow DC/PCB - *07*	70	87
371-353	**60059** ***Swinden Dalesman*** Loadhaul black+ orange DC/PCB - *09*	70	87
371-350Y	**60061** ***Alexander Graham Bell*** Transrail triple grey Sp Edn 504 (Buffers) - *07*	70	90
371-351	**60078** Mainline blue DC/PCB - *07*	70	87
371-350Z	**60081** ***Isambard Kingdom Brunel*** EWS green Ltd Edn 512 (Kernow MRC) - *07*	70	90
371-352	**60084** ***Cross Fell*** Transrail triple grey DC/PCB - *08*	70	87

L51a. Class 66 Diesel Co-Co (B) (2005)

'DCC ready' and headlamps. Upgraded mechanism, balanced twin flywheel 5-pole skew wound motor. Interchangeable couplings.

371-375	**66010** EWS maroon+yellow - *not made*	NA	NA
371-380A	**66098** EWS maroon+yellow DC/PCB - *09*	68	83
371-375	**66135** EWS maroon+yellow - *05*	65	78
371-380	**66200** ***Railway Heritage Committee*** EWS maroon+yellow DC/PCB - *06*	65	78

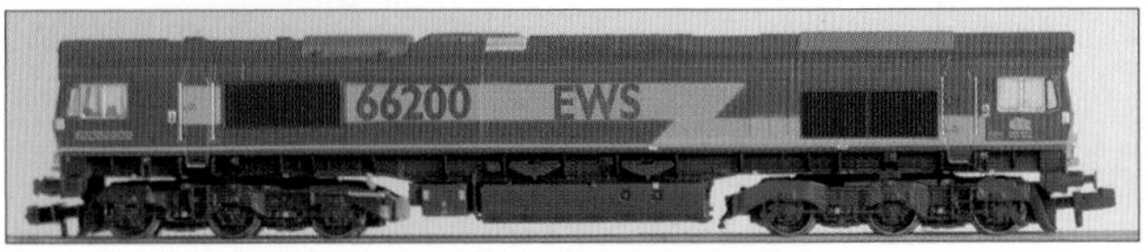

EWS Class 66 No.66200 [L51b]

371-381	**66405** Malcolm Logistics blue DC/PCB - *08*	68	83
371-376	**66502** Freightliner green - *not made*	NA	NA
371-378	**66522** Freightliner/Shanks 2 greens - *06*	65	78
371-378	**66610** Freightliner/Shanks green - *not made*	NA	NA
371-376	**66610** Freightliner green - *05*	65	78
371-377	**66701** ***Whitemoor*** GBRailfreight blue+yellow DC/PCB - *05*	68	83
371-379	**66709** ***Joseph Arnold Davies*** GBf/Medite black+yellow DC/PCB - *06*	68	83
371-383	**66152** DB Schenker red.- *09*	68	83

L51b. Class 66/9 Diesel Co-Co (2007) (B)

The environmentally friendly Class 66. 'DCC ready' and headlamps. Upgraded mechanism, balanced twin flywheel 5-pole skew wound motor. Interchangeable couplings.

371-393	**66301** Fastline grey DC/PCB - *10*	70	86
371-391	**66411** ***Eddie the Engine*** DRS/Stobart dark blue DC/PCB- *07*	68	83
371-382	**66412** DRS Malcolm Rail dark blue - *09*	68	83
371-394	**66623** Freightliner Bardon Aggregates violet-blue DC/PCB - *10*	70	86
371-392	**66725** ***Sunderland AFC*** First GBRF violet DC/PCB - *08*	68	83
371-390	**66952** Freightliner green 40th Anniv. DC/PCB - *07*	68	83

L52. Class 70 'Powerhaul' Co-Co (2011) (B)

The new 75 Mph Co-Co 'PowerHaul' locomotives feature innovative designs such as Dynamic Braking and AC traction technology and will be utilised across all parts of the extensive Freightliner route network.

371-?	**70001** ***Powerhaul*** Freightliner green+yellow Sp Edn (Freightliner) - *11*	NPG	NPG
371-?	? Freightliner green+yellow - *11*	NPG	NPG
371-?	? Freightliner green+yellow - *11*	NPG	NPG

Electric Locomotives

These were reissued in 2005 with brand new chassis with twin flywheels, 5-pole skew wound motors as previously used in the Class 158. The mouldings are crisper and the glazing better fitting that the old GF models.

L53. Class 87 Electric Bo-Bo (2005)

Unique chassis.

Virgin Trains Class 8T No.87019 Sir Winston Churchill [L53] (Bachmann)

371-750	**87001** ***Royal Scot*** Virgin red+black - *05*	65	77
371-751	**87019** ***Sir Winston Churchill*** Virgin red+black - *07*	65	82

L54. Class 90 Electric Bo-Bo (2005)

371-776	**90004 *City of Glasgow*** Virgin red+black - *05*	65	77
371-775	**90030 *Crewe Locomotive Works*** EWS maroon+yellow - *05*	65	82
371-777	**90046** Freightliner green - *09*	65	82

L55. Class 91 Electric Bo-Bo (2005)

371-801	**91004 *Grantham*** GNER navy + **82212** DVT - *05*	75	92
(371-810)	**91004 *Grantham*** GNER navy on its own - *05*	60	NA
371-800	**91126 *York Minster*** GNER navy + **82226** DVT - *05*	70	87
(371-800)	**91126 *York Minster*** GNER navy on its own - *05*	60	NA

Multiple Units

L56a. Class 101 2-Car DMU (B) (2011)

The re-release of this model was delayed due to problems in upgrading the existing tooling.

371-500	**?+?** BRc green speed whiskers DC6 - *11*	70	91
371-502	**?+?** BRe blue DC6 - *11*	70	91
371-500	**?+?** ScotRail - *not made*	NA	NA
371-501	**?+?** BR Regional Railways blue DC6 - *11*	70	91

L56b. Class 101 3-Car DMU (B) (2011)

Structual details as above.

371-510	**W50329?+?+?** BRc green whiskers - *not made*	NA	NA
371-510	**?+?+?** BRe blue DC6 - *11*	85	103
371-511	**?+?+?** BRe blue+grey DC6 - *11*	85	103

L57a. Class 108 2-Car DMU (B) (2006)

The units have a 6 pin NEM 651 DCC socket fitted and it is the first ready-to-run British N gauge model released that is able to accommodate a LokSound sound decoder and 13mm speaker (speaker frame included). The models also have a detailed interior, all wheel pick-up, a fly-wheel driven motor, NEM coupling pockets and working lights.

Class 108 DMU [L57a]

371-875	**M50628+M56214** BRc green speed whiskers DC6 - *08*	70	89
371-879	**M51563+M51562** BRc green with whiskers DC6 - *10*	85	103
371-875A	**M56263+M50980** BRc green speed whiskers DC6 - *09*	80	100
371-876	**M50976+M56224** BRe blue DC6 - *08*	70	89
371-878	**E53931+E51562** BRe blue DC6 - *10*	85	103
371-877	**53959+54243** BRe blue+grey DC6 - *08*	80	100
371-876A	**?+?** BRe blue DC6 - *09*	80	100

L57b. Class 108 3-Car DMU (B) (2010)

The units have a 6 pin NEM 651 DCC socket fitted and it is the first ready-to-run British N gauge model released that is able to accommodate a LokSound sound decoder and 13mm speaker (speaker frame included). The models also have a detailed interior, all wheel pick-up, a fly-wheel driven motor, NEM coupling pockets and working lights.

371-886	**E50644+E59388+E50622** BRc green DC6 - *09*	90	113
371-885	**E50626+E59384+E50636** BRe blue DC6 - *10*	90	113

L58. Class 150 2-Car Sprinter DMU (B) (2009)

'DCC ready'. Upgraded mechanism, twin flywheel 5-pole skew wound motor and tinted glazing. Both 150/1 and 150/2 subclasses. Directional lights.

371-325	**150144** (**57144+52144**) First North Western violet 150/1 DC6 - *09*	75	92
371-326	**150102** Centro green+blue 150/1 DC6 - *not made*	NA	NA
371-326	**150125** (**57125+52125**) Central Trains green+blue 150/1 DC6 - *09*	75	92
371-327	**150256** (**57256+52256**) Arriva Trains Wales light blue 150/2 DC6 - *09*	75	92
371-328	**150270** (**57270+52270**) BR Reg Rlys violet+pale grey 150/2 DC6 - *09*	75	92
(370-105)	**150148** (**57148+52148**) BR Provincial original Sprinter livery violet+pale grey 150/1 ex-set - *09*	75	NA

L59a. Class 158 DMU (2002)

From 2005, upgraded mechanism developed for the Class 170, twin flywheel 5-pole skew wound motor and tinted glazing.

	2-car unit		
371-554	**158726** (**57726+52726**) ScotRail Woosh! white+purple - *not made*	NA	NA
371-554	**158741** (**57741+52741**) ScotRail Woosh! white+purple - *05*	65	86
371-552	**158745** (**57745+52745**) Alphaline Wales & West silver - *02*	55	70
371-553	**158746** (**57746+52746**) Wessex Trains Alphaline silver - *05*	65	83
371-551	**158758** (**57758+ 52758**) FNW blue - *02*	55	70
371-550	**158783** (**57783+52783**) Central green - *02*	65	86
371-557	**158783** (**57783+52783**) East Midlands Trains blue+white+red - *10*	80	105
371-556	**158791** (**57791+52791**) Northern Rail mauve+ violet - *10*	80	105
371-550A	**158797** (**57797+52797**) Central green - *05*	65	83
371-554	**158823** Northern Spirit light blue - *not made*	NA	NA
371-555	**158823** (**52823+57823**) Arriva lt.blue - *07*	65	86
	3-car unit		
371-525	**158811** (**52811+57811+58811**) Northern Spirit TPE purple - *02*	60	75

L59b. Class 159 3-Car DMU (2005)

Upgraded mechanism, twin flywheel 5-pole skew wound motor and tinted glazing.

371-526	**159019** (**52891+58736+57891**) SWT white, blue, red + orange - *05*	72	88

L60. Class 168 Clubman 3-Car DMU (2006)

Upgraded mechanism, twin flywheel 5-pole skew wound motor.

Chiltern Railways Class 168 DMU [L60]

371-435	**168111** (**58161+58461+58261**) Chiltern Railways white+violet 168/1 - *06*	80	99

L61a. Class 170 Turbostar DMU (2004)

Upgraded mechanism, twin flywheel 5-pole skew wound motor. In the case of the 3-car units, the power car is in the centre.

	2-car unit		
371-425	**170105** (**50105+79105**) MML teal green 170/1 - *04*	65	84
371-429	**170270** (**50270+79270**) Anglia/One blue 170/2 - *07*	70	90
371-427	**170302** (**50302+79302**) SWT white+red+ blue 170/3 - *05*	70	88

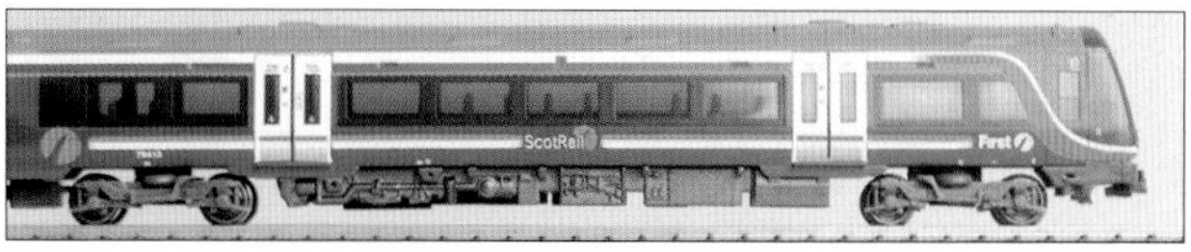

First ScotRail Class 170 'Turbostar' DMU [L61a]

371-432	**171504** (**50504+79504**) London Midland pale grey+green 170/5 - *09*	70	88
371-426	**170514** (**50514+79514**) Central green 170/5 - *04*	65	84
371-431	**170519** (**50519+79519**) Cross Country silver+ purple 170/2 - *10*	80	100
	3-car unit		
371-428	**170413** (**79413+56413+50413**) First ScotRail purple 170/4 - *06*	80	99

L61b. Class 171 Turbostar 2-Car DMU (2007)

Upgraded mechanism, twin flywheel 5-pole skew wound motor.

371-430	**171721** (**50721+79721**) Southern green+white 171/7 - *07*	70	90

L62. Class 220 Voyager 4-Car DMU (B) (2008)

'DCC Ready' with 6-pin decoder sockets. Heavy twin fly-wheel chassis, working bi-directional lighting, detailed interiors and optional N gauge couplings, allowing the purchaser to fit standard N gauge couplings if required.

371-675	**220001** ***Maiden Voyager*** (**60301+60701+60201+60401**) Virgin red+silver DC6 - *08*	110	132
371-678	**220017** (**60317+60717+60217+60417**) Cross Country grey+purple DC6 - *08*	110	132

L63. Class 222 Meridian/Pioneer DMU (B)

This had been planned for 2009, but in July 2010 it was announced that Bachmann had decided to no proceed with this model for the time being.

371-676	**222011**MML (Meridian) white+blue+grey DC6 - *not made*	NA	NA
371-679	**222017** East Midlands (Meridian) white+ blue DC6 - *not made*	NA	NA
371-677	**222101** Hull Trains green+grey (Pioneer) DC6 - *not made*	NA	NA

L64. GWR Railcar (2005)

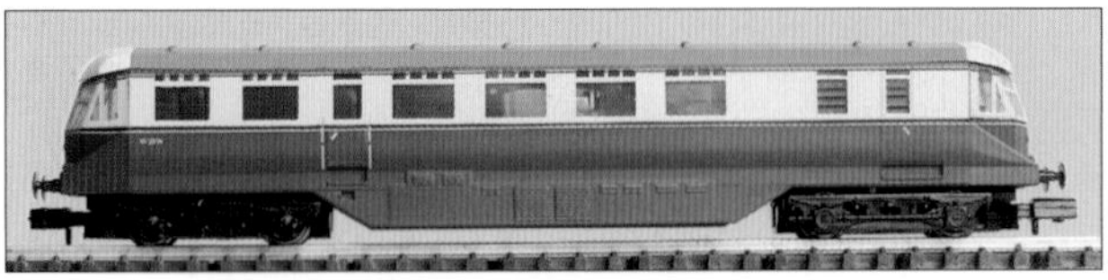

Ex-GWR railcar No.W20W [L64]

371-626	**19** GWR (shirt button) brown+cream - *05*	55	69
371-626A	**21** GWR brown+cream - *06*	NPG	NPG
371-626B	**22** GWR (button) brown+cream - *07*	60	76
371-625	**W22W** BRc green - *not made*	NA	NA
371-627	**W27W** BR red+cream - *05*	55	69
371-627A	**W20W** BR red+cream - *06*	60	76
371-625A	**W30W** BRc green - *07*	60	76
371-625	**W32W** BRc green - *05*	55	69

COACHES

Cat No.	Company, Number, Colour, Dates	£	£

LMS Coaches

C1a. LMS Stanier Brake 3rd (B) (2008)

374-825	**LMS** 5789 maroon - *08*	10	15
374-825A	**LMS** 5810 maroon - *10*	12	16
374-826	**BR** M5805M red+cream - *08*	10	15
374-826A	**BR** M5772M red+cream - *10*	12	16
374-827	**BR** M5789M maroon - *10*	12	16

C1b. LMS Stanier Corridor All 3rd (B) (2008)

374-835	**LMS** 2040 maroon - *08*	10	15
374-835A	**LMS** 1674 maroon - *10*	12	16
374-836	**BR** M1971M red+cream - *08*	10	15
374-836A	**BR** M1981M red+cream - *10*	12	16
374-837	**BR** M1674M maroon - *09*	12	16

C1c. LMS Stanier Vestibule 1st/3rd (B) (2008)

374-850	**LMS** 9755 maroon - *08*	10	15
374-850A	**LMS** 9750 maroon - *10*	10	16

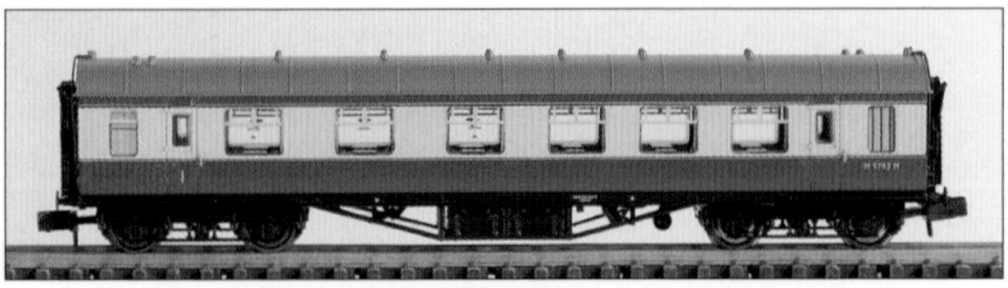

Stanier ex-LMS composite coach [C1c]

374-851	**BR** M9752M red+cream - *08*	10	15
374-851A	**BR** M9743M red+cream - *10*	12	16
374-852	**BR** M9755M maroon - *10*	12	16

C1d. LMS Stanier Brake 1st (B) (2008)

374-830	**LMS** 5062 maroon - *08*	10	15
374-830A	**LMS** 5060 maroon - *10*	10	16
374-831	**BR** M5053M red+cream - *08*	12	16
374-831A	**BR** M5055M red+cream - *10*	10	16
374-832	**BR** M5062M maroon - *10*	12	16

C1e. LMS Stanier Vestibule 3rd (B) (2008)

374-840	**LMS** 9443 maroon - *08*	10	15
374-840A	**LMS** 4964 maroon - *10*	12	16
374-841	**BR** M9491M red+cream - *08*	10	15
374-841A	**BR** M9502M red+cream - *09*	12	16
374-842	**BR** M9443M maroon - *10*	12	16

C1f. LMS Stanier Corridor 1st (2008)

374-845	**LMS** 1062 maroon - *08*	10	15
374-845A	**LMS** 1066 maroon - *10*	10	16
374-846	**BR** M1077M red+cream - *08*	10	15
374-846A	**BR** M1066M red+cream - *10*	12	16
374-847	**BR** M1062M maroon - *10*	12	16

BR Mk1 Pullman Coaches

C2a. BR Mk1 Pullman Parlour 1st (FP) (B) (2006)

Mk1 Pullman 1st parlour car Amathyst [C2a]

374-200	**Pullman** *Emerald* dark brown+cream - *07*	12	15
374-200A	**Pullman** *Amber* dark brown+cream - *08*	12	16
374-200B	**Pullman** *Amethyst* dark brown+cream - *09*	15	19
374-201	**Pullman** E326E grey+blue - *07*	15	19
374-201A	**Pullman** E327E grey+blue - *10*	15	19

C2b. BR Mk1 Pullman Kitchen 1st (FK) (B) (2006)

374-220	**Pullman** *Eagle* dark brown+cream - *06*	12	15
374-220A	**Pullman** *Magpie* dark brown+cream - *08*	12	16
374-220B	**Pullman** *Falcon* dark brown+cream - *09*	15	19
374-221	**Pullman** E315E grey+blue - *07*	15	19

C2c. BR Mk1 Pullman Parlour 2nd (SP) (B) (2006)

374-210	**Pullman** Car 347 dark brown+cream - *07*	12	15
374-210A	**Pullman** Car 348 dark brown+cream - *08*	12	16
374-210B	**Pullman** Car 349 dark brown+cream - *09*	15	19
374-211	**Pullman** E252E grey+blue - *07*	15	19
374-211A	**Pullman** E347E grey+blue - *10*	15	19

C2d. BR Mk1 Pullman Kitchen 2nd (SK) (B) (2006)

374-230	**Pullman** Car 332 dark brown+cream - *07*	12	15
374-230A	**Pullman** Car 333 dark brown+cream - *07*	12	16
374-230B	**Pullman** Car 334 dark brown+cream - *09*	15	19
374-231	**Pullman** E334E grey+blue - *07*	15	19

C2e. BR Mk1 Pullman Bar Car 2nd (BSP) (B) (2006)

374-240	**Pullman** *The Hadrian Bar* dark brown+cream - *07*	15	19
374-241	**BR** M354E *Nightcap Bar* blue+grey - *07*	15	19

BR Mk1 Suburban Coaches

C3a. BR 57' Suburban Coach (B) (2002)

374-276	**BR** W5490 maroon lined all 2nd - *02*	8	11
374-277	**BR** M11497 red - *02*	8	11
374-278	**BR** M16751 red - *02*	8	11
374-275	**BR** W6680 maroon lined - *02*	8	11
(370-075)	**BR** W6680 maroon lined ex-set - *03*	8	NA

C3b. BR 57' Suburban Brake End (B) (2002)

374-300	**BR** W6494 maroon lined - *02*	8	11
374-301	**BR** M20525 red (also in set 370-075) - *02*	8	11

C3c. BR Mk1 57' Suburban Compartment 2nd (B) (2005)

374-270	**BR** W46012 red - *05*	10	14
374-270A	**BR** M46081 maroon - *10*	10	16
374-271	**BR** M46071 maroon lined - *05*	10	13
374-271A	**BR** M46073 maroon lined - *09*	10	14

C3d. BR Mk1 57' Suburban Composite (B) (2005)

374-280	**BR** W41045 red - *05*	10	14
374-280A	**BR** M41004 maroon - *10*	10	16
374-281	**BR** M41014 maroon lined - *05*	10	13
374-281A	**BR** W41058 maroon lined - *09*	10	14
(370-076)	**BR** M41012 maroon lined ex-set - *05*	8	NA

C3e. BR Mk1 57' Suburban Open 3rd (2nd) (B) (2005)

Mk1 suburban open 2nd class [C3e]

374-290	**BR** W48033 red - *05*	10	14
374-290A	**BR** W48030 maroon - *10*	10	16
374-291	**BR** M48032 maroon lined - *05*	10	13
374-291A	**BR** W48029 maroon lined - *09*	10	14

C3f. BR Mk1 57' Suburban Brake 3rd (2nd) (B) (2005)

(370-076)	**BR** M43268 maroon lined ex-set - *05*	8	NA
374-310	**BR** M43269 maroon lined - *05*	10	14
374-310A	**BR** W3266 maroon lined - *10*	10	15
374-311	**BR** W43270 red - *05*	10	14

BR Mk1 Main Line Coaches

C4aa. BR Mk1 Open 2nd (SO) (2005)

374-000	**BR** E34796 red+cream - *not made*	NA	NA
374-000	**BR** E3737 red+cream - *05*	10	13
374-000A	**BR** M4421 red+cream - *07*	10	13
374-001	**BR** S4040 green - *05*	10	13
374-002	**BR** W4739 brown+cream - *05*	10	13
374-002A	**BR** W26093 brown+cream - *07*	10	13
374-003	**BR** M4899 maroon - *05*	10	13
374-006	**BR** E3457 blue+grey - *08*	11	14
374-004	**InterCity** 4909 grey+beige - *05*	11	14
374-005	**Regional Railways** 4873 blue+grey - *05*	10	13
-	**'BR RTC'** Test Coach 5	16	NA
-	**'BR RTC'** Laboritory Coach 12	16	NA
374-000Z	above 2 coaches Sp Edn 504 (ModelZone) - *10*	NA	40

C4ab. BR Mk1 Open 2nd (SO) New (B) (2010)

374-010	**BR** M3471 red+cream - *10*	14	18
374-011	**BR** S3824 green - *10*	14	18
374-014	**BR** W3821 dark brown+cream - *10*	14	18
374-012	**BR** M4929 maroon - *10*	14	18
374-013	**BR** M4430 blue+grey - *10*	14	18

C4b. BR Mk1 Full Brake (BG) (2002)

WR Mk1 full brake [C4b]

374-026	**BR** M80541 red+cream - *03*	9	12
374-026A	**BR** M80549 red+cream - *04*	10	13
374-026B	**BR** E86308 red+cream - *07*	10	13
374-026C	**BR** E80623 red+cream - *09*	11	14
374-027	**BR** E80798 maroon - *02*	9	12
374-027A	**BR** E80792 maroon - *04*	10	13
374-027B	**BR** M81299 maroon - *07*	10	13
374-027C	**BR** M80950 maroon - *09*	12	15
374-028	**BR** S81510 green - *02*	10	13
374-028A	**BR** ? green - *?*	NPG	NPG
374-029	**BR** W81205 brown+cream - *02*	9	12
374-029A	**BR** W81216 brown+cream - *05*	10	13
374-029B	**BR** W81019 brown+cream - *07*	10	13
374-029C	**BR** W80668 brown+cream - *09*	11	14
374-025	**BR** E80617 blue+grey Newspapers - *02*	9	12
374-025A	**BR** E80629 blue+grey - *05*	10	13
374-025B	**BR** M80871 blue+grey - *07*	10	13
374-025C	**BR** M? blue+grey - *?*	NPG	NPG
374-030	**Inter-City** 92151 grey+beige NEA* - *03*	11	14
374-031	**Regional Rlys** E92058 blue+grey NEA - *03*	11	14
374-032	**RES** 92322 red+dark grey NEX - *03*	10	13
374-032A	**RES** 92327 red+dark grey NEX - *08*	11	14
(370-125)	**RES** 92418 red+dark grey NFA ex-set - *03*	9	NA

* Box marked NHA but model marked NEA.

C4ca. BR Mk1 Corridor 2nd (SK) (2002)

374-050	**BR** M24446 red+cream - *02*	9	12
374-050A	**BR** M24813 red+cream - *03*	9	12
374-050B	**BR** E24807 red+cream - *04*	9	12
374-050C	**BR** E24783 red+cream - *05*	9	12
374-050D	**BR** M24159 red+cream - *06*	10	13
374-050E	**BR** M25889 red+cream - *07*	10	13
374-051	**BR** S24311 green - *02*	9	12
374-051A	**BR** S24324 green * - *04*	9	12
374-051B	**BR** S24309 green - *06*	10	13
374-051C	**BR** S24318 green - *08*	10	14
(370-225)	**BR** S24327 green ex-set - *03*	9	NA
(370-225)	**BR** S24309 green ex-set - *03*	9	NA
374-052	**BR** W24165 brown+cream - *02*	9	12
374-052A	**BR** W25051 brown+cream - *03*	9	12
374-052B	**BR** W25093 brown+cream - *04*	9	12
374-052C	**BR** W26099 brown+cream - *06*	10	13
374-052D	**BR** W26128 brown+cream - *08*	10	14
(370-150)	**BR** W25050 brown+cream ex-set - *03*	9	NA
374-053	**BR** E24538 maroon - *02*	9	12
374-053A	**BR** M25400 maroon - *03*	9	12
374-053B	**BR** M25437 maroon - *04*	9	12
374-053C	**BR** M25409 maroon - *05*	9	12
374-053D	**BR** E24237 maroon - *06*	10	13
374-053E	**BR** E25491 maroon - *07*	10	13
374-053F	**BR** E26057 maroon - *08*	11	14
(370-100)	**BR** M24399 maroon ex-set - *03*	9	NA
(370-100)	**BR** M24823 maroon ex-set - *03*	9	NA
(370-101)	**BR** M24824 maroon ex-set - *05*	9	NA
(370-101)	**BR** M24400 maroon ex-set - *05*	9	NA
(370-135)	**BR** M24567 red+cream ex-set - *02*	9	NA
(370-135)	**BR** M24819 red+cream ex-set - *02*	9	NA
374-055	**BR** E25039 blue+grey - *03*	9	12
374-055A	**BR** E25011 blue+grey - *04*	9	12
374-055B	**BR** E2603 blue+grey - *06*	10	13
374-055C	**BR** M25893 blue+grey - *07*	10	13
374-055D	**BR** E2603 blue+grey - *08*	11	14
374-054	**BR Intercity** M18753 grey+beige - *03*	9	12
374-054A	**BR** E24448 grey+beige - *06*	11	14

* Also shown as 374-051B in the catalogue.

C4cb. BR Mk1 Corridor 2nd (SK) New (B) (2010)

Mk1 corridor 2nd class [C4cb] new tooling

374-060	**BR** M24135 red+cream - *10*	14	18
374-064	**BR** W24328 dark brown+cream - *10*	14	18
374-063	**BR** S24317 green - *10*	14	18
374-061	**BR** M24911 maroon - *10*	14	18
374-062	**BR** SC18551 blue+grey - *10*	14	18

C4d. BR Mk1 Corridor Brake Comp (BCK) (2002)

374-075	**BR** M21026 red+cream - *02*	9	12
374-075A	**BR** E21093 red+cream - *05*	9	12
374-075B	**BR** W21071 red+cream - *05*	9	12
374-075C	**BR** E21217 red+cream - *06*	10	13
374-075D	**BR** E21053 red+cream - *08*	11	14
(370-135)	**BR** M21030 red+cream ex-set - *02*	9	NA
(370-135)	**BR** M21238 red+cream ex-set - *02*	9	NA
374-076	**BR** S21268 green - *02*	9	12
374-076A	**BR** S21271 green - *04*	10	13
374-076B	**BR** S21275 green - *08*	10	14
(370-225)	**BR** S21264 green ex-set - *03*	9	NA
(370-225)	**BR** S21272 green ex-set - *03*	9	NA
374-077	**BR** W21067 brown+cream - *02*	9	12
374-077A	**BR** W21083 brown+cream - *04*	9	12
374-077B	**BR** W21135 brown+cream - *06*	10	13
374-077C	**BR** W21192 brown+cream - *08*	10	14
374-078	**BR** E21202 maroon - *02*	9	12
374-078A	**BR** M21226 maroon - *03*	9	12
374-078B	**BR** E21219 maroon - *05*	9	12
374-078C	**BR** E21259 maroon - *06*	9	12
374-078D	**BR** E21234 maroon - *08*	11	14
(370-100)	**BR** M21033 maroon ex-set - *03*	9	NA
(370-100)	**BR** M21198 maroon ex-set - *03*	9	NA
(370-101)	**BR** M21199 maroon ex-set - *05*	9	NA
(370-101)	**BR** M21034 maroon ex-set - *05*	9	NA
374-080	**BR** M21241 blue+grey - *03*	9	12
374-080A	**BR** E21037 blue+grey - *06*	10	13
374-080B	**BR** E21216 blue+grey - *08*	11	14
374-079	**BR Intercity** 21266 grey+beige - *03*	11	14

C4e. BR Mk1 Mini Buffet (RMB) (2003)

374-100	**BR** red+cream - *not made*	NA	NA
374-100	**BR** S1881 green - *03*	9	12
374-100A	**BR** S1864 green - *05*	11	14
374-100B	**BR** ? green - *?*	NPG	NPG
374-101	**BR** green - *not made*	NA	NA
374-101	**BR** W1814 brown+cream - *03*	9	12
374-101A	**BR** W1821 brown+cream - *05*	10	13
374-101B	**BR** W1816 brown+cream - *06*	10	13
374-101C	**BR** ? brown+cream - *?*	NPG	NPG
374-102	**BR** brown+cream - *not made*	NA	NA
374-102	**BR** E1871 maroon - *03*	9	12
374-102A	**BR** E1879 maroon - *05*	9	12
374-102B	**BR** E1864 maroon - *06*	10	13
374-102C	**BR** M1821 maroon - *08*	11	14
374-102D	**BR** ? maroon - *?*	NPG	15
374-103	**BR** maroon - *not made*	NA	NA
374-104	**BR** E1871 blue+grey - *03*	10	13
374-104A	**BR** M1869 blue+grey - *08*	11	14
374-105	**BR** blue+grey - *not made*	NA	NA
374-103	**BR Intercity** 1832 grey+beige RBR - *03*	11	14
374-104	**BR Intercity** grey+beige - *not made*	NA	NA

C4f. BR Mk1 Corridor 1st (FK) (2005)

Mk1 corridor 1st class [C4f]

374-150	**BR** M13004 red+cream - *05*	10	13
374-150A	**BR** M13062 red+cream - *08*	11	14
374-150B	**BR** ? red+cream - *?*	NPG	NPG
374-151	**BR** S13143 green - *05*	10	13
374-151A	**BR** S13003 green - *09*	10	14
374-151B	**BR** ? green - *?*	NPG	NPG
374-152	**BR** W13074 brown+cream - *05*	10	13
374-152A	**BR** W13137 brown+cream - *08*	11	14
374-152B	**BR** ? brown+cream - *?*	NPG	NPG
374-153	**BR** W13030 maroon - *05*	10	13
374-153A	**BR** E13245 maroon - *07*	10	13
374-153B	**BR** M13070 maroon - *09*	12	15
374-153C	**BR** ? maroon lined - *?*	NPG	NPG
374-156	**BR** E13107 blue+grey - *08*	11	14
374-156A	**BR** E? blue+grey - *?*	NPG	NPG
374-154	**BR Intercity** M13341 grey+beige - *05*	11	14
374-155	**BR Regional Railways** 13225 blue - *05*	11	14

C4ga. BR Mk 1 Corridor Brake 2nd (BSK) (2005)

374-175	**BR** E34226 red+cream - *05*	10	13
374-175A	**BR** red+cream - *not made*	NA	NA
374-176	**BR** S35021 green - *05*	10	13
374-177	**BR** W34751 brown+cream - *05*	10	13
374-178	**BR** M35486 maroon - *05*	10	13
374-178A	**BR** maroon - *not made*	NA	NA
374-181	**BR** blue+grey - *not made*	NA	NA
374-179	**BR Intercity** M35465 grey+beige - *05*	11	14
374-180	**BR Regional Railways** 35452 blue - *05*	11	14

C4gb. BR Mk1 Corridor Brake 2nd (BSK) New (B) (2010)

374-185	**BR** M34288 red+cream - *10*	14	18
374-186	**BR** S34641 green - *10*	14	18
374-189	**BR** W34290 brown+cream - *10*	14	18
374-187	**BR** M34140 maroon - *10*	14	18
374-188	**BR** M35040 blue+grey - *10*	14	18

C4ha. BR Mk1 Corridor Composite (CK) (2005)

374-250	**BR** M15019 red+cream - *05*	10	13
374-251	**BR** S15904 green - *05*	10	13
374-252	**BR** W15770 brown+cream - *05*	10	13
374-253	**BR** E15145 maroon - *05*	9	12

C4hb. BR Mk1 Corridor Composite (CK) New (B) (2010)

BR (SR) Mk1 corridor composite 1st/2nd [C4hb] new tooling

374-255	**BR** M15192 red+cream - *10*	14	18
374-259	**BR** S15904 green - *10*	14	18
374-256	**BR** W13110 brown+cream - *10*	14	18
374-257	**BR** M15196 maroon - *10*	14	18
374-258	**BR** E15768 blue+grey - *10*	14	18

C4i. BR Mk1 Restaurant Car (RU) (2006)

374-117	**BR** W1902 brown+cream - *06*	11	14
374-117A	**BR** ? brown+cream - *?*	NPG	NPG
374-116	**BR** E1926 maroon - *06*	10	13
374-116A	**BR** W1915 maroon - *09*	12	15
374-115	**BR** E1938 blue+grey - *06*	11	14
374-118	**BR Intercity** 1981 grey+beige - *06*	11	14

C4j. BR Mk1 Restaurant Car (RFO) (2005)

374-802	**BR** M4 red+cream - *05*	10	13
374-802A	**BR** W8 red+cream - *09*	11	14
374-803	**BR** S9 green - *05*	11	14
374-803A	**BR** ? green - *?*	NPG	NPG
374-804	**BR** W7 brown+cream - *05*	11	14
374-804A	**BR** ? brown+cream - *11*	10	15
374-801	**BR** E3 maroon - *05*	11	14
374-801A	**BR** ? maroon - *101*	10	15
374-800	**BR** E3 blue+grey - *05*	11	14

C5. BR Mk1 General Utility Van (GUV) (2003)

374-128	**BR** ? green - *?*	NPG	NPG
374-129	**BR** ? maroon - *?*	NPG	NPG
374-125	**BRe** W86359 blue Express Parcels - *03*	9	12
374-125A	**BRe** W93180 blue Express Parcels - *05*	10	13
374-125B	**BRe** 93469 blue - *08*	11	14
374-125C	**BRe** ? blue - *?*	NPG	NPG
374-126	**BR** M93337 blue+grey Intercity Motorail - *03*	10	13
374-127	**BR RES** 95197 red+dark grey - *03*	9	12
374-127A	**BR RES** 95193 red+dark grey - *05*	11	14
374-127B	**BR RES** ? red+dark grey - *?*	NPG	NPG
(370-125)	**BR RES** 95199 red+dark grey NOX ex-set - *03*	10	NA

C6. BR Mk1 Full Brake Super BG (2005)

These are the first Farish coaches to be entirely tooled in China. Detailed underframes.

374-775	**RES** 94451 red+dark grey - *05*	11	14
374-776	**RES/Royal Mail** 94520 red+dark grey - *05*	11	14
374-777	**EWS/Royal Mail** 94420 red+dark grey - *05*	11	14
374-778	**Royal Mail** 94486 red+black - *05*	11	14

C7. BR Mk1 Travelling Post Office TPO (2010)

374-901	**BR/Royal Mail** W80300 red - *10*	NPG	NPG
374-902	**BR Royal Mail** M80300 blue+ grey - *10*	NPG	NPG
374-903	**BR Royal Mail** Letters 80300 red NSV - *10*	NPG	NPG
374-900	**BR Travelling Post Office** 80305 red NSX - *10*	NPG	NPG

BR Mk2 Coaches

C8a. BR Mk2D/F Brake 2nd Open (BSO) (2004)

374-677	**BR IC** E9482 blue+grey Mk2F - *04*	9	12
374-677A	**BR IC** E9491 blue+grey Mk2F - *06*	10	13
374-677B	**BR IC** E9481 blue+grey Mk2F - *09*	11	14
374-675	**Virgin** 9516 red+black Mk2F - *04*	11	14
374-676	**FGW** 9492 green MK2D - *04*	11	14

C8b. BR Mk2 Buffet Open 1st (RFB/RMBF/TSOT) (2004)

374-702	**BR IC** E6614 blue+grey Mk2F TSOT - *04*	9	12
374-702A	**BR IC** E6605 blue+grey Mk2F TSOT - *06*	10	13
374-702B	**BR IC** E6601 blue+grey Mk2F TSOT - *09*	11	14
374-700	**Virgin** 1208 red+black Mk2F RFB - *04*	11	14
374-701	**FGW** 6723 green Mk2D RMBF - *04*	11	14

C8c. BR Mk2D/E Trailer 2nd Open (TSO) (2004)

374-727	**BR IC** E5675 blue+grey Mk2E - *04*	9	12
374-727A	**BR IC** E5709 blue+grey Mk2E - *06*	10	13
374-727B	**BR IC** E5681 blue+grey Mk2E - *10*	11	14
374-725	**Virgin** 5966 red+black Mk2E - *04*	10	13
374-726	**FGW** 5657 green Mk2D - *04*	9	12
374-726A	**FGW** 5669 green Mk2D - *06*	11	14

C8d. BR Mk2E/F Trailer 1st Open (TFO) (2004)

Virgin Trains Mk2 trailer 1st open [C8d]

374-752	**BR IC** E3186 blue+grey Mk2F - *04*	9	12
374-752A	**BR IC** E3171 blue+grey Mk2F - *06*	10	13
374-752B	**BR IC** M3210 blue+grey Mk2F - *09*	11	14
374-750	**Virgin** 3381 red+black Mk2E - *04*	10	13
374-750A	**Virgin** 3385 red+black Mk2E - *09*	11	14
374-751	**FGW** 3381 green Mk2E - *04*	11	14

BR Mk3 Coaches

C9a. BR Mk3 Trailer Standard (TS) (2001)

347-329	**BR ICs** 42010 grey+beige - *07*	10	13
-	**BR ICs** 42074 grey+beige ex-pack - *07*	10	NA
347-327	**GNER** 42057 [C] navy blue - *01*	9	12
-	**GNER** 42064 [B] navy blue ex-pack - *01*	9	NA
(371-480)	**GNER** 42058 [B] navy+red ex-pack - *07*	10	NA
(371-481)	**GNER** 42377 [?] navy+red ex-pack - *09*	11	NA
374-327A	**GNER** 42235 [G] navy blue, red doors - *08*	11	14
374-327B	**GNER** 42243 [F] navy blue, red doors - *08*	11	14
374-327C	**GNER** 42057 [E] navy blue, red doors - *08*	11	14
374-327D	**GNER** 42219 [C] navy blue, red doors - *08*	11	14
347-328	**Virgin** 42171 [?] red+black - *02*	9	12
-	**Virgin** 42127 [?] red+black ex-pack - *02*	9	NA
374-325	**MML** 42149 [C] teal green+cream - *01*	9	12
-	**MML** 42157 [B] green+cream ex-pack - *01*	9	NA
374-325A	**MML** 42335 [E] white+blue+grey - *07*	11	14
(371-475A)	**MML** 41100 [L] white+blue+grey ex-pack - *07*	10	NA
347-326	**FGW** 42025 [C] purple - *02*	9	12
347-326A	**FGW** [C] purple - *not made*	NA	NA
-	**FGW** 42072 [D] purple ex-pack - *02*	9	NA
374-331	**Arriva Cross Country** 42378 silver - *10*	11	15

C9b. BR Mk3 Trailer 1st (TF) (2001)

347-354	**BR ICs** 41036 grey+beige - *07*	11	14
347-352	**GNER** 41091 [G] navy blue - *01*	9	12
374-352A	**GNER** 41100 [L] navy blue, red doors - *08*	11	14
347-353	**Virgin** 41081 [?] red+black - *02*	9	12
374-350	**MML** 41064 [G] teal green+cream - *01*	9	12
374-350A	**MML** 41057 [J] white+blue+grey - *07*	11	14
347-351	**FGW** 41005 [H] purple - *02*	9	12
374-355	**Arriva Cross Country** 41195 silver - *10*	11	15

C9c. BR Mk3 Trailer Buffet 1st (TRFB) (2001)

347-379	**BR ICs** 40708 grey+beige - *07*	11	14
347-378	**GNER** 40705 [F] navy blue - *01*	10	13

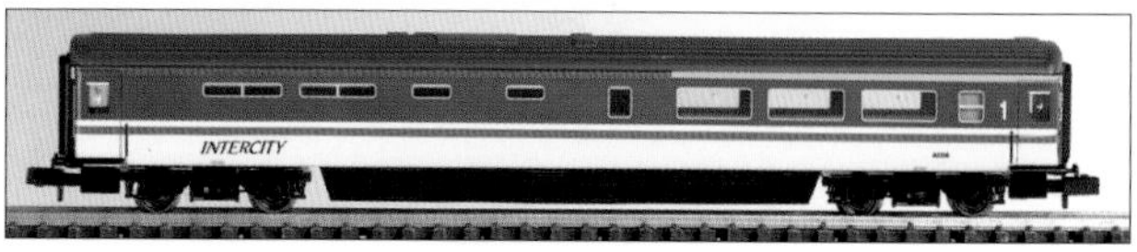

Mk3 trailer buffet 1st [C9c]

374-378A	**GNER** 40711 [J] navy blue, red doors - *08*	11	14
347-377	**Virgin** 40732 red+black - *02*	9	12
347-375	**MML** 40729 [F] teal green+cream - *01*	9	12
374-375A	**MML** 40708 [F] white+blue+grey - *07*	11	14
347-376	**FGW** 40707 [F] purple - *02*	11	14
374-380	**Arriva Cross Country** 45003 silver - *10*	11	15

C9d. BR Mk3 Trailer Guard's Standard (TGS) (2001)

347-404	**BR ICs** 44018 grey+beige - *07*	11	14
347-403	**GNER** 44098 [A] navy blue - *01*	10	13
374-403A	**GNER** 44019 [A] navy blue, red doors - *08*	11	14
347-402	**Virgin** 44076 [A] red+black - *02*	9	12
347-400	**MML** 44041 [A] teal green+cream - *01*	11	14
347-400A	**MML** 44041 [A] white+blue+grey - *07*	11	14
347-401	**FGW** 44023 [A] purple - *02*	11	14
374-405	**Arriva Cross Country** 44052 silver - *10*	11	15

C9e. BR Mk3 Trailer Buffet Standard (TRSB)

374-425	**Virgin** ? red+black - *not made*	NA	NA

C9f. BR Mk3 Trailer Buffet 1st (TRB)

374-450	**FGW** ? purple - *not made*	NA	NA

C9g. BR Mk3 Sleeper Car (SLEP) (2007)

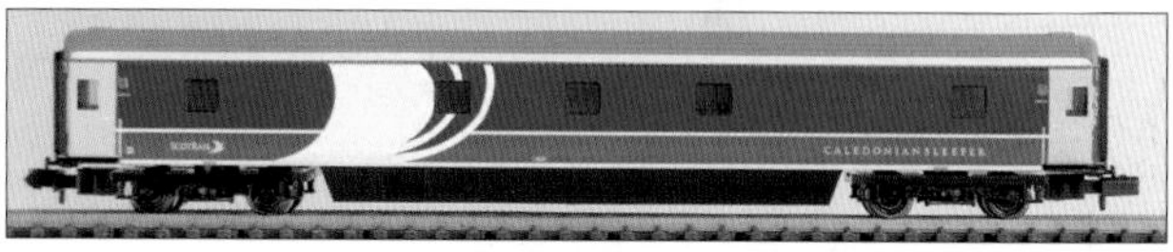

ScotRail Mk3 Caledonian Sleeper [C9g]

374-475	**FGW** 10590 green (fag packet) - *07*	11	14
374-476	**Scotrail Caledonian** 10681 purple - *07*	10	13

C9h. BR Mk3 Restaurant Buffet 1st (RFM) (2007)

374-500	**Virgin** 10202 red+black - *07*	11	14

BR Mk4 Coaches

C10a. BR Mk4 Open Standard (TSOD) (2006)

374-525	**GNER** 12313 [F] navy blue - *07*	11	14

C10b. BR Mk4 Open Standard (End) (TSOE) (2006)

374-550	**GNER** 12212 [B] navy blue - *07*	11	14

C10c. BR Mk4 Open Standard (TSO) (2006)

374-575	**GNER** 12489 [E] navy blue - *07*	11	14

C10d. BR Mk4 Open 1st (TFO) (2006)

374-600	**GNER** 11254 [K] navy blue - *07*	11	14

C10e. BR Mk4 Kitchen Buffet Standard (RSB) (2006)

374-625	**GNER** 10323 [H] navy blue - *07*	10	13

C11. BR Mk4 Driving Brake Van (DLV) (2005)

374-650	**GNER** ? navy blue - *not made*	NA	NA
(371-810)*	**GNER** 82212 navy blue DVT trailer - *05*	10	NA
(371-800)*	**GNER** 82226 navy blue DVT trailer - *05*	10	NA

* These came in a pack twinned with Class 91 electric locomotives.

WAGONS

Most of the wagons have been based on the original Graham Farish range but by 2005, Bachmann were totally retooling some of them, basing the new wagons on their own 00 range. The first samples of a whole new range of open wagons arrived in the summer and, where appropriate, they had separate brakes and V hanger mounted brake handles and there were both spoked and 3-hole disc wheels. They also had turned brass buffers and a choice of timber or steel type floors. The new wagons also had clip plate couplings with an enclosed spring as is common in the USA range of products from Bachmann.

Cat No.	Company, Number, Colour, Dates	£	£

Flat Wagons

W1. 'Conflat' with Container (B) (2009)

377-327	**GW** 39326 dark grey + GWR AF container AF-2100 white - *not made*	NA	NA
377-327	**GW** 39354 dark grey + GWR AF container AF-2098 white - *09*	5	7

'Conflat B' with 2 'Birds Eye' AFP containers [W1]

377-326	**BR** B709437 brown + AF container AF16392B ice blue - *09*	5	7
377-325	**BR** B505569 brown + BD Speedfreight BD46491B silver+yellow - *09*	5	7
377-328	**BR** 709708 brown + BD50150B container ? red - *09*	5	7
377-340	**BR** B704954 brown + 2 AF containers BR AF 16098B + AF 65098B white - *09*	5	7
377-341	**BR** B740503 brown + 2 AFP containers Birds Eye AFP66348B+AFP66358B blue+white - *09*	5	7

Planked Open Wagons

W2. 3-plank Wagon (B) (2007)

377-500	**'Imperial Chemical Industries'** 48 grey - *07*	3	4
377-500A	**'Imperial Chemical Industries'** 46 grey - *10*	4	5
377-502	**LMS** 473449 grey - *07*	3	4
377-502A	**LMS** 473215 grey - *10*	4	6
377-501	**BR** Medfit B457203 brown - *07*	3	4
377-501A	**BR** M470105 brown - *08*	4	5

W3a. 5-plank Wagon (2001)

373-155	'Joshua **Grey'** 3 brown - *02*	3	4
373-150Z	**'Foster Yeoman'** 36 black Sp Edn 500 (Buffers) - *05*	4	5
373-159	**'George Lovegrove'** 215 red sf - *05*	4	5
373-152	**'Hopton-Wood Stone'** 2 grey - *01*	4	5
373-153	**'ICI Lime'** 3034 grey - *01*	4	5
373-150	'EA **Stevenson'** 10 blue - *01*	4	5
373-158	'J&R **Stone'** 245 grey - *05*	3	4
373-157	**'Tarslag'** 836 grey - *02*	3	4
373-154	'Harry **Whitehouse'** 16 red - *02*	3	4
373-151	**'Worcester Co-op'** 20 red - *01*	4	5
373-156	**BR** P143165 grey (also used in sets) - *02*	3	4

W3b. 5-plank Wagon 9ft (steel floor) (B) (2005)

Spoked wheels and separately assembled brake gear. sf = steel floor. wf = wooden floor.

377-026	**'Arenig Granite'** 207 red sf - *05*	4	5
377-026A	'Nath'l. **Atrill'** 6 black - *10*	5	6
377-025A	**'Constable Hart & Co.'** 1004 black - *10*	5	6
377-025	**'Hopton-Wood Stone'** 2 grey sf - *05*	4	5
377-028	**'Lilleshall'** 1750 red - *10*	5	6
(377-075K5)	**'Lochgelly'** 1898 red Sp Edn 504 (BCC) - *09*	5	NA
377-027	'George **Lovegrove'** 215 red sf - *05*	4	5
377-027A	**BR** M318256 grey - *10*	5	6

W3c. 5-plank Wagon 9ft (wood floor) (B) (2005)

Spoked wheels and separately assembled brake gear.

5-plank wagon - 'R.Fred Cole' [W3c]

377-053	'R Fred **Cole'** 11 red - *10*	5	6
377-050	'James **Durnford & Son'** 37 black - *05*	4	5
377-050A	'James **Durnford & Son'** 30 black - *10*	5	6
377-052	**'Hucknall'** 3422 red - *05*	3	4
377-051	'FH **Silvey'** 191 dk.brown - *05*	3	4
377-054	**BR** M318256 grey - *10*	4	5

W4a. 6-plank Wagon 10ft (2001)

Although labelled 7-plank, the model appears to have 6 planks.

373-175U	**'Bradford & Sons'** 1 brown Sp Edn 500 (Buffers) - *05*	4	5
373-175S	'G **Bryer Ash'** 1110 black Sp Edn 500 (Buffers) - *05*	4	5

6-plank 'Charles Roberts & Co' [W4a] (Bachmann)

(370-025)	**'Carlton Main'** 5014 red* ex-set- *03*	3	NA
373-175	**'Charles Roberts'** 70001 black Sp Edn club (BCC) - *04*	4	5
373-178	**'Cosy Fires'** 778 grey - *01*	4	5
373-183	**'Douglas Bank Colliery'** 454 brown - *05*	3	4
373-175X	**'Dunkerton Colliery'** 10 blue Sp Edn 500 (Buffers) - *05*	4	5
373-181	**'Florence Coal & Iron'** 1017 grey - *02*	3	4
373-177	**'Flower & Son'** 7 grey-green - *01*	4	5
373-182	**'Gellyceidrim'** 719 light grey - *02*	3	4
373-183	'The **Great Western Railwaymen's Coal Association'** 1 grey - *not made*	NA	NA
373-175	**'ICI Salt'** 326 brown *(also used in 370-200 set) - 01*	4	5
373-2003	'James **Kenworthy'** 47 brown Ltd Edn (BCC) - *03*	3	4
373-175T	**'Kilmersdon Colliery'** 25 green Sp Edn 500 (Buffers) - *05*	4	5
373-176	**'Kobo'** 15 grey - *01*	4	5
373-179	**'Lunt'** 724 grey+black - *02*	3	4

373-175R	'The **Mains Coal & Cannel Co.**' 475 light grey Sp Edn 500 (Buffers) - *05*	4	5
373-175Z	**'Royal Leamington Spa'** 22 maroon Ltd Edn 500 - *04*	3	4
(370-175)	**'South Leicester'** 373 red ex-set - *03*	3	NA
373-180	**'Sycobrite'** 650 yellow+black - *02*	3	4
373-175W	**'Timsbury Colliery'** 14 red Sp Edn 500 (Buffers) - *05*	4	5
373-184	**'Webb, Hall & Webb'** 19 grey - *not made*	NA	NA
373-184	'WE **Wise**' 18 black - *05*	3	4
(370-050)	'JR **Wood Co.**' 346 yellow* ex-set - *03*	3	NA
373-175Y	**'Writhlington Colliery'** 160 light blue Sp Edn 500 (Buffers) - *05*	4	5
373-175V	**'Yeovil Gas Works'** 24 brown Sp Edn 500 (Buffers) - *05*	4	5

* shade variations.

W4b. 7-plank Wagon 9ft (end door & fixed end) (B) (2005)

Spoked wheels and separately assembled brake gear.Some have end doors (end) and some have fixed ends (fix) and should not be confused with the 2001 model.

377-075K2	**'Aberpergwn'** 941 red Sp Edn 504 (BCC) - *05*	7	10
377-081Z	'The **Arley Colliery**' 27 red fix Sp Edn 504 (Castle Trains) - *08*	4	6
377-080	**'Bradleys Weardale'** 246 brown end - *06*	4	6
377-076	**'Douglas Bank Colliery'** 454 brown end - *05*	4	6
377-075K3	**'Cains'** 3 black Sp Edn 504 (BCC) - *05*	7	10
377-075K	'The **Cambrian Wagon Co.**' 188 ? Sp Edn (BCC) - *05*	7	10
377-076K	'Edward **Eastwood**' 2 very dark green Sp Edn (BCC) - *08*	6	9
377-075K1	**'Fife Coal'** 1655 brown Sp Edn 504 (BCC) - *05*	7	10

7-plank 'Firestone' [W4b]

377-079	**'Firestone'** 2004 blue end - *06*	4	5
377-079A	'**Firestone**' 2005 blue end - *10*	5	6
(377-075K4)	**'Fleetwood Fish'** 2 brown Sp Edn (BCC) - *05*	7	NA
377-075?	**'Gloucester Gas Light Company'** 37 black Sp Edn 500 (*British Railway Modelling*) - *09*	4	6
377-075?	**'Gloucester Gas Light Company'** 51 black Sp Edn 500 (*British Railway Modelling*) - *09*	4	6
377-075	**'Goldendale Iron Co.'** 598 grey - *05*	4	6
377-081A	'DVend**Gostick** 1 blue fix - 10	5	6
(377-075K4)	**'Guard Bridge Paper Co.'** 67 grey fix Sp Edn (BCC) - *05*	7	NA
377-081	**'GWR Railwaymans Coal Assn.'** 1 grey fix - *06*	4	6
377-075A	**'Harrisons'** 5038 grey end - *10*	5	6
377-2009K	'Thomas **Hunter**' brown Sp Edn (BCC) - *09*	6	8
(377-075K5)	**'Jenkerson & Sons'** 277 black Sp Edn 504 (BCC) - *09*	5	NA
377-082	**'Kobo'** 15 grey end - *10*	4	6
377-075Y	**'Leamington Priors Gas Co.'** 10 bright red fix Sp Edn - *06*	4	5
(377-075K4)	**'Lewis Merthyr Navigation Colliery'** 674 black Sp Edn (BCC) - *05*	7	NA
377-2010K	**Pickering [R.Y.] & Co. 1002**, ?, Sp Edn (BCC) - *10*	NPG	NPG
(377-075K5)	**'St Helens Industrial Co-operative Society'** 17 grey Sp Edn 504 (BCC) - *09*	5	NA
377-075K	**'Standard Wagon'** 1923 yellow Sp Edn (BCC) - *05*	7	10
377-075U	**'Walker & Rogers'** 3 red Sp Edn (Castle Trains) - *09*	5	6
377-075V	**'Warwick Gas Co.'** 6 grey Sp Edn (Castle Trains) - *09*	5	6
377-077	**'Wimberry Colliery Co.'** 2 black end - *05*	4	6
377-078	**BR** M608163 grey end - *08*	4	6
377-078A	**BR** P36147 grey end - *10*	5	6

W5a. Coal Traders Wagon Sets (2002)

373-900	6 assorted coal wagons - *02*	NA	20

W5b. Coal Traders Wagon Sets 9ft (B) (2005)

Some have end doors and some have fixed ends (fix) and should not be confused with the 2001 model.

-	**'MA Ray & Sons'** 123 light grey fix	6	NA
-	**'Fred C Holmes'** 104 red-brown	6	NA
-	**'FW Wacher'** 6 black fix	6	NA
373-075Z	above 3 wagons Kent Coal Traders pack Sp Edn 504 (ModelZone) - *06*	NA	24
-	**'St Helens Industrial Coal Department Co-operative Society'** 17 grey 7-plank	6	NA
-	**'Lochgelly'** 1898 red-brown 4-plank	6	NA
-	'T **Jenkerson & Sons**' 277 black 7-plank	6	NA
377-075K5	set of above 3 Sp Edn 504 (BCC) - *08*	NA	21
-	**'Pilkington Brothers'** 1412, red	6	NA
-	**'Smith Anderson & Co.'** 10, brown	6	NA
-	**'David Jones & Sons'** 650, black	6	NA
337-077K	above set of 3, Sp Edn 500 (BCC) - *10*	NA	21

Coal Traders Set [W5b] (Bachmann)

W6a. 7-plank with Coke Rail 10ft

373-375	**'POP'** - *not made*	NA	NA
373-376	**'Stringer & Jaggar'** - *not made*	NA	NA

W6b. 7-plank with Coke Rail 9ft (B) (2005)

Spoked wheels and separately assembled brake gear. Some have end doors (end) and some have fixed ends (fix) and should not be confused with the 2001 model.

377-175	**'New Cransley'** 166 red end - *05*	4	6
373-175A	**'POP'** 215 grey end - *10*	5	6
377-176	**BR** P368515 grey fix - *05*	3	4
377-176A	**BR** P368502 grey fix - *08*	4	6
377-176B	**BR** P167248 grey fix - *10*	5	6

W7a. 8-plank Wagon 9ft (fixed ends) (B) (2005)

Spoked wheels and separately assembled brake gear.

377-150K	**'Metropolitan'** 188 brown Sp Edn (BCC) - *06*	7	10

8-plank wagon 'Osborne & Son' [W7a]

377-151	'Henry **Musgrave**' 2 grey - *05*	4	6
377-151A	'Henry **Musgrave**' 1 grey - *05*	4	6
377-152A	**'Osborne & Son'** 10 green - *10*	5	6
373-125A	'Pearse & Partners, **Thorne**' 740 red - *10*	5	6

377-150	'AJ **Salter**' 202 brown - *05*	4	6
373-150A	**'Stewart and Lloyds'** 6301 grey - *10*	5	6
377-152	'Charles **Ward'** 4265 red - *05*	4	6

W7b. 8-plank Wagon 9ft (end door) (2005) (B)

Spoked wheels and separately assembled brake gear.

377-125	**'Bagley'** 38 red - *05*	4	6
377-126	'The **Boston Deep Sea Fishing'** 86 blue - *05*	4	6
377-125K	'T **Burnett & Co.'** 1907 red Sp Edn (BCC) - *07*	7	10
373-127A	**'Great Mountain'** 930 brown - *10*	5	6
373-126A	**'Ketton Cement'** S89 red - *10*	5	6
377-127	'JR **Wood & Co.'** 346 orange - *05*	4	6

W8. 8-plank with Coke Rail 9ft (B) (2005)

Spoked wheels and separately assembled brake gear. Some have end doors (end) and some have fixed ends (fix) and should not be confused with the 2001 model.

8-plank wagon with coke rail 'Birley' [W8]

377-200	**'Birley'** 1605 black fix - *05*	4	6
377-200A	**'Birley'** 1610 black fix - *10*	4	6
377-201	**'Modern Transport'** 110 black end - *05*	4	6
377-202	**'Stamford'** 101 light grey fix - *05*	3	4
377-203	**'Reading'** 112 black end - *10*	4	6

W9. OAA 31T 5-plank Open Wagon (2003)

373-400	**BRe** 100013 brown - *03*	4	5
373-402	**BRe** 100078 brown ABN - *05*	5	7
373-401	**Railfreight** 100090 grey+red - *03*	4	5
373-403	**BRe Railfreight** 100005 grey+red - *05*	4	5
373-403A	**BRe Railfreight** 100039 grey+red - *08*	5	7
373-403B	**BRe Railfreight** 100081 grey+red - *10*	5	7

W10a. OBA 31T 5-plank Open (low-end) (B) (2007)

373-626	**BRe Railfreight** 110264 grey+red - *07*	5	7
373-626A	**BRe Railfreight** grey+red - *not made*	NA	NA
373-626B	**BRe Railfreight** 110583 grey+red - *made?*	NPG	NPG
373-626B	**BRe Railfreight** 110332 grey+red - *09*	7	9
373-625	**EWS** 110678 maroon+yellow - *07*	5	7
373-625A	**EWS** 110332 maroon+yellow - *08*	6	8
373-625B	**EWS** 110351 maroon+yellow - *made?*	NPG	NPG
373-625B	**EWS** 110583 maroon+yellow - *09*	7	9
373-625C	**EWS** 110740 maroon+yellow - *09*	7	9

W10b. OBA 31T 5-plank Open (high-end) (B) (2007)

373-627	Railfreight **'Plasmor'** 110701 red+green - *07*	5	7
373-627A	Railfreight **'Plasmor'** 110662 red+grn W - *08*	6	8
373-627B	Railfreight **'Plasmor'** 110737 red+green W - *09*	7	9
373-628	**EWS** 110636 maroon+yellow - *07*	5	7
373-628A	**EWS** 110639 maroon+yellow - *08*	6	8
373-628B	**EWS** 110545 maroon+yellow - *09*	7	9

Steel Open Wagons

W11a. BR 16T Steel Mineral Wagon (2002)

This wagon has pressed steel end and side doors.

373-200	**BR** B38066 grey (also in set 370-175) - *02*	4	5
373-200A	**BR** B38059 grey - *04*	4	5
373-202	**BR** B258683 light grey MCO - *02*	4	5
373-203	**BR** B38066 light grey - *not made*	NA	NA
373-203	**BR** B38071 light grey - *05*	4	5
(370-201)a	**BR** B68992 brown ex-set - *05*	5	NA
(370-201)b	**BR** ADB562927 olive ex-set - *05*	5	NA
(370-201)C	**BR** DB388868 grey+yellow ex-set - *05*	5	NA
(370-201)D	**BR** DB388869 grey+yellow ex-set - *05*	5	NA
373-201A	**BR** B68998 brown - *04*	4	5
373-201	**BR** B564872 brown Coal (also in set 370-051) - *02*	4	5

W11b. BR 16T Steel Mineral Wagon (no flap) (B) (2006)

Diagram 102

377-250	**BR** B227229 grey - *not made*	NA	NA

16 ton steel mineral wagons [W11b + W11c]

377-250	**BR** B38066 grey - *06*	3	4
377-250A	**BR** B38059 grey - *08*	3	5
377-250B	**BR** B? grey - *09*	4	6
377-251	**BR** B121830 grey MCO - *not made*	NA	NA
377-251	**BR** B258683 light grey MCO - *06*	3	4
377-251A	**BR** B? light grey MCO - *09*	4	6
377-252	**BR** ADB562927 olive green ZHV - *06*	4	6

W11c. BR 16T Steel Mineral Wagon (top flap) (B) (2006)

Diagram 108

377-225	**BR** B80200 grey - *not made*	NA	NA
377-225	**BR** B100071 grey - *06*	3	4
377-225A	**BR** B100083 grey - *08*	3	5
377-225B	**BR** B107071 grey - *09*	4	6
377-227	**BR** B106979 grey W - *06*	4	6
377-227A	**BR** B107071 grey W - *10*	4	6
377-226	**BR** B68901 brown - *not made*	NA	NA
377-226	**BR** B68900 brown - *06*	4	6
377-226A	**BR** B69007 brown - *10*	4	6

(377-225Z)	**BR** B77701 grey	4	NA
(377-225Z)	**BR** 80200 grey	4	NA
(377-225Z)	**BR** 168553 grey	4	NA
(377-225Z)	**BR** 140952 grey	4	NA
(377-225Z)	**BR** 257058 grey	4	NA
(377-225Z)	**BR** 82219 grey	4	NA
377-225Z	above 6 grey wagons Sp Edn 504 (Hattons) - *08*	NA	37

W12. BR 27T Steel 'Tippler' Wagon (B) (2006)

377-275	**BR** B383560 Iron Ore - *not made*	NA	NA
377-275	**BR** B381550 Iron Ore - *not made*	NA	NA
377-275	**BR** B381500 Iron Ore - *06*	4	6
377-275A	**BR** B381934 Iron Ore - *10*	4	6
377-276	**BR** B382888 grey Chalk - *not made*	NA	NA
377-276	**BR** B381293 grey Chalk - *06*	4	6
377-277	**BR** B380005 grey W Iron Ore - *not made*	NA	NA
377-277	**BR** B383476 grey W Iron Ore - *06*	3	4
377-277A	**BR** B380005 grey W Iron Ore - *10*	4	6

W13. BR 16T Slope-Sided Mineral Wagon (B) (2006)

Riveted door.

377-450	**BR** B11532 grey - *not made*	NA	NA
377-450	**BR** B8128 grey - *06*	4	6
377-450A	**BR** B115332 grey - *10*	4	6
377-451	**MWT** 11532 brown - *06*	4	6
377-451A	**MWT** 9512 brown - *10*	4	6

W14. MEA 46t Open Mineral Wagon (2002)

373-576	**Railfreight Coal** 391045 grey+yellow - *02*	5	7
373-576A	**Railfreight Coal** ? grey+yellow - *not made*	NA	NA
373-577	**Mainline** M391139 blue - *02*	5	7
373-577A	**Mainline** ? blue - *not made*	NA	NA
373-575	**EWS** 391262 maroon - *02*	5	7
373-575A	**EWS** 391307 maroon - *04*	5	7
373-575B	**EWS** 391549 maroon - *07*	5	7
373-575C	**EWS** 391537 maroon - *08*	5	7
373-575D	**EWS** ? maroon - *10*	5	7

W15. MFA 24t Open Box Mineral Wagon (2003)

373-877	**Rft Coal** 391070 grey+yellow - *03*	5	5
373-877A	**Rft Coal** 391078 grey+yellow - *04*	5	7
373-877B	**Rft Coal** 391075 grey+yellow - *07*	6	8
373-875	**EWS** 391102 in Mainline blue - *03*	5	6
373-875A	**EWS** 391146 in Mainline blue - *04*	5	7
373-876	**EWS** 391572 maroon - *03*	5	6
373-876A	**EWS** 391575 maroon - *?*	6	8
373-878	**EWS** 391102 maroon+yellow - *06*	5	7
373-878A	**EWS** ? maroon+yellow - *10*	6	8

W16. POA/MKA 46t Open Box Mineral Wagon (B) (2007)

Loadhaul open box mineral wagon [W16]

373-976	**'ARC'/Tiger** TRL5323 yellow PNA - *07*	7	9
373-975	**'Yeoman'/Tiger** TRL5352 very pale grey - *07*	7	9
373-978	**'Yeoman'/Tiger** TRL5154 very pale grey - *07*	5	7
373-978A	**'Yeoman'/Tiger** TRL? very pale grey - *09*	7	9
373-977	**Loadhaul** 393030 black+orange MKA - *07*	7	9
373-979	**Tiger** TRL5165 very pale grey - *07*	5	7
373-979A	**Tiger** TRL5164 very pale grey - *10*	7	9

W17. OCA 31t Drop-side Open Wagon (B) (2009)

377-550	**BR Departmental** 112115 grey+yellow - *09*	8	11
377-550A	**BR Departmental** 112092 grey+yellow - *10*	8	11
377-551	**BR Railfreight** 112342 red - *09*	8	11
377-551A	**BR Railfreight** 112391 red - *10*	8	11
377-552	**EWS** 112256 maroon+yellow - *09*	8	11
377-552A	**EWS** 112173 maroon+yellow - *10*	8	11

Open Hopper Wagons

W18. HEA/HSA 46t Hopper (2002)

See also the HEA listed in the earlier Graham Farish N section.

373-502	**BR** 360075 brown HSA - *02*	5	7
373-502A	**BR** 360226 brown HSA - *07*	5	7
373-502B	**BR** ? brown HSA - *09*	5	7
373-503	**BRe Railfreight** 361862 red+grey - *02*	5	7
373-503A	**Railfreight** red+grey - *not made*	NA	NA
373-507	**BRe Railfreight** 360644 red+grey - *06*	5	7
373-507A	**Railfreight** ? red+grey - *06*	5	7
373-501	**Railfreight** Coal 360601 grey+yellow - *not made*	NA	NA
373-501	**Railfreight** Coal 361554 grey+yellow - *02*	5	7
373-501A	**Railfreight** Coal grey+yellow - *not made*	NA	NA
373-506	**Rft Coal Load** 361579 grey+yellow - *06*	5	7
373-506A	**Rft Coal Load** 361581 grey+yellow - *08*	5	7
373-508	**Mainline** 360643 blue - *07*	5	7
373-508A	**Mainline** ? blue - *not made*	NA	NA
373-504	**ex-Mainline** 360940 blue + graffiti - *03*	5	7
373-500	**EWS** 361870 maroon+yellow - *02*	5	7
373-505	**EWS** 361328 maroon+yellow - *not made*	NA	NA
373-505	**EWS** 360042 maroon+yellow - *06*	5	7
373-505A	**EWS** maroon+yellow - *not made*	NA	NA
373-505B	**EWS** 360059 maroon+yellow - *08*	5	7
373-036C	**Railease** SRW? white - *10*	5	7

W19a. HAA 46t Hopper (B) (2005)

373-900	**BR** 351540, 352752, 352871, 353269 silver+brown - *05*	5	7
373-900A	**BR** 353687 silver+brown - *07*	5	7
373-900B	**BR** 353855 silver+brown W - *08*	7	9
373-900C	**BR** ? silver+brown W - *11*	7	9
373-902	**Railfreight Coal** 356263, 356281, 356297 silver+yellow - *06*	7	9
373-901	**EWS** 350122, 350357, 350461 silver+ maroon - *06*	5	7
373-901B	**EWS** ?, ?, ? silver+maroon - *09*	7	9

W19b. HFA Hopper with Dust Cover (B) (2006)

Transrail HFA hopper wagon [W19b]

373-950	**TransRail** 365034 silver+red-brown - *06*	5	7
373-950A	**TransRail** 365908 silver+red-brown - *07*	7	9
373-951	**Railfreight** red W - *not made*	NA	NA
373-951	**Mainline** 355512 silver+yellow - *06*	5	7
373-951A	**Mainline** 355786 silver+yellow W - *08*	7	9

W19c. CEA 46t Covered Hopper (B) (2006)

373-475	**LoadHaul** 361841 black+orange - *06*	5	7
373-475A	**LoadHaul** 361845 black+orange - *10*	5	7
373-476	**EWS** 360726 maroon - *06*	5	7
373-476A	**EWS** 360955 maroon - *10*	5	7

W20. PGA Bulk Aggregate Hopper (2003)

373-027	**'ARC'** AR14245 yellow - *03*	4	6
373-037	**'ARC'**/Caib PR14707 yellow - *04*	4	6
373-037A	**'ARC'**/Procor PR14726 yellow - *06*	5	7
373-037B	**'ARC'**/Procor PR14716 yellow - *08*	5	7
373-037C	**'ARC'**/Procor PR? yellow - *09*	5	7
373-030	**'British Industrial Sand'** BIS7987 white no ladders - *04*	5	7
373-030A	**'British Industrial Sand'** BIS7986 off-white - *08*	5	7
373-030B	**'British Industrial Sand'** BIS? off-white - *10*	5	7
373-025	**Caib** PR14455 grey - *03*	4	6
373-031	**'ECC Quarries'** PR14360 blue - *06*	5	7
373-031A	**'ECC Quarries'** PR14374 blue - *07*	5	7
373-031B	**'ECC Quarries'** PR? blue - *09*	5	7
373-033	**'Lafarge'** REDA14783 pale cream - *05*	5	7
373-033A	**'Lafarge'** REDA14796 pale cream - *07*	5	7
373-033B	**'Lafarge'** REDA? pale cream - *10*	5	7
373-036	**Railease** PR14466 white - *03*	4	6
373-036A	**Railease** SRW18506 white - *05?*	4	6
373-036B	**Railease** SRW18511 white - *07*	5	7
373-036C	**Railease** SRW? white - *10*	5	7
373-035	**Railease** SRW18506 white - *not made*	NA	NA
373-035	**'Redland'** - *not made*	NA	NA
373-028	**'Redland'** REDA14792 pale green - *04*	4	6
373-028A	**'Redland'** REDA14506 pale green - *06*	5	7
373-028B	**'Redland'** REDA14514 pale green - *07*	5	7
373-028C	**'Redland'** REDA? pale green - *09*	5	7
373-038	**'Tarmac'** TAMC14682 white+brown - *04*	5	7
373-038A	**'Tarmac'** TAMC14667 white+brown - *07*	5	7
373-026	**'Tarmac Quarry Products'** TAMC14863 green - *03*	4	6
373-026A	**'Tarmac Quarry Products'** ? green - *?*	4	6

'ARC' & 'Yeoman' PGA bulk aggragate hoppers [W20]

373-032	**VTG** VTG14372 Light grey - *06*	5	7
373-032A	**VTG** VTG? Light grey - *11*	5	7
373-035	**'Yeoman'** PR14466 very pale grey - *03*	5	7
373-035A	**'Yeoman'** PR14333 very pale grey - *05*	5	7
373-035B	**'Yeoman'** PR14363 very pale grey - *07*	5	7
373-035C	**'Yeoman'** PR? very pale grey - *09*	5	7
373-029	**'Yeoman'/Caib** PR14189 blue+grey - *04*	5	7

373-029A	**'Yeoman'/Caib** PR14196 blue+grey W - *07*	5	7
373-029B	**'Yeoman'/Caib** PR? blue+grey W - *09*	5	7

Dry Powder Hopper Tanks

W21. 22T 'Presflo' (2005)

373-526	**'Blue Circle'** PF20 yellow - *05*	4	5
373-526A	**'Blue Circle'** PF17 yellow W - *07*	4	5
373-526B	**'Blue Circle'** PF14 yellow W - *08*	5	7
373-527	**'Pozzolanic'** B888974 brown - *05*	5	7
373-525	**'Rugby Cement'** B8873811 brown - *05*	4	5
373-525A	**'Rugby Cement'** B8873814 brown - *08*	5	7

W22. PCA Bulk Powder (2003)

373-000	**'Alcan'** 55552 silver - *03*	4	6
373-003	**'Alcan'** 55552 silver - *not made*	NA	NA
373-002	**'Blue Circle'** DP102 pale grey - *03*	4	6
373-005	**'Blue Circle'** pale grey - *not made*	NA	NA
373-003	(unbranded) BCC11118 very pale grey - *04*	4	6
373-003A	(unbranded) BCC10994 very pale grey W - *05*	4	6
373-003B	(unbranded) BCC11138 very pale grey W - *06*	5	7
373-003C	(unbranded) BCC11122 very pale grey W - *08*	5	7
373-003D	(unbranded) BCC11017 very pale grey W - *10*	5	7
373-007	**'Castle Cement'** RLS10319 grey W - *06*	5	7
373-007A	**'Castle Cement'** RLS10327 pale grey W - *08*	5	7
373-007B	**'Castle Cement'** RLS10311 pale grey W - *10*	5	7
373-008	**'ICI'** 10120 white - *07*	5	7
373-008A	**'ICI'** 10111 off-white - *08*	5	7

Weathered 'RMC' & 'Blue Circle' PCA bulk powder tank wagons [W22]

373-005	**'RMC'** RC10025 orange - *04*	4	6
373-006	**'RMC'** RC10034 orange W - *06*	5	7
373-006A	**'RMC'** RC10041 orange W - *08*	5	7
373-006B	**'RMC'** RC10045 orange W - *10*	5	7
373-002A	**'Rugby Cement'** PR9420 white - *04*	4	6
373-002B	**'Rugby Cement'** PR9409 white - *06*	5	7
373-002B	**'Rugby Cement'** PR9417 white - *08*	5	7
373-002D	**'Rugby Cement'** PR9414 white - *10*	5	7
373-001	**'Tunnel Cement'** RLS10321 very pale grey - *03*	4	6
373-004	**'Tunnel Cement'** PL510327 very pale grey W - *04*	4	6

W23. PCA Taper Bulk Powder V Tank (2003)

373-075	**'Blue Circle'** 9343 pale grey - *03*	4	6
373-076A	(unbranded) BCC10834 very pale grey - *04*	5	7
373-076B	(unbranded) BCC10821 very pale grey - *07*	5	7
373-076C	(unbranded) BCC10771 very pale grey - *10*	5	7
373-077	(unbranded) APCM9138 very pale grey - *04*	4	6
373-077A	(unbranded) BCC10809 very pale grey - *06*	5	7
373-077B	(unbranded) BCC9171 very pale grey - *07*	5	7
373-077D	(unbranded) APCM9278 very pale grey - *10*	5	7
373-075A	**'Ketton Cement'** PR9468 yellow - *04*	4	6
373-075B	**'Ketton Cement'** PR9469 yellow - *06*	5	7
373-075C	**'Ketton Cement'** PR9471 yellow - *07*	5	7
373-075D	**'Ketton Cement'** TLG9464 yellow - *10*	5	7
373-078	**'Lever Brothers'** TRL10527 purple - *05*	5	7
373-078A	**'Lever Brothers'** TRL10523 purple - *07*	5	7
373-078B	**'Lever Brothers'** TRL10525 purple - *10*	5	7
373-076	**'Rockware Glass'** 10563 blue - *03*	4	6

Tank Wagons

W24a. 14T Small Tank Wagon (small cap) (B) (2005)

With gantry and ladders.

373-652	**'Bitumuls'** 12 black - *06*	4	5
373-653	**'ICI'** 159 blue - *08*	5	7
373-653A	**'ICI'** ? blue - *11*	5	7
373-650	**'National Benzole'** 734 silver - *06*	5	7
373-650A	**'National Benzole'** 755 silver - *10*	5	7
-	**'Shell BP'** 3971 black W large cap	5	NA
-	**'Shell BP'** 5103 black W	5	NA
-	**'Shell BP'** A4282 black W	5	NA
373-650Z	above three wagons Sp Edn 504 (Signalbox) - *07*	NA	21
373-651	**'Shell Electrical Oils'** SM1302 brown - *05*	4	5
373-651A	**'Shell Electrical Oils'** SM3116 brown - *08*	5	7
373-651B	**'Shell Electrical Oils'** SM2202 brown - *10*	5	7

W24b. 14T Small Tank Wagon (large cap) (B) (2005)

With cross stays.

373-677	**'Carburine Motor Spirit'** 6 yellow - *05*	4	5
373-678	**'Fina'** 136 silver - *08*	5	7
373-678A	**'Fina'** 135 silver - *10*	5	7

14 ton tank wagon 'The Kalchester Manufacturing Co.' [W24b]

373-676	'The **Kalchester Manufacturing Co.**' 101 red - *06*	4	5
373-675	**'Mobil'** 1624 black - *06*	5	7
373-675A	**'Mobil'** 5294 black - *10*	5	7
373-679	**'Shell/BP'** A5281 black - *08*	5	7
373-679A	**'Shell/BP'** A7287 black - *10*	5	7

W25. TTA 45t 'Monobloc' Tank Wagon (B) (2006)

373-775	**'BP'** BPO53774 green - *07*	6	8
373-775A	**'BP'** BPO53779 green - *08*	7	9
-	**'BP'** BPO60873 green	7	NA
-	**'BP'** BPO60880 green	7	NA
-	**'BP'** BPO60586 green	7	NA
373-775?	above 3 wagons in a set Sp Edn (*Model Rail*) - *08*	NA	24
373-776	**'Esso'** 57575 light grey - *07*	6	8
373-776A	**'Esso'** 57534 light grey - *08*	7	9
373-776B	**'Esso'** 5961 light grey - *10*	7	9
373-777	**'Shell/BP'** 67391 light grey - *07*	6	8
373-777A	**'Shell/BP'** 67389 light grey - *08*	7	9

Unbranded Grey

373-575T	56050 W	NA	NA
373-575U	56039 W	NA	NA
373-575V	56177 W	NA	NA
373-575W	56103 W	NA	NA
373-575T	set of above 4 wagons Sp Edn 500 (Kernow MR Centre) - *not made**	NA	NA
373-575W	56050 W Ltd Edn 504 - *08*	8	10
373-575X	56039 W Ltd Edn 504 - *08*	8	10
373-575Y	56177 W Sp Edn 504 - *08*	8	10
373-575Z	56103 W Sp Edn 504 - *08*	8	10

* This set of four wagons was ordered but later cancelled due to rising prices. As production was already under way, Bachmann decided to release them themselves as limited editions through selected retailers.

Covered Vans

W26. 10T Salt Van

373-350	**'Shaka Salt'** - *not made*	NA	NA
373-351	**'Stafford Salt Works'** - *not made*	NA	NA

Tools were unsuitable and so none were made.

W27a. 12T Cattle Van (2003)

373-250	**LMS** M14390 light grey - *03*	3	4
373-250A	**LMS** M14393 light grey - *04*	3	4
373-252	**NE** 55787 grey - *03*	3	4
373-254	**NE** 55783 grey - *05*	3	4

373-251	**BR** B891416 brown (also in set) - *03*	3	4
373-251A	**BR** B891419 brown - *04*	3	4

W27b. 8T Cattle Van (B) (2009)

373-261	**GW** 106881 dark grey - *09*	5	7
373-260	**BR** B893343 brown - *09*	5	7

W28. 12T Fish Van (2005)

373-225	**NE** 27456 brown - *not made*	NA	NA
373-225	**NE** 414124 brown - *05*	3	4

W29. 12T LMS Single Vent Van (2002)

(370-025)	**'Worthington'** 5 brown ex-set - *03*	3	NA
373-100	**LMS** 505969 grey (also in set 370-050) - *02*	4	5
373-103	**LMS** 505953 light grey - *04*	3	4
373-101	**BR** M504891 grey (also in set 370-200) - *02*	4	5
373-104	**BR** M504883 light grey - *04*	3	4
373-102	**BR** ? brown - *probably not made*	NPG	NPG
373-105	**BR** E568037 brown - *04*	3	4

W30. 12T GWR Twin Vent Van (2002)

373-125Z	**'Axminster Carpets'** B895006 grey Sp Edn 500 (Buffers) - *05*	4	6
373-125	**GW** 139956 dark grey - *02*	4	6
373-128	**GW** 139948 dark grey - *04*	4	6
373-130	**BR** W134035 grey - *04*	4	6
373-127	**BR** W134030 light grey - *probably not made*	NPG	NPG
373-126	**BR** W124480 brown (also in sets) - *02*	4	6
373-129	**BR** W124483 brown - *04*	4	6

W31a. BR 12T Fruit Van (Plywood) (B) (2010)

377-625	**BR** B875800 (early) brown - *10*	5	7
377-626	**BR** B875640 (late) brown - *10*	5	7

W31b. BR 12T Ventilated Van (Plywood Doors) (B) (2010)

377-627	**BR** B? (early) brown - *11*	5	7
377-628	**BR** B? (late) brown - *11*	5	7

W32a. BR 12T Ventilated Van (Planked) (B) (2007)

373-700	**BR** B755180 brown - *07*	4	6
373-700A	**BR** B755197 brown - *08*	5	7
373-701	**BR** B762318 brown Margarine - *07*	4	6

3 BR standard vans [W32a]

373-701A	**BR** B762324 brown Margarine - *08*	5	7
373-701B	**BR** ? brown Margarine - *08*	5	7
373-702	**BR** ADB780575 grey+blue Railstores - *07*	4	6

W32b. BR 10T Insulated Van (Planked) (B) (2007)

373-725	**BR** B872187 white - *07*	4	6
373-725A	**BR** B872171 white - *08*	5	7
373-726	**BR** 041421 brown - *07*	4	6
373-726A	**BR** B872042 brown - *08*	5	7
373-727	**BR** ? pale blue - *09*	5	7

W32c. BR 12T Ventilated Van (Plywood) (B) (2006)

373-750	**BR** ? grey - *07*	4	6
373-751	**BR** B784873 brown - *07*	4	6
373-751A	**BR** B784887 brown - *08*	4	6

W33. VBA/VBB 29T Box Van (2003)

373-050	**Railfreight** 200287 brown VBB - *03*	4	5
373-051	**Railfreight Dist**. 200155 olive green VBA - *03*	4	5
373-052	**Railfreight** 200611 grey+red VBA - *06*	4	6
373-052A	**Railfreight** 200629 grey+red VBA - *08*	5	7
373-052B	**Railfreight** 200602 grey+red VBA - *10*	5	7
373-053	**EWS** 200571 maroon VBA - *06*	4	6
373-053A	**EWS** 200537 maroon VBA - *07*	5	7
373-053B	**EWS** 200569 maroon VBA - *10*	5	7

W34. VGA 46t Sliding Wall Van (B) (2006)

373-601	**Railfreight Speedlink** 210452 silv+red - *06*	6	8
373-601A	**Railfreight Speedlink** 210646 silver+red W - *08*	7	9

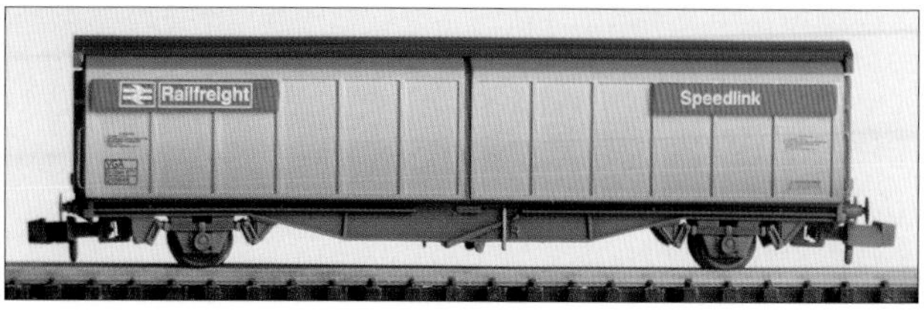

Railfreight VGA van [W34]

373-601B	**Railfreight Speedlink** 210630 silver+red W - *09*	8	10
373-602	**Railfreight Distribution** 210639 silver+ yellow Carlisle Currock motif - *06*	6	8
373-602A	**Railfreight Distribution** 210595 silver+yellow W Carlisle Currock motif - *09*	7	9
373-602B	**Railfreight Distribution** 210493 silver+yellow W Carlisle Currock motif - *09*	8	10
373-600	**EWS** 210444 maroon - *06*	6	8
373-600A	**EWS** 200537 maroon W - *08*	7	9
373-600B	**EWS** 200430 maroon W - *09*	8	10

Brake Vans

W35a. GWR 20T 'Toad' Brake Van (2002)

373-325	**GW** 56683 grey Severn Tunnel Junc.- *02*	5	7
373-325A	**GW** 114800 grey Rhymney - *03*	5	7
373-325B	**GW** 68690 grey Dowlais Cae Harris - *09*	5	6
373-327	**BR** W35960 grey Shrewsbury (Coton Hill) - *03*	5	6
373-326	**BR** W11496 brown (also in set) - *03?*	5	6
373-326A	**BR** W114961 brown - *03*	5	7
373-326B	**BR** W? brown - *09*	5	6
373-328	**BR** DW17455 brown S&T Department - *05*	5	6
373-328A	**BR** DW? brown S&T Department - *09*	5	6

W35b GWR 20T 'Toad' Brake Van (B) (2010)

377-375	**GW** 687613 grey Birkenhead - *10*	5	7
377-376	**BR** W68834 grey Stourbridge RU - *10*	5	7
377-377	**BR** W114854 brown (early) - *10*	5	7
377-378	**BR** DW68786 brown S&T Department - *10*	5	7

W36. LMS 20T Brake Van (B) (2008)

377-310	**LMS** 730026 grey - *08*	5	7
377-311	**LMS** 730670 brown - *08*	5	7
377-301	**BR** M730836 grey - *08*	5	7
377-301A	**BR** B950197 grey - *10*	5	7
377-300	**BR** M732396 brown - *08*	5	7
377-300A	**BR** M731460 brown - *10*	5	7

W37a. 20T Brake Van (2003)

(370-025)	**SR** no number ex-set - *03*	3	NA
(370-050/1)	**NE** 151752 brown ex-set - *03-04*	3	NA
373-301	**BR** M732484 grey - *?*	NPG	NPG
373-300	**BR** S? brown - *?*	NPG	NPG
(370-201/2)	**BR** DS62864 grey+yellow ex-set - *05-07*	3	NA

W37b. BR 20T Standard Brake Van (2005)

NE versions do not have full-length step boards.

BR standard brake van [W37b]

377-527	**NE** 260922 brown - *07*	5	7
377-527A	**NE** 234998 brown - *10*	7	9
377-525	**BR** B954762 brown - *07*	5	7
377-525A	**BR** B951094 brown - *08*	7	9
377-525B	**BR** B951759 grey - *10*	7	9
377-526	**BR** B951480 grey - *07*	5	7
377-526A	**BR** B950884 grey - *08*	7	9
377-526B	**BR** B951759 grey - *10*	7	9
377-527	**BR Railfreight** B? grey+red - *not made*	NA	NA

W37c. BR 20T Standard Brake Van (2005)

This version had flush ends.

377-535	**Railfreight** B955247 red+grey - *07*	7	9

Bogie Wagons

W38. LMS 30T Bogie Bolster C Wagon (B) (2009)

373-927	**LMS** 314000 light grey - *09*	9	12
373-926	**BR** B943405 grey - *09*	9	12
373-925	**BR S&T** DB997636 red Prawn - *09*	9	12

W39. BDA 80T Bogie Bolster Wagon (B) (2010)

377-600	**Loadhaul** 950414 black+orange with heavy duty bolsters and stanchions - *10*	15	18
377-601	**BR Railfreight** 950954 red with standard bolsters and stanchions - *10*	15	18
377-602	**EWS** 950026 maroon with heavy duty bolsters and stanchions - *10*	15	18

W40a. 63' Freightliner Flat + 2 x30ft Containers (2004)

373-450	**Freightliner** 602307 + containers **'Freightliner'** white+red 56N08, 56N23 - *04*	7	9
373-450A	**Freightliner** B601483 + containers **'Freightliner'** white+red 56N05, 56N26 - *05*	7	9
373-452	**Freightliner** B602389 + containers **'Freightliner'** red 51N37, 60N53 - *05*	7	9

W40b. 63' Freightliner Flat + 3 x20ft Containers (2004)

373-451	**Freightliner** 602160 + containers**'Freightliner'** grey+ red 08L25, 20L69, 05B04 - *04*	7	9
373-451A	**Freightliner** B6020637 black + containers **BRe 'Freightliner'** grey+red 08L46, 22L37, 05B17 - *05*	7	9
373-453	**Freightliner** B601237 dark blue + containers **'Freightliner Limited'** grey+red 26L24, 24L17, 25L09 - *05*	7	9
373-454	**Freightliner** B602359 black + containers **'P&O Nedlloyd'** grey PONU61807[8], PONU093276[7], PONU16267[7] - *08*	8	11
373-454A	**Freightliner** B602305 black + containers**'P&O Nedlloyd'** grey PONU162679, PONU093273, PONU061808 - *10*	10	13
373-455	**Freightliner** B602291 black + containers **'P&O'** blue PONU041942[6], PONU050018[4], PONU032814[1] - *06*	7	9
373-455A	**Freightliner** B602235 black + containers **'P&O'** blue POCU032812, POCU050019, POCU041943 - *10*	10	13

W40c. 63' Freightliner Flat + 20ft & 40ft Containers (2008)

373-456	**Freightliner** B602379 + containers 40' **'Hanjin'** blue HJCU769573+ 20' **'MSC'** yellow containers MSCU251403 - *08*	9	12
373-456A	**Freightliner** B602351 + containers 40' 'Hanjin' blue HJCU769577[3] + 20' **'MSC'** yellow MSCU251404[5] - *10*	10	13
373-457	**'Freightliner** B602394 + containers 40' **'Maersk'** silver MAEU638436[?] + 20' **'Cosco'** grey CBHU328736[?] - *08*	9	12
373-457A	**Freightliner** B602544 + containers 40' **'Maersk'** silver MAEU638434 + 20' **'Cosco'** grey CBHU328738 - *09*	9	12

W41. 'Intermodal' Wagons + 45ft Containers (B) (2008)

373-350	**EWS** (pair) pale green + 2x **'Seawheel'** green containers SWLU965245+SWLU451349 - *08*	20	28
373-350A	**EWS** (pair) pale green + 2x **'Seawheel'** green 45' containers SWL451345+SWLU965241 - *10*	25	30
373-351	**EWS** (pair) pale green + 2x **'Axis'** pale grey 45' containers AXIU716457+AXIU716309 - *08*	20	28

EWS 'Intermodal' wagons with 45ft 'Malcolm' containers [W41]

373-351A	**Rft Distribution** 33 70 4938 004-9 (pair) black + 2x **'Axis'** white 45' containers AXIU716451+ AX16370 - *10*	25	30
373-352	**EWS** (pair) pale green + 2x **'Seaco'** blue 45' containers SCZU147605+SCZU146922 - *08*	20	28
373-352A	**Rft Distribution** (pair) pale green + 2x **'Seaco'** blue 45' containers SCZU147600+ SCZU146924 - *10*	20	30
373-354	**EWS** 33 70 4938510-3 (pair) pale green + 2x **'Malcolm'** dark blue 45' containers WHMU450015+WHMU450020 - *10*	25	30
373-355	**Rft Distribution** (pair) black + 2x 'DHL' yellow 45' containers ?+? - *10*	25	30

W42. Container Packs (2008)

379-350	**'China Shipping'** CCLU314404/**'K Line'** KKTU740156 - *08*	NA	4
379-351	**'Maersk Sealand'** MSKU206820 /**'OCL'** OOLU33664 - *08*	NA	4
379-352	**'Yang Ming'** YMLU317786/**'Hyundai'** HDMU235691 - *08*	NA	4
379-353	**'Hapag Llyod'** HLXU222317/**'Hanjin'** HJCU810266 - 08	NA	4
379-354	**'MSC'** MSCU251438/**'Hamburg Sud'** SUDU370512 - *08*	NA	4
379-360	**'Hapag'** HXLU414034/**'China Shipping'** CCLU465009 - *08*	NA	4
379-361	**'K Line'** KKFU150171/**'CoscoL'** CBHU172455- *08*	NA	4
379-362	**'P&O Nedlloydd'** PONU1675046/**'Yang Ming'** YMLU496931 - *08*	NA	4
379-370	**'Eucon'** EUCU459120/**'ECS'** ECBU450106 - *08*	NA	4
379-371	**'EFS'** EFSU452044/**'P&O Ferrymaster'** FMBU001799 - *08*	NA	4
379-372	**'Powerbox'** PWRU450209/**'Consent Leasing'** NEVU220200 - *08*	NA	4
379-373	**'DHL'** DZ5141+DZ7005 x2 - *08*	NA	4
379-374	**'Asda'** WHMU450825+WHMU450819 x2 - *08*	NA	4
379-325	**'K Line'** KXYU740516/ **'Yang Ming'** YMLU317786/ **'Hapag Lloyd'** PONU167504/ **'P&O Nedlloyd'** HLXU414034 - *08*	NA	4

W43. 50T Bogie Sulphate Wagon (2004)

373-425	**NE** Sulphate 164852 - *04*	5	6

W44. MBA 'Megabox' (High-sided) (B) (2010)

Introduced in 1999 by EWS, 200 were built and made up into sets of five wagons.

EWS MBA 'Megabox' [W44]

377-650	**EWS** 500028 maroon with buffers - *10*	16	20
377-651	**EWS** 500178 maroon without buffers - *10*	16	20

W45. MOA 'Megabox' (Low-sided) (B) (2010)

Some of the 'Megabox' sets were cut down to reduuce their capacity.

377-652	**EWS** 500327 maroon with buffers - *10*	16	20

W46. YGA/B/H 40T 'Sealion'/'Seacow' (B) (2009)

The 'Seacows' are ex-'Sealions'

377-000	**BR** Eng DB982637 olive green YGH - *09*	15	18

377-000A	**BR** Eng DB982887 olive green YGH - *10*	15	18
377-001	**BR** DB982473 grey+yellow -YGB - *09*	15	18
377-001A	**BR** DB982554 grey+yellow -YGB - *10*	15	18
377-002	**EWS** DB982696 maroon - YGA -*09*	15	18
377-002A	**EWS** DB980220 maroon - YGA - *10*	15	18

W47. JGA 90t Bogie Hopper Wagon (B) (2009)

373-802	**'Buxton Lime'** - *not made*	NA	NA
377-101	**'Buxton Lime Industries'** BLI19206 blue+ white - *09*	15	18
377-101A	**'Buxton Lime Industries'** BLI19218 blue+wht - *10*	15	18
373-801	**'RMC'** - *not made*	NA	NA
377-100	**'RMC'** RMC19228 orange+white - *09*	15	18
377-100A	**'RMC'** RMC19238 orange+white - *10*	15	19
373-800	**'Tilcon'** - *not made*	NA	NA
377-102	**'Tarmac'/NACCO** NACCO19175 v.pale grey - *09*	15	18
377-102A	**'Tarmac'/NACCO** NACCO19175 v.pale grey - *10*	15	19

W48. BYA/BRA 104t Bogie Steel Carriers (B) (2009)

373-825	**EWS** 960015 maroon coil BYA - *09*	15	18
373-826	**EWS** 964014 maroon strip BRA - *09*	15	18
373-826A	**EWS** ? maroon strip BRA - *10*	15	18

W49. HTA 102t Bulk Coal Hopper (2006)

373-850	**EWS** 310222 maroon+yellow - *06*	14	17
373-850A	**EWS** 310078 maroon+yellow - *08*	14	19
373-850B	**EWS** 310103 maroon+yellow - *10*	17	21

W50. HHA 100t GLW Bogie Coal Hopper (B) (2007)

Freightliner Heavy Haul HHA coal hopper [W50]

373-800	**'Freightliner Heavy Haul'** 370258 grey - *07*	15	18
373-800A	**'Freightliner Heavy Haul'** 370270 grey - *08*	15	19
373-800B	**'Freightliner Heavy Haul'** 370429 grey - *10*	17	21
373-801	**'Freightliner Heavy Haul'** 370001 grey - *07*	15	18
373-801A	**'Freightliner Heavy Haul'** 370037 grey - *08*	15	19
373-801B	**'Freightliner Heavy Haul'** ? grey - *09*	17	21

W51. HYA 102t GLW Bulk Coal Hopper (B) (2009)

377-575	**First GBRf** ? pale grey - *09*	15	18
377-575A	**First GBRf VGT** ? pale grey - *10*	16	20
377-576	**'Fastline'** 37 70 6791 087-9 pale grey - *09*	16	20

W52. JPA 100t Cement Tank Wagon (B) (2010)

377-675	**VTG 'Lafarge'** VTG12434 silver - *10*	15	18
377-676	**VTG 'Castle Cement'** VTG12461 pale grey - *10*	15	18

W53. TEA 100T Bogie Tank Wagon (2004)

373-552	**'BP'** BPO83786 black - *05*	7	9
373-553	**'BP'** BPO87467 grey - *05*	7	9

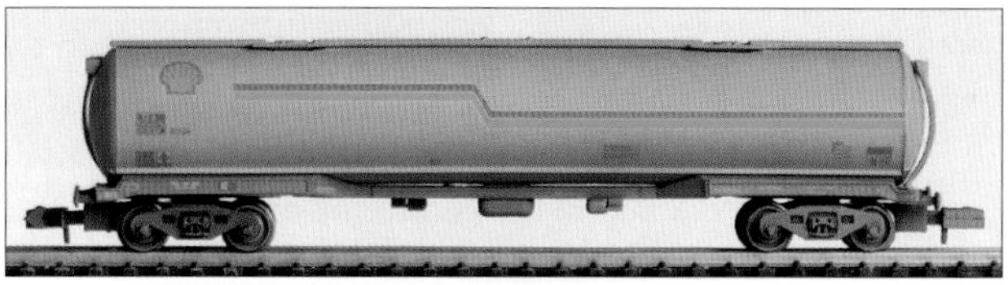

'Shell' TEA bogie tank wagon [W53]

373-554	**'BP'** BPO83681 black W - *06*	7	10
373-554A	**'BP'** BPO83693 black W - *08*	10	13
373-554B	**'BP'** BPO83588 black W - *10*	10	13
373-551	**'Fina'** 508 grey - *04*	7	9
373-551A	**'Fina'** 503 grey - *05*	7	9
373-556	**'Fina'** FINA85519 grey - *06*	7	10
373-556A	**'Fina'** FINA85527 grey W - *06*	10	13
373-556B	**'Fina'** FINA? grey W - *10*	10	13
(370-250)	**'Fina'** 504 grey - *06*	7	NA
(370-250)	**'Fina'** 505 grey - *06*	7	NA
373-550	**'Shell BP'** 4001 grey - *04*	7	9
373-550A	**'Shell BP'** 4007 grey - *05*	7	9
(370-250)	**'Shell BP'** 4008 grey - *06*	7	NA
(370-250)	**'Shell BP'** 4009 grey - *06*	7	NA
373-555	**'Shell'** 87317 grey - *06*	7	10
373-555A	**'Shell'** SHELL87324 grey W - *08*	10	13
373-555B	**'Shell'** SHELL97321 grey W - *10*	10	13

Those in set 370-250 are also in set 370-251

The Bachmann model of a Class 4900 'Hall' from computer artwork by Robbie McGavin

Graham Farish N gauge - Mk1 Coaches

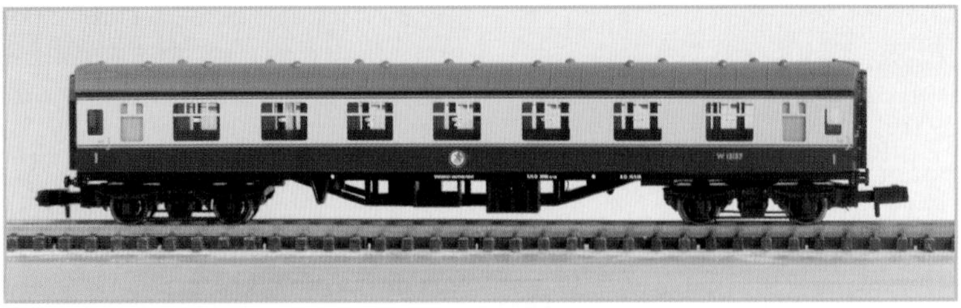

FK (corridor first)

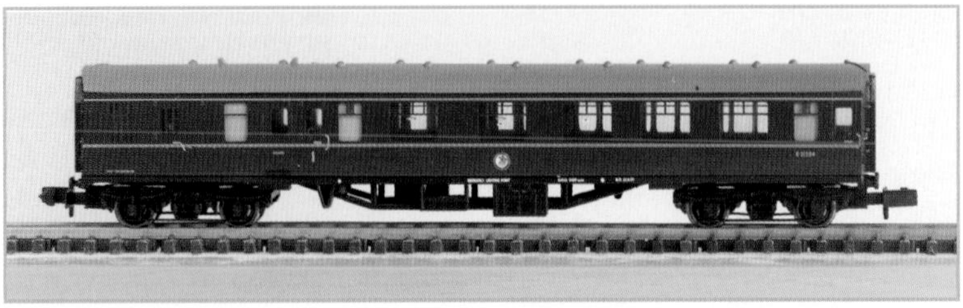

BSK (corridor brake second)

BG (gangwayed full brake)

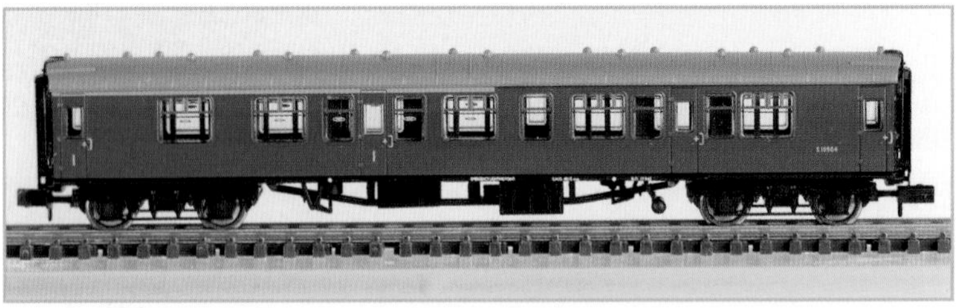

CK (corridor composite)

RFO (restaurant first open)

SK (corridor second)

Heljan 00 (British)

Please note that due to several additions to this range, it has been necessary to renumber the tables.

HISTORY

Based in Sonderso, Denmark, Heljan has made quality kits, in their own factory, for over 40 years. More recently they expanded into ready-to-run locomotives and rolling stock of a high quality, especially for the Scandinavian market but also exporting to other parts of Europe and North America.

Class 15 BTH-Clayton diesel [L2] (Hattons)

The firm was started by Niels-Christian Nannestad, a tool-maker by trade, in 1957 in the basement of a very small apartment in Copenhagen. With very little funds, Nannestad collected sawdust from local carpenters, stained it green and sold it as the first Heljan product. Next he turned his hands to wooden structures and found a ready market. This led to the purchase of tooling machines and a range of building kits. After this, the range and company both expanded to serve a much wider market. In the 1970s Heljan received a bulk order for kits from a Marklin subsidiary and later Revell. When the Marklin contract took a nose dive, Heljan concentrated on their own range and had a ready market in the USA through Walthers, Atlas and others. Besides building kits they also made rolling stock for other suppliers and in the late 1980s started to produce a Heljan range as well, starting with Danish wagons and coaches. Locomotives and multiple units followed.

The company passed to Nannestad's son Jan and grandsons Bo and Kim. In 2001 they decided to tackle the UK market with an 00 gauge Class 47 diesel.

Heljan were initially approached by a syndicate of UK H0 modellers concerning the possibility of producing diesels in H0 scale. This proved to be uneconomical due to the small number of people interested in this scale in Britain but 00 scale was felt to hold possibilities. Initially, Heljan had been asked to make a Class 37 diesel but the project later changed to a Class 47. When the sponsors dropped out, the company decided to go ahead with an 00 gauge model anyway. This was developed quite quickly and arrived in the shops in May 2001.

The models are designed and tooled in Denmark and the tools are then shipped out to China for production. The models are assembled and finished in China and then shipped back to Denmark. The blue loco boxes state 'Made in Denmark' and the outer boxes say 'Made in China'.

Numbering - All catalogue numbers are prefixed with '1100' but are abbreviated here to save space.

Weathered - Some models have been weathered and these are shown with a 'W' after the colour.

LOCOMOTIVES

The locomotives have a heavy diecast Continental chassis with H0 bogies, a 5-pole Buhler motor, Cardan shaft drive, pickups on both bogies, moulded plastic bodies with a high level of detail, working headlights, finescale blackened wheel sets, flush glazing, separately moulded handrails and other detail, NEM coupling sockets, tension-lock couplings and have a DCC board fitted ready to take a chip.

Cat No.	Company, Number, Colour, Dates	£	£

Diesel Locomotives

L1. Class 14 'Teddy Bear' 0-6-0 (2009)

The tooling of this model was paid for by Hattons who have exclusive rights to models produced from them.

Class 14 'Teddy Bear' 0-6-0 diesel shunter in National Coal Board livery [L1] (Hattons)

1402	**31** NCB purple-blue Sp Edn 400 (Hattons) - *09*	90	115
1406	**45** British Steel green+grey W Sp Edn (Hattons) - *10*	90	115
1400	**D9500** BRc green Sp Edn 1600 (Hattons) - *09*	90	115
1404	**D9521** BRc green+grey Sp Edn (Hattons) - *10*	90	115
1405	ex-**D9526** Blue Circle green+grey W Sp Edn (Hattons) - *10*	90	115
1403	**D9535** BRc green+grey W Sp Edn (Hattons) - *10*	90	115
1401	**14029** BRe blue Sp Edn 600 (Hattons) - *09*	90	115
1407	**14701** Loadhaul black+orange Sp Edn 200 (Hattons) - *10*	90	115

L2. Class 15 BTH/Clayton (2009)

1500	**D8200** BRc plain green - *09*	75	89
1504	**D8201** BRc gloss green, plain ends - *10*	75	89
1505	**D8202** BRc green, small yellow panels - *10*	75	89
1507	**D8215** BRc plain green - *10*	75	89
1501	**D8219** BRc plain green with small yellow ends - *09*	75	89
1502	**D8229** BRc plain green with full yellow ends - *09*	75	89
1503	**D8233** BRc green, small yellow panels (as preserved) Lt Edn 1000 - *10*	90	109
1506	**D8235** BRe green, yellow ends - *10*	75	89
1508	**D8239** BRc green, yellow ends, TOPS panels - *10*	75	89

L3. Class 17 'Clayton' Bo-Bo (2009)

1712	**D8501** BRc gloss green, small yellow panels - *10*	75	89
1708	**D8507** BRe blue full yellow ends - *09*	75	89
1711	**D8512** BRc blue, full yellow ends, Derby research variant - *10*	75	89

Class 17 'Clayton' in Ribble Cement livery [L3] (Hattons)

1700	**D8568** BRc green small yellow panels - *09*	75	89
1701	**8561** BRc green full yellow ends - *09*	75	89
-	**D8599** BRc green W full yellow ends Ltd Edn - *09*	75	89

1702	**D8529** BRe blue full yellow ends - *09*	75	89
-	**D8529** BRe blue W full yellow ends Lt Edn - *09*	75	89
1705	**D8545** BRe blue full yellow ends - *09*	75	89
1706	ex-**D8568** 'Ribble Cement' white Ltd Edn 1000 - *09*	75	89
1799	**D8574** BRe blue W snow ploughs Sp Edn 250 (Modelfair.com) - *09*	75	89
1704	**8592** BRc green full yellow ends - *09*	75	89
1798	**D8599** BRc green W small yell panels Sp Edn 250 (Modelfair.com) - *09*	75	89
1714	**D8600** BRc green small yellow panels - *10*	75	89
1713	**D8601** BRc green, small yellow panels - *10*	75	89
1703	**D8603** BRc green small yellow panels - *09*	75	89
1710	**D8606** BRe blue with yellow ends - *10*	75	89
1707	**D8612** BRc green small yellow panels - *09*	75	89

L4. Class 23 'Baby Deltic' Bo-Bo (2010)

2300	**D5900** BRc green, small yellow panel - *10*	90	120
2301	**D5903** BRc green, yellow end - *10*	90	120
2302	**D5908** BRe blue, yellow end - *10*	90	120
2303	**D5909** BRe blue, yellow end - *10*	90	120

L5a. Class 26/0 Bo-Bo (2010)

Based on the 26/1 model below, it uses several parts from that model but has a new body. 20 of the locomotives were delivered to BR between mid 1958 and the Spting of 1959. They were numbered D5300-19.

Class 26 diesel No.26015 in BR blue livery [L5b]

2654	**26001/D5301 *Eastfield*** BRc Heritage green - *10*	70	99
2652	**26003** BRe Engineers grey+yellow - *10*	70	99
2653	**26004** BRe Railfreight Coal grey - *10*	70	99
2651	**26006** BReLL Railfreight red stripe grey - *10*	70	99
2650	**26015** BRe blue - *10*	70	99

L5b. Class 26/1 Bo-Bo (2006)

A new body was in use by the end of 2009.

2606	**D5320** BRe blue full yellow panels & oval buffers - *07*	50	60
2605	**D5323** BRc green small yellow panels - *07*	50	64
2604	**D5325** BRe blue full yellow ends - *07*	50	64
2601	**D5326** BRc green small yellow panels - *06*	50	60
2602	**D5331** BRe blue - *06*	50	60
2607	**D5332** BRc green, small yellow panels - *10*	70	85
2600	**D5335** BRc green, full yellow panel - *06*	50	60
2603	**D5340** BRe blue - *06*	50	60
2636	**26024** BRe blue full yellow ends West Highland motifs - *08*	50	64
2631	**26025** Railfreight red stripe West Highland motifs - *08*	50	64
2612	**26027** BRe blue full yellow ends - *08*	50	64
2610	**26028** BRe blue full yellow ends - *08*	50	64
2613	**26029** BRe blue full yellow ends - *08*	50	64
2611	**26031** BRe blue full yellow ends - *08*	50	64
2634	**26032** Railfreight red stripe - *08*	50	64
2630	**26037** Railfreight red stripe - *08*	50	64
2633	**26038** BRe Eng grey+yellow - *08*	50	64
2635	**26041** Railfreight red stripe - *08*	50	64
2637	**26043** BRe Eng grey+yellow Eastfield motifs - *08*	50	64
2632	**26046** BRe blue full yellow ends - *08*	50	64

L6. Class 27 BRCW Bo-Bo (2006)

Sc = Scottish version with tablet catcher recesses, front cab doors and sliding cab windows.

2722	**D5348** BRe blue full yellow ends Sc - *08*	60	79
2720	**D5356** BRc green original Sc - *08*	60	79
2721	**D5362** BRc green small yell panels Sc - *08*	60	79
2704	**5377** BRc green full yellow ends NER freight version with no boiler tank - *07*	60	79
2701	**5380** BRe blue - *06*	60	79
2705	**D5382** BRc 2-tone green small yellow panels - *07*	60	79
2706	**D5385** BRc green small yellow panels - *07*	60	79
2700	**D5401** BRc green small yellow panels - *06*	60	79
2702	**27034** BRe blue - *06*	60	79
2703	**27105** BRe blue - *06*	60	79

L7. Class 28 Co-Bo (2011)

This model was commissioned by Hattons of Liverpool for exclusive distribution by them.

2800	**D5700** BRc green with plain green ends - *11*	100	125
2805	**D5701** BRe blue - *11*	100	125
2806	**D5701** BRe blue W - *11*	100	125
2801	**D5705** BRc green with small yellow panels - *11*	100	132
2802	**D5707** BRc green with full yellow ends - *11*	100	132
2804	**D5708** BRc green W with full yellow ends - *11*	100	132
2803	**D5718** BRc green W with small yellow panels - *11*	100	132

L8. Class 33 Bo-Bo (2005)

Sprung metal buffers, screw couplings, full bufferbeam pipework included. From 2006 these had improved headcodes and headlight arrangements. 'Slim Jim' = narrower body.

Class 33 in Railfreight Distribution livery [L8] (Hattons)

3362	**D6517** BRc green Lt Edn 500 - *10*	70	89
3341	**D6520** BR blue yellow ends 33/1 - *06*	50	62
3363	**D6526** BRc green W Lt Edn 500 - *10*	70	89
3383	**D8545** BRe blue, full yellow ends - *10*	70	89
3310	**D6553** BRc green full yellow ends - *05*	50	62
3381	**D6563** BRc green, full yellow ends - *10*	70	89
3382	**D8579** BRe blue, full yellow ends - *10*	70	89
3346	**D6580** BRc green, small yellow panels - *10*	70	89
3360	**D6581** BRc green Sp Edn 300 (Kernow Model Rail) - *07*	65	85
3380	**D6582** BRc green, small yellow panel - *10*	70	89
3361	**D6583** BRc green Sp Edn 300 (Kernow Model Rail) - *09*	70	89
3318	**D6585** BRc early green - *06*	55	79
3311	**6572** BRe blue with yellow ends - *05*	50	62
3322	**6591** BR blue Slim Jim 33/2 - *06*	50	62
3317	**33002** BR Departmental grey 33/0 - *06*	50	62
3313	**33004** BRe DCE* blue, blue roof - *05*	50	62
3301	**33008 *Eastleigh*** BRc green 33/0 - *06*	50	62
3314	**33012** BRe blue, grey roof, yell ends - *06*	50	62
3315	**33019** BRe blue, grey roof - *06*	50	62
3312	**33025 *Sultan*** BR blue, light grey roof - *05*	50	62
3370	**33025 *Glen Falloch*** West Coast purple 33/0 - *09*	70	89
3316	**33027 *Earl Mountbatten of Burma*** BRe blue, full yellow end, grey roof - *06*	50	62
3371	**33029 *Glen Loy*** West Coast purple 33/0 - *09*	70	89
3303	**33030** EWS maroon+yellow 33/0 - *06*	50	62
3302	**33035 *Spitfire*** NSE bright blue 33/0 - *06*	50	62
3300	**33059** BRe blue 33/0 - *not made*	NA	NA
3300	**33065 *Sealion*** BR Eng grey+yellow 33/0 - *05*	50	62
3351	**33101** BR Departmental grey 33/1 - *07*	50	62
3354	**33103 *Swordfish*** Fragonset black 33/1 - *07*	50	62
3340	**33105** BR blue Bagpipes 33/1 - *06*	50	62
3342	**33108** BR Eng grey+yellow Bagpipes 33/1 - *06*	65	79
3350	**33108 *Vampire*** Fragonset black 33/1 - *07*	50	62
3352	**33109 *Captain Bill Smith RNR*** BR Departmental grey 33/1 - *07*	50	62
3345	**33112 *Templecombe*** BR blue full yellow ends 33/1 - *07*	50	62
3344	**33114 *Ashford 150*** NSE blue 33/1 - *07*	50	62
3353	**33116/D6535 Hertfordshire Rail Tours** BRe blue - *10*	70	89
3347	**33117** BRe blue, all yellow ends - *10*	70	89

3343	**33118** BR blue full yellow ends 33/1 - *07*	50	62
3332	**33201** BR Eng grey+yellow 33/2 - *07*	50	62
3325	**33201** BR grey 33/2 - *07*	50	62
3326	**33202** BRe blue 33/2 - *10*	70	89
3334	**33202 *Meteor*** Fragonset black 33/2 - *06*	65	79
3333	**33204** BRe Mainline triple grey - *?*	65	79
3321	**33206** Rft Distribution grey Slim Jim 33/2 - *06*	50	62
3323	**33207 *Earl Mountbatten of Burma*** Rft Construction grey 33/2 - *07*	50	62
3331	**33207** DRS blue 33/2 - *07*	50	62
3335	**33207** West Coast Railway maroon 33/2 - *06*	50	62
3324	**33211** BR blue full yellow ends 33/2 - *07*	50	62
3330	**33211** Railfreight Distribution grey 33/2 - *07*	50	62
3320	**33212** BR blue Slim Jim 33/2 - *06*	50	62

* DCE = Department of Civil Engineers.

L9. Class 35 'Hymek' Bo-Bo (2003)

Centrally mounted 5-pole motor with twin flywheels.

3514	**D7000** BRe green, full yellow ends - *10*	70	89
3505	**D7009** BRc green - *04*	55	75
3500	**D7017** BRc 2-tone green - *03*	55	75
3511	**7017** BRe blue, full yellow ends - *09*	70	89
3508	**D7035** BRe blue full yellow ends - *04*	55	75
3502	**D7036** BRe blue small yellow panel white window frames - *03*	55	75
3501	**D7039** BRc 2-tone green small yellow panel - *03*	55	75
3507	**D7040** BRe blue small yellow ends, grey windows - *04*	55	75
3503	**D7042** BRe blue full yellow ends - *03*	55	75
3506	**D7044** BRc green, small yellow ends - *04*	55	75
3510	**D7051** BRe blue W small yellow panels - *09*	70	89
3512	**D7061** BRe blue full yellow ends - *10*	70	89
3513	**D7093** BRe green, small yellow panels, TOPS panels - *10*	70	89
3504	**D7097** BRc green, full yellow ends - *04*	55	75
3509	**D7100** BRe green, lime band - *09*	70	89

L10. Hawker Siddeley/Brush *Kestrel* Co-Co (2009)

This was a Brush/Hawker Siddeley development and a one-off experimental locomotive which ran on the national network for three years from 1968. The model has a 5-pole central motor with twin flywheels, directional lights and an 8-pin socket for DCC.

Hawker Siddeley/Brush experimental diesel Kestrel [L10] (Antics)

4000	**HS 4000 *Kestrel*** yellow+dark brown Ltd Edn - *09*	100	120

L11. BRCW-Sulzer-AEI *Lion* Co-Co (2011)

This was developed as a privately sponsored prototype locomotive in 1962 by Birmingham RC&W, Sulzer Brothers and Associated Electrical Industries. It survived 18 months in service but BR chose the Brush design for its Type 4 diesels instead. The model has a 5-pole central motor with twin flywheels, directional lights and an 8-pin socket for DCC.

4005	**D0260 *Lion*** white Ltd Edn 4000 - *11*	100	120

L12. Class 47 Co-Co (2002)

LB = late body. This was the original body developed by Heljan. EB = early body (1965 to 1982 period). The completely new body features radiator slats as before but with authentic interchangeable illuminated four character headcodes and a boiler flue outlet. The current chassis has been adapted to include under-slung boiler water tanks and a full buffer beam cowling. IB = intermediate body (without water tanks and with unmodified cabs, together with marker light panels and headlamps). Ibf = intermediate body with flush No.2 end. esn = etched stainless steel nameplates.

4700	**D1100** BRc 2-tone green small yellow panels EB - *02*	65	80
4790	**D1501** BR 2-tone green, small yellow panels as preserved Ltd Edn 500 - *11*	70	89
4751	**1562** BRc 2-tone green full yellow front - *05*	65	80
46513	as above but weathered Ltd Edn 75 - *05*	70	90
4794	**D1661 *North Star*** BR green W full yellow ends Ltd Edn 500 - *11*	70	89
4701	**D1662 *Isambard Kingdom Brunel*** BRc 2-tone green small yellow panels EB - *02*	65	80
4752	**D1733** BRe XP64 blue - *05*	65	80
4699	**D1733/47853** *(see 47853 below)*	-	-
4750	**D1734** BRc 2-tone green small yellow panels - *05*	65	80
4792	**D1916 (47812)** Riviera Trains in BR 2-tone green (heritage) full yellow ends Ltd Edn 500 - *11*	70	89
4730	**D1932** BRe blue EB - *02*	65	80
4702	**D1942** BRc 2-tone green small yellow panels EB - *02*	65	80
4703	**1934** BRc 2-tone green, full yellow ends 0000 headcode EB - *02*	65	80

Class 47 in Railfreight Construction livery [L12] (Hattons)

4731	**47059** BRe blue EB - *02*	65	80
46313	as above but weathered Ltd Edn 75 - *05*	70	85
4812	**47063** Railfreight Construction grey - *05*	55	60
4732	**47076 *City of Truro*** BRe blue EB - *02*	65	80
4732	**47077 *North Star*** BRe blue EB - *not made*	NA	NA
4675	**47079** Freightliner grey IBf - *not made*	NA	NA
4831	**47094** Railfreight Petroleum grey IB - *02*	65	80
4753	**47122** BRe blue - *05*	65	80
4661	**47145 *Merddin Emrys*** Railfreight Distribution Tinsley blue - *05*	65	80
4680	**47193** Freightliner green - *05*	65	80
4664	**47200 *The Fosse Way*** Cotswold Rail silver - *05*	65	80
4802	**47211** BReLL Rft grey yellow ends IB - *03*	65	80
4805	**47212** BRe Railfreight Petroleum 2-tone grey W IB - *03*	55	65
46053	as above but weathered Ltd Edn 75 - *05*	70	85
4697	**47237** DRS blue IBf Sp Edn 750 (Rail Express) - *03*	65	80
4630	**47245 *The Institute of Export*** Rft Distribution European grey LB - *01*	65	80
4640	**47258 *Forth Ports Tilbury*** Freightliner green LB - *02*	65	80
46403	as above but weathered Ltd Edn 75 - *05*	70	85
4733	**47278** BRe blue, pale grey roof EB 0000 headcode - *02*	65	80
4663	**47298** DRS blue - *05*	65	80
4695	**47299 *Ariadne*** BR blue - *05*	65	80
4677	**47321** unbranded triple grey IBf - *not made?*	NPG	NPG
4677	**47321** Railfreight unbranded triple grey IBf - *03*	60	65
4675	**47334 *P&O Nedlloyd*** Freightliner triple grey W IBf - *03*	60	65
46753	as above but weathered Ltd Edn 75 - *05*	70	85
4803	**47340** BReLL Railfreight red stripe grey IB - *03*	65	80
4804	**47361 *Wilton Endevour*** Railfreight Distribution grey Thornaby motif IB - *03*	65	80
46043	as above but weathered Ltd Edn 75 - *05*	70	85
4678	**47375 *Tinsley Traction Depot*** Railfreight Distribution - *05*	65	80
4811	**47476 *Night Mail*** Parcels red - *05*	65	80
4808	**47500** GWT green - *05*	65	80
4791	**47508 *SS Great Britain*** BRe blue Ltd Edn 500 - *11*	70	89
4793	**47555 The Commonwealth Spirit** BR blue W Ltd Edn 500 - *11*	70	89
4809	**47581** NSE bright blue - *05*	65	80
4800	**47591** BReLL blue IB - *03*	65	80
4806	**47593 *Galloway Princess*** InterCity grey IB - *03*	65	80
4696	**47596 *Aldeburgh Festival*** BRe blue, grey roof IB Sp Edn 250* (47401 Project) - *03*	60	65
4813	**47635** BReLL blue? Highland - *05*	65	58
4801	**47636 *Sir John de Greame*** BReLL blue small numbers IB - *03*	65	80
4821	**47643** ScotRail red stripe grey IB - *02*	65	80

4679	**47711 *County of Hertfordshire*** NSE revised blue LB - *02*	65	80
4679	**47711 *County of Hertfordshire*** NSE revised blue IBf - *03*	65	80

Class 47 in Colas livery 47727 Rebecca [L12] (Hattons)

4662	**47714** Anglia Railways turquoise - *05*	60	65
4807	**47715 *Haymarket*** ScotRail blue stripe grey IB - *03*	65	80
4744	**47727 *Rebecca*** Colas yellow+orange Ltd Edn - *09*	70	89
4650	**47744** EWS maroon+yellow - *02*	65	80
46503	as above but weathered Ltd Edn 75 - *05*	70	85
4745	**47749 *Demelza*** Colas yellow+orange Ltd Edn - *09*	70	89
4620	**47778 *Irresistible*** RES red+grey LB - *01*	65	80
4622	**47781 *Isle of Iona*** RES red+grey - *05*	65	80
4621	**47782** RES red+grey LB - *01*	60	65
4698	**47787 *Windsor Castle*** EWS maroon+yellow no headcode recesses esn Ltd Edn 1000 LB - *02*	65	75
4651	**47792 *Robin Hood*** EWS maroon+yellow - *05*	65	80
4660	**47798 *Prince William*** EWS dark purple LB - *02*	65	75
4610	**47805** InterCity swallow grey LB - *01*	65	80
4601	**47806** Virgin red+dark grey LB - *01*	65	70
4610	**47807** InterCity swallow grey LB - *?*	65	80
4676	**47810 *Porterbrook*** Virgin red+dark grey - *05*	65	80
4670	**47815 *Abertawe Landore*** First Great Western dark green LB - *02*	65	72
4611	**47826 *Springburn*** Intercity grey - *05*	65	80
4665	**47829** Police livery white+stripes LB - *03*	75	85
4667	**47840 *North Star*** BRe blue LB - *03*	65	80
4600	**47843 *Vulcan*** Virgin red+dark grey LB - *01*	60	65
4668	**47847 *Railway World Magazine*** BReLL Heritage blue LB - *03*	65	80
4666	**47851/D1966 *Traction Magazine*** BRc Heritage 2-tone green LB - *03*	65	80
4699	**47853/D1733 *Rail Express*** BRe XP64 blue no headcode recesses esn LB Sp Edn 750 (*Rail Express*) - *02*	65	80
4810	**47981** BR Engineer's grey+yellow - *05*	60	75
	Unnumbered Models		
4740	BRc 2-tone green small yellow panels - *07*	40	50
4741	BRe blue full yellow ends - *07*	40	50
4742	BReLL blue, light grey roof - *07*	40	50
4743	Railfreight Sector triple grey - *07*	40	50

* 750 were planned but only 250 made. The rest were sold off as spare chassis and bodies with the name and number removed.

L13. Class 52 'Western' Diesel Hydraulic C-C (2005)

5204	**D1000 *Western Enterprise*** BRd desert sand - *05*	60	65
5213	**D1000 *Western Enterprise*** BRd desert sand - *10*	75	89
5214	**D1001 *Western Pathfinder*** BRc gloss maroon - *10*	75	89
5207	**D1004 *Western Crusader*** BRc green - *05*	60	65
5200	**D1007 *Western Talisman*** BRc maroon small yellow panels - *04*	60	65
5209	**D1010 *Western Campaigner*** ? ? - *05*	60	65
5215	**D1012 *Western Firebrand*** BRc maroon - *05*	75	89
5212	**D1013 *Western Ranger*** BRe blue - *05*	60	65
5203	**D1015 *Western Champion*** BRc golden ochre small yellow panels - *04*	60	65
5216	**D1023 *Western Fusilier*** BRe blue, yellow ends - *10*	75	89
5210	**D1036 *Western Emperor*** BRc green, small yellow panels - *05*	60	65
5201	**D1037 *Western Empress*** BRc green small yellow panels - *04*	60	65
5206	**D1039 *Western King*** BRc maroon, yellow bufferbeam - *05*	60	65
5211	**D1041 *Western Prince*** maroon full yellow front - *05*	60	65
5205	**D1047 *Western Lord*** BRe blue, small yellow ends - *05*	60	65
5208	**D1058 *Western Nobleman*** BRe blue - *05*	60	65
5202	**D1067 *Western Druid*** BRe blue full yellow ends - *04*	60	65

Class 52 'Western' in BR maroon D1010 Western Campaigner [L13] (Hattons)

L14. Class 53 *Falcon* Co-Co (Prototype) (2008)

Supplied with non-scale alternative bufferbeams for use with couplings. en = etched metal nameplates

5300	**D0280 *Falcon*** BRb lime green+chestnut brown Ltd Edn 800 - *08*	90	110

Experimental diesel loco Falcon in blue livery [L14] (Antics)

5303	**D0280 *Falcon*** BRb lime green+chestnut brown en Ltd Edn 800 - *08*	90	110
5305	**D0280 *Falcon*** BRb lime green Ltd Edn 500 - *10*	90	110
5301	**D1200 *Falcon*** BRc 2 tone green small yellow panels Ltd Edn 800 - *08*	90	110
5306	**D1200 *Falcon*** BRc 2 tone green small yellow panels Ltd Edn 500 - *10*	90	110
5302	**1200 *Falcon*** BRe blue full yellow ends Ltd Edn 800 - *08*	90	110
5304	**1200 *Falcon*** BRe blue W Ltd Edn 1,200 - *08*	95	129

L15. Class 57/3 Co-Co (2005)

Has directional lighting and tail lighting.

5700	**57301** Virgin red+silver - *05*	65	89
5701	**57307** Virgin red+silver - *05*	65	89
5703	**57310** Virgin red+silver - *05*	65	89
5702	**57602** FGW green+gold - *05*	65	89
5704	**57604** FGW green+gold - *05*	65	89
5705	**57605** FGW green+gold - *05*	65	89

L16. Class 58 Co-Co (2008)

1 = version 1 with no body-side panel handles and CP3 bogies. 2 = version 2 with body-side panel handles and the later CP3a bogies.

5802	**58001** Railfreight red stripe grey 1 - *08*	60	75

Class 58 in Railfreight 'red stripe' livery [L16] (Hattons)

5800	**58004** Mainline ex-Railfreight triple grey 1 - *08*	60	75
5806	**58009** Railfreight triple grey 'Mainline' - *08*	60	75
5801	**58014** ***Didcot Power Station*** Rft Coal grey 1 - *08*	60	75
5807	**58024** EW&S maroon+yellow - *08*	60	75
5803	**58037** Railfreight red stripe grey - *08*	60	75
5808	**58038** Railfreight red stripe grey - *08*	60	75
5804	**58047** EWS maroon+yellow - *08*	60	75
5809	**58048** ***Coventry Colliery*** Railfreight Coal grey - *08*	60	75
5805	**58050** ***Toton Traction Depot*** Mainline blue - *08*	60	75

L17. Class 66 Co-Co

Six versions were planned but the project was cancelled.

Electric Locomotives

L18. Class 86 Bo-Bo Electric (2010)

8600	**86205** ***City of Lancaster*** Virgin red+grey - *10*	90	110
8601	**86214** ***Sans Pareil*** InterCity Swallow grey - *10*	90	110
8602	**86215** ***Round Tabler*** Anglia light blue - *10*	90	110
8603	**86233** ***Alstom Heritage*** BRd Electric blue - *10*	90	110
8604	**86605** Freightliner green - *10*	90	110

L19. Class 76 EM1 Electric (2011)

The model has been commissioned by Olivia's Trains of Sheffield. Heavy Diecast Chassis, 5-pole motor with flywheels, all wheel drive, sprung buffers, 21-pin DCC socket, pre-fitted speaker, functionable LED lamps (including a red lense cover over the lamp as per the real thing).

76??	**26020** BRb lined black - *11*	NPG	149
76??	as above DCC fitted	NPG	165
76??	as above with sound	NPG	249
76??	**26049** BRc lined green, small yellow panel - *11*	NPG	149
76??	as above DCC fitted	NPG	165
76??	as above with sound	NPG	249
76??	**E26051** BRe blue, yellow front - *11*	NPG	149
76??	as above DCC fitted	NPG	165
76??	as above with sound	NPG	249
76??	**76014** BRc blue, yellow front - *11*	NPG	149
76??	as above DCC fitted	NPG	165
76??	as above with sound	NPG	249
76??	**76022** BRc blue, yellow front - *11*	NPG	149
76??	as above DCC fitted	NPG	165
76??	as above with sound	NPG	249

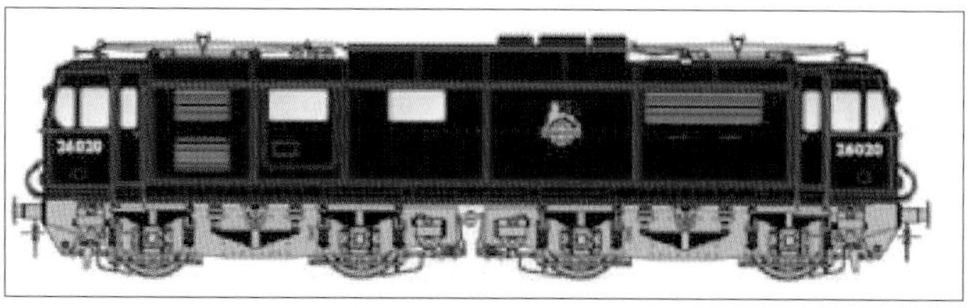

Proposed Class 76 (EM1) electric locomotive [L19] (Olivia's Trains)

L20. Class 77 EM2 Electric (2011)

The model has been commissioned by Olivia's Trains of Sheffield. Heavy Diecast Chassis, 5-pole motor with flywheels, all wheel drive, sprung buffers, 21-pin DCC socket, pre-fitted speaker, functionable LED lamps (including a red lense cover over the lamp as per the real thing).

77??	? BRb lined black - *11*	NPG	165
77??	as above DCC fitted	NPG	181
77??	as above with sound	NPG	271
77??	? BRc lined green - *11*	NPG	165
77??	as above DCC fitted	NPG	181
77??	as above with sound	NPG	271
77??	? BRc bright blue - *11*	NPG	165
77??	as above DCC fitted	NPG	181
77??	as above with sound	NPG	271

Rail Buses

L21. Waggon und Maschinenbau Railbus (2011)

8700	**E79960** light green - *11*	NPG	115
8701	**E79962** green - *11*	NPG	115
8702	**E79963** green, small yellow panels - *11*	NPG	115
8703	**M79964** green, large yellow panels - *11*	NPG	115

Diesel Multiple Units

L22. Class 251 'Blue Pullman'

The model was commissioned by Olivia's Trains of Sheffield but when, in July 2010, Bachmann revealed their intention to produce the model, Olivia's Trains withdrew from the arrangement with Heljan.

WAGONS

Cat No.	Company, Number, Colour, Dates	£	£

W1. ZFV 'Dogfish' (2004)

Ballast transporting wagons. M = 'Mainline'.

	BR Engineers		
4088	DB993057 olive green - *04*	12	15
4089	DB993413 olive green - *04*	12	15
4090	DB993634 olive green ZFV - *04*	12	15
4085	DB993016 grey+yellow - *04*	12	15
4086	DB983192 grey+yellow M on hopper - *04*	12	15
	Sets		
4087	DB993314 grey+yellow M on solebar - *04*	12	15

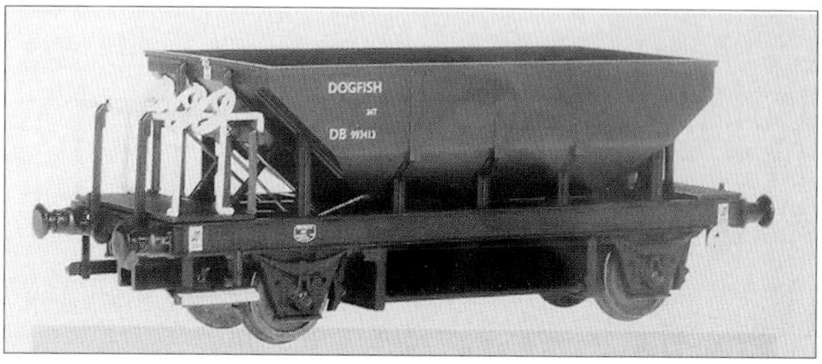

'Dogfish' hopper wagon [W1] (Heljan)

-	DB983577 grey+yellow + ballast	12	NA
-	DB993188 grey+yellow + ballast	12	NA
-	DB992908 grey+yellow + ballast	12	NA
-	DB992982 grey+yellow + ballast	12	NA
4095	above 4 wagons in a pack - *09*	NA	69
-	DB983135 olive green + ballast	12	NA
-	DB993626 olive green + ballast	12	NA
-	DB993608 olive green + ballast	12	NA
-	DB993586 olive green + ballast	12	NA
4096	above 4 wagons in a pack - *09*	NA	69
-	DB983217 red	12	NA
-	DB983596 black	12	NA
-	DB993225 black	12	NA
-	DB993602 olive green	12	NA
4097	above 4 wagons in a pack - *10*	NA	69
-	DB983037 grey+yellow	12	NA
-	DB983210 grey+yellow	12	NA
-	DB983260 grey+yellow	12	NA
-	DB993111 Loadhaul black	12	NA
4098	above 4 wagons in a pack - *10*	NA	69
-	DB983195 olive green W	12	NA
-	DB993605 olive green W	12	NA
-	DB993952 black W, 'TLF South East'	12	NA
-	DB992748 black W, 'NE Return to Ladybank'	12	NA
4099	above 4 wagons in a pack - *10*	NA	69
-	DB983187 grey+yellow W	12	NA
-	DB992929 grey+yellow W	12	NA
-	DB982307 grey+yellow W	12	NA
-	DB983032 grey+yellow W	12	NA
4100	above 4 wagons in a pack - *10*	NA	69

(* As supplied, these had non-insulated wheels and shorted out. Replacement wheel sets were supplied by Heljan.

W2. IGA Bogie Flat Wagon (2008)

Based on a late 1970s design for transporting long welded rails. They were originally used for transporting imported steel.

	DB 'Cargowaggon'		
5100	464-7-044 blue - *08*	16	19
5101	464-7-049 blue 'Corus Rail' - *08*	16	19
5102	464-7-035 blue - *08*	16	19
5103	464-7-030 blue W - *08*	20	23
4103	464-7-030-2 blue - *09*	20	25
5104	464-7-026 blue W + timber load - *08*	22	25
4104	464-7-026-8 blue + grey pipe load - *09*	22	27
5105	474-7-??? blue Corus Rail - *10*	NPG	NPG
5106	474-7-000 blue - *10*	NPG	NPG
5107	474-7-028 blue W - *10*	NPG	NPG
5108	464-7-041 blue with load - *10*	NPG	NPG

W3. IWA/IWB Bogie Van (2007)

Long bogie vans used for various domestic and Channel Tunnel traffic. Based on a late 1970s design.

	'Blue Circle'		
5002	2797669 yellow+blue - *07*	17	20
5003	2797683 yellow+blue - *07*	17	20
5008	2797699 yellow+blue W - *07*	17	20
	'Cargowaggon'		
5000	2797695 silver+ blue - *07*	17	20
5001	2797678 silver+ blue - *07*	17	20
5004	2797650 silver+ blue - *07*	17	20
5005	2797670 silver+ blue - *07*	17	20
5006	2797673 silver+ blue W - *07*	17	20
5007	2797591 silver+ blue W - *07*	17	20
5009	2797682 silver+ blue W - *07*	17	20
5011	2797581 silver+ blue W - *07*	17	20
5010	unbranded 2797692 silver+blue W - *07*	17	20

Two Hornby standards from computer artwork by Robbie McGavin

Heljan 0 (British)

Please note that due to two new additions it has been necessary to renumber the tables in this section.

HISTORY

Ready-to-run 0 gauge models were announced by Heljan at the end of 2004. They are built to 1:43.5 scale.

LOCOMOTIVES

These are being produced to the same high standard as the Heljan 00 models but with both bogies being driven. They have NEM pockets for interchangeable couplings.

Cat No.	Company, Number, Colour, Dates	£	£

L1. Class 20 Bo-Bo (2009)

The models are supplied unnumbered.

2000	BRc green small yellow panels - *09*	NPG	525
2001	BRe blue full yellow ends - *09*	NPG	525

L2. Class 26/1 BRCW Type 2 Bo-Bo (2011)

The models are supplied unnumbered.

2670	BRc green small yellow panels - *11*	NPG	525
2671	BRe blue full yellow ends - *11*	NPG	525

L3. Class 31 A1A-A1A (2011)

The models are supplied unnumbered.

?	BRc green - *11*	NPG	NPG
?	BRe blue - *11*	NPG	NPG

L4. Class 33 Bo-Bo (2011)

The models are supplied unnumbered.

?	BRc green - *11*	NPG	525
?	BRe blue - *11*	NPG	525

L5. Class 35 'Hymek' Bo-Bo (2005)

Rotating roof fan, two 5-pole motors, screw couplings, 4-character headcodes where appropriate, directional LED marker lights and sound insulated.

'Hymek' No.D7039 in BR green [L5] (Heljan)

3580	**D7039** BRc green full yellow ends - *05*	300	365
3581	**D7040** BRe blue - *05*	300	375
3581	**D7042** BRe blue - *not made*	NA	NA
3580	**D7097** BRc green full yellow ends - *not made*	NA	NA
3582	* BRc green no yell panel Ltd Edn 125 - *08*	NPG	349
3583	* BRc green full yell ends Ltd Edn 125 - *08*	NPG	349
3584	* BRe blue full yell ends Ltd Edn 125 - *08*	NPG	349

*The models are supplied unnumbered.

L6. Class 37/0 Co-Co (2008)

Rotating roof fan, two 5-pole motors, screw couplings, illuminated 4-character split headcodes where appropriate, directional LED marker lights and sound insulated. The models are supplied unnumbered. At the time of going to press,a centre codebox version was said to be on the cards.

3700	BRc green small yellow panels (100 made) - *08*	475	525
3701	BRe blue full yellow ends - *08*	475	525
3703?	BRe blue - *08*	475	525

L7. Class 47 Co-Co (2007)

Rotating roof fan, two 5-pole motors, screw couplings, illuminated 4-character headcodes, directional LED marker lights and sound insulated.

4880	* BRc 2-tone green, half yellow ends - *07*	375	425
4881	* BRe blue, full yellow ends - *07*	375	425

Class 47 No.D1662 Isambard Kingdom Brunel in BR blue [L7] (Hattons)

488x	**D1660 *City of Truro*** BRc two-tone green - *09*	NPG	525
4883	**D1662 *Isambard Kingdom Brunel*** BRe blue Ltd Edn 150 - *08*	NPG	525
4884	**D1664 *George Jackson Churchward*** BRc 2-tone green Ltd Edn 150 - *08*	NPG	525
4882?	**D1942** BRc 2-tone green, half yellow ends Sp Edn 100 (Tower Models) - *07*	375	425

* The models were supplied unnumbered.

L8. Class 55 'Deltic' Co-Co (2011)

The early version has been modelled with the sandbox fillers still in place.

?	BRc green - *11*	NPG	NPG
?	BRe blue - *11*	NPG	NPG

COACHES

Cat No.	Company, Number, Colour, Dates	£	£

The coaches listed in the following 5 tables are provided un-numbered.

C1a. BR Mk1 2nd Corridor (SK) (2010)

4900	red+cream - *10*	200	250
4901	maroon - *10*	200	250
4902	blue+grey - *10*	200	250
4903	brown+cream Lt Edn - *10*	240	309
4904	green Lt Edn - *10*	240	309

C1b. BR Mk1 Tourist 2nd Open (TSO) (2010)

4910	red+cream - *10*	200	250
4911	maroon - *10*	200	250
4912	blue+grey - *10*	200	250
4913	brown+cream Lt Edn - *10*	240	309
4914	green Lt Edn - *10*	240	309

C1c. BR Mk1 Brake 2nd Corridor (BSK) (2010)

4920	red+cream - *10*	200	250
4921	maroon - *10*	200	250
4922	blue+grey - *10*	200	250
4923	brown+cream Lt Edn - *10*	240	309
4924	green Lt Edn - *10*	240	309

C1d. BR Mk1 1st Corridor (FK) (2010)

4930	red+cream - *10*	200	250
4931	maroon - *10*	200	250
4932	blue+grey - *10*	200	250
4933	brown+cream Lt Edn - *10*	240	309
4934	green Lt Edn - *10*	240	309

C1e. BR Mk1 Miniature Buffet (RMB) (2010)

4940	red+cream - *10*	200	250
4941	maroon - *10*	200	250
4942	blue+grey - *10*	200	250
4943	brown+cream Lt Edn - *10*	240	309
4944	green Lt Edn - *10*	240	309

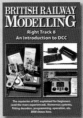

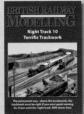

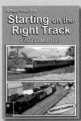

Hornby 0

These models were made by Meccano Ltd at Binns Road, Liverpool, between 1920 and 1962.

HISTORY

The Hornby Series was started by Frank Hornby, the inventor of Meccano, in 1920 during a time, following the First World War, when there was strong anti-German feeling. Hitherto, toy trains had been principally imported from Germany by companies like Bassett-Lowke and Gamages. Although marked 'made in England', the first cheap tinplate LNWR 0-4-0 tender locomotive and coaches, sold under the Hornby name, were based on German designs. However, the backbone of the new Hornby range was the more expensive, better made, nut and bolt constructed series of 0-4-0s in LNWR, GNR and MR company colours. These set a quality standard which was to remain until the demise of Hornby 0 gauge in the early 1960s.

In 1910, Hornby had taken on two very competent men in key positions within the company. Beardsley was in charge of production and Jones dealt with sales. This proved to be a powerful combination.

Milestones

1901 Frank Hornby invented Meccano.
1908 Meccano Ltd founded.
1914 Meccano Ltd moves to Binns Rd, Liverpool.
1915 Frank Hornby announces he is to make steam engines.
1920 Toy train production starts at Binns Road.
1922 'Zulu' trains first appear.
1923 Post-grouping liveries.
1924 'Hornby Series' name adopted.
1924 First tab and slot models appear.
1925 Metropolitan electric model introduced.
1926 M Series arrives.
1927 No.3 Pullman sets.
1927 'Hornby Lines' produced in Meccano's American factory.
1928 Meccano Ltd sell their American factory to AC Gilbert.
1928 First Southern Railway liveries.
1929 No.2 Special locomotives.
1930 Meccano make a bid for the Canadian market.
1931 Automatic couplings.
1932 Electrically lit accessories.
1932 Countryside sections.
1933 Colour changes on many models.
1934 Automatic reversing in electric locos.
1936 Death of Frank Hornby and Roland Hornby becomes Chairman and George Jones becomes Managing Director.
1937 *Princess Elizabeth* and *Eton* released.
1938 Arrival of Hornby Dublo points to the future.
1939 First year with no new 0 gauge models.
1941 Toy production closes down.
1946 Post-war products reach the shops and are now called 'Hornby Trains' or just 'Hornby'.
1951 Plastic wheels introduced to rolling stock.
1952 M Series models reappeared.
1954 BR liveries begin to appear.
1957 No.50 series wagons arrive as a last ditch attempt to retain interest in Hornby 0 gauge.
1962 Possibly last year of 0 gauge tinplate production.
1964 Lines Bros. invited to take over Meccano Ltd.
1965 Hornby name transferred to Tri-ang Railway, hence Tri-ang Hornby.
1965 Meccano Ltd release a plastic Percy Play Train.

Most of the locomotives were freelance in design and although all were beautifully made and finished, some, like the No.3s and the 4-4-2s, were peculiar in character. Products of more prototypical appearance were the No.2 Special Tender Locomotive 4-4-0, the No.4 'Schools' Class *Eton* and the top of the range 4-6-2 *Princess Elizabeth*. The latter was introduced in 1937, packed in a very attractive wooden box and cost £5.5.0 at a time when the average weekly wage was about £2.

At the other end of the scale, the market was catered for by the 'M' series, still very nicely made but much more basic.

The locomotives were supported by a large and colourful range of rolling stock, buildings and other accessories, the private owner wagons being particularly attractive. There was also a good range of colourful catalogues to whet the appetite (including *The Hornby Book of Trains* series) and sales leaflets.

On the death of Frank Hornby, in 1936, his son Roland replaced him as Chairman and George Jones was appointed Managing Director. With a marketing man in charge, Hornby continued to expand its base particularly with the 00 scale Hornby Dublo range introduced in 1938. On the death of Jones after the war, Beardsley became Managing Director and George Jones' marketing skills were very much missed during the 1950s.

After the Second World War the product name had changed from 'Hornby Series' to 'Hornby Trains'. The large locomotives did not return and only 0-4-0 locomotives were made. Bogie rolling stock was scarce and the range of accessories more limited. The reason was not a shrinkage in the market; indeed, in the first few years after the war the Hornby 0 gauge system was selling quite well. Trains were no longer the toys of the better-off but had become the toy that every boy wanted. To feed this fast expanding market, and to be more suitable for the typical suburban home, the smaller 00 gauge held preference. Thus British 00 gauge quickly displaced 0 gauge as the country's most popular scale and, as the demand for 00 increased, that for Hornby 0 gauge waned.

At the Meccano factory in Liverpool, special attention was now being given to expanding the Hornby-Dublo range which, for a while in the early 1950s, enjoyed its place as the market leader in Britain. Hornby 0 gauge limped on into the 1960s but production had already ceased when, in 1964, Meccano Ltd invited the toy manufacturing giant, Lines Bros. Ltd, to take them over.

After several months studying the problems at the Meccano factory, Lines Bros. decided to develop the Dinky Toy and Meccano ranges but not to restart the loss-making railway production lines. Instead they set about disposing of the large amount of unsold stock that had built up in the factory and, until the late 1960s, Hornby 0 gauge wagons and accessories could be bought for very attractive prices.

No.2 Special - GWR 4-4-0 County of Bedford [L16] (Wallis & Wallis)

Further Reading

For further reading on this subject, the most complete study will be found in *The Hornby 0 Gauge System* by Chris and Julie Graebe and published by New Cavendish Books (ISBN 0 904568 35 0). By the same authors and publishers there is also the *Gauge 0 Compendium* (ISBN 0 904568 90 3) which lists model variations and is an excellent guide to dating variations. Both books contain many more variations than we have been able to include here and are strongly recommended for an in-depth study of Hornby 0 gauge.

Collectors Club

You may also wish to join the Hornby Railway Collectors Association (HRCA) who publish, for their members, a monthly magazine, called *The Hornby Railway Collector*, devoted to the toy train and model railway products of Meccano Ltd. Details of this organisation may be obtained from the membership secretary, John Harwood, tel: 01935 474830.

Series Numbering - Meccano Ltd used '0', '1', '2' etc. to denote series, with the higher number being used for higher standard models. Having started with '1', '0' was used when they decided to produce a cheaper series and, when they wanted to produce a series even further down market, they adopted the prefix 'M'. Top of the range were No.2 bogie wagons and No.2 electrically lit lineside accessories. With coaches and locomotives, the numbering went even higher to '3' and '4'. Many special wagons do not have a series number.

Zulu - This was an early cheaper range which was superseded by No.0 and M3 items.

No. 2 Special Pullman car Zenobia [C3c] (Vectis)

M Series - As we have seen, these form the bottom end of the range being cheaper, smaller and more toy-like than their relatives and were introduced to compete with the cheaper tin trains of Wells, Brimtoy, Chad Valley etc. The series which started with the M3 goods set late in 1926, was colourful and a complete system in its own right with locomotives, rolling stock, buildings and other accessories.

The M items were later divided into the M1/M3 range and M0 items which were even simpler and cheaper. The M1/M3 items had rudimentary drop-link couplings while M0 models had a simple tab and slot coupling. None of the M items had buffers.

Today, the series is probably more admired by toy-collectors than model railway collectors. M0 and M1 are the only product series names carried through to the post-war locomotives at the recommencing of manufacture in 1946.

No one is sure what the 'M' referred to but it has been suggested that it was derived from 'minor' or even 'mechanical', which was used when selling the products abroad instead of the term 'clockwork'.

The 'British Express' was an unusual variation within this series as it was especially made for chain stores and shops which were not normal Hornby outlets. In order to perpetuate this price cutting, these M0 products had special tin printings and were devoid of maker's marks.

Prices - The chance of finding mint boxed Hornby 0 gauge is so small that the use of the 'mint/boxed' column (right hand one) for this purpose would have no meaning. We have therefore used both price columns to indicate the price range one may expect for examples in very good condition (except for *Princess Elizabeth* models which had a much higher rate of box survival). The difference between top and bottom price may seem erratic, but this is because actual auction prices are used and differences sometimes bear little relevance to relative scarcity. Thus a poorer quality example can sometimes sell for more than a better quality version of the same model, sold at a different time and in a different auction. **Once again we caution readers not to take the values quoted in this guide too literally.**

Pricing 0 gauge Hornby is extremely difficult. Due to the large range of variations in colour and transfer positions, most sellers are unaware of the rarity of some of these and so they can be bought quite cheaply. This means that prices range greatly, limiting the value of prices quoted here.

Four different versions of the No 1 side-tipping wagon [W32] (Vectis)

Wheels - the earliest items of rolling stock had pressed silver tinplate wheels which were replaced by black tinplate wheels around 1928. Some of the more expensive items were fitted with realistic cast wheels with white painted rims ('United Dairies' and 'Colas' tank wagons are examples). Cast Mansell-type wheels were also catalogued and sold separately at 3d per pair for the more discerning to fit to their stock. Snowploughs always had cast wheels to improve traction necessary to drive the rotating plough.

Couplings - Early models had a drop-link type coupling which required each item to be connected to its neighbour by hand. Around 1931, 'automatic' couplings were introduced which allowed vehicles to couple on their own when shunted together. It seems that the changeover from one coupling type to the other was not instantaneous but took place over a number of years thus allowing old stock to be cleared. Not all vehicles were converted to automatic couplings.

Loco Search by Type

If you know the type of Hornby 0 gauge locomotive you are looking for, this table will tell you in which section you should look.

Locomotive.	**Wheels**	**Table**
George V Tender Loco	0-4-0	L4
Princess Elizabeth	4-6-2	L19
Silver Link, Tender Loco	0-4-0	L5
'Zulu' Tender Loco	0-4-0T	L8
'Zulu' Tank	0-4-0	L9
LE1	0-4-0	L21
LE2	0-4-0	L22
M0 Tender Loco	0-4-0	L1
M1 Tender Loco	0-4-0	L2
M3 Tender Loco	0-4-0	L4
M3 Tank	0-4-0T	L6
Metropolitan	0-4-0	L20
No.0 Tender Loco	0-4-0	L8
No.00 Tender Loco	0-4-0	L4
No.1 Tank	0-4-0T	L9
No.1 Tender Loco	0-4-0	L10
No.1 Special Tank	0-4-0T	L11
No.1 Special Tender Loco	0-4-0	L12
No.101 Tank	0-4-0T	L7
No.2 Tank	4-4-4T	L13
No.2 Special Tank	4-4-2T	L15
No.2 Tender Loco	4-4-0	L14
No.2 Special Tender Loco	4-4-0	L16
No.20 Tender Loco	0-4-0	L1
No.30 Tender Loco	0-4-0	L3
No.3C Tender Loco	4-4-2	L17
No.4 *Eton* Tender Loco	4-4-0	L18
No.40 Tank	0-4-0T	L7
No.50 Tender Loco	0-4-0	L10b
No.501 Tender Loco	0-4-0	L10b
No.51 Tender Loco	0-4-0	L10b
Streamlined Tender Locos	0-4-0	L5

Loco Search by Running Number

In order to help you find your Hornby 0 Gauge locomotive we have listed below, in the left column, the numbers that appear on the side of models (running numbers) and, in the right column, the number of the table(s) in which you will find the model.

Loco Tables	Nos.	Loco Tables	Nos.	Loco Tables	Nos.
		234	L16	516	L11
0-4-0	L9a	326	L9a+9b	551	L8
2	L20	4-4-4	L13	600	L8
6	L15	460	L6,7,13	623	L9a+9b
29	L9b	463	L9a	700	L16
70	L11	483	L4	793	L8+10a
111	L9b	492	L15	826	L9b
201	L16	500	L8	850	L17

Loco	Nos. Tables	Loco	Nos. Tables	Loco	Nos. Tables
900	L18	2728	L2+4	7202	L13
1000	L10b	2810	L8+10b	7283	14
1019	L13	2900	L9b	7391	L5
1179	L12	2930	L2	8108	L11
1185	L16	3031	L2	8123	L11
1368	L12	3132	L2	8324	L8+10a
1452	L4	3133	L2	8327	L8+10a
1504	L8	3233	L1	8329	L15
1534	L13	3435	L2	8712	L12
1759	L16	3580	L11	9319	L10b
1784	L15	3821	L16	10655	L21+22
1842	L10b	3917	L5	15500	L11
2051	L13	4073	L17	16045	L11
2052	L13	4300	L10b	31240	L17
2091	L15	4312	L12	31290	L17
2107	L13	4472	L1+17	31801	L17
2115	L9b	4525	L12	45746	L3
2120	L11	4560	L9b	50153	L10b
2162	L11	4700	L12	60199	L10b
2180	L15	4703	L15	60985	L1
2221	L15	4797	L8	82011	L7
2243	L13	5096	L8+10a	A129	L11
2251	L8	5097	L8	A179	L12
2270	L6+7	5097	L10a	A504	L8+10b
2290	L10b	5154	L15	A600	L9
2301	L12	5165	L13	A759	L8,10a+16
2323	L15	5399	L8	A760	L14
2329	L15	5500	L11	A950	L11
2449	L8+10a	5508	L8	B28	L11
2509	L5	5600	L8+10b	B343	L12
2526	L2+4	6097	L10b	B604	L13
2527	L4	6100	L1+17	B667	L9a
2586	L11	6161	L1	E29	L9b
2595	L1	6201	L19	E111	L9b
2663	L4	6380	L8	E126	L6+7
2691	L12	6418	L11	E492	L13+15
2694	L12	6600	L6+7	E509	L8+10a
2700	L12	6781	L15	E510	L14
2710	L4,8+10a	6954	L15	E793	L8+10b
2711	L14	7140	L9b	E850	L17

LOCOMOTIVES

Cat No.	Company, Number, Colour, Dates	£	£

L1. M0 and No.20 0-4-0 (1930)

These were tinprinted, without cylinders and rods but having a fixed key until 1936. From then on it had fitted cylinders, connecting (not coupling) rods and a removable key. The tenders carried numbers only, with no railway companies decals. The 'British Express' trains were produced for sale to non-Hornby agents and so carried no Meccano Ltd identification.

No.20 tender loco of 1954 [L1] (D.J. Auctions)

Cat No.	Company, Number, Colour, Dates	£	£
M0	**4472** green, black base, cutout cab windows c/w - *30-32*	20	35
M0	**2595** green, red or green base c/w - *33-36*	25	35
M0	**2595** green, cylinders, round printed splashers (1938-41) c/w - *36-41*	25	35
M0	**6100** red, black base, cutout cab windows c/w - *30-32*	20	35
M0	**6161** red, red or green base c/w - *33-36*	20	35
M0	**6161** red, cylinders c/w - *36-37*	25	35
M0	**6161** red, cylinders, round printed splashers c/w - *38-41*	25	35
M0	**6161, 2595** red or green, wheels unpainted c/w - *46-54*	20	35
-	**3233** red 'British Express' locomotive, black base, no cylinders or trademark, c/w - *32-36*	300	350
20	**60985** BRb green lined out in orange+black, black chassis c/w - *54-68*	25	45

The red 6100 represented the LMS *Royal Scot* while 6161 was the number of *The King's Own Regiment*. The green 4472 represented *Flying Scotsman* but the number 2595 belonged to LNER A1 loco *Trigo*.

L2. M1 0-4-0 (1926)

These tin-printed models were sturdier than the M0, the early examples being copied from a Bing design. The engines had a non-reversible clockwork mechanism, without rods and there were no cylinders or company decals - only numbers. They were almost all green with black chassis and lined out in black and white. The M1 was revised from 1930 with a more modern shaped body (with single piece forming boiler and cab) and a new reversing mechanism. In 1934 two inexpensive electric motors were introduced, EM120 (20 volt) and EM16 (6 volt), both AC.

Pre-war M1 tender loco of 1934 [L2] 3-rail electric (Vectis)

Cat No.	Company, Number, Colour, Dates	£	£
M1	**2526** on tender and cab side, green, black base, cast chimney unpainted wheels c/w - *26-32*	30	50
M1	**2728** as above - *27-29*	30	55
M1, M2930	**2930** as above, tin chimney - *29-32*	30	55
M1	**3031** on tender green or red new shape, blk base, red wheels, c/w - *30*	30	70
M1	**3132** as above but tin printed windows - *31-33*	30	60
M1	**3132** as above dark red - *31-33*	30	60
M1	**3132** as above green or red but green base - *33-34*	30	60
M1	**3132** as above dark red - *33-34*	40	60
M1	**3133** as above but green - *33-34*	30	40
M1	**3435** green or red, bases green, red or black c/w - *34-41*	30	40
EM16	as above green 6v - *34-38*	105	175
EM16	as above red 6v - *34-38*	150	215
EM120	as above green 20v - *34-38*	110	185
EM120	as above red 20v - *34-38*	160	230
M1	**3435** green, black base, Hornby on cabsides, red wheels, c/w - *46-58*	20	30
M1	**3435** red, black base, Hornby on cabsides, red wheels, c/w - *46-58*	25	45

No.30 tender loco of 1956 [L3]

L3. No.30 0-4-0 (1956)

Initially designed in 1954 to replace the one-piece pressing M1, it was late in being issued and failed to stop the Hornby decline. The No 30 had a larger, squarer, separate cab, an improved tender and was finished in BR green with lion and wheel emblem on the tender. However, the mechanism was the same as the M1 but had very crudely cast con-rods.

30	**45746** green, lined orange+black with black chassis + wheels c/w - *56-65*	30	55

L4. No.00 and M3 'George V' 0-4-0 (1920)

This was an 0-4-0 locomotive with outside cylinders. It was a very early tin-printed design and was based on a Bing original. It was finished in early company colours and had an underscale tender. A clockwork reversing mechanism was fitted until 1924 after which a larger non-reversing mechanism was fitted. It was referred to as the No.00 engine in 1925 (nothing to do with '00' scale), becoming the M3 tender locomotive in 1926 and finally being paired with the larger M1 style tender with modified open coal rail. Coupling rods were fitted in 1927. No railway company markings were used on the engines in the last two years of the model, when the colour was enamelled instead of tin-printed. There were many sub-variations, especially in the last two years of production, and below we have listed only the main ones.

00, M3	**1452** on cab **GNR** on tender, green c/w - *20-26*	70	150
00, M3	**2663** on cab ***George the Fifth***, **LNWR** on tender, black c/w - *20-26*	115	150
00, M3	**483** on tender **MR** crest on cab, red c/w - *20-26*	140	160

00/M3 tender loco of 1920 [L4] (Vectis)

M1 style tender with cutout coal rails

M3	**2526, 2728** on tender green c/w - *26-28*	70	100
M3	**2527, 2710** on tender **MR** crest on cab, red c/w - *26-28*	140	160
M3	**2710, 2527, 2663** on tender ***George the Fifth***, black c/w - *26-28*	115	130
M3	**2728, 2710** (red or black) on tender, No.0 style body, green c/w - *28-29*	60	90

L5. Streamlined 0-4-0s (1936)

The streamlined 0-4-0 tender locomotives were clockwork and belonged to the 'M' series. It was an 'M' sheep in wolf's clothing! It was heart breaking when you think of the real A4s. They were sold in sets with special articulated coaches. Those for *Silver Link* were silver, numbered 1584 and 1585 and carried the name 'The Silver Jubilee'.

'Silver Link' and coaches of 1936 [L5] (Lacy, Scott & Knight)

0	**2509 *Silver Link* LNER** silver c/w - *36-41*	200	380
0	**7391** on loco + tender, 2 greens c/w - *37-40*	200	300
0	**3917** on loco + tender, maroon+cream c/w - *37-40*	200	300

L6. M3 0-4-0T (1931)

This was an 0-4-0 locomotive without cylinders and connecting rods until 1936. Earlier locos that were repaired at the factory were often fitted with rods. It had a tin-printed body and no handrail knobs. The engine was fitted with 8-spoke red wheels, except between 1932 and 1936 when they were 12-spoke. From 1936, cylinders and rods were fitted.

M3	**6600 Great Western**, green c/w - *31-41*	55	165
EM36	as above 6v - *34-41*	135	205
EM320	as above 20v - *32-34*	135	205
M3	**2270 LMS** red c/w - *31-41*	55	110
EM36	as above 6v - *34-41*	125	175
EM320	as above 20v - *32-34*	125	175
M3	**460 LNER** green c/w - *31-41*	50	155
EM36	as above 6v - *34-41*	150	250
EM320	as above 20v - *32-34*	150	250

M3 0-4-0T of 1932 20v electric [L6] (Vectis)

M3	**E126, E492 Southern** dark green c/w - *31-41*	60	140
EM36	as above 6v - *34-41*	130	190
EM320	as above 20v - *32-34*	130	190

L7. No 101 and No.40 0-4-0T (1947)

A post-war 0-4-0 tank locomotive with cylinders, connecting rods and coupling rods, this was a continuation of the pre-war M3 with the same mechanism and body with minor changes in the tinprinting.

No.101 0-4-0T of 1947 [L7]

101	**6600 GW** green c/w - *47-54*	80	275
101	**2270 LMS** red c/w - *47-54*	45	110
101	**460 LNER** green c/w - *47-54*	45	105
101	**E126 SR** green c/w - *47-54*	85	290
101	**E111 SR** black c/w - *47-54*	85	290
40	**82011 BRb** lined black c/w - *54-60*	40	110
40	**82011 BRc** lined black c/w - *60-65*	40	110

Note: Red lining sometimes has pinkish metallic finish.

L8. 'Zulu' and No.0 0-4-0 (1923)

Early examples of this 0-4-0, with outside cylinders and a coal rail tender, had 'Zulu' on the smokebox door but this was later replaced with 'Hornby'. Up until 1928 the wheel splashers were over the rear wheels only but from then on they stretched to cover both sets. In 1931 the whole locomotive was redesigned (see below) and from now on the tender coal rails were not cut out. All locos were lined out but were made without cylinders until 1937 when outside cylinders were reintroduced to the range. There were many variations of this model, only some of which are listed below. Note: In most production runs of Hornby models there were fewer black locomotives, so they normally sell for 30% to 50% more than the coloured ones. Rare numbers, such as 1504, add further value.

No.0 tender loco of c1923 [L8] (Wallis & Wallis)

-	***Zulu*** on splashers in red/gold, black c/w - *23-24*	110	140
0	**2710 GW** on splasher, diecast GWR type safety valve, green c/w - *26-29*	95	235
0	**2710** red with MLdL logo on splashers and tender - *23-24*	100	130
0	**2710** on tender, **LMS** on splashers, red c/w - *24-29*	60	130
0	as above but black - *24-29*	75	170
0	**2710 LNER** green c/w - *24*	85	180
0	as above but lined c/w - *25-27*	85	105
0	as above but red wheels c/w - *28-29*	80	100
0	**2710 LNER** black c/w - *24*	120	170
0	as above but lined c/w - *25-27*	115	165
0	as above but red wheels c/w - *28-29*	100	160
0	**E509** on tender **Southern** black, red wheels c/w - *28-31*	190	260
0	**A759** on tender **Southern** green, red wheels, c/w - *28-31*	145	210
0	**2449** on cab, **Great()Western** on tender, green c/w - *29-31*	130	235
0	**8327, 8324, 600 LMS** on tender, red c/w - *29-31*	85	130
0	as above but black - *29-31*	140	200
0	**5097, 5096** + **LNER** on tender, green c/w - *29-31*	85	130
0	as above but black - *29-31*	140	200
0	**2251, 5399 Great()Western** green body redesigned c/w - *31-41*	95	235
E06	as above 6v - *34-35*	170	270
E020	as above 20v - *34-41*	240	310
0	**600, 8324, 500, 551, 5600 LMS** red body redesigned c/w - *31-41*	60	130
E06	as above 6v - *34-35*	120	200
E020	as above 20v - *34-41*	150	240
0	**600, 8324, 500, 551, 5600 LMS** black body redesigned c/w - *31-41*	100	150
E06	as above 6v - *34-35*	220	270
E020	as above 20v - *34-41*	270	310
0	**6380, 2810, 5508, 4797 LNER** green body redesigned c/w - *31-41*	100	155
E06	as above 6v - *34-35*	170	220
E020	as above 20v - *34-41*	200	250
0	**6380, 2810, 5508, 4797 LNER** black body redesigned c/w - *31-41*	160	210
E06	as above 6v - *34-35*	220	270
E020	as above 20v - *34-41*	270	310
0	**A504, 1504, E793, 793 Southern** green body redesigned c/w - *31-41*	145	210
E06	as above 6v - *34-35*	800	1200
E020	as above 20v - *34-41*	850	1250
0	**A504, 1504, E793, 793, E111 Southern** black body redesigned c/w - *31-41*	380	450
E06	as above 6v - *34-35*	800	1200
E020	as above 20v - *34-41*	850	1250

L9a. No.1 0-4-0T (original body) (1922)

These were 0-4-0 tank locomotives with cylinders and connecting rods. A brass dome was carried until 1928 (except Zulu) after which it was painted. There were wire handrails on the smokebox with a brass knob each side and the body was enamelled. In 1931 it received a revised body (see 9a below). **Mechanisms**: Clockwork 1922-41, 6 volt DC. 1929-31.

1	**'Zulu'** on tank in red/gold, red edge to spectacles, black c/w - *22-23*	85	280
1	**'Zulu'** on smokebox front, **LMS** black c/w - *23-24*	85	160
1	**Great Western** green c/w - *26-31*	85	165
E16	as above 6v DC - *29-34*	240	340
1	**Great()Western** green c/w - *30-31*	100	170
E16	as above 6v DC - *30-31*	260	355
1	**0-4-0** + **LMS** on tank, red c/w - *24-26*	80	145
1	as above but black c/w - *24-26*	70	150
1	**623, 326 LMS** black, wheels black or red c/w - *26-31*	80	170
E16	as above but 6v DC - *29-34*	240	350
1	**0-4-0 LNER** green c/w - *24-26*	70	170
1	as above but black c/w - *24-26*	80	210
1	**623, 326, 463 LNER** green c/w - *26-31*	70	170
1	as above but black c/w - *26-31*	80	210
E16	**463 LNER** green 6v DC - *29-34*	160	280
E16	as above but black 6v DC - *29-34*	280	900
1	**A600, B667** on tanks **Southern** green c/w - *28-31*	100	120
1	as above but black c/w - *28-31*	100	120

No 1 0-4-0T LMS of 1924 [L9a] (Vectis)

E16	as above green 6v DC - *29-34*	260	300
E16	as above black 6v DC - *29-34*	260	300

L9b. No.1 0-4-0T (revised body) (1931)

In 1931 a revised body design was adopted for the No.1 tank which was heavier looking with lower chimney, dome, cab and flared bunker. Control rods were now above the bunker (not through its bunker plate as previously). No black body versions were made after 1936. **Mechanisms**: Clockwork 1931-41; 6 volt DC. 1931-34; E16 (6 volt); 1934-36 LST1/20 (20 volt); 1934-41 E120 (20 volt).

1	**4560 Great Western** green c/w - *31-34*	85	165
EPM16	as above 6v - *34-35*	210	250
LTS1/20	as above 20v - *32-34*	230	300
1	**4560 GWR** button green c/w - *35-41*	80	165
E120	as above 20v - *35-41*	180	240
1	**7140, 623, 326, 2115 LMS** red c/w - *31-41*	95	145
EPM16	as above 6v - *34-35*	130	220
LTS1/20	as above 20v - *32-34*	170	330
E120	as above 20v - *34-41*	180	350
1	**7140, 623, 326, 2115 LMS** black c/w - *31-41*	90	225
EPM16	as above 6v - *34-35*	170	300
LTS1/20	as above 20v - *32-34*	240	350
E120	as above 20v - *34-41*	240	350
1	**826, 2900 LNER** green c/w - *31-35*	80	180
EPM16	as above 6v - *34-35*	130	180
LTS1/20	as above 20v - *32-34*	150	220
E120	as above 20v - *34-35*	150	220
1	**826, 2900 LNER** darker green c/w *36-41*	80	180
E120	as above 20v - *36-41*	150	220
1	**826, 2900 LNER** black c/w - *31-41*	90	230
EPM16	as above 6v - *34-35*	200	650
LTS1/20	as above 20v - *32-34*	300	900
E120	as above 20v - *34-41*	300	900

The updated No.1 0-4-0T of 1931 with larger boiler [L9b] (Vectis)

1	**E111, 111, E29, 29 Southern** green c/w - *31-41*	100	350
EPM16	as above 6v - *34-35*	200	400
LST1/20	as above 20v - *32-34*	220	420
E120	as above 20v - *34-41*	220	420
1	**E111, 111, E29, 29 Southern** black c/w - *31-41*	150	295
EPM16	as above 6v - *34-35*	400	500
LST1/20	as above 20v - *32-34*	450	600
E120	as above 20v - *34-41*	450	600

L10a. No.1 0-4-0 (original body) (1920)

The No.1 0-4-0 locomotive had cylinders and connecting rods and was similar to No.0 locomotive but with brass handrail knobs instead of diecast ones. They had cylinders on all variations and the bodies were enamelled. Some early examples had nickel base plates. In 1931, a completely revised and modernised body was fitted (see 10b).
Mechanism: Clockwork 1920-31. N&B = nut and bolt construction

No.1 tender loco of 1920 with small boiler [L10a] (Vectis)

1	**2710 LNWR** style black N&B ML Ltd c/w - *20-23*	155	260
1	**2710 MR** style maroon, N&B ML Ltd c/w - *20-23*	110	200
1	**2710 CR** style blue, N&B, ML Ltd c/w - *20-23*	230	280
1	**2710 GN** style green, N&B some had red sides to running plate ML Ltd c/w - *20-23*	165	220
1	**2710** on coal rail tender **GW** on splasher, crest on cab, green c/w - *26-29*	90	160
1	**8327** on coal rail tender, **Great()Western** black c/w - *26-29*	90	160
1	**2449** on cabside **Great()Western** coal rail tender, long splashers, green c/w - *29-31*	100	170
1	**2710** on cabsides **LMS** on RH splasher red or black c/w - *23-24*	100	150
1	**2710** on tender **LMS** on both splashers red or black c/w - *25-29*	100	150
1	**2710** on cabsides **LNER** on RH splasher red side plates, green c/w - *23-24*	100	150
1	**2710** on tender **LNER** on both splashers, red sides till '26, c/w green - *25-29*	100	150
1	**2710** on tender **LNER** on both splashers, black c/w - *24-29*	120	180
1	**8324** on cabside **LMS** on coal-rail tender, long splashers, red c/w - *29-31*	80	135
1	**8327** on cabside **LMS** on coal-rail tender, long splashers, black c/w - *29-31*	80	135
1	**5096** + **LNER** on tender, 232 on cabside, long splashers, green c/w - *29-31*	80	135
1	**5097** + **LNER** on tender, 232 on cabside, long splashers, black c/w - *29-31*	150	180
1	**8324** + **LNER** on tender, 232 on cabside, long splashers, green c/w - *30-31*	200	240
1	**A759** + **Southern** on tender green c/w - *28-29*	200	240
1	**E509** + **Southern** on tender black + green lining c/w - *28-29*	200	450
1	**A759** + **Southern** on coal rail tender 232 on cabside long splashers, green c/w - *29-31*	150	340
1	**E509** + **Southern** on coal rail tender 232 on cabside, long splashers, black c/w - *29-31*	200	400

Note: There were numerous detailed variations on the No.1 tender locomotives.

L10b. No.1, No.501, No.50 and No.51 0-4-0 (1931)

The new body for the No1 tender locomotive, introduced in 1931, had a larger diameter boiler, long splashers, low chimney and dome and a cab with two windows each side. Driving wheels were normally red and a heavier type tender with solid top rails was used. The No.501 was a post WWII continuation of the No.1. The enamel was finished with a matt varnish (as were the very late No.1's from 1939). Electric 20 volt versions, numbered E502, are quite rare, having all been sent for export. No black liveries were made in the 501 series and wheels were black except for the LNER c/w locomotive which was produced with green wheels. New details were: a centre lamp bracket above the front coupling and lamp brackets on the rear of the tender. The No 50 and 51 were basically the same as the No.501 but updated with the introduction of BR liveries, emblems and numbers, being smartly lined out and finished in gloss. They were made only in clockwork. **Mechanism**: Clockwork 1931-41, E16 (6 volt) 1934-35, E120 (20 volt) 1934-41. N&B = nut and bolt construction

1	**4300** on cabside, **Great()Western** on tender, green c/w - *31-34*	95	160
E16	as above 6v - *34-35*	195	450
E120	as above 20v AC - *31-34*	250	550
1	**4300** on cabside, **GWR** button on tender, green c/w - *35-38*	100	160
E120	as above 20v - *34-38*	250	550
1	**9319** on cabside **GWR** button on tender, green c/w - *38-41*	95	160
E120	as above 20v - *38-41*	250	550
1	**1000** on cabside **LMS** on tender red c/w - *31-41*	80	200
1	**2290** on cabside **LMS** on tender black c/w - *31-36*	100	280
1	**5600** on cabside **LMS** on tender red c/w - *36-41*	80	200
E16	**1000, 2290** on cabside **LMS** on tender red 6v - *34-35*	230	375
E16	as above but black 6v - *34-35*	170	270
E120	**1000, 2290, 5600** on cabside **LMS** on tender, red 20v - *34-41*	230	375
E120	as above but black 20v - *34-41*	200	320
1	**2810** on cabside **LNER** on tender green (darker from '36) c/w - *31-35*	75	130
1	as above but darker - *36-41*	75	130
1	**6097** on cabside, **LNER** on tender, black c/w - *31-36*	120	370
1	**1842** on cabside, **LNER** on tender green c/w - *39-41*	75	130
E16	**2810, 6097** on cabside, **LNER** on tender, green 6v - *34-35*	220	355
E16	as above but black 6v - *34-35*	270	330
E120	**2810, 6097, 1842** on cabside, **LNER** on tender, green 20v - *34-41*	140	260
E120	as above but black 20v - *34-41*	280	360
1	**E793** on tender **Southern** green c/w - *31-33*	170	340
1	**793** on tender **Southern** green c/w - *33-41*	130	300
E16	as above 6v - *34-35*	360	700
E120	as above 20v - *34-41*	460	800
1	**A504** on tender **Southern** black c/w - *31-36*	310	450
E16	as above 6v - *34-35*	350	600
E120	as above 20v - *34-36*	400	650
501	**9319** on cab **G()W** green c/w - *48-49*	300	500
E502	as above 20v - *48-49*	400	550
501	**5600** serif on cab **LMS** red c/w - *48*	60	160
E502	as above 20v - *48*	220	365
501	**5600** sans-serif on cab **LMS** red c/w - *49-54*	65	170
E502	as above 20v - *49-54*	220	365
501	**1842** serif on cab **LNER** green c/w - *48*	65	170
E502	as above 20v - *48*	190	375
501	**1842** sans-serif on cabside **LNER** green c/w - *49-54*	75	165

No.50 (ex-revised No.1) of 1954 in BR livery [10b] (Wallis & Wallis)

E502	as above 20v - *49-54*	180	390
50	**60199 BRb** black lined red+grey c/w - *54-61*	70	175
51	**50153 BRb** green lined orange+black c/w - *54-61*	70	165

Note: There were numerous detailed variations on the No.1 tender locomotives.

L11. No.1 Special 0-4-0T (1929)

These were heavy 0-4-0 locomotives with cylinders and connecting rods. They were larger than other 0-4-0 tanks and had more powerful mechanisms. They were finished in the four railway company colours, and in black liveries (except for the GWR version). Red and black engines had red wheels while green engines had green wheels. **Mechanisms**: Clockwork 1929-41, EPM16 (6 volt) 1934-39, and E120 special (20 volt) 1934-41.

1	**3580 Great Western** green 7 boiler bands c/w - *29*	130	260
1	**3580 Great Western** green 8 boiler bands c/w - *30*	130	260
1	**5500 Great Western** number not on plate green c/w - *30-31*	140	260
EPM16	as above 6v - *30-31*	280	390
E120	as above 20v - *30-31*	320	460

1	**5500 Great Western** green c/w - *32-35*	140	260
EPM16	as above 6v - *32-35*	280	390
E120	as above 20v - *32-35*	320	460
1	**5500 GWR** button green c/w - *36-41*	140	250
EPM16	as above 6v - *36-39*	280	390
E120	as above 20v - *36-41*	320	460
1	**6418 LMS** sans-serif letters and numbers shadowed, red c/w - *29-30*	130	230
1	**2120 LMS**, serif letters and numbers, shadowed, red c/w - *30-34*	130	230
1	**15500 LMS**, serif letters and numbers, shadowed, red c/w - *34-36*	140	280
EPM16	as above 6v - *34-36*	220	350
E120	as above 20v - *34-36*	250	400

No.1 Special 0-4-0T of 1929 [L11] (Vectis)

1	**70** (serif) **LMS** red c/w - *36-41*	130	230
EPM16	as above 6v - *36-39*	220	350
E120	as above 20v - *36-41*	250	400
1	**70** (sans-serif) **LMS** red c/w - *37-39*	140	280
EPM16	as above 6v - *37-39*	220	330
E120	as above 20v - *37-39*	240	380
1	**16045 LMS** (sans-serif) black c/w *29-30*	125	285
EPM16	as above 6v - *34-35*	250	450
E120	as above 20v - *34-35*	320	490
1	**16045 LMS** (serif) black c/w - *30-36*	125	285
EPM16	as above 6v - *35-36*	250	450
E120	as above 20v - *35-36*	320	530
1	**8123 LNER** green 7 bands c/w - *29*	115	360
EPM16	as above 6v - *34*	220	430
E120	as above 20v - *34*	250	530
1	**8123 LNER** green 8 bands c/w - *30-35*	115	350
EPM16	as above 6v - *35*	220	430
E120	as above 20v - *35*	250	530
1	**2162 LNER** green c/w - *35*	140	380
EPM16	as above 6v - *35*	295	530
E120	as above 20v - *35*	240	500
1	**2162 LNER** darker green c/w - *36-41*	130	370
EPM16	as above 6v - *36-39*	230	450
E120	as above 20v - *36-41*	260	500
1	**8108 LNER** black c/w - *29-30*	130	380
1	**2586 LNER** black c/w - *30-36*	150	410
EPM16	as above 6v - *34-36*	350	470
E120	as above 20v - *34-36*	400	520
1	**A950 Southern** sans-serif letters, green with white+black lining c/w - *29-30*	170	320
1	**B28 Southern** serif letters, green with white+ black lining c/w - *30-35*	170	420
EPM16	as above 6v - *34-35*	400	1100
E120	as above 20v - *34-35*	520	1400
1	**516 Southern** green with white+black lining c/w - *35-41*	170	320
EPM16	as above 6v - *35-39*	350	950
E120	as above 20v - *35-41*	450	1250
1	**A129 Southern** black with green lining c/w - *29-30*	590	770
1	**A950 Southern** now with serif letters, black c/w - *30-36*	700	900
EPM16	as above 6v - *34-36*	800	1300
E120	as above 20v - *34-36*	1000	1525

L12. No.1 Special 0-4-0 (1929)

These were similar to the previous models but with splashers over the wheels instead of side tanks. They were paired with a four-wheeled tender that was larger than that used with other 0-4-0 models. Other details were those already described for the No.1 Special Tank Loco except that 6 volt mechanisms were not fitted to this model.

1	**2301 Great()Western** on tender, green c/w - *29-35*	230	500
1	**4700 Great()Western** on tender, green c/w - *34-35*	200	470
E120	as above 20v - *34-35*	425	595
1	**4700 GWR** button on tender, green c/w - *36-41*	190	450
E120	as above 20v - *36-41*	425	595
1	**4312 LMS** (serif), lined tender, red c/w - *30-31*	130	390
1	**8712** on cabside **LMS** (serif), lined tender, red c/w - *31-35*	130	390
E120	as above 20v - *34-35*	300	585
1	**2700 LMS** letters on lined tender, red c/w - *35-41*	110	310
E120	as above 20v - *35-41*	300	585
1	**4525 LMS** gold on tender, black c/w - *29*	155	495
1	as above letters shadowed c/w - *30-36*	155	480
E120	as above 20v - *34-36*	500	550
1	**1368** on cab, **LMS** on tender, red c/w (error) - *?*	1000	1200
1	**2694** + **LNER** on tender, small no. on cab, blk boiler bands, green c/w - *29*	150	320
1	as above, white boiler bands - *30-31*	150	320

No.1 Special 0-4-0 tender loco of 1929 [L12] (Vectis)

1	**1368** on cab, **LNER** on tender, green c/w - *31-35*	150	320
E120	as above 20v - *34-35*	300	730
1	as above but darker green c/w - *36-41*	280	520
E120	as above 20v - *36-41*	300	730
1	**2691** in gold + **LNER** on tender, oval on cabsides, black c/w - *29-36* -	250	440
E120	as above 20v - *34-36*	500	650
1	**A179** on cab **Southern** green c/w - *29-35*	240	400
E120	as above 20v - *34-35*	800	1500
1	**1179** + **Southern** on tender, green c/w - *35-41*	240	800
E120	as above 20v - *35-41*	560	1650
1	**B343** + **Southern** on tender, black lined green c/w - *29-36*	810	1000
E120	as above 20v - *34-36*	950	4800

L13. No.2 4-4-4T (1923)

This was the only 4-4-4 locomotive made by Hornby and had the character of tank engines of the early years of the 20th century, especially on the LNWR. Produced from 1923-29 in clockwork only, there were many detail variations including 24 on LMS locos alone! We have not been able to deal with all of them here. Two lamps were fixed on front of the locomotive from 1924 onwards.

No.2 4-4-4T of 1923 [L13] (Vectis)

2	**Great Western** green crest on cab c/w - *26*	210	505
2	**7202, 2243 Great()Western** green c/w - *27-29*	180	400
2	**1019 LM&SR** red part lined c/w - *23*	170	350
2	**LM&S** red part lined c/w - *23*	170	350

2	as above but black c/w - *23*	160	280
2	**4-4-4 LMS** red fully lined c/w - *24-26*	150	320
2	as above but black c/w - *24-26*	140	260
2	**2052 LMS** crest on bunker, red c/w - *26-28*	150	320
2	as above but black c/w - *26-28*	140	260
2	**2107, 2051, 2052 LMS** on bunker plate, later on tank, red c/w - *28-29*	150	320
2	as above but black c/w - *28-29*	140	260
2	**L&NER** green with red side plates, lined bunker c/w - *23*	200	320
2	**1534 L&NER** green with red side plates, lined tanks c/w - *23*	200	320
2	**4-4-4 L&NER** green + red side plates, full lining c/w - *24-25*	180	300
2	as above but black c/w - *24-25*	165	435
2	**4-4-4 LNER** green, full lining c/w - *25-26*	180	310
2	as above but black c/w - *25-26*	170	420
2	**460 LNER** green with crest on cab c/w - *26*	200	320
2	as above but black c/w - *26*	180	440
2	**460, 5165 LNER** green with crest on bunker c/w - *27-29*	230	450
2	as above but black c/w - *27-29*	170	370
2	**B604** Southern green c/w - *28-29*	250	850
2	**E492** Southern black c/w - *28-29*	240	1150

L14. No.2 4-4-0 (1921)

These were elegant 4-4-0 locomotives of early 20th century character. They were powered by clockwork only, except for very special orders. Produced between 1921 and 1929, they had a 6-wheeled coal rail tender which usually carried the number '2711'; although there are other variations. For the first two years, the locos were made in pre-grouping colours (GN - green, MR - red, CR - blue, LNWR - black) but, after this, the colours of the four grouped companies were introduced. Black engines were again available for all companies except the GWR. The driving wheels were covered by long splashers and the domes were mainly brass. The model was of nut and bolt construction, using Meccano nuts and bolts. The locos had two fixed front lamps from late 1924 onwards. **Electric Models** : These exceptionally rare examples were Hornby's first venture into electric mechanisms. No sound price guide is available on the electric versions as they are very rare and usually in poor condition when found. £1300 is a very broad guide.

2	**2711** on brass cab plate **MR** style red, Meccano transfers, c/w - *21-23*	190	520
2	as above **LNWR** style black - *21-23*	250	800
2	as above **CR** style blue - *21-23*	450	1200
2	as above **GNR** style green, red valences - *21-23*	380	920
2	**2711** on tender, **GW** on splashers, GWR crest on cab, green c/w - *26*	295	380
2	**2711** on tender, **Great()Western** on splashers, **7283** on cab, green c/w - *27-28*	295	380
2	**7283** on cabsides, **Great()Western** on tender, green c/w - *29*	340	780
2	**2711** metal on cab, red, **LM&S** on splashers, pre-group tender c/w - *23*	200	520
2	as above but black c/w - *23*	225	870
2	red as above but trademark transfer on RH and **LMS** on LH splasher - *23*	200	520
2	as above but black - *23*	250	870
2	red as above but **LMS** on splashers and tender c/w - *24*	200	520
2	as above but black - *24*	225	870
2	red as above but number only on tender, crest on cab c/w - *24-29*	150	450
2	as above but black - *24-29*	240	580
2	**2711 GN** crests on splashers, metal cabside number, green c/w - *23*	250	500
2	**2711** (metal on cab) **L&NER** on LH and **GN** crest on RH splasher, green c/w - *23*	240	500
2	**2711** (metal on cab) **L&NER** on both splashers and tender, green c/w - *23*	210	450
2	**2711** on tender **LNER** on both splashers, green c/w - *24-29*	150	400
2	**2711 LNER** on splashers, crest on cabsides, black c/w - *24-27*	160	500
2	**2711 LNER** crest on cab, no letters on splashers, black c/w - *28-29*	160	500
2	**A760** + **Southern** on tender, green c/w - *28-29*	480	900
2	**E510** + **Southern** on tender, black c/w - *28-29*	1200	1700

No.2 4-4-0 tender loco of 1921 [L14] (Vectis)

L15. No.2 Special 4-4-2T (1929)

This was a 4-4-2 updated replacement for the No.2 tank and was produced from 1929 until 1941. Larger driving wheels were fitted to the later improved mechanisms and smokebox bulbs were used from 1933 onwards. It was a heavier looking engine than the No.2 with higher boiler and lower chimney, dome and cab. It had no outside cylinders but there were two fixed front lamps until 1930 when they were replaced by four brackets front and rear. **Mechanisms**: powered by clockwork, 6V 30-34, 6V E26 34-41, 20V LST2/20 33-34, 20V E220 34-41. The early electric motors had protruding brushes.

2	**4703 Great Western**, green c/w - *29-30*	250	300
2	**2221 Great Western** green c/w - *30-31*	140	230
2	as above 6v - *30-31*	170	300
LST 2/20	as above 20v - *30-31*	200	380
2	**2221** plate on cabside **Great Western** green c/w - *32-36*	140	230
2, E26	as above 6v - *32-36*	170	300
LST 2/20	as above 20v - *32-34*	200	380
E220	as above 20v - *34-36*	200	380
2	**2221** on cabside **GWR** button, green (late ones matt) c/w - *36-41*	140	230
E26	as above 6v - *36-41*	170	300
E220	as above 20v - *36-41*	200	380
2	**2323** + **LMS** sans-serif, red c/w - *29-30*	170	300
2	**2180** + **LMS** serif, red c/w - *30-36*	140	330
2, E26	as above 6v - *30-36*	180	355
LST 2/20	as above 20v - *33-34*	210	370
E220	as above 20v - *34-36*	210	370
2	**6954** + **LMS** serif, red c/w - *36*	140	330
E26	as above 6v - *36*	180	300
E220	as above 20v - *36*	200	355
2	**6954** + **LMS** serif, matt red c/w - *40-41*	140	330
E26	as above 6v - *40-41*	180	355
E220	as above 20v - *40-41*	200	365
2	**6954** + **LMS** sans-serif matt red c/w - *37-39*	140	330
E26	as above 6v - *37-39*	180	500
E220	as above 20v - *37-39*	200	350
2	**6781 LMS** sans-serif, black c/w - *29-30*	160	270
2	**6781 LMS** serif, black c/w - *31-36*	160	250
2, E26	as above 6v - *30-36*	210	340
LST 2/20	as above 20v - *33-34*	240	425
E220	as above 20v - *34-36*	240	425
2	**6 LNER** green c/w - *29-32*	125	220
2	**1784 LNER** green, green wheels c/w - *32-35*	140	265
2, E26	as above 6v - *32-35*	180	270
LST 2/20	as above 20v - *32-34*	200	350
E220	as above 20v - *34-35*	200	350
2	**1784 LNER** darker green, green wheels c/w - *36-38*	140	265
E26	as above 6v - *36-38*	185	270
E220	as above 20v - *36-38*	200	350
2	**1784 LNER** darker matt green, green wheels c/w - *39-41*	140	265
E26	as above 6v - *39-41*	185	270
E220	as above 20v - *39-41*	200	350
2	**5154** + **LNER** gold on tank, red lining, black wheels, black c/w - *29-36*	145	320
2, E26	as above 6v - *30-36*	185	290
LST 2/20	as above 20v - *33-34*	325	350
E220	as above 20v - *34-36*	325	350
2	**8329** + **Southern** on tanks serif, green c/w - *30-33*	180	300
2	as above 6v - *30-33*	210	470
2	**2329 Southern** green c/w - *33-35*	175	300
2, E26	as above 6v - *33-35*	210	470
LST 2/20	as above 20v - *33-34*	250	500
E220	as above 20v - *34-35*	250	500

No.2 Special 4-4-2T of 1929 [L15] (Wallis & Wallis)

2	**2091 Southern** green c/w - *35-38*	175	300
E26	as above 6v - *35-38*	210	470
E220	as above 20v - *35-38*	250	500
2	**2091 Southern** matt green c/w - *39-41*	175	300
E26	as above 6v - *39-41*	210	470
E220	as above 20v - *39-41*	250	500
2	**E492** on bunker + **Southern** sans-serif, red wheels, black c/w - *29*	NPG	NPG
2	**E492** + **Southern** on tanks serif, wheels (early red late black), black c/w - *30-33*	175	550
2	as above 6v - *30-33*	350	650
2	**492 Southern**, black c/w - *33-36*	175	550
2, E26	as above 6v - *33-36*	300	550
LST 2/20	as above 20v - *33-34*	350	650
E220	as above 20v - *34-36*	350	650

The production of black 'goods' engines was stopped after 1936 but they were obtainable by special order at extra cost.

L16. No.2 Special 4-4-0 (1929)

These were 4-4-0 tender locomotives and were Hornby's first real venture into true-to-type models. They were and are a very attractive and popular range embodying the character of the prototypes. **Mechanisms**: Clockwork 1929-41, E220 (20 volt) 1934-41, 6V special order.

3821 *County of Bedford* - Green

2	Great()Western, green running plates, red nameplates c/w - *29-30*	600	1100
2	Great()Western, black running plates, black nameplates c/w - *30-36*	350	800
E220	as above 20v - *34-36*	600	1100
2	GWR button, black running plates c/w - *36-41*	350	800
E220	as above 20v - *36-41*	600	1100

LMS 1185 'Compound' - Maroon

2	sans-serif, red drivers + running plate, unlined tender c/w - *29-30*	300	420
2	serif, black drivers + running plate, lined tender c/w - *31-36*	310	580
E220	as above 20v - *34-37*	400	850
2	sans-serif, black drivers + running plate, lined tender c/w - *37-38*	310	580
E220	as above 20v - *37-38*	400	850
2	serif, black drivers + running plate, lined tender, matt finish c/w - *39*	310	580
E220	as above 20v - *39*	400	850
2	**700 LMS** black Class 2P no cylinders, special order, beware imitations - *38*	3000	4000

LNER 234 *Yorkshire* - Green

No.2 Special of 1929 [L16] (Wallis & Wallis)

2	LNER + number on tender, small cab numberplates c/w - *29*	500	900
2	LNER on tender, number on cabside, green running plate c/w - *30-31*	500	900
2	LNER on tender, number on cabside, black running plate c/w - *31-35*	500	900
E220	as above 20v - *34-35*	780	2800
2	LNER special order black with white lining - *31-32*	4000	5500

LNER 201 *Bramham Moor* - Green

2	LNER c/w - *35-36*	400	630
E22	as above 20v - *35-36*	690	1625
2	LNER darker green c/w - *36-41*	400	630
E220	as above 20v - *36-41*	690	1625

SR Class L1 - Green

2	**A759** lined cab unlined tender c/w - *29*	1000	3250
2	**A759** lined tender c/w - *30-35*	615	1275
E220	as above 20v - *34-35*	1100	3250
2	**1759** lined tender c/w - *35-41*	615	1275
E220	as above 20v - *35-41*	1100	3250

L17. Riviera 'Blue Train' and No.3 4-4-2 (1926)

These 4-4-2 tender engines were of rather odd freelance appearance with their large cylinders and double thickness running plates. They were nothing like the top expresses they are named after. This was almost 'badge engineering', and ironically they were coupled to the excellent No 2 special tenders (except for the 'Nord' which has a bogie tender and was made for the Riviera 'Blue Train' Set). **Mechanisms**: Clockwork 26-40, 3E 4 volt 26-29, 3E 6 volt 29-34, E36 6 volt 34-36, E3/20 20 volt 33-34, E320 20 volt 34-40.

Nord 31240 - Brown

3C	31801 on tender, black running plate, brass domes c/w - *26-27*	190	330
3E	as above 4v - *26-27*	250	500
3C	31801 on tender, brown running plate and domes c/w - *28-29*	195	330
3E	as above 4v - *28-29*	250	500

Nord 31801 - Brown

3C	brown smokebox c/w - *29*	195	330
3E	as above 6v - *29*	250	500
E3/20	as above 20v - *29*	265	550

No.3 4-4-2 tender loco 1929 version [L17] (Vectis)

3C	black smokebox c/w - *30-33*	195	330
3E	as above 6v - *30-33*	250	500
E3/20	as above 20v - *30-33*	265	550
3C	black smoke deflectors c/w - *34-36*	230	380
E36	as above 6v - *34-36*	250	500
E320	as above 20v - *34-36*	265	550
3C	brown deflectors + smokebox c/w - *36-38*	230	380
E320	as above 20v - *36-38*	265	400
E320	**3.1290** brown deflectors + smokebox, cab lined gold only, 20v - *38-41*	380	500

4073 *Caerphilly Castle* - Green

3C	Great()Western coal-rail tender, green smokebox c/w - *27-28*	245	435
3E	as above 4v - *27-28*	295	500
3C	Great()Western, black smokebox, brass whistle c/w - *29*	245	435
3E	as above 6v - *29*	295	500
3C	Great()Western, black smokebox, brass whistle, No.2 tender c/w - *30-36*	245	435
3E, E36	as above 6v - *30-36*	295	500
E3/20, E320	Great()Western, black smoke box, brass whistle, 20v - *33-36*	300	650
3C	GWR button c/w - *36-38*	245	435
E320	as above 20v - *36-38*	300	650
3C	GWR button, nameplate black+gold c/w - *39-41*	260	435
E320	as above 20v - *39-41*	300	650

	LMS 6100 *Royal Scot* - Maroon		
3C	crest on cab and number on coal rail tender c/w - *27-29*	220	400
3E	as above 4v - *27-29*	250	440
3C	gold number on cab and number or LMS on tender c/w - *29-30*	220	400
3E	as above 4v - *29-30*	250	440
3C	gold number on cab and number or LMS on lined tender c/w - *30-32*	220	400
3E	as above 6v - *30-32*	250	440
3C	gold number on cab and number or LMS (shaded) on lined tender c/w - *33-36*	220	400
3E, E36	as above 6v - *33-36*	250	440
E3/20	as above 20v - *33-34*	300	480
E320	as above 20v - *34-36*	300	480
3C	smoke deflectors, gold number on cab and number or LMS shaded on lined tender c/w - *36-41*	300	500
E320	as above 20v - *36-40*	350	550
	LNER 4472 *Flying Scotsman* - Green		
3C	LNER + number on coal-rail tender, crest on cab, grn smokebox c/w - *27*	190	350
3E	as above 4v - *27*	270	455
3C	LNER + number on coal-rail tender, crest on cab, black smokebox c/w - *28*	190	350
3E	as above 4v - *28*	270	455
3C	LNER + number on coal-rail tender, gold number on cab, black smokebox c/w - *29*	190	350
3E	as above 4v - *29*	270	455
3C	LNER on No2 tender, gold number on cab, black smokebox c/w - *30-32*	190	350
3E	as above 6v - *30-32*	270	455
3C	LNER shadowed on No2 tender, gold number on cab, black smokebox c/w - *33-36*	190	350
3E, E36	as above 6v - *33-36*	270	455
E3/20, E320	LNER shadowed on No2 tender, gold number on cab, black smokebox 20v - *33-36*	210	420
3C	as above but darker green c/w - *36-41*	260	420
E320	as above 20v - *36-41*	350	465
3C	with smoke deflectors, rare - *34-36?*	NPG	NPG
E320	black, extremely rare, fakes! - *37*	2500	3500
	SR E850 *Lord Nelson* - Green		
3C	coal-rail tender c/w - *28-29*	230	380
3E	as above 4v - *28-29*	300	420
3C	No.2 Special tender c/w - *29-33*	230	360
3E	No as above 4v - *29-33*	300	420
	SR 850 *Lord Nelson* - Green		
3C	c/w - *33-36*	230	380
3E, E36	6v *-33-36*	300	420
E3/20	20v - *33-34*	400	480
E320	20v - *34-36*	400	480
3C	smoke deflectors fitted c/w - *36-41*	260	430
E320	as above 20v - *36-41*	450	560

L18. No.4 'Schools' Class 4-4-0 (1937)

This was a 4-4-0 'Schools' Class tender locomotive. A most attractive and popular model, it was Hornby's final engine based on a prototype. The tender (a No.2 special) was incorrect for prototype. **Mechanisms**: Clockwork and E240 (20 volt motor).

No.4 tender loco of 1937 'Schools' Class 900 Eton [L18] (Wallis &Walis)

4	**900 *Eton*** Southern grn c/w - *37-41*	550	1270
4	as above 20v - *37-41*	770	1600
4	**900 *Eton*** Southern black, mainly for export, watch out for fakes! - *37-41*	3000	5000

L19. 'Princess Royal' Class 4-6-2 (1937)

The 4-6-2 'Princess Royal' Class locomotive was Hornby's largest and most impressive piece of motive power. However, incorrect proportions on the locomotive give a distorted appearance to line of boiler and firebox. Early wooden presentation cases were red with blue lining and marked in gold - 'Meccano Ltd. Liverpool *Princess Elizabeth*. Boxes from the middle period of production were red with cream lining and later ones were blue with green lining. Both of the latter had a nice printed description and picture inside the lid. **Prices** - those in the right-hand column include the wooden presentation case. **Mechanism**: 20 volt electric motor.

'Princess Royal' Class Princess Elizabeth of 1937 [L19] (Wallis & Wallis)

-	**6201 *Princess Elizabeth*** LMS (serif) maroon, cab inside sand - *37*	1230	2100
-	as above but sans-serif - *38*	1230	2100
-	as above but cab inside maroon - *39-40*	1230	2100

L20. Metropolitan 0-4-0 (1925)

This was an 0-4-0 with its wheels tucked under its skirt instead of being a double bogied model like the real locomotive. One wonders what could have been achieved if Hornby had developed a motor bogie like Bassett-Lowke and the Leeds Model Company. This was Hornby's first production electric motored model as well as its first prototypical one. It was colourful and attractive but it initially worked on 125 volt AC! Re-railing without the controller turned off could give you an additional thrill! This would appear to be the only Hornby Series locomotive not to be fitted with automatic couplings in later days. **Mechanisms**: 1925-29 H.V. (125), 1926-39 clockwork, 1927-29 4V, 1929-39 6V, 1938-39 20V. In about mid production, clockwork and 6 volt motors were improved.

Metropolitan loco of 1925 [L20] (Wallis & Wallis)

	2 Metropolitan - Maroon		
1, HV	125v AC - *25, 27-29*	300	495
2, LV	4v - *27-29*	300	495
3, C	rear windows not punched out, coupling rods c/w - *26-39*	210	370
LV, E36	protruding brush-caps 6v - *29-39*	300	495
E320	20v - *38-39*	340	530

There were numerous mechanical variations of this model but the main ones are listed above.

LE1 Swiss 0-4-0 of 1932 [L21] (Vectis)

L21. LE1 Swiss Type 0-4-0 (1932)

Here was an 0-4-0 locomotive with a Swiss type body for overhead power collection. Dummy pantographs were fitted and there were coupling rods on the clockwork models but rarely on electric ones. This was a somewhat odd production model which lasted only four years and had five colour changes in this time! These were dark green, light green, red, cream and blue and the roofs were grey, cream, red or yellow. **Mechanisms**: 1932-36 LEC1, clockwork. 1932-34 LE1/20, 20V. 1934-36 LE120, 20V.

LEC1	**10655** various colours c/w - *32-36*	350	600
LE1/20	as above 20v - *32-34*	400	700
LE120	as above 20v - *34-36*	400	700

L22. LE2 Continental 0-4-0 (1932)

Another 0-4-0 locomotive and a very strange looking object being basically a Metropolitan loco without the skirts. Apart from the *Princess Elizabeth*, it was the sole Hornby model not to have a clockwork version. The body was fitted with overhead pantographs and it carried the same transfers as LE1. Some models had coupling rods and the body colours that may be found are dark green, light green, red or cream. roof colours were grey, cream or blue. **Mechanisms**: 1932-34 LE2/20, 20V 1934-36 LE220, 20V.

LE220	**10655** Swiss, Metropolitan body various colours 20v - *32-36*	650	1700

COACHES

Until the middle of the 1920s, rolling stock was of nut and bolt (Meccano type) construction. After that, tabs and slots were used to join pieces together when items were assembled. Below we provide a means of identifying the age of coaches by their structure and finish.

Cat No.	Company, Number, Colour, Dates	£	£

M Series Coaches (4-wheel)

C1a. M0 Pullman Coaches (1930)

This was a small coach with no buffers, tin hook and loop couplings, cream and brown livery and named *Joan* or *Zena*.

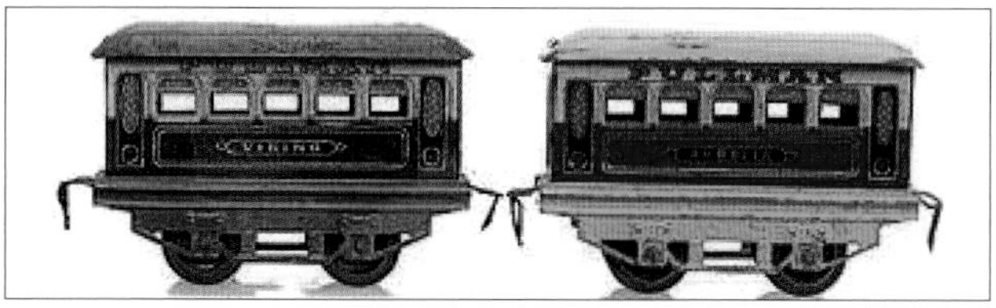

M1 Pullman cars [C1b] (Vectis)

M0	red or green roof, marked 'Hornby Series' - *30-41*	10	14
No.0	as above but with automatic couplings - *31-41*	10	14
M0	grey roof, marked 'Hornby' - *46-54*	8	12
No.21	**BR** red+cream same body no names - *54-59*	5	10

C1b. M1/2 and M1 Pullman Coaches (1926)

This was larger than the M0 Pullman coach. All had drop-link couplings, cream and brown livery and were named 'Pullman' (1926-28), *Marjorie, Aurelia* or *Viking*.

M1/2	yellow+green+cream, red or brown roofs and bases - *26-41*	15	22
M1	white or grey roofs and black bases - *46-57*	15	22

C1c. No.31 Coaches (1956)

Replaced M series Pullman Coaches in 1956 and were larger than No. 21 but smaller than 41/51 series coaches. They were fitted with No. 30 series combined loop and hook non-automatic couplings and no buffers.

No.31	**BR** red+cream composite - *56-62*	8	12
No.31	**BR** red+cream brake 2nd - *56-62*	8	12

No1 Coaches (4-wheel)

C2a. 1921 No.1 Passenger Coaches (1921)

These were of nut and bolt construction, had brass numbers on the doors, grey roofs, coats of arms on the sides, cut-out windows and 4 silver wheels.

No.1	**CR** orange-brown, ochre doors - *21-23*	80	110
No.1	**GN** orange-brown, ochre doors - *21-24*	60	75
No.1	**LNWR** brown+white - *21-23*	60	75
No.1	as above tinprinted doors - *23-24*	60	75
No.1	**MR** maroon, brown-pink doors - *21-24*	60	75

No.1 4-wheel coaches of 1921 [C2a] (Vectis)

C2b. 1924 No.1 Passenger Coaches (1924)

This had a completely different body of tab and slot construction and a full brake was also made from now onwards. The coaches had grey clerestory roofs (until 1929), three opening doors in each side and printed windows. The wheelbase was short for the length of body making them look toy-like.

No.1	**GWR** brown+cream, clerestory roof - *24-28*	55	70
No.1	**GWR** brown+cream - *28-34*	35	50
No.1	**LMS** red, clerestory roof - *24-28*	40	55
No.1	**LMS** 1136? red - *28-34*	30	45
No.1	**LNER** brown, clerestory roof - *24-28*	40	55
No.1	**LNER** brown - *28-34*	30	45
No.1	**SR** 1728 green - *28-32*	55	70
No.1	**SR** 2891 green - *32-34*	55	70

C2c. 1934 No.1 Passenger Coaches (1934)

These coaches were completely redesigned models which were wider and higher than previous ones, with wheels further apart, non-opening doors and closed axle springs. Roofs were grey (lighter shade after the war) and post-war versions were marked 'Hornby' or 'Hornby Trains'.

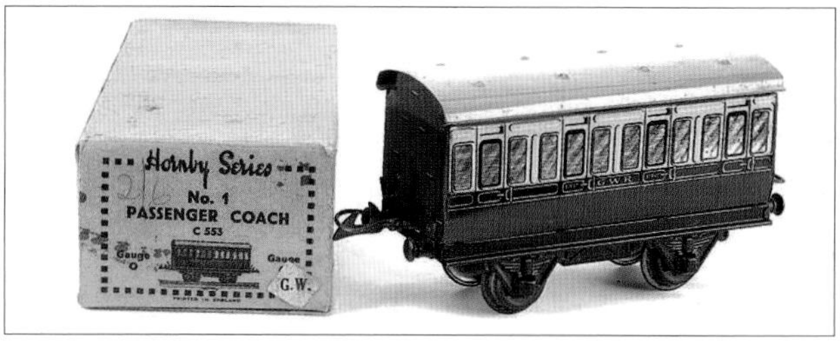

No.1 GWR coach of 1934 [C2c] (Vectis)

No.1	**GWR** brown+cream - *34-41*	50	65
No.1	**GWR** brown+cream - *47-49*	70	85
No.1	**LMS** red+yellow+black detail - *34-41*	25	40
No.1	**LMS** red - *47-59*	20	35
No.1	**LNER** light brown wood-grain - *34-41*	30	45
No.1	**LNER** light brown - *47-59*	20	35
No.1	**SR** green+yellow printed detail - *34-41*	80	95
No.1	**SR** green - *47-49*	90	120
No.41	**BR** red+yellow lining, no black lined panels - *54-58*	20	25
No.51	**BR** red+cream - *54-58*	30	45

C2d. 1928 No.1 Pullman Coach (1928)

Both coach and brake end versions were made over a long period so mums and dads must have loved them but to kids they were hideous! They had rounded roof ends and recessed end doors. They had brown and cream tin-printed sides and were named *Corsair, Cynthia, Niobe, Ansonia* or *Aurora*. Roofs were cream, grey, red, green or blue.

No.1	opening doors - *28-35*	20	30
No.1	non-opening doors - *35-41*	20	30

No.2 Bogie Coaches (with compensating bogies)

The passenger coaches were 1st/3rd composites and the brake coaches were all 3rd class. They were similar in style and colour to the 1934 No.1 coaches but twice as long.

C3a. 1921 No.2 Pullman and Dining Saloon. (1921)

These were the first bogie coaches to be made by Hornby and were a light cream and green and had greenish grey roofs. They were of nut and bolt construction and had celluloid windows. Until 1923 the doors were fixed but from then they were hinged.

No.2 dining saloon of 1921 [C3a] (Vectis)

No.2	**CR** crest Dining Saloon green+cream - *21-23*	100	140
No.2	**GN** crest Dining Saloon green+cream - *21-23*	100	140
No.2	**LNWR** crest Dining Saloon green+cream - *21-23*	100	140
No.2	**MR** crest Dining Saloon green+cream - *21-23*	90	130
No.2	**Pullman** crests, green+cream - *21-25*	90	130
No.2	**Pullman** crests as above but scrolled box around name - *25*	90	130
No.2	**Pullman** crests as above but livery now brown +cream - *25-27*	90	130
No.2	**Pullman** crests Dining Saloon green+cream - *23-25*	90	130

C3b. Metropolitan Coaches (1926)

This was a suburban bogie coach with a fine wood grain tin-printed finish made specially to go with the Metropolitan electric locomotive. Two versions were made - 1st class and brake/3rd. They had grey roofs, yellow windows, brass buffers, drop-link couplings and were available in both lit and unlit versions.

-	**Met** 1st class brown coach - *26-39*	180	250
-	**Met** brake 3rd brown coach - *26-39*	180	250

C3c. 1928 No.2/3 or No.2 Special Pullmans (1928)

These replaced the No.2 and No.3 Pullmans in sets. They had a restyled body with smaller, better shaped, windows which had more elegant window frames. They had square accumulator boxes beneath the coach instead of cylinders. They also had snap-on roofs, seven windows in their sides and they had a curved roof with rain gullies and ventilators. All were brown and cream and a brake end (or composite) was now produced. They were called No.2/3 Pullmans until 1930/31 when they were renamed No.2 Special Pullmans.

Pullman

No.2/3	***Iolanthe*** all cream upper half, cream roof with blue vents - *28-30*	90	130
No.2/3	***Iolanthe*** or ***Zenobia*** all cream upper half, cream roof with blue vents - *29-30*	90	130
No.2/3	***Arcadia*** brake, all cream upper half, cream roof with blue vents - *28-30*	90	130
No.2/3	***Arcadia*** or ***Alberta*** brake, all cream upper half, cream roof, blue vents - *29-30*	90	130
No.2	***Iolanthe, Zenobia*** or ***Grosvenor*** brown above windows, grey roof - *30-35*	120	180
No.2	***Zenobia, Grosvenor*** or ***Loraine*** as above - *35-41*	120	180
No.2	***Arcadia, Alberta*** or ***Montana*** brake, brown above windows, grey roof - *30-35*	120	180
No.2	***Alberta, Montana*** or ***Verona*** as above, luggage compartment now all brown - *35-41*	120	180

No.2 GWR coach of 1935 [C3a] (Vectis)

C3d. 1935 No.2 Passenger Coaches (1935)

These were the first Hornby bogie coaches for general passenger stock of the four railway companies despite the fact that Bing and Bassett-Lowke had issued theirs in the early 1920s. The coaches consisted of a 1st/3rd composite and an all 3rd brake end and looked like suburban stock.

No.2	**GWR** brown+cream with badge in lower half - *35-41*	180	250
No.2	**GWR** brown+cream with badge in lower half - *48-50*	225	295
No.2	**LMS** red + black/yellow lining - *35-41*	110	170
No.2	**LMS** red + black/yellow lining - *48-50*	155	200
No.2	**LNER** light brown teak effect - *35-41*	150	195
No.2	**LNER** light brown teak effect - *48-50*	185	240
No.2	**SR** green + yellow/black lining - *35-41*	200	300
No.2	**SR** green + yellow/black lining - *48-50*	250	350

C3e. 1937 No.2 Corridor Coaches (1937)

This was a later design to go with the larger express locomotives. They had large windows and the end panels were cut to take the 'concertina' type corridor connections. All were composites except the Southern coach which was an all-3rd. There were destination board brackets above windows.

No.2	**GWR** brown+cream with badge in lower half, white roof, composite - *37-41*	160	220
No.2	**GWR** 4073 brown+cream with badge in lower half, white roof, brake/3rd - *37-41*	160	220
No.2	**LMS** 3888 red, yellow lining, matt chassis after 1939, grey roof, composite - *37-41*	100	160
No.2	**LMS** 6844 red, yellow lining, matt chassis after 1939, grey roof, brake composite - *37-41*	100	160
No.2	**LNER** 186 teak, yellow lining, white roof, composite - *37-41*	125	180
No.2	**LNER** teak, yellow lining, white roof, brake composite - *37-41*	125	180
No.2	**SR** green, yellow lining, white roof, all-3rd - *37-41*	200	300
No.2	**SR** green, yellow lining, white roof, deep orange round door windows, brake/3rd - *37-41*	200	300

No.3 Bogie Coaches

C4a. Riviera 'Blue Train' & Mitropa Coaches (1926)

The Riviera Blue Train coaches were the first Hornby coaches to be made with corridor connectors and were for use with the Nord locomotive. Two types, a sleeper and a diner, were available but these were structurally the same but with different celluloid strips at the windows. From 1931 onwards, they were fitted with compensating bogies and a Mitropa version of each was produced in red livery. The latter had white roofs and were a strange choice because Hornby did not have an appropriate locomotive to pull them. They could perhaps have been put behind the Nord as a through train!

No.3	**CIE** Dining Car, blue - *26-41*	150	190
No.3	**CIE** Sleeping Car, blue - *26-41*	150	190
No.3	**Mitropa** Schlafwagen, red+gold - *31-41*	500	600
No.3	**Mitropa** Speisewagen, red+gold - *31-41*	500	600

C4b. No.3 (No.2) Pullman & Saloon Coaches (1927)

Based on the Riviera Blue body, these Pullmans originally came with the No.3 train sets. They also had corridor connections and brown corridor end plates but used the same transfers as the No.2 Pullmans and carried the same livery with cream roofs. From 1930 the No.3 was renamed the 'No.2 Pullman Coach' and LMS and LNER 1st class end vestibule saloon coaches were made to the same design.

No.3	**Pullman**, large crests, drop-link couplings - *27-28*	60	80
No.2	**Pullman**, small crests, automatic couplings - *30-41*	60	80

No.2 LNER coach of 1930 [C4b] (Vectis)

No.2	**LMS** 402 red saloon - *30-41*	60	80
No.2	**LNER** 137 brown saloon - *30-41*	60	80

C5. American Pullman Cars (1930)

Made for export to America, but available in the UK.

-	***Madieson*** green+black - *30-36*	NPG	NPG

-	***Madieson*** green+red - *33-34*	NPG	NPG
-	***Madieson*** yellow+black - *30-36*	NPG	NPG
-	***Madieson*** yellow+orange - *33-34*	NPG	NPG
-	***Washington*** green+black - *30-36*	NPG	NPG
-	***Washington*** green+red - *33-34*	NPG	NPG
-	***Washington*** yellow+black - *30-36*	NPG	NPG
-	***Washington*** yellow+orange - *33-34*	NPG	NPG

WAGONS

The first Hornby 0 gauge wagons appeared in 1920 and were of nut and bolt construction. These were in liveries representing pre-grouping companies and were priced 3/9 each.

Company Lettering - Meccano Ltd were quick to introduce the new liveries after Grouping in 1923; LNER and LMS being the first to appear followed by GWR and SR. Around 1928, 'LNER' was dropped in favour of 'NE'.

Earlier lettering on pre-grouping stock consisted of white painted tinplate letters stamped out and fixed to the sides of vehicles by the tongue and slot method. This changed to transfers around 1925 and around 1928 to transfers with shaded white lettering. On some later vehicles, gold transfer lettering was used.

As the range evolved, realism was further pursued by overall tinprinting. The SR vans are good examples where this method achieved both realistic colouring and detail representation.

Transfer Dating - most wagons carry transfers and the position in which these were placed varied according to the period in which the batch of wagons was being made. The position can help to date the wagon but space does not allow us to include the many variations here. We refer you to Chris and Julie Graebe's *Hornby Gauge 0 Compendium* published by New Cavendish Books which provides extensive listing of these along with dates.

Base Writing - A number of earlier vehicles had their description, e.g: 'Cattle Truck', in small white letters on each side of their underframe.

Chassis - Over the years five basic types of wheelbase were fitted to the standard wagons, the main visual difference being the representation of springs and axleboxes. In addition there were longer, narrower, bases used on a few wagons and denoted here by an 'L' suffix.

Type 1: (1921-25) Solid and plain. These had deep solebars and unfretted axle supports. Extra slots for drop-link couplings were added sometime in 1921 and a further revision was made the following year for thinner axles. Last stocks were used up in 1925 (T1).
Type 2: (1922-41) An open chassis with embossed and pierced springs etc. (T2).
Type 2L: (1924-49) This was a little used long and narrow wheelbase found on open wagons in the mid '20s, double wine wagons and M series open wagons (T2L).
Type 3: (1930-40) Introduced at the time auto couplings came in. Solid with embossed springs (not cut-out) and can also be found on some wagons released immediately after WW2 (T3).
Type 3L: (1934-41) this had a long narrow wheelbase and was made from a carriage chassis. It saw very little use on wagons (T3L).
Type 4: (1949-57) Simple embossed spring shapes which did not show leaves as the previous type did. This was the post-war version of the T3 (T4).
Type 4L: This was a long base used on M wagons after the war (T4L).
Type 5: (1957-63) Known as the No.50 wheelbase, this had cast ends and buffers, no brake rod connecting the axleboxes but had a separate silver coloured brake lever (T5).
Dating wagons by their bases can be harder than it might seem, due to stocks of old bases sometimes coming back into use on later wagons in

Early Chassis Types
(Drawings by John King)

Type 1 brass buffers and hook coupling plus early round trade mark clip on lettering

Type 1 with drop link coupling

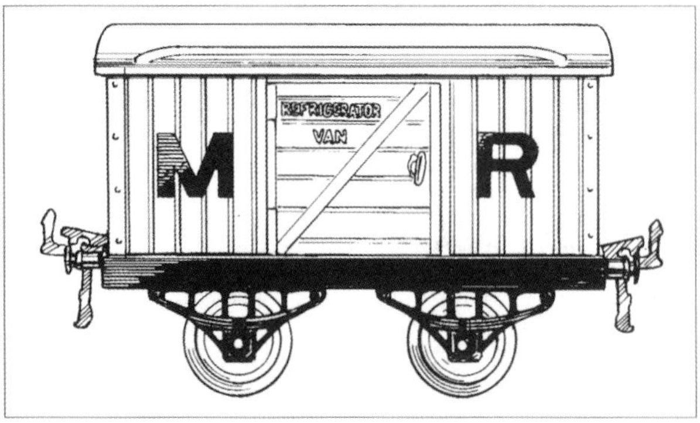

Type 2 open chassis 1923 -32 drop link coupling

Type 3 closed chassis 1933 - 62 with automatic couplings which were introduced in 1931

order to use them up. However, the trademark variations will help here and an illustrated guide to these is provided in this section.

Watch out for Replicas - The colourful and attractive private owner wagons were a very effective way for manufacturers to advertise as they were toy versions of real wagons on the railways in the '20s and '30s. Hornby usually encouraged the companies, whose names appeared on the vans, to contribute towards the cost of the transfers.

Many of these are now much sought after. The 'Colman's Mustard' van was based on the first nut and bolt No.1 van and had a very short life before being replaced by the 'Seccotine' van in 1925. A number of replica 'Colman's' vans are around and so buyer beware! If it is not a nut and bolt item it is by definition a replica but some replicas are nut and bolt vans that have been repainted.

Some of the private owner transfers were also applied to Dinky toys including 'Seccotine', 'Palethorpes', 'Shell', 'Esso' and 'Pratts'.

There was a more sophisticated tank wagon which was larger and had more detail including ladders. The transfers were 'United Dairies' or 'Nestles Milk' on white tanks and 'Colas' on blue or red tanks. Genuine examples of the latter are quite rare and so beware of reproductions!

In general, wagons in Southern Railway (SR) livery are much rarer than the others and some sell for very high prices. Consequently replicas exist - so beware!

M0 Freight Stock

The M0 series were small, toy-like, tinplate wagons designed to go with the M0 locomotives. They were to a smaller scale while still being 0 gauge, so they look small alongside the other 0 gauge wagons. They were printed in red before the war and mostly in green during the post-war period (but some were red). The couplings were very simple consisting of a broad loop at one end of the wheelbase and a hook at the other.

Cat No.	Company, Number, Colour, Dates	£	£
W1.	**M0 Wagon (open wagon)** (1930)		
M0	red on black base - *30-41*	10	15
M0	green on black base - *33-41*	10	15
M0	**'British Express'** Wagon - *32-36*	10	20
M0	red on black base - *46-54*	5	10
M0	green on black base - *46-54*	5	10
W2.	**M0 Rotary Tipping Wagon** (1935)		
M0	green on black base - *35-36*	10	15
M0	green on red base - *36-41*	10	15
M0	blue top on red base - *36?*	10	15
M0	green top on red base - *52-64*	5	10
W3.	**M0 Side Tipping Wagon** (1935)		
M0	yellow on black base - *35-36*	10	15
M0	same but green base - *36-41*	10	10
M0	yellow top on green base - *52-64*	5	10
W4.	**M0 Petrol Tank Wagon** (1935)		
M0	**'Shellmex and BP'** cream on black base - *35-36*	10	25
M0	same but red base - *36-38*	10	25
M0	**'Shell'** or **'BP'** cream on red base - *38-41*	10	25
M0	**'Shell'** or **'BP'** silver on red base - *52-60*	10	25
W5.	**M0 Crane Truck** (1935)		
M0	blue crane, black base - *35-36*	10	15
M0	same but green base - *36-41*	10	15
M0	same but post-war - *52-54*	5	10

No.20 Freight Stock

A wagon used only in the No.20 post-war train set.

W6.	**No.20 Wagon (open wagon)** (1954)		
	This was very like the M0 wagon but was now in a BR livery.		
No.20	**BR** 163502 grey - *54-64*	5	10

M0 crane truck [W5]

W7.	**No.20 Crane Truck** (1954)		
No.20	blue crane on green base - *54-64*	5	10
W7A.	**No.20 Rotary Tipping Wagons** (1954)		
No.20	red+green - *54-64*	5	10

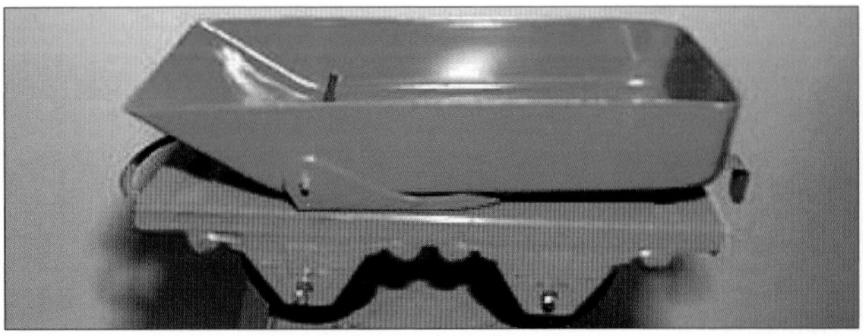

No.20 rotary tipper wagon [W7A]

M/M1 Freight Stock

The only wagons made to go with the M1 train sets were open wagons. Early ones had plain grey enamelled bodies printed in white and later ones had tin-printed bodies that showed planking and bracing detail.

W8a. M Wagon (early) (1926)

This used the long thin base and had an enamelled grey open wagon body with or without buffers. They had drop-link couplings. Letters printed in white on a plain grey body.

M GWR open wagon [W8a]

M	**GW** W grey *-26-27*	5	20
M	same with gold 'LMS' - *27-29*	5	15
M	**LMS** W grey - *26-27*	5	10
M	same with gold 'LMS' - *27-29*	5	15
M	**NE** W grey - *29*	5	10
M	**SR** W grey - *29*	20	35
W8b.	**M1 Wagon (late)** (1929)		
	Long thin tin-printed wagons and carrying the number 12530.		
M	**GW** plain grey - *29-30*	5	20

M1	**GW** detailed grey - *30-33, 35-41*	5	20
M1	same but green base - *33-35*	5	20
M	**LMS** plain grey - *29-30*	5	10
M1	**LMS** detailed grey - *30-33, 35-41*	5	10
M1	same but green base - *33-35*	5	10
M	**NE** plain grey - *29-30*	5	10
M1	**NE** detailed grey - *30-33, 35-41*	5	10
M1	same but green base - *33-35*	5	10
M	**SR** plain grey - *29-30*	20	35
M1	**SR** detailed grey - *30-33, 35-41*	20	35
M1	same but green base - *33-35*	20	35

W8c. M1 Wagon (post-war) (1946)

This was similar to the late pre-war M1 wagons but with different printing. Usually black interiors.

M1	**LMS** buff or grey - *46-48*	5	10
M1	**LMS** brown - *48-57*	5	10
M1	**LNE** buff or grey - *46-48*	5	10
M1	**LNE** brown - *48-57*	5	10

No.30 Freight Stock

These were 1956 replacements for the M1 wagons and were of a completely new design. They were available separately as well as in the No.30 train sets and had loop and hook couplings like the M0 wagons.

W9. No.30 Wagon (open wagon) (1956)

M30	**BR** grey - *56-64*	5	10

W10. No.30 Van (1956)

M30	**BR** brown - *56-64*	10	15

M3 Freight Stock

These enamelled wagons were available only in M3 goods train sets and could not be bought separately. Consequently individual boxed examples will not be found. They can be recognised by the absence of buffers on all but the pre 1927 open wagons.

W11. M3 Wagon (open wagon) (1931)

Long and thin, these open wagons were grey enamelled and, from 1927, were not fitted with buffers. They had drop-link couplings and gold transfers.

M3	**GW** 12530 detailed grey T2L - *31-33, 35-41*	15	25
M3	same but green base - *33-35*	15	25
M3	**LMS** 12530 detailed grey T2L - *31-33, 35-41*	15	25
M3	same but green base - *33-35*	15	25
M3	**NE** 12530 detailed grey T2L - *31-33, 35-41*	15	25
M3	same but green base - *33-35*	15	25
M3	**SR** 12530 detailed grey T2L - *31-33, 35-41*	30	45
M3	same but green base - *33-35*	30	45

W12. M3 Tank Wagon (1931)

This was like the No.1 Shell tank wagon but without buffers.

M3	**'Royal Daylight'** red T3 *36-41*	20	35
M3	**'Shell'** red T3 *31-36*	20	35

W13. M3 Timber Wagon (1931)

This was like the No.1 timber wagon but without buffers.

M3	red base green stanchions T3 *31-39*	15	25
M3	black base red stanchions T3 *39-41*	15	25

W14. M3 Fibre Wagon (1935)

Found in the M11 set, this was like the No.1 fibre wagon but without buffers.

-	**LMS** grey T3 *35-41*	25	45

No.0 Freight Stock

While to the same scale and basic design as the No.1 wagons, the No.0 series were a cost cutting exercise. They were tin-printed instead of being enamelled, had non-opening doors and a cheaper chassis, sometimes without buffers. Some of the latter were designated M1 and others, for tank goods sets, were labelled M3. Beware of replicas!

W15. No.0 Open Wagon (1929)

This replaced the Zulu open wagon and was tin-printed; first plain and then with detail.

No.0	**GW** plain grey T2 - *29-30*	10	20
No.0	**GW** detailed grey T2 - *30*	15	30
No.0	now with T3 base - *30-41*	10	20
No.0	**GW** detailed brown T2 - *30*	15	30
No.0	now with T3 base - *30-41*	10	20
No.0	**LMS** plain grey T2 - *29-30*	10	20
No.0	**LMS** detailed grey T2 - *30*	15	30
No.0	now with T3 base - *30-41*	10	20
No.0	**NE** plain grey T2 - *29-30*	10	20
No.0	**NE** detailed grey T2 - *30*	15	30
No.0	now with T3 base - *30-41*	10	20
No.0	**SR** plain grey T2 - *29-30*	25	45

W16. No.0 Rotary Tipping Wagon (1934)

Unlike the No.1 rotary tipping wagon, this had curved tipper supports.

No.0	**'Meccano'** blue T2 (red) - *34-35*	20	30
No.0	blue T2 (red) - *35-39*	10	20
No.0	now with black base - *39-41*	15	25

W17. No.0 Refrigerator Van (1937)

Tin-printed with fixed doors.

No.0	**GW** 59823 white Mica B T3 - *37-41*	60	80
No.0	**LMS** grey T3 - *37-41*	40	70
No.0	**NE** white T3 - *37-41*	40	70
No.0	**SR** buff T3 - *37-41*	60	110

No.0 GWR 'Mica' refrigerator [W17] and meat [W19] vans

W18. No.0 Milk Traffic Van (1931)

Tin-printed with sliding doors until 1935, then fixed.

No.0	**GW** 28127 grey T3 (black) - *31-33*	40	70
No.0	same but green base - *33-55*	40	70
No.0	**GW** 28127 brown T3 - *35-41*	30	50

W19. No.0 Meat Van (1931)

Tin-printed with sliding doors until 1935, then fixed.

No.0	**GW** 59791 grey 'Mica' T3 - *37-41*	80	150
No.0	**LMS** 19631 grey T3 (black) - *31-33, 35-41*	40	60
No.0	same but green base - *33-35*	40	60
No.0	**NE** brown T3 - *37-41*	50	70

W20. No.0 Fish Van (1931)

Tin-printed with sliding doors until 1935, then fixed. Normally a black base.

No.0	**GW** 7101? red-brown T3 - *37-41*	50	100
No.0	**LMS** 7674? red T3 - *37-41*	50	100
No.0	**NE** 12630 grey T3 (black) - *31-33*	40	70
No.0	as above but green base - *33-35*	40	70
No.0	**NE** 12630 red-brown T3 - *35-41*	40	70

W21. No.0 Banana Van (1935)

Tin-printed with no sliding door. It had a black base and white or grey roof and was marked 'Avonmouth' in black or white.

No.0	**LMS** grey T3 *35-41*	40	70

No.1 Freight Stock

This was the basic series characterised by embossed, stamped, detail with an enamel finish. Where applied, they had quality transfer markings and vans had sliding doors.

W22a. No.1 Flat Truck (1934)

No.1	**GW** 32804 grey T3 - *34-41*	5	20
No.1	**GW** 32804 grey T3 - *48*	20	40
No.1	now with T4 base - *48-54*	15	30
No.1	**LMS** 219493 grey T3 - *34-41*	5	15
No.1	**LMS** 219493 brown T3 - *48*	10	15
No.1	now with T4 base - *48-54*	5	15
No.1	**NE** 35968 grey T3 - *34-41*	5	15
No.1	**NE** 35968 brown T3 - *48*	10	15
No.1	now with T4 base - *48-54*	5	10
No.1	**SR** 39010 brown T3 - *34-41, 48*	25	45
No.1	now with T4 base - *48-54*	25	45
No.1	**BR** E35968 brown T4 - *54-59*	5	10

W22b. No.1 Flat Truck with Cable Drum (1934)

No.1 flat truck & cable drum [W22b] (Vectis)

No.1	**GW** 32804 grey T3 + Bl cable drum - *34-41*	25	40
No.1	same but Liverpool Cables - *37-39*	20	30
No.1	same but post-war - *48*	30	60
No.1	now with T4 base - *48-51*	30	60
No.1	**LMS** grey T3 + Bl cable drum - *34-41*	20	30
No.1	same but Liverpool Cables - *37-39*	30	45
No.1	**LMS** 219493 brown T3 + Liverpool drum - *48*	20	30
No.1	now with T4 base - *48-54*	10	20
No.1	**LMS** + Electric Cables drum - *?*	250	300
No.1	**NE** 35968 grey T3 + Bl cable drum - *34-41*	20	30
No.1	same but Liverpool Cables - *37-39*	30	45
No.1	**NE** 35968 brown T3 + Liverpool drum - *48*	20	30
No.1	now with T4 base - *48-54*	10	20
No.1	**SR** 39010 brown T3 + Bl cable drum - *34-41*	35	70
No.1	same but Liverpool Cables - *37-39*	35	70
No.1	same but post-war - *48*	55	100
No.1	now with T4 base - *48-51*	35	70
No.1	**BR** E35958 brown T4 + Liverpool Cables - *54-59*	10	20

W22c. No.1 Flat Truck with Container (1936)

The container was of wood and covered with printed paper.

No.1	**GW** 32804 grey T3 + GWR FX-1642 container - *36-41*	25	50
No.1	**GW** 32804 grey T3 + GWR FX-1642 container - *48*	50	90
No.1	now with T4 base- *48-51*	40	80
No.1	**LMS** grey T3 + LMS K61 container - *36-41*	20	40
No.1	**LMS** 219493 brown T3 + LMS K61 container - *48*	25	40
No.1	now with T4 base- *48-54*	15	30
No.1	**NE** grey 35968 T3 + LNER BL3297? container - *36-41*	20	40
No.1	**NE** brown 35968 T3 + LNER BL3297? container - *48*	25	40
No.1	now with T4 base- *48-54*	15	30
No.1	**SR** 39010 brown T3 + SR K544 container - *36-41*	35	70
No.1	same but post-war - *48*	190	230
No.1	now with T4 base - *48-51*	160	210
No.1	**BR** E35968 brown T4 + furniture container - *55-59*	15	30
No.1	**BR** brown T4 + insulated meat container - *55-59*	15	30

No.1 SR flat truck with SR container [W22c] (Vectis)

W23. Fibre Wagon (1931)

Examples without buffers were for the M series.

-	red T3 - *31-33*	15	25
-	blue T3 - *33-39*	15	25
-	black T3 - *39-41*	15	25

W24. No.1 Lumber Wagon (1923)

This was a base with a pair of red or black bolsters. Some were inscribed 'No.1 Lumber Wagon'.

No.1	**GW** olive green T2 - *26-30*	20	40
No.1	**LMS** olive green T2 - *24-30*	10	20
No.1	**L&NER** olive green T2 - *24*	60	120
No.1	**LNER** olive green T2 - *24-26*	20	40
No.1	**NE** olive green T2 - *26-30*	10	20
No.1	**SR** brown + blue bolsters T2 - *28-30*	90	170
No.1	brown + blue bolsters T2 - *30*	60	120
No.1	olive green T2 - *23-24*	20	40
No.1	olive green T2 - *30*	30	60
No.1	same with T3 base - *30-33*	10	20
No.1	light green + yellow bolsters T3 - *33-39*	10	20
No.1	black + red bolsters T3 - *39-41*	10	20
No.1	same but post-war - *48*	10	20
No.1	now with T4 bases - *48-57*	8	20

W25. No.1 Timber Wagon (1922)

This was a flat base with two vertical projections each side to retain a planks load. Some were inscribed 'Timber Wagon'.

No.1 timber wagon [W25]

No.1	**GW** green & red T2 - *26-30*	10	20
No.1	**LMS** olive green T2 - *24-30*	10	20
No.1	**LNER** olive green T2 - *24-26*	20	40
No.1	**NE** olive green T2 - *26-30*	10	20
No.1	**SR** brown T2 - *28-30*	80	160
No.1	brown T2 with red stanchions - *30*	70	150
No.1	olive T2 with olive stanchions - *22-24*	20	40
No.1	olive T2 with red stanchions - *30*	30	60
No.1	now with T3 base - *30-31*	25	50
No.1	now red with yell stanchions - *31-32*	20	40
No.1	same with green stanchions - *31-39*	10	20
No.1	now black with red stanchions - *39-41*	6	20
No.1	now black with red stanchions - *47-48*	10	20
No.1	now with T4 base - *48-59*	6	20

W26. Gas Cylinder Wagon (1923)

Inscription or lettering on side of cylinders. The position of 'Gas Cylinders' and company lettering varies.

-	**GW** red T2 - *26-30*	20	40
-	**LMS** red T2 - *24-30*	10	20
-	**L&NER** red T2 - *24*	20	40
-	**LNER** red T2 - *24-26*	10	20
-	**NE** red T2 - *26-30*	10	20
-	**SR** green T2 - *28-30*	70	140
-	red T2 - *23-24*	10	20
-	red T3 - *30-33, 39-41, 48*	10	20
-	as above but with blue base - *33-39*	10	20
-	red T4 - *48-57*	5	20

W27a. Open Wagon (1st type) (1920)

These wagons started life as constructional trucks, square-ish in shape, had silver wheels, brass buffers and clip-on letters. From 1922-23 they had thinner axles.

-	**LNWR** grey T1 - *20-23*	30	60

No.1 type 1 open wagon LNWR [W27a]

-	now with T2 base - *22-23*	30	50
-	**MR** grey T1 - *20-23*	30	60
-	now with T2 base - *22-23*	30	50
-	**CR** grey T1 - *21-22*	50	100
-	**GN** grey T1 - *20-23*	35	60
-	now with T2 base - *22-23*	30	50
-	**GE** grey T1 - *21-22*	50	100
-	**LBSC** grey T1 - *21-22*	400	500
-	**SECR** grey T1 - *21-22*	250	350

W27b. Zulu Wagon (1st type) (1922)

The letters were sprayed on but otherwise these were similar to the 1920 open wagons. The body was fixed to the base by eyelets and fitted with cast buffers.

No.1	**LNW** W grey T1 - *22-23*	30	60

W27c. Open Wagon (1st type) (1923)

This was as the 1920 wagon but with transfers and cast or brass buffers.

-	**GW** W grey T1 - *26*	25	50
-	same with T2 base - *26-27*	25	50
-	**LMS** W grey T1 - *23-24, 26-27*	20	45
-	same with T2 base - *23-24*	20	45
-	**LNER** W grey T2 - *23-24*	20	45
-	same with T2 base - *23-26*	20	45
-	**NE** W grey T2 - *26-27*	20	45

W27d. Open Wagon (2nd type) (Long) (1924)

These were long thin wagons with transfers. Some had brass buffers and other with cast ones.

-	**LMS** grey T2L - *24-25*	25	45
-	**LNER** grey T2L - *24-25*	25	45

W27e. Open Wagon (3rd type) (1927)

This was a new design of enamelled body introduced late 1925 and of tab construction with transfers.

-	**GW** G grey T2 - *27-30*	15	25
No.1	now with T3 base - *30*	15	30
No.1	now with white 'GW' - *30-32*	15	30
No.1	now with green base - *33*	15	30
-	**LMS** G grey T2 - *27-30*	10	20
No.1	now with T3 base - *30*	15	25
No.1	now with white 'LMS' - *30-32*	10	20
No.1	now with green base - *33*	15	25
-	**NE** G grey T2 - *27-30*	10	20
No.1	now with T3 base - *30*	15	25
No.1	now with white 'NE' - *30-32*	10	20
No.1	now with green base - *33*	15	25
-	**SR** G brown T2 - *27-30*	25	45
No.1	now with T3 base - *30*	25	45
No.1	now with white 'SR' - *30-32*	25	45
No.1	now with green base - *33*	25	45

W27f. Open Wagon (4th type) (tin-printed) (1932)

A tin-printed range introduced in 1932. The planking, ironwork and sole bar detail were now printed on. Variants exist.

No.1	**GW** 12530 grey T3 - *32-41*	10	30
No.1	**GW** buff T3 - *47-48*	30	50

No.1 type 4 open wagon LMS [W27f]

No.1	**LMS** 12530 grey T3 - *32-41*	10	20
No.1	**LMS** 12530 buff T3 - *47-48*	10	20
No.1	**LMS** 12530 brown T3 - *48*	10	20
No.1	now with T4 base - *48-49*	10	20
No.1	**LMS** (small) 210112 brown T4 - *49-54*	5	20
No.1	**NE** 12530 grey T3 - *32-41, 48*	10	20
No.1	now with T4 base - *48-49*	5	20
No.1	**NE** buff T3 - *47-48*	5	20
No.1	**NE** (small) 404844 grey T4 - *49-54*	5	20
No.1	**SR** 12530 brown T3 - *32-41*	25	45
No.1	**SR** 12530 brown T3 - *47-48*	30	55
No.1	**BR** M210112 grey T4 - *54-58*	5	20

W28a. Sheet Rail Open Wagon B (1931)

As above but with sheet rail added. Lettering was always white and the rail was blue or black.

B	**GW** black T3 (green) - *31-33*	25	50
B	**GW** blue T3 (green) - *33-35*	25	50
B	now with black base - *35-41*	25	50
B	**LMS** black T3 (green) - *31-33*	20	40
B	**LMS** blue T3 (green) - *33-35*	20	40
B	now with black base - *35-41*	20	40
B	**NE** black T3 (green) - *31-33*	20	40
B	**NE** blue T3 (green) - *33-35*	20	40
B	now with black base - *35-41*	20	40
B	**SR** 12530 black T3 (green) - *31-33*	50	90
B	**SR** blue T3 (green) - *33-35*	50	90
B	now with black base - *35-41*	50	90

W28b. Wagon with Sheet Rail (1948)

Post-war version of above.

-	**LMS** brown T3 - *48*	20	30
-	**LMS** (small) brown T4 - *49-54*	10	20
-	**NE** grey T3 - *48*	20	30
-	**NE** (small) grey T4 - *49-54*	10	20
-	**BR** grey T4 - *54-58*	10	20

No.1 coal wagon 'Hornby Railway Company' [W29] (Vectis)

W29. Coal Wagon (1931)

This was the same as the No.1 open wagon but fitted with a load of embossed coal. G = company letters in gold transfers.

-	**'Meccano'** G red T3 - *31-36*	75	110
-	as above but white transfer - *40?*	120	180
-	**'Hornby Railway Company'** G red or maroon T3 - *36-40*	100	120
-	as above but white transfer - *40-41*	100	150

W30. Hopper Wagon (1923)

Some early examples were inscribed 'Hopper Wagon'. G = company letters in gold transfers.

-	grey T2 - *23-24*	45	60
-	**GW** G grey T2 - *26-27*	45	70
-	**GW** G green T2 - *27-30*	45	70

-	now with T3 base - *30-39*	30	60
-	bow with black base - *39-40*	30	60
-	now with white 'GW' - *40-41*	30	60
-	**LMS** G grey T2 - *24-27*	45	60
-	**LMS** G green T2 - *27-30*	20	30
-	now with T3 base - *30-39*	20	30
-	same with black base - *39-40*	20	40
-	now with white 'LMS' - *40-41*	20	40
-	now with white 'LMS' - *48*	25	60
-	now with T4 base - *48-54*	10	20
-	**LNER** G grey T2 - *24-26*	40	60
-	**LNER** G green T2 - *26-27*	40	60
-	**NE** G green T2 - *27-30*	20	30
-	now with T3 base - *27-30*	20	30
-	bow with black base - *39-40*	20	40
-	now with white 'NE' - *40-41*	20	40
-	**SR** G red T2 - *28-30*	70	140
-	now with T3 base - *30-40*	55	110
-	now with white 'SR' - *40-41*	75	150
-	**BR** B40177 grey T4 - *48-59*	10	20

W31. No.1 Rotary Tipping Wagon (1923)

Early ones inscribed 'Rotary Tipper'.

No.1 rotary tipping wagon 'Meccano' [W31] (Vectis)

No.1	grey T2 (black) - *23*	30	60
No.1	**'McAlpine'** grey T2 (black) - *23-26*	20	45
No.1	same with olive green base - *23-26*	20	45
No.1	now with orange base and top - *26-29*	20	45
No.1	**'Meccano'** orange T2 - *29-30*	55	110
No.1	now with T3 base - *30-32*	55	110
No.1	now with blue base + yell top - *32-36*	55	110
No.1	**'Trinidad Lake Asphalt'** buff T3 (blue) - *36-39*	20	45
No.1	now with black base - *39-41, 48*	20	45
No.1	now with T4 base - *48-59*	10	25

W32. Side Tipping Wagon (1923)

These had drop-link couplings and black or red lining. Early ones were inscribed 'Tilting Wagon'.

-	grey T2 (black) - *23-24*	20	60
-	**'McAlpine'** grey T2 (black) - *24-27*	25	45
-	**'McAlpine'** blue T2 (blue) - *27-30*	25	45
-	**'Robert Hudson'** blue T2 (blue) - *29-30*	25	45
-	now with T3 base - *30-33*	25	45
-	**'Robert Hudson'** yell T2 (blue) - *33-38*	25	45
No.1	**'McAlpine'** yellow T3 (blue) - *38-39*	25	45
No.1	now with black base - *39-41, 48*	25	45
No.1	**'McAlpine'** buff T4 (black) - *48-56*	15	25
No.1	**'McAlpine'** green T4 (black) - *57-64*	15	25

W33. Barrel Wagon (1931)

This was sold as a Continental type wagon. The long thin wagon base with auto couplings was used. 2 chains secured the wooden barrels on the T2L wheelbase and a single chain on the T3L one.

-	blue barrels T2L (red) - *31-33*	10	20
-	yellow barrels T2L (red) - *33-35*	10	20
-	same with green barrels - *33-35*	10	20
-	yellow barrels T3L (red) - *35-37*	10	20
-	same with green barrels - *35-37*	10	20
-	**'Castrol'** yellow barrels T3L (red) - *37-41*	30	40
-	same with green barrels - *37-41*	30	40

No.1 barrel wagon 'Castrol' [W33]

W34. Single Wine Wagon (1929)

-	green with red barrels T2 - *29-30*	60	140
-	now with T3 base - *30-35*	50	120

W35. Double Wine Wagon (1928)

Long thin wheelbase.

-	green with red barrels T2L - *28-39*	50	100
-	black with red barrels T2L - *39-41*	50	100

W36. Petrol Tank Wagon (1922)

-	**'Shell Motor Spirit'** red T1 - *22-23*	50	80
-	**'Shell Motor Spirit'** red T2 - *25-30*	20	35
No.1	**'Shell Motor Spirit'** red T3 - *30-36*	20	35
No.1	**'Shell Motor Spirit'** red T3 - *48*	90	135
No.1	now with T4 base - *48-50*	80	110
-	**'BP Motor Spirit'** Petroleum cream T2 - *27-30*	50	120
-	**'BP Motor Spirit'** Petroleum cream T3 - *30-32*	90	135
-	**'BP Motor Spirit'** cream T3 - *32-36*	90	135
No.1	**'Shellmex BP Motor Spirit'** cream T3 - *36-38*	35	65
No.1	**'Shell Lubricating Oil'** yell T4 - *55-57*	25	45
-	**'Pratt's Motor Spirit'** green T2 - *25-30*	45	90
-	**'Pratt's Motor Spirit'** orange T3 - *30*	55	110

No.1 early tank wagons 'National Benzol' & 'Pratts' [W36] (Vectis)

-	**'Pratt's High Test'** orange T3 - *31-33*	45	90
-	now yellow T3 - *33-36*	35	65
-	**'National Benzole'** yellow T2 - *23-29*	35	65
No.1	**'National Benzole'** 918? silver T4 - *53-55*	15	30
-	**'Redline'** dark blue T2 - *28-30*	45	90
-	now with T3 base T3 - *30-32*	45	90
-	**'Redline-Glico'** dark blue T3 - *32-41*	45	90
-	**'Castrol'** green T3 - *30-41*	50	100
-	**'Mobiloil'** grey T3 - *31-41*	45	90
-	**'Royal Daylight'** red T3 - *36-41*	20	35
No.1	**'Royal Daylight'** grey T3 - *47-48*	220	320
No.1	**'Esso'** cream T3 - *36-41*	65	130
No.1	**'Esso'** silver T4 - *50-53*	12	25
No.1	**'Power Ethyl'** green T3 - *38-41*	180	270
No.1	**'Pool'** grey T3 - *40-41*	45	90
No.1	**'Pool'** grey T3 - *47-48*	120	170
No.1	**'Manchester Oil Refineries'** 114 green T4 - *55-57*	35	65

W37a. Milk Tank Wagon (1929)

This was a better quality tank wagon with ladders.

-	**'United Dairies'** white+grey T2 - *29-31*	360	650
-	**'United Dairies'** white+blue T2 - *29-31*	360	650
-	now with T3 base - *31-37*	360	650
-	**'Nestle's Milk'** white+green T3 - *36-41*	400	750
-	**'Nestle's Milk'** white+blue* T3 - *36-41*	380	700

* Also seen with black base.

W37b. Bitumen Tank Wagon (1929)

A better quality tank wagon.

No.1 bitumen tank wagon 'Colas' [W37b] (Vectis)

-	**'Colas'** 33 blue T2 red stays - *29-30*	300	500
-	same with blue stays - *30-36*	300	500
-	**'Colas'** 33 red T3 (blue) - *36-39*	500	800
-	same with black base - *39-41*	500	800

W38. Cement Wagon (1922)

This was a van with a pitched roof and had 'Cement Wagon' on it in white or gold in various positions. The position of company lettering also varied.

-	**GW/Cement** grey T2 - *26-27*	30	60
-	as above but red T2 - *27-30*	30	60
-	**LMS/Cement** grey T2 - *24-27*	25	50
-	as above but red T2 - *27-30*	25	50
-	**LNER/Cement** grey T2 - *24-27*	25	50
-	as above but red T2 - *27-30*	25	50
-	**SR/Cement** red T2 - *28-30*	85	170
-	**Cement** grey T2 - *22-24*	30	55
-	**Cement** red T2 - *30*	40	60
-	now with T3 base - *30-37*	25	50
-	**'Portland Blue Circle Cement'** yellow T3 - *37-41*	20	40
-	same post-war - *48*	20	40
-	now with T4 base - *48-57*	15	25

W39. No.1 Cattle Truck (1923)

G = gold transfers.

No.1	grey T2 (olive green) - *23*	20	40
No.1	**GW** G grey T2 (olive green) - *26-27*	20	40
No.1	**GW** G grey+blue T2 (blue) - *27-30*	20	40
No.1	now with T3 base - *30-32*	20	40
No.1	now with red base - *32-33*	20	40
No.1	now with green base - *33-34*	20	40
No.1	**GW** G grey T3 (black) - *34-39*	20	40
No.1	now with while letters - *39-41*	20	40
No.1	**GW** (small) 26001 grey T3 (black) - *48*	200	350
No.1	now with T4 base - *48-51*	40	80
No.1	**LMS** G grey T2 (olive green) - *24-25*	20	40
No.1	now without writing - *25-27*	20	40
No.1	**LMS** G grey+blue T2 (blue) - *27-30*	20	40
No.1	now with T3 base - *30-32*	20	40
No.1	now with red base - *32-33*	20	40
No.1	now with green base - *33-34*	20	40
No.1	**LMS** G grey T3 (black) - *34-39*	10	20
No.1	now with while letters - *39-41*	20	40
No.1	**LMS** (small) 48744 brown T3 (black) - *48*	15	30
No.1	now with T4 base - *48-54*	10	20
No.1	**LNER** G grey T2 (olive green) - *24-25*	20	40
No.1	now without writing- *25-26*	20	40
No.1	**NE** G grey T2 (olive green) - *26-27*	20	40
No.1	**NE** G grey+blue T2 (blue) - *27-30*	10	20
No.1	now with T3 base - *30-32*	10	20
No.1	same with red base - *32-33*	15	30
No.1	now with green base - *33-34*	15	30

No.1 LNER cattle wagon [W39]

No.1	**NE** G grey T3 (black) - *34-39*	10	20
No.1	now with while letters - *39-41*	15	30
No.1	**NE** (small) 15058 brown T3 (black) - *48*	20	40
No.1	now with T4 base - *48-54*	10	20
No.1	**SR** G brown T2 (black) - *28-30*	50	95
No.1	now with T3 base - *30-33*	50	95
No.1	**SR** G brown+green T3 (green) - *33-34*	50	95
No.1	now with black base - *34-35*	50	95
No.1	**SR** G brown T3 (black) - *34-39*	50	95
No.1	now with while letters - *39-41*	50	95
No.1	**SR** (small) 8338 brown T3 (black) - *48*	75	130
No.1	now with T4 base - *48-51*	50	95
No.1	**BR** B893151 brown T4 - *54-57*	8	20

W40. No.1 Milk Traffic Van (1923)

This was inscribed 'Milk Traffic' until 1925. Earliest ones had an internal clip for cans. 4 milk churns, made specially for the van, were supplied with it.

No.1	grey T2 (olive green) - *23-24*	20	40
No.1	**GW** grey T2 (olive) - *26-27*	20	40
No.1	**GW** blue T2 (green) - *27-30*	20	40
No.1	**LMS** grey T2 (olive) - *24-27*	20	40
No.1	**LMS** blue T2 (green) - *27-30*	20	40
No.1	**LNER** grey T2 (olive) - *24-26*	20	40
No.1	**NE** grey T2 (olive) - *26-27*	20	40
No.1	**NE** blue T2 (green) - *27-30*	20	40
No.1	**SR** 2435 green T2 (black) - *28-30*	45	90
No.1	**SR** 2435 green T3 black) - *48*	85	170
No.1	same with green base - *48*	95	190
No.1	same with T4 base - *48-54*	35	65
No.1	**BR** S2435 maroon T4 - *54-57*	20	40
No.1	blue T2 (green) - *30*	20	40
No.1	now with T3 base - *30-33*	10	20
No.1	now with red base - *33-35*	10	20
No.1	now with black base - *35-41*	10	20
No.1	green T3 - *48*	20	40

W41. Gunpowder Van (1922)

This had 'Gunpowder Van' on white and the position of this was moved over time and was sometimes absent. W = company lettering white. G = company lettering gold.

-	**LNWR** red T1 inscription in black - *22*	150	200
-	as above but white inscription - *22*	150	200
-	now with T2 base - *22-24*	150	200

No.1 GWR gunpowder van [W41] (Vectis)

-	**GW** W red T2 - *26-27*	50	100
-	now with gold 'GW' - *27-28*	60	120
-	**GW** G grey T2 GPV + red cross - *28-29*	100	180

-	now with T3 base - *30-39*	60	120
-	now with white 'GW' - *39-41*	80	150
-	**LMS** W red T2 - *24-27*	35	60
-	now with gold 'LMS' - *28-30*	40	100
-	now with T3 base - *30-39*	60	100
-	now with white 'LMS' - *39-40*	70	110
-	**LNER** W red T2 - *24-26*	130	180
-	**NE** W red T2 - *26-27*	150	200
-	now with gold 'NE' - *27-30*	40	100
-	now with T3 base - *32-39*	60	100
-	now with white 'NE' - *39-41*	70	110
-	**SR** G red T2 - *28-30*	150	260
-	now with T3 base - *30-39*	150	260
-	now with white 'SR' - *39-41*	180	310

W42. Private Owner Vans (1923)

This was of nut and bolt construction. and most versions may be found with either sliding or hinged doors. Beware of replicas!

-	**'Colman's Mustard'** pale yellow T2 (white) - *23-24*	450	750
-	**'Seccotine'** blue with orange or red roof T1 (black) - *25*	250	370
-	same with T2 base - *23-31*	250	370
-	now with T3 base - *31-34*	250	370
-	**'Carr's Biscuits'** dark blue or blue-grey body + roof T2 (black) - *24-30*	150	210
-	now with T3 base - *30-41*	100	210
-	**'Crawford's Biscuits'** red body + roof T2 (black) - *24-31*	150	210
-	now with T3 base - *31-34*	150	210
-	as above but 'By Appointment' added - *34-38*	150	210
-	as above but 'By Appointment to the Late King' - *38-41*	150	260
-	**'Jacob & Co's Biscuits'** maroon T2 (black) - *24-30*	200	320
-	now with T3 base - *30-40*	125	210
-	as above but brown - *40-41*	150	260

No.1 P.O. van 'Cadbury's' [W42] (Vectis)

-	**'Fyffes Bananas'** yellow with red or white roof T3 (green, red or black) - *31-41*	75	160
-	**'Cadbury's Chocolate'** * blue with white roof T3 (black or green) sliding doors - *32-41*	150	230
-	**'Palethorpe's Sausages'** maroon body T3 (black) sliding doors - *38-41*	500	900
-	**'Huntley & Palmers'** **	200	320

* May be found with serif or sans-serif (later) style letters. ** This was one of only a few private owner wagons produced by the French factory

W43. No.1 Luggage/Goods Van (1921)

This was of nut and bolt construction until around 1924 and during the mid '20s it usually carried the inscription 'Luggage Van' either on the vans doors or base. W = company lettering white. G = company lettering gold.

No.1	**MR** (clip-on) grey T1 - *21-23*	30	60
No.1	now with T2 base - *23-24*	30	60
No.1	**GW** W grey T2 - *26-27*	20	40
No.1	now with gold 'GW' - *27-30*	20	40
No.1	now with T3 base - *30-39*	20	40
No.1	now with white 'GW' - *39-41*	20	40
No.1	**GW** (small) 145371 grey T3 - *48*	120	220
No.1	same with T4 base - *48-51*	70	150
No.1	**LMS** W grey T2 - *24-27*	20	40
No.1	same with gold 'LMS' - *27-30*	20	40
No.1	same with T3 base - *30-39*	20	40
No.1	now with white 'LMS' - *39-41*	20	40
No.1	**LMS** (small) 282095 brown T3 - *48*	30	60
No.1	same with T4 base - *48-54*	10	30
No.1	**LNER** W grey T2 - *24-26*	20	40
No.1	**NE** W grey T2 - *26-27*	20	40
No.1	now with gold 'NE' - *27-30*	20	40
No.1	now with T3 base - *30-39*	20	40
No.1	now with white 'NE' - *39-41*	20	40
No.1	**NE** (small) 18253 brown T3 - *48*	30	60
No.1	same with T4 base - *48-54*	10	30
No.1	**SR** G brown T2 - *28-30*	70	150
No.1	now with T3 base - *30-39*	70	150
No.1	now with white 'SR' - *39-41*	70	150
No.1	**SR** (small) 59941 brown T3 - *48*	180	230
No.1	same with T4 base - *48-51*	45	80
No.1	**BR** E82153 brown T4 - *54-57*	10	20

W44a. Refrigerator Van (1923)

This was of nut and bolt construction with clip-on letters and with or without the inscription 'Refrigerator Van'.

-	**MR** white T1 - *23*	35	65
-	**MR** white T2 - *23-24*	35	65

W44b. Refrigerator Van (1924)

Tab and slot construction and lettering in black (except G = gold). It was inscribed 'Refrigerator Van'.

No.1 refrigerator van [W44b]

-	**GW** white T2 - *26-30*	40	80
-	now with T3 base T3 - *30-41*	40	80
-	same but base and roof blue - *33-34*	50	90
-	**LMS** white T2 - *24-30*	30	60
-	now with T3 base T3 - *30-41*	30	60
-	same but base and roof blue - *33-34*	40	80
-	**LMS** (small) 279770 buff T3 - *48*	20	40
-	now with T4 base - *48-54*	20	40
-	**LMS** white T4 base - *48-54*	40	60
-	**LNER** white T2 - *24-27*	30	60
-	**NE** 15275 white T2 - *27-30*	30	60
-	now with T3 base - *30-41*	30	60
-	same but base and roof blue - *33-34*	40	80
-	**NE** (small) 15270? white T3 - *48*	20	40
-	now with T4 base - *48-54*	20	40
-	**SR** G pink T2 - *28-29*	650	850
-	**SR** white T2 - *29-30*	130	180
-	now with T3 base T3 - *30-34*	130	180
-	**SR** pink T3 - *34-41*	340	450
-	**BR** E165642 white T4 - *54-57*	20	40

W45. LNWR Brake Van (single ended) (1922)

This was of nut and bolt construction until around 1924 and had a black base (green 1933-34) and white roof (grey post-war). There was a hinged door at one end and pairs of windows at both ends. W = white lettering sprayed on. G = gold transfer lettering. Post-war examples had very small lettering and lamp brackets fitted on the sides and ends.

-	**LNW** W grey T1 - *22-23*	30	45
-	now with T2 base - *23-24*	30	45
-	**GW** W grey T2 - *26-27*	10	20
-	now with gold 'GW' - *27-30*	10	20
-	same with T3 base - *30-32*	10	20
-	now with white 'GW' - *32-41*	10	20
-	**GW** (small) 17551 grey T3 - *48*	140	180
-	now with T4 base - *48-51*	100	150
-	**LMS** W grey T2 - *24-27*	10	20
-	now with gold 'LMS' - *27-30*	10	20
-	same with T3 base - *27-33*	10	20
-	now with white 'LMS' - *34-41*	5	10

-	**LMS** (small) 1663 brown T3 - *48*	20	40
-	now with T4 base - *48-54*	10	20

W46. GN Brake Van (double ended) (1922)

Nut and bolt construction until around 1924. Black base (green 1933-34) and white roof. Hinged door and large single window at each end. W = white lettering sprayed on. G = gold transfer lettering. Post-war examples has very small lettering and lamp brackets fitted on the sides and ends.

-	**GN** W brown T1 - *22-23*	40	80
-	now with T2 base - *23-24*	40	80
-	**LNER** W brown T2 - *24-27*	20	40
-	**NE** G brown T2 - *27-30*	10	20
-	now with T3 base - *30-32*	10	20
-	now with white 'NE' - *32-41*	10	20

No.1 LNER brake van [W46]

-	**NE** 22604 small, brown T3 - *48*	10	20
-	now with T4 base - *48-54*	10	16
-	**SR** G brown T2 - *28-30*	40	90
-	now with T3 base - *30-33*	40	90
-	now with white 'SR' - *32*	50	100
-	**SR** G dark brown T3 - *33*	50	100
-	now with white 'SR' - *33-41*	40	90
-	**SR** small, brown T3 - *48*	150	230
-	now with T4 base - *48-51*	120	230
-	**BR** E22604 brown T4 - *54-57*	10	20

W47. Crane Truck (1924)

-	**GW** grey T2 - *26-27*	30	50
-	**GW** brown+blue T2 - *27-30*	30	50
-	**LMS** grey T2 - *24-27*	20	40
-	**LMS** brown+blue T2 - *27-30*	20	40
-	**LNER** grey T2 - *24-26*	30	60
-	**NE** grey T2 - *26-27*	20	40
-	**NE** brown+blue T2 - *27-30*	20	40
-	**SR** brown+blue T2 - *28-30*	55	110
-	brown+blue T2 - *30*	20	40
-	same with T3 base - *30-33*	10	20
-	blue+yellow T3 - *33-35*	10	20
-	blue T3 - *35-38*	10	20
-	grey T2 - *23-24*	30	50
-	grey T3 - *38-41*	10	20
-	red T3 - *48*	20	40
-	now with T4 base - *48-57*	8	20

W48a. Rotary Snow Plough (1923)

Inscribed 'Snow Plough'.

-	grey T2 (black) - *23-24*	70	100
-	**GW** grey T2 (black) - *26*	100	180
-	**LMS** grey T2 (black) - *24-26*	80	150
-	**LNER** grey T2 (black) - *24-26*	80	150

W48b. Rotary Snow Plough (tin-printed) (1926)

Tin-printed and inscribed 'Snow Plough'.

-	**GW** grey T2 (black) - *26-27*	150	200
-	now with green base - *27-30*	150	200
-	**LMS** grey T2 (black) - *26-27*	100	150
-	now with green base - *27-30*	100	150
-	**LNER** grey T2 (black) - *26*	100	150
-	**NE** grey T2 (black) T2 - *26-27*	70	100
-	now with green base - *27-30*	70	100

-	**SR** grey T2 (green) - *28-30*	220	350
-	grey T2 (green) - *30*	80	120
-	now with T3 base - *30-32*	50	80
-	now with red base - *32-33*	50	80
-	yellow T3 (green) - *33*	80	120
-	now with blue base - *33-36*	80	120
-	now with black base - *36-41*	50	80
-	two tone green - *?*	120	160

No.2 Freight Stock

W49a. Trolley Wagon (1923)

This was a well wagon with a bolster on each raised platform over the bogies. Most were inscribed '50 Ton Trolley'.

-	**GW** G grey with red bolsters - *26-27*	30	60
-	**GW** G brown + blue bolsters - *27-30*	30	60
-	**LMS** G grey with red bolsters - *24-27*	20	40
-	**LMS** G brown + blue bolsters - *27-30*	20	40
-	**NE** W grey with black bolsters - *23*	30	50
-	same with red bolsters - *23-24*	20	40
-	same with gold 'NE' - *26-27*	20	40
-	**NE** G brown with blue bolsters - *27-30*	20	40
-	**LNER** G grey with red bolsters - *24-26*	30	45
-	**SR** G brown with blue bolster - *28-30*	120	160
-	brown with blue bolster - *30-33*	15	30
-	red with green bolsters - *33-39*	30	60
-	grey with green bolsters - *33-39*	15	30
-	red with red bolsters - *39-41*	15	30
-	grey with red bolsters - *49-50*	200	300

No.2 trolley wagons [W49a + W49b] (Vectis)

W49b. Trolley Wagon + Cable Drums (1936)

This was the trolley wagon with two cable drums in the well. The drums were the same as those used on the flat truck. The cable drum being made of wood and the detail provided by printed paper stuck to the surface. Most were inscribed '50 Ton Trolley'.

-	red with green bolsters + **'BI Cables'** - *36-37*	40	60
-	same with **'Liverpool Cables'** - *37-39*	40	60
-	grey with red bolsters + **'BI Cables'** - *39-41*	40	60

W50. No.2 Timber Wagon (1930)

Some were inscribed 'No.2 Timber Wagon'. With the exception of the first version, the stanchions were pressed out from the floor of the wagon.

-	olive green, steel stanchions riveted to base, 5 planks - *22*	100	120
No.2	**GW** olive green - *26-27*	40	80
No.2	now with red stanchions - *27-30*	30	60
No.2	**LMS** olive green - *24-27*	30	60
No.2	now with red stanchions - *27-30*	30	60
No.2	**L&NER** olive green - *24*	30	60
No.2	**LNER** olive green - *24-26*	30	60
No.2	**NE** olive green - *26-27*	30	60
No.2	now with red stanchions - *27-30*	30	60
No.2	**SR** brown with red stanchions - *28-30*	120	160
No.2	olive green - *22-24*	30	50
No.2	olive with red stanchions - *30-33*	30	60
No.2	red with green stanchions - *33-39*	30	50
No.2	grey with red stanchions - *39-41*	20	40

No.2 timber wagons [W50] and lumber wagons [W51] (Vectis)

W51. No.2 Lumber Wagon (1923)

This was the bogie base with 2 (usually red) bolsters and three logs chained to the bolsters.

No.2	**GW** olive green - *26-30*	40	80
No.2	**LMS** olive green - *24-30*	30	60
No.2	**LNER** olive green - *24-26*	30	60
No.2	**NE** olive green - *26-30*	30	60
No.2	**SR** light brown - *28-29*	120	160
No.2	**SR** dark brown - *29-30*	120	160
No.2	olive green - *23-24*	30	60
No.2	olive green - *30-33*	30	60
No.2	yellow - *33-39*	15	30
No.2	grey - *39-41, 49-50*	30	60

W52. No.2 High Capacity Wagon (1936)

No.2	**GW** 53962 Loco Coal grey - *36-41*	75	100
No.2	**GW** 53962 Loco Coal grey - *49-50*	150	200
No.2	**LMS** Loco Coal grey - *36-41, 49-50*	50	80
No.2	**LMS** Loco Coal brown - *?*	120	160
No.2	**NE** 163535 Brick Wagon red-brown - *36-41, 49-50*	60	90

W53. No.2 Cattle Truck (1923)

No.2	**GW** W grey+olive green - *26-27*	50	90
No.2	**GW** W grey+blue - *27-28*	50	90
No.2	*now* with gold 'GW' - *28-33*	50	90
No.2	as above but grey+green - *33-35*	50	90
No.2	now with grey base - *35-38*	50	90
No.2	as above but white letters - *38-41*	50	90
No.2	now with black base - *39*	50	90
No.2	**LMS** W grey on olive green- *24-27*	30	60
No.2	**LMS** W grey+blue on blue - *25-27*	30	60
No.2	now with gold 'LMS' - *28-33*	40	80
No.2	as above but green base - *33-35*	30	60
No.2	now with grey base - *35-38*	30	60
No.2	as above but white letters - *38-41*	45	90
No.2	now with black base - *39*	30	60
No.2	**LNER** W grey on olive green- *24-26*	30	60
No.2	**NE** W grey on olive green - *26-27*	30	60
No.2	**NE** W grey+blue on blue - *25-27*	30	60
No.2	now with gold 'NE'- *28-33*	40	80
No.2	as above but green base - *33-35*	30	60
No.2	now with grey base - *35-38*	30	60
No.2	as above but white letters - *38-41*	30	60
No.2	now with black base - *39*	30	60
No.2	**SR** G brown - *28-39*	90	150
No.2	as above but white 'SR' - *39-41*	90	150
No.2	**SR** brown+green - *33-34*	90	150
No.2	grey on olive green - *23-24*	30	60
No.2	brown - *49-50*	50	75

No.2 goods van [W54] & cattle truck [W53] (Vectis)

W54. No.2 Luggage/Goods Van (1923)

Early versions were inscribed 'Luggage Van'.

No.2	grey + olive green - *23-24*	60	100
No.2	**GW** W grey+olive green - *26-27*	60	120
No.2	**GW** W blue+olive green - *27-28*	60	120
No.2	now with gold 'GW' - *28-33*	60	120
No.2	**GW** G grey - *33-36*	60	120
No.2	same with grey base - *36-38*	60	120
No.2	**GW** W grey - *39*	60	120
No.2	**GW** W grey with grey base - *38-41*	60	120
No.2	**LMS** W grey+olive green - *24-27*	50	90
No.2	**LMS** W blue - *27-28*	60	100
No.2	now with gold 'LMS' - *28-33*	60	100
No.2	**LMS** G grey - *33-39*	50	90
No.2	**LMS** W grey - *38-41*	50	90
No.2	**LMS** brown - *48-50*	80	120
No.2	**LNER** W grey+olive green - *24-26*	50	90
No.2	**NE** W grey+olive green - *26-27*	60	100
No.2	**NE** W blue - *27-28*	60	100
No.2	now with gold 'NE' - *28-33*	60	100
No.2	**NE** G grey - *33-35*	50	90
No.2	same with grey base - *36-38*	50	90
No.2	**NE** W grey with grey base- *38-41*	50	90
No.2	**NE** 106303 brown - *48-50*	80	120
No.2	**SR** G brown - *28-39*	250	350
No.2	now with white 'SR' - *39-41*	250	350

W55. Breakdown Van & Crane (1923)

This bogie wagon had the van body at one end and a crane at the other end. G = gold transfers. Early doors were hinged and later ones sliding.

-	grey with red cross - *23-24*	45	70
-	now without red cross - *23-24*	45	70
-	**GW** grey + red cross - *26*	50	80
-	**GW** G brown+blue + red cross - *27-32*	50	80
-	now without red cross - *32-33*	60	100
-	**GW** G green+blue- *33-41*	50	80
-	**LMS** grey + red cross - *24-27*	40	70
-	**LMS** G brown+blue + red cross - *27-32*	40	70
-	same without red cross - *32-33*	45	70

No.2 breakdown van & crane [W55] (Vectis)

-	**LMS** G green+blue - *34-37*	30	60
-	**LMS** G grey+black - *38-41*	40	70
-	**LMS** brown with red crane - *49-50*	60	100
-	same without 'LMS' - *49-50*	60	100
-	**LNER** grey + red cross - *24-27*	45	70
-	**NE** G brown+blue + red cross - *27-32*	50	90
-	now without red cross - *32-33*	50	90
-	**NE** G green+blue - *34-37*	30	60
-	**NE** G grey - *37-41*	40	70
-	**SR** G brown + red cross - *28-31*	100	160
-	now without red cross - *31-33*	100	160
-	**SR** G green+blue - *33-37*	100	160
-	**SR** G grey - *37-41*	110	180

No.50 Freight Stock

This was a new series of tin-printed four wheels wagons produced late in the life of Hornby 0 gauge and all were fitted with the T5 wheelbase.

W56a. No.50 Flat Truck (1957)

No.50	**BR** brown - *57-64*	15	30

W56b. No.50 Flat Truck with Cable Drum (1957)

No.50	**BR** brown + **'Liverpool'** drum - *57-64*	25	40

W57. No.50 Flat Truck with Container (1957)

No.50	**BR** brown + furniture container - *57-64*	20	30
No.50	**BR** brown + insulated meat container - *57-64*	20	30

W58. No.50 Gas Cylinder Wagon (1957)

No.50	red - *57-64*	10	20

W59. No.50 Lumber Wagon (1957)

No.50	red bolsters - *57-64*	10	20

W60. No.50 Wagon (open wagon) (1957)

Tin-printed.

No.50	**BR** grey - *57-64*	15	30

W61. No.50 Hopper Wagon (1957)

No.50	**BR** B40177 grey - *57-64*	15	30

No.50 an assortment of 1957 wagons (Vectis)

W62. No.50 Rotary Tipping Wagon (1957)

No.50	**'Trinidad Lake Asphalt'** buff - *57-64*	15	35

W63. No.50 Side Tipping Wagon (1957)

No.50	**'McAlpine'** green - *57-64*	15	30

W64. No.50 Salt Wagon (1957)

No.50	**'Saxa Salt'** 431? yellow - *57-64*	60	80

W65. No.50 Tank Wagon (1957)

No.50	**'Shell Lubricating Oil'** yellow - *57-64*	25	45
No.50	**'Manchester Oil Refineries'** green - *57-61*	45	85

No.50 an assortment of 1957 wagons (Vectis)

W66. No.50 Cattle Truck (1957)

No.50	**BR** brown T5 - *57-64*	20	40

W67. No.50 Goods Van (1957)

No.50	**BR** brown - *57-64*	20	40

W68. No.50 Refrigerator Van (1957)

No.50	**BR** white - *57-64*	20	40

W69. No.50 BR Goods Brake Van (1957)

This was tin-printed with no opening doors.

No.50	**BR** brown T5 - *57-63*	15	30

W70. No.50 Crane Truck (1957)

No.50	red jib on black base - *57-64*	15	30

W71. American Freight Cars (1930)

Made for export to America but also available in the UK.

-	Caboose orange+green - *30-41*	NPG	NPG
-	Caboose red+green - *30-41*	NPG	NPG
-	box car brown - *30-41*	NPG	NPG
-	box car orange+green - *30-41*	NPG	NPG
-	tank car red -*30-41*	NPG	NPG
-	tank car red, green filler - *30-41*	NPG	NPG

ACCESSORIES

Hornby 0 Gauge was a very complete system providing scores of lineside features with which to embellish your train and track. Some of these are now quite rare, as they are the items that were thrown away when your mother gave your trains to your younger cousins.

Many of the accessories continued in production throughout the life of the company; obviously with many style and colour variations, including a fair number during the post-war period. The 'Hornby' (or 'Meccano' on very early examples) trade marks appeared on all but the smallest pieces so identification is fairly easy. In this catalogue we are unable to provide a complete listing (with description and price) of all variations, or even all products, but the following is a basic listing giving you some idea of what is of interest and roughly what it is worth. With the exception of fields, hedges, trees, tunnels and cuttings which are made of wood and fabric, all of Hornby's accessories were made from printed tinplate.

***Buffers* -** No.1 buffers were the short spring type in various colours (£3-£5) while No.2 buffers were the long hydraulic type as seen in large terminus stations (£15-£20). There were also versions of both types with electric lamps coded No.1E (£25-£30) and No.2E (£40-£60).

***Countryside Sections* -** These were made from thick card and printed paper and came in various shapes to fit around the track (£20-£40 per piece).

Cuttings - There were straight and curved sections of the embankments that formed the cuttings (£40-£80).

Engine Sheds - These were Hornby's finest buildings and were made between 1928 and 1941. They were constructed of printed tinplate and featured a late 19th Century industrial building, the best having a roof ventilator and smoke vents. The No.2 engine shed was twice the length of the No.1 and may be found with either clockwork 2-rail fittings or electric 3-rail with electric interior lighting (£150-£600).

***Footbridges and Lattice* Girder *Bridge* -** Over the years these were made in blues, creams and white. The No.2 footbridge had two signals on it (£30-£65). The much larger lattice girder bridge was made only between 1921 and 1934 (£90-£150).

Goods Platform - This had a rectangular platform and a simple building shape on which the detail was printed. It had a gabled overhanging roof and came in various colours. The No.2 version had an operating crane and sliding doors while a No.2E also had an electric light (£60-£300).

Hedges and Trees - Hedges were made from dyed loofah fixed to a wooden base to fit around fields. The trees were of similar construction but had lead bases to give them stability (£6-£12).

***Island Platform* -** This had a long platform with ramps at either end and two posts supporting a central canopy. Before the war the posts were latticed but after the war they were plain. They may be found in various colours and with an assortment of names. There was also an electrically lit version (£80-£350).

Lamp Standards - These had latticed posts and hanging glass globe lamps; two in the case of the No.2 version. The standard models were non-lighting (£60-£90) but there were No.1E and No.2E lit versions, with simpler brackets, lampshades and bulbs, as well (£70-£150)

Level Crossings - The No.1 and No.E1 level crossings had single track, one for 2-rail clockwork and the other for 3-rail electric respectively. There was also a 3-rail No.E1E which had lamps on the gates (£10-£30). It is therefore logical that the No.2 level crossing had double track with No.2, No.E2 and No.E2E versions (£30-£100) being available. Over the years there were many variations in the attractive printing on the bases, showing road and verges, while gates were white with red diamonds.

Loading Gauge - Early loading gauges (1920s) had round bases but later ones were square. While the posts were white, the bases were usually blue, but green and black examples may be found (£40-£60).

Platelayers Hut - This was an attractive feature with its red brick finish, chimney, blue roof and green door which opens on some models (£40-£75).

Platform Crane - This was an operating crane on a square base with steps. Some came in bright colours (£15-£30).

Platform Accessories - There were platform machines (ticket and nameplate), pillar box, fire hut, seats and luggage consisting of hampers and trunks - all made in printed tinplate (£8-£35 each). Between 1924 and 1926 the trunk was made with a 'Carlisle' label on it. This version is much sought after and has been valued at £90.

Watchman's Hut - The hut had an open front and was blue with a red roof. It came with a shovel and poker hanging on its sides and a brazier standing in front (£25-£35).

Signal Cabins - All the signal cabins had a gabled roof and a chimney stack. No.1 had printed windows while on the No.2 version they were pierced and the cabin had separate steps. The box was unnamed except for those made between 1924 and 1928 which carried the name 'Windsor'. The No.2E had a lamp inside while the Control Cabin had an opening roof and a base for a lever frame (£25-£85).

Signal Gantries - The No.1 signal gantry was of simple construction consisting of two supporting posts and four signal posts which push-fitted together on the gantry (£30-£50). The No.2 gantry was larger with lattice posts and had railings and a ladder. The signals were worked by a series of wires (£250-£450). There was also a No.2E which had electric lights behind each signal (£1,000-£2,000).

Signals - There were many colour variations although the main part was always white - single arm, double arm, home, distant and bracket. Most post-war examples have non-latticed posts (£10-£50). There were also electrically lit examples (£50-£120).

Stations - Many variations in stations were made during 1923-41 and 1948-57. These included variations in colour and printing, the latter providing an interesting study of changing clothes fashion and car design etc.. Sadly, the long gable ended shape with two chimneys (missing from cheaper stations) is less interesting than stations designed by other manufacturers such as Bing and Marklin. Fences, an open booking hall concourse and electric lamps may be found on some Hornby stations. Prices vary from £60-£90 for fairly basic units to £120-£250 for more elaborate ones.

Staff and Passengers - These were cast in lead, the size of them being slightly reduced around 1938. The range included six station staff, six passengers, six engineering staff and five train and hotel staff. There were also sets of farmyard animals, a shepherd and sheep. Single figures in good condition sell for £5-£10 while boxed sets range from £50-£120 depending on which set it is.

Telegraph Pole - This was over-scale and was fixed to a square tinplate base. Until 1929 the two cross bars were tin after which they were cast in lead (£30-£45 each).

Tunnel - Between 1924 and 1931 the tunnel was printed tin to represent moorland (£70-£90) but from then until 1937 the picture represented countryside with hikers (£70-£120). From 1932, up to the Second World War, many were made of wood and fabric and finished with coloured sawdust. The latter were made in various lengths and available curved or straight (£20-£60).

Viaduct - This was single track and the centre section had grey or green girder sides. There were ramp sections at both ends and they came with either clockwork (£30-£35) or electric (£70-£80) track.

Water Tank - During the 1930s the No.1 water tank was red with a green base, black ladder and yellow or buff column. Post-war it was black and red with a plastic column (£15-£35). The No.2 water tank was more like gauge 1 in scale and came with a blue or green base and column and a red or yellow tank (£75-£85). There was also a No.2E version with a blue electric light fitting on the tank (£800-£1200).

SETS

If one counts the many company and colour variations, Meccano Ltd produced 223 different Hornby 0 gauge train sets before the outbreak of World War 2 and a further 34 after the war.

The Hornby train sets were released in attractive packaging and very early boxes were brown or maroon with pictures of locomotives tastefully embossed in gold on their lids.

From 1921 onwards, inspiring coloured pictures of fast-moving prototypical trains appeared on most sets; only from 1925 until 1931 did Hornby show their own products on the lid. These were a 2711 4-4-0 in LMS livery, with smoke coming from the chimney, pulling No.2 Pullman cars at speed through a country scene.

The *Royal Scot* and *Flying Scotsman* were the most common images on set boxes and were continued in 1945. In this last period, a No.41 tank passenger set had a picture of a 'Castle' Class locomotive on the box lid while another 0-4-0 locomotive set showed a 'Britannia' Class engine racing along the word 'Hornby'. This was before the Trade Description Act and one thing is for sure - the contents did not match the picture!

Boxes for sets had stoutly made compartments and each contained a circle of clockwork or electric track. There were also a small box of track clips, a locomotive and either coaches or wagons. Clockwork sets also had a key in a packet and some sets had a packet of locomotive lamps and/or coach connectors. The sets contained a 'tested' label, guarantee slip, instructions and an application form for the Hornby Railway Association which the purchaser was invited to join.

Collecting sets is a specialist field which is ignored by many who prefer to run their trains. Constant use of the contents of sets can lead to destructive and devaluing wear and tear. Replacement inserts are available for some boxes through the Hornby Railway Collectors Association.

A rough guide to the value of a run-of-the-mill set is the sum of the contents plus a bit extra for the box. A 3C set of the late '30s, containing a 4-4-2 and two coaches has a value of £550-£850 in nice condition; depending on the exact contents. A rare electric set containing a large locomotive will be upwards of £1000. On the other hand, pre-war clockwork sets with No.1 locomotives (either tender or tank) are valued at £150-£250.

M series items are generally inexpensive and small attractive sets, with good pictures on their lids, sell for £40-£60.

There are obviously more post-war 0-4-0 sets about in good order and one can expect to pay between £100-£150; unless it is uncommon in which case it could cost as much as £200.

Some of the pre-war sets were given impressive names of real named trains. These include 'The Pines Express' on a No.1 0-4-0 passenger set of 1939, 'The Dover Pullman', 'The Golden Arrow' and the 'Cornish Riviera', all of which contained various No.3 4-4-2s with bogie coaches or Pullman cars. From 1945 the romantic names disappeared but the enticing pictures remained.

Hornby Dublo

These models were made by Meccano Ltd at Binns Road, Liverpool, between 1938 and 1964.

HISTORY

In pre-Second World War Britain, 0 gauge ruled supreme, but as early as the 1920s a bid had been made to have a smaller gauge accepted. That was the Bing Table Top Railway which was a victim of the growth of Nazi influence in Germany. The German Trix system sprang from the Bing version and when the inventors fled to Britain to avoid Nazi persecution, a British version of the system was developed at Northampton in association with Bassett-Lowke.

Milestones

1901 Frank Hornby invents Meccano.
1914 Meccano Ltd moves to Binns Rd, Liverpool.
1915 Frank Hornby announces he is to make 'toy trains'.
1920 Toy train production starts at Binns Road.
1938 Launch of electric and clockwork Hornby Dublo through *Meccano Magazine*.
1941 Toy production closes and this sees the end of the clockwork system.
1947 Hornby Dublo returns and now has Peco type automatic couplings.
1948 *Duchess of Atholl* released.
1950 New motors introduced.
1953 Change to British Railways liveries.
1957 *Bristol Castle* released.
1957 Dublo Dinky Toys arrive.
1958 The first plastic wagons appear.
1958 Head and coach boards introduced.
1958 First diesel added to the range (Class 20).
1959 First plastic building appears.
1959 2-rail electric system introduced.
1960 Ringfield motor announced.
1960 Plastic couplings first appear.
1962 Decals on loco models now show only left facing lion.
1963 First beginners sets released
1964 Last model, the AL1 electric, released after other Hornby Dublo production had stopped.
1964 Lines Bros. Ltd invited to take over Meccano Ltd.
1964 Official end of 3-rail system.
1965 Announcement of 'amalgamation' with Tri-ang Railways.
1966 Hornby Dublo tools sold to G&R Wrenn.

Standard tank No.80059 [L4] (Vectis)

Seeing the possible risk this created for Hornby's market, Meccano Ltd decided to launch their own 00 scale system. Thus, in 1938, Hornby Dublo was born.

Initially it was a small version of the 0 gauge system except that the locomotives had cast metal bodies, the track looked like that sold by Marklin and the buildings were made of wood. Both clockwork and electric sets were available before the war but the couplings could not be uncoupled automatically. Pre-war locomotives were limited to a valanced LNER A4 'Pacific' named *Sir Nigel Gresley* and an 0-6-2 tank engine which looked like an LNER Class N2 but which, in true Hornby tradition, was available in the liveries of the big four companies (with detail concessions to the GWR).

After the war, the Peco automatic coupling was adopted as standard and the buildings, when they reappeared, were diecast in aluminium. Clockwork did not reappear but the long awaited LMS *Duchess of Atholl* did.

In 1953 the system was 'Nationalised' and the old liveries, which had been gradually dropped until only the LMS was left, were finally replaced by BR ones. One of Hornby Dublo's finest locomotives was soon to appear - the 2-6-4 Standard tank. The 'Castle', 8F and Bo-Bo diesel quickly followed. By 1957 it was clear that Hornby Dublo was losing ground to the Tri-ang Railways system and something drastic had to be done. The first change was the adoption of plastic for wagon bodies. The first, the grain wagon, appearing the following year.

The possibility of a 2-rail electric system had been discussed as long ago as 1938 but was not adopted until 1959. Plastic buildings arrived the same year and the 'Super Detail' coaches followed the year after. Too late, it was realised that the system was not gaining the loyalty of beginners, whose parents were being wooed by the low prices of Tri-ang and Playcraft sets. In 1963, in a last ditch attempt to save the system, two beginner's sets were launched but, with unsold stock piling up in the factory, production of the Hornby Dublo system was halted.

Super detailed restaurant car [C8] (Vectis)

With Meccano Ltd facing strong competition in the areas of railways (Tri-ang), diecast cars (Corgi) and construction systems (Lego), it had nowhere to go and consequently invited Lines Bros. (the makers of Tri-ang) to take them over - which they did. The name Hornby was transferred to the Tri-ang Railways system. This was done in the guise of an amalgamation but the only Hornby Dublo models to be adopted into the newly named Tri-ang Hornby range (and then only for a few years) were the terminus station and the AL1 Class AC electric locomotive. Thus Tri-ang Railways carried on, renamed Tri-ang Hornby (later renamed Hornby Railways), and the Hornby products in the shops today are therefore direct descendants of Tri-ang Railways and not Hornby Dublo. The name 'Hornby Dublo', was retained by Tri-ang although not used again and it is still owned by Hornby Hobbies who are also still based in Margate.

The Hornby Dublo tools were sold to Tri-ang subsidiary, G&R Wrenn, and formed the basis of the Wrenn Railways model range which started to appear in the late 1960s and is described elsewhere in this book.

At the time Meccano Ltd were taken over by Tri-ang they had various models planned. With the approval of Hornby Hobbies, two of the proposed locomotives were later produced by Michael Foster, in association with the Hornby Railway Collectors Association (HRCA), using former Hornby Dublo chassis. These are the V2 and the 56XX 0-6-2 tank.

Further Reading

Anyone interested in further study of this important and popular model railway system is recommended to read *Hornby Dublo Trains* by Michael Foster and published by New Cavendish Books (ISBN 0 904568 18 0). There is also a compendium to this work by Alan F Ellis, called *Hornby Dublo Compendium*, which is also published by New Cavendish Books (ISBN 0 904568 80 6). A small but comprehensive listing of the post-war 3-rail system will be found in Tony Oakes' *Post-war 3-rail Collectors Guide*, published by Mayfield Publishing (ISBN 0 9516757 0 2).

Collectors Club

You may also wish to join the Hornby Railway Collectors Association (HRCA) who publish, for their members, an excellent monthly magazine, called *The Hornby Railway Collector*, devoted to the toy train and model railway products of Meccano Ltd. Details of this organisation may be obtained from the membership secretary, John Harwood, tel: 01935 474830.

Prices - The chance of finding mint boxed Hornby Dublo is relatively small and so the use of the 'mint/boxed' column (right hand one) for this purpose would have little meaning. We have therefore used both price columns to indicate the price range one may expect for examples in very good condition - top quality examples being in their original and correct box. We do, however, refer you to the section on values near the front of the book.

Dates - The dates used in the following tables are those when models were being advertised by the manufacturer or, in the case of short term variations, when it is thought likely they were made. Although they are thought to be fairly accurate, they are for guidance only and should not be taken too literally. There were large unsold stocks in the factory after production ceased and these took several years to clear. This time is not included in the dates given.

Couplings - pre-war models had flat sprung metal couplings while post-war they were fitted with Peco style couplings. These were metal until 1961 but had been altered in design in 1954 to give them greater depth. In 1961 rather clumsy plastic couplings replaced the metal ones but these were unpopular and in 1963, a coupling with a thinner profile and made of Delrin was introduced.

Wheels - Rolling stock initially had diecast mazak wheels, forced onto steel axles without insulating bushes, making them unsuitable for 2-rail systems. Mazak was replaced by sintered iron in 1950. The wheels were held in place by metal tabs bent over the underside of each axlebox. In 1957, one-piece wheels/axle nylon mouldings appeared for the first time, and were used in both disc and spoked form on rolling stock, again held in place by tabs.

LNER horse box [W5]

2-rail/3-rail - Unless otherwise stated, all of the locomotives in this section have three rail power contact (i.e. power is collected from a centre rail and returned through the wheels via the outer rails) . Clockwork models (c/w) are suitable for use on both systems but not on 2-rail track at the same time as it is being used for electric locomotives. Rolling stock with metal wheels was suitable only for 3-rail operation while those with plastic wheels could be used on either 3-rail or 2-rail layouts.

Export Models - Couplings were attached with a rivet but models for export in 1962-63 usually had their couplings fixed on with screws so that they could be changed. They also had an export label on the end of the box and had different catalogue numbers. Bogie and open wagons could not be made this way, nor could locomotives with couplings attached to bogies. No 3-rail locos are known with screw-fitted couplings, other than those diesel and electric types which had them anyway. Models in boxes marked with export labels have been known to sell at prices many times higher than the equivalent for the home market. For example, in 2003, a group of four different 2-rail tank wagons in export boxes sold for £600.

Oddities - Errors do turn up from time to time and include such things as inverted printing on the side of the flat wagon, incorrect printing of the mineral wagon, mismatching bogies on bogie wagons and mismatched body sides on various items of rolling stock. Coaches with ends lacking printing detail appear to be corrections of wrongly assembled coaches.

Buyer beware! Some oddities can be 'manufactured' by the unscrupulous. For example: chassis can be swapped around as too can roofs. Many coach and van roofs were interchangeable and so models may be found with the wrong roof colour. Before buying one as a 'rarity' make sure that it cannot have been 'manufactured' by a bit of roof swapping.

With the arrival of 2-rail models, the bodies of 2-rail and 3-rail locomotives were often swapped over by retailers to offer their customers choice. The only exceptions to this were the Class R1 0-6-0T which had no 3-rail equivalent, the plain green 'Deltic' type diesel which was unnumbered and the EMU which shared a common number.

LOCOMOTIVES

Other Identification Aids - Pre-war and early post-war models did not have the model number (e.g. EDL7) under the running board while later ones did. On early post-war tank locomotives the maker's decal, on the back of the bunker, was a gold block with a red border and inscribed 'Hornby Meccano Ltd, Made in England'. This was replaced by a silver coloured decal with a red border in late 1949 when the motor changed. *Sir Nigel Gresley* only ever had a silver-backed label on both loco and tender (some pre-war tenders had none).

[1]***After-Sale Factory Variations*** - Hornby Dublo variations marked [1] resulted from the model being returned to the factory for a repair and a revised part being used, thus altering the model. Others include *Sir Nigel Gresley* with black driving wheels, *Duchess of Montrose* with nickel-plated driving wheels and the 0-6-2 tank with no coal in the bunker, but nickel-plated driving wheels.

Cat No.	Company, Number, Colour, Dates	£	£
L1.	**Starter Tank 0-4-0T** (1963)		

Plastic moulded body. All starter locomotives were 12v DC electric and were available only in sets.

(2001)	BRd black, riveted couplings ex 'Ready to Run' set - *63-64*	25	NA
(2001)	BRd black, clipped couplings ex 'Ready to Run' set - *63-64*	25	NA
(2002)*	blue, map of Australia, from Commonwealth set for Australia - *64*	90	NA

* Those sold in the UK through non-Meccano dealers were coded 2002 but some that reached Australia were coded 2003. The latter had power units wound for Australian power supply.

L2. SR Class R1 0-6-0T (1959)

Plastic moulded body.

A pair of Class R1 0-6-0Ts [L2] (Vectis)

2206	**31337** BRc black 2-rail - *59-64*	50	70
2206	as above but red buffers - *63-65*	75	100
2207	**31340** BRc green 2-rail 31337 on front - *59-61*	50	70

2207	as above but 31340 on front - *61-65*	40	60
2207	as above but red buffers - *63-65*	60	80

L3. **LNER Class N2 0-6-2T** (and similar) (1938)

Diecast body. p-wb = pre-war body (one without notch in buffer beam for post-war coupling). p-wc = pre-war couplings.

	GWR		
DL7	**6699** green p-wc c/w - *38-40*	700	800
EDL7	**6699** green p-wc - *38-41*	500	600
EDL7	**6699** green p-wb - *48*	NPG	NPG
EDL7	**6699** green - *47-53*	200	700
EDL7	**6231** green *Duchess of Atholl* number and not on plate, very rare* - *53-54*	700	900
	LMS		
DL7	**6917** black p-wc c/w - *38-40*	400	450
EDL7	**6917** black p-wc - *38-41*	300	400
EDL7	**6917** black, serif letters - *47-49*	175	250
EDL7	**6917** black, sans serif letters - *49-53*	50	100
	LNER		
DL7	**2690** black p-wc c/w - *38-40*	450	550
EDL7	**2690** black p-wc - *38-41*	300	400
EDL7	**9596** black very rare - *47-48*	300	NPG
EDL7	**9596** green - *48-49*	110	175
EDL7	**9596** green letters changed - *50-53*	110	175
	Southern		

Pre-war clockwork SR 0-6-2T [L3] (Vectis)

DL7	**2594** olive green p-wc c/w - *38-40*	700	800
EDL7	**2594** olive green p-wc - *38-41*	600	700
EDL7	**2594** olive green p-wb - *48*	500	700
EDL7	**2594** on bunker olive green - *48*	550	700
EDL7	**2594** malachite green - *48-53*	250	800
	BR		
EDL7	**E9560** BRa green - *53?*	NPG	NPG
EDL7	**69567** BRb gloss black no coal - *53-54*	100	150
EDL17	**69567** BRb matt black no coal - *54-61*	40	70
3217	**69567** BRc matt black with coal - *61-62*	150	300
2217	**69550** BRc black 2-rail small safety valve coal in bunker - *60-63*	80	150
2217	**69550** BRc black 2-rail large safety valve dome coal in bunker - *63-64*	100	150

*Thought to have been an export-intended disposal of remaining GWR-type 0-6-2T bodies, unsuited to BR livery, with surplus '6231' numbers deputising for lack of '6699' ones.

L4. **BR Class 4MT Standard Tank 2-6-4T** (1954)

From 1959 the model had a more accurately shaped chimney.

EDL18	**80054** BRb black - *54-61*	60	80
2218	**80033** BRc black 2-rail* - *59-65*	90	120
3218	**80059** BRc black - *61-64*	300	400

* There is a rare version of 80033 on the casting for 80054 with a different chimney.

L5. **GWR 'Castle' Class 4-6-0** (1957)

Diecast body.

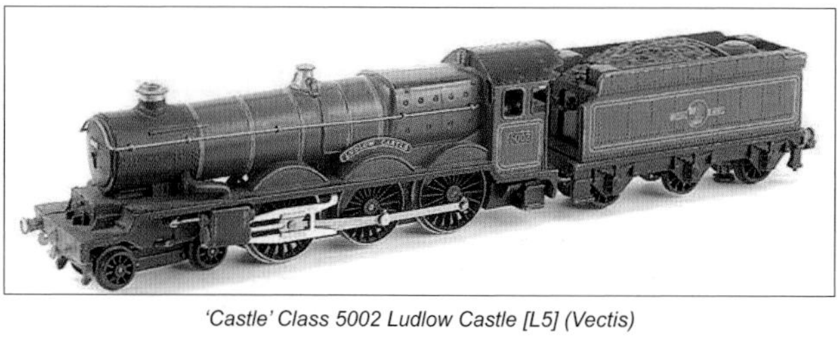

'Castle' Class 5002 Ludlow Castle [L5] (Vectis)

EDLT20	**7013 *Bristol Castle*** BRc green - *57-61*	90	120
2220	**7032 *Denbigh Castle*** BRc 2-rail green - *59-60*	120	200
2221	**4075 *Cardiff Castle*** BRc 2-rail green - *60-65*	100	150
3221	**5002 *Ludlow Castle*** BRc green - *61-64*	300	400

L6. **LMS 'Duchess' Class 4-6-2** (1948)

Diecast body. A different nameplate, with smaller letters, was used for a short time on this model around 1949. The BR maroon livery versions had a modified body with cut away front to the footplate, modified cab, recessed safety valves and a tender with a moulded plastic body.

	LMS 6231 Duchess of Atholl		
EDL2	maroon, horseshoe magnet - *48-49*	125	300
EDL2	maroon block magnet and 'EDL2' under cab roof - *49-51*	125	300
EDL2	nameplate with yellow letters on maroon - *50*	300	425
EDL2	lump replaced depression beneath one nameplate (factory error) - *51?*	150	325
EDL2	maroon longer nameplate and rib along footplate edge* - *51-53*	125	300
EDL2	+ defectors 'EDL12' in cab roof[1] ** - *?*	350	500
EDL3	**1215** Canadian Pacific black revised smokebox *** - *52-63*	400	600
EDL12	**46232 *Duchess of Montrose*** BRb gloss green - *53-54-58*	100	150
EDL12	as above but matt green - *54-58*	60	130
L12	as above but 'L12' under cab roof - *58-61*	80	120
2226	**46245 *City of London*** BRc maroon 2-rail **** - *59-64*	150	300

'Duchess' City of Liverpool [L6]

3226	**46247 *City of Liverpool*** BRc maroon - *61-65*	275	400
3226	as above but numbered '46245' on left-hand cab - *64*	475	600

*This was the final *Duchess of Atholl* body casting which had been designed with a BR livery and *Duchess of Montrose* in mind (the rib was to aid lining). Introduction of the BR livery was delayed due to shortages resulting from the Korean War. ** These were models re-bodied in the Service Department using a *Duchess of Montrose* body, spraying it maroon and then fitting smoke deflectors because the body had been modified to take them. *** These were used in three batches of sets but were also available as solo releases in 1953, the tender being sold separate from the loco. The loco body casting used was the final version for the *Duchess of Atholl* still with 'EDL2' in the cab roof. **** *City of London* had 2 styles of cab lining.

L7. **LNER Class A4 4-6-2** (1938)

Diecast body. Around 1950 the nameplates, for a short period, had rounded end borders. Some post-war examples of the A4 from sets released around 1949 have tenders with pre-war lettering (red shaded).

Pre-war LNER Class A4 Sir Nigel Gresley [L7]

EDL1	**4498 *Sir Nigel Gresley*** LNER blue valances and p-w couplings - *38-41*	300	480
DL1	as above but clockwork - *38-41*	600	800
EDL1	**7 *Sir Nigel Gresley*** LNER blue horseshoe motor - *48-50*	80	120
EDL1	as above but block-magnet motor + 'EDL1' inside cab roof - *50-53?*	80	120

EDL1	as above but 'EDL11' inside cab roof and raised front number plate[1]	300	400
EDL1	prewar loco, postwar tender[1] - *48-53*	150	200
EDL11	**60016 *Silver King*** BRb gloss green - *53-54*	100	150
EDL11	ditto but no raised front no. plate * - *53-54*	NPG	NPG
EDL11	**60016 *Silver King*** BRb matt green - *54-58*	85	120
EDL11	ditto but no raised front no. plate * - *54*	NPG	NPG
L11/3211	**60022 *Mallard*** BRc green ** - *58-61*	100	150
3211	ditto but now with plated driving wheels and thin handrails - *61-64*	250	320
2211	**60030 *Golden Fleece*** BRc green 2-rail - *59-65*	120	200

* An extra '1' stamped under the cab roof to read 'ED11'. These possibly resulted from the use of old tooling while the EDL11 tool was under repair. ** On early examples of *Mallard* the tender wheels were zinc but these were later changed for plastic ones - possibly with the arrival of *Golden Fleece*.

L8. BR Rebuilt 'West Country' Class 4-6-2 (1961)

Diecast body. *Barnstaple* stocks were taken into the Tri-ang Hornby range with the model being included in the 1966 Tri-ang Hornby catalogue.

2235	**34005 *Barnstaple*** BRc green 2-rail - *61-66*	150	250
3235	**34042 *Dorchester*** BRc green - *61-64*	250	350

8F 2-8-0 [L9] & 'West Country' Dorchester [L8] (Vectis)

L9. LMS Class 8F 2-8-0 (1958)

Diecast body.

LT25/ 3225	**48158** BRc black - *58-61*	90	120
2225	**48109** BRc 2-rail black - *59-60*	75	150
2224	**48073** BRc 2-rail black - *60-65*	75	150
3224	**48094** BRc black - *61-64*	250	350

L10. Starter Diesel Shunter 0-4-0DS (1964)

This was the Class 08 diesel body on an 0-4-0 chassis and has a shortened body housing so as to fit the chassis, with side rods omitted.

(2004)	yellow ex 'Ready to Run' set - *64*	35	NA
(2005)	as above but from sets sent to Australia - *64*	35	NA

L11. Diesel Shunter (Class 08) 0-6-0DS (1961)

Plastic moulded body. Both single and 2-part coupling rods may be found, the former being the older. The body differs from the Wrenn one (which was from different tooling) in having 'Hornby Dublo - Meccano Ltd - Made in England' inside.

2231	**D3302** BRc green 2-rail - *61-63*	60	80
2231	ditto 2-piece coupling rod - *63-65*	60	80
3231	**D3763** BRc green * - *61-63*	100	150
3231	ditto 2-piece coupling rod - *63-64*	100	150

* D3763 may be found with transfer numbers instead of heat-printed ones. These are thought to have been due to the heat-printing not coming out properly first time round.

L12. Type 1 (Class 20) Diesel Bo-Bo (1958)

The first loco in the Hornby Dublo range with a plastic moulded body.

L30/3230	**D8000**** BRc green - *58-62*	70	120
L30/3230	**D8000** BRc green no buffers * Canadian - *59-62*	550	700
L30/3230	**D8000** BRc green no buffers * no motor Canadian - *59-62*	650	800
2230	**D8017** BRc green 2-rail - *59-62*	80	150

*These were released for the Canadian market and had the buffers sawn-off leaving rounded studs instead. They were both sold in the normal 3-rail blue box and were not particularly successful. A further batch of 2-rail models (powered and non-powered) were sent over in normal UK boxes in 1962. Some of these non-powered examples are very strangely assembled with motor bogies but with the armature missing.

L13. Metro-Vic (Class 28) Diesel Co-Bo (1961)

Diecast body. Stocks of the 2-rail version were taken into the Tri-ang Hornby range with the model being included in the 1966 Tri-ang Hornby catalogue.

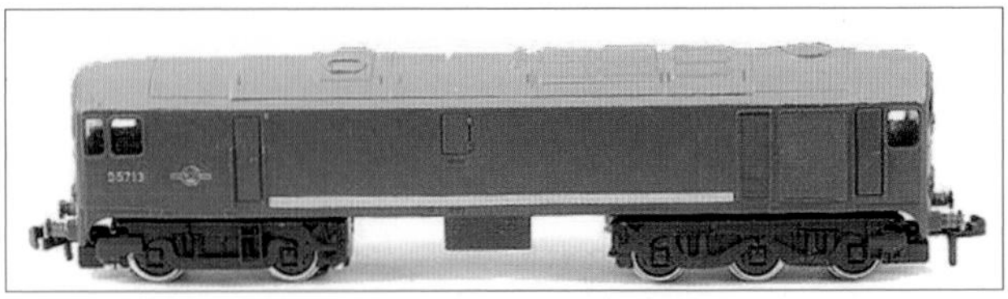

Met-Vic Class 28 [L13] (Vectis)

2233	**D5702** BRc green 2-rail * - *61-66*	60	120
3233	**D5713** BRc green - *61-64*	150	250

* A rare variation has a pair of strengthening ribs to the outline of the battery box between the bogies.

L14. 'Deltic' Type (Class 55) Diesel Co-Co (1961)

Diecast body. The modell was released before the real locomotives were put into service, which could explain the initial error of the plain green livery, and, like them, started life without names for the first year.

2232	BRc green 2-rail - *61-64*	60	100
2232	the same with plastic bogie sides - *64-65*	80	120
3232	BRc green - *61-64*	120	180
3234	**D9001 *St Paddy*** BRc 2-tone green - *62-65*	300	400
2234	**D9012 *Crepello*** BRc 2-tone green 2-rail - *62-64*	70	140

L15. Class AL1 (Class 81) AC Electric Bo-Bo (1964)

Plastic moulded body.

Class 81 AC electric [L15] (Vectis)

2245	**E3002** BRd blue 2-rail - *64-65*	300	500

L16. Class 501 Suburban EMU (1962)

Tinplate body. Caution: Examples with a different livery or number have been altered after leaving the factory and are therefore not listed here.

2250+ 4150	**S65326+S77511** BRc green 2-car unit 2-rail - *62-65*	150	475
2250	power car 2-rail with green rear end moulding instead of black - *?*	180	500
3250 + 4150	**S65326+S77511** BRc green 2-car 3-rail unit - *62-64*	300	600
3250	power car 3-rail with green rear end moulding instead of black - *?*	330	650
2350 + 4250	**S65326+S77511** BRc green 2-car unit 2-rail boxes marked 'Export' - *?*	NA	1000

COACHES

The first coaches were lithographed tinplate (including windows). Construction was tab-and-slot and the bogies were diecast, as were the wheels. Pre-war diecasting often contained impurities that later led to metal fatigue resulting in much pre-war rolling stock die castings becoming crazed or crumbling.

The LMS coaches, introduced after the war, were the first to have punched out and glazed windows, a feature which the Gresley stock never achieved. Tinplate was retained for coach production right to the end although the final range of Super Detail Mk1 coaches had only tinplate sides. The only plastic coaches produced were Pullman cars.

Cat No.	Company, Number, Colour, Dates	£	£

Tinplate Coaches

These were all tinplate with metal roofs, some with printed windows and others with clear windows. With the exception of the restaurant cars, they had no interior detail.

C1. LNER Gresley Stock (1938)

All had printed windows and curved round ends in typical Gresley style. p-wc = pre-war couplings. LNER versions had white roofs and BR versions, grey ones. The all 3rd LNER coaches were introduced after the change to BR livery in order to use up a residue of tinprinted parts produced for the articulated coaches.

LNER teak

D251	42759 D1 composite pre-war couplings - *38-41*	70	120
32010	as above, post-war couplings - *48-53*	25	40
D252	45401/45402 D2 all 3rd+brake 3rd articulated p-wc - *38-41*	500	850

Gresley pre-war articulated coaches [C1] (Vectis)

D252	45401/45402 D2 all 3rd+3rd/brake articulated export only - *48-49*	750	1000
-	45402/45401/45402 articulated brake+3rd+ brake* - *not made*	NA	NA
32011	45402 D1 brake/3rd brown ends - *48-53*	25	40
32011	45402 D1 brake/3rd teak** ends - *48-53*	40	55
32012	45401 D1 all 3rd brown ends - *early 54*	25	40
32012	45401 D1 all 3rd teak ends - *late 54*	25	40
32012	as above with grey roof - *late 54-55*	35	50
	BR red+cream		
32013	E42759E D11 composite Gresley bogies - *53-54?*	20	25
32013	as above but BR bogies - *54?-56*	20	25
32014	E45402E D11 brake/3rd Gresley bogies - *53-54?*	20	25
32014	as above but BR bogies - *54?-56*	20	25

* A pre-production sample was made, after the war, from two 2-car units at Binns Road and sent to Canadian Meccano Ltd. office for their approval but the project was abandoned. ** These teak ends were from the articulated coaches and lacked the dark brown corridor detail. They were used up on all 3rd coaches but, in error, some were used on the brake/3rd coaches.

C2. LMS Stanier Stock (1948)

Although planned for release before the last war, it was not released until after hostilities had ended. All had punched out and glazed windows. Early LMS coaches had a silver grey roof while later ones had a pale grey one. p-wc = pre-war couplings. The BR coaches gained plastic wheels in 1958, before the change to red boxes with 4XXX numbers.

LMS maroon (D3)

-	4183 composite p-wc - *not made*	NA	NA
32015	4183 composite dark metallic coloured roof - *48-49*	40	60
32015	as above but light metallic roof - *50-51*	40	60
32015	as above but light grey roof - *52-53*	30	50
-	26133 brake/3rd p-wc - *not made*	NA	NA
32016	26133 brake/3rd dark metallic coloured roof - *48-49*	40	60
32016	as above but light metallic roof - *50-51*	40	60
32016	as above but light grey roof - *52-53*	30	50

Stanier BR restaurant car [C2]

BR red+cream

32017	M4183 D12 comp LMS bogies - *53*	20	25
32017	as above but BR bogies - *53-58*	12	18
4005	as above but plastic wheels - *58-61*	18	35
4005	as above but plastic couplings - *61*	40	50
32018	M26133 D12 brake/2nd/3rd LMS bogies - *53*	20	25
32018	as above but BR bogies - *53-58*	12	18
4006	as above but plastic wheels - *58-61*	15	35
4006	as above but plastic couplings - *61*	30	45
32097/ 4048	W9562 restaurant car plastic wheels - *57-64*	15	25
	BR brown+cream		
32094	W15862 D21 composite - *57-58*	15	25
4009	as above but plastic wheels - *58-61*	20	40
4009	as above but plastic couplings - *61*	40	50
32095	W34881 D21 brake/2nd - *57-58*	15	25
4010	as above but plastic wheels - *58-61*	15	35
4010	as above but plastic couplings - *61*	30	45
32096/ 4047	W9572 D20 restaurant car plastic wheels - *57-64*	20	30
	BR maroon		
32022	M4193 D22 composite - *57-58*	20	25
4013	as above but plastic wheels - *58-62*	25	40
4013	as above but plastic couplings - *61*	40	50
32023	M26143 D22 brake/2nd - *57-58*	20	25
4014	as above but plastic wheels - *58-61*	25	40
4014	as above but plastic couplings - *61*	40	50
4049	W4966W red restaurant car red window detail, plastic wheels - *59-61*	30	40
4049	as above, cream window detail (factory error) - *59*	20	30

C3. BR Mk1 Suburban Stock (1954)

Suburban stock was a post-war introduction and originally had printed windows. These were improved by stamping out and glazing them in 1956. They were eventually replaced by super detail coaches in 1962. These models are hard to find without scratch marks at their ends caused by staples used in box assembly. pw = plastic wheels. They gained plastic wheels in 1958, before the change to red boxes with 4XXX numbers.

32090	**BR** maroon D13 composite printed windows - *54-57*	15	25
32090	as above but with Gresley bogies (factory error) - *?*	30	40
32092	as 32090 but glazed D14 - *56-58*	20	30
32092	as above but windows in one end - *56-57*	30	40
4021	as D14 but plastic wheels - *59-65*	15	25
32091	**BR** maroon D13 brake/3rd/2nd printed windows - *54-57*	15	25
32093	above but glazed D14 - *56-58*	15	25
4022	as above but plastic wheels - *59-65*	15	25
4025	**BR** S41060 green comp - *59-65*	25	40
4026	**BR** S43374 green brake/2nd - *59-65*	25	40
4026	as above but with plain ends - *?*	35	50

C4. GWR Travelling Post Office (1957)

This was available only in the TPO set which included the lineside apparatus and mail bags. The value suggested in the right-hand column is for the complete set.

Royal Mail coach from TPO set [C4]

32098	**BR** W807 maroon coach only (the cat. no. of the set is 32099) - *57-59*	15	20
4401	as above but plastic wheels one side (the cat. no. of the set is 2400) - *59-65*	15	20

Plastic Bodied Coaches

These had the body and roof as a single moulding.

C5. Pullman Cars (1961)

These had plastic bodies and were later made by Wrenn. They were based on 1928 vehicles built for the LNER. The prototypes were transferred to steam-hauled services on the Southern Region in the 1950s. Watch out for broken buffers (imperfect mouldings) on these models. Early Pullman cars had Gresley compensating bogies and a three colour coat of arms but, by 1963, BR bogies were being used and a single colour was being used for the coat of arms.

4035	**Pullman** *Aries* brown+cream 1st class Gresley bogies - *61-63*	20	30

4035	as above but BR bogies and one colour crest - *63-65*	20	30
4036	**Pullman** Car 74 brown+cream 2nd class Gresley bogies - *61-63*	20	30

Pullman car Aries [C5]

4036	as above but BR bogies and one colour crest - *63-65*	20	30
4037	**Pullman** Car 79 brown+cream brake 2nd Gresley bogies - *61-63*	20	30
4037	as above but BR bogies and one colour crest - *63-65*	20	30

Super Detail Corridor Stock

These had plastic roofs, underframes and body ends but tinplate sides. They were modelled on BR Mk1 stock but were of a reduced length. Most BR and WR side corridor stock had compensating bogies.

The interior units used in these coaches were usually a tan colour or blue (1st class) but a rare variant is white which has turned up in some suburban stock and will add to the value of the item.

Caution: examples with a different livery of number to any given in the tables below have been altered after leaving the factory and consequently are not listed here.

C6. BR Mk1 Passenger Coaches (1960)

	BR maroon		
4052	E15770 composite* - *60-65*	20	30
4053	E35173 brake/2nd* - *60-65*	20	30
4062	M3002 1st open - *61-65*	25	30
4063	M3716 2nd open - *61-65*	25	30
	BR chocolate & cream		
4050	W15870 composite* - *60-65*	20	30
4051	W34290 brake/2nd* - *60-65*	20	30
4060	W3085 1st open - *61-65*	25	30
4061	W3984 2nd open - *61-65*	25	30
	BR green		
4054	S15573 composite - *62-65*	35	50
4055	S35001 brake/2nd - *62-65*	35	50

* Introduced with compensating bogies and found, usually, only in sets.

C7. BR Mk1 Sleeping Car (1961)

Found only with compensating bogies.

4078	**BR** W2402 maroon - *61-65*	20	30

C8. BR Mk1 Restaurant Car (1963)

4070	**BR** W1910 brown+cream - *63-65*	110	130
4071	**BR** E1939 maroon - *63-65*	120	180

Mk1 full brake [C9] & Mk1 'Stove' [C11] (Vectis)

C9. BR Mk1 Passenger All Brake (1961)

Found only with compensating bogies.

4075	**BR** E81312 maroon - *61-65*	20	30

C10. BR Mk1 Suburban Stock (1962)

4081	**BR** S46291 green composite - *62-65*	50	70
4082	**BR** 543381 green brake 2nd - *62-65*	50	60
4082	as above but S43381* - *62-65*	110	130
4083	**BR** M41012 maroon composite - *62-65*	50	70
4084	**BR** M43277 maroon brake/2nd - *62-65*	45	60

* It is possible that these were hand altered at the factory.

C11. BR Mk1 'Stove' 6-Wheeled Passenger Brake (1963)

4076	**BR** M32958 maroon - *63-65*	100	150

WAGONS

Initially wagons were all lithographed tinplate with the flat spring pre-war couplings. Construction was tab-and-slot and the chassis and bogies were diecast, as were the wheels. Pre-war wagons frequently suffer from metal fatigue which has caused the diecast chassis to crumble and so care must be taken when buying these. The tinplate wagons reappeared after the war, with open wagons, vans and brake vans in train sets only in 1947 and all solo models the following year for export only (and the UK market in 1949). They now had Peco couplings and, in some cases such as the tank wagons, with black instead of coloured caps.

Prior to 1953 customers had a wide choice of wagons as they were produced in the liveries of the big four companies but, that year, the whole system changed to BR liveries and where there had previously been four open wagons or vans there was now only one. This was partly compensated for with the release of the first of a series of wagons with diecast bodies, starting that year with the mineral wagon and bogie bolster.

The original diecast standard 10' wagon chassis was a rather crude affair with no daylight visible between the brake rods. Late in the day, this was improved but the chassis could not compare with the plastic ones made by other manufacturers at the time.

The first Hornby Dublo vehicle to have a plastic body was the grain wagon which arrived in 1958. Once plastic wagons started to appear, wagons with larger wheelbases followed and these had plastic chassis made specially for them and were to a high standard. A plastic standard 10' wagon chassis was made at the very end but this was for wagons in the starter sets. Tinplate survived to the end for just one wagon - the 4-wheel tanker in all its variations.

Cat No.	Company, Number, Colour, Dates	£	£

Tinplate Series

W1. D1 Open & Coal 5-plank Wagons (1938)

The coal version of the wagon had a single moulding representing the top of a coal load. This had the ends turned down to act as feet to hold the 'coal' surface near the rim of the wagon. As it was a separate moulding it was interchangeable. p-wc = pre-war couplings

-	**GW** 109458 grey p-wc - *38-41*	25	35
-	as above with coal - *38-41*	25	35
32075	**GW** 109458 grey - *47-50*	20	35
32025	as above with coal - *48-50*	20	35
-	**LMS** 210112 brown p-wc - *38-41*	25	35
-	as above with coal - *38-41*	25	35
32075	**LMS** 210112 brown - *47-51*	15	25
32025	as above with coal - *48-51*	15	25
32075	**LMS** 210112 lighter brown - *51-53*	15	25
32025	as above with coal - *51-53*	15	25
-	**NE** 404844 green-grey p-wc - *38-41*	25	35
-	as above with coal - *38-41*	25	35

LMS 5-plank wagon [W1]

32075	**NE** 404844 green-grey - *47-51*	15	18
32025	as above with coal - *48-51*	15	18
32075	**NE** 404844 grey - *51-52*	15	18
32025	as above with coal - *51-52*	15	18
-	**SR** 19260 dark brown p-wc - *38-41*	40	100
-	as above with coal - *38-41*	40	100
32075	**SR** 19260 dark brown - *47-50*	30	100
32025	as above with coal - *48-50*	30	100
32075	**BR** E404844 grey - *54-58*	10	12
32025	as above with coal - *54-58*	10	12

W2. D2 High Sided Wagon (7-plank) (1938)

The coal version of the wagon had a single moulding representing the top of a coal load. This had the ends turned down to act as feet to hold the 'coal' surface near the rim of the wagon. p-wc = pre-war couplings

-	**LMS** 608344 brown p-wc - *38-41*	25	35
-	as above with coal - *38-41*	25	35
32055	**LMS** 608344 brown - *48-51*	15	20
32030	as above with coal - *48-51*	15	20
32055	**LMS** 608344 lighter brown - *51-53*	15	20
32030	as above with coal - *51-53*	15	20
-	**NE** 91508 grey p-wc - *38-41*	40	50
-	as above with coal - *38-41*	40	50

BR high-sided wagon [W2]

32055	**NE** 91508 grey - *48-51*	30	50
32030	as above with coal - *48-51*	30	50
32055	**BR** M608344 grey - *54-58*	10	15
32030	as above with coal - *54-58*	10	15

W3. D1 'Tube' Wagon(1956)

32076	**BR** W73349 brown - *56-58*	10	15
4690	as above but plastic wheels - *59-60*	10	15

W4. D1 Short Tank Wagon (1938)

This was the only wagon to retain its tinplate body with cast ends to the end of production. p-wc = pre-war couplings.

Esso tank wagon [W4]

-	**'Esso'** buff p-wc buff cap - *38-41*	80	150
32081	as above post-war black cap - *48-51*	80	100
36676	**'Esso'** silver - *52-58*	12	20
4676	as above but plastic wheels - *59-62*	15	25
4676	as above but open brake-gear - *62-64*	20	30
-	**'Power Ethyl'** green p-wc green cap - *38-41*	80	150
32080	as above post-war black cap - *48-51*	70	120
32080	**'Power'** * green - *54-55*	15	35
32080	as above but in 'Power Petrol' box - *55*	NA	100
-	**'Royal Daylight'** red p-wc red cap - *38-41*	80	150
32070	as above post-war black cap - *48-51*	100	120
32070	**'Esso Royal Daylight'** red - *52-55*	16	30
32082	**'Shell Lubricating Oil'** yellow - *55-58*	16	25
4678	as above but plastic wheels - *59-62*	16	25
4678	as above but open brake-gear - *62-64*	18	25
32083	**'Vacuum'** red - *55-56*	17	35
32084	**'Mobil Oil'** red (cat.4677) - *56-57*	17	30
32084	**'Mobil'** red (cat.4677) - *57-58*	17	30
32084	as above but plastic wheels - *59-62*	15	20
32084	as above but open brake-gear - *62-64*	20	30
4680	**'Esso'** black plastic wheels - *60-62*	20	20
4680	as above but open brake-gear - *62-64*	25	35

* Power tank wagons were sold in 'Power Ethyl' boxes for a long time after introduction. 'Power Petrol' boxes are extremely rare.

W5. D1 Closed Vans (1938)

Vans have white roofs except for the LMS versions which started silver grey and finished light grey and the BR vans which had light grey roofs. The SR meat van was available for a while with the LMS silver grey roof and examples sell at a higher price than those with white roofs, however, as roofs were interchangeable, it is not included in the list below. p-wc = pre-war couplings

	GWR		
32040	112699 green-grey goods van p-wc - *38-41*	55	75
32040	as above, post-war couplings - *47-50*	50	70
32020	106324 green-grey cattle van p-wc - *38-41*	25	35
32020	ditto post-war, two small windows - *48-51*	30	40
32020	as above but now grey - *51-53*	30	40
32020	as above but one long window - *52-53*	30	40
	LMS		
32040	508194 brown goods van p-wc - *38-41*	25	35
32040	as above, post-war couplings - *48-51*	15	25
32040	as above but lighter brown - *51-53*	15	25
32065	19631 brown meat van p-wc - *38-41*	25	35
32065	as above, post-war couplings - *47-53*	15	20
32020	710018 brown cattle van p-wc - *38-41*	45	65
32020	as above, post-war couplings - *48-53*	80	120
	LNER		
32035	168975 brown fish van p-wc - *38-41*	25	35
32035	as above, post-war couplings - *48-53*	18	25
32060	2337 teak horse box p-wc - *38-41*	25	35
32060	as above, post-war couplings - *48-53*	18	25
32040	182153 brown goods van p-wc - *38-41*	25	35
32040	as above, post-war couplings - *47-53*	18	25
	SR		

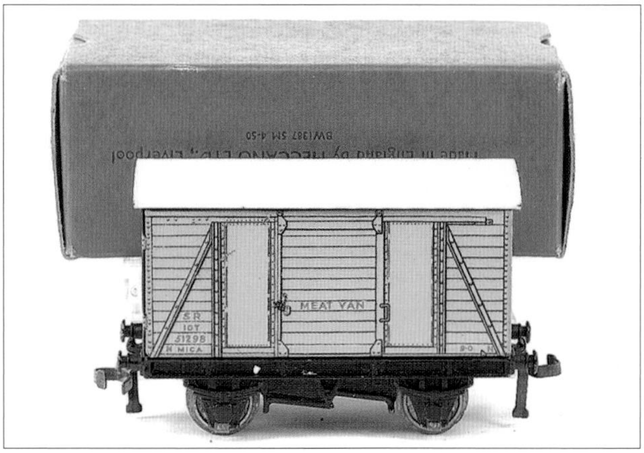

SR Meat van [W5]

32040	48277 dark brown goods p-wc - *38-41*	75	85
32040	as above, post-war couplings - *47-50*	80	120
32065	51298 buff meat van - *48-53*	60	80
	BR		
32040	B755414 brown goods van - *54-58*	12	16
32020	B893344 brown cattle van - *56-58*	12	18
32035	E168975 brown fish van - *54-58*	12	16

32060	E2337 red horse box - *54-58*	12	16
32065	S50494 white meat van - *54-58*	12	16

W6. D1 GWR Long Wheelbase Van (1954)

32058	**BR** W28798 brown - *54-58*	15	25
4326	as above but plastic wheels - *59*	20	30

W7. D1 GWR Goods Brake Van (1938)

-	**GW** 68796 grey Park Royal no chimney, pre-war couplings - *38-41*	45	65
32045	as above, post-war couplings - *47-50*	50	70
32047	**BR** W68796 grey Park Royal, with chimney - *56-58*	10	18

W8. D1 LMS Goods Brake Van (1938)

p-wc = pre-war couplings

-	**LMS** 730026 brown, no chimney, pre-war couplings - *38-41*	25	35

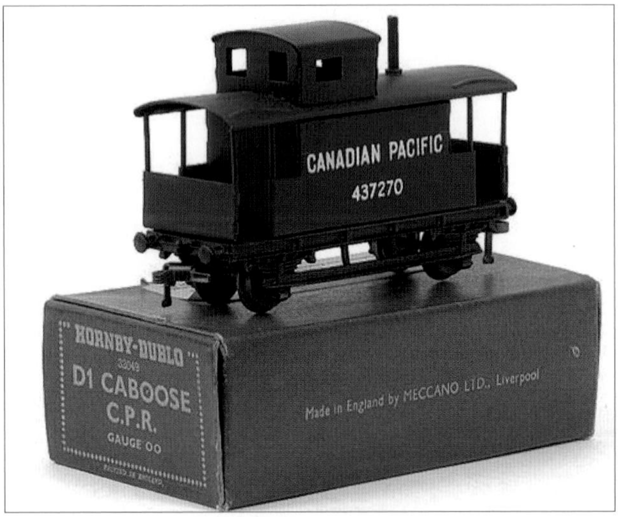

Canadian CPR 'Caboose' [W8] (Vectis)

32045	as above but post-war - *47-51*	15	25
32045	as above but lighter brown - *51-53*	15	25
32045	**BR** M730026 grey plain roof - *53-54*	15	25
32045	as above with chimney * - *54-58*	10	12
32049	**Canadian Pacific** 437270 black 'caboose' - *54-61*	100	250

* Rain strips also added.

W9. D1 LNER Goods Brake Van (1938)

p-wc = pre-war couplings

-	**NE** 178717 brown, pre-war couplings, no chimney - *38-41*	25	35
32045	ditto but post-war, white roof - *47-51*	15	20
32045	as above but grey roof - *53*	25	30
32046	**BR** E178717 brown, white roof - *53*	25	30
32046	as above but plain grey roof - *53-54*	15	25
32046	as above with chimney * - *54-58*	8	16

* Rain strips also added.

W10. D1 SR Goods Brake Van (1938)

p-wc = pre-war couplings

-	**SR** 55975 dark brown, no chimney, pre-war couplings - *38-41*	125	150
32045	as above but post-war couplings, one window on end - *47-50*	100	150
32045	as above but window each side of end door (factory error*) - *48*	100	120

* This detail comes from the LMS brake van. More usually they are found with the wrong detail at one end only.

W11. D1 LNER Bogie Brick Wagon (1938)

p-wc = pre-war couplings. All but one version had brown chassis.

-	**NE** N163535 brown p-wc - *38-41*	60	70
-	as above with black chassis *	150	160
32050	as above post-war - *48-53*	15	20
32050	**BR** E163535 brown - *53*	25	30
32050	as above but black chassis - *54-58*	10	16

* These were pre-war wagons returned for repair after the war.

Diecast Wagons

W12. D1 Low-Sided Wagon (1953)

The flat wagon with wooden cable drums had six holes in the base through which the drums were held in place with Meccano green string. Around 1960 the number of holes was reduced to two and black tube elastic was used to fix the drums. pw = plastic wheels.

32085	**BR** B459325 brown - *53-58*	8	12
4645	as above but plastic wheels - *59-64*	12	15
32087	**BR** B459325 brown + maroon furniture container - *56-58*	10	15
4647	as above but plastic wheels - *59-64*	15	20
32088	**BR** B459325 brown + white Insul-meat container - *56-58*	10	15
4648	as above but plastic wheels - *59-64*	15	20
4649	**BR** B459325 brown + tractor load, plastic wheels - *59-64*	40	55

Cable drum wagon [W12]

32086	**BR** M486 grey + **'Liverpool Cables'** wood drums - *53-59*	10	15
4646	as above but plastic wheels - *59-62*	12	18
4646	**BR** M486 grey, **'Aluminium Wire & Cable'** plastic drums + wheels - *61-64*	30	40
4646	as above but wood drums with silver advert - *61*	200	300

W13. BR Double Bolster Wagon (1956)

pw = plastic wheels.

32052	**BR** B920022 grey - *56-58*	10	15
32052	as above but plastic wheels - *59*	10	15
4615	**BR** B920022 grey + timber pw - *59-64*	15	20

W14. D2 BR 16T Mineral Wagon (1953)

32056	**BR** B54884 grey - *53-58*	10	15
32056	as above, markings at wrong end - *53*	25	30
32056	wagon number and weights panel reversed on one side (error) - *53?*	25	30
4654	Rail Cleaning Wagon * black - *64*	350	600

* Beware of forgeries

W15. D1 BR Bogie Well Wagon (1955)

32053	**BR** B901006 grey diamond bogies - *55-58*	10	15
32053	as above but plate bogies - *58*	15	20
4605	as above but plastic wheels - *59-64*	10	20

W16. D1 LMS Bogie Bolster Wagon (1953)

Early models had the stanchions 3mm longer than standard. While the shortening undoubtedly saved metal, it was probably done to stop them poking out of their boxes, with a card insert to keep them tight fitting.

32051	**BR** M720550 grey diamond bogies - *53-58*	10	15
32051	as above but plate bogies - *58-59*	20	25
4610	as above but plastic wheels - *59-64*	15	20

W17. Breakdown Crane (1959)

4620	**BR** No.133 + DE961665 matt red - *59-61*	40	50
4620	as above but gloss red, red box - *61-?*	70	120

4620	as above but yellow box top * - *?-64*	70	180

* This should contain a gloss red crane with delrin couplings, all diecast hook and plastic grips on the metal handles. Not all gloss cranes had plastic grips or delrin couplings.

SD6 Plastic Wagons

W18. BR 'Lowmac' Machine Wagon (1961)

4652	**BR** B904631 gloss brown ballast weights beneath - *61-64*	10	15
4652	as above but matt brown ballast weights - *61-64*	10	15

W19. BR 5-plank Open Wagon (1958)

SD6 sand wagons [W19]

4660	**'The United Glass Bottle Manufacturers'** 82 yellow (also 32069) - *58-61*	8	12
4660	as above but open brake-gear - *61-62*	15	20
4660	**'United Glass'** 82 yellow - *62-64*	35	45
-	yellow, plastic chassis ex sets - *63-64*	10	NA
4670	**BR** B477015 grey (also 32074) - *58-62*	8	12
4670	as above but open brake-gear - *62-64*	10	16
4635	**BR** B477015 grey + coal - *58-62*	10	18
4635	as above but open brake-gear - *62-64*	10	20

W20. BR Steel Open Wagon (1953)

4640	**BR** B486865 brown (also 32071) - *58-62*	10	15
4640	as above but open brake-gear - *62-65*	12	16
-	buff, plastic chassis ex sets - *63-64*	8	NA

W21. BR 16T Mineral Wagon (1953)

4655	**BR** B54884 grey (also 32057) - *58-62*	10	12
4655*	as above but open brake-gear - *62-64*	25	35
4656	**BR** B550200 brown open brake gear - *62-64*	30	45

* Watch out for chassis swapping. The body should be riveted to the chassis.

W22. BR 21T Hopper Wagon (1963)

4644	**BR** B414029 grey - *63-64*	60	100
4644	as above, reversed transfers - *?*	100	125
4644	with nicks in end support rib - *?*	70	110

W23. BR Grain Wagon (1958)

Make sure that the small lugs at the base of the grain container are not missing.

4625	**BR** B885040 grey Grain (also 32067) - *58-64*	15	25

W24. 'Presflo' Wagon (1961)

SD6 'Presflos' [W24]

4626	**BR** brown 'Presflo' - *61-64*	10	18
4627	**'ICI'** blue green Bulk Salt - *61-64*	10	18

W25. BR 'Prestwin' Silo Wagon (1962)

4658	**BR** B873000 brown 'Prestwin' - *62-64*	12	18

W26. Chlorine Tank Wagon (1960)

Care must be taken when cleaning this model as the paint easily comes off!

4675	**'ICI'** 124 white end supports - *60-64*	10	18
4675	as above but cream supports - *60-64*	10	18

W27. 6-wheel Tank Wagon (1962)

4657	**'UD'** off-white high supports - *62-63*	28	50
4657	**'UD'** off-white high and low supports - *63-64*	22	40
4657	**'UD'** off-white low supports - *64*	60	80

W28. Ferry Tank Wagon (1960)

Check that the top piping is not missing.

4679	**'Traffic Services Ltd'** 500836 silver - *60-64*	15	25

W29. Salt Wagon (1958)

4665	**'Saxa Salt'** 248 yellow (also 32068) - *58-62*	10	15
4665	as above but open brake-gear - *62-64*	15	25

W30. BR Cattle Wagon (1958)

4630	**BR** B893344 brown (also 32021) - *58-64*	12	15

W31. BR Standard Horse Box (1960)

This model is often missing the horse or has door lugs broken off.

4316	**BR** S96412 green + horse - *60-64*	60	85
4315	**BR** E96435 maroon + horse - *60-64*	60	80

W32. BR Gunpowder Van (1962)

4313	**BR** B887002 brown open brake gear - *62-64*	15	18

W33. BR Banana Van (1962)

4301	**BR** B881967 brown open brake-gear - *62-64*	20	25

W34. GWR Passenger Fruit Van (1960)

4305	**BR** W2910 maroon - *60-64*	20	30

W35. BR Ventilated Van (and Packing Van) (1958)

4325	**BR** B757051 brown white roof (also 32041) - *58-62*	10	14
4325	as above but open brake gear - *62-65*	10	14
4318	**BR** DE545523 red grey roof * - *62-64*	20	30

* packing van for breakdown crane.

W36. SR Utility Van (1961)

This model had a plastic chassis. The under-van brake gear etc. was fragile on this model and easily broken. Also watch out for broken buffers (imperfect mouldings).

SD6 SR CCT utility van [W36]

4323	**BR** S2380S green CCT - *61-64*	35	50

W37. GWR 6T 'Mica B' Refrigerator Van (1958)

4320	**BR** W59850 white/cream 9also 32062) - *58-62*	10	16
4320	as above but open brake gear - *62-65*	10	16

W38. LNER 'Blue Spot' Fish Van (1961)

This model had a plastic chassis. The under-van brake gear etc. was fragile on this model and easily broken. Also watch out for broken buffers (imperfect mouldings).

4300	**BR** E87231 white or cream Insul-fish - *61-64*	25	35

W39. GWR Goods Brake Van (1958)

4312	**BR** W56421 grey Southall RU (also 32048) - *58-64*	10	14
4312	**BR** W35247 brown - *not made*	NA	NA

W40. LMS Goods Brake Van (1958)

4310	**BR** M730012 grey (also 32044) - *58-61*	10	14
4310	**BR** M730012 brown - *62-64*	35	50
4310	**BR** M730973 brown - *62-64*	35	50

W41. BR Standard Goods Brake Van (1959)

4311	**BR** B950350 brown - *59-64*	10	15
-	red, short plastic chassis ex starter sets - *63-64*	10	NA

W42.	**Caustic Liquor Bogie Tank Wagon** (1962)		
4685	**'ICI'** 5710 blue-green diamond bogies - *62*	200	350
4685	as above but plate bogies - *62-64*	60	95

SD6 ICI bogie tank wagon [W42]

ACCESSORIES

Pre-war wooden station buildings, which were made with either a red or green roof, are the most sought-after lineside accessories. They include: the main station building, the arched roof, island platform (green roof), engine shed and goods depot (£200-£250), red roof island platform and the through station (£150-£175), platforms from the central station (£20-£40), sets of boxed staff or passengers figures (£75-£100), wooden signal cabin (£50-£75), tunnels (340-£50), buffer-stops (£15-£20) and signals (£7-£12).

After the war the buildings were made of cast aluminium. These included the through station (£50-£70), island platform (£30-£40), straight platform extensions for either (£35-£45), footbridge or red roof signal cabin (£20-£30), green roof signal cabin (£120 -£150), metal girder bridge (£40-£50), 6 station staff or 6 passengers (£25-£30) and level crossing (£10-£15). Also from this period is the turntable (£35-£40).

Plastic kits for stations and lineside buildings came in 1959 replacing the aluminium ones. Most expensive are the large terminus station (£150-£300), station extension canopy in red and yellow box (£400-£500), the same in a white box (£180-£250), plastic girder bridge (£400-£500) and set of 12 railway staff (£50-£60). Other items from this period to look for include: 2-road engine shed (£60-£70), engine shed extension kit (£30-£50), suburban station kit (£30-£40), plastic tunnel (£50-£100), double track tunnel (£100-£140), island platform kit (£30-£40), goods depot kit (£30-£50), buff coloured water crane (£35-£45), buffers with electric lights on them (£8-£12), 12 plastic passengers and goods (£30-£40), lighting kit (£10-£15), set of 12 gradient and mile posts (£40-£50), set of 6 lineside notices (£25-£35) and box of 12 telegraph poles (£50-£75).

Signals sell for between £7 and £18 while lever switches are £4-£5 or, in the case of green coloured ones, £5-£6.

The most expensive item of track is the clockwork track point at £15-£20 each. Pre-war 3-rail points, in contrast, are £6-£12 and other pieces of track usually sell at between £1 and £2 each. Of post-war track, the most demanded are 3-rail straights (£1-£2), hand points (£5-£10) and electric points (£10-£15). There is little demand for 2-rail plastic sleeper track.

NEVERWAZZAS

These are models that were not made by Meccano Ltd but have been produced by enthusiasts in the style of Hornby Dublo or as miniaturisation of Hornby 0 gauge wagons. While some are one-offs, others are produced in limited runs for sale to other enthusiasts. Some are merely repaints, while others have structural alteration. A number of interesting ones are those based on models that Meccano Ltd. planned to produce but, in the end, did not. These include two locomotives - a V2 and a GWR 0-6-2 tank. There are also a double level crossing and a log carrier using a coach chassis. Some excellent replica boxes have been produced by Tony Cooper including boxes for some neverwazzas. Recommending values is very difficult and really outside the scope of this book, but at auction the boxed double level crossing will fetch £100-£150 while neverwazza wagons tend to be a lot cheaper at around £25 each.

Neverwazza gas tank wagon

SETS

As one might expect, pre-war train sets fetch the highest prices. Clockwork passenger DP1 sets are priced £1,000-£1,250 and DG1 clockwork goods sets sell for £300-£900; with the level of price depending on which livery is carried. Pre-war electric passenger EDP1 sets are £900-£1,250 but, again the goods sets vary: EDG7 GWR and LMS (£300-£900), EDG7 LNER and SR (£700-£900) while EDGA7 GWR sets are in the £500-£750 price range.

Amongst post-war sets, ones to look out for are the very first ones released in 1947 and 1948. They differ slightly, in various ways, from those produced after 1948 and the date on instruction leaflets will help to identify them. For these the prices are as follows: LNER passenger EDP1 (£600-£800), LMS passenger EDL7 (£300-£400), LNER goods EDL7 (£500-£900) and SR goods (£1,000-£1,500).

Other post-war pre-Nationalisation sets are priced: LNER passenger EDP1 (£150-£200), LMS passenger EDL2 (£120-£160), LMS, LNER and SR goods EDL7 sets (£300-£900), GWR goods EDL7 (£300-£500). Either of the Canadian Pacific sets sells for £650-£850.

As with the solo models, the BR liveried sets replaced the pre-Nationalisation ones in 1953 following which the range of sets grew quite fast. The following are some of the sets worth looking for: EDP15 with matt locomotive finish (£150-£200), G19 (£350-£450), P15 or P20 (£350-£450), P22 (£250-£350), 2015, 2020, 2021, 2022, 2025, 2033, 2034, 2035, 2049 or 2050 (£200-£300) and 2035 (£1,000-£1,250). Other sets are mostly priced £100-£125 for good boxed examples. Others that have turned up at auction mint boxed are 2023 (£140) and 2030 (£120).

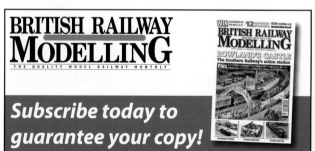

Ixion

HISTORY

Ixion Model Railways Ltd is an Anglo-Australian company registered in the United Kingdom. It was formed in September 2007 by three friends, Phil Badger, Chris Klein and Lindsay O'Reilly, with the purpose of manufacturing high quality ready-to-run UK prototype locomotives in British N scale 1:148.

Dapol Model Railways Ltd was appointed as the sole retailer of Ixion's products in the UK, Europe and North America. All sales elsewhere are handled directly by Ixion via the Internet and exhibitions.

GWR 'Manor' class No.7816 Frilsham Manor [L2] (Mercig Studios)

Phil Badger is Australia's pre-eminent N scale modeller, manufacturing his own range of etched brass and polyurethane cast kits in N scale (1:160). He also produces kits by himself, and in collaboration with others, in H0, 7mm and 1/4" scales for standard and narrow gauge prototypes. He produces limited-run RTR N scale locomotives of NSW and Victorian prototypes.

Chris Klein has been a railway modeller for more than 40 years, and is best known for the more than 25 articles he has written for the Railway Modeller. He has written about his BR(WR) 4mm scale Abersoch and Boduan Junction layouts, and, more recently, his explorations into 7mm modelling, especially his essays into locomotive kit-building.

Lindsay O'Reilly describes himself as an incurable scale-gauge schizophrenic, having built models of standard and narrow gauge prototypes in N, H0, and 0 scales, and even gauge 3 (1:22.5 standard gauge). He has written for a number of Australian modelling magazines, generated the instructions for a range of NSW 7mm kits, and is well known for his layout designs and presentations on building small layouts in 7mm scale.

The models are manufactured in China.

LOCOMOTIVES

The first model produced was announced in March 2008 and was a GWR 'Manor'. The model was launched later that year but it was discovered that it was 8% out of scale. Models were recalled and after five revisions to the CAD/CAM drawings, in May 2009 work started on new tooling. It had been intended to release it 'DCC ready' but with the reduction in scale it was found that the small 'Manor' tender had insufficient room for a chip to be fitted.

After the 'Manor' and 'Mogul', an Australian Railways 'Coffee Pot' steam motor coach was made for sale in Australia.

Cat No.	Company, Number, Colour, Dates	£	£

L1. GWR 63xx Mogul Class 4-6-0 (2010)

The model will have RP25.57, darkened, spoked see-through wheels, a highly detailed loco body and 3500 gallon tender. NEM coupling pockets with alternate couplers will be fitted and spare air pipes and coupling chains provided. The model will have etched brass factory fitted nameplates and cab side number plates, backhead detail, fire irons with 2 man crew, hand lamps and front steps (for customer fitting). It will have a tender powered loco drive mechanism using a 'super creep' motor, 40:1 gear ratio for super slow running, phospor-bronze self lubricating wheel axle bearings and a positively sprung front bogie.

INX63?	? - *10*	NPG	NPG
INX63?	? - *10*	NPG	NPG
INX63?	? - *10*	NPG	NPG
INX63?	? - *10*	NPG	NPG

L2. GWR Manor Class 4-6-0 (2009)

The model has RP25.57, darkened, spoked see-through wheels and stainless steel rods. 12-wheel pick-ups and stainless steal coupling and connecting rods, a highly detailed loco body and 3500 gallon tender, NEM coupling pockets with alternate couplers, spare air pipes and coupling chains, etched brass factory fitted nameplates and cab-side number plates, backhead detail, fire irons with 2 man crew, hand lamps and front steps (for customer fitting). Tender powered, the loco drive mechanism uses a 'super creep' 5-pole skew-wound motor, 40:1 gear ratio for super slow running, phospor-bronze self lubricating wheel axle bearings and a positively sprung front bogie.

INS-7816	**7816 *Frilsham Manor*** GWR plain green - *10*	80	105
INS-7808	**7808 *Cookham Manor*** GWR (button) plain green - *10*	80	105
INS-7823	**7823 *Hook Norton Manor*** BRb plain black - *10*	80	105
INS-7800	**7800 *Torquay Manor*** BRc lined green - *10*	80	105

7816 Frilsham Manor [L2] (Mercig Studios)

Bachmann Jubilee by Robbie McGavin

Jouef 00 (British)

HISTORY

Jouef was a French company which had come into being at the end of the Second World War. They released their first tinplate train set onto the French market around 1949. Their first 6 volt electric set followed in 1950. The Jouef range remained small until around 1960 when it expanded rapidly and improved in quality.

This was the time when the company entered into an agreement with the British company, Mettoy Ltd, to supply them with an inexpensive British system which Mettoy would market under the Playcraft brand (see separate listing).

It would seem that this enlargement of their market provided the impetus for them to also expand the French H0 range and Jouef took off!

It would seem that part of the deal with Mettoy was that Jouef would handle distribution of the Corgi range of diecast cars in France.

Late Playcraft models were mainly from the Jouef Continental range, packaged in Jouef boxes specially for the British market.

Playcraft eventually died out in the early 1970s but this was not the end of the company's involvement in the British market. By 1977 they had produced a Class 40 diesel and some Mk3 coaches. These are unlike most models made for the British market by a Continental manufacturer in being to 00 scale and not H0. Although some of the Continental models were, for a while, made in BR blue livery in the mid 1970s, these were displaced when the more suitable 00 models arrived. These had been manufactured in France and the moulds were later transferred to Ireland.

Class 40 No.D285 [L2]

With the help of a grant from the Irish government, Jouef opened a factory at Shannon Airport International Trading Estate, in the Irish Republic, late in 1979. The subsidiary company was called Hobby Developments Ireland (HDI) and they assembled a variety of products which carried the letters 'HDI' and also published a catalogue. The company did not survive beyond 1981 but offered 18 different locomotive types before its demise. One interesting H0 model was the German V200 sold as a Warship Class loco in BR corporate blue as 825 *Intrepid*.

There was also what looked like a CIE black and orange C Class numbered 1306. This was in fact the body, without pantographs, of a Jouef German outline E10 electric locomotive, mounted on the French Monomoteur Bo-Bo chassis, and finished in an Irish livery. BR Mk3 coaches may also be found, rather crudely repainted in CIE livery, which would have been produced by HDI. There was also a CIE repaint of the standard SNCF Y Class 4-wheel diesel shunter.

The idea had been to not only assemble models from parts made in France, but to manufacture the parts in Ireland, right down to the packaging. It was felt that this would make the models cheaper in Ireland and Britain. Certainly Continental models have been found with 'HDI' on their bases.

The subsidiary folded in 1981 and, in the November of 1986, Hobbyphoto of Dublin were selling off the remaining stock. The tools for the British outline models were purchased from the liquidators and, by April 1987, The Southern Model Railway Company of Blessington, County Wicklow, were advertising a limited run of the Class 40 locomotive in either green or blue livery.

Thought had been given to introducing a 'Pacific' loco in the form of a Gresley A1 and A3 for 1978 but the project was abandoned. Both were to be turned out in 'strict LNER livery'.

In the 1990s, Jouef was again in financial difficulty and was taken over by Lima, who closed down the independent Jouef production base and moved the company to Italy. Lima themselves were to find themselves in difficulty a few years later and their entire group, including Jouef, was bought by Hornby and became part of Hornby International in 2004.

LOCOMOTIVES

Only one loco, the Class 40, was produced in a choice of two liveries. The green version came unfinished with a sheet of transfers which included: two BRc totems, two *Mauretania* nameplates, four D285 numbers, two *Empress of Britain* nameplates, 4 D210 numbers, one 'Empress Voyager' headboard and six white headcode discs. The buffer stocks were sprayed red.

Cat No.	Company, Number, Colour, Dates	£	£

L1. LNER Class A1/A3 2-6-4

These were planned in 1978.

?	LNER A1 - *announced but not made*	NA	NA
?	LNER A3 - *announced but not made*	NA	NA

A display of Irish made Jouef (Dave McCarthy)

L2. Class 40 1Co-Co1 Diesel (1977)

The models came with a choice of two headboards one of which was 'Irish Mail' and the other 'Empress Voyager'. The model had a 5-pole motor, working headlights and glazed windows. The model also had floating bogies for the non-driven wheels.

8913	**D210 *Empress of Britain*** green BRc - *78*	20	NA
8913	**D211 *Mauretania*** green BRc - *78*	20	NA
8912	**D285** blue BRe - *77*	15	25
8913	green + transfers - *78*	NA	30

L3. Class 42 'Warship' Diesel Hydraulic B-B (1980?)

This was a German V200 disguised as a Warship.

8921	**825 *Intrepid*** blue BR - *80?*	20	25

COACHES

Cat No.	Company, Number, Colour, Dates	£	£

C1. BR Mk3 Stock (1977)

These were based on loco hauled WCML stock.

5751	**BR** M12004 blue+ grey InterCity 1st - *77*	10	15
5752	**BR** M11017 blue+ grey InterCity 2nd - *77*	10	15
5753	**BR** blue+ grey buffet - *78*	10	15
?	**CIE** orange+black 2nd (HDI) - *82?*	15	25

ROSEBUD
Kitmaster
PLASTIC SCALE MODELS
Catalogue 1961
92220
ROSEBUD
Kitmaster
TRADE MARK
PLASTIC SCALE MODELS
46225

Kitmaster

HISTORY

Nene Plastics Ltd was founded in Raunds by T Eric Smith in 1940, immediately prior to his call-up for war service. On his return, he set about developing and launching his Rosebud Dolls range. In 1954 a new injection moulding plant was brought into operation. The following year the name of the company was changed to Rosebud Dolls Ltd. with a target of five million dolls per year.

In 1958, Rosebud Kitmaster was formed to make kits using spare capacity in the injection moulding room. The subject was chosen because kits were a growing market and at that time locomotive kits in plastic were not being done by anyone else. In the UK, the kits were available between 1959 and 1962 and were moulded in polystyrene. They were complementary to a range of railway kits made by Airfix but were much more expensive. The subjects were chosen by Dennis Franklin, who was Rosebud's Assistant Technical Manager and who took charge of the Kitmaster project. He travelled far and wide, choosing and studying the models to be made and obtaining official drawings for them.

A crucial error was an early decision to model only in a 'constant' 00 scale which meant that models of foreign locomotives would not sell abroad where H0 scale was the norm. The foreign outline models were generally of little interest to the British public and, with tools costing between £6,000 and £10,000 per model, income from sale of these kits fell a long way short of repaying the development costs.

Trix had made a similar mistake in modelling in H0 for the British market and an interesting connection with Trix Products Ltd was through the latter's chief designer, Michael Catalani. He had designed the new range of Trix plastic coaches but was not prepared to move to Birmingham when that company was moved there. Instead, he went to work for Rosebud Kitmaster for three weeks before being lured back by his previous employer. While at Rosebud he was involved with the design of the Pullman cars.

ROSEBUD
Kitmaster
PLASTIC SCALE MODELS
AUTHENTIC MODEL WITH MOVING PARTS · KIT INCLUDES PLASTIC CEMENT

Kitmaster logo

Initially, the Kitmaster kits were released at a rate of one a month but after the first year the strain of this was beginning to show. As a result of pressure put on them, a number of skilled staff left. Up until the release of the 'Beyer-Garratt' model in 1960, the pattern making was done in-house but, after that, it was subcontracted to freelance model makers. Most of these patterns were made in brass by model-maker Jack Gain.

The Kitmaster project was clearly over-ambitious and badly planned as described above. Within a short time this was creating financial strains on the company. The policy of a new model every month required large amounts of capital for new tools and Rosebud Kitmaster had been slow in getting their distribution and marketing sorted out. As a result, money was not coming into the company as fast as it was going out with the result that a crisis was looming.

The solution was to sell the Kitmaster business and the obvious buyer was Airfix Ltd. Late in 1962 the Kitmaster tools and stock were sold to that company. Some of the surplus kits were released to the public through a Shredded Wheat promotion conducted by the Hermes Supply Company; a subsidiary of Airfix Ltd.

A number of the British subjects were absorbed into the Airfix kit range and were later acquired by Palitoy and then by Dapol, who are still making them!

TT Mk1 corridor brake 2nd kit [3]

By 1964 things were looking desperate for Rosebud Dolls Ltd and in June that year the Receiver was called in. The Company remained in administrative receivership, with the doll business recovering, until July 1967 when it merged with Mattel Inc (famed for the Barbie doll), to form Rosebud Mattel Ltd. (renamed Mattel (UK) Ltd in 1971).

Further Reading

The book *Let's Stick Together* by Stephen Knight contains everything you are ever likely to want to know about the Kitmaster range and what happened to the kits in later years. This very thorough work was published in 1999 by Irwell Press (ISBN 1-871608-90-2) and is strongly recommended to anyone interested in further study.

Collectors Clubs

Enthusiasts of the Kitmaster kit range are well catered for by the Kitmaster Collectors Club which was founded in 1980. The Club publishes a magazine called *Signal* twice a year and includes in the subjects covered the railway kits by Airfix and Dapol. The Club has a website at www.kitmaster-club.org.uk and for enquiries regarding membership fax: 01787 478226.

Boxed kit of a Barreite 23 locomotive [1] (Vectis)

KITS

Dates - The dates given below are those when the kit is believed to have first been available in the shops. Remaindered stock was available in shops, often for considerable periods, after the demise of Kitmaster.

Prices - The two prices given show the range of prices one can find on unmade kits; the second column being for mint examples in their original cellophane wrapping.

Cat No.	Company, Number, Colour, Dates	£	£
1.	**00 Kits**		
Note that Continental outline models are to 4mm/1ft in this table.			
1	**L&M 0-2-2** *Rocket* yellow - *59*	15	25
2	**0-6-0DS** D3421 black - *59*	15	25
4	**'Princess Coronation' Class** 46225		

	Duchess of Gloucester black - *59*	35	50
5	**'Schools' Class** 30919 *Harrow* black - *59*	5	15
6	**ex-L&Y 0-4-0ST** 51212 black - *59*	5	12
7	**Class 6100 2-6-2T** 6167 black - *59*	5	12
8	**Italian Class 835 0-6-0T** 162 black - *59*	35	50
9	**Stirling 'Single' 4-2-2** No.1 green - *59*	35	50
10	**Prototype Diesel** *Deltic* blue - *60*	35	50
11	**'Battle of Britain' Class** 34057 *Biggin Hill* black - *60*	15	25
12	**Swiss 'Crocodile'** Series Be6/8 13305 black - *60*	25	35
13	**Mk1 Corridor Composite** M16001, M15627, M15019, M15243, W15111, W15598, W15430, E15307, E15144, E16017 maroon - *60*	10	20
13	**Mk1 Corridor Composite** S15042, S 15573, S15888, S15903, S15580, S15873 green - *60*	15	25
14	**Mk1 Corridor 2nd** M25589, M24133, M24405, M24861, W24165, W24341, W24719, E24222, E24531, E25027 maroon - *60*	10	20
14	**Mk1 Corridor 2nd** S24320, S24305, S24169, S24326, S24318, S24311 green - *60*	15	25
15	**Mk1 Corridor Brake 2nd** M35114, M34090, M34105, M34671, W34152, W34297, W34763, E34422, E34590, E35157 maroon - *60*	10	20

Lancashire & Yorkshire 0-4-0ST 'Pug' [1] (Rosebud)

15	**Mk1 Corridor Brake 2nd** S34256, S34621, S34158, S34945, S34279, S35020 green - *60*	15	25
19	**German 'Baureihe' Class 23** 23001, 23008, 23014 black - *60*	35	50
22	**Class 9F 2-10-0** 92220 *Evening Star*, 92203, 92134 black - *60*	15	25
23	**French 241P 'Mountain'** 241P.026, 241P.027, 241P.029 black - *60*	35	50
24	**GWR 'City' Class** 3440 *City of Truro* black - *60*	15	25
25	**LMS 'Beyer-Garratt' 2-6-6-2** 7971, 7987, 47994 black - *61*	70	100
26	**J94 0-6-0ST** 68022, 68028, 68051, 68076 black - *61*	15	25
28	**Mk1 Restaurant Car** M4, M5, M6, S9, W7, W8, E1, E2, E3, E10, E11 maroon - *61*	15	25
28	**Mk1 Restaurant Car** M4, M5, M6, S9, W7, W8, E1, E2, E3, E10, E11 green - *61*	25	35
30	**Class 4MT** BR Mogul 76000, 76093, 76114 black - *61*	25	35
31	**'Midland Pullman'** Power Car A F blue - *61*	35	60
32	**'Midland Pullman'** Kitchen Car B E blue - *61*	50	70
33	**'Midland Pullman'** Parlour Car C D blue - *61*	25	35
35	**USA 0-6-0T** - *not made*	NA	NA
36	**Class A3** *Flying Scotsman - not made*	NA	NA

2. H0 Kits

Note that these are genuine 3.5mm/1ft models.

3	**Early American 'General' 4-4-0** *General* black - *59*	35	50
27	**DB B4yge** coach - *61*	5	10
29	**SNCF A9 myfi/1958** coach silver - *61*	5	10
34	**New York Central 'Hudson' J3a 4-6-4** 5405 black - *61*	70	100
37	**Canadian National U-4-A** - *not made*	NA	NA

Rebuilt 'Merchant Navy', The General, L&Y 'Pug' and French 'Mountain' engine.

3. TT Kits

16	**Rebuilt 'Royal Scot'** 46100 *Royal Scot*, 46110 *Genadier Guardsman*, 46169 *The Boy Scout* black - *60*	35	50
17	**Mk1 Corridor Brake 2nd** M35114, M34090, M34105, M34671, W34152, W34297, W34763, E34422, E34590, E35157 maroon - *60*	5	10
17	**Mk1 Corridor Brake 2nd** S34256, S34621, S34158, S34945, S34279, S35020 green - *60*	5	10
18	**Mk1 Corridor Composite** M16001, M15627, M15019, M15243, W15111, W15598, W15430, E15307, E15144, E16017 maroon - *60*	5	10
18	**Mk1 Corridor Composite** S15042, S15573, S15888, S15903, S15580, S15873 green - *60*	5	10
20	**Mk1 Corridor 2nd** M25589, M24133, M24405, M24861, W24165, W24341, W24719, E24222, E24531, E25027 maroon - *60*	5	10
20	**Mk1 Corridor 2nd** S24320, S24305, S24169, S24326, S24318, S24311 green - *60*	5	10
21	**Mk1 Restaurant Car** M4, M5, M6, S9, W7, W8, E1, E2, E3, E10, E11 maroon - *60*	5	10
21	**Mk1 Restaurant Car** M4, M5, M6, S9, W7, W8, E1, E2, E3, E10, E11 green - *60*	5	10

4. Presentation Sets

P1	**100 Years of British Steam** - *Rocket*, *Duchess of Gloucester* and Stirling 'Single' - *59*	100	150
P2	**'Battle of Britain' Set** 34057 *Biggin Hill* and 3 Mk1 coaches - *60*	NPG	200
P3	**'Royal Scot' Set** (TT) Rebuilt 'Royal Scot' and 4 Mk1 coaches - *61*	NPG	300

5. Motor Kits

KM1	Motor Bogie 00 - *60*	10	15
KM2	Motor Box Van 00 - *60*	10	15
KM3	Motor Bogie TT - *not made*	NA	NA

Footnote: Airfix produced two locomotive kits of their own, not using Kitmaster tools. These were the Park Royal Railbus (R201) in green (1960) which sells for £15 in good condition and £25 when mint and the 204HP Drewry shunter (R7) in black (1961) for which you might expect to pay £7 for a good example or £10 for a mint one.

Leeds (LMC)

HISTORY

The Leeds Model Company was started by Rex Stedman, an engineer, and was founded in 1912, at Halton, near Leeds. His first products were 7mm scale diecast parts for signals, rolling stock wheels, buffers and axleguards. The models were handmade and, due to the war, tool making did not get underway properly until 1919; Stedman doing most of the design work himself. During the war Stedman worked on aircraft design and a wind-driven cine-camera for aerial photography. With the coming of peace, he moved his fledgling company to new premises at Balm Road, Hunslet, in Leeds. With the financial help of a wealthy model railway enthusiast, GP Keen, the company was incorporated in March 1920 as The Leeds Model Company Limited and Keen became its chairman.

The retail catalogue released that year was priced 6d and listed 11 establishments which stocked LMC products, all, it was claimed, made in their own works although the alloy castings were bought in.

Mansted Foundry

In the mid 1920s, after GP Keen had given up the chairmanship of the Leeds Model Company, Rex Stedman built locomotives specifically for Keen's own 0 gauge model railway which he had at home and called 'K Lines'. These unique and mainly freelance models, produced in the mid to late '20s, were supposed to come from a fictitious Mansted Foundry, the first part of the name being an anagram of 'Stedman'.

The name 'Mansted Foundry' was inscribed on the models along with the serial number. A report in the model railway press at the time indicated that some parts were supplied by Winteringhams who were part of the Bassett-Lowke group, and with whom GP Keen also had business links.

The bodies of the locomotives were brass instead of tinplate and the 20V DC mechanisms had cobalt steel magnets and 8-pole armatures.

K Lines was broken up a number of years ago, following the death of Keen, but several of the Mansted Foundry models have survived. Probably Stedman's finest work was an LNER Garrett.

A further link with Bassett-Lowke occurred in the early 1920s when LMC made two locomotive models exclusively for the Bassett-Lowke range (see main text).

In Britain, the Leeds Model Company ranked third, after Hornby and Bassett-Lowke, during the 1920s and 1930s, the emphasis being on reasonably affordable 0 gauge models rather than toy trains. The principles Stedman adopted were that his designs must provide the widest possible product range, at minimum cost, to give the customer maximum choice at the lowest possible price. To achieve this he had to produce standard models that shared parts and could look good in a range of liveries. The result was a series of freelance tank engines which were released in the early 1920s.

The 1920 catalogue illustrated the first of these - the 0 gauge 4-4-0 tank engine. The body was enamelled tinplate and much of the clockwork mechanism was in brass. The first testing model was in North Eastern Railway livery but other liveries were planned - several of these were illustrated in the 1921 catalogue. There were also pictures of some of the rolling stock they had already produced.

Next, Stedman needed to make an impact in the market to get noticed and the subject he chose was a Great Central Railway 4-4-0 'Director Class', 437 *Charles Stuart Wortley*. This, together with an LNWR Claughton, a GNR A1 and further standard tank designs, appeared in the 1922/23 catalogue. Using much of the 'Director' tooling, Stedman went on to make another Great Central locomotive - the 4-6-0 *Sir Sam Fay*.

Production went on apace with Stedman doing most of the design work himself. Besides producing their own models to sell from the start, LMC had also sold a large range of parts for customers to build their own models.

The company went on to produced a full range of rolling stock, accessories and wooden sleepered track. The rolling stock made by the company falls into three categories. The early, high quality, handmade wagons offered through their catalogues, which started before the First World War, remained available, all be it in a much restricted range, until after the Second World War. Many of these handmade models were also available in gauge 1 as well as 0 gauge.

LMC are best known for their lithographically printed, paper covered, wooden wagons and coaches which were available between 1923 and 1966 (an embossed card NE open wagon had actually been made from 1920 but was soon dropped). Kits were available up to the time the company ceased trading.

The third type of rolling stock arrived in the late '30s and had bodies moulded in bakelite with the detail added with transfers. This was the first time this material had been used for rolling stock production and the result was very pleasing. It continued as the 'True Scale' range after the war.

Clockwork LMS 2-4-0T possibly made to order (Vectis)

Their cast metal wheels are much closer to scale and have finer flanges than either Hornby or Bassett-Lowke products. Some locomotives had smoke units fitted after the Second World War, pre-empting Tri-ang by a number of years.

In 1922, an 0 gauge exhibition layout, built using LMC equipment, was exhibited at the first post-war model engineering exhibition at Wembley. It then toured the country, visiting places such as York, Leeds and Blackpool. All the locomotives were electric, as too were the signals, which had interlocking levers.

Late in 1925, The Leeds Model Company merged with the Bristol Model Co. and Stedman was reduced from Managing Director to Chief Engineer and Designer. The Bristol directors, headed by Hugh Leader, had money to invest in new designs and are largely responsible for the appearance of GWR locomotives in the range including a Churchward 4-4-0 'County' for Bassett-Lowke. This was followed by a Caledonian Railway Class 72 Pickersgill 4-4-0. While under the agreement with Bassett-Lowke, LMC could not sell these two models in their own range, they did use the tooling to produce their own GWR 'Mogul' and Pickersgill 0-6-0. Also, from 1925, an 8V DC mechanism was available alongside the clockwork one.

Within the Leeds catalogues, models were classified under a maximum of four headings. Those for locos were as follows:

A - Freelance designs.
B - Scale models of actual types.
C - Super-detailed exact scale models.
D - Exhibition or 'glass case' models.

Rolling Stock fell into three categories:

A - Scale models with lithographed sides and wooden construction.
B - Wooden construction, handmade scale models.
C - Super-detailed models

By the 1930s the term 'super-detailed' had virtually disappeared. With the introduction, in the mid '30s, of a new range of generic tank engines which were closer to scale models, the only locomotive referred to as 'freelance' was the 0-4-0ST.

Things, however, did not continue to run smoothly. Stedman had invested heavily in producing models of the pre-grouping companies, but by 1924 the public had been wanting the liveries of the Big Four. During an acute financial crisis in 1928, Rex Stedman left LMC and set up a new company called RF Stedman & Co Ltd at Jack Lane, Hunslet, Leeds. At the same time, The Leeds Model Company started cutting its prices by up to 20%. A few months later Stedman purchased the entire stock and plant as well as trade mark of LMC. He continued to manufacture under the name of RF Stedman & Co Ltd and work now went into extending and updating the range of models with the new liveries. The changes included a switch from clockwork to electric mechanisms and the dropping of the expensive to produce hand-built rolling stock.

Back in 1927, Stedman had visited the Bing factory in Nuremberg and been impressed by the new developments in die-casting with alloys. However, in 1931, he again relinquished control of the Company (this time for good) and the name reverted to Leeds Model Company or, later, just 'LMC'. George Simpson now took over as Managing Director with RS Moore as Chairman.

As a sign of their success, LMC were the victim of Japanese imitation when Stromlite marketed copies of several models in the 1930s. These included *Sir Sam Fay*, the 0-4-0ST, 'Brighton Belle' set and several of the coaches and wagons.

Bakelite had been considered for wagon production as long ago as 1925, but was not used by the LMC until the late 1930s. Trix, of course, had been using it for their track bases since the mid '30s but LMC were the first company in the UK to produce coach and wagon bodies in the material.

Meanwhile, Stedman used his cinematography skills to form a new line of business in Stedman's Cinematography Laboratory Ltd. However, with the coming of the Second World War, Stedman returned to the aircraft industry and became chief test pilot to Chrislea Aircraft Co. Ltd. In 1949 he returned to the model railway industry as a partner in S&B Productions of South Norwood. The 'S' in the name of the company stood for Stedman and the company are particularly remembered for their 00 scale signal parts.

After the Second World War, the Leeds Model Company concentrated on supplying retailers with their models instead of supplying the public direct. Model parts for scratch builders became available again, followed by the standard locomotive range. Shortage of materials and a shrinking market meant that the large scale models were no longer viable and so did not reappear. Instead, a standard 4-4-0 was designed and tooled up.

In 1953, LMC became Ellemsee Accessories, supplying a wide range of parts for 0 gauge scratch builders. Despite an initial post-war rallying of demand for 0 gauge railways, the 1950s saw the popularity of the newer 00 gauge explode into a major industry. Against this competition, those companies who were totally committed to the 0 gauge market stood little chance of success. While the Company survived until 1966 before being wound up, the product range was shrinking from the mid '50s, so that there was not much left at the end.

Electric LNER 0-6-4 possibly made to order (Vectis)

Buyers Beware! **-** Sadly the description of a model for sale today as 'possibly Leeds' is often a misnomer and should be described as 'origin unknown'! Beware! LMC models are very well constructed from tinplate and the chief fault is flaking paint due to poor cleaning and priming before they were painted. In consequence of this, professional repaints are relatively common and do not greatly affect the value of Leeds locomotives. However, original paintwork can be stabilised by a carefully applied light spray of matt or satin finish varnish.

The electric mechanisms of the earlier models had brass side frames, but in the 1930s these were replaced by diecast parts some of which, over the years, have suffered from swelling and cracking due to impurities in the alloy. This is sometimes difficult to see, however, so look carefully for distortion and cracks and, when buying, ask if the locomotive is in good working order.

Further Reading

We are unaware of a book on the Leeds Model Company but there have been several articles written about it. Two articles appeared in *Model Railway Constructor*, one in the August 1981 issue and the other in May 1984. The first was by David Peacock of the Leeds Stedman Trust and the second by David Peacock and Adrian Stedman - Rex Stedman's son. David Peacock, to whom we are indebted for much of the information provided here, has also written a series of articles called 'Leeds Lines' for the *Gauge O Guild Gazette* - the magazine of the Gauge O Guild.

Collecting Organisation

The Leeds Stedman Trust is an organisation run by David Peacock to look after the Stedman archives and to help collectors and operators of LMC models to keep them running by supplying spare parts. It is not a club, but you can be placed on a mailing list for the annual price list of parts. The email address for the Leeds Stedman Trust is dpeacock@btconnect.com

Prices - The prices quoted show the range that examples in good condition usually sell within.

Dates - It is difficult to be accurate with these, as catalogues provide only a rough guide to what was available each year and a catalogue for each year is not available. Dates quoted should therefore be taken only as a guide.

Electric Pickersgill style 0-6-0 [L17] (Vectis)

Construction Notes

Rolling Stock Bogies - Most early coaches had a fitted plywood bearing pad between the bogie and the floor of the coach but these were missing on later ones. There were at least three different types of bogies used:

1. Full white metal castings (1919-1922/3) which were fitted to hand-built stock and possibly retrofitted by owners to some early litho stock.

2. White metal dummy axleboxes and springs and a tinplate carrier (1922-35). During this long period of production, tools became worn or were replaced and this shows in the castings. The tinplate carrier also varied in height. These were fitted to all litho coaching and bogie wagon stock, except the GWR 'Siphon G' and 'Monster' bogie vans which had American style bogies made by replacing the usual axle boxes by an integral white metal equalising bar and square axle boxes.

3. Fully diecast zinc units for bakelite coaches and LMS and GWR litho stock (from 1936/7).

LMC also made both tinplate (CO18) and diecast (CO14) 6-wheel bogies and, while these were available to scratch-builders, in the factory they were fitted only to special coaches made to order. Similarly, diamond bogie frames (WO/20 and WO/22 - equalised) were also available for scratch-builders and were fitted to the top of the range bolster and high capacity bogie vans.

Cast iron wheels were available for all the bogies at an extra cost.

Rolling Stock Wheels - Dissatisfied with the coarse standards of the day, Rex Stedman launched his own range of white metal wheels in 1915. These were closer to scale and had finer flanges than either Hornby or Bassett-Lowke products. However, white metal was not a particularly suitable material and soon Stedman was experimenting with zinc alloys. This led to redesigning both coach and wagon wheels for the litho stock of the late '20s.

Wheels on wagons dating from 1928 which carry the word 'Remod' on them, and have a tyre width of 5.5 mm, were from a batch of zinc alloy wheels bought from Bing to tide the company over until their own casting plant was operational. This was working in 1929 and the rolling stock wheels being turned out had a tyre width of 5 mm. The zinc alloy wheels had finer spokes and a bronze look about them and were nearly as good as the optional cast iron wheels used on locomotive models.

In 1930, Stedman introduced a new range of locomotive zinc alloy wheels which he called 'Newalloy' and it is thought that, by 1935, LMC were using this material for a finer scale range of coach and wagon wheels with a tyre width of just 4 mm. There were three types of rolling stock wheels available: both spoked and disc wagon wheels and Mansell coach disc wheels.

As far as we know, all standard rolling stock made in the factory was fitted with non-insulated wheels (i.e. for 3-rail operation).

Metal Fatigue - LMC wheels frequently suffered from a process popularly called 'metal fatigue' caused by impurities in the alloy mix. Some 80% of wheels (even higher immediately after the last war) show signs of disintegration or loosening on the axle. As a result, many coaches and wagons around today have been re-wheeled.

Woodworm - Later LMC vehicles were made of plywood bought from Finland. It has been prone to woodworm infestation and this should be born in mind when buying these later models. For some strange reason, reported examples have often been LNER subjects but, in fact, the problem occurs on any of the plywood bodies.

GCR Robinson Class B2 City of London [L23]

Litho Sheets - Original LMC/Stedman litho coach and wagon papers are still relatively inexpensive and an interesting line to collect. These sheets have a unique patina, which is very difficult to colour photocopy, and have self-sticky backs.

Repairs and Restoration - Repairs to wooden rolling stock can be easily and sympathetically achieved. Principal problems are fatigue of the glue, warping, detached bogies, fatigued buffers and wheels and broken couplings and buffer beams. All can be rectified: re-gluing as necessary, introducing pine strips internally along the corner edges and fixing them with PVA glue and by replacing missing and broken parts. The latter may be available from the Leeds Stedman Trust (see above) or by salvaging them from scrap vehicles. Warping is difficult to rectify but not impossible. On coaches and vans it can be achieved by gluing a horizontal wooden tie-plate internally, just below the roof line, remembering to leave spaces at either end of the vehicle to give access to the inside.

LOCOMOTIVES

Locomotives were built in heavy gauge soldered tinplate and all were fitted only with Stedman's own design of clockwork motor until 1925 when their 6-8V DC mechanism was also available as an alternative. This had a laminated 3-pole motor and a permanent magnet field which was self reversing. They had an adjustable double centre rail pickup suitable for raised or level centre rails. 20V AC mechanisms, with a hand reverse switch, were supplied between 1934 and 1939. When Stedman bought back his company in 1929, he set about modernising the range and one of his decisions was to drop the clockwork mechanism. Wheels were cast iron until 1929/30 and then cast alloy ones, called Newalloy, were fitted. They were insulated from 1959 and smoke units were fitted to some locomotives from late 1949.

Repaints were often done in later years when models were restored but some repaints were done in the factory in the 1920s with the introduction of the post grouping liveries. This was a service advertised in the catalogue along with rebuilding models and repairs.

Catalogue Numbering - The 'LO' prefix was used up until 1937/8 after which 'LA' or 'LD' prefixes were used according to whether an AC or DC mechanism was fitted.

Cat No.	Company, Number, Colour, Dates	£	£

First Freelance or 'Standard' Models

As we have seen, LMC produced a series of cost saving tank locomotives which were basically freelance in design and available in a variety of liveries. The character of individual railway companies was established by the changing of chimneys, domes and other detail fittings.

Standard 0-4-0ST in LMS livery [L1] (Vectis)

L1. Standard Saddle Tank 0-4-0ST (Freelance) (1922)

One of the most distinctive of the freelance models was the 0-4-0 tank, which is easy to recognise because of its very square appearance, although it was one of the models copied by Stromlite. This was the very basic 'starter' locomotive in the range and its unusual shape was almost certainly chosen to give plenty of room for the clockwork motor. There was a choice of a clockwork or (from 1925) 12v DC electric mechanism. Between 1934 and 1939 an AC mechanism was also available. In addition to the liveries listed below, freelance liveries were also supplied to customer's requirements.

LO/150	NER green? - *22-24*	180	230
LO/151	L&NWR black - *22-24*	180	230
LO/152	MR black - *22-24*	180	230
LO/153	**5** GCR green? - *22-24*	180	230
LO/154	GNR green? - *22-24*	180	230
LO/155	GER blue? - *22-24*	180	230
LO/156	**No3, 12** CR blue - *22-24*	120	170
LO/157	**6** LB&SCR brown? - *22-24*	180	230
LO/158	**60** SE&CR green? - *22-24*	180	230
LO/159	**4** GWR green? - *22-24*	120	170
LO/160	**78, 73** LNER green - *25-40?*	120	170
LO/160	**78, 73** LNER black - *25-40?*	120	170
LO/161	**93, 99** LMS black - *25-40?*	120	170
LO/162	**1, 701** GWR green - *25-40?*	180	230
LO/163	**75** Southern green - *25-40?*	180	230
LO/163	**31117** Southern black - *25-40?*	180	230

LD/10	**68116** BR ex train sets - *c50-66*	180	230
LD/10	**68116** BR ex sets, smoke - *c50-66*	180	230
LD/10	**68113** BR ex sets shorter, outside cylinders smoke - *c50-66*	180	230
L/10	loco kit - *?*	180	230
-	**'Leeds Model Company'** green - *c50-66*	NPG	NPG

The freelance, or 'Standard' range, included several wheel combinations, the largest being 4-6-0. There were two distinct series of these. The first, starting in 1920, had high mounted boilers (to take a tall and powerful clockwork mechanism), high side tanks and squat cabs with ribbed roofs. Another feature of this series is the clearly displayed 'LMC' trade mark which was less obvious on the second series. The original plan was to top wind these locos through the cab roof (the very earliest 4-4-0Ts have a key hole covered with a ventilator plate) but the idea was dropped. Electric drive was available from 1925 and all models had standard 1½" driving wheels. It is possible that some of the pre-grouping liveries listed in the catalogue, and therefore included in our tables, were never made unless hand painted. Archive material includes NE, LNWR and GCR examples.

L2. Standard Tank 4-4-0T (Freelance) (1920)

This was Stedman's first locomotive which he started in 1919. It had clockwork or (from 1925) 6-8v electric mechanisms available. Enamelled finish.

Standard 4-4-0T in NER livery [L2] (Vectis)

LO/100	**723** North () Eastern green - *20-23?*	230	250
LO/101	**3267, 3268** L&NWR black - *20-23?*	280	300
LO/102	**2908** MR red - *20-23?*	360	380
LO/103	**276** GCR green - *21-23?*	360	440
LO/103	GNR green? - *21-23?*	360	380
LO/105	**52** GER blue? - *21-23?*	360	380
LO/106	CR blue - *21-23?*	360	380
LO/107	**910** LB&SCR brown - *21-23?*	360	380
LO/108	**695** SE&CR green? - *21-23?*	360	380
LO/109	**6412** LNER lined green - *25-32*	220	250
LO/109	**2686** LNER green - *25-32*	280	370
LO/109	**78, 6412** LNER black - *25-32*	160	250
LO/110	**3754** LMS red - *25-32*	300	330
LO/110	LMS black - *25-32*	300	330
LO/111	GWR green - *25-32*	350	380
LO/112	**2664** Southern green? - *25-32*	280	250
?	**2686** green - *25-32*	300	370

L3. Standard Tank 0-4-4T (Freelance) (1922)

Clockwork or (from 1925) 6-8v electric mechanisms available.

LO/170	**314** L&SWR green? *-22-23?*	360	380
LO/171	MR red *-22-23?*	360	380
LO/172	SE&CR green? *-22-23?*	360	380
LO/173	**23, 185, E453, E508** SR lined green * - *26-32*	360	380
LO/173	**E508** Southern black * - *26-32*	360	380
LO/174	LMS red - *25-32*	360	380
LO/17?	**9067** LNER green - *25-32*	360	380

The Urie style dome and chimney die castings were available for this model from 1926 and were based on those of a Class 736.

L4. Standard Tank 4-4-2T (Freelance) (1922)

This was said to look like an L&NWR Precurser tank or one of the LB&SCR tanks used on express duties. Clockwork or (from 1925) 6-8v electric mechanisms available. Enamelled finish.

LO/120	**3495** L&NWR black c/w - *22-23?*	330	360
LO/121	LB&SCR brown c/w *-22-23?*	360	380

Standard 4-4-2T in GCR livery [L4] (Brooks)

LO/122	**276** Great()Central green c/w *-22-23?*	190	380
LO/123	**3754** LMS lined red - *25-32*	360	380
LO/124	Southern green - *25-32*	360	380
LO/125	**6412** LNER green - *25-32*	360	380
LO/125	**9064** LNER black - *25-32*	360	380
LO/125	**56** LNER - *25-32*	360	380
LO/126	GWR green - *25-32*	360	380

L5. Standard Tank 0-6-2T (Freelance) (1922)

Clockwork or (from 1925) 6-8v electric mechanisms available.

LO/180	**510** LB&SCR brown *-22-23?*	360	380
LO/181	GNR green? *-22-23?*	360	380
LO/182	GER blue? *-22-23?*	360	380
LO/183	**E148** Southern green - *25-32*	360	380
LO/184	**5756, 5769** LNER green - *25-32*	360	380

L6. Standard Tank 4-6-0T (Freelance) (1922)

Clockwork or (from 1925) 6-8v electric mechanisms available.

Standard 4-6-0T in NER livery [L6] (Vectis)

LO/130	**690** North () Eastern green *-22-23?*	330	360
LO/131	**2673** L&NWR black *-22-23?*	360	380
LO/132	**271** GCR green *-22-23?*	360	380
LO/133	**386, 396** LNER lined green - *25-32*	330	360
LO/134	LMS red - *25-32*	330	360
LO/134	LMS black - *25-32*	330	360

Second Series of Tank Engines

Production of the first series standard tanks ended in 1932 and the second series was delayed until 1935, because of a disastrous factory fire at the Jack Lane Works on 29th June 1932. This second range, in tables 7-13 below, was nearer to scale in appearance and wheel arrangements, and locomotive numbering related to prototype examples. Company character, however, was still achieved by the changing of detail fittings, but a particular characteristic of this series that separates it from the last is the tall dome fitted to each model. They are the products by which LMC is best remembered but, ironically, although designed by Stedman, they were not produced until after he had left the Company. A reduced selection of these tank engines was continued in the late 1940s until the closure of LMC, although towards the end only kits were available.

After 1949 it is likely that the interchangability of parts increased as castings became used up. In later years lining was simplified or left off altogether. AC and DC versions available. Bodies only were also available.

L7. GCR Class G5 0-4-4T (1935)

LD/10	**8120** LNER black, red lining - *35-39*	230	280

Other numbers were applied.

L8. LSWR Adams Class T1 0-4-4T (1935)

LD/22	**126** SR black, yellow lining - *35-39*	280	620
LD/22	**126** SR green, yellow lining - *50-60*	280	620

Other numbers were applied.

L9. L&YR 2-4-2T (1935)

L&Y 2-4-2T [L9] (Vectis)

LD/21	**6720, 6723, 10763** LMS black, red lining - *35-60*	160	280
LD/21/S	**6720, 6723, 10763** LMS black + smoke - *52-?*	160	280
L/21	kit - *35-60?*	NPG	NPG

Other numbers were applied. The body only was sold as L/21/B.

L10. GER Class F4 2-4-2T (1935)

LD/11	**7102, 7105** LNER black, red lining - *35-39*	230	280

Other numbers were applied.

L11. Standard Tank 0-6-0T (Freelance) (1948)

This model was close to a 'Jinty' in appearance but also very like a Furness Railway shunter. It could be bought with or without a smoke unit. Those with, had an 'S' suffix to the catalogue number. The model had a 12V DC mechanism and bodies only were also available. * Bodies only carried the catalogue number with a 'B' suffix.

LD/15*	**8410, 8415, 8417, 8418, 8419** LMS black, posing as a 'Jinty' - *48-60*	120	170
LD/16*	**8305, 8302** LNER green, posing as a J72, black and white lining - *48-60*	120	170
LD/17*	**126, 259, 260, 261, 269, 75** SR green, lining - *48-60*	180	230
LD/18	BRb black - *c50-60*	120	170
LD/18	**67627,** BRb black ex-kit - *c50-60*	120	170
L/15	LMS black kit - *c50-60*	NPG	NPG

Other numbers were applied. A GWR version is known to exist but this was not catalogued.

L12. L&YR 0-6-2T (1935)

L&Y 0-6-2T in LMS livery, electric [L12] (Vectis)

LD/20	**6530** LMS red, black lining - *?*	280	330
LD/20	**6550** LMS red, yellow lining - *?*	280	330
LD/20	**6530** LMS black, red lining - *35-60*	170	330
LD/20/S	**6530** LMS black + smoke - *52-?*	170	330
LD/20	BRb black, red lining - *52-?*	170	330

Other numbers were applied. The body only was sold as L/20/B.

L13. GCR Class N5 0-6-2T (1935)

-	**524** GCR black, red lining - *?*	300	330
LD/12	**5773** LNER black, red lining - *35-60*	300	330
LD/12	**5773, 9348, 9354, 9356** LNER green, black and white lining - *52-54?*	300	330
L/12	kit - *50-?*	NPG	NPG

Other numbers were applied. The body only was sold as L/12/B.

Freelance Tender Loco

After the Second World War, the Leeds Model Company introduced a basic inside cylinder 4-4-0 tender locomotive with an affinity to their pre-war 'Director' Class model, however, there was no provision for GWR fans! In fact, the 1948 catalogue carried an apology to these people and a promise to provide some GWR locomotives as well as describing present productions as a 'stop gap' measure. The shape of the model was obviously wrong for the GWR. Within a short time the model was being offered with outside cylinders as an alternative and the model was also available in BR livery. Other names and numbers were available on these late products.

L14. 4-4-0 Tender Loco (Freelance) (1947)

This post-war standard locomotive model was based roughly on the pre-war Director Class but was also thought to have a close resemblance to an LMS 2P and a Southern L1. From late 1949 the model was offered with a smoke unit fitted although the 1952 catalogue shows that only the models with outside cylinders were so fitted. The LMS, LNER, SR and tender bodies were also available on their own. The model had a 12V DC mechanism. oc = outside cylinders.

Standard 4-4-0 in LMS livery, electric [L14] (Vectis)

LD/50	**570, 621** LMS lined black - *47-54*	120	170
?	**564, 673, 624** LMS black 12vDC - *?*	250	NPG
LD/50/S	**570, 582** LMS lined black, oc + smoke - *52-54?*	120	170
-	**570** LMS red - *50-60*	120	170
LD/51	**2683, 2685** LNER green, lined black+white - *47-60*	120	170
LD/51/S	**2683, 2685, 2686, 2689, 2608** LNER green, lined black+white, oc + smoke - *52-54?*	120	170
LD/52	**1756** SR green, lined yellow + black - *47-60*	170	220
LD/52/S	**1756, 1783, 1754** Southern green, lined yellow, oc + smoke - *52-54?*	170	220
LD/53	GWR green - *52-54?*	170	220
LD/53/S	GWR green, oc + smoke - *53-54?*	170	220
LD/53	**30875, 60734** BRb black - *52-54?*	120	170
LD/53/S	**60734** BR black, oc + smoke - *52-54?*	120	170
L/50	LMS loco kit - *52-54?*	NPG	NPG
L/51	LNER loco kit - *52-54?*	NPG	NPG
L/52	SR loco kit - *52-54?*	NPG	NPG
L/49	tender kit - *52-54?*	NPG	NPG

Scale Models

The development of the 'Director' and *Sir Sam Fay* classes has already been described above, and these were certainly the mainstay of the Scale range, but several other scale model locomotives were made by the Leeds Model Company during the years from 1920 to 1939. Some of them were generally available while others were only made to order.

After the war only a few prototypical locomotives were introduced. Most examples were reasonably detailed and could be further enhanced if required. Special models were manufactured to order and you got what you paid for. These included, in 1952, a nice 4-6-0 'County' Class and enthusiasts of the LMS were also tempted by the introduction of a 'special order' 4-6-0 'Jubilee' Class.

L15a. GCR Class D10 'Director' 4-4-0 (1922)

The D10 was the original 'Director' Class developed by Robinson on the Great Central Railway in 1913. In 1920 it was modified to form the 'Improved Director' Class which was also modelled by LMC. From 1930, alloy wheels were fitted and, from 1935, diecast frames replaced brass ones. While mass production of the model ceased in 1939, it was available by a special order from the mid 1950s and there was a choice of clockwork or electric mechanism.

	Great () Central Green D10		
LO/200	**429 *Sir Douglas Haig*** - *22-24*	500	600
LO/200	**436 *Sir Berkeley Sheffield*** - *22-29*	500	600
LO/200	**437 *Charles Stuart Wortley*** - *22-26*	500	600
	LNER Green D10		
LO/201	**5436 *Sir Berkeley Sheffield*** - *25-29*	500	600
LO/201	**5437 *Charles Stuart Wortley*** - *25-37*	500	600

Ex-GCR Director Class Prince George [L15a]

LO/201	**5437** on cab ***Prince George*** - *28-31*	500	600
LO/201	as above but no. on tender - *31-39*	500	600

Other names and numbers could be had at an extra cost of 1/6. One named *John Arnott* was presented to the Lord Mayor of Leeds in 1925.

L15b. GCR Class D11 'Improved Director' 4-4-0 (1929)

The D11 cab versions (with 2 windows each side) had Ross pop safety valves replacing the larger GCR twin lever units. From 1930 alloy wheels were fitted and from 1935, diecast frames replaced brass ones. While mass production of the model ceased in 1939, it was available by a special order from the mid 1950s. Choice of clockwork or electric mechanism.

	LNER Green D11		
LO/202	**5501 *Mons*** - *29-39-?*	550	750
LO/202	**5503 *Somme*** - *29-39-?*	550	750
LO/202	**5504 *Jutland*** - *29-39-?*	550	750
LO/202	**5505 *Ypres*** - *29-39-?*	550	750
LO/202	**5506 *Butler Henderson*** - *29-39-?*	450	550

Other names and numbers could be had at an extra cost of 1/6.

L16. GNR 'Atlantic' 4-4-2 (1925)

Made to special order only.

GNR 'Atlantic' [L16]

LO/353	**1443** * L&NER green - *25-35?*	500	600
LO/353	***St Cuthman*** LNER green c/w - *c33*	550	750
LO/353	**1421** GNR green electric - *25-?*	550	750

*Customers were offered any number.

L17. CR 'Pickersgill Goods' 0-6-0 (1927)

Based on a Caledonian Railway goods locomotive. Choice of clockwork or electric mechanism.

LO/358	**17602, 17604, 17608, 17609** * LMS black c/w - *27-39, c54-60*	380	440
LO/358	**17602, 17604, 17608, 17609** * LMS black - electric *27-39, c54-60*	380	440

*Customers were offered any number between 17560 and 17660 but those indicated above are ones seen.

L18. GWR Class 43XX 'Mogul' 2-6-0 (1926)

Clockwork or 6-8v electric mechanisms available.

GWR Mogul Class 43xx [L18]

LO/348	**4362, 4371, 6362** * Great Western green - *26-39?, c54-60*	380	440

Customers were offered any number between 6362 and 6369 but those shown are ones seen.

L19. GWR 'Star' or 'Abbey' Class 4-6-0 (1925)

Made to special order only. The customer chose the name.

LO/354	Great () Western green - *25-35?*	550	750

L20. GWR 'Castle' Class 4-6-0 (1925)

Made to special order only. The customer chose the name.

LO/355	**4078 '*Pembroke Castle*'** * Great () Western green - *25-35?*	550	750

*customer's choice

L21. GWR Hawksworth 'County' Class 4-6-0 (1952)

Fitted with smoke apparatus.

LD/54	**1024 *County of Pembroke*** * Great Western green - *52-60*	550	750
LD/54	**1010 *County of Caenarvon*** * GWR green - *52-60*	550	750

*Customers were offered any name. In GWR livery *Caenarvon* should have been spelt 'Carnarvon' as the spelling was not changed to the former until November 1951.

L22. LNWR 'Claughton' Class 4-6-0 (1922)

	L&NWR Black		
LO/350	**2222 Sir *Gilbert Claughton*** - *22-24*	500	650
LO/350	**5931 *Captain Fryatt*** - *22-24*	550	750
LO/350	**5919 *Lord Kitchener*** - *22-24*	550	750
LO/350	**1019** - *22-24*	550	750
LO/350	**2431** - *22-24*	550	750
LO/350	**162** - *22-24*	550	750
	LMS Maroon		
LO/351	**5900 *Sir Gilbert Claughton*** - *25-35*	500	650
LO/351	**5931 *Captain Fryatt*** - *25-35*	550	750
LO/351	**5919 *Lord Kitchener*** - *25-35*	550	750
LO/351	un-named - *25-35*	550	750

L23. GCR Robinson Class B2 (B19) 4-6-0 (1924)

Clockwork or 6-8v electric mechanisms available.

	Great () Central Green + Maroon		
LO/352	**423 *Sir Sam Fay*** - *24?-28*	NPG	NPG
LO/352	**427 *City of London*** - *24?-28*	NPG	NPG

GCR Robinson Class B2 4-6-0 Sir Sam Fay [L23] (SAS)

	LNER green		
LO/352	**5423 *Sir Sam Fay*** - *26-39, c54-60*	450	550
LO/352	**5427 *City of London*** - *29-39*	550	750
LO/352	**5423 *City of Lincoln*** * - *29-39*	550	750
LO/352	**5426 *City of Chester*** * - *29-39*	550	750
LO/352	**5425 *City of Manchester*** * - *29-39*	550	750
LO/352	**5428 *City of Liverpool*** * - *29-39*	550	750

* Initially these were an optional extra for which there was a charge of 1/6.

L24. GCR Robinson Class B3 4-6-0 (1926)

Standard Leeds 8-pole 8V motor and engraved brass nameplates.

	LNER Green		
LO/356	**6169 *Lord Faringdon*** - *26-35?*	550	750
LO/356	**6164 *Earl Beatty*** - *26-35?*	550	750
LO/356	**6166 *Earl Haig*** - *26-35?*	550	750
LO/356	**6168 *Lord Stuart of Wortey*** - *26-35?*	550	750
LO/357	**6165 *Valour*** * - *26-35?*	550	750

* Brass nameplates engraved 'In memory of G.C.R. employees, 1914-1918'.

L25. SR 'Schools' 4-4-0

-	? SR green - *?*	500	650

L26. GWR Class 57XX Pannier Tank 0-6-0PT (1959)

-	**GWR green** - *59-60*	**140**	**200**

L27. GWR Class 51XX 'Prairie' Tank 2-6-2T (1959)

-	GWR green - *59-60*	140	200

Super Detailed Models

These were models constructed by a special department at the works and handled individually. These were specially high class models, beautifully finished. Each was as complete as possible in every detail. The Walschaerts valve gear was complete, the radius rod traversing the links automatically as the loco was reversed.

They were usually made to order only and each was built to its own specification. There was also usually an option to have further detail added at extra cost. They were available with either clockwork or electric drive. Initially, some were offered in two standards of finish, the cheaper one having simpler lining, valve gear and fittings.

L28. GWR Class 3150 'Prairie' Tank 2-6-2T (1953)

GWR 2-6-2T Class 51xx [L28] (Brooks)

-	**3169** GWR (button) green - *53-60*	280	400

L29. L&SWR Urie 4-6-2T (1922)

Made to special order only.

LO/550	**516** LSWR green - *22-29*	550	750
LO/551	**516** LSWR green simpler lining, valve gear and fittings - *22-24?*	500	700
LO/550	**E516** Southern green - *26-29*	550	750

L30. CR McIntosh 140 'Dunalastair IV' 4-4-0

-	**140** CR blue - *?*	650	800

L31. LMS 'Jubilee' Class 4-6-0 (1952)

Made to special order only.

	LMS Maroon		
-	**5553 *Canada*** - *52-60*	550	750
-	**5581 *Bihar and Orissa*** - *52-60*	550	750

Customers were offered other names.

L32. LMS 'Princess Royal' Class 4-6-2 (1959)

-	**The *Princess Royal*** - *59-60*	NPG	NPG

L33. GNR/LNER A1 4-6-2 (1922)

High quality enamel finish, lined by hand. Made to special order only. Customers were offered any name/number and those given here are known to exist.

LO/300	**1470 *Great Northern*** GNR green - *22-28*	650	950
LO/301	**1470 *Great Northern*** GNR green simpler lining, valve gear and fittings - *22-24*	600	850
LO/?	**1471 *Sir Fredrick Banbury*** - *24-27*	850	1300
LO/300	**4472 *Flying Scotsman*** LNER green - *29-39*	650	850

L34. NER Raven A2 'Pacific' 4-6-2 (1924)

Made to special order only.

Ex-GCR Raven Class A2 4-6-2 City of York [L34]

	LNER Green		
LO/?	**2402 *City of York*** - *24-27*	850	1300

Customers were offered any number.

L35. LNER Sentinel-Cammell Rail Car (1935)

Wooden body covered with lithographed paper providing detail. Black roof.

SC/1	**233 *Nettle*** LNER green+cream - *35-60*	120	170

L36. Pullman 'Brighton Belle' EMU (1935)

Wooden body covered with lithographed paper providing detail.

	Pullman Brown & Cream		
CD/154	**Car No.89** drive car - *35-50*	90	130
CD/155	**Car No.88** drive car - *35-50*	90	130
CD/156	***Hazel*** 1st class car - *35-50*	50	70
CD/157	***Doris*** 1st class car - *35-50*	50	70
CD/158	**Car No.86** 3rd class - *35-50*	50	70
CD/159	above 5-car train - *35-50*	400	550
CD/153	**Cars Nos. 88 + 89** 2 - *35-50*	170	260

COACHES

The very first Leeds coaches were made of wood and painted. They were built to order to a very high standard. The 1920 catalogue illustrated and described a 12-wheel GNR dining saloon with an interior detailed in 'after-dinner style'. The tables were littered with books, papers, bottles, packs of cards and soda siphons. The coach could even be lit from an accumulator in the guards van. The first were being offered in MR livery.

By 1922, these painted coaches were added to by the new range of cheap off-the-shelf coaches made with lithograph paper prints pasted onto boxwood sides and, later, a thinner plywood. The first to arrive were in MR livery and these were followed by NER and LNWR designs and later by those of the Big Four which took precedence. In 1922 the new coaches cost 10/6 (£0.52) compared with around £8 for the super detailed models. A set of Pullman cars based on the 'Brighton Belle' were introduced in 1935. From 1929, both suburban and corridor coaches had been made and LNER lithographed articulated sets had been introduced in 1925. Other articulated coach sets were made by cutting and splicing the lithographs of full length coaches.

LNER railcar Nettle [L35] (Vectis)

In the late 1930s, as we have seen, Leeds scored another first by using bakelite instead of wood for their coaches.

Roof Ventilators - Two types were used: torpedo and shell. Up until 1928, all coaches either had torpedo vents or none at all. From 1928, all GWR coaches had shell vents and these were fitted to LMS bakelite coaches when they were introduced. Full brakes had 8 ventilators and pre-grouping coaches had 12. They were arranged down the centre line on LMS open stock and offset on GWR, SR and LNER coaches with side corridors. Over the years roofs have become turned round and swapped over and care should be taken to ensure that you have the right roof for the coach.

Buffers - The 1st series standard coaches (table C1 below) had pre-grouping thin buffers which, when bought separately, had the catalogue number CO/10. Those in tables 2, 3 and 4 had non-locking buffers which had the catalogue number WO/11.

Trusses - The under-floor trusses on the 1st Series Standard coaches, whether solebar type or individual, had facsimiles of the tension bar boss protruding downwards. All later trusses, with the exception of those for True-Scale coaches did not have these protrusions.

Corridor Connections - These, introduced in 1930, were standard only on bakelite coaches. They were not as good as others on the market and comprised steel end plates joined by single cloth bellows, with No.4 screw holes in the plate which adjoined the coach end door and 0.25" diameter clearance holes in the other end for screwdriver access. Their part number was CO/30. Over the years those of other makes, including the better looking Exley type, have been used and so it is worth checking whether yours are genuine LMC.

Cat No.	Company, Number, Colour, Dates	£	£

C1. Early Super-Detailed Exact Scale Coaches

There is no record of all the variety of caches made by LMC. After the introduction of standard coaches in 1921, LMC maintained a special department where super-detailed coaches and brake vans were produced by hand. They never carried a large stock of finished models but tended to make them to order. We are told in their catalogue that the variety of these was large and covered practically every railway company of the time. The bodies and underframes were of hardwood, the windows glazed and some had curtains. Door handles were brass plated and the roofs had individually fitted torpedo vents, roof boards, lamp tops and other detail found on the prototypes. The underframes had buffing and draw gear fitted while dynamo and brake cylinders were fitted where required. The coaches, which were available in both 0 and gauge 1, were available in teak finish or enamel painted and lined.

C2. 1st Series Standard Coaches (1921)

These were 1' long bogie non-corridor coaches made of wood with litho printed paper pasted on to provide the colour and detail. The first series coaches were characterised by having their ends turned under. Early models had tinplate solebar, integral with the truss and solebar detail provided by a litho paper. Later models had wooden solebars painted black.

NER luggage van [C2]

Cat No.	Company, Number, Colour, Dates	£	£
CO/120	**LNWR** 2307 cream+brown composite - *21-28*	70	80
CO/121	**LNWR** 5410 cream+brown full brake - *21-28*	80	90
CO/136	**MR** 578 maroon composite - *21-28*	70	80
CO/136	as above overprinted **'LMS'** 578 maroon - *25-27*	80	80
CO/137	**MR** 159 maroon full brake - *21-28*	70	80
CO/137	as above overprinted **'LMS'** 159 maroon - *25-28*	80	90
CO/106	**NER** 840 maroon 1st/3rd composite - *21-28*	60	70
CO/107	**NER** 106 red full brake - *21-28*	70	80
CO/135	**LMS** 358 maroon brake 3rd - *28-30*	60	70

C3. Twin & Triple Sets (1925)

The individual coaches were 9.375" long and had short under-floor trusses as a result. They were made up into two or three coach articulated sets. A selling point at the time was that they took up less room on the track. The LMS and GWR versions were made from cutting and splicing the standard coach lithographs while those for the LNER sets were specially printed lithographs and they had white tinplate roofs. The catalogue numbers changed over the years and those shown are for 1937. The intermediate bogies were the same as the standard tinplate bogies but with the usual central 'top hat' bolster turned through 90° and soldered to each end of the bogie.

LNER teak triple articulated coach set [C3] (Leeds Stedman Trust)

Cat No.	Company, Number, Colour, Dates	£	£
CO/151	**GWR** (button) 6927+3275 brown+cream twin articulated set (brake+composite) - *31-39*	140	170
CO/153	**GWR** (button) 6927+3275+3275 brown+ cream triple articulated set (brake+composite + composite) - *31-39*	170	200
CO/148	**LMS** 15478+3395 maroon twin articulated set (brake+composite) - *34-39*	140	170
CO/149	**LMS** 15478+3395+3395 maroon triple articulated set (brake+composite+ composite) - *34-39*	170	200
CO/150*	**LNER** 6021N+6022N teak twin articulated set (brake+composite) - *25-39*	100	140
CO/152*	**LNER** 6021N+6022N+6023N teak triple articulated set (brake+composite+ composite) - *25-39*	120	170

* After WW2, these catalogue numbers were used for the sheets of litho papers, of each of these two types, to go with coach kits (SOP/2) which had to be adapted for length.

C4. 2nd Series Standard Coaches

This was the new series of coaches released in 1929. They were the same length as the first series but had straight ends and no litho papers on the solebars. Initially they had tinplate bogies but from 1938, diecast bogies were used. To economise, corridor coaches used the suburban stock litho on the compartment side and so it was necessary for the corridor and suburban coaches to have the same number.

C4a. GWR Panelled Coaches (1929)

These had a panelled effect and the 1912 GWR gartered coat-of-arms. They were replaced by standard coaches with the button logo in 1934.

Cat No.	Company, Number, Colour, Dates	£	£
CO/138	**GWR** 3275 brown+cream corridor 1st/3rd composite - *29-33*	70	80

GWR panelled coach of 1929 [C4a]

Cat No.	Company, Number, Colour, Dates	£	£
CO/139	**GWR** 6927 brown+cream corridor brake 3rd - *29-33*	70	80
CO/140	**GWR** 3275 brown+cream suburban coach - *29-33*	70	80
CO/141	**GWR** 6927 brown+cream suburban brake - *29-33*	70	80

C4b. Standard Coaches (1934)

These were made of wood with litho printed paper stuck to the sides and a tinplate roof. The maroon models are often faded or discoloured to brown with age.

Cat No.	Company, Number, Colour, Dates	£	£
CO/138*	**GWR** (button) 3275 brown+cream corridor 1st/3rd composite - *34-39*	35	45
CO/139*	**GWR** (button) 6927 brown+cream corridor brake 3rd - *34-39*	35	45
CO/140*	**GWR** (button) 3275 brown+cream suburban 1st/3rd composite - *34-39*	35	45
CO/141*	**GWR** (button) 6927 brown+cream suburban brake 3rd - *34-39*	35	45
CO/134	**LMS** 18572 maroon corridor 3rd - *31-39*	35	45
CO/135*	**LMS** 18503 maroon corridor brake 1st - *31-39*	35	45
CO/136*	**LMS** 3395 maroon suburban composite - *31-39*	35	45

LMS suburban brake 3rd [C4b]

Cat No.	Company, Number, Colour, Dates	£	£
CO/137	**LMS** 358 maroon suburban brake 3rd - *31-39*	35	45
CO/106	**LNER** 2253 teak corridor 1st/3rd coach - *31-39*	35	45
CO/107	**LNER** 3627 teak corridor 1st/3rd brake - *31-39*	35	45
CO/108	**LNER** 38295 teak suburban 1st/3rd - *31-39*	25	35
CO/109	**LNER** 38364 teak sub. 1st/3rd brake - *31-39*	25	35
CO/142	**SR** 4526 green corridor coach - *27-35*	60	70
CO/143	**SR** 2127 green corridor brake - *27-35*	60	70
CO/144	**SR** 4526 green suburban coach - *27-35*	60	70
CO/145	**SR** 2127 green suburban brake - *27-35*	60	70

* After WW2, these catalogue numbers (with an 'L' suffix) were used only for the sheets of litho papers, of these designs, to go with a coach kit (SOP/2). Other litho sheets were:
CO/126/L LNER corridor coach
CO/127/L LNER corridor composite
CO/128/L LNER suburban coach
CO/129/L LNER suburban brake composite

C5. Pullman Cars (1935)

These were 14" long and among the most detailed and attractive models in the LMC range. The five listed below make up the 'Brighton Belle' set. Litho papers, besides being available separately for these five, were also sold without names or numbers for those who wanted to choose their own.

Pullman car Hazel [C5]

CD/154	**Pullman** 89 brown+cream driver ** - *35-39*	90	140
CD/155	**Pullman** 88 brown+cream driver ** - *35-39*	90	140
CO/156*	**Pullman** *Hazel* brown+cream 1st - *35-39*	45	70
CO/157*	**Pullman** *Doris* brown+cream 1st - *35-39*	45	70
CO/158*	**Pullman** 86 brown+cream 3rd - *35-39*	45	70

* After WW2, these catalogue numbers (with an 'L' suffix) were used only for the sheets of litho papers, of these designs. ** these are also featured as a pair in Part 1 of the catalogue under the catalogue number CD/153 while the complete five car train was catalogued as CD/159.

C6. True Scale Coaches (1937)

These had moulded bakelite bodies and glazed windows. They were under scale length and examples may be found that have been lengthened by cutting a section out of another coach and adding it in. These were initially available between 1937 and 1940. They were self coloured bakelite and the black parts (or cream also in the case of GWR) were over-painted as appropriate. After the war all coach bodies were made black and the livery colour(s) painted on, so the LNER was dropped. BR (blood and custard) was introduced after 1949 or so. SR coaches never had window frets, all the others did, but some later GWR sets had the frets painted on the window glass. Lining, numbers, company insignia were all hand applied transfers. In the case of numbers, a large range was available as transfers. scp = self coloured bakelite for coach sides, other colours painted on. bp = black bakelite, liveries painted on.

CM/54	**GWR** brown+cream saloon, scp - *37-40*	45	60
CM/54	**GWR** brown+cream saloon, bp - *46-66*	45	60

True scale bakelite LMS coach [C6] (SAS)

CM/55	**GWR** brown+cream saloon brake, scp - *37-40*	45	60
CM/55	**GWR** 5065? brown+cream saloon brake, bp - *46-66*	45	60
CM/50	**LMS** maroon vestibule 3rd, scp - *37-40*	45	60
CM/50	**LMS** maroon vestibule 3rd, bp - *46-66*	45	60
CM/51	**LMS** maroon vestibule 3rd brake, scp - *37-40*	45	60
CM/51	**LMS** maroon vestibule 3rd brake, bp - *46-66*	45	60
CM/52	**LNER** teak saloon, scp - *39-40*	90	120
CM/53	**LNER** teak saloon brake, scp - *39-40*	90	120
CM/56	**SR** green 3rd saloon, scp - *37-40*	60	80
CM/56	**SR** green 3rd saloon, bp - *46-66*	60	80
CM/57	**SR** green 3rd brake, scp - *37-40*	60	80
CM/57	**SR** green 3rd brake, bp - *46-66*	60	80
CM/52	**BR** red+cream saloon, bp - *50-66*	45	70
CM/53	**BR** red+cream saloon brake, bp - *50-66*	45	70

C7. Rigid Litho Coach (1948)

These were made up from a single litho printed card, folded to form the sides and roof, and held in place by diecast ends and a timber floor. The litho was to the existing 1931 design (see table C3 above). Window apertures were cut out and glazed and it had the 1935 bogies, non-locking buffers, roof vents and 3-link couplings. It was also available as a kit without bogies.

?	**LMS** 3395 maroon suburban - *48-50*	NPG	NPG

WAGONS

The methods of manufacture of wagons were the same as those used for coaches.

Buffers **-** All wagons had non-locking buffers.

Cat No.	Company, Number, Colour, Dates	£	£

Litho Wagons (Type A)

Wagons made after the First World War were initially embossed paper on pine, but by 1923 wagons covered with litho printed paper, spayed with matt varnish, were produced and the variety of these grew over the years. The wooden wagon bodies had lock jointed corners and sides grooved to locate the floor. Non-lock buffers and three link couplings were fitted.

Wagons are marked on their solebars with 'LMC' or 'Leeds Model Co. Ltd.' or 'RF Stedman & Co. Ltd.' This reflects the change of name in 1928. Some designs may be found in more than one version, showing that the litho papers were reprinted from time to time.

W1. Embossed Open Wagon (1920)

-	**NE** M132 grey - *20-21*	30	35

W2a. Open Wagon - 1st Series (1923)

These had 4.62" long bodies, a wheelbase of 2.62" and the interiors were painted to match the colour of the litho paper. These pre-grouping wagons had the litho paper butting up to the corner. All had standard buffers and single link couplings fitted. These carry 'LMC' plates on the solebars.

GNR 4-plank wagon [W2a]

WO/51	**LNWR** 8004 grey 4-plank - *23-32*	20	25
WO/52	**MR** 12709 light grey 5-plank - *23-32*	20	25
WO/54	**GN** 33225 brown 4-plank - *23-32*	20	25
WO/50	**NE** V363 light grey 6-plank - *23-32*	20	25
WO/53	**GC** 8124 grey 5-plank - *23-32*	25	28
WO/55	**GW** 12509 grey 5-plank - *23-32*	25	28

W2b. Open Wagon - 2nd Series (1928)

GWR 5-plank wagon [W2b]

These had 4.62" long bodies, a wheelbase of 2.62" and the interior was painted black (except the LMS ones which were painted pale grey to match the litho paper). These post-grouping wagons had the paper wrapped round the corner to simulate a stanchion. Non-lock buffers and three link couplings fitted. These carry 'R.F.Stedman & Co. Ltd' plates on the solebars.

WO/57*	**GW** 109458 black 5-plank - *28-66*	20	20
WO/59*	**LMS** 304719 grey 5-plank - *28-66*	20	25
WO/58*	**NE** 36503 black 6-plank - *28-66*	15	20
WO/56	**SR** 12340 dark brown 8-plank wagon - *28-35*	25	25

*These catalogue numbers (with an 'L' suffix) were used for the sheets of litho papers, of these designs, to go with a wagon kit (SOP/4).

W3. Private Owner Open Wagon (1927)

These were said to be to Railway Clearing House (RCH) design. These usually carry 'Leeds Model Co. Ltd' plates on the solebars but some have 'RF Stedman & Co. Ltd' plates.

WO/62	**'Brentnall & Cleland'** 684 black Stedman plates - *29-34*	30	35
WO/62	**'Brentnall & Cleland'** 684 black LMC plates - *34-66*	30	35
WO/66*	**'Cawoods'** 1499 black - *36-66*	20	25
WO/64*	**'Coote & Warren'** 2176 brown - *34-39*	30	35

Private owner coal wagon Manchester Collieries [W3]

-	**'Hargreaves Coal'** 2340 black Sp Edn ** - *27*	30	40
-	**'Hargreaves Coal'** 2342 blue Sp Edn ** - *27*	60	75
WO/65*	**'Manchester Collieries'** 12001 maroon - *35-58*	25	30
WO/67*	**'Michael Whitaker Ltd'** 100 maroon - *36-66*	20	25
WO/60	**'RF Stedman & Co. Ltd'** 36 green - *29-36*	35	40
WO/63*	**'Warrens'** 1603 brown - *34-39*	30	35
WO/61	'JR **Wood & Co. Ltd'** 300 orange Stedman plates - *29-34*	30	35
WO/61	'JR **Wood & Co. Ltd'** 300 orange LMC plates - *34-38*	30	35

* These catalogue numbers (with an 'L' suffix) were used for the sheets of litho papers, of these designs, to go with a wagon kit (SOP/3). ** Ordered specially by a Leeds based coal exporting company associated with the Whiting family. It had Stedman plates, white lettering and planking lines and the end papers were identical to those of the 'Cawoods' wagon (although wagons with SR end papers have also been found). The blue version of the wagon has been found in Australia!

W4. Cattle Wagon (1929)

These had 5.31" long wooden bodies with litho papers, a 3" wheelbase and had white roofs. These carry 'R F Stedman & Co. Ltd' plates on the solebars.

GWR cattle truck [W4]

WO/176	**GW** 106324 very dark grey - *29-39*	20	25
WO/177	**LMS** 107877 light grey - *29-39*	20	25
WO/174	**NE** 150882 brown - *29-39*	20	25
WO/175	**SR** 764 very dark brown - *29-39*	20	25

W5. Pre-Grouping GWR Box Van (1923)

The body of this van was 4.62" long. This carries 'LMC' plates on the solebars.

WO/170	**GWR** 1408 mid-grey double axleguards - *23-28*	25	30

W6. Box Van (1929)

These vans had bodies 4 81" long, a 2.75" wheelbase, although these dimensions have been known to vary slightly. The roof was white. These carry 'R F Stedman & Co. Ltd' plates on the solebars.

WO/171	**GW** 114294 dark brown double doors, double vent 12T - *29-39*	20	25
WO/170	**LMS** 260723 light grey sliding door - *29-39*	25	30
WO/172	**NE** 140092 black single doors 12T - *29-39*	20	25
WO/173	**SR** 44556 dark brown triple door, single vent 10T - *29-39*	20	25

W7. Brake Vans (1923)

These were individual designs to suit each company and all had white roofs. Litho papers for the NER and GWR brake vans were still available in the late 1950s.

LNER brake van [W7]

WO/201	**LNWR** 382 grey, 1 verandah - *23-31*	30	35
WO/202	**MR** M946 light grey, 1 verandah + 1 open platform - *23-31*	30	35
WO/200	**NE**(R) 71911 maroon, 2 verandahs Newport - *23-30*	30	35
WO/201	**GW** 17954 very dark grey Toad Cardiff - *31-39*	25	30
WO/200	**LMS** 917 light grey no platforms - *31-39*	30	35
WO/202	**NE** 71911 brown as NER brake van - *31-39*	20	25
WO/203	**SR** 55975 very dark brown 2 verandahs + platforms - *31-39*	25	35

W8. Bogie Open Wagon (Gondola) (1929)

These carry 'R.F.Stedman & Co. Ltd' plates on the solebars.

WO/253	**LMS** 13768 grey 30T steel high capacity 'gondola' - *29-36*	45	60
WO/254	**NE** 51001 brown 50T brick wagon - *29-36*	60	70

W9. LNER 25T High Capacity Box Van (1931)

This carries 'R.F.Stedman & Co. Ltd' plates on the solebars.

WO/252	**NE** 102497 very dark grey spoked wheels - *31-39*	40	45

W10. GWR 14T 'Siphon G' (1930)

This carries 'R.F.Stedman & Co. Ltd' plates on the solebars.

WO/250	**GW** 1270 dark brown American bogies spoked wheels - *30-39*	45	60

W11. GWR 10T 'Monster' (1930)

This carries 'R.F.Stedman & Co. Ltd' plates on the solebars.

WO/251	**GW** 591 dark brown American bogies spoked wheels - *30-39*	45	60

GWR 'Monster' bogie van [W11]

Handmade Wagons (Type B)

For those who wanted top quality models LMC made them by hand, initially entirely of wood, but later using as near as possible the materials used for the real wagon - or so they claimed. The following is a list of handmade wagons, made from 1922. Most of them were also available in gauge 1 until 1928 and these would have had 'W1' prefixes to their catalogue numbers.

Some of these wagons date from 1918 and possibly some from as early as 1912, but records of production in the early days of the company are unavailable and so we have been conservative with the dates quoted. By the 1930s, high quality wagons were still made to order but there was no list of types available in the catalogue. By now they were referred to as 'Super Detail' wagons and catalogues carried a photograph of a GWR drop-door 7-plank wagon numbered 63051 as an illustration of the quality that could be achieved in the 'Super Detail Goods Vehicle Department'. They offered to produce a wagon within two weeks of an order being placed. The lengths quoted below are taken over the buffers. TCS = to customers specification.

W12. LBSC Single Bolster Timber Wagon (1922)

These came as a coupled pair of four-wheel wagons each with a single swinging bolster on a special rubbing plate. Together they were 10" long and were complete with chains and hooks to fix the load. They were fitted with scale couplings and buffers, metal axle guards and wheels on steel axles.

WO/545	**LBSC** - *22-28*	35	40
	other liveries	35	40

W13. MR Stores Drop-side Wagon (1922)

This was a 10.5" long 4-wheel flat wagon based on a MR design. It was fitted with scale couplings, buffers, anti-friction axle guards and wheels on steel axles.

WO/550	**MR** - *22-28*	25	30
WO/550	**LMS** - *26-28*	25	30
	other liveries	25	30

W14. GWR Shunter's Truck (1925)

This was 4.62" long and the tool box has a hinged lid and was fitted with cast iron wheels.

WO/590	**GW** 708 Swindon - *25-28*	30	35

W15. LNER 'Tube' Wagon (1926)

This was 6.62" long. They were fitted with scale couplings, non-locking buffers, and spoked cast iron wheels.

WO/551	**LNER** 756363? brown - *26-28*	30	35

W16. Open Wagon (1922)

5.5" long, these 5-plank wagons were described as also being available in 4-plank or 3-plank forms at extra cost. They were painted and lettered as standard but for a higher price they could be fitted with working brakes and cast iron wheels.

WO/500	**L&WNR** - *22-28*	25	30
WO/500	**NER** - *22-28*	25	30
WO/500	**MR** - *22-28*	25	30
WO/500	**GNR** - *22-28*	25	30
WO/500	**GCR** - *22-28*	25	30
WO/500	**GWR** - *22-28*	25	30
WO/500	? TCS - *22-28*	25	30

W17. Ballast Wagon (1925)

6.5" long, the 4-wheel 6-plank Engineer's wagon, with imitation bottom doors. It was fitted with cast iron wheels.

WO/580	**GW** - *25-28*	30	35
WO/580	**LMS** - *25-28*	30	35
WO/580	**NE** 63567 grey - *25-28*	30	35
WO/580	**SR** - *25-28*	30	35
WO/580	TCS	30	35

Standard oil wagon 'BP Motor Spirit' [W18] (Vectis)

W18. Standard Oil Wagon (1922)

6" long, the 4-wheel tank wagon, with a large manhole cap, came with braces and tie-wires. It was fitted with scale couplings, buffers, anti-friction axle guards and wheels on steel axles.

WO/570	**'BP Motor Spirit'** 1098 buff (transfers) - *26-33*	170	180
WO/570	**'Royal Daylight'** black (hand painted) - *22-28*	170	180

W19. Standard Rectangular Tar Tank Wagon (1922)

Fitted with tie-bars, braces and a manhole, the wagon was 5" long. It was fitted with scale couplings and buffers, metal axle guards and wheels on steel axles.

WO/575	Tar Wagon 50261 - *22-28*	40	45

W20. Standard Cattle Wagon (1922)

This 5.5" van was constructed with open board sides. It was fitted with scale couplings, buffers, axle guards and wheels on steel axles.

WO/565	**L&NWR** - *22-28*	30	35
WO/565	**MR** - *22-28*	30	35
WO/565	**GNR** - *22-28*	30	35
WO/565	**NER** - *22-28*	30	35
WO/565	**GCR** - *22-28*	30	35
WO/565	**SE&CR** - *22-28*	30	35
WO/565	**GWR** - *26-28*	30	35
WO/565	**LMS** - *26-28*	30	35
WO/565	**LNER** - *26-28*	30	35
WO/565	**SR** - *26-28*	30	35
WO/565	TCS	30	35

W21a. LNER Horse Box (1925)

This wagon was fitted with cast iron wheels.

WO/585	**LNER** 368 - *25-28*	40	45

W21b. GWR Horse Box (1926)

This wagon was 6.37" long and fitted with scale couplings and non-locking buffers. It had glazed windows and correct GWR pattern ventilators. It had cast iron disc wheels and carriage axle guards.

WO/586	**GWR** brown - *26-28*	40	45

W22. 10T Box Wagon (1922)

5.5" long, these wood planked vans were fitted with scale couplings and buffers, anti-friction axle guards and wheels on steel axles. Painted and lettered.

WO/510	**L&NWR** - *22-28*	25	30
WO/510	**MR** - *22-28*	25	30
WO/510	**GNR** - *22-28*	25	30
WO/510	**NER** - *22-28*	25	30
WO/510	**GCR** - *22-28*	25	30
WO/510	**SECR** - *22*	25	30
WO/510	**GWR** - *22-28*	25	30
WO/510	**GWR** - *26-28*	25	30
WO/510	**LMS** - *22-28*	25	30
WO/510	**LNER** - *26-28*	25	30
WO/510	**SR** 5738 - *26-28*	25	30
WO/510	? TCS - *26-28*	25	30

W23. LNER 12T Box Wagon (1926)

This wagon was described as being to 'correct scale' with 'magnificent' detail. It had cast iron wheels.

WO/511	**LNER** - *26-28*	40	45

W24. 4-wheel Mineral Brake Vans (1922)

5.5" long and with four wheels, these were fitted with handrails, chimney, footboards, scale couplings and buffers, anti-friction axle guards and wheels on steel axles. Painted and lettered.

WO/520	**LNWR** 10T - *22-28*	30	35
WO/520	**MR** 10T - *22-28*	30	35
WO/520	**GNR** 10T - *22-28*	30	35
WO/520	**NER** 10T - *22-28*	30	35
WO/523	**GWR** 12T - *26-28*	30	35
WO/519	**LMS** (MR type) 10T - *26-28*	30	35
WO/520	**LNER** (GN type) 10T - *26-28*	30	35
WO/524	**SR** (LSWR type) 20T - *26-28*	30	35

W25. 6-wheel Mineral Brake Vans (1922)

6.25" long and with six wheels, these were fitted with handrails, chimney, footboards, scale couplings and buffers, anti-friction axle guards and wheels on steel axles. Painted and lettered.

WO/521	**LNWR** 20T- *22-28*	30	35
WO/521	**MR** 20T - *22-28*	30	35
WO/521	**GNR** 20T - *22-28*	30	35
WO/521	**LMS** (LNWR type) 20T - *26-28*	30	35
WO/522	**LNER** (GNR type) 20T - *26-28*	30	35

W26. 30T Bogie Timber Truck (1922)

This was a bogie bolster wagon, of MR design, built in metal except for the bolsters which were wood. They were fitted with ring plates for securing the load. Slightly under scale, the wagon measures 11" long and was mounted on equalised diamond bogies. It was fitted with scale couplings and buffers.

WO/555	**MR** - *22-28*	40	45
WO/555	**LMS** - *26-28*	40	45

W27. High Capacity Bogie Wagon (1922)

This was a bogie steel type open wagon, 11" long, but shorter than scale, these were fitted with scale couplings and buffers, and painted and lettered. Fitted with cast iron wheels.

WO/540	**MR** - *22-28*	35	40
WO/540	**GNR** - *22-28*	35	40
WO/540	**NER** - *22-28*	35	40
WO/540	**LMS** - *26-28*	35	40

W28. NER 25T High Capacity Box Van (1922)

This was a bogie closed van. It was fitted with tie-bars, scale couplings and buffers. It was fitted with diamond bogie frames. Fitted with cast iron wheels.

WO/560	**NER** - *22-28*	45	50
WO/560	**LNER** - *26-28*	45	50

W29a. GWR 'Siphon G' (1926)

This was a bogie van 14.75" long and fitted with flexible corridor connectors. It had tie-bars, gas cylinders, non-locking buffers and scale couplings. It had equalising bogies and cast iron disc wheels.

WO/562	**GWR** dark brown - *26-28*	45	50

W29b. GWR 'Siphon H' (1926)

This was a bogie van 14.75" long and fitted with flexible corridor connectors. It had tie-bars, gas cylinders, non-locking buffers and scale couplings. It had equalising bogies and cast iron disc wheels.

WO/563	**GWR** dark brown - *26-28*	45	50

Super Detailed Wagons *(Type C)*

These were first referred to in the 1922/23 catalogue and were a cut-above the handmade wagons in being closer to scale and with more detail. LMC claimed that the range available was large but it seems likely that there was no set list but rather an undertaking to build whatever the customer wanted. Three examples quoted in the catalogue are listed below.

W30. NER Agriculture Implement Wagon (1922)

This was a short flat wagon, with upward curved platform ends, and made of brass and sheet steel.

WO/545	**NER** 6391 brown - *22-?*	50	70

W31. 12T Sheet Rail Wagon (1922)

This was a 5-plank wagon fitted with brake pipes and a dummy vacuum cylinder as well as working hand-brakes. Metal corner plates, crown plates and strapping had raised bolt heads. They had 8-spoke wheels mounted on steel axles and anti-friction axle guards.

WO/545	**GWR** 451 grey - *22-?*	50	70

W32. WD 'Parrot' Bogie Wagon (1922)

This was a flat wagon as used by the War Department in the transportation of tanks at the time and during the First World War. Detail includes ring-plates, rivet heads and two screw-jacks at each end. The model was made of metal with a wood planked floor.

WO/545	**WD** - *22-?*	40	60

'True Scale' Wagons *(Type D)*

There were two mouldings, an open wagon and a box van. Before the war, self coloured bakelite was used which had detail, such as running numbers and broad diagonal stripes to show drop ends, applied as transfers. Post war open wagons had a thin white line painted on the diagonal strapping at the drop end (the end with a door) and the livery colour range was painted onto black bakelite. They had non-locking buffers and 3-link couplings.

The bodies could also be bought separately, ready printed, to fit to your own chassis or to make up into larger wagons by joining bodies together. After the war, catalogues showed examples of bogie stock made in this way.

W33. 'True Scale' Standard 7-plank 12T Open Wagon (1937)

A range of running numbers was available on a sheet of transfers. scp = self coloured bakelite with other detail painted on. Finished bodies were also available on their own - with the same catalogue number but with a 'B' suffix. An LNER red-brown body on its own was catalogued as WM/2/RO. bp = black bakelite with liveries painted on.

WM/3	**GW** 245157 dark grey scp - *37-40*	15	20
WM/3	**GW** 271025 * dark grey scp - *37-40*	15	20
WM/3	**GW** dark grey bp - *46-66*	15	20
WM/1	**LMS** 51432, 604707 * red-brown scp - *37-40*	15	20
WM/1	**LMS** red-brown bp - *46-66*	15	20
WM/2	**NE** 588263 * dark grey scp - *37-40*	15	20
WM/5	**NE** red-brown fitted with brake pipes scp - *37-40*	25	30
WM/2	**NE** 563562 dark grey bp - *46-66*	15	20
WM/5	**NE** red-brown fitted with brake pipes bp - *46-66*	20	25
WM/4	**SR** dark brown scp - *37-40*	15	20
WM/4	**SR** dark brown bp - *46-66*	15	20

* example of number seen.

W34. 'True Scale' Standard 12T Goods Van (1937)

The moulding on the vans showed vertical planking, dummy sliding doors with moulded rollers, slide bar, stops and T end stanchion. A range of running numbers was available on a sheet of transfers. Finished bodies were also available on their own - with the same catalogue number but with a 'B' suffix. An LNER red-brown body on its own was catalogued as WM/11/RO. scp = self coloured bakelite with other colours painted on. bp = black bakelite, liveries painted on.

True Scale bakelite LNER van [W34]

WM/14	**GW** 203002 dark grey goods van scp - *37-40*	15	20
WM/14	**GW** dark grey goods van bp - *46-66*	15	20
WM/8	**LMS** 190875* bauxite goods van scp - *37-40*	15	20
WM/9	**LMS** bauxite goods van brake pipes ventilators scp - *37-55*	20	25
WM/10	**LMS** maroon 6T fish van brake pipes scp - *37-40*	25	30
WM/8	**LMS** bauxite goods van bp - *46-66*	15	20
WM/10	**LMS** maroon 6T fish van brake pipes bp - *46-66*	25	30
WM/11	**NE** 588263 dark grey goods van scp - *37-40*	15	20
WM/12	**NE** red oxide goods van brake pipes scp - *37-40*	20	25
WM/13	**NE** red oxide fruit van brake pipes ventilators scp - *37-55*	20	25
WM/11	**NE** dark grey goods van bp - *46-66*	15	20

WM/12	**NE** red oxide goods van brake pipes bp - *46-66*	20	25
WM/15	**SR** brown goods van scp - *37-40*	20	25
WM/15	**SR** brown goods van bp - *46-66*	20	25

* example of number seen.

W35. 'True Scale' Handmade Goods Brake Vans (c1937)

Brake vans to go with the bakelite range were handmade in the factory - before the war in wood and after the war in tinplate. Pre-war, there were three types offered - LMS in bauxite, LNER in red oxide and SR in brown. Only the LMS van was offered after the war (those for the other three companies were to have followed but did not arrive). Initially, the post-war brake van had the long wheelbase (7.5" overall) but, from about 1950, a shorter version (6" overall), was produced to accompany the boxed goods train sets. A choice of numbers was available on sheets of transfers.

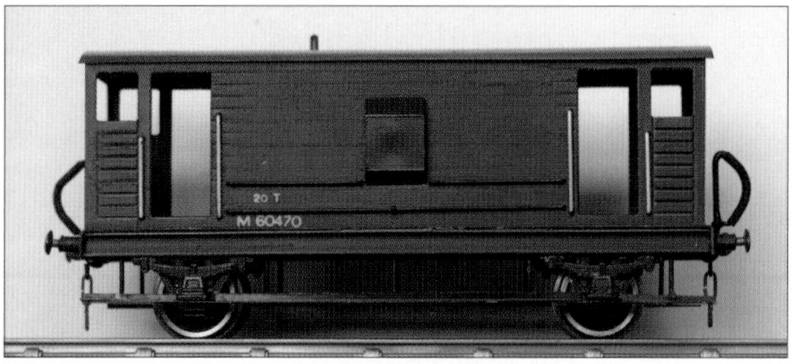

Post-war brake van [W35]

WF/50	**LMS** brown 20T express brake - *c37-40*	45	60
WF/50	**LMS** brown 20T express brake 6" - *c50-66*	45	60
WF/50	**LMS** brown 20T express brake 7.5" - *c46-66*	45	60
WF/51	**NE** brown 20T express brake - *c37-40*	60	70
WF/52	**SR** brown 25T goods brake - *c37-40*	60	70
?	**BR** M60470 dark brown 20T LMS type goods brake 6" - *c50-66*	35	45

ACCESSORIES

A full range of brass/steel, wooden sleepered, track was made. The electric type had the centre third rail raised 3mm above the running rails. Wooden stations, goods depots, signal boxes, huts, tunnel mouths and signals provided the enthusiast with a complete railway system.

Hornby Rebuilt Royal Scot from computer artwork by Robbie McGavin

Lima N (British)
Wrenn Micromodels

HISTORY
The name Lima comes from the initials of Lavarazione Italia Metalli ed Affini (Italian Production of Metalwork, etc.). The company was founded in 1949 to produce toy cars, boats etc. and trains were not made until 1958. This was the HO range. Lima commenced production of an Italian range of 1:160 N gauge in 1966. From the start it was a 12v 2-rail system and was available in the UK.

Lines Bros., the makers of Tri-ang Hornby, did not actually want to make N gauge, but they did wish to keep their finger on the pulse. As early as the Summer of 1964 Lines had been approached by Stan Perrin of Lone Star to ask if they would take the Treble-O-Lectric system off their hands.

Class 4MT 2-6-4T GWR [L3] (Lima)

Perrin thought that Rovex would be able to make his trains cheaper than he could but the men at Rovex did not agree. The offer came at the time they were realising that their own TT system was not going to be profitable and a time when they were considering how they could merge the Tri-ang and Hornby-Dublo systems. On 14th August 1964 the offer was diplomatically turned down.

In 1967, however, Lines did a deal with Lima under which Lima N gauge would be sold through the Rovex subsidiary, G & R Wrenn Ltd and, in exchange, Lima would be allowed to make Tri-ang Big-Big trains under licence.

The Lima agreement was different from the Lone Star proposal. From the start it was clear that the trains were to be made by Lima and just marketed as Micromodels under the name of G & R Wrenn Ltd. A good range of track, locomotives and rolling stock would be available by June 1967, together with two boxed sets which would include British outline models. The first of the British locomotives was to be the AL1 type Bo-Bo 3001.

Rumours about Tri-ang Hornby entering the N gauge field had been rife for sometime when the 1967 Toy Fair opened and the first models were seen. A full page advertisement for the 'new' system was to be found in July model railway magazines but all the models illustrated with drawings were of Continental outline. A fully illustrated coloured brochure and a price list were also available.

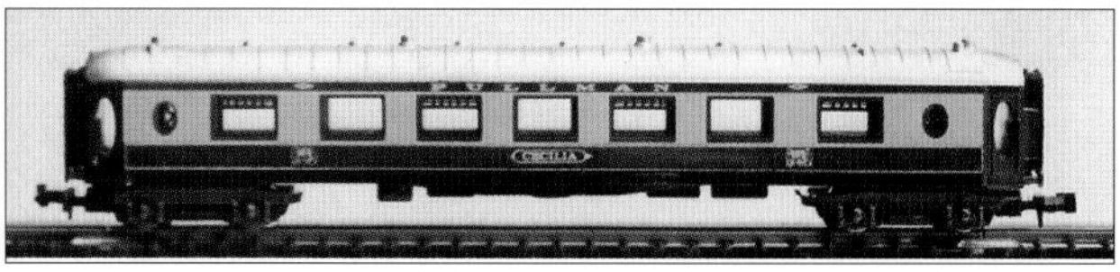

Pullman car Cecilia [C1] (Lima)

The following month a magazine advert included photographs of the first three wagons to be included in the British range. These were a mineral wagon, a brake van and a BP tank wagon. The first two were clearly models of British prototypes, the standard BR brake van having been adopted for the model. The tank wagon was clearly an existing Continental model produced in a familiar livery.

By November the promised two sets were offered for the Christmas trade. Set No1 had the E3001 and 2 coaches and set No2 had the same loco but with four wagons. At the same time the loco was available as a solo purchase.

It was not until the Summer of 1968 that we heard any more about new British outline models and then it was the availability of the two coaches in maroon livery and a buffet car in both maroon and blue/grey. Then, in November, the Wrenn full page advertisement showed the British and Swedish 2-6-4 tanks, a parlour car Wagon Lits and one of the BR Mk1 coaches in blue and grey livery.

Rovex continued to sit on the fence with regard to N gauge and Graham Farish saw an opportunity and took it to become Britain's leading developer of the system. Wrenn's association with Lima continued for a while after the collapse of Lines Bros. and the cutting loose of G&R Wrenn as an independent company.

Rovex, under new management, reviewed its N gauge policy but were still unconvinced that there was a good market for it. However, when Trix closed down their operations in Britain and were looking for a British company to import their British Minitrix range from Germany, Rovex seemed the obvious choice and thus Hornby Minitrix appeared in the shops.

Wrenn withdrew from the Lima agreement in 1977 and Eisenmann & Co. Ltd became the British importers of Lima N gauge. From 1983 Richard Kohnstam Ltd took it over but production of the British range ceased two years later as it could not compete with Graham Farish and Hornby Minitrix. Around 1991 a new attempt at launching a British range under the Lima MiniTrains label came to nothing.

GWR horse box [W16]

Packaging
Although sold under the Wrenn Micromodels name, the models carried the name 'LIMA' on their undersides and the grey and yellow packaging was inscribed "Made in Italy by Lima for G+R Wrenn Limited, Basildon, Essex, England."

The sets, locos and rolling stock came in window boxes but other models had simple end flap boxes. All had the catalogue number and contents roughly printed onto a white panel on the box ends.

In the early 1970s, the livery of the packaging changed to dark blue and orange and all reference to Lima was dropped. Around this time, the locomotives and rolling stock were sold in clear plastic boxes which had proved popular on the Continent for smaller scale models.Other changes in packaging style followed.

Dates - The dates quoted below are years when we believe the models were initially released.

Catalogue Numbers - Items were given new catalogue numbers in 1978 and three digit prefixes were added. These prefixes have not been included here.

LOCOMOTIVES
The small size of locomotive prototypes in Britain meant that it was difficult to fit the existing motor inside models of them. The result was British locomotives which had an 'over fed' look to them.

Cat No.	Company, Number, Colour, Dates	£	£
L1.	**GWR Class 94XX Pannier Tank 0-6-0PT**		
240	**9400** GWR green - *not made*	NA	NA
241	**9420** BR black - *not made*	NA	NA
L2.	**LNER Class J50 Tank 0-6-0T**		
254	**8920** LNER green - *not made*	NA	NA
255	**68920** BRb black - *not made*	NA	NA
L3.	**BR Class 4MT Tank 2-6-4T** (1968)		

This was a badly proportioned model due to it having to accommodate a motor which was too large.

Cat No.	Company, Number, Colour, Dates	£	£
228	**8230** GWR green - *68*	25	40
252/227	**80033** BR black - *77*	25	40
251	**S1** Swedish - *68*	NPG	NPG
253	**383** Pennsylvania - *70*	NPG	NPG
257	**Ci.66** DB black - *not made*	NA	NA
L4.	**LMS Class 4F 0-6-0** (1975)		
258	**4547** LMS black - *75*	20	30
259	**11683** LMS red - *not made*	NA	NA
259	**4683** LMS red - *75*	18	30
260	**1905** black (Australian) - *83*	NPG	NPG
?	? black CIE - *?*	NPG	NPG
L5.	**GWR 'King' Class 4-6-0**		

BR Express blue King Charles II [L5] (Lima)

Cat No.	Company, Number, Colour, Dates	£	£
256	**6000 *King George V*** GWR green - *not made*	NA	NA
256	**6009 *King Charles II*** BRb green - *not made*	NA	NA
257	**6009 *King Charles II*** BRb blue - *not made*	NA	NA
257	**? *King* ?** Caledonian blue - *not made*	NA	NA
L6.	**Diesel Shunter 0-4-0** (1973)		

Based on a German design.

Cat No.	Company, Number, Colour, Dates	£	£
210	**D2785** BRc green - *73*	15	20
211	**D2790** BRe blue - *73*	15	20
L7.	**Centre Cab Diesel Bo-Bo** (1973)		

Based on a German design but looking similar to a 'Clayton' Class 17.

Cat No.	Company, Number, Colour, Dates	£	£
212	**D8900** BRc green - *73*	30	40
213	**D8915** BRe blue - *73*	30	40
L8.	**Class 31 Diesel A1A-A1A** (1970?)		

BR Class 31 diesel [L8]

Cat No.	Company, Number, Colour, Dates	£	£
214	**D5509** BRc green - *73?*	35	50
209	**D5518** BRe blue - *70?*	35	50
209	**D5572** BRe blue - *not made*	NA	NA
245L	**31004** BRe blue - *not made*	NA	NA
245	**31246** BReLL blue - *83?*	40	60
244L	**31275** BR Railfreight Coal - *not made*	NA	NA
242L	**31402** BRe blue - *not made*	NA	NA
240L	**31423** BR Mainline - *not made*	NA	NA
241L	**31541** BR 'Dutch' grey+yellow - *not made*	NA	NA
243L	**31970** BR Research - *not made*	NA	NA
218	**2158** RENFE green+yellow - *76*	NPG	NPG
?	? CIE deep yellow - *?*	NPG	NPG
L9.	**Class 52 'Western' Diesel Hydraulic C-C**		
299	**D1000 *Western Enterprise*** BRc desert sand - *not made*	NA	NA
244	**D1003 *Western Pioneer*** BRc green - *not made*	NA	NA
242	**D1016 *Western Gladiator*** BRc maroon - *not made*	NA	NA
243	**D1071 *Western Renown*** BRe blue - *not made*	NA	NA
L10.	**Class 55 'Deltic' Diesel Co-Co** (1978)		
253	**D9003 *Meld*** BRc green - *78*	60	70
217	**9006 *The Fife & Forfar Yeomanry*** BRe blue - *78*	60	70
217	**9009 *Alycidon*** BRe blue - *not made*	NA	NA
L11.	**Class 81/86 Electric Bo-Bo** (1967)		

BR Class 86 electric loco [L11]

Cat No.	Company, Number, Colour, Dates	£	£
205	**E3001** BRd electric blue - *not made*	NA	NA
205	**E3185** BRd electric blue - *67*	50	70
249	**86235 *Novelty*** BReLL blue - *83*	60	75

COACHES

These were quite accurate 1:160 scale models and had bright metal wheels with oversize flanges. Up until 1980 the liveries used had an exaggerated brightness but these were darkened from 1980 onwards. Early examples had correct running numbers.

Cat No.	Company, Number, Colour, Dates	£	£
C1.	**Pullman (Continental Type)** (1976)		

Based on the Wagon Lits vehicles as used on the Victoria-Paris services in the UK.

Cat No.	Company, Number, Colour, Dates	£	£
355	**Pullman** *Anne* brown+yellow - *not made*	NA	NA
355	**Pullman** *Cecilia* brown+yellow - *76*	12	15
356	**Golden Arrow** 23085 blue+grey - *76*	12	15
-	**Chesapeake & Ohio** ? blue+silver - *?*	20	25
-	**Santa Fe** ? red+silver - *?*	20	25
-	**New Haven** ? red+silver - *?*	20	25

C2a. BR Mk1 Corridor Composite (CK) (1967)

361	**GWR** 3015 brown+cream - *76*	12	15
357	**BR** 15865 red+cream - *75*	12	15
357	**BR** M24628 red+cream - *80*	12	15

BR Mk1 corridor coach [C2a]

352	**BR** 534257 green - *78*	12	15
352	**BR** S37483 green - *80*	12	15
353	**BR** 534257 green - *73*	12	15
361	**BR** W24624 brown+cream - *80*	12	15
314	**BR** M25276 maroon 2nd - *68*	12	15
314	**BR** M26810 maroon - *80*	12	15
306/307	**BR** 15865 blue+grey - *67*	12	15
306	**BR** W43671 blue+grey - *80*	12	15
354	**Pennsylvania** 1410 red+gold *-68*	NPG	NPG
364	**Wabash** 142 grey+blue - *68*	NPG	NPG
374	**Baltimore & Ohio** 186 blue+grey - *68*	NPG	NPG
384	**Santa Fe** 1418 grey+red - *68*	NPG	NPG
394	**New Haven** 1410 grey+red - *68*	NPG	NPG
?	**CIE** deep yellow - *?*	NPG	NPG
395	**CIE** green - *c96*	NPG	NPG
-	**Chesapeake & Ohio** ? blue+silver - *?*	20	25
-	**Santa Fe** ? red+silver - *?*	20	25
-	**New Haven** ? red+silver - *?*	20	25

C2b. BR Mk1 Brake 2nd (BSK) (1967)

362	**GWR** 5104 brown+cream - *76*	12	15
358	**BR** 35024 red+cream - *75*	12	15
358	**BR** M24374 red+cream - *80*	12	15
352/353	**BR** S1297 green - *73*	12	15
353	**BR** S75469 green - *80*	12	15
362	**BR** W24528 brown+cream - *80*	12	15
362	**BR** W24756 brown+cream - *80*	12	15
315	**BR** 72234 maroon - *not made*	NA	NA
315	**BR** 35024 maroon - *70*	12	15

BR Mk1 brake 2nd coach [C2b]

315	**BR** M25290 maroon - *80*	12	15
306	**BR** 35024 blue+grey - *67*	12	15
307	**BR** 35024 blue+grey - *74*	12	15
307	**BR** W43281 blue+grey - *80*	12	15
355	**Pennsylvania** 7093 red+gold - *68*	NPG	NPG
365	**Wabash** 2697 grey+blue - *68*	NPG	NPG
375	**Baltimore & Ohio** 86 blue+grey - *68*	NPG	NPG
385	**Santa Fe** 2602 grey+red - *68*	NPG	NPG
395	**New Haven** 2609 grey+red - *68*	NPG	NPG
?	**CIE** deep yellow - *?*	NPG	NPG
-	**Chesapeake & Ohio** ? blue+silver - *?*	20	25
-	**Santa Fe** ? red+silver - *?*	20	25
-	**New Haven** ? red+silver - *?*	20	25

C2c. BR Mk1 Buffet Car (RMB) (1968)

363	**GWR** 5208 brown+cream - *76*	12	15
359	**BR** 1823 red+cream - *75*	12	15
359	**BR** M34276 red+cream - *80*	12	15
354	**BR** S1297 green - *73*	12	15
354	**BR** S33760 green - *80*	12	15
363	**BR** W24760 brown+cream - *80*	12	15
316	**BR** 1823 maroon - *68*	12	15
316	**BR** M25486 maroon - *80*	12	15
313	**BR** 1823 blue+grey - *68*	12	15
313	**BR** W43212 blue+grey - *80*	12	15

C2d. BR Mk1 Full Brake (BG) (1977)

369	**BR** M80855 red+cream - *77*	12	15
369	**BR** M34752 red+cream - *80*	12	15
366	**GWR** 4476 brown+cream - *77*	12	15
366	**BR** W24589 brown+cream - *80*	12	15
367	**LMS** 30964 maroon - *77*	12	15
367	**BR** M25742 maroon - *80*	12	15
368	**BR** M80855 blue+grey - *77*	12	15
368	**BR** W43462 blue+grey - *80*	12	15

WAGONS

Re-liveried Continental tanks and silos made their appearance in the catalogues along with various other Continental designs. It is likely that versions of these wagons made for other countries turned up in Britain, but we have listed here only the Continental type wagons marked in the catalogues as being for Britain. Specifically, British outline wagons were also made and these are listed separately.

The mineral wagon and brake van are overscale as they were copies of Tri-ang Hornby wagons which Lima draughtsmen wrongly took to be H0 scale. However, for later BR wagons, BR drawings were used and these are to 1:160 scale.

Cat No.	Company, Number, Colour, Dates	£	£

Continental Style Wagons

W1. Twin Bolster Wagon (1969)

482	brown + 3 pipes - *69*	6	9
483	brown + timber - *69*	6	9

W2. Open Wagon (no doors)

725	**BR** WT3 grey - *?*	3	5

W3. Steel Open Wagon (with doors) (1975)

725	**BR** WT3 blue - *not made*	NA	NA
725	**BR** WT3 grey - *75*	3	5
726	**'NCB'** WT3 grey+red - *76*	3	5

W4. Twin Silo Wagon (1973)

461	? Cement - *73*	3	5
729	**'Blue Circle'** yellow - *75*	3	5

W5. Small Tank Wagon (1967)

454	**'BP'** green - *67*	4	6
451	**'Esso'** silver - *68*	4	6
451	**'Esso'** silver/red - *75*	5	7
780	**'Gulf'** white+red - *75*	5	7
782	**'ICI Chemicals'** white - *76*	5	7
784	**'Mobil LP Gas'** cream - *79*	5	7
781	**'Mobil Oil'** white - *75*	5	7
452	**'Shell'** yellow - *68*	4	6
455	**'Texaco'** red - *77*	5	7

W6. Van (long wheelbase) (1976)

462	**'East Anglian Meat'** light green - *76*	4	6

Continental van 'East Anglian Meat' [W6]

W7. Refrigerator Van (long wheelbase) (1976)

479	**'Coca-Cola'** white - *76*	4	6
463	**'Grimsby Fish'** NE26426 blue - *77*	4	6
474	**'Schweppes'** 2416S beige - *76*	4	6
?	**'Sundries' (CIE)** yellow/orange - *made?*	NPG	NPG

W8. Liner Train Flat + Containers (1969)

484	**'Freightliner'** x3 grey+red (N484) - *69*	8	12
487	**'Kuhne & Nagel'+'ACL'+'Sealand'** - *73*	8	12
795	**'Pickfords'+'Fyffes'+'Containerway'** - *73*	8	12
485	**'CNC'+'Danzas'+'LEP'** - *73*	8	12
486	**'Hapag Lloyd'+'CTI'+DB** - *73*	8	12
486	**'Hapag Lloyd'+RENFE+DB** - *76*	8	12
486	**'Fyffes'+'Danzas'+'Freightliner'** - *?*	8	12
486	**'Hapag Lloyd'+'Danzas'+'Freightliner'** - *?*	8	12
486	**'Hapag Lloyd'+'CTI'+'Freightliner'** - *?*	8	12
486	**'Hapag Lloyd'+'CTI'+'CNC'** - *?*	8	12
486	**CIE+RENFE+DB** - *?*	8	12
760	**'ACL'+'CP Ships'** - *79*	8	12
796	**'ACL'+'TNT'+'RACE'** - *79*	NPG	NPG

W9. Ferry Van (1975)

400	**BR** TFV2 brown - *75*	5	7

W10. Car Carrier (1973)

792	**'British Leyland'** black + 6 cars - *76*	18	25
481	**'Sitfa'** + 6 cars - *73*	18	25

W11. USA Type 'Gondola' Brick Wagon (1973)

420/720	**'London Brick'** red - *73*	5	7

W12. Bogie Tanker (1980)

622	**'Amoco'** A1090 white - *80*	7	9
625	**Milk** 152 blue+yellow - *80*	6	8
623	**'Texaco'** J62417 red - *not made*	NA	NA

British Style Wagons

W13. 7-plank Open Wagon (1974)

604	**'Barrow Barnsley'** yellow - *80*	4	6
602	**'Black Park'** 2021 brown - *80*	4	6

7-plank wagon - 'Black Park Colliery' [W13]

610	**'Buxton Gas Dept.'** 24 grey - *79*	4	6
735	**'Caxton'** 32 lime green - *74*	3	5
601	**'Clay Cross'** 1791 brown - *77*	3	5
605	**'Dearne Valley'** 61 blue - *77*	3	5
603	**'Evans & Bevan'** 1759 black - *77*	3	5
602	**'Glasshoughton'** 126 yellow - *77*	3	5
734	**'Hall & Dean'** 115 yellow - *74*	3	5
607	'JK **Harrison'** red - *79*	4	6
738	**'Kendall & Co.'** 26 grey - *75*	3	5
407	**'North Thames Gas'** 357260 brown - *75*	3	5
604	**'Oxford District Gas'** 18 green - *77*	3	5
609	**'Pinxton'** 930 black - *79*	4	6
608	'PW **Spencer'** yellow - *79*	4	6
606	**GWR** 122060 grey - *77*	3	5
-	**CIE** brown - *80*	NPG	NPG

The 1980 illustration is not of a 7-plank wagon but looks more like a ventilated van without a roof. It is not known whether any of the CIE wagons were made in N gauge

W14. 16T Mineral Wagon (1967)

?	**'Caxton'** 32 lime green - *?*	3	5
?	**'Hall & Dean'** 115 yellow - *?*	3	5
?	**'Kendall & Co.'** 26 grey - *?*	3	5
?	**'North Thames Gas'** 357260 brown - *?*	3	5

16T steel mineral wagon [W14]

406	**BR** B554430 grey - *67*	3	5
407	**BR** B54884 brown - *?*	3	5

W15. Vee Cement Tank Wagon

633	**'Albright & Wilson'** green - *not made*	NA	NA
630	**'Blue Circle'** grey - *not made*	NA	NA
632	**'Castle Cement'** white - *not made*	NA	NA
631	**'Ketton Cement'** yellow - *not made*	NA	NA
634	**'Lever Bros.'** purple - *not made*	NA	NA
635	**BR** 9398 grey - *not made*	NA	NA

W16. Horse Box (1978)

616	**GWR** 5463 brown - *not made*	NA	NA
616	**GWR** 546 brown - *80*	9	12
617	**LMS** red - *78*	9	12
619	**SR** green - *not made*	NA	NA

W17. Ventilated Van (1974)

619	**'Birds Custard'** blue - *81*	4	6
739	**'Castrol GTX'** grey - *80*	4	6
736	**'Ford'** S52272 blue - *74*	4	6
737	**'Fyffes'** yellow - *74*	4	6
612	**'Homepride'** SHP2225 blue+white - *not made*	NA	NA
618	**'Lucas Batteries'** M3245 black - *81*	4	6
613	**'Michelin'** M1245 brown - *not made*	NA	NA

Ventilated van - 'Castrol GTX' [W17]

614	**'St Ivel'** 68837 white - *77*	4	6
476	**'Tate & Lyle'** green - *76*	4	6
611	**'Typhoo Tea'** S1200 red - *77*	4	6
615	**GWR** 59701 grey - *77*	5	7
477	**LMS** 59673 red - *76*	4	6
412	**LNER** 167349 brown - *not made*	NA	NA
740	**SR** 45826 brown - *75*	5	7
?	**CIE** brown - *80*	NPG	NPG

W18. CCT Van (1975)

868	**'Tartan Arrow'** M94220 white+red - *?*	5	7
869	**BR** E94606 blue - *made?*	NPG	NPG
869	**BR** M94291 blue - *80*	5	7
870	**BR** M94823 maroon - *80*	5	7

W19. 20T GWR Brake Van (1975)

410	**GWR** 47342 grey - *not made*	NA	NA
410	**GWR** 114756 grey - *75*	5	7

W20. 20T BR Standard Brake Van (1967)

405	**BR** B954521 brown - *67*	3	5
?	**CIE** grey - *80*	NPG	NPG

W21. GWR 'Siphon G' (1980)

863	**'Palethorpes'** 2766 dark brown - *81*	7	9
862	**GWR** 2792 brown - *80*	7	9
864	**BR** W2982 blue - *80*	7	9
865	**BR** W2938W brown - *80*	7	9
865	**BR** M2928 maroon - *80*	7	9
867	**BR** RDW150423 blue 'Enparts' - *80*	7	9

Hornby 'Great Western Heavy Goods 1936' from computer artwork by Robbie McGavin

Hornby 4MT 4-6-0 from computer artwork by Robbie McGavin

Lima H0 (British)

HISTORY

Following some success with N gauge in Britain (sold through G&R Wrenn) Lima decided to try and compete in the British 00 market which by 1973 had only one principal supplier. As in the rest of Europe, Lima's middle scale was H0 and so they produced their first British models in this smaller scale. This meant that they looked too small alongside the British 00 models and Lima realised that in order to compete in the UK they would have to change to 00 scale. Lima 00 had completely replaced H0 in the British catalogue in 1977.

Because of its short life, the Lima British outline H0 range did not extend to any great size and, coming as it did from a company that made models for many countries, there was some compromising done which resulted in certain foreign subjects turning up in British liveries. Only models in UK liveries or of British subjects in foreign liveries are listed here.

The lists have been made from the full range of catalogues including the Lima Irish Collection issue of 1979/80 and Wrenn price lists of the mid 1970s (Wrenn were UK agents for Lima until Eisenmann took it over).

Some models in the H0 range were up-scaled for the 00 system and sometimes they took their catalogue number with them. Today, interest in Lima H0 British models is increasing and after a long period when you could hardly give them away, we are at last seeing their prices rise. This especially applies to mint boxed models as will be seen from the prices quoted here.

Dates: Those given are those when we believe the models were sold and do not always tie up with their appearance in the catalogues. Some models such as the 'Deltic', J50 and 'King' were shown in the 1976 catalogue as H0 models but were in fact 00 scale when they arrived. They have therefore been included in our Lima 00 lists.

LOCOMOTIVES

Cat No.	Company, Number, Colour, Dates	£	£

L1. US Tank 0-4-0T (1974)

1710	**40106** red white lining, headlamp, outside cylinders - *74-76*	15	20
1711	**4572** SR green, headlamp, outside cylinders full valvegear - *76*	18	25
1711	**4572** SR green, headlamp, outside cylinders simplified valve gear, ex sets - *76*	15	NA

These engines also came with NMRA couplings.

L2. LMS Class 4F 0-6-0 (1974)

Tender drive with a pancake type motor.

1701	**4547** LMS lined black - *74-78*	22	30
1701	**4547** LMS unlined black - *74-78*	22	30

LMS Class 4F 0-6-0 [L2] (Lima)

1702	**4168** LMS lined red - *not made*	NA	NA
1702	**4683** LMS (black) lined red - *74*	15	25
1702	**4683** LMS (yellow) lined maroon - *75-76*	15	25
1707	**628** CIE black - *77-79*	35	NPG
1715	**1908** black as Australian Class 219 - *76-83*	35	45

L3. GWR 'King' Class 4-6-0

1713	**6000 *King Charles*** BRb green - *not made*	NA	NA
1704	**6000 *King Charles*** BRb blue - *not made*	NA	NA
1704	CR blue - *not made*	NA	NA

L4. Continental Diesel Shunter 0-4-0DS (1974)

American design (Plymouth MDT). Simplified versions without handrails and the roof not painted black are from train sets. These were still being sold after 1977.

1651	**D2785** BRc green - *74-76*	12	15
1650M	**D2785** BRe blue - *?*	12	15
1650	**D2790** BRe blue - *74-76*	12	15

L5. German Class V100 Diesel Bo-Bo (1975)

This was a centre cab loco. It was probably supposed to be a Class 14 or 17

-	**D8900** BRc green ex-starter sets - *75*	15	NA
-	**D8900** BRe blue ex-starter sets - *75*	15	NA

L6. Class 33 Diesel Bo-Bo (1973)

1646	**D6514** BRc green, white window surrounds - *76*	25	35
1646	**D6514** BRc green with yellow window surrounds - *?*	40	50

Class 33 diesel [L6] (Robert Forsythe)

1646	**D6514** BRc green with yellow ends and window surrounds - *76*	40	50
1646	**D6506** BRc green with yellow ends and white window surrounds - *?*	40	50
8049	**D6524** BRe dark blue no lights, ex-sets - *73-76*	15	20
8049/L	**D6524** BRe chromatic blue with lights - *73-74*	20	30
8015	CIE orange+black - *76*	40	50

L7. Class 55 'Deltic' Diesel Co-Co

Planned for release in H0 and orange-brown packaging printed ready but then the decision was taken to produce the model in 00 scale.

1645	**9009** BRe blue - *not made*	NA	NA

COACHES

The choice of running numbers was sometimes haphazard but the Mk1s and Mk2s were attractive models.

Cat No.	Company, Number, Colour, Dates	£	£

Original Continental Style Coaches

C1a. Pullman (panelled sides) (1975)

9199	***Anne*** dark brown+yellow - *75*	5	10
9200	**'Golden Arrow'** 23085 blue+grey - *75*	5	10
9200	**'Golden Arrow'** 23085 green+grey - *75*	8	15

C1b. Pullman (smooth sides) (1976)

9146	***Louisa*** dark brown+yellow - *76*	5	10
9200	**'Golden Arrow'** 23085 blue+grey - *76*	5	10
9200	**'Golden Arrow'** 23085 green+grey - *76*	20	25

C1A. Continental Coaches (1976)

These were 18cms long. Continental coaches produced in British liveries for use in early starter train sets. These were later produced with tension-lock couplings.

-	**LMS** red+yellow - *76*	5	NA
-	**LMS** maroon - *76*	5	NA
-	**SR** green - *76*	5	NA
-	**BR** blue+grey - *76*	5	NA

C2. Travelling Post Office (1973)

970	**BR** W80062 blue+grey Royal Mail - *73-75*	8	12

Continental model of travelling post office in BR blue & grey [C2] (Lima)

British Design Coaches

C3a. BR Mk1 Corridor Composite (1975)

9151	**GWR** 5014 dark brown+cream - *76*	5	10
9146	**LMS** 2257 maroon - *75-76*	5	10
9145	**BR** 15210 red+cream - *75-76*	5	10
9145	**BR** 15215 red+cream - *?*	8	12
9152	**BR** S15865 green - *76*	5	10
?	**BR** W5449 blue+grey - *not made*	NA	NA
5346	**CIE** green - *?*	NPG	NPG
5347	**CIE** orange+black - *not made*	NA	NA

C3b. BR Mk1 Brake 2nd (1975)

9326	**GWR** 5103 dark brown+cream - *76*	5	10
9321	**LMS** 5051 maroon - *75-76*	5	10
9320	**BR** 34100 red+cream - *75-76*	5	10
9327	**BR** S1297 green - *76*	5	10
9327	**BR** S15895 green - *not made*	NA	NA
?	**BR** blue+grey - *not made*	NA	NA

C3c. BR Mk1 Restaurant Buffet Car (1976)

9233	**GWR** 9542 dark brown+cream - *76*	5	10
9234	**LMS** 270 maroon - *76*	5	10
?	**BR** red+cream - *not made*	NA	NA
9235	**BR** S3056 green - *76*	5	10
9232	**BR** W1652 blue+grey - *76*	5	10
9232	**BR** M1704 blue+grey - *not made*	NA	NA

C4a. BR Mk2b Open Coach TSO (1973)

8 windows per side.

9136	**BR IC** W5449 blue+grey - *73-76*	5	10
9144	**CIE** orange - *75-?*	15	25

C4b. BR Mk2b Brake 1st BFK (1973)

9137	**BR IC** W16084 blue+grey - *73-76*	5	10

C4c. BR Mk2b Open 1st FO (1973)

7 windows per side.

9135	**BR IC** W13493 blue+grey - *73-76*	5	10

WAGONS

Again, a large variety considering the short life of the range. Also re-liveried Continental tanks and silos made their appearance in the catalogues. It is likely that versions of these wagons made for other countries turned up in Britain but we have listed here only the Continental type wagons marked in the catalogues as being for Britain.

The specifically British outline wagons consisted of just four designs. The goods van and open wagon were produced in a number of private owner liveries. There were also Irish and Australian examples of some of the British models and these are particularly sought by British collectors and so have been included here. It will be noted that the Irish and Australian models came late and it seems likely that this was Lima attempting to get back some of their investment in the British H0 tooling. In time, the Australian models also transferred to 00 scale.

Original Continental Style Wagons

These often differed from the 00 versions of them in having Continental couplings instead of the British tension-lock type.

Cat No.	Company, Number, Colour, Dates	£	£

W1. Continental 4-wheel Container Wagon (1975)

2871	2 x 20' **'Freightliner'** containers - *made?*	NPG	NPG
2871	2104290324 + 40' **'Freightliner'** grey+red - *75-76*	5	6
2852	2104290324 + **'Scotch Beef'+'LHB'** blue+orange - *75-76*	5	6

W2. Continental LWB Mineral Wagon (1973)

3173	**'NCB'** Cardiff 1879 light grey - *76*	4	5
3175	**BRe** 100027 brown - *73-76*	3	5

W3. Continental Covered Hopper

3194	**BR** brown - *not made*	NA	NA

W4. Continental Twin Silo Wagon (1973)

2805	**'Blue Circle'** 7504 yellow (yellow circle on blue background) - *75*	8	12
2805	**'Blue Circle'** 7504 yellow (blue circle) - *75-76*	3	5
2805	**'Prestwin'** brown - *73 (made?)*	4	6
2805	**'Prestwin'** grey - *73-74*	4	6

W5. Continental 3-cask Beer Wagon (1973)

2822	**'Watneys'** P650513 red+brown - *73-76*	4	6

W6. Continental Small Tanker (1973)

L = ladder and gantry.

2715	**'BP'** 577128 green + black band L - *73-76*	3	5
2711	**'Esso'** ? silver + black band L - *?*	3	5
2711	**'Esso'** ? silver + red stripe- *?*	3	5
2720	**'ICI'** Chemicals C1182 white + yell stripe - *76*	4	6
2713	**'Shell'** 557128 yellow + black stripe - *not made*	NA	NA
2713	**'Shell'** 535204 yellow + black band L - *73-75*	3	5
2713	**'Shell'** 557128 yellow - *not made*	NA	NA
2713	**'Shell'** 005 7 426-3 yellow L - *75-76*	3	5

W7. Continental LWB Tank (1975)

265?	**'Mobiloil'** red ex-sets - *75-76*	4	NA
2651	**'Shell'** yellow ex-sets - *75-76*	4	NA
265?	**'Texaco'** red ex-sets - *75-76*	4	NA

W8. Continental Ferry Van (1976)

2008 *	**'Derrate Alamentan'** E75 white - *76*	8	12
3155	**'East Anglian Meat'** E75 lime green - *76*	4	6
3165	**BR** 217021003910 brown - *76*	3	5
3162	**BR** 217021003910 brown converter van - *78*	5	7

* Probably not released in the UK.

W9. Continental Refrigerator Van (1976)

3118	**'Schweppes'** 2416S yellow - *76*	3	5
3113	**'Coca-Cola'** white - *76*	3	5

W10. Continental Car Transporter (1974)

9057	**'British Leyland'** 518098800213 black - *76*	10	15
9053	**BR 'Motorail'** 518098800213 blue - *74-76*	10	15

W11. Continental Bogie Tanker (1975)

2913	**'Amoco'** A1090 white - *76*	6	8
2911	**Milk** 152D blue - *76*	6	8
2904	**'Shell Covengas'** 500314 yellow - *75*	6	8

Continental bogie tank wagon - 'Traffic Services Ltd'/ 'Pfizer' [W11] (Lima)

2904	**'Shellgas'** 036 4 291-5 yellow - *76*	5	7
2653 *	**'Texaco'** 65324 red - *76*	8	12
2911	**'Traffic Services Ltd'/'Pfizer'** green - *75*	7	9

* Probably not released in the UK.

W12. Continental Bogie Ferry Van (1974)

3194	**'Traffic Services Ltd'/'Pfizer'** cream - *74-76*	8	12
3194	**BR Railfreight** BRT yellow - *76*	8	12

British Design Wagons

W13. 12T 7-plank Open Wagon (1974)

3177	**'Caxton'** 32 lime green - *74-76*	4	6
3176	**'Hall & Dean'** 115 yellow - *74-76*	4	6
3179	**'Kendall'** 26 grey - *75-76*	4	6
3178	**'North Thames Gas'** 357260 brown - *75-76*	4	6
3180	**BR** grey - *75-76*	4	6
3511	**VR** 7354 (Australian) blue - *78-83*	15	20
?	**CIE** brown - *made?*	NPG	NPG

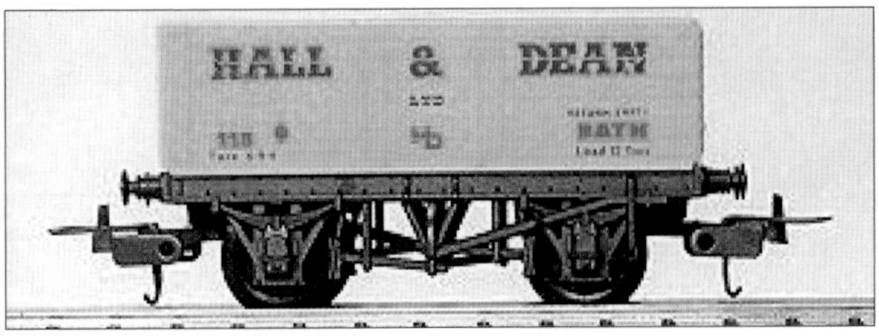

7-Plank coal wagon ' Hall & Dean' [W13] (Lima)

W14. 12T Corrugated End Van (1975)

3169	**'Castrol GTX'** grey - *75-76*	4	6
3160	**'Ford'** blue - *75-76*	4	6
3168	**'Fyfes'** yellow - *75-76*	4	6
3156	**'Tate & Lyle'** green - *76*	5	7
3157	**LMS** red - *76*	3	5
3170	**SR** brown - *75-76*	5	7
3515	**'Explosives'** PV11065 (Australian) - brown - *78-83*	15	20
?	**CIE** brown - *made?*	NPG	NPG

W15. 20T BR Standard Brake Van (1976)

3152	**BR** B954521 brown - *76*	3	5
3153	**NE** 159486 grey - *76*	3	5
?	**CIE** grey - *made?*	NPG	NPG

W16. GWR 'Toad' Brake Van (1974)

3166	**GW** 57740* light grey - *not made*	4	6
3166	**GW** 114756 light grey - *74-76*	4	6

* This appears to have been a Hornby model fitted with Continental couplings for the catalogue illustration.

SETS

Our information on Lima H0 sets is incomplete at present, but we are aware of at least eight having been catalogued, of which at least one was not produced. These were either clockwork or battery powered and were released between 1974 and 1976. One of the most attractive and best selling was the 5608A Inter-City set with its blue Class 33 and three Mk2 coaches.

The 8614A set contained a BR blue Continental design diesel shunter with the 'Schwepps' and 'Coca-Cola' vans and the Continental style long wheelbase open wagon in BR brown. The set has a circle of track and a battery powered controller.

Sets are not much in demand yet and rarely fetch more than £20. As interest in Lima H0 grows, good quality sets should come into their own.

Hornby Class 28xx (R2915) and 'Schools' (R2742) from computer artwork by Robbie McGavin

Virgin
XC
CrossCountry

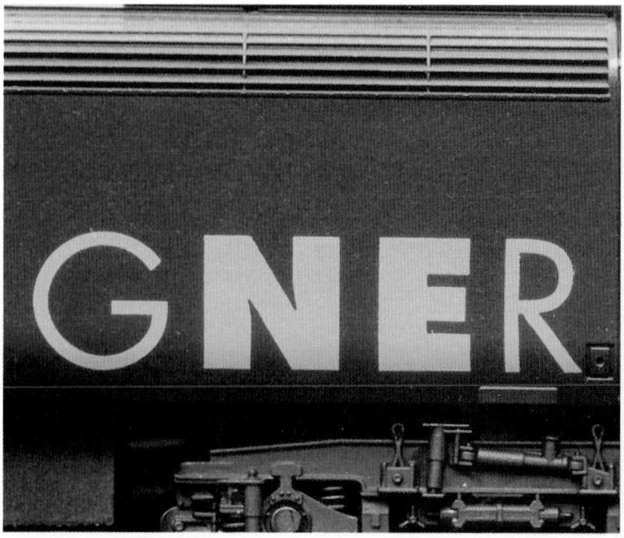
GNER

MIDLAND

"Blackpool Rock"
BLACKPOOL ROCK

First
43172

Great Western

Lima 00

Mk2 coach tables have been renumbered to put them in a more logical order.

HISTORY

The initials, that form the name Lima, stand for 'Lavarazione Italia Metalli ed Affini'. The company has been one of a handful of model railway manufacturers that are truly international; producing models for many different overseas markets. They date from 1949 but did not enter the British market until 1967. Their N gauge system was the first to arrive and this was sold through G&R Wrenn as Wrenn Micromodels. In 1973 they tried a range of British H0 which they sold direct but this was unsuccessful. Recognising that, if they were to sell to British modellers, they would need to make their products in the uniquely British 00 scale, they started a very successful British 00 gauge range in 1976.

Milestones

1949 Lavarazione Italia Metalli ed Affini (Lima) formed.
1966 Lima introduce N gauge.
1967 Wrenn market Lima N gauge in UK.
1973 Lima try both British H0 and 0 gauge ranges.
1976 Lima change production for the British market to 00 scale.
1977 'Deltic' model appears.
1979 Last steam outline models launched.
1983 Riko become UK importers of Lima.
1985 The Class 73 is released.
1987 The most prolific UK model, Lima's Class 47, is launched.
1994 The highly detailed Class 59 is released.
1999 Lima become the first manufacturer to market a model of the new Class 66.
2000 The Hobby Company take over the importing of Lima from Riko.
2002 Lima part company with The Hobby Company.
2003 Lima Group goes into liquidation.
2004 Hornby purchase the Lima Group assets.
2005 Tooling is transferred to China.
2006 The first 11 former Lima models reappear in the Hornby range.

Class 20 in Hunslet livery as No.20903 [L14]

In the 1980s Lima made a serious bid for the modern image market and greatly improved the quality of their models. They recognised that modern image modellers were interested in the minor variations between different members of a class of locomotives. They employed batch production, which meant that a limited number of each model were made before it was replaced by another version of it. As a result, the range in shops was constantly changing with new releases each month.

Diesel & Electric Range Development

Lima modern image locomotives were introduced in the following years:
1977 Classes 33 and 55
1978 Class 09
1979 Classes 52 and 87
1980 Classes 42, 117 and GWR railcar
1982 Class 43
1984 Class 50 and 20
1986 Classes 37 and 73
1987 Class 47
1988 Class 40
1989 Classes 26, 27 and 31
1990 Class 60
1992 Class 156
1994 Classes 59 and 92
1996 Class 373 (ex-Jouef)
1997 Class 101
1998 Class 121
1999 Classes 57 and 66
2001 Class 67

Lima's production for the British market has been almost exclusively diesel and electric locomotives and 'modern' coaching stock, with collectors forming a major part of their market. At one time, Lima, more than any other manufacturer supplying the British market, were prepared to accept commissions from retailers, to produce exclusive short runs of special editions. This resulted in a vast range of model variations over the last twenty five years.

The models were made at Vicenza in Italy and, since 1983, were imported by Riko International Ltd based in Hemel Hempstead and the importer recommend what should be made. In 2000 the dealership changed to The Hobby Company Ltd but, after disagreements between the importer and Lima, the two parted company in 2002. Lima indicated their intention to upgrade many of their models saying that they would be sold under the Rivarossi label while the remainder would be sold in Hobby Line packaging. However, on 12th July 2003 the Lima Group went into liquidation.

Class 31 as No 31970 in Research Division livery [L17]

Late in 2004, Hornby bought most of the assets of the Lima Group which, besides Lima, includes Rivarossi, Arnold, Pocher and Jouef, and established Hornby International to manage these brands. The purchase included the tooling, trademarks and other intellectual assets of the group but did not include the group's premises and did not leave Hornby responsible for the debts. Hornby established a small company in Italy called Hornby Italia but transferred production to China. The first Lima Continental models were marketed again under the Lima name in 2006. Any British outline 00 models from the former Lima range that Hornby subsequently produce were upgraded and re-released as Hornby models - some in their main range but the poorer models, such as the 'Deltic', in their RalRoad budget range. 2006 saw 11 former Lima British models reappearing in the Hornby catalogue and more followed in subsequent years.

Dates - Only single years are shown in the tables below. This is because most Lima models are produced in single batches and therefore production is not spread over several years.

Listing - The locos are listed in order of size starting with tank engines followed by tender locos and ending with diesels, electrics and multiple units. The coaches are listed in order of introduction of the real vehicles but with a special section for parcels vans which are a speciality of Lima. Wagons are listed in the order of: flats, open wagons, hoppers, tanks, vans, brake vans and bogie stock.

LOCOMOTIVES

Common abbreviations - The following abbreviations have been used in the tables below:
ccb = central codebox
scb = split codebox
disc = disc codes
hyp = half yellow end panels
syp = small yellow end panels
fyp = full yellow end panels
sno = fitted with snow ploughs

Cat No.	Company, Number, Colour, Dates	£	£

Steam

L1. Freelance 0-4-0T (1979)

This was used in starter sets.

-	**148** Great Western green - *79*	10	NA
-	**41312** BRb black - *80*	10	NA

L2. GWR Class 94xx Pannier 0-6-0PT (1979)

A late pannier tank development introduced in 1947 by Hawksworth, just before Nationalisation

L205117	**9400** GWR green - *79*	25	35
L204815A6	**9401** GWR green * - *94?*	25	35
L205118	**9420** BRb black - *79*	30	40
L204815	**9401** BRb black - *94*	30	40

* Sold in Continental box.

L3. LNER Class J50 0-6-0T (1976)

A Gresley designed tank introduced in 1922.

(L102606)	**8920** LMS red ex-Midland Express train set - *81*	12	NA
L205101	**8920** LNER dark shade of green, no steps to smokebox and works plate, plastic whistle - *76*	25	NA
L205101	**8920** LNER lighter shade of green - *77*	25	30
L205102	**68920** BRb black - *77*	25	35
(L152300)	**8920** lined red, ex-set - *82*	12	NA
(L152301)	**8920** lined green, ex-set - *82*	12	NA
(L152400)	**8920** lined blue, ex-set - *82*	12	NA

L4. GWR Class 45xx Small 'Prairie' 2-6-2T (1978)

A Churchward design introduced to the GWR in 1906.

L205111	**4589** GWR green - *78*	25	35
L205015	**4581** GWR green - *93*	25	35

Ex-GWR Class 45xx 2-6-2T [L4]

L205110	**5574** BRb black, lined - *79*	30	40
L205014	**5557** BRb lined black - *93*	30	40
L100000	**5549** BR black - *?*	45	60

L5. Freelance American Style 0-4-0 (1980)

Sold mainly in South Africa and Australia. Sloping back to tender.

-	Great Western, H0 couplings, ex-set - *80*	NPG	NA

L6. LMS 'Mogul' 'Crab' 2-6-0 (1980)

A Hughes designed 'Mogul' introduced to the LMS in 1926.

L205119	**13000** LMS maroon, no. on tender - *80*	30	45
L205057	**2724** LMS unlined black - *94*	NPG	NPG
L205120	**42700** BRb lined black - *80*	35	50
L204814	**42760** BRc black, Ltd Edn 850 - *94*	40	65

L7. *Davy Crockett* 2-6-0 (ex-Tri-ang Hornby) (1968)

The TC models were supplied by Rovex ready-made and were sold in Lima boxes with Lima couplings fitted.

L208102	**1863 *Davy Crockett*** red+yellow Lima couplings in Lima packaging - *68*	100	250

L8. LNER Class V2 2-6-2 (1980)

A Gresley design. This would have been a nice model with separate handrails throughout. It was probably dropped because the company decided to concentrate on modern image models in future.

L205130	**4771 *Green Arrow*** LNER light green, planned for 1980 - *not made*	NA	NA
L205131	**60964 *The Durham Light Infantry*** BRb lined black, planned for 1980 - *not made*	NA	NA

L9. GWR Class 6000 'King' 4-6-0 (1978)

Released at the same time as the Hornby 'King' and led directly to Hornby retooling theirs.

L205103	**6000 *King George V*** Great (crest) Western green, single boiler bands, crests separate - *78*	30	42
L205103	**6000 *King George V*** Great (crest) Western green, separate handrails, double boiler bands, crests joined - *78*	30	42
L205056	**6012 *King Edward VI*** Great (crests) Western green, separate handrails, bell, Ltd Edn 850 (Riko) - *93*	55	70
L205104	**6009 *King Charles II*** BRb bright blue, moulded handrails, thin lining - *78*	30	45

Ex-GWR 'King' Class 4-6-0 King Charles II [L9]

L205104	**6009 *King Charles II*** BRb blue, moulded handrails, thick lining - *78*	30	45
L205104	**6009 *King Charles II*** BRb blue, separate handrails, thick lining - *78*	40	55
L205176	**6026 *King John*** BRb green, separate handrails, double boiler bands - *90*	55	70

L10. LMS 'Princess Royal' Class 4-6-2

This was announced to the model railway press around 1981 but not made.

L11. Class 23 4-6-2 (ex-Tri-ang Hornby) (1968)

The TC Pacific models were supplied by Rovex ready made and were sold in Lima boxes with Lima couplings fitted.

L208100	**2335 *Hiawatha*** black Lima couplings in Lima packaging - *68*	100	250

Diesels

L12. Freelance 0-4-0DS (1979)

This was used in starter sets.

-	**D2785** BRe blue - *79*	10	20

L13. Classes 08/09/10/11 0-6-0DS (1978)

From 1999, the 08 chassis had all of its six wheels driven.

L205108	**3004** BRc green bright con rods - *78*	25	30
L205109	**7120** LMS black bright con rods - *78*	25	30
L205151	**D3489 *Colonel Tomline*** Townsend Thoresen light green, chevron ends, yellow rods - *83*	28	35
L205297	**08331** GNER navy + red stripe - *00*	25	30
L205297	**08331** GNER black + red stripe, error 48 made - *00*	50	70
L205297/A	As above with RFS roundels - *00*	50	70
L204638	**08611** Virgin red - *99*	25	30
L205259	**08720** EWS maroon - *00*	25	30
L205200	**08874** Silverlink blue+green - *99*	25	30
L204658	**08887** Virgin Pit Stop black - *99*	25	30
L204677	**08899** Midland Mainline teal green - *99*	25	30
L149972	**08899** Midland Mainline teal green + coaches in a train pack - *99*	NA	50

Class 08 diesel shunter 08899 in Midland Mainlilne livery [L13]

L204701	**09007** Mainline blue - *96*	30	40
L204758	**09009 *Three Bridges CED*** EW&S maroon - *97*	32	45
L205090	**09012 *Dick Hardy*** I-C Executive - *89*	28	40
L205201	**09023** EWS maroon - *99*	30	40
L205107	**09026** BRe blue, chevron ends, bright con rods - *79*	25	30

L20?	**09026** BRe blue no chevron ends - *?*	25	NPG
(L101806TW)	**09026** NSE bright blue no con rods ex-set - *88*	15	NA
(L101806TW)	**09026** BRe blue no con rods ex-set - *88*	15	NA
L205225	**09026** NSE bright blue, bright rods - *88*	28	35
L205112	**09027** Railfreight red stripe grey, Eastfield motifs - *86*	25	35
(L103409)	**09027** BRe blue no rods or yellow ends, Eastfield motifs ex-set - *86*	35	NA
L205058	**09101** BRe Departmental plain grey - *94*	30	40
L205123	Swedish livery brown - *83*	NPG	NPG
L205124	Swedish livery orange - *83*	NPG	NPG
L205129	**511** Dutch livery yellow+grey - *83*	NPG	NPG

L14. Class 20 Bo-Bo (1985)

ccb - centre code boxes. disc - disc codes. light - sealed beam headlight. gr = grey roof. ocr = orange cant rail. ov = oval buffers. syp = small yellow panel.

L204905	**D8000** BRc green disc gr ocr ov - *01*	35	50
L204900	**D8001** BRc green disc gr ob - *01*	35	50

Class 20 No.D8001 in BR green [L14]

(L205031)	**D8020** BRc green disc gr, sold with D8163 see below - *00*	35	NA
L205031	**D8020 + D8163** sold as pair - *00*	NA	80
L204827	**D8040** BRc green gr 1st with 5-pole motor sold with D8041 Sp Edn (MR&ME) 475 - *93*	35	50
L204828	**D8041** as above - *93*	35	50
-	above two sold together - *93*	NA	100
L205156	**D8138** BRc green, ccb gr syp - *85*	30	45
(L205031)	**D8163** BRc green gr 7D58 ccb paired with D8020 see above - *00*	35	NA
L205156	**D8170** BRc green planned for 1985 but D8138 made instead	NA	NA
L205066	**2014** RFS all over grey - *93*	30	40
L205069	**20001** Eddie Stobart Ltd green Ltd Edn 750 (Trafford MC) - *01*	40	65
L204707	**20042** Waterman black, disc - *96*	30	45
L205220	**20048** BRe blue, disc, Eastfield motifs Sp Edn 550 (Harburn) - *99*	30	50
L149779	as above + 3 Mk1 coaches in Sp Edn pack 250 (Harburn Hobbies) - *99*	NA	80
L204865	**20059** Railfreight red stripe grey, disc - *95*	30	40
L205240	**20064** ***River Sheaf*** BRe green red solebars disc + Oleo buffers - *88*	30	45
L205067	**20066** BRe blue disc - *94*	30	40
L205241	**20088** Railfreight unspecified triple grey - *89*	30	45
L204821	**20092** BRe Central Services pink+grey dummy, see below*** - *93*	35	NA
-	*****20092 + 20169** BRe Central Services pink+grey, sold as pair, Sp Edn 475 (Greenyard +Hatton) - *93*	NA	140
L205203	**20112** BRe blue Ltd Edn 850 - *92*	75	90
L204944	**20121** BRe blue disc - *02*	30	45
L204836	**20131** ***Almon B Strowager*** BRT grey, ccb - *94*	30	40
L204982	**20164** BRe blue - *02*	NPG	55
L204822	**20169** BRe Central Services pink +grey, light, see ***20092 - *93*	35	NA
L205158	**20171** BReLL blue * ccb, light grey roof - *84*	30	40
(L149974)	**20172** ***Redmire*** BRe blue, grey cab roof, name on red solebar Thornaby motif - *00*	50	NA
(L149974)	**20173** ***Wensleydale*** as above - *00*	50	NA
L149974	above two Sp Edn 300 (Beatties) - *00*	NA	125
L205157	**20183** BRe (on body side) blue, ccb, domino style headcodes - *85*	30	40
(L103807TW)	**20183** BRe blue, no detail ex-set - *85*	65	NA
L205068	**20187** BRT grey+green * ccb - *93*	30	40
L204881	**20188** Waterman black, ccb 3D94 - *96*	25	35
L205159	**20215** BReLL Railfreight red stripe grey - *85*	30	40
L204634	**20222** BRe blue, ccb, light, large numbers, Haymarket motifs - *98*	25	35
L204662	**20227** ***Traction*** Railfreight red stripe grey Sp.Edn. 500 (Traction) - *98*	35	50
L204902	**20227** ***Sir John Betjeman*** maroon Met. livery Class 20 Loco Society - *01*	35	50
L205263	**20901** DRS blue Sp Edn 750 (*Rail Express*), disc - *00*	35	50
L205263	**20901** DRS blue Sp Edn 750 (*Rail Express*), disc, 'Kosovo Train for Life' headboards - *00*	50	70
L204249	**20903** ***Allison*** Hunslet-Barclay grey disc - *00*	30	40
L205113	**20904** DRS blue, red sole, disc - *01*	35	50
L204813	**20906** ***Kilmarmock 400*** Hunslet- Barclay grey Ltd Edn 850 - *93*	50	65
L204914	**20906** DRS blue, red sole, ccb - *01*	35	50

* Not authentic.

L15. Class 26 Bo-Bo (1989)

sno = snowploughs.

L204699	**D5300/26007** BRc green Sp Edn 550 (Harburn) etched plaques and shedplates, plastic headlights - *99*	30	40
L205075	**D5301** ***Eastfield*** BRc green Ltd Edn 550 - *93*	65	80
L204878	**D5310** BRc green - *94*	25	35
L205242	**26001** Railfreight Coal grey - *90*	25	35
L205246	**26003** BRe blue Haymarket motif - *89*	25	35
L205008	**26004** BRe Dutch grey+yellow, Eastfield shedplates - *91*	25	35
L205245	**26004** BRe Railfreight red stripe grey - *90*	25	38
L204677	**26006** BReLL Railfreight red stripe grey - *99*	25	35
(L106306)	**26010** Railfreight grey ex-set - *90*	35	NA
L205244	**26027** BRe blue, discs sno - *90*	20	35
L205243	**26038** BRe Railfreight red stripe grey, Eastfield motif - *90*	30	40
L205173	**26040** BRe Dutch grey+yellow Eastfield motif - *00*	30	40

L16. Class 27 Bo-Bo (1989)

L205248	**D5394** BRc green, yellow half panels, headcode 1Z98 - *90*	25	35
L204671	**27001** BRe blue, Eastfield motif - *99*	25	35

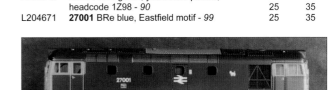

Class 27 No.27001 in BR blue livery [L16]

L205252	**27037** BRe blue, Eastfield motif - *89*	30	40
L205247	**27102** BRe blue - *89*	30	40

L17. Class 31 A1A-A1A (1989)

L205239	**D5500** BRc green, discs, no yellow panels - *90*	30	40
L205093	**5518** BRe green Royal Train white roof - *00*	32	45
L205282	**D5528** *(see 31110)*	-	-
L204640	**D5551** BRc green Sp Edn 550 (MR&ME) - *98*	30	60
L204614	**D5578** BRc experimental blue, code ccb 7M68 - *98*	25	36
L204624	**D5579** BRc experimental 'golden ochre' - *98*	25	40
L204859	**D5583** ***Stratford Major Depot*** BRc green, BR No.31165, yellow panel and white wrap windows - *94*	30	40
L205092	**D5679** BRc green - *89*	30	40
L205093	**D5830** BRc green, half yell panel - *89*	30	40
L205238	**31004** BRe blue, discs - *90*	30	40
L204868	**31105** ***Bescot TMD*** Transrail triple grey - *96*	30	40
(L204637)	**31106** ***The Black Countryman*** BRe Dutch grey+yellow see below - *98*	35	50
(L204637)	**31107** ***John H. Carless VC*** BRe Dutch grey+ yellow see below - *98*	35	50
L204637	above two locos sold as pair Sp Edn 300 (Langdale) - *98*	NA	100
L205109	**31107** BReLL Railfreight red stripe grey, headcode boxes removed - *01*	30	40

L204908	**31108** original Railfreight - *02*	NPG	55
L205282	**31110/D5528** ***Traction Magazine*** BRc green 81A plates Sp Edn 550 (Warners Group/Rails) - *00*	30	40
L204704	**31112** Transrail grey+yellow - *96*	30	40
L205072	**31116** ***Rail 1981-1991*** BRe Dutch grey+yellow (sold in Scotland) - *91*	40	65
-	**31116** ***Rail 1981-1991*** BRe Dutch grey+yellow, with headcodes Sp Edn 500 (Rail) - *91*	30	55
L205114	**31116** ***Rail Celebrity*** BRe Infrastructure yellow +grey Bescot motifs - *00*	30	40
L205172	**31019** BRe blue grey roof - *99*	30	40
L204967	**31130** ***Caulder Hall Power Station*** BRe Coal Sector 2-tone grey Crewe Diesel motifs - *02*	NPG	55
L205232	**31160** ***Phoenix*** BRe Railfreight Distribution grey, Tinsley plates - *90*	30	40
L204940	**31185** BRe Petroleum Sector triple grey Immingham plates - *02*	NPG	55
-	**31199** BReLL Railfreight Distribution grey - *?*	320	400
L205095	**31201** ***Fina Energy*** BRe Railfreight Petroleum grey, Fina logo - *91*	30	40
L205031	**31206** BRe Railfreight red stripe grey - *91*	30	40
L205237	**31275** BRe Railfreight Coal grey, Canton shedplates - *89*	30	40
L205236	**31283** BRe blue, large numbers, Thornaby motifs - *90*	30	40
L205213	**31296** ***Amlwch Freighter/Tren Nwyddau Amlwch*** BReLL Railfreight grey, yellow cabs - *90*	30	40
L205190	**31309** ***Cricklewood*** BRe blue Sp Edn 500 (Beatties) - *99*	30	45
L205091	**31325** BRe blue - *89*	30	40
L205234	**31327** ***Phillips Imperial*** Railfreight red stripe grey, large numbers - *89*	30	40
L205235	**31402** BRe blue - *89*	30	40
L204730	**31407** Mainline blue - *96*	30	40
L205255	**31410** ***Granada Telethon*** BRe Regional Railways grey+blue - *00*	30	40
L204946	**31411** BRe blue, white stripe - *02*	30	45
L205032	**31413** ***Severn Valley Railway*** BRe Severn Valley blue unofficial Provincial Services livery - *91*	30	50
L204845	**31421** ***Wigan Pier*** BRe Regional Railways grey+blue - *96*	30	40
L205233	**31423** BRe I-C Mainline grey - *90*	60	80
L205069	**31439** BRe Regional Railways grey+blue Ltd Edn 850 - *93*	45	60
L204673	**31452** Fragonset Railways black - *99*	30	40

Class 31 in Regional Railways livery as No.31455 Our Eli [L17]

L205196	**31455** ***Our Eli*** BRe Regional Railways grey+ blue - *99*	30	40
L204980	**31467** BRe blue - *02*	NPG	50
L204661	**31466** EWS maroon - *98*	25	37
L204687	**31468** Fragonset Railways black - *99*	30	40
L205096	**31541** BRe Dutch grey+yellow, Immingham shedplates - *91*	30	40
L205094	**31568** ***The Enginemans Fund*** BRe Departmental grey - *90*	30	40
L205094	**31601** ***Bletchley Park Station X*** Fragonset Railways black - *00*	30	40
L205229	**31970** BRe Research Division red+grey - RTC Derby - *90*	30	40

L18. Class 33 Bo-Bo (1977)

Body improved in 1986. sno = snowploughs.

L205115	**D6506** BRc green, big numbers, half yellow front - *78*	25	35
L205129	**D6506** BRc green, big numbers, no yellow panel - *88*	25	35
L205114	**D6524** BRe blue, yellow window frames - *77*	25	35
L205114	**D6524** BRe chromatic blue - *77*	25	35
	D6535 ***Herefordshire Rail Tours*** (see 33116)		
L205116	**215** CIE orange+black - *78*	NPG	NPG
(L105100)	**015** IR orange+black Sp Edn (Murphy's Models) - *97*	NA	40
L205221	**33008** ***Eastleigh*** BRc green half yellow ends sno - *87*	25	47
L205126	**33008** ***Eastleigh*** BRe green full yellow ends - *86*	25	35
L204911	**33021** ***Eastleigh*** BRe Post Office red, Eastleigh motif - *01*	25	35
L205114	**33024** BRe blue, yellow fronts - *81*	25	38
L205115	**33025** BReLL blue logo too small - *82*	30	40
-	**33025** BRe blue, small nos. ex-set - *82*	28	NA
L204660	**33025** EWS maroon - *98*	30	40
L205114	**33027** ***Earl Mountbatten of Burma*** BRe blue, white cab roofs, red buffer beams - *83*	30	40
(L103706V)	**33027** ***Earl Mountbatten of Burma*** BRe blue, white cab roofs, black buff beam ex-set - *83*	28	NA
L204660	**33030** EWS maroon - *98*	25	45
(L104313)	**33033** Railfreight Construction grey, ex-set - *92*	28	NA
L205070SI	**33033** triple grey for Railwayana, no body markings - *89*	25	40
L205074	**33035** revised NSE bright blue, sno - *93*	25	35
L204610	**33046** ***Merlin*** BRe grey+yellow - *98*	25	40
L205228	**33050** ***Isle of Grain*** BRe Railfreight Construction grey - *89*	25	40
(L105111)	**33051** ***Shakespeare Cliff*** Railfreight Construction grey ex-set - *89*	28	NA
L204756	**33051** ***Shakespeare Cliff*** BRe grey+ yellow Sp Edn 500 (Rail Express) - *97*	40	55
L205142	**33052** ***Ashford*** BRe blue sno - *01*	30	40
L205174	**33056** ***The Burma Star*** BRe blue, red beam, white roof, large buffers - *87*	30	40
(L174MWG)	**33056** ***The Burma Star*** BRe blue, red beam, white roof, small buffers ex-set - *87*	28	NA
(L103407V)	**33056** ***The Burma Star*** BRe blue, black beam large buffers, white roof, ex-set - *87*	28	NA
-	**33056** ***The Burma Star*** BRe blue, black beam small buffers, white roof ex-set - *87*	28	NA
L204705	**33063** BRe Mainline triple grey - *95*	25	42
L205030	**33065** BRe Dutch grey+yellow small numbers on body sides - *91*	25	42
L205116	**33105** BRe blue push-pull - *87*	30	40

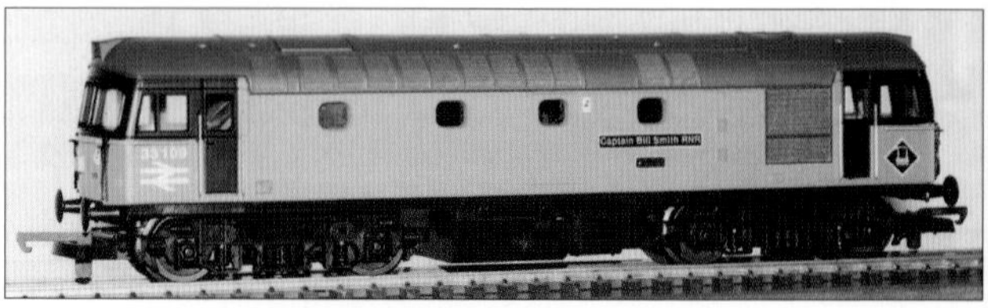

Class 33 as 33109 Captain Bill Smith RNR [L18]

L205073	**33109** ***Captain Bill Smith RNR*** BRe Departmental plain grey - *94*	30	45
L205185	**33114** ***Ashford 150*** Revised NSE bright blue, headboard, Ltd Edn 850 - *92*	70	100
L204841	**33116/D6535** ***Hertfordshire Rail Tours*** BRe blue Sp Edn 500 (Hertfordshire Rail Tours Sales) - *94*	40	55
L205070	**33205** Railfreight Distribution grey, side body numbers small - *89*	30	45
L204986	**33207** DRS blue - *02*	NPG	55

L19. Class 37 Co-Co (1986)

sno = snowploughs fitted. syp = small yellow panels. scb = split codebox. ccb = central codebox. ib = improved body.

L204858	**D6607** ***Ben Cruachan*** BRc green Sp Edn 500 (Harburn Hobbies) etched Eastfield Depot motifs + nameplates, syp, sno - *94*	90	150
L204644	**D6700** BRc green, small yellow panels, Sp Edn 500 (Model Rail) - *98*	35	50
L205222	**D6722** BRc green, no yellow ends - *87*	30	45
L205173	**D6755** BRc green, half yellow panel oversize nos. scb headcode 0F75 - *87*	30	45
L204834	**D6916** ***Great Eastern*** BRc green Ltd Edn		

	1000 216 on ends, syp - *94*	50	65
L204772	**D6999** BRc green Sp Edn 550 (MR&ME) 300th diesel electric, 5T17 code in boxes - *97*	50	65
L205172	**37012 *Loch Rannoch*** BRe blue, white stripe, red buffer beams, silver handrails, sno, Eastfield motif, scb - *87*	45	50
(L106206)	**37012 *Loch Rannoch*** BRe blue, white stripe, black buffer beams sno Eastfield motif scb no end detail ex-set - *87*	35	NA

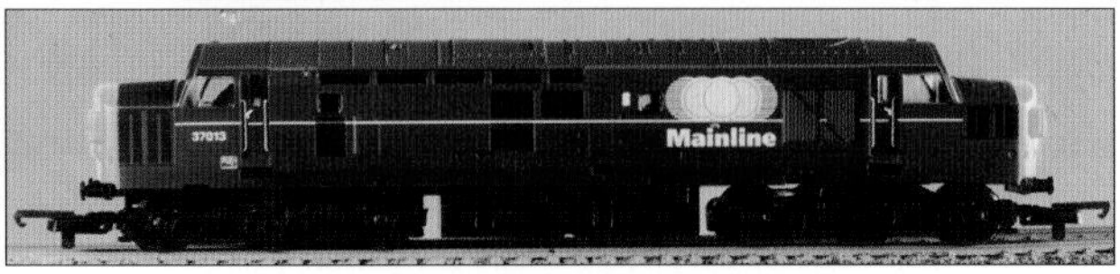

Class 37 Mainline blue No.37013 [L19]

L204717	**37013** Railfreight triple grey unspecified Sp Edn 500 (Geoffrey Allison) - *96*	40	55
L205198	**37013** Mainline blue, scb - *99*	30	45
L204866	**37023 *Stratford TMD Quality Approved*** Mainline blue, Stratford motif, split headcodes - *94*	35	50
L204879	**37025 *Inverness TMD*** BReLL blue (extended) Sp Edn 500 (Harburn Hobbies) etched nameplates yellow cab, Inverness motif, sno, scb - *95*	70	100
L20?	**37026 *Shap Fell*** Speedlink grey Sp Edn 500 (Collectable Models) - *01?*	NPG	NPG
L204693	**37027 *Loch Eil*** BReLL blue Sp Edn 550 (Geoffrey Allison) Eastfield motif, yellow cab, sno, scb - *99*	30	45
L204786	**37032 *Mirage*** Railfreight red stripe grey, Sp Edn 550 (Macclesfield Model Centre), unofficial name - *98*	35	47
L204968	**37042** BRe Mainline triple grey - *03*	NPG	50
L205189	**37043 *Loch Lomond*** BRe blue, Sp Edn 550 (Harburn Hobbies) etched metal nameplates small Eastfield motif - *99*	35	49
L205294	**37049** BRe blue, scb - *89*	30	45
-	**37051** Railfreight Metals grey, ex set L106307 - *92*	50	NA
L204613	**37057 *Viking*** EW&S maroon - *98*	28	37
-	**37063** Railfreight Distrib grey, ex-set L106307 - *89*	50	NA
L205076	**37069** BRe Dutch grey+yellow scb - *91*	30	45
L205190	**37081 *Loch Long*** BReLL blue, small Eastfield motif, 'computer' style numbers, sno, scb, yellow cabs - *87*	50	65
L205171	**37082** BReLL, Railfreight grey 8 - *87*	30	45
L205177	**(37093)** BR painted in Police car white livery for a TV advert, no number carried - *87*	45	85
L204760	**37095 *British Steel Teeside*** BRe blue, white cantrail stripe, Thornaby motif, scb - *97*	30	45
L205077	**37099 *Clydesbridge*** BRe grey Railfreight Metals, scb, Motherwell plates - *93*	30	45
L20?	**37100** Railfreight Metals grey, flush No.2 end Sp Edn (Moray's) - *cancelled*	NA	NA
L204680	**37111 *Loch Eil Outward Bound*** BReLL blue Eastfield motif Sp Edn 500 (Moray's) - *98*	30	45
L205091	**37112** BRe blue, scb, wrap round yellow ends, 1981 hybrid livery - *00*	30	45

Class 37 BR blue 37112 [L19]

L205286	**37113** BRe blue, scb, large Eastfield motif - *89*	30	45
L205288	**37114 *Dunrobin Castle*** BReLL blue, numbers and logo too small, Inverness motif, scb - *89*	55	80
L205128	**37114 *City of Worcester*** EW&S maroon, Inverness motif, scb - *01*	45	50
L204714	**37116 *Sister Dora*** Transrail on Rail blue Sp Edn 500 (Rail Express) etched plates enclosed - *96*	60	100
L205299	**37133** BRe Departmental grey - *91*	30	45
L205218	**37137 *Clyde Iron*** Railfreight Metals grey sno - *99*	30	40
L205289	**37140** BRe blue Stratford motif ccb - *89*	30	45
L204973	**37154** BRe Transrail triple grey - *02*	NPG	55
L205124	**37180 *Sir Dyfed/County of Dyfed*** Railfreight all-over grey, sno, ccb - *87*	35	50
L205018	**37184** Railfreight Petroleum grey, Immingham motif - *91*	30	45
L205019	**37185** Railfreight Distribution grey - *91*	30	45
L204948	**37188 *Jimmy Shand*** BReLL blue Sp Edn 500 (Harburn Hobbies) Eastfield motif - *02*	35	50
-	**37190** BReLL blue see ** below - *cancelled*	NA	NA
L204985	**37194 *British International Freight Association*** Mainline grey - *02*	NPG	50
L204700	**37201 *Saint Margaret*** Transrail on BRe Dutch grey+yellow - *96*	30	45
L205033	**37207 *William Cookworthy*** BRe blue, Cornish Railways on cab fronts with Cornish and BR flags - *00*	30	45
L204788	**37209 *Phantom*** BReLL blue Sp Edn 550 (Geoffrey Allison) sno - *98*	30	45
L208434	**37216 *Great Eastern*** green Ltd Edn 1000, D6916 - *94*	45	60
L204711	**37219** Mainline blue, number at wrong end one side - *96*	30	45
L205297	**37223** BRe Railfreight Coal grey, Canton motif - *90*	40	55

Class 37 Railfreight coal livery No.37223 [L19]

L205017	**37232 *The Institution of Railway Signal Engineers*** grey+yellow - *91*	35	50
L205079	**37251 *The Northern Lights*** InterCity Swallow grey - *93*	30	45
(L20?)	**37260 *Radio Highland*** BReLL blue Inverness motif (see ** below) - *cancelled*	NA	NA
L20?	**above model **+** 37190 Sp Edn (Moray's) - *cancelled*	NA	NA
(L205262)	**37261 *Caithness*** BReLL blue see below - *00*	40	NA
(L205262)	**37262 *Dounreay*** BReLL blue see below - *00*	40	NA
L205262	above 2 models Ltd Edn 300 (Geoffrey Allison) - *00*	NA	100
L204663	**37275 *Oor Wullie*** BRe blue, Sp Edn 500 (Rails) - *98*	30	44
L204938	**37308** BRe blue, new body, Sp Edn 500 (Much Ado About Toys) - *02*	NPG	50
L205123	**37310 *British Steel Ravenscraig*** BReLL blue, dark roof, small logo Glasgow South motif, ccb - *87*	50	80

Class 37 Transrail No.37351 [L19]

L205287	**37350/D6700** BRc green, small yellow panel - *89*	35	50
L205193	**37351** Transrail on grey+yellow scb - *99*	30	45
L205215	**37370** BReLL Railfreight red stripe grey, Glasgow South motif, sno - *99*	30	45
L204960	**37379 *Ipswich WRD Quality Approved*** Mainline blue - *02*	NPG	55
L205290	**37401 *Mary Queen of Scots*** InterCity Mainline grey, sno, ccb - *89*	35	50
L204771	**37401 *Mary Queen of Scots*** BRe Railfreight Distribution triple grey Sp Edn 500 (Harburn Hobbies), sno, etched nameplates and arrows - *97*	75	90

L204975	**37401** ***Mary Queen of Scots*** EWS maroon - *02*	NPG	55
L205178	**37402** ***Oor Wullie*** BReLL blue, incorrect mould, no sealed beam headlight - *87*	35	50
L204773	**37402** ***Bont-y-Bermo*** Railfreight unspecified triple grey, Sp Edn 550 (Geoffrey Allison), sno - *97*	30	45
L20?	**37403** ***Glendarroch*** BRe triple grey unbranded, Eastfield motif, Railfreight Distribution + Railfreight General decals, etched nameplates Sp Edn (Moray's) - *cancelled*	NA	NA
L205129	**37404** ***Ben Cruachan*** InterCity Mainline grey Sp Edn 275 (Harburn) + metal etched nameplates sno - *00*	50	150
L204812	**37405** ***Strathclyde Region*** BReLL blue, small nos., small logo, large Eastfield motif, sno, ccb - *94*	35	50
L205241	**37405** ***Strathclyde Region*** InterCity Mainline grey Sp Edn 350 (Moray's) sold with 37417 - *00*	35	50
L205219	**37406** ***The Saltire Society*** Transrail on triple grey Sp Edn 550 (Harburn), sno, etched nameplates - *99*	35	49
L204863	**37407** ***Blackpool Tower*** Transrail, triple grey 407 on front end - *95*	30	45
L204863	**37407** ***Blackpool Tower*** Transrail, triple grey - *95*	30	45
L204696	**37407** ***Loch Long*** InterCity Mainline red stripe grey Sp Edn 500 (Morays) sno - *99*	35	50
L204882	**37408** ***Loch Rannoch*** BReLL blue, large Eastfield motif, sno - *95*	30	70
L204882	**37408** ***Loch Rannoch*** BReLL blue, large Eastfield motif, sno, no detail on front, ex-set - *95*	45	NA
L204675	**37409** ***Loch Awe*** BReLL blue Sp Edn 550 (Harburn) sno, Eastfield motif, etched nameplates, yellow cabs - *98*	35	47
L204949	**37410** ***Aluminium 100*** Transrail grey Sp Edn 500 (Harburn) - *02*	35	50
L204762	**37411** ***Ty Hafan*** EWS maroon, sno - *97*	30	45
L20?	**37412** ***Loch Lomond*** BReLL blue Sp Edn 500 (Collectable Models) - *01?*	NPG	NPG
L204632	**37413** ***Scottish Railway Preservation Society*** EWS maroon Sp Edn 700 (Harburn and SRPS), etched nameplates + SRPS Railtours headboard, ticket - *98*	35	50
L204817	**37414** ***Cathays C&W Works 1846-1993*** BRe Reg Rlys grey+blue Ltd Edn 850 - *93*	100	130
L149442	**37415/416/419/426** InterCity Mainline grey Sp Edn 300 (Rails) set of 4 models - *01*	NA	180
(L149442)	**37415** ***Mt Etna*** InterCity Mainline grey, Sp Edn see below*** - *01*	40	NA
(L149442)	**37416** ***Mt Fuji*** InterCity Mainline grey, Sp Edn see below *** - *01*	40	NA
L149442	*****37415/416/419/426** InterCity Mainline grey Sp Edn set 300 (Rails) - *01*	NA	180
L205241	**37417** ***Highland Region*** InterCity Mainline grey Sp Edn 350 (Moray's) sold with 37405 - *00*	35	50
L205266	**37417** ***Rail Magazine*** EWS maroon black and gold nameplates sno - *00*	30	45

Class 37 EWS 37417 Rail Magazine [L19]

L204625	**37418** ***East Lancashire Railway*** BRe Regional Railways grey+blue - *98*	30	45
L204820	**37418** ***Pectinidae*** Railfreight Petroleum grey Sp Edn 250 (Langdales) paired with 37421 - *99*	35	50
L205027	**37418** ***An Comunn Gaidhealach*** BReLL blue, Inverness motif + metal etched nameplates Sp Edn 550 (Harburn Hobbies) - *01*	35	50
(L104311)	**37419** InterCity Mainline grey ex-set - *92*	65	NA
(L149442)	**37419** ***Mt Pinatubo*** InterCity Mainline grey, Sp see above *** - *01*	40	NA
L204641	**37420** ***The Scottish Hosteller*** blue BReLL Sp Edn 550 (MR&ME) - *98*	30	45
L204697	**37420** ***The Scottish Hosteller*** BRe Regional Railways bright blue, etched nameplates and logo, sno, Sp Edn 1000 (Morays + Geoffrey Allison) - *99*	35	50
L204731	**37421** ***The Kingsman*** BRe Regional Railways grey+blue sno - *96*	55	70
L204819	**37421** ***Strombidae*** Railfreight Petroleum triple grey Immingham plates sno Sp Edn 250 (Langdales) paired with 37418 - *99*	35	50
L204763	**37422** ***Robert F Fairlie*** BRe Regional Railways grey+blue, spelling mistake, sno - *97*	30	45
L149932	**37423** ***Sir Murray Morrison...*** Railfreight Distribution grey, sno, Sp Edn 330 (Langdales) paired with 37428 - *98*	30	45
L204784	**37424** ***Isle of Mull*** Mainline grey Sp Edn 550 (Harburn Hobbies) sno, etched nameplates - *98*	35	50
L204782	**37425** ***Sir Robert McAlpine/ Concrete Bob*** BRe Regional Railways grey+ blue Sp Edn 550 (Rails) sno - *97*	50	65
L204897	**37425** ***Sir Robert McAlpine/ Concrete Bob*** Railfreight Construction grey Sp Edn 500 (Rails) sno - *96*	55	70
L204655	**37425** ***Sir Robert McAlpine/ Concrete Bob*** BReLL blue Sp Edn 550 (Rails) sno yellow cab Eastfield motif - *98*	30	45
L204612	**37426** EWS maroon - *98*	30	45
-	**37426** ***Mt Vesuvius*** InterCity Mainline grey, Sp Edn see above *** - *01*	40	NA
L204842	**37427** ***Highland Enterprise*** BRe Regional Railways/ScotRail grey+blue, Sp Edn 500 (D&F) uncertificated - *94*	70	100
L149932	**37428** ***David Lloyd George*** Railfreight Petroleum grey, sno, Sp Edn 330 (Langdales) paired with 37423 - *98*	30	45
L204659	**37428** Royal Claret livery for the Royal Scotsman/GSWR EWS motif Sp Edn 550 (Harburn Hobbies) sno - *98*	50	70
L204887	**37429** ***Eisteddfod Genedlaethol*** BRe Regional Railways grey+blue - *94*	30	60
L205298	**37430** ***Cwmbran*** InterCity Mainline grey, number wrong end one side - *92*	50	80
L205176	**37431** ***County of Powys'/'Sir Powys*** BReLL blue, red dragon motif, coat of arms, yellow cabs - *00*	30	45
L204824	**37431** ***Bullidae*** IC Mainline grey Petroleum train load logos sno Sp Edn 335 (Langdales) - *99*	55	70
L205230	**37501** ***Teeside Steelmaster*** BReLL British Steel blue, Thornaby motif, BSC logo - *90*	50	65
L205231	**37502** ***British Steel Teeside*** BReLL Railfreight red stripe grey, large nos. - *90*	45	60
L204983	**37505** ***British Steel Workington*** Transrail - *03*	45	60
L205078	**37506** ***British Steel Skinningrove*** BReLL Railfreight red stripe grey, Thornaby motif - *94*	30	45
L204843	**37510** InterCity Swallow grey - *95*	30	60
L205293	**37511** ***Stockton Haulage*** BRe Railfreight Metals grey, large numbers, Thornaby motif - *89*	50	65
L204709	**37517** ***St. Aidens*** Loadhaul black+orange - *96*	30	45
(L107157)	**37519** Railfreight red stripe grey, large nos, ex-set Thornaby motif - *89*	55	NA
L204647	**37605** EPS triple grey Tunnel motifs - *98*	55	70

Class 37 DRS No.37607 [L19]

L204684	**37607** DRS blue Ltd Edn 750 - *99*	40	60
L204796	**37609** DRS blue - *98*	50	70
L204605	**37610** DRS blue Sp Edn 550 (Rail Express) - *98*	60	100
L204683	**37611** DRS blue - *99*	50	70
L204737	**37671** ***Tre Pol And Pen*** Railfreight Distribution triple grey, St Blazey motif, sno - *97*	60	100
L205285	**37673** Rft Distribution grey St Blazey motif - *87*	45	60

L204937	**37674 *Saint Blaise Church 1445-1995*** Transrail grey, upgrade tool - *02*	35	50
L205208	**37675 *William Cookworthy*** Railfreight red stripe grey Ltd Edn 850 - *92*	50	65
L204754	**37682 *Hartlepool Pipe Mill*** EW&S maroon - *97*	30	45
L205178	**37684 *Peak National Park*** BRe Railfreight Construction grey Buxton motif ib Sp Edn 500 (Geoffrey Allison + DPS) - *01*	30	45
L205296	**37688 *Great Rocks*** BRe Railfreight Construction grey Buxton motif - *90*	40	70
L204891	**37692 *The Lass O Ballochmyle*** BRe Rft Coal grey Sp Edn 500 (D&F Models) Eastfield motif - *95*	70	100
L205025	**37693 *Sir William Arrol*** BRe Railfreight Coal grey, Eastfield motif, ib, etched nameplates, Sp Edn 550 (Harburn) - *00*	35	50
L204979	**37697** original Railfreight - *02*	NPG	55
L204765	**37698 *Coed Bach*** Railfreight Coal grey British Coal, Canton plates - *97*	30	45
L204735	**37702 *Taff Merthyr*** Railfreight Coal triple grey, Canton motif - *96*	30	45
(L204922)	**37711 *Tremorfa Steel Works*** Railfreight Metals triple grey, see below - *01*	40	NA
(L204922)	**37712 *The Cardiff Rod Mill*** Railfreight Metals triple grey see below - *01*	40	NA
L204922	above two models Canton motifs Sp Edn 350 (Geoffrey Allison) - *01*	NA	96
L204856	**37713** Loadhaul sticker attached black+orange - *94*	30	45
L204793	**37714** EWS maroon - *98*	25	38
L204892	**37715 *British Petroleum*** BRe Mainline on Railfreight unspecified triple grey Stewarts Lane motif, BP logo - *95*	30	45
L204964	**37715 *British Petroleum*** Railfreight Construction/Petroleum triple grey Stewarts Lane motif - *02*	NPG	65
L204740	**37717 *Maltby Lilly Hall*** EW&S maroon - *97*	30	45
L204886	**37798** Mainline blue, revised moulding, Stewarts Lane motif - *94*	30	45
L204622	**37884 *Gartcosh*** Loadhaul black+orange - *98*	22	34
L20?	**37887 *Castell Caerfilli/ Caerphilly Castle*** Railfreight Coal grey Sp Edn (Collectable Models) - *01*	NPG	NPG
L20?	**37888 *Petrolea*** Railfreight Petroleum grey Sp Edn (Collectable Models) - *01*	NPG	NPG
L205034	**37890 *The Railway Observer*** BRe Railfreight Petroleum triple grey Ripple Lane motif - *00*	30	45
L205284	**37892 *Ripple Lane*** Railfreight Petroleum triple grey, Ripple Lane motif - *87*	50	65
L204954	**37899** GIF light blue Spanish infrastructure livery - *not released*	NPG	NPG
L20?	**37901 *Mirlees Pioneer*** Railfreight Metals grey Sp Edn (Collectable Models) - *01?*	NPG	NPG
L205285	**37905 *Vulcan Enterprise*** BRe Railfreight Metals triple grey Canton motif, 700 - *00*	30	45
L205096	**37906 (*Slug 6*)** Transrail triple grey, only 300 made - *00*	50	80
L204910	**37906** BReLL grey, Railfreight logos, wrap round yellow ends, red buffer beams - *?*	NPG	NPG
L204910	**37906 (*Slug 6*)** Railfreight grey, Canton motif, 700 - *01*	35	50
L204932	**37906 *Star of the East*** Transrail triple grey, new body shell, Slug 6 motif, Canton plates - *01*	35	50

* Not an authentic livery.

L20. Class 40 1Co-Co1 (1988)

scb = split codebox. ccb = central codebox. hyp - yellow half panels. fyp = full yellow panels.

L204939	**200** BRc blue - *02*	30	45
L205064	**D205** BRc green no yellow panels, discs - *89*	30	45
L205233	**D210 *Empress of Britain*** BRc green Sp Edn (Rails) - *99*	30	40

BR green Class 40 No.40337 [L20]

L204728	**D233 *Empress of England*** BRc green, discs Sp Edn 550 (Rails) hyp - *97*	40	55
L205060	**D261** BRc green, ccb 3E28 light grey roof, fyp - *88*	30	45
L205065	**D334** BRc green scb, hyp - *89*	30	45
L205201	**D335** BRc green scb - *88*	30	45
L205062	**D354** BRc green ccb 1A75 hyp - *89*	30	45
L204642	**337** BRc green scb - *98*	30	45
L205189	**40001** BRe blue discs - *88*	30	45
L204698	**40012 *Aureol*** BRe blue Sp Edn 500 (Moray's) - *99*	35	50
L205063	**40052** BRe blue discs - *90*	30	45
L205104	**40052** BRc green full yellow panels - *00*	30	40
L205217	**40063** BRe blue ccb - *89*	30	45
L205187	**40066** BRe blue ccb - *89*	30	45
L205188	**40106 *Altantic Conveyor*** BRc revised green, discs fyp - *88*	35	50
L205200	**40122/D200** BRc green, discs - *88*	30	45
L205278	**40126** BRe blue scb - *89*	30	45
L205202	**40140** BRe blue scb - *90*	30	45
L205061	**40145** BRe blue ccb - *88*	30	45
L204972	**40155** BRe blue, red bufferbeam - *02*	NPG	NPG
L204972	**40155** BRe blue, black bufferbeam - *03*	NPG	NPG

L21. Classes 42 & 43 ('Warships') B-B (1980)

L205127	**D801 *Vanguard*** BRe blue, planned 1980 replaced by 'Dragon' - *not made*	NA	NA
L204894	**D807 *Caradoc*** BRe blue- *96*	30	38
L204669	**D809 *Champion*** BRc maroon - *99*	30	38
L149966	**D809 *Champion*** BRc maroon train pack with 3 coaches - *99*	NA	70
(L107307)	**D814 *Dragon*** BRe blue ex-set - *80*	35	NA

BR Class 42 'Warship' No.D809 Champion [L21]

L205127	**814 *Dragon*** BRe blue, headcode 1A15 - *80*	30	38
L204861	**D815 *Druid*** BRc maroon - *95*	30	38
L204837	**D819 *Goliath*** BRc green Ltd Edn 1000, spelling error, red nameplates - *94*	35	50
L205083	**828 *Magnificent*** BRe blue, headcodes 7C39, 1V13 - *93*	30	38
L205128	**D838 *Pathfinder*** BRc maroon planned 1980 replaced by 'Rapid' - *not made*	NA	NA
L205129	**D838 *Rapid*** BRc maroon yellow half panels, headcode 1A15 - *80*	30	45
L205135	**D843 *Sharpshooter*** BRc green headcode 1A15 - *80*	30	45

L22. Class 43 HST Power & Dummy Cars (1982)

The Lima model is of the later DM unit with no guard's compartment windows and with an exhaust baffle on the cab roof. It therefore needed a TGS coach to provide guard's accommodation. I-C = InterCity. Ics = InterCity Swallow.

L205253	**43024 + 43025** FGW 'fag packet' grn - *00*	NPG	NPG
L149909	**43043 *Leicestershire County Cricket Club* + 43075** Midland Mainline teal green 4-car train pack - *98*	50	65
L205080	**43051 *Duke and Duchess of York*** ICs grey - *89*	25	35
L205082	**43051 *Duke and Duchess of York* + 43072** ICs grey ex-set L106520 - *89*	50	NA
L205197/ L205199	**43053 *County of Humberside* + 43136** BRe I-C 125 exec grey ex-L149811 set - *87*	50	NA
L149806	**43058 *Midland Pride* + 43059** Midland Mainline teal green 4-car train pack - *98*	65	78
L14?	**43108 *Old Course St Andrews* + 43105 *City of Inverness*** GNER navy Sp Edn 250 pack (Harburn) - *02*	65	85
L205160	**43113 *City of Newcastle Upon Tyne* + 43063**		
L205164	BRe I-C 125 blue L149751 train pack - *84*	45	60
L205164	**43063** BRe I-C 125 blue, dummy - *84*	18	25
L205169	**43085 *City of Bradford*** BRe I-C 125 grey - *87*	25	35

L205198	**43091 *Edinburgh Military Tattoo*** BRe I-C 125 grey dummy - *87*	18	25
L205198/ L205197L	**43091 *Edinburgh Military Tattoo* + 43053 *County of Humberside*** BRe I-C 125 grey - *87*	NA	50
L149849	**43093 *Lady in Red* + 43155 *The Red Arrows*** Virgin XC red 4-car pack - *98*	65	NA
L149872	**43096 *The Great Racer* + 43110** GNER navy, white lettering, 4-car pack - *97*	60	75
L204681	**43100 *Blackpool Rock* + 43101 *The Irish Mail*** Virgin red - *99*	35	50

Virgin Trains Class 43 No.43101 Irish Mail [L22]

L149624	**43105 *City of Inverness* + 43108 *Old Course St Andrews*** + 2 Mk3s GNER navy Sp Edn 260 (Harburn Hobbies) - *02*	NA	70
L149908	**43109 + 43167** GNER navy, pearl lettering, 4-car train pack - *98*	45	60
L205160	**43113 *City of Newcastle Upon Tyne* (253042)** BRe InterCity 125 blue (also ex-107006 set) - *84*	25	35
L149918	**43117 + 43118** GNER navy gold lettering, 4-car train pack - *98*	50	65
(L106506)	**43122 + 43178** Virgin red ex-set - *99*	45	NA
L205180/ L205184	**43125 + 43126 (253028)** BRe I-C 125 executive grey - *85*	50	NA
L204733	**43129** ICs grey dummy - *96*	15	20
L149849	**43155 *The Red Arrows*** Virgin XC red - *98*	NPG	NPG
L205254	**43157 *HMS Penzance*** Virgin XC red - *99*	25	35
L149916	**43160 *Storm Force* + 43090** Virgin red 4-car train pack - *98*	50	65
L205160 L205164	**W43167 + W43168** BRe I-C 125 blue ex L149751 train pack and L103416V set - *82*	40	NA
L205160	**W43167** BRe I-C blue 125 - *82*	25	35
L205164	**W43168** BRe I-C 125 blue dummy - *82*	18	25
L149975	**43172 + 43009** First Great Western green + 2 Mk3 coaches - *00*	80	95
(L106522)	**43177 *University of Exeter* + 43139** ICs grey ex-set - *97*	65	NA
(L106522)	**43177 + 43139** ICs grey ex-set- *98*	65	NA
L205081/ L205082	**43178 + 43072** ICs grey ex-set - *89*	40	NA
L204732	**43181 *Devonport Royal Dockyard*** ICs grey - *96*	35	40
L149871	**43185 *Great Western* + 43168** GWT Merlin green 4-car train pack - *97*	65	NA
L205165/ L205168	orange+silver ex-Australian XPT L205165 pack, no numbers export only - *84*	35	NA
L149759	blue+grey ex-Australian Countrylink NSW 4-car pack - *92*	NA	70

L23. Classes 45/46 1Co-Co1

This was shown as a proposed model in the 1989/90 catalogue but was dropped, possibly because there was already a model on the market and it was felt that it did not offer adequate variations in livery. ccb = central codeboxes. scb = split codeboxes.

L205203	**D100 *Sherwood Forester*** BRc green no yellow panels - *not made*	NA	NA
L205207	**45012** BRe blue ccb - *not made*	NA	NA
L205205	**45032** BRe blue scb - *not made*	NA	NA
L205204	**45054** BRe blue scb - *not made*	NA	NA
L205206	**46004** BRe blue+grey plated nose with lights - *not made*	NA	NA

L24. Class 47 Co-Co (1987)

sno = snowploughs fitted.

L205103	**D1111** BRc 2-tone green, - *02*	40	50
L204904	**D1524** BRc 2-tone green, headcodes 0F70 + 1E07 - *01*	30	40
L205215	**D1574** BRc 2-tone green, original as built livery - *89*	30	40
L204718	**D1664 *George Jackson Churchward*** BRc 2-tone green Sp Edn 480 (MR&ME) - *96*	50	90
L204775	**D1733** blue Sp Edn 240 (Langdales) headcode XP64, no red panels - *97*	70	85
L204775	**D1733** blue Sp Edn 280 (Langdales) headcode XP64, with red panels fitted after leaving the factory - *97*	60	80
L205049	**1761** BRc 2-tone green, headcode 1A09 - *89*	35	50
L205219	**D1842** BRc 2-tone green, headcode 1M35 - *89*	35	50
L205192	**D1957** BRe blue - *99*	30	40
	D1962 (*see* **47833**)		
L204835	**47004/D1524 *Old Oak Common T&RSMD*** BRc 2-tone green, headcode 0F70 - *95*	40	60
L205255	**47006** Railfreight Construction grey, sno - *90*	35	50
L149930	**47010 *Xancidae*** Railfreight Petroleum grey Sp Edn 200 (Macclesfield Model Centre) part of 4 pack - *98*	50	65
L205210	**47016 *Atlas*** BReLL Railfreight grey, '1546', yellow cabsides - *99*	30	45

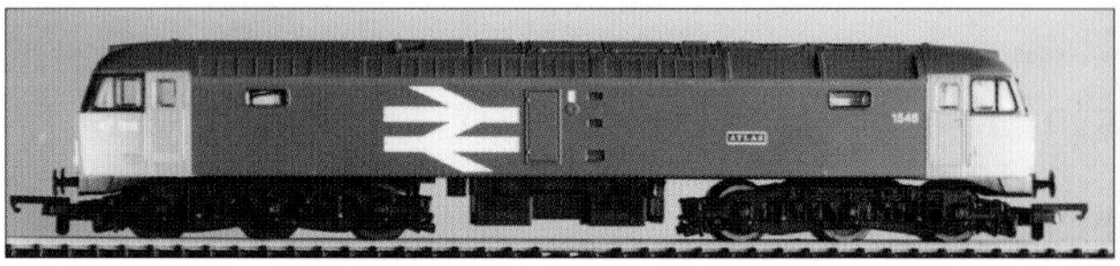

Railfreight Class 47 No.47016 Atlas [L24]

L204710	**47033 *The Royal Logistics Corps*** Railfreight Distribution European grey, Tunnel motif - *96*	30	50
L205266	**47079** Railfreight Metals grey - *88*	30	40
L204600	**47114 *Freightliner Bulk*** Freightliner 2-tone green Sp Edn 550 (*Rail Express*) - *97*	50	75
L149930	**47125 *Tonnidae*** Railfreight Petroleum grey Sp Edn 200 (Macclesfield Model Centre) part of 4 pack - *98*	60	65
L204789	**47142 *Traction*** Railfreight red stripe grey Sp Edn 550 (Macclesfield Model Centre), unofficial name - *98*	35	50
L204860	**47145 *Merddin Emrys*** Tinsley blue, Speedlink logo Ltd Edn 850 - *94*	50	75
L204885	**47157** Railfreight unspecified triple grey Sp Edn 500 (Geoffrey Allison) - *95*	50	65
L205081	**47163** BRe blue Stratford Union Jack Silver Jubilee finish - *01*	30	45
L205210	**47164** BRe blue Stratford Union Jack Silver Jubilee finish - *87*	30	60
L205043	**47190 *Pectinidae*** Railfreight Petroleum grey, flush both ends - *89*	30	40

Freightliner Class 47 No.47193 [L24]

L205298	**47193** Freightliner green - *00*	30	46
L204945	**47207 *Bulmers of Hereford*** BR Railfreight Distribution grey - *03*	NPG	65
L205092	**47210 *Blue Circle*** BRe Railfreight Construction grey, Eastfield motif - *00*	55	70
L205044	**47213 *Marchwood Military Port*** Railfreight Distribution (faded) triple grey Tinsley motifs - *03*	NPG	65
L149930	**47233 *Strombidae*** Railfreight Petroleum grey Sp Edn 200 (Macclesfield Model Centre) part of 4 pack - *98*	50	65
L204844	**47241** Railfreight Distribution European grey, Tunnel motif, Tinsley shedplates - *95*	30	40

L149930	**47278** ***Vasidae*** Railfreight Petroleum grey, Sp Edn 200 (Macclesfield Model Centre) part of 4 pack - *98*	50	65
L205045	**47283** ***Johnnie Walker*** Railfreight Distribution grey - *89*	30	45
L205048	**47298** BRe blue - *89*	30	40
L205035	**47299** ***Ariadne*** BRe blue - *00*	30	45
L205039	**47301** BReLL Railfreight red stripe grey, large numbers, Thornaby motif - *89*	35	50
L205260	**47305** Chemical blue, yell stripe - *88*	30	40
L204903	**47306** ***The Sapper*** Railfreight European grey, blue roof, regimental badge, Tinsley motif - *01*	35	50
L205257	**47315** Departmental plain grey - *90*	30	40
L205044	**47317** ***Willesden Yard*** Railfreight Distribution grey - *89*	30	45
L205075	**47323** ***Rover Group Quality Assured*** Railfreight European grey, Tinsley motif Sp Edn 500 (Geoffrey Allison) - *01*	30	40
L204962	**47324** RES red+dark grey - *02*	NPG	55
L20?	**47325** ***Red Rum*** Railfreight grey, Sp Edn (Collectable Models) - *01*	30	45
L204759	**47348** ***St Christopher's Railway Home*** Railfreight Distribution European Channel Tunnel grey - *97*	30	40
L205212	**47363** ***Billingham Enterprise*** BReLL Railfreight grey, Thornaby motif - *87*	30	40
L204832	**47365** ***Diamond Jubilee*** Railfreight Distribution European grey, Tunnel motif, Tinsley shedplates - *95*	30	40
L204633	**47369** BRc 2-tone green with yellow cab - *98*	25	35
L204889	**47375** ***Tinsley Traction Depot*** Railfreight Distribution grey - *95*	30	40
L204874	**47376** ***Freightliner 1995*** triple grey Freightliner, Crewe Diesel motif - *95*	30	40
L205033	**47380** ***Immingham*** Railfreight Petroleum grey - *91*	30	40
L205269	**47401** ***North Eastern*** BRe blue - *89*	30	40
L204666	**47402** ***Gateshead*** BRe blue, yellow cab windows - *99*	30	40

BR blue Class 47 No.47402 Gateshead [L24]

L204920	**47423** ***(Sceptre)*** BRe blue, NSE flashes - *01*	30	40
L205216	**47455** BReLL (extended), blue - *88*	40	60
(L107210)	**47461** ***Charles Rennie Mackintosh*** ScotRail blue+grey, Inverness motif, no front detail ex-set - *88*	50	NA
L205264	**47461** ***Charles Rennie Mackintosh*** ScotRail blue+grey, Inverness motif - *88*	30	NA
L205209	**47471** ***Norman Tunna G.C.*** I-C grey, yellow cabs + cab roofs, No.1 end flush - *99*	35	40
L205036	**47474** ***Sir Rowland Hill*** Parcels red - *90*	30	50
L205254	**47475** Provincial blue - *90*	30	40
(L104318)	**47475** ***Restive*** RES red, ex-set - *93*	50	NA
(L105114)	**47476** ***Night Mail*** Parcels red, ex-set - *91*	50	NA
L205040	**47484** ***Isambard Kingdom Brunel*** BRe Brunswick green, GWR 150, No.1 end flush - *89*	40	60
L205218	**47487** BRe blue - *87*	30	40
L205214	**47487** BRe InterCity executive grey, yellow doors, Stratford motif - *88*	40	60
L204682	**47488** Fragonset Railways, 2-tone green - *99*	30	40

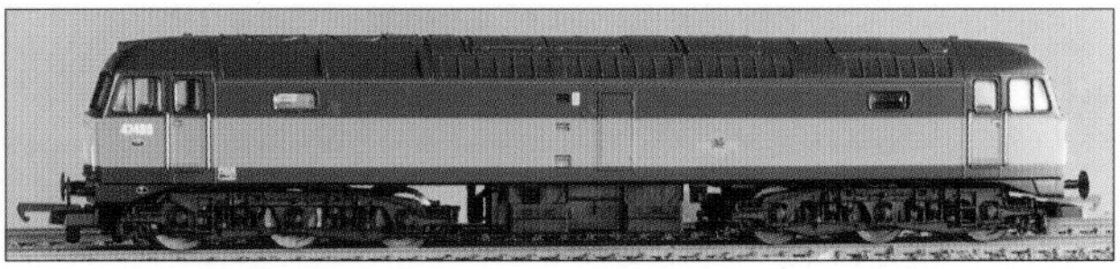

Fragonset two tone green Class 47 No.47488 [L24]

L205071	**47489** ***Crewe Diesel Depot*** Parcels red - *91*	35	50
(L104318)	**47490** ***Restive*** RES red, as 47475 but incorrect number, should have been *Resonant* ex-set - *93*	40	NA
L20?	**47492** ***The Enterprising Scot*** I-C ScotRail red stripe grey, Inverness motifs Sp Edn (Moray's) - *cancelled*	NA	NA
L205046	**47508** ***SS Great Britain*** InterCity Mainline grey - *89*	30	60
L204619	**47513** ***Severn*** BReLL blue, grey roof, yellow cabs - *98*	30	40
L204923	**47517** ***Andrew Carnegie*** BReLL blue, blue roof, yellow cabs, Inverness motif - *01*	35	50
L205042	**47522** ***Doncaster Enterprise*** BRe Parcels, LNER green, flush both ends - *89*	55	70
L204969	**47528** ***The Queen's Own Mercian Yeomanry*** InterCity Mainline - *03*	NPG	65
(L105112)	**47530** Revised NSE bright blue ex-set - *90*	50	NA
L205184	**47535** ***Saint Aidan*** RES red, Crewe Diesel motif - *99*	30	40
L205211	**47541** ***The Queen Mother*** InterCity ScotRail red stripe grey+ Inverness motif, plinth, coat of arms, etched nameplates Sp Edn 550 (Harburn) - *00*	60	77
(L107206)	**47549** ***Royal Mail*** InterCity Executive grey, ex-set - *91*	50	NA
L204734	**47555** ***The Commonwealth Spirit*** BRe blue, small logo, yellow cab windows - *96*	30	40
L204774	**47564** ***Colossus*** BReLL blue Sp Edn 550 (MR&ME) - *97*	30	45
L204729	**47565** ***Responsive*** RES red, headboard, Crewe Diesel motif - *96*	30	40
L205259	**47567** ***Red Star*** BRe blue - *88*	35	50
L204947	**47568** ***Royal Engineers Postal & Courier Corps*** BR InterCity Mainline grey - *02*	35	50
(L105110)	**47569** ***The Gloucestershire Regiment*** Parcels red, ex-set - *90*	50	NA
L205220	**47573** ***The London Standard*** BRe NSE bright blue, planned for 1987 but replaced by 47581 - *not made*	NA	NA
(L107108)	**47576** ***Kings Lynn*** NSE bright blue, ex-set - *88*	70	NA
L205038	**47579** ***James Nightall VC*** BRe Revised NSE original blue, nameplates both at one end - *89*	35	50
L205220	**47581** ***Great Eastern*** BRe NSE bright blue, Stratford motifs - *87*	30	60
L205209	**47582** ***County of Norfolk*** NSE bright blue, Stratford motifs - *87*	35	50
L205261	**47583** ***County of Hertfordshire*** NSE bright blue - *88*	35	50
L205127	**47583** ***County of Hertfordshire*** BReLL (extended), bright blue Sp Edn 500 (Langdale) - *00*	30	45
L205084	**47588** ***Resurgent*** BRe red RES, Crewe motifs - *93*	35	50
(L104314)	**47594** ***Resourceful*** BRe RES red, ex-set - *92*	50	NA
L205047	**47596** ***Aldeburgh Festival*** BRe blue, grey roof - *89*	35	50
L205034	**47599** Railfreight Metals grey, wrong size symbols - *91*	35	50
L205268	**47609** ***Fire Fly*** I-C executive grey - *89*	35	50
-	**47613** ***North Star*** I-C executive grey, no details to front end, ex-set - *88*	55	NA
L205262	**47613** ***North Star*** I-C executive grey - *88*	50	NA
L205041	**47620** ***Windsor Castle*** InterCity Executive grey, flush No.2 end - *89*	30	60
L204962	**47624** ***Saint Andrew*** RES red+grey Crewe Diesel motifs - *03*	NPG	65
L205205	**47625** ***Resplendent*** RES red - *92*	35	50
L205213	**47628** ***Sir Daniel Gooch*** Brunswick green, GWR 150 - *87*	30	60
L205206	**47635** ***Jimmy Milne*** BReLL extend, blue, Inverness motif Ltd Edn 850 - *92*	50	65
L205258	**47637** InterCity ScotRail red stripe grey, Inverness motifs - *88*	65	80
L20?	**47641** ***Fife Region*** BReLL blue, Eastfield motifs Sp Edn (Moray's) - *cancelled*	30	45
L204976	**47676** ***Northamptonshire*** ICs - *02*	NPG	65
L204818	**47701** ***Old Oak Common T&RSMD*** Revised NSE later blue, flush No.2 end - *94*	35	50

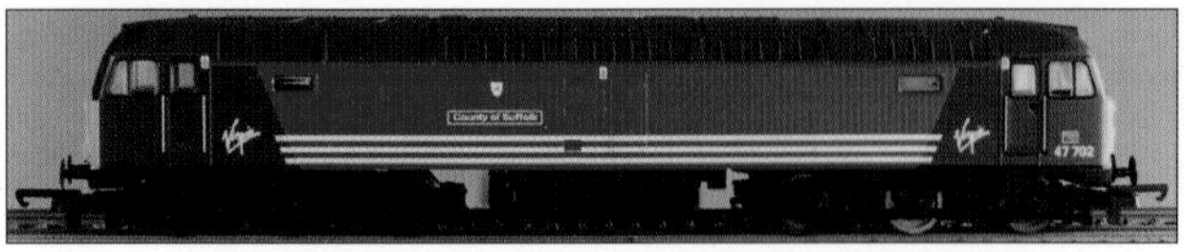

Virgin Trains Class 47 No.47702 County of Suffolk [L24]

L204636	**47702 *County of Suffolk*** Virgin red Sp.Edn - *99*	35	50
L204898	**47703** Fragonset black - *98*	30	40
L204999	**47703 *Hermes*** Fragonset black - *03*	NPG	65
L205211	**47705 *Lothian*** ScotRail grey+blue, one side incorrect - *87*	30	60
L204703	**47705 *Guy Fawkes*** Waterman Railways black - *96*	30	40
L205267	**47709 *The Lord Provost*** ScotRail grey+blue - *88*	30	60
L204880	**47710 *Lady Godiva*** Waterman Railways black - *95*	30	40
L204688	**47710** Fragonset Railways black with logos (also in pack 149971) - *99*	30	40
L149779	**47711 *Greyfriars Bobby*** BRe ScotRail grey+ blue, yellow cab roof Sp Edn 300 (Harburn) ex-train pack - *95*	70	NA
L205037	**47711 *Greyfriars Bobby*** BRe ScotRail grey+ blue, etched name + workplates, Scottie figurine Sp Edn 200 (Harburn Hobbies) - *95*	70	85
L204921	**47711 *County of Hertfordshire*** NSE revised blue, Stratford motif, flush No.2 end - *01*	35	50
L205032	**47712 *Lady Diana Spencer*** BReLL blue, light grey roof, yellow cabs - *00*	40	70
L204959	**47712 *Lady Diana Spencer*** BRe Parcels red+ grey Ltd Edn 1200 - *02*	NPG	65
L20?	**47713 *Tayside Region*** I-C ScotRail grey Sp Edn 350 (Moray's) sold with 47714 - *00*	35	50
L20?	**47714 *Grampian Region*** I-C ScotRail grey Sp Edn 350 (Moray's) sold with 47713 - *00*	35	50
L205037	**47716 *The Duke of Edinburgh's Award*** BRe ScotRail grey+blue, blue line, Haymarket motif - *88*	30	40
L204739	**47726 *Manchester Airport Progress*** RES red Sp Edn 500 (Langdale) - *96*	30	45
L204931	**47738 *Bristol Barton Hill*** RES maroon part of twin set with 67013 - *02*	NPG	NA
L149784	**47747 *Res Publica*** BRe RES red, ex-train pack - *95*	50	NA
(L149808)	**47749 *Atlantic College*** RES red, ex-train pack - *97*	50	NA
L149808	**47749 *Atlantic College*** RES red, with NFX 92714, NOX 95133 + NJX 95138 train pack - *97*	NA	100
L204690	**47758 *Regency Rail Cruises*** EWS maroon - *99*	30	40
L205258	**47760 *Ribblehead Viaduct*** EWS maroon - *00*	30	46

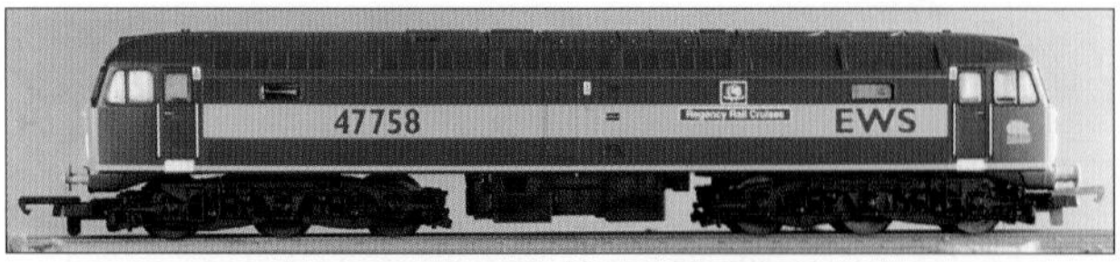

EWS Class 47 No.47758 [L24]

L204767	**47785 *Fiona Castle*** EWS maroon - *97*	30	45
L204792	**47786 *Roy Castle OBE*** EWS maroon- *98*	30	40
L204864	**47798 *Prince William*** RES royal dark purple, Crewe Diesel motif - *95*	30	40
L204794	**47798 *Prince William*** EWS Royal dark purple, new logos - *98*	30	40
L204888	**47799 *Prince Henry*** RES Royal dark purple, Crewe Diesel motif - *95*	30	40
L204795	**47799 *Prince Henry*** EWS Royal dark purple, new logos - *98*	30	40
L204853	**47803** Infrastructure yellow (transfers optional) Sp Edn 500 (Greenyards/ Hattons) - *93*	50	65
L204753	**47807** Porterbrook Leasing Co. purple+white - *97*	45	60
L205085	**47809 *Finsbury Park*** ICs grey - *94*	70	80
L149949	**47810** ICs Porterbrook grey? Ltd Edn 200 (Macclesfield MC) ex 4-pack - *99*	35	50
L149949	**47811** ICs grey Ltd Edn part of 4-pack - *99*	35	50
L204825	**47811** First Great Western green - *00*	30	43

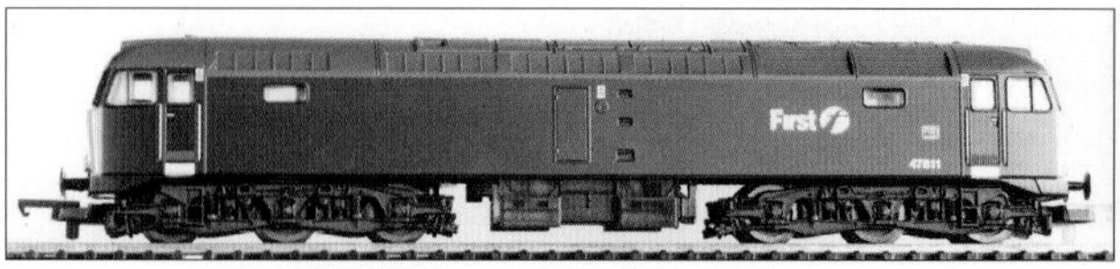

First Group Class 47 No.47811 [L24]

L204645	**47813 *SS Great Britain*** GWT green - *98*	25	35
L204761	**47814 *Totnes Castle*** Virgin red - *98*	30	40
L204727	**47817** Porterbrook purple+white - *96*	30	40
L204635	**47827** Virgin red - *99*	30	40
L204685	**47830** GWT green (also in 149970 sleeper pack) - *99*	30	40
L204685	**47830** Virgin red, issued in error, most recalled, reissued as 47827 - *99*	60	100
L205283	**47832** First Great Western revised green yellow stripe livery - *00*	30	40
(L105108)	**47833** ICs grey, ex-set - *93*	65	NA
L205089	**47833/D1962 *Captain Peter Manisty RN*** BRc 2-tone green Ltd Edn 850 - *93*	60	80
L205013	**47835 *Windsor Castle*** ICs grey, flush No.2 end Sp Edn 650 (Cheltenham Model Centre) - *93*	45	65
L205256	**47838** ICs grey, incorrect white skirting to body sides - *90*	35	50
L205256	as above, correct white skirting - *90*	35	50
L149960	**47840 *North Star*** ICs grey Ltd Edn part of 4-pack - *99*	35	50
L205202	**47841 *Institute of Mechanical Engineers*** ICs grey, Ltd Edn 500 (Macclesfield Model Centre) - *99*	30	45
L204621	**47844** Virgin red - *98*	30	40

Virgin Trains Class 47 No.47844 [L24]

L205171	**47846 *Thor*** GWT green - *99*	30	40
L205268	**47849 *Cadeirlan Bangor Cathedral*** Virgin red Ltd Edn 550 - *00*	30	45
(L149960)	**47853** InterCity Swallow grey, Ltd Edn, part of 4-pack - *99*	35	50
(L149960)	**47840 *North Star*** + **47853** as above Sp Edn 250 (Macclesfield Model Centre) - *99*	NA	120
L20?	**47791 *VSOE*** RES red+grey Sp Edn (Collectable Models) - *01*	30	45
L204823	**47972 *Royal Army Ordnance Corps*** BRe RTC (Tech Services) red+grey Sp Edn 850 (Beatties) - *93*	50	65
L205035	**47976 *Aviemore Centre*** Dutch grey+yellow - *91*	30	40
L205253	**97561 *Midland Counties Railway* 150** maroon, yellow cabs + lined border - *90*	40	50

L25. Class 50 Co-Co (1984)

The model used the bogies from the Class 55 which were to H0 scale. sno = snowploughs fitted

L205009	**D400** BRe blue Sp Edn 400 (Rail Magazine) headboard - *91*	110	140
L205009	**D400** BRe blue, headcode 1S57 - *92*	30	45
L205170	**50001 *Dreadnought*** BRe blue - *99*	30	45
L205265	**50003 *Tremeraire*** Revised NSE bright blue, these were 750 of *Ark Royal* refinished in UK - *92*	55	80
L205140	**50007 *Sir Edward Elgar*** BRe Brunswick green, original mould - *85*	30	45
L205140	**50007 *Sir Edward Elgar*** BRe Brunswick green,		

	modified mould - *91*	30	45
L205121	**50008 *Thunderer*** BRe blue, grey roof Ltd Edn 550 - *92*	85	120
L204811	**50009 *Conqueror*** BReLL blue - *94*	30	45
L205232	**50010 *Monarch*** BReLL blue, blue roof Sp Edn 550 (Traction magazine) - *99*	35	47
L205226	**50015 *Valiant*** BReLL blue - *87*	30	45
L205007	**50015 *Valiant*** BRe Dutch grey+yellow - *91*	30	45
L205135	**50017 *Royal Oak*** BRe NSE bt.blue - *86*	30	45

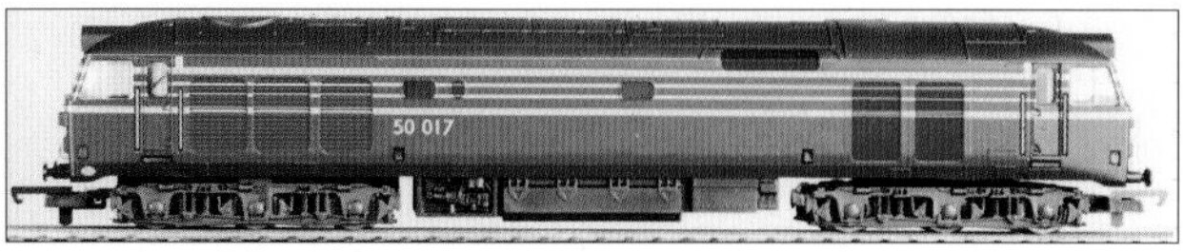

VOSE Northern Pullman Class 50 No.50017 Royal Oak [L25]

L205175	**50017** VSOE Northern Pullman maroon (LMS Royal Scot livery) - *00*	30	45
L204896	**50019 *Ramillies*** BRe blue, grey roof, Sp Edn 600 (Model Railway Enthusiast) - *94*	45	60
L205141	**50020 *Revenge*** BRe blue, original mould - *84*	30	45
L205279	**50021 *Rodney*** BReLL blue - *89*	30	45
L205131	**50023 *Howe*** BRe NSE bright blue - *86*	30	45
(L103408)	**50023 *Howe*** BRe NSE bright blue, ex-set no cab detail - *86*	35	NA
L205177	**50025 *Invincible*** BRe NSE bt.blue - *93*	30	45
L205291	**50027 *Lion*** NSE Revised bt.blue, sno - *01*	30	45
L205280	**50028 *Tiger*** BRe Revised NSE bright blue - *89*	30	45
(L107208)	**50030 *Repulse*** BRe Revised NSE bright blue ex-set - *89*	40	NA
L205011	**50031 *Hood*** BReLL blue Sp Edn 650 (Cheltenham Model Centre) - *93*	60	75
L205179	**50033 *Glorious*** Revised NSE bright blue ex-set - *90*	45	NA
(L104317)	**50033 *Glorious*** Revised NSE bright blue ex-set - *93*	45	NA

NSE Class 50 No.50033 Glorious [L25]

(L105179)	**50033 *Glorious*** Revised NSE bright blue ex-set - *00*	30	NA
L205027	**50034 *Furious*** Revised NSE bt.blue - *91*	30	45
L205207	**50035 *Ark Royal*** Revised NSE bright blue Ltd Edn 850 - *92*	50	65
L204787	**50036 *Victorious*** BReLL blue, yellow cab, grey roof - *98*	30	40
L205227	**50038 *Formidable*** BReLL blue - *87*	30	45
L204961	**50040 *Leviathan*** BReLL blue Ltd Edn 1100 - *02*	30	45
(L104312)	**50041 *Bulwark*** Revised NSE bright blue ex-set - *92*	45	NA
(L106207)	**50042 *Triumph*** BReLL blue, black cab surrounds ex-set - *89*	100	NA
L205142	**50043 *Eagle*** BReLL blue, original mould, light grey roof - *84*	30	40
L205142	**50043 *Eagle*** BReLL blue, revised mould - *84*	40	55
L205224	**50044 *Exeter*** NSE bright blue - *87*	30	45
L206920	**50046 *Ajax*** BReLL blue, black roof yellow cab, Ltd Edn 550 (MR&ME) - *99*	30	45
L204716	**50050 *Peco Golden Jubilee 1946- 1996*** BReLL blue Sp Edn 500 (Peco) - *96*	30	45
L205281	**50149 *Defiance*** BRe Railfreight General grey Laira motif (experimental motif) - *87*	30	45

L26. Class 52 C-C (1979)

hyp = half yellow end panels. fyp = full yellow end panels.

L205130	**D1001 *Western Pathfinder*** BRc maroon - *01*	30	40
L205134	**D1003 *Western Pioneer*** BRc green, hyp, headcode 1A66 - *80*	30	40
L204800	**D1004 *Western Crusader*** BRc green, red nameplate, hyp, headcode 1V23 - *94*	30	45
L204846	**D1013 *Western Ranger*** BRe blue - *95*	30	40
L205010	**D1015 *Western Champion*** BRc golden ochre Sp Edn 500 (Cheltenham Model Centre) - *92*	70	120
L205121	**D1016 *Western Gladiator*** BRc maroon, headcode 1A66, hyp - *79*	30	40
L205126	**D1023 *Western Enterprise*** BRd sand, wrong name, headcode 1V86, fyp - *79*	30	40
L204776	**D1023 *Western Fusilier*** BRe blue Ltd Edn 550 (Langdale) - *98*	30	45
L204668	**D1043 *Western Duke*** BRe blue - *99*	30	40

BR Class 52 No.D1043 Western Duke [L26]

L205122	**D1071 *Western Renown*** BRe blue, headcode 1A66 - *79*	30	40

L27. Class 55 Co-Co (1977)

hyp = half yellow end panels. fyp = full yellow ends. pcl = plated codeboxes with lights. This model had H0 scale bogies as the model was originally to have been made to this scale.

L204651	**D9000 *Royal Scots Greys*** BRc 2-tone green Sp Edn 550 (Geoffrey Allison) - *98*	35	50
L204781	**D9001 *St Paddy*** BRc 2-tone green Sp Edn 550 (Rails) - *97*	50	80
L205222	**D9002 *Kings Own Yorkshire Light Infantry*** BRc 2-tone green, no name on side, etched plates supplied Sp Edn 500 (Moray's) - *00*	35	50
L205105	**D9003 *Meld*** BRc 2-tone green, headcode 1S14 - *77*	30	40
L204951	**D9005 *The Prince of Wales's Own Regiment of Yorkshire*** BRc 2-tone green Ltd Edn 350 (Rails) - *02*	NPG	50
L205105	**D9008 *The Green Howards*** BRc 2-tone green, handrails not picked out, headcode 1A35 - *82*	30	40
L204657	**D9009 *Alycidon*** BRc 2-tone green, Sp Edn 550 (Rails/DPS) - *98*	30	45
L204952	**D9012 *Crepello*** BRc 2-tone green Ltd Edn 350 (Rails) - *02*	NPG	50

BR Class 55 No.D9018 Ballymoss [L27]

L204816	**D9013 *The Black Watch*** BRc 2-tone green, hyp, windows not picked out Sp Edn 650 (MR&ME) - *93*	60	75
L204656	**D9015 *Tulyar*** BRc 2-tone green, Sp Edn 550 (DPS/Rails) - *98*	30	45
L204607	**D9016 *Gordon Highlander*** BRc 2-tone green, Ltd Edn 850 - *98*	30	60
L205269	**D9018 *Ballymoss*** BRc 2-tone green, hyp - *00*	30	45
L204743	**D9019 *Royal Highland Fusilier*** BRc 2-tone green, hyp, steps not picked out Sp Edn 550 (MR&ME) - *97*	40	55
L204953	**D9020 *Nimbus*** BRc 2-tone green Ltd Edn 350 (Rails) - *02*	NPG	50
L201645	**9006 *Fife and Forfar Yeomanry*** BRe blue also chromatic blue, headcode 1G09 window bars painted on, box numbered '1645MW' & '5106MW' - *77*	35	85
L205106	**9006 *Fife and Forfar Yeomanry*** BRe blue also chromatic blue, headcode 1G09 - *77*	30	40
L205260	**9016 *The Gordon Highlander*** Porterbrook purple Ltd Edn 1200 - *00*	80	100
L205299	**55001 *St Paddy*** BRe blue Ltd Edn 700 - *00*	35	50
L204802	**55002 *Kings Own Yorkshire Light Infantry*** BRc 2-tone green, fyp, pcl Ltd Edn 500 - *94*	40	60

L204801	**55007** ***Pinza*** BRe blue, white cab surround, pcl - *93*	30	60
L204869	**55009** ***Alycidon*** BRe blue, silver grills and batteries - *94*	30	60
L204936	**55010** ***The King's Own Scottish Borderer*** BRe blue - *02*	45	60
L204738	**55015** ***Tulyar*** BRe blue Sp Edn 550 (DPS + Rails) - *96*	45	60
L205191	**55017** ***The Durham Light Infantry*** BRe blue, Ltd Edn 1000 - *99*	30	45
L205230	**55019** ***Royal Highland Fusilier*** BRe blue Sp Edn (DPS) - *00*	30	45

BR Class 55 No.55017 The Durham Light Infantry [L27]

L204702	**55021** ***Argyll and Sutherland Highlander*** BRe blue, etched crests and nameplates + replica Argyll's badge Sp Edn 500 (Harburn Hobbies) - *96*	35	60
L205106	**55022** ***Royal Scots Grey*** BRe blue, handrails not picked out - *82*	30	40

L28. Class 57 Co-Co (1999)

L204649	**57001** ***Freightliner Pioneer*** Freightliner green Ltd Edn 750 (*Rail Express*) - *99*	60	75
L204686	**57002** ***Freightliner Phoenix*** Freightliner green - *99*	30	50

Freightliner Class 57 No.57007 [L28]

L204686	**57003** ***Freightliner Evolution*** green Freightliner - *99*	30	50
L205250	**57007** ***Freightliner Bond*** Freightliner green - *00*	30	50

L29. Class 59 Co-Co (1994)

L204838	**59001** ***Yeoman Endeavour*** original Foster Yeoman silver+blue livery - *94*	40	50
L204804	**59002** ***Yeoman Enterprise*** original Foster Yeoman silver+blue livery - *94*	40	55
L205029	**59002** ***Alan J Day*** Mendip Rail green+orange Sp Edn 750 (Rail Express) - *01*	40	50
L204849	**59003** ***Yeoman Highlander*** original Foster Yeoman silver+blue livery - *96*	40	60
L204643	**59003** ***Yeoman Highlander*** DB/ Yeoman silver+red+blue Sp Edn 500 (Beatties) - *98*	45	70
L204850	**59005** ***Kenneth J Painter*** original Foster Yeoman silver+blue livery - *95*	40	55
L204646	**59005** ***Kenneth J Painter*** revised Foster Yeoman silver+blue livery - *99*	30	45
L204851	**59101** ***Village of Whatley*** original ARC yellow livery - *96*	40	55
L204667	**59101** ***Village of Whatley*** revised ARC silver+ yellow livery - *99*	30	45

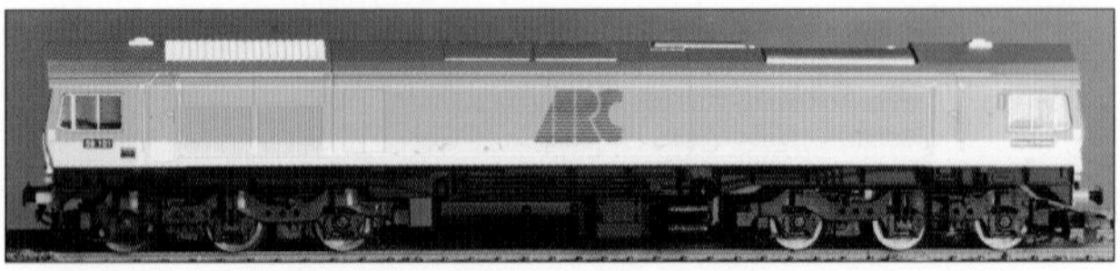

ARC Class 59 No.59101 Village of Whatley [L29]

L204839	**59102** ***Village of Chantry*** original ARC yellow livery - *94*	40	55
L204803	**59103** ***Village of Mells*** original ARC yellow livery - *94*	40	55
L204665	**59103** ***Village of Mells*** Hanson orange+blue livery - *99*	40	55
L204852	**59104** ***Village of Great Elm*** original ARC yellow livery - *95*	35	50
L205257	**59104** ***Village of Great Elm*** Hanson orange+ blue livery - *99*	40	52
L204805	**59201** ***Vale of York*** National Power blue - *94*	45	60
L204664	**59201** ***Vale of York*** EWS maroon - *99*	35	50
L204674	**59203** ***Vale of Pickering*** EWS maroon - *99*	30	50
L205292	**59206** ***Pride of Ferrybridge*** National Power blue - *00*	40	52

L30. Class 60 Co-Co (1990)

hyp = half yellow end panel. OB = original body.

L204867	**60000** Loadhaul black+orange Sp Edn 100 for Loadhaul personnel - *95*	250	450
L205020	**60001** ***Steadfast*** Railfreight Construction grey OB - *90*	30	45
L204957	**60001** ***The Railway Observer*** EWS maroon - *03*	NPG	NPG
L205021	**60002** ***Capability Brown*** Railfreight Petroleum grey OB, wrong side grill, Immingham motif - *90*	30	45
L204764	**60003** ***Freight Transport Association*** EWS maroon - *97*	30	45
L205024	**60003** ***Christopher Wren*** Railfreight Petroleum grey OB - *91*	35	50
L205022	**60004** ***Lochnager*** Railfreight Coal grey OB - *90*	35	50
L204783	**60006** ***Scunthorpe Ironmaster*** British Steel blue - *98*	30	45
L204926	**60006** ***Scunthorpe Ironmaster*** EWS Corus silver - *01*	35	50

BR 'Steel' Class 60 No.60006 Scunthorpe Iron Master [L30]

L205023	**60008** ***Moel Fammau*** Railfreight Metals grey OB - *90*	35	50
L204736	**60008** ***Gypsum Queen II*** Loadhaul black+ orange - *97*	50	70
L204715	**60011** Mainline blue - *96*	30	45
L204755	**60012** EW&S maroon - *97*	30	45
L204875	**60015** ***Bow Fell*** Transrail on triple grey Cardiff Canton plates - *95*	30	45
L204933	**60016** ***Rail Magazine*** EWS maroon, yellow snow ploughs - *01*	35	50
L204741	**60019** EW&S maroon - *97*	30	45
L204806	**60032** ***William Booth*** BRe Railfreight Coal grey, Toton shedplates - *93*	35	60
L204799	**60033** ***Tees Steel Express*** British Steel blue - *98*	35	50
L204918	**60033** ***Tees Steel Express*** EWS Corus silver - *01*	35	50
L204807	**60039** ***Glastonbury Tor*** BRe Railfreight Construction grey, Stewarts Lane shed plates - *93*	35	50
L204876	**60040** ***Brecon Beacons*** BRe Mainline on 3-grey Railfreight, Stewarts Lane motif - *95*	30	45
L205169	**60044** ***Ailsa Craig*** Mainline blue - *99*	30	45
L204808	**60050** ***Roseberry Topping*** BRe Railfreight Metals grey, Thornaby shedplates - *94*	30	45
L204857	**60050** ***Roseberry Topping*** BRe Loadhaul on Railfreight grey Thornaby motif sno - *95*	30	45
L204854	**60051** ***Mary Somerville*** Railfreight Petroleum grey - *95*	30	45
L205025	**60055** ***Thomas Barnardo*** Railfreight Coal triple grey sno - *91*	35	50
L204867	**60059** ***Swinden Dalesman*** Loadhaul black +orange - *95*	30	45
L204768	**60063** ***James Murray*** Transrail on triple grey - *97*	30	45

L204909	**60081** ***Isambard Kingdom Brunel*** GWR green, decals, lined, yhp, No.081 on front, Ltd Edn 1,000 - *01*	45	70
L204620	**60083** ***Mountsorrel*** EWS maroon - *99*	30	40
L204924	**60093** ***Jack Stirk*** Transrail on triple grey - *01*	35	50
L205025	**60098** ***Charles Francis Brush*** BRe Railfreight Construction grey Sp Edn 250 for Brush personnel - *93*	230	320
L205026	**60100** ***Boar of Badenoch*** BRe Railfreight Construction grey Ltd Edn 850 - *92*	45	60

L31. Class 66 Co-Co (1999)

emp = etched metal plates

L204679	**66001** EWS maroon - *99*	35	75
L204691	**66016** EWS maroon - *99*	35	75

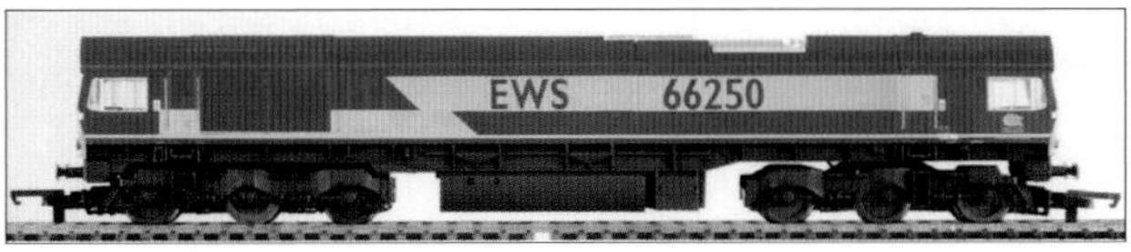

EWS Class 66 No.66250 [L31]

L205002	**66068** EWS maroon - *02*	35	75
L205197	**66100** EWS maroon Ltd Edn - *99*	40	75
L204906	**66250** EWS maroon - *01*	40	75
L205229	**66501** Freightliner green Sp Edn 750 (Rail Express) - *99*	45	75
L205229	**66501** ***Japan 2001*** Freightliner green Sp Edn 750 (Rail Express) emp - *99*	45	75
L205227	**66502** Freightliner green - *99*	40	75
L205284	**66504** Freightliner green Ltd Edn 700 - *00*	40	75
L204901	**66506** ***Crewe Regeneration*** Freightliner green, Railtrack - *01*	40	75
L205059	**66527** ***Don Raider*** Freightliner green, Railtrack - *03*	40	75
L204917	**66601** ***The Hope Valley*** Freightliner green - *01*	40	75
L205122	**66701** ***Railtrack National Logistics*** GBRf blue Sp Edn 750 (Rail Express) - *02*	50	75
L204966	**66703** GBRf blue - *03*	40	75
L204943	**66706** GBRf blue - *02*	50	75

L32. Class 67 Bo-Bo (2001)

The model has a 5-pole motor, all wheel pickup and drive, precision helical gears, high rigidity ABS chassis construction with low set ballast, custom electronics control via PCB, scale starting acceleration control and dual directional lighting. The body is highly detailed with separately moulded handrails and super detail parts included. Glazing is flush and the couplings detachable.

L205261	**67001** ***Night Mail*** EWS maroon - *02*	40	70
L204963	**67002** ***Special Delivery*** EWS maroon - *03*	35	45
L204929	**67003** EWS maroon - *02*	40	70
L204942	**67004** ***Post Haste*** EWS maroon - *03*	35	45
L204978	**67005** ***The Queen's Messenger*** EWS maroon - *03*	40	50
L204931	**67013** EWS maroon part of twin set with 47738 - *02*	35	NA
L149619	**67025** EWS maroon + 3 Super GUVs (94123+94157+94208) - *02*	NA	NPG
L205095	**67030** EWS maroon Ltd Edn 750 - *03*	35	45

Electro Diesels

L33. Class 73 Electro-Diesel Bo-Bo (1986)

L205276	**E6001** BRc 2 tone green (SR EMU green with lime green bottom band) - *87*	40	60
L205192	**E6003** BRc Brunswick green - *87*	50	70

BR Electric blue Class 73 No.E6012 [L33]

L149929	**E6003 Sir *Herbert Walker*** BRc green Sp Edn 375 (Rails) paired with 73128 - *98*	30	45
L205223	**E6012** BRe in original blue with grey bottom band - *87*	30	50
L205275	**73001** BRe blue - *87*	30	50
L205275	**73001** BRe blue, grey roof - *87*	30	50
L205274	**73002** BReLL blue, large number - *89*	30	50
L205273	**73004** ***The Bluebell Railway*** BRe NSE bright blue, yellow cab roofs - *89*	30	50
L205272	**73005** ***Watercress Line*** BRe NSE bright blue, shown in 1989/90 catalogue - *not made*	NA	NA
L204618	**73101** ***Brighton Evening Argus*** Pullman brown+cream - *98*	30	75
L205186	**73101** ***The Royal Alex*** Pullman brown+cream, commemorative edition first 3000 * certificated - *92*	35	75
L205270	**73105** BReLL blue - *90*	25	40
L205170	**73108** BRe early blue, roof dark grey - *87*	30	50
L205001	**73109** ***Battle of Britain 50th Anniversary*** Revised NSE bright blue, Ltd Edn 550 - *92*	100	130
L205001	**73109** ***Battle of Britain 50th Anniversary*** Revised NSE bright blue original Ltd Edn body without lights and other detail - *92*	NPG	250
L205090/ L205016	**73109** ***Battle of Britain 50th Anniversary*** SWT bright blue - *01*	35	50
L204862	**73114** ***Stewarts Lane Traction Maintenance Depot*** Mainline blue, Stewarts Lane motif - *94*	25	40
L204877	**73118** triple grey EPS, code 73 - *94*	25	40
L205193	**73123** ***Gatwick Express*** BReLL I-C executive grey, large numbers, full yellow ends, light grey roof - *87*	30	40
L205193	I-C Executive grey full yellow ends, light grey roof no number or detail, 2 only - *87*	NPG	150
L205191	**73125** ***Stewarts Lane 1860-1985*** BReLL I-C executive grey, half yellow and half black cab ends - *86*	30	40
(L103406)	**73125** ***Stewarts Lane 1860-1985*** I-C executive grey, no running numbers, enlarged shed plate on cabside ex-set - *86*	90	NA
L205012	**73126** ***Kent & East Sussex Railway*** Revised NSE bright blue Sp Edn 650 (Signal Box) - *93*	75	80
L204742	**73128** EW&S maroon - *96*	30	40
L149929	**73128** ***OVS Bulleid*** BRe Dutch grey+ yellow Stewarts Lane motif Sp Edn 375 (Rails) paired with E6003 - *98*	30	45
L205178	**73129** ***City of Winchester*** NSE bright blue without branding, city coat of arms - *00*	30	45
L205277	**73130** ***City of Portsmouth*** BRe Intercity Mainline grey - *89*	30	40
L204757	**73131** EW&S maroon - *97*	30	45
L204648	**73133** ***Bluebell Railway*** BRe Dutch grey+ yellow - *98*	25	40
L205194	**73134** ***Woking Homes 1885-1985*** BReLL InterCity black+grey, yellow cab roof - *99*	30	45
L205169	**73136** BRe Departmental plain grey, code 20 - *91*	25	40
L205271	**73138** ***Poste Haste*** BRe I-C Mainline grey, full yellow to front end only - *89*	30	40
L205169	**73142** ***Broadlands*** BReLL blue - *86*	30	40
L205194	**73142** ***Broadlands*** BReLL I-C Executive grey, dark roof, yellow cab roofs - *87*	30	40
L204847	**73212** ***Airtour Suisse*** Gatwick Express grey - *94*	25	35
L204770	**73901** Merseyrail yellow Sp Edn 500 (Langdale) - *97*	40	55

* Certificate number 3,190 has been found!

Electrics

L34. Class 87 Bo-Bo (1979)

L204810	**87002** ***Royal Sovereign*** ICs grey - *94*	30	45
L205195	**87003** ***Patriot*** Virgin red+black - *99*	30	45

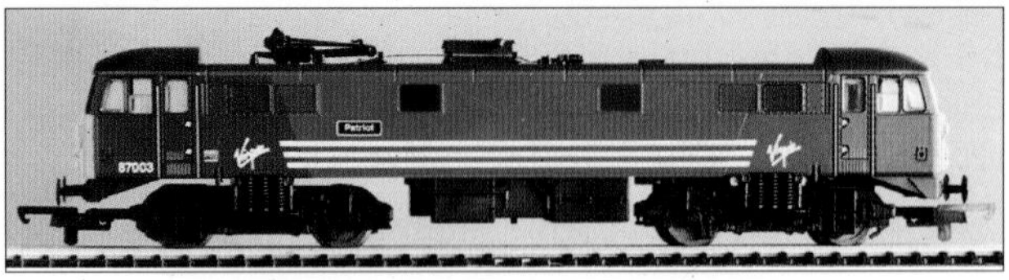

Virgin Trains Class 87 No 87003 Phoenix [L34]

L205125	**87005 *City of London*** BRe blue - *79*	30	40
L205125	**87005 *City of London*** BRe I-C Executive grey - *87*	30	40
L204631	**87006 *George Reynolds*** Virgin red+black - *98*	30	35
L204798	**87009** Virgin red+black - *98*	30	40
L205195	**87009 *City of Birmingham*** BRe I-C Executive grey - *86*	30	40
L205130	**87012 *Couer de Lion*** BRe I-C Executive grey - *85*	30	40
L205185	**87018 *Lord Nelson*** BRe I-C Executive grey - *85*	30	40
L205175	**87019 *Sir Winston Churchill*** BRe blue - *84*	30	40
L204925	**87021 *Robert the Bruce*** BRe InterCity Executive grey - *01*	35	50
L205155	**87022 *Cock O' The North*** BReLL, non-authentic LL blue livery - *82*	30	40
L205179	**87031 *Hal O' The Wynd*** InterCity Mainline grey - *90*	30	40
L204809	**87101 *Stephenson*** BRe Railfreight Distribution grey, Falcon shed plates - *93*	30	40

L35. Class 90 Bo-Bo

This was shown as a proposed model in the 1989/90 catalogue but was dropped, possibly because Hornby had launched their model in 1988.

L205291	**90002** ICs grey - *not made*	NA	NA

L36. Class 91 Bo-Bo

This was shown as a proposed model in the 1989/90 catalogue but was dropped, possibly because Hornby had launched their model in 1988.

L205295	InterCity Swallow grey - *not made*	NA	NA

L37. Class 92 Co-Co (1994)

L204855	**92001 *Victor Hugo*** BRe Railfreight Distrib grey, Tunnel + Crewe Electric motifs, Commemorative Edn. 3000 certificated - *94*	30	40
L204672	**92001 *Victor Hugo*** EWS maroon, Tunnel motif - *99*	30	45

EWS Class 92 No.92001 Victor Hugo [L37]

L204893	**92003 *Beethoven*** BRe Railfreight EPS grey, Tunnel+Crewe Electric motifs - *95*	35	50
L204672	**92015 *DH Lawrence*** Railfreight Unspecified grey - *95*	30	40
L204871	**92017 *Shakespeare*** BRe Railfreight Unspecified grey, Tunnel motif - *95*	35	40
L204870	**92022 *Charles Dickins*** BRe Railfreight Distribution grey, Tunnel motif - *94*	35	40
L204873	**92023 *Ravel*** Railfreight SNCF grey, Tunnel + Crewe Electric motifs - *94*	35	50
L204708	**92030 *Ashford*** BRe Railfreight Distribution grey, Ltd Edn 850 *, Tunnel + Crewe Electric motifs - *98*	30	40
L204984	**92031 *The Institute of Logistics and Transport*** EWS maroon Tunnel motifs - *03*	NPG	NPG
L204884	**92034 *Kipling*** Railfreight Unspecified grey - *96*	30	45
L204777	**92041 *Vaughan Williams*** Railfreight Unspecified grey Sp Edn 300 (Beatties) - *97*	75	90

* Both 300 and 850 appear on certificates.

Multiple Units

L38. Class 101 (1997)

L149894	**51228/51506** BRe grey+blue Regional Railways - *97*	40	60
L149895	**M50321/M50303** BRc green, white stripe and whiskers - *97*	45	65
L149896	**53311/53322** NSE bright blue - *97*	40	60
L149897	**M50304/M50338** BRe blue - *97*	40	60
L149898	**51188/53268** BRe Regional Railways ScotRail grey+blue - *97*	40	60
L149899	**E51433/E51503** BRc green - *97*	45	60
L149814	**SC51800/SC51808** BRc green, destination Dundee - *98*	45	60
L149915	**E51425/59108/E51503** BRe blue+grey - *99*	35	55
L149927	**51177/59303/53269** BRe Regional Railways grey+blue - *99*	35	55
L149959	**51253/53171** Strathclyde PTE maroon 2-car set Sp Edn 300 (D&F) - *99*	50	85
L149973	**M53331/M59125/M53308** BRe, blue/ grey rework, destination Crewe - *00*	60	75
L149612	**E51206/E56364** BRc green, whiskers - *01*	45	60

L39. Class 117/2 (1980)

Although these are listed as sets, cars could be purchased individually in most cases.

-	**117305 (51410/59520/51368)** BRc GWR brown+cream Sp Edn 300 (*Model Railway Enthusiast* magazine) - *94*	NA	140
L204829	**51410** BRc GWR brown+cream power car from above set - *94*	55	NA

BR Class 117 No.51410 [L39]

L204830	**59520** BRc GWR brown+cream centre car from above set - *94*	20	NA
L204831	**51368** BRc GWR brown+cream dummy power car ex above set - *94*	20	NA
L149809	**W51342/W59518/W51340** BRc 1959 green livery 3-car pack, yellow half panels, headcode 1A20 - *84*	NA	65
L149851	as above pack - *93*	40	65
L205137	**W51342** BRc green motor brake 2nd powered - *80*	20	25
L205146	**W59518** BR green composite trailer - *82*	10	15
L205139	**W51340** BRc green motor brake 2nd non-powered - *80*	10	15
L149816	**W51334/W59493/W51332** BRe 1974 blue 3-car pack, headcode 2A71 - *85*	NA	60
L149852	as above pack - *93*	40	65
L205136	**W51334** BRe blue motor brake 2nd powered - *80*	20	25
L205145	**W59493** BR blue composite trailer - *82*	10	15
L205138	**W51332** BRe blue motor brake 2nd non-powered - *80*	10	15
L149810	**W51350/W59508/W51332** BRe 1981 blue+grey livery 3-car pack - *84*	NA	60
L149854	as above pack - *93*	40	65
L205147	**W51350** BRe blue+grey motor brake 2nd powered - *81*	20	25
L205148	**W59508** BR blue+grey composite trailer - *82*	10	15
L205149	**W51332** BRe blue+grey motor brake 2nd		

	non-powered - *81*	10	15
L149815	**W51350/W59484/W51346** BRe white+blue refurbished livery 3-car pack - *85*	NA	60
L205152	**W51350** BRe white+blue motor brake 2nd powered - *82*	20	25
L205153	**W59484** BR white+blue composite trailer - *82*	10	15
L205154	**W51346** BRe white+blue motor brake 2nd non-powered - *82*	10	15
L149850	**117306 (51369/59521/51411**) BRe Regional Railways grey+blue 3-car pack - *93*	NA	60
L205086	**51369** BRe Regional Railways grey+blue motor brake 2nd powered - *91*	20	25
L205087	**59521** BRe Regional Railways grey+blue composite trailer - *91*	10	15
L205088	**51411** BRe Regional Railways grey+blue motor brake 2nd non-powered - *91*	10	15
L149853	**L424 (51362/59514/51404**) BRe NSE bright blue 3-car pack - *93*	NA	60
L205097	**51362** BRe NSE grey+blue motor brake 2nd powered - *92*	20	25
L205098	**59514** BR NSE grey+blue composite trailer - *92*	10	15
L205099	**51404** BRe NSE grey+blue motor brake 2nd non-powered - *92*	10	15

L40. Class 121/2 'Bubble Car' (1998)
(see also table L43 for Class 960)

L205030	**W55020** BRc brown+cream, yellow front, white roof, 500 made - *00*	40	60
L204630	**W55025** BRc green, whiskers - *98*	30	45
L204617	**W55026** BRc green, small yellow warning panel, code 2T55 - *98*	30	45
L204611	**55027** NSE bright blue - *98*	30	40

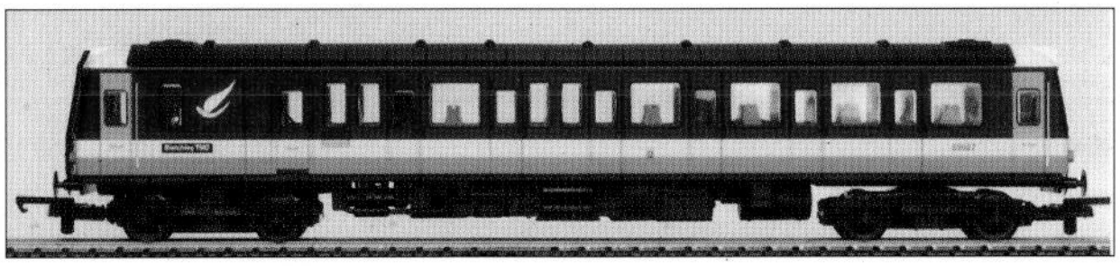

Silverlink Class 121 No.55027 Bletchley TMD [L40]

L204623	**W55028** BRe blue+grey - *98*	30	40
L204912	**55029 *Marston Vale*** Silverlink blue+green - *01*	30	40
L204608	**W55035 (B135)** BRe blue, destination Bath - *98*	30	40
L205028	**55027 *Bletchly MD*** Silverlink blue+green - *00*	30	40

L41. Class 156 (1989)

L205053	**156470 (52470)** BRe Provincial blue, single car only - *92*	15	35
L204706	**156402 (52402+57402)** BRe 158 Class style grey Regional Railways Express, - *96*	40	55
L204935	**156407 (5740+/52407)** Central Trains green - *02*	45	60
L204895	**156420 (52420+57420)** BRe Regional Railways grey+blue, green stripe - *96*	40	55

SPT Class 156 The Kilmarnock Edition [L41]

L204791	**156433 *The Kilmarnock Edition* (52433 +57433)** Strathclyde PTE carmine+cream, etched nameplates Sp Edn 300 (Harburn Hobbies) - *98*	75	125
L205050	**156443 (52443+57443)** BRe Provincial blue - *89*	35	55
L205050D	**156443** BRe Provincial blue, dummy car - *?*	NPG	NPG
L205119	**156447** ScotRail Whoosh grey etc. Sp Edn 400 (Harburn Hobbies) - *01*	30	60
L204676	**156454 *Whitby Endeavour* (52454 +57454)** BRe Provincial blue - *99*	30	50
L204712	**156465 *Bonnie Prince Charlie* (52465+57465)** Provincial ScotRail blue, etched nameplates Sp Edn 400 (Harburn Hobbies) - *96*	40	65
L205051	**156480 (52480+57480)** BRe Provincial Blue - *89*	35	50
L205052	**156481 (52481+57481)** BRe Provincial Blue - *92*	35	50
L205036	**156490 (57491+52491)** Northern Spirit blue-green - *01*	40	55
L205054	**156501 (52501+57501)** BRe Strathclyde Transport orange+black - *89*	40	55
L205054D	**156501 (57501)** BRe Strathclyde Transport orange+black, dummy car only - *93*	25	30
L204840	**156502 (52502+57502)** BRe Strathclyde Transport orange+black Sp Edn 500 (D&F) uncertificated - *94*	60	75
L20?	**156510 (?+?)** carmine+cream Sp Edn (D&F Models) - *02*	60	75
L205055	**156512 (52512+57512)** BRe Strathclyde Transport orange+black Sp Edn 500 (Harburn) uncertificated - *92*	65	90
L204713	**156513 (52513+57513)** BRe Strathclyde Transport orange+black Sp Edn 400 (D&F Models) uncertificated - *96*	40	65
L204927	**156510 (52510+57510)** Strathclyde PT carmine +cream Sp Edn 400 (Harburn Hobbies) - *01*	50	66

L42. Class 373 'Eurostar' H0 (ex-Jouef) (1996)

(L106530)	**F5 (3211+3212**) Eurostar grey ex-set - *96*	40	NA*

L43. Class 960 Sandite Unit 'Bubble Car' (2001)

L204907	**ADB97723** Railtrack Clearing the Way brown - *01*	35	50
L204928	**977858** Railtrack Clearing the Way maroon - *01*	35	50

L44a. GWR Railcar (1980)

L205132	**No.22** GWR (button) brown+cream, white roof - *80*	30	55
L205133	**W22** maroon+cream 1948 numbering - *80*	30	45
L204639	**No.29** Great()Western brown+cream - *98*	25	40
L205150	**W30W** BRc green, whiskers - *83*	30	40
L205267	**W32W** BRc green, white roof domes, whisker stripes - *00*	30	40
L205267	**W32W** BRc green, white roof (error, approx. 10 exist) whisker stripes - *00*	65	80
L204913	**W34** BRc maroon - *01*	30	45

L44b. GWR Parcels Railcar (1982)

L205143	**No.34** GWR (button) brown+cream Express Parcels - *82*	30	40
L205144	**W34** Express Parcels maroon - *?*	30	40
L205144	**W34W** Express Parcels maroon - *82*	30	40

COACHES

Lima coaches have been limited to only a few prototypes. These fall into two categories - BR standard coaching stock and non-passenger stock. The latter includes 'Syphons', CCTs and GUVs while the former are made up of Mk1s, Mk2s and Mk3s. In addition to there are centre cars for DMUs. As with Lima locomotives, the emphasis has been on extending the range of liveries that can be carried by each basic model.

Cat No.	Company, Number, Colour, Dates	£	£

C1. Pullman (1977)

This was available for only one year with tension-lock couplings.

L309199	**Pullman *Louisa*** brown+cream - *77*	6	10
L309200	**Pullman Golden Arrow** blue - *77*	6	10

BR Mark 1 Stock

C2a. BR Mk1 Corridor 2nd (SK) (1982)

L305363	**BR** M24437 red+cream - *82*	8	12
L305363	**BR** W24490 red+cream - *82*	8	12
L305365	**BR** S25916 green - *82*	8	12
L305362	**BR** W26070 brown+cream - *82*	8	12

MK1 SK W26070 [C2a]

L305362	**BR** W26178 brown+cream - *82*	8	12
L305364	**BR** M25623 maroon - *82*	8	12
L305361	**BR** M25308 blue+grey - *82*	8	12
L305350	**BR** W18611 blue+grey - *99*	8	12
L305326	**BR IC** M18753 grey - *86*	8	12
L305317	**Sealink** SC24850 - *87*	8	14
L305306	**NSE** 18711 early blue - *87*	8	14
L305306	**NSE** 18711 late blue - *90*	8	14

C2b. BR Mk1 Open 2nd (SO) (1985)

L305329	**BR** E4630 blue+grey - *95*	NPG	NPG
L305383	**BR** E4630 blue+grey - *87*	8	12
L305330	**IC** swallow 4998 grey - *85*	8	12
L305384	**BR IC** M4479 grey - *87*	8	12
	ScotRail 'West Highland' Green+Cream		
L305444	Sc4243 Sp Edn 150 (Harburn Hobbies) - *99*	18	20
L305445	Sc4610 Sp Edn 150 (Harburn Hobbies) - *99*	18	20
(L149441)	Sc4419 Sp Edn 250 (Harburn Hobbies) ex-train pack - *01*	18	NA
(L149441)	Sc4435 Sp Edn 250 (Harburn Hobbies) ex-train pack - *01*	18	NA
(L149441)	Sc4900 Sp Edn 250 (Harburn Hobbies) ex-train pack - *01*	18	NA

C2d. BR Mk1 Corridor Composite (CK) (1977)

L305313	**GWR** 5014 brown+cream - *77*	8	12
L305312	**LMS** 2257 maroon - *77*	8	12
L305311	**BR** 15215 red+cream - *77*	8	12
L305311	**BR** M34628 red+cream - *79*	8	12
L305311	**BR** M5248 maroon+cream - *?*	8	12
L305314	**BR** S15865 green - *77*	8	12
L305314	**BR** S33472 green - *79*	8	12
L305313	**BR** W24624 brown+cream - *79*	8	12
L305312	**BR** M25264 maroon - *79*	8	12

MK1 CK Engineering Dept. mess car DE2513961 [C2d]

L305310	**BR** DE2513961 Eng. drab - *83*	8	12
L305315	**BR** W43671 blue+grey - *79*	8	12
L305351	**BR** W45198 blue+grey - *99*	8	12
L305318	**Sealink** Sc7997 - *87*	8	14
L305346	**CIE** green - *78*	15	30
L305347	**CIE** orange+black - *78*	15	30

C2e. BR Mk1 Corridor Brake 2nd (BSK) (1977)

L305333	**GWR** 5103 brown+cream - *77*	8	12
L305333	**GWR** 5104 brown+cream - *77*	8	12
L305332	**LMS** 5051 maroon - *77*	8	12

MK1 BSK LMS 5051 [C2e]

L305331	**BR** 34100 red+cream - *77*	8	12
L305331	**BR** M34376 red+cream - *79*	8	12
L305334	**BR** S1297 green - *77*	8	12
L305334	**BR** S33454 green - *79*	8	12
L305333	**BR** W24528 brown+cream - *79*	8	12
L305332	**BR** M25290 maroon - *79*	8	12
L305335	**BR** W43281 blue+grey - *79*	8	12
L305372	**BR IC** M35465 grey - *87*	8	12
L305307	**NSE** 35193 early blue - *87*	8	14
L305307	**NSE** 35193 late blue - *90*	8	14
L305316	**Sealink** Sc35070 - *87*	8	12
L305397	**BRT** KDB977167 silver grey Engineering Dept. Telecommunications - *94*	8	12
	ScotRail 'West Highland' Green+Cream		
L305446	Sc9312 Sp Edn 150 (Harburn Hobbies) - *99*	18	20
(L149441)	Sc21241 Sp Edn 250 (Harburn Hobbies) ex-train pack - *01*	18	NA

C2f. BR Mk1 Restaurant Buffet (RBR) (1977)

L305322	**GWR** 9542 brown+cream - *77*	8	12
L305323	**LMS** 270 maroon - *77*	8	12
L305325	**BR** M34642 red+cream - *79*	8	12

MK1 RBR M34642 [C2f]

L305324	**BR** S3056 green - *78*	8	12
L305324	**BR** S33465 green - *79*	8	12
L305322	**BR** W24760 brown+cream - *79*	8	12
L305323	**BR** M25486 maroon - *79*	8	12
L305321	**BR** W1652 blue+grey - *77*	8	12
L305321	**BR** W43212 blue+grey - *79*	8	12
L305352	**BR** W92069 blue+grey - *99*	8	12
L305320	**BR InterCity** IC1698 grey - *87*	8	12

BR Mk1 Gangwayed Full Brake (BG)

(found under 'PARCELS STOCK' after 'COACHES' section)

BR Mark 2 Stock

C3a. BR Mk2b TSO Tourist Open (1977)

L305302	**BR** W5449 blue+grey 2b - *77*	8	12
L305305	**BR** M5940 blue+grey 2f - *85*	8	12
L305337	**BR IC** M5804 grey 2e - *87*	8	15
(L104311)	**ICs** 6025 grey 2e ex-set - *?*	8	NA
L305309	**BR IC** swallow livery 2e - *not made*	NA	NA
L305395	**Regional Railways** 5304 blue 2b Sp Edn (Signal Box) - *92*	15	20
L305386	**NSE** 5448 early blue 2b - *87*	8	14
L305386	**NSE** 5448 late blue 2b - *89*	8	14
(L104312)	**NSE** 5454 blue 2b ex-set - *?*	8	NA
(L104312)	**NSE** 5456 blue ex-set - *?*	8	NA
L305395	**Trans-Pennine** 5479 2b - *90*	8	12
L205264	**ScotRail** Sc5813 grey 2e ex-set - *?*	12	NA
L305306	**CIE** orange+black - *78*	15	30
-	**IE** standard open *(see C3i)*	-	-

C3b. BR Mk2b FK Corridor 1st (1977)

L305301	**BR** W13493 blue+grey 2b - *77*	8	12
L305387	**NSE** 13442 early blue 2a - *87*	NPG	NPG
L305387	**NSE** 13442 late blue 2a - *89*	NPG	NPG
(L104312)	**NSE** 13482 blue ex-set - *?*	8	NA
(L104312)	**NSE** 13435 blue ex-set - *?*	8	NA
L305394	**Trans-Pennine** 13520 2c - *90*	8	12

C3c. BR Mk2b Brake Corridor 1st (BFK) (1977)

L305303	**BR** W16084 blue+grey 2b - *77*	8	12
L305319	**BR IC** swallow livery - *not made*	NA	NA
L305388	**Regional Railways** 17123 blue 2c Sp Edn (Signal Box) - *89*	15	20
L305388	**NSE** 17086 early blue 2a - *87*	8	12
L305388	**NSE** 17086 late blue 2a - *89*	8	12
L305338-1	**IE** 5102 orange+black Sp Edn 200		

	(Murphy's Models) - *98*	20	30
L305607	**CIE** orange+black - *?*	15	30

C3d. BR Mk2b TSO (RSO) Restaurant Car (1986)

This vehicle did not exist in reality. The number is from a Mk1 RMB and the model used is the TSO made to look like a RSO (non-kitchen restaurant car).

L305327	**BR IC** 1883 grey - *86*	8	12

C3e. BR Mk2b Micro-Buffet (TSOT) (1982)

L305308	**BR** E6524 blue+grey - *82*	8	12
L305327	**BR IC** 1583 grey Restaurant/Buffet - *?*	8	12

C3f. BR Mk2b in Irish Liveries (2003)

The NIR coaches came in boxes branded Lima Jouef. The models are of the Lima Mk2b/c.

(LT600003)	**NIR** 911 blue+grey brake/2nd open generator - *03*	20	NA
(LT600003)	**NIR** 924 blue+grey open 2nd - *03*	20	NA
(LT600003)	**NIR** 933 blue+grey open 2nd - *03*	20	NA
LT600003	above 3 coaches in '80s Enterprise livery Sp Edn 500 (Murphy Models) - *03*	NA	80

C3g. BR Mk2f TSO Tourist Open (1998)

L305423	**Virgin** 6157 [B] red+black - *98*	8	13
L305424	**Virgin** 6064 [C] red+black - *98*	8	13
L305425	**Virgin** 6067 [D] red+black - *98*	8	13
L305426	**Virgin** 6170 [E] red+black - *98*	8	13

MK2f TSO Virgin Trains 6170 [C3g]

L305427	**Virgin** 5976 [F] red+black - *98*	8	13
L305337	**Inter-City** M5804 grey - *?*	10	15
L305305	**BR** M5940 blue+grey - *?*	10	15

C3h. BR Mk2f Open 1st (FO) (1985)

L305304	**BR** M3310 blue+grey 2f - *85*	8	12
L305336	**BR IC** M3229 grey 2e - *87*	8	12
(L104311)	**ICs** 3228 grey 2e ex-set - *?*	8	NA
L305329	**ScotRail** 3265 grey 2e - *86*	12	15
L305380	**ScotRail** Revised Sc11008 grey - *87*	12	15
-	**IC** 3524 grey ex-train pack Sp Edn (Harburn Hobbies) ex-Deerstalker train pack - *01*	15	NA

C3i. BR Mk2f in Irish Liveries (2001)

The models came in boxes branded Lima Jouef.

(LT149439)	**IE** 5225 standard open - *01*	20	NA
(LT149439)	**IE** 5216 standard open - *01*	20	NA
(LT149439)	**IE** 5235 standard open - *01*	20	NA
LT149439	above 3 coaches of the Galway Line Sp Edn 300 (Murphy Models) - *01*	NA	80
(LT600001)	**IE** 5209 standard open - *03*	20	NA
(LT600001)	**IE** 5232 standard open - *03*	20	NA
(LT600001)	**IE** 5233 standard open - *03*	20	NA
LT600001	above 3 coaches of the Galway Line Sp Edn 500 (Murphy Models) - *03*	NA	80

C3j. BR Mk2 (unidentified) in Irish Liveries

Insufficient information is available to determine what type the coaches were.

(L105100X33)	**IR** 5228 standard open Ltd Edn (Murphy Models) ex-train set - *97*	20	NA
(L149801)	**IE** 5201 standard open Ltd Edn 300 (Murphy Models) ex-3-coach set - *97*	20	NA
(L149801-1)	**IE** 5102 standard open - *98*	20	NA
(L149801-1)	**IE** 5223 standard open - *98*	20	NA
(L149801-1)	**IE** 5228 standard open - *98*	20	NA
L149801-1	above 3 coaches of the Galway Line Sp Edn 300 (Murphy Models) - *98*	NA	80
(L149439-1)	**IE** 5228 standard open Ltd Edn 300 (Murphy Models) ex-3-coach set (also in train set L105100X33 of 1997) - *00*	20	NA

BR Mark 3 Stock

C4a. BR Mk3 Trailer Standard Open (TSO) (1985) (HST Stock)

L305368	**BR IC** 42252 grey - *85*	10	15
L305391	**BR ICs** 42191 grey - *89*	10	15
(L106522)	**BR ICs** 42197 grey ex-set - *89*	10	NA
L305402	**GNER** 42106 [B] navy blue - *98*	10	15
L305437	**GNER** 42181 [C] navy blue - *98*	10	15
L305438	**GNER** 42180 [D] navy blue - *98*	10	15
L305439	**GNER** 42179 [E] navy blue - *98*	10	15
(L149624)	**GNER** 42179 Sp Edn 260 (Harburn Hobbies) - *02*	10	NA
L305460	**GNER** 42323 [?] navy blue - *?*	10	15

MK3 TSO GNER [C4a]

L305458	**GNER** 42058 [?] navy blue - *?*	10	NA
(L149872)	**GNER** 42242 navy blue ex-train pack - *98*	10	NA
(L149908)	**GNER** 42154 [B] navy blue ex-train pack - *98*	10	NA
(L149908)	**GNER** 42150 [C] navy blue ex-train pack - *98*	10	NA
(L149918)	**GNER** 42215 [E] navy blue ex-train pack - *98*	10	NA
L305412	**Mid Mainline** 42228 [B] green+beige - *98*	10	15
L305416	**Mid Mainline** 42227 [C] green+beige - *98*	10	15
L305417	**Mid Mainline** 42229 [D] green+beige - *98*	10	15
L305418	**Mid Mainline** 42194 [E] green+beige - *98*	10	15
L305453	**Mid Mainline** 42121 [B] green+beige Sp Edn - *?*	15	24
L305454	**Mid Mainline** 42120 [C] green+beige Sp Edn - *?*	15	24
L305455	**Mid Mainline** 42119 [D] green+beige Sp Edn - *?*	15	24
L305456	**Mid Mainline** 42337 [E] green+beige Sp Edn - *?*	15	24
(L149806)	**Mid Mainline** 42230 green+white ex-train pack - *98*	10	NA
(L149909)	**Mid Mainline** 42157 [C] green+beige ex-train pack - *98*	10	NA
L305404	**Virgin XC** 42189 [B] red+black - *98*	10	15
L305420	**Virgin XC** 42188 [C] red+black - 98	10	15
L305421	**Virgin XC** 42187 [D] red+black - 98	10	15
L305422	**Virgin XC** 42326 [F] red+black - *98*	10	15
(L149859)	**Virgin XC** 42239 red+black ex-train pack - *98*	10	NA
L305429	**Virgin** 42317 [B] red+black - *99*	10	15
L305430	**Virgin** 42316 [C] red+black - *99*	10	15
L305431	**Virgin** 42315 [D] red+black - *99*	10	15
L305432	**Virgin** 42195 [F] red+black - *99*	10	15
(L149916)	**Virgin** 42314 [B] red+black ex-train pack - *?*	10	NA
L305414	**GWT** 42350 [D] green+ivory - *99*	10	15
L305441	**GWT** 42295 [E] green+ivory - *99*	10	15
(L149871)	**GWT** 42296 green+ivory ex-train pack - *98*	10	NA
(L149871)	**GWT** 42297 green+ivory ex-train pack - *98*	10	NA
L305449	**FGW** 43032 [B] green+ivory - *99*	10	15
L305478	**FGW** 42014 [C] - *99*	10	15
L305480	**FGW** 42068 [E] - *99*	10	15

C4b. BR Mk3a Open Second (SO) (1984)

L305366	**BR** M12004 blue+grey - *84*	10	15
L305379/1	**ScotRail** Revised Sc12020 grey+blue Ltd Edn 200 (Harburn Hobbies) - *95*	15	20
L305379/2	**ScotRail** Revised Sc12030 grey+blue Sp Edn 200 (Harburn Hobbies) - *95*	15	20
L305328	**ScotRail** 12025 grey - *86*	12	15
L305379	**ScotRail** Revised 12024 grey - *87*	12	15

C4c. BR Mk3 Open Composite (CO) (1987)

L305385	**ScotRail** 11907 grey - *87*	12	15
L305385/1	**ScotRail** Sc11908 grey+blue Sp Edn 200 (Harburn Hobbies) - *95*	15	20

C4d. BR Mk3 Trailer First Open (TFO) (1982) (HST Stock)

L305161	**BR** 41163 blue+grey - *82*	10	15
L305181	**BR IC** 41121 grey - *87*	10	15
L305392	**BR ICs** 41097 grey - *89*	10	15
(L106522)	**BR ICs** 41097 grey ex-set - *89*	10	NA
L305403	**GNER** 41092 [G] navy blue - *98*	10	15

L305440	**GNER** 41091 [H] navy blue - *98*	10	15
(L149872)	**GNER** 41092 navy blue ex-pack - *98*	10	NA
(L149624)	**GNER** 41092 Sp Edn 260 (Harburn Hobbies) - *02*	10	NA
L305411	**Mid Mainline** 41069 [G] green+beige - *98*	10	15
L305419	**Mid Mainline** 41112 [?] green+beige - *98*	10	15
L305451	**Mid Mainline** 41041 [G] green+beige *?*	15	24
L305452	**Mid Mainline** 41061 [H?] green+beige Sp Edn - *98*	15	24
(L149806)	**Mid Mainline** 41062 [G] green+white ex-train pack - *98*	10	NA
(L149909)	**Mid Mainline** 41079 [H] green+beige ex-train pack - *98*	10	NA
L305405	**Virgin XC** 41095 [H] red+black - *98*	10	15
(L149859)	**Virgin XC** 41081 red+black ex-train pack - *98*	10	NA
L305434	**Virgin** 41107 [H] red+black - *99*	10	15
(L149916)	**Virgin** 41168 [H] red+black ex-train pack - *98*	10	NA

MK3 TFO GWT Intercity [C4d]

L305415	**GWT** 41143 [H] green+ivory - *99*	10	15
L305442	**GWT** 41144 [G] green+ivory - *99*	10	15
L305450	**FGW** 41032 [G] green+ivory - *99*	10	15
L305482	**FGW** 41094 [G] - *99*	10	15
L205166	**Australian** XPT silver+orange - *?*	10	15

C4e. BR Mk3 Pullman First Open (PFO) (1987)

L305374	**BR IC** 11076 *John Lennon* grey - *87*	18	20
L305375	**BR IC** 11091 grey - *87*	10	15
L305376	**BR IC** 11093 *L.S.Lowry* grey - *87*	18	20
L305377	**BR IC** 11091 *Sir Stanley Matthews* grey - *87*	18	20
L305378	**BR IC** 11085 *Sir John Barbirolli* grey - *87*	18	20

C4f. BR Mk3 Trailer Guard Standard (TGS) (1982)

This is HST stock with a guards compartment in one end of a standard class coach.

L305162	**BR** 44080 blue+grey - *82*	20	25
L305182	**BR** 44028 IC grey - *87*	20	25
L305390	**BR ICs** 44071 grey - *89*	20	25
L305400	**GNER** 44058 [A] navy blue - *98*	20	25
(L149918)	**GNER** 44094 [A] navy blue ex-pack - *98*	20	NA
L305410	**Mid Mainline** 44073 [A] green+beige - *98*	20	25
L305428	**Virgin** 44090 [A] red+black - *99*	20	25
L305406	**Virgin XC** 44060 [A] red+black - *98*	20	25
L305408	**GWT** 44039 [A] green+ivory - *99*	20	25
L305448	**FGW** 44005 [A] green+ivory - *99*	20	25
L205167	**Australian** XPT silver+orange - *?*	20	25

C4g. Mk3 Trailer Restaurants (HST Stock) (1982)

L305163	**BR** 42258 blue+grey - *82*	10	15
L305183	**BR** 40322 IC grey (TRUB) - *87*	10	15
L305393	**BR ICs** 40619 (TRFM) grey - *89*	10	15
L305433	**Virgin** 40418 [G] red+black (TRSB) - *98*	10	15
L305407	**Virgin XC** 40432 [G] red+black - *98*	10	15
L305401	**GNER** 40704 [F] navy blue (TRFB) - *98*	10	15
L305413	**Midland Mainline** 40749 [F] green+ beige (TRFB) - *98*	10	15
L305409	**GWT** 40733 [F] green+ivory (TRFB) - *99*	10	15
L305447	**FGW** 40727 [F] green+ivory (TRFB) - *99*	10	15
L305481	**FGW** 40707 [F] (TRFB) - *99*	10	15
(L105100X33)	**IR** 7115 orange+black? Sp Edn 300 (Murphy's Models) ex-train set - *97*	20	NA
L305340	**IE** 7403 orange+black? Sp Edn 300 (Murphy's Models) - *97*	20	25
(L149437)	**IE** 7411 orange+black? Sp Edn 300 (Murphy's Models) ex 3-coach set - *01*	20	NA

C4h. Mk3a Sleeper (SLE) (1984)

L305367	**BR** E10646 blue+grey - *84*	10	15
L305369	**BR IC** E10645 grey - *85*	10	15
L305484	**IC Mainline** 10506 grey Sp Edn (Harburn Hobbies) - *01*	12	NA

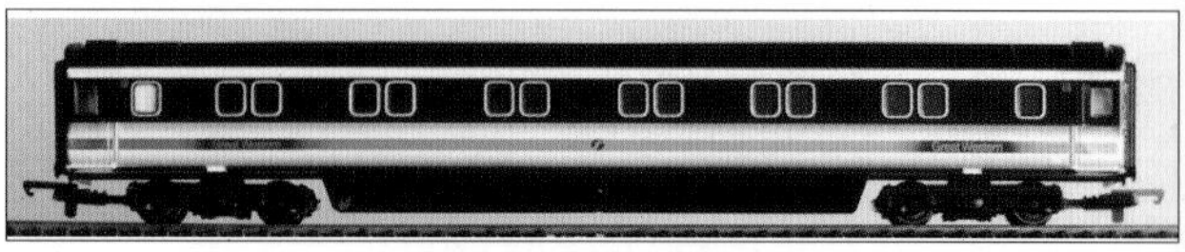

Mk3 SLE FGW 10588 [C4h]

L305443	**FGW** 10532 green+ivory - *99*	10	15
L305483	**FGW** 10588 - *99*	10	15

C4i. Mk3 in Irish Liveries (various types) (1997)

The models came in boxes branded Lima Jouef.

(L149801)	**IE** 7115 orange+black? Sp Edn 300 (Murphy's Models) ex 3-coach set - *97*	20.	NA
(L149801)	**IE** 7411 orange+black? Sp Edn 300 (Murphy's Models) ex 3-coach set - *97*	20	NA
L305339	**IE** 7132 orange+black ? Sp Edn 300 (Murphy's Models) - *98*	20	25
LL305339-1	**IE** 7135 orange+black ? Sp Edn 300 (Murphy's Models) - *98*	20	25
(L149801-2)	**IE** 7135 orange+black? - *98*	20	NA
(L149801-2)	**IE** 7141 orange+black? - *98*	20	NA
(L149801-2)	**IE** 7165 orange+black? - *98*	20	NA
L149801-2	above 3 coaches in a set Sp Edn 300 (Murphy's Models) - *98*	NA	80
(L149439-1)	**IE** 7135 orange+black? Sp Edn 300 (Murphy's Models) ex 3-coach set - *00*	20.	NA
(L149439-1)	**IE** 7141 orange+black? Sp Edn 300 (Murphy's Models) ex 3-coach set - *00*	20	NA
(L105500X05)	**IE** (no number) orange+black? Sp Edn (Murphy's Models) ex-train set - *01*	20	NA
(L149437)	**IE** 7129 orange+black? Sp Edn (Murphy's Models) ex 3-coach set - *01*	20	NA
(L149437)	**IE** 7151 orange+black? Sp Edn (Murphy's Models) ex 3-coach set - *01*	20	NA
(LT600002)	**IE** 7161 dark maroon Executive - *03*	18	NA
(LT600002)	**IE** 7161 dark maroon Executive - *03*	18	NA
LT600002	above 2 coaches in 1990s Executive livery Sp Edn (Murphy Models) - *03*	NA	60

C5. Class 101 Centre Car (TSL) (1999)

L305398	**BR** E59523 green - *99*	10	15
L305399	**BR** Sc59553 green - *99*	10	15
L305382	**BR** M59115 blue - *99*	10	15
(L149915)	**BR** 59108 blue+grey ex-train pack - *99*	10	NA
L305381	**ScotRail** 59539 grey+blue - *99*	10	15
(L149927)	**Regional Railways** 59303 white+blue ex-train pack - *99*	10	NA
-	**NSE** blue - *99*	10	15

C6. Class 117 Centre Car (1981)

L204830	**BRc** 59520 GWR brown+cream Ltd Edn 300 - *94*	20	NA
L205146	**BRc** W59518 green - *81-95*	10	15
L205145	**BRe** W59493 blue - *81-90*	10	15
L205148	**BRe** W59508 blue+grey - *81-94*	10	15
L205153	**BRe** W59484 white - *82-90*	10	15
L205087	**BR Reg Rlys** 59521 blue+grey - *94-?*	10	15
L205098	**NSE** 59514 blue+white - *94-?*	10	15

C7. 'Eurostar' Cars (1996)

(L106530)	**EPS** 3211 grey ex-set - *96*	8	NA
(L106530)	**EPS** 3212 grey ex-set - *96*	8	NA

PARCELS STOCK

More than any other manufacturer, Lima have catered for parcels traffic and often found it hard to decide whether to classify the models as coaches or wagons. To avoid the confusion, we have included them all here under a new heading.

Cat No.	Company, Number, Colour, Dates	£	£
P1.	**GWR Bogie Parcel Van Siphon G** (1978)		
L305351	**GWR** 2792 dark brown - *78*	8	12
L305352	**GWR** '**Palethorpes**' 2766 brown - *78*	8	12
L305350	**BR** W2938W red - *81*	8	12
L305353	**BR** 2982 blue - *78*	8	12
L305354	**BR** ADW150426 blue Enparts - *79*	8	12
P2.	**LMS GUV Bogie Parcel Van** (1980)		
L305358	**LMS** 37762 maroon - *80*	8	12
L305359	**BR** M37794 red+cream - *80*	8	12
L305371	**BR** M37776M maroon - *83*	8	12
L305370	**BR** DM395929 Engineering Dept. olive Air Compressor Van - *83*	8	12
L305360	**BR** M37926 blue - *80*	8	12
P3.	**BR Mk1 Gangwayed Full Brake (BG)** (1977)		
L305345	**GWR** 4476 brown+cream - *77*	8	12
L305342	**LMS** 30964 maroon - *77*	8	12
L305344	**BR** M80855 red+cream - *77*	8	12
L305344	**BR** M34722 red+cream - *79*	8	12
L305348	**BR** S33456 green - *79*	8	12

Mk1 BG BR (SR) green S33456 [P3]

Cat No.	Company, Number, Colour, Dates	£	£
L305345	**BR** W24680 brown+cream - *79*	8	12
L305342	**BR** M25742 lined maroon - *79*	8	12
L305341	**BR** B80855 blue Parcels Express - *77*	8	12
L305341	**BR** M80855 Express Parcels blue - *84*	8	12
L305343	**BR** M80855 blue+grey - *77*	NPG	NPG
L305343	**BR** W43462 blue+grey - *79*	8	12
L305373	**BR IC** M92001 grey - *87*	8	12
-	**IC Mainline** 92194 grey ex-train pack Sp Edn (Harburn Hobbies) - *01*	15	NA
L305346	**Scotrail** 92128 - *87*	12	15
L305396	**Trans-Pennine** 92092 - *90*	8	12
L305389	**NSE** 92236 late blue - *89*	8	12
L305347	**Post Office** 80861 NDX red - *90*	8	12
L305340	**RES** 93134 red - *?*	10	12
L305349	**RES** 92355 NEX red - *93*	8	12
(L149808)	**RES** 92714 red ex-pack - *99*	12	NA
(L149784	**RES** 92750 red ex-pack - *?*	12	NA
-	**RES/Royal Mail** 92244 red NDX - *?*	12	NA
P4.	**BR CCT/NOV Parcel Wagon** (1979)		
L305355	**Tartan Arrow** M94229 - *79*	6	10
L305356	**BR** M94291 blue - *79*	6	10
L305357	**BR** M94292 red - *79*	6	10
P5a.	**BR 57' GUV Bogie Parcel Van** (1982)		
L305657	**BR** W34674 maroon - *82*	8	12
L305657	**BR** W86470 lined maroon - *82*	8	12
L305611	**BR** W96175 Motorail blue+grey - *90*	8	12
L305610	**BR** 96102 Motorail Intercity grey - *90*	8	12
L305656	**BR** M86117 Express Parcels blue+grey - *82*	8	12
L305612	**NSE** 93852 Express Parcels late blue - *91*	8	12
L305658	**BR** yellow Engineering Dept Tool Van - *82*	8	12
L305640	**BR RES** 95134 NJX red - *92*	10	12
(L149784)	**RES** 93143 red ex-pack - *?*	12	NA
(L149808)	**RES** 95133 red ex-pack - *99*	12	NA
(L149808)	**RES** 95138 red ex-pack - *99*	12	NA
L305613	**Post Office** 93395 NIX red - *91*	10	12
(L105110)	**Post Office** 93849 NIX red - *90*	12	NPG

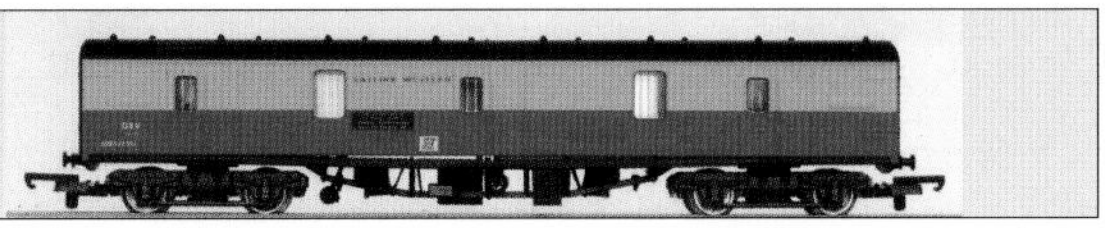

Mk1 GUV 'Satlink Western' No.KDB977557 [P5a]

Cat No.	Company, Number, Colour, Dates	£	£
L305658	'**Satlink Western**' KDB977557 bright red+yellow - *91*	8	12
L305658	'**Theakstons**' Brewer yellow - *82*	8	12
P5b.	**BR 57' NKA Super GUV** (2001)		
L305614	**RES** 94153 red+grey - *02*	12	17
L305721	**RES** 94123 red - *02*	12	17
L305723	**RES** 94208 red - *01*	12	17
L305722	**RES** 94157 Royal Mail red - *02*	12	17
L305724	**RES** 94209 Royal Mail red - *01*	12	17
L305619	**RES** 94212 EWS red - *01*	12	17
L305725	**RES** 94212 EWS red - *01*	12	17

WAGONS

In comparison with the locomotive range, the range of Lima wagons is limited to a few types which vary considerably according to the age of the model design. Early models were taken from Lima's Continental ranges and given liveries that might have been seen in Britain if the wagons had run there, but models based on British prototypes gradually displaced the Continental ones. Some of these survived in the British range for many years.

Even early British wagon types, such as the 7-plank wagon and closed van were somewhat simplified, but later models were more sophisticated and detailed. With Lima's concentration on modern image locomotives, understandably, the emphasis in recent years has been on modern wagons.

Cheap versions of some wagons, which incorporated body and chassis in one, were produced for starter sets but carried the same printing as the better wagons they were based on. They can be quickly recognised because the chassis is the same colour as the body (this does not include any black bodied wagons). If Lima wagons ever become targeted by collectors, these cheap versions, made exclusively for sets, are likely to become much sought after.

To add confusion, some wagons were in the original Lima H0 range and were transferred to the 00 range in the mid '70s. Some very non-British wagons were fitted with British tension-lock couplings and used in train sets for sale in the UK. These included the following which are not listed in the tables: a long (60') flat wagon which came with the container loading facility and carried two semi-trailers, an American style bulk head flat car (self- unloading) lettered SNCF with two tubes and a brown unlettered match truck with American Bettendorf bogies and an ACL semi-trailer load.

Cat No.	Company, Number, Colour, Dates	£	£

Original Continental Style Wagons

W1. Continental 30' 4-wheel Container Wagon (1977)

This was of Continental design and carried either one 40' H0 size container or two 20' ones. The wagon was black and those used in starter sets had no printing on them.

Cat No.	Company, Number, Colour, Dates	£	£
L302871	2104290324 + '**Scotch Beef**' grey - *?*	5	10
L302870	2104290324 + 2 '**Freightliner**' red - *84*	5	10
L302852	2104290324 + '**Scotch Beef**'+'**LHB**' blue+ orange - *77*	5	10
L302871	2104290324 + '**Freightliner**' grey+red - *77*	4	6
L302870	2104290324 + 2 x '**ACL**' grey - *80*	5	10
L302874	wagon + 2 x '**ACL**' grey - *84*	3	NA
L302682	wagon + 2 cars ex-starter sets - *84*	3	NA
W2.	**Continental Twin Flat Bolster Wagons** (1977)		
L309039	brown + tubes - *77*	6	10
L309038	brown + planks - *77*	6	10
W3.	**Continental LWB Mineral Wagon** (1977)		
	scc = chassis the same colour as the body.		
L303173	'**NCB**' Cardiff 1879 light grey - *77*	4	5
L303134	'**NCB**' Cardiff 1879 light grey scc - *77*	4	5
L303194	'**Traffic Services**' brown - *?*	NPG	NPG

'NCB' Continental mineral wagon [W3]

L303318	**BR** brown scc ex-sets - *80*	4	NA
L303133	**BR** 100027 brown scc ex-sets - *84*	3	NA
L303175	**BRe** 100027 brown - *77*	3	NA

W4. Continental Twin Silo Wagon (1977)

L302805	**'Blue Circle'** Cement 7504 yellow - *77*	4	5

W5. Continental 3-cask Beer Wagon (1977)

L302822	**'Watneys'** P660513 red+brown - *77*	4	5

W6. Continental Small Tank (1977)

L302720	**'Amoco'** AMOCO85600 white - *79*	4	5
L305691	**'Amoco'** AMOCO85600 white - *85*	4	5
L302715	**'BP'** 21RIV 005 7426 3 green - *77*	4	5
L302718	**'Gulf'** white+red - *77*	4	5
L302720	**'ICI'** Chemicals C1182 white - *77*	4	5
L302717	**'Mobil'** 57882 yellow LP-Gas - *79*	4	5
L302713	**'Shell'** 557128 yellow - *77*	4	5
L302721	**'Unigate'** S252 white - *77*	4	5

W7. Continental LWB Tank (1980)

Previously in the Lima H0 series.

L30265?	**'BP'** dark green ex-sets - *80*	4	NA
L30265?	**'Mobiloil'** red ex-sets - *80*	4	NA
L302651	**'Shell'** 557128 yellow ex-sets - *80*	4	NA
L30265?	**'Texaco'** red ex-sets - *80*	4	NA

W8. Continental Ferry Van (1977)

L303155	**'East Anglian Meat'** E75 lime green - *77*	7	10
L302991	**NE** 167349 brown - *77*	7	10
L303165	**BR** 217021003910 brown - *77*	4	6
L303162	**BR** 217021003910 brown * - *78*	5	7

* This was a converter van having a Lima continental coupling on one end and a tension-lock coupling at the other end.

W9. Continental Refrigerator Van (1977)

St = with steps each end. scc = chassis the same colour as the body.

L303104	**'Bell'** white - *?*	4	5
L303142	**'Coca-Cola'** white scc ex-sets - *84*	3	NA
L303114	**'Grimsby Fish'** N82642H St blue - *77*	4	5
L303135	**'Grimsby Fish'** N82642H St blue scc - ex-sets *77*	3	NA
L303545	**'Heinz'** 24516S St yellow - *79*	4	5
L303145	**'Heinz'** 24516S yellow scc ex-sets - *84*	3	NA
L303110	**'Infrigo'** blue - *?*	4	5
L303146	**'Pepsi'** white+red+blue scc ex-sets - *80*	3	NA
L303118	**'Schweppes'** 2416S yellow - *77*	4	5
L303144	**'Schweppes'** 2416S yellow scc ex-sets - *77*	3	NA

W10. 'Tierwag' Type Car Carrier (1980)

L302681	brown ex-sets - *80*	4	NA

W11. Continental Car Transporter (1977)

L309057	**'Austin Rover'** - *84?*	NA	NA
L309057	**'British Leyland'** 518098800213 black - *77*	10	15
L305697	**'Austin Rover'** 518098800213 black - *85*	10	15

Continental car transporter [W11]

L305696	**BR Motorail** 518098800213 black - *87*	10	15
L309053	**BR Motorail** 518098800213 blue - *77*	10	15

W12. 26T Bogie Hopper (1982)

L302892	**'ICI'** Bulk Salt - *not made*	NA	NA
L302892	**'NCB'** 6763532 light grey - *82*	6	10

W13. Continental Bogie Tanker (1977)

L302913	**'Amoco'** A1090 white - *77*	6	8
L302908	**'Esso'** 30000 red+white - *79*	6	8
L302908	**'Esso'** 30000 red+silver - *c82*	6	8
L302911	**Milk** 152D blue - *77*	7	10
L302904	**'Shellgas'** 21RIV 03642915 yellow - *77*	7	10
L302916	**'Texaco'** J62417 red - *77*	5	8
L302909	**'Total'** PR82620 red - *79*	7	10

W14. Bogie Refrigerator Van (1977)

L303199	**'BP Offshore'** S42746 light blue - *77*	8	12
(L?)	**'Inter Frigo'** 11RIV 83FS 0876517[1] off-white ex-set - *?*	8	NA
(L?)	**'Martini'** 21RIV 80DB 0820784[5] light grey ex-set - *?*	8	NA
(L?)	**'Martini'** 21RIV 80DB 0820784[5] greeny-grey ex-set - *?*	8	NA
(L?)	**'Traffic Services Ltd'** (Pfizer Chemicals & TSL London) 21RIV 80DB 0820784[5] buff ex-set - *?*	8	NA

W15. Bogie Sliding Door Van (1977)

L303204	**BR Railfreight** BRT yellow - *77*	8	12
L303203	**'Sundries'** (Irish) yellow - *83*	8	12

W16. 35T Continental Breakdown Crane (1977)

This was an 8-wheel mobile crane with a bogie match truck which had a gantry to carry the weight of the jib.

L309059	**LNER** red - *77*	7	10
L305698	**BRe** ADRC96708 yellow - *85*	7	10
L309048	**BR** 654414 yellow - *?*	7	10

W17. 20-wheel Articulated Heavy Carrier (1977)

L309067	**'BSC'** Foundry wagon white - *79*	10	15
L309052	**'Calf'** Foundry wagon grey - *77*	10	15
L309068	**'GEC'** transformer load green - *79*	10	15
L309056	**'Phillips'** transformer load grey - *77*	10	15

British Design Wagons

W18. 12T 7-plank Open Wagon (1977)

scc = chassis the same colour as the body.

L305690	**'Austin Rover'** 9191 grey + coal - *84*	4	5
L303365	**'Austin Rover'** 9191 grey scc ex-sets - *85*	3	NA
L305614	**'Barrow & Barnsley'** cream - *80*	4	5
L305673	**'Black & Decker'** B44191 white + coal - *83*	4	5
L305612	**'Black Park'** Colliery 2021 maroon - *80*	4	5
L305634	**'Buxton'** 24 light grey - *79*	4	5
L305611	**'Clay Cross'** 1791 brown - *77*	4	5
L305669	**'Clarks'** 9 green + coal - *84*	4	5
L30?	**'Clarks'** 9 green scc ex-sets - *94*	3	NA

7-plank wagon 'Clay Cross' [W18]

L305678	**'Courtaulds'** 18 green + coal - *84*	4	5
L305615	**'Dearne Valley'** 61 bright blue - *77*	4	5
L305679	**'Ebbw Vale'** 6117 black - *84*	4	
5L305613	**'Evans & Bevan'** 1759 black - *77*	4	5
L305612	**'Glasshoughton'** 126 yellow - *77*	4	5
L305631	'JK **Harrison & Co.'** maroon + coal - *79*	4	5

L305677	**'Harrods'** 45 brown + coal - *84*	4	5
L305674	**'NCB'** 423 black + coal - *83*	4	5
L305614	**'Oxford & District'** 18 yellow-green - *77*	4	5
L305670	**'Pilkington Glass'** 1928 red + coal - *83*	4	5
L305633	**'Pinxton Collieries'** 930 black - *79*	4	5
L305671	**'Prince of Wales'** 3133 grey + coal - *83*	4	5
L305676	**'Raleigh Burner'** 1117 blue + coal - *84*	4	5
L305672	**'Royal Arsenal'** 144 brown + coal - *83*	4	5
L305632	'PW **Spencer'** 3 buff-yellow - *79*	4	5
L30?	'PW **Spencer'** yellow scc ex-sets - *94*	3	NA
L3056??	**'Tomkins Coal Merchants'** black ex-set - *?*	10	NA
L305616	**GWR** 122060 light grey - *77*	4	5
L305675	**BR** M3132 light grey + coal - *83*	4	5
L303364	**SNCF** 7354 blue ex-starter sets - *84*	3	NA
L303362	**Australian** brown ex-starter sets - *84*	10	NA
L305617	**CIE** 21411 brown - *78*	10	14

W19. 50T PGA Aggregate Hoppers (1980)

L305636	**'ARC Amey Roadstone'** AR14228 cream - *80*	6	8
L305637	**'ARC'** (revised) AR14214 yellow - *86*	6	8
L305668	**'BP'** Chemicals PR8264 grey - *83*	6	8

'Tarmac' PGA aggregate hopper wagon [W19]

L305639	**'Tarmac'** 14007 white - *81*	6	8
L305638	**'Tilcon'** 14099 light grey - *80*	6	8
L305635	**'Yeoman'** PR14001 grey - *80*	6	8
L305638	**'Yeoman'** (revised) PR14019 grey - *87*	6	8
L305637	**BR** brown - *80*	6	8

W20. 45T Grain Hopper (1982)

L305653	**'Bass Charringtons'** 7 red - *83*	7	11
L305652	**'Black and White'** 6046 yellow - *82*	7	10
L305654	**'Grainflow'** BRT7780 green - *84*	7	10
L305651	**'Haig'** 5834 blue - *82*	7	10
L305650	**'Vat 69'** 5835 pale blue - *82*	7	12

W21. PCA Depressed Centre Tank (1989)

L305604	**'Albright & Wilson'** TRL10529 green - *89*	10	15
L305601	**'Blue Circle'** light grey - *89*	10	15
L305603	**'Castle'** TRL9154 white - *89*	10	15
L305602	**'Ketton'** TRL9470 lime green - *89*	10	15
L305605	**'Lever Bros.'** TRL10537 purple - *89*	10	15
L305607	**'Tiger'** TRL10521 yellow - *89*	10	15
L305608	**'Tiger APG'** TRL10523 blue - *91*	10	15
L305606	**BR** APCM9398 light grey - *89*	10	15

W22. 6-wheel Tank (1980)

Based upon an ex-GWR vehicle but the brake gear was not representative of any of the grouping railways.

L305640	**'Corn Products'** 37 W44520 black - *82*	6	8
L305644	**'CWS'** W44520 very dark green - *81*	6	8
L305644	**'CWS'** W44520 very dark green+orange - *82*	10	13
L305643	**'Express Dairies'** black - *80*	7	10
L305643	**'Express Dairies'** white - *81*	6	8
L305643	**'Express Dairies'** W44520 blue - *83*	7	10
L305642	**'IMS'** 22 W44520 black - *80*	6	8
L305641	**'St Ivel'** W44520 white+orange - *80*	6	8

'St Ivel' - 6-wheel milk tank wagon [W22]

L305641	**'St Ivel'** W44520 white+black - *81*	10	13
L305703	**'United Dairies'** W2009 white - *02*	7	10
L305702	**BR** ADW2592 oil storage blue *02*	7	10

W23. GWR Horse Box (1979)

L305625	**GWR** 546 brown - *79*	4	5
L305626	**LMS** red - *79*	4	5
L305628	**Southern** green - *79*	4	5

W24. 20T Corrugated End Van (1977)

scc = chassis the same colour as the body.

L303???	**'Agfa'** red scc ex-set - *?*	10	NA
L305607	**'Birds Custard'** deep blue - *80*	4	5
L303???	**'Birds Custard'** deep blue scc ex-set - *80*	4	NA
L305685	**'Birds Eye'** 441 white - *84*	4	5
L303375	**'Birds Eye'** 441 white scc ex-set - *85*	3	NA
L303157	**'Castrol'** light grey scc ex-sets - *84*	3	NA
L305608	**'Castrol GTX'** B785242 grey - *80*	4	5
L303???	**'Coca-Cola'** red scc ex-set - *?*	10	NA
L303056	**'Ever Ready'** M3245 black - *83*	4	5
L305681	**'Ford'** B16771 white - *83*	4	5
L305602	**'Home Pride'** BHP3228 white+blue - *77*	4	5
L303374	**'Lima'** brown scc ex-sets - *84*	3	NA
L305606	**'Lucas Batteries'** M3245 black - *80*	4	5
L305687	**'McCain'** Beefeater yellow - *84*	4	5
L305603	**'Michelin'** M3245 brown (red letters) - *77*	4	5
L305603	**'Michelin'** M3245 brown (pink letters) - *77*	4	5
L305682	**'Pearl of Cyprus Services'** blue - *83*	4	5
L305684	**'Shredded Wheat'** 714 yellow - *84*	4	5
L305688	**'Stork Margarine'** 100 yellow - *84*	4	5
L305604	**'St Ivel Unigate'** 68837 white - *77*	4	5
L305601	**'Typhoo'** S1200 red - *77*	4	5
L305686	**'Walls'** 469 brown - *84*	4	5
L305689	'R **White'** 305689 white - *84*	4	5
L303373	explosives van brown scc ex-set - *84*	3	NA
L303372	**SAR** * 78-056142 light grey scc ex-sets - *84*	3	NA
L305605	**GWR** 59701 light grey - *77*	4	5
L305680	**BR** DE1240 tool van red - *83*	4	5
L305606W	**CIE** 13141 brown - *78*	10	14

* On South African versions, the inscription is in English on one side and Afrikaans on the other side. In this case it is English both sides and the van turned up in a starter set.

W25. 20T BR Standard Brake Van (1977)

L305621	**NE** 159486 grey - *77*	4	5
L305620	**BR** B954521 brown - *77*	4	5
L305623	**Civil Link** DB950406 grey+yellow - *93*	4	5

BR Civil Link standard brake van [W25]

L305622	**BRe Post Office** B954735 red - *91*	4	5

L305622	**CIE** 41005 grey - *78*	10	NPG

W26. 30T Bogie Bolster Wagon (1980)

L305629	**GWR** 70897 grey + rails - *81*	6	8
L305630	**BR** B924162 brown + rails - *80*	6	8
L305631	**Civil Link** yellow + bogie load - *93*	6	8

W27. 102T PTA Bogie Ore Tippler (1983)

The model is based on the BREL built batch.

L305670	**'ARC'** PR25735 yellow - *87*	12	15
L305663	**'BSC'** Iron Ore grey - *83*	12	15
L305664	**'BSC'** Iron Ore grey+red - *83*	12	15
L305671	**'Yeoman'** PR26513 white - *89*	12	15
L305672	**'Yeoman'** PR26548 grey - *95*	12	15

W28a. 'Seacow' Bogie Ballast Hopper (1984)

L305667	**BR** Eng DB982881 grey+yellow - *84*	12	25
L305699	**BR Loadhaul** DB982878 - *95*	12	22
L305624	**EWS** DB980003 maroon - *99*	12	20
L305628	**EWS** DB890064 maroon - *99*	12	20
L305629	**EWS** DB892138 maroon - *99*	12	20

BR 'Seacow' bogie hopper wagon [W28a]

L305633	**EWS** DB890004 maroon - *99*	12	20
L305642	**EWS** DB890076 maroon - *99*	12	20
L305682	**EWS** DB890015 maroon - *00*	12	20
L305683	**EWS** DB890072 maroon - *00*	12	20
L305693	**EWS** DB890067 maroon - *00*	12	20
L305694	**EWS** DB890068 maroon - *00*	12	20
L305695	**EWS** DB890069 maroon - *00*	12	20
L149967	**EWS** DB892835 maroon ex-set - *99*	12	NA
L149967	**EWS** DB891401 maroon ex-set - *99*	12	NA

W28b. 'Sealion' Bogie Ballast Hopper (1984)

L305665	**BR** Eng DB982861 olive green - *84?*	12	20
L305665	**BR** Eng DB982833 olive green - *84*	12	20
L305666	**BR** DB982924 brown - *84*	12	20

W29. 102T 'Procor' Bogie Tank (1983)

L305645	**'Esso'** PR78537 white - *83*	12	15
L305646	**'Fina'** black - *83*	12	15
L305647	**'Phillips'** white - *83*	12	15

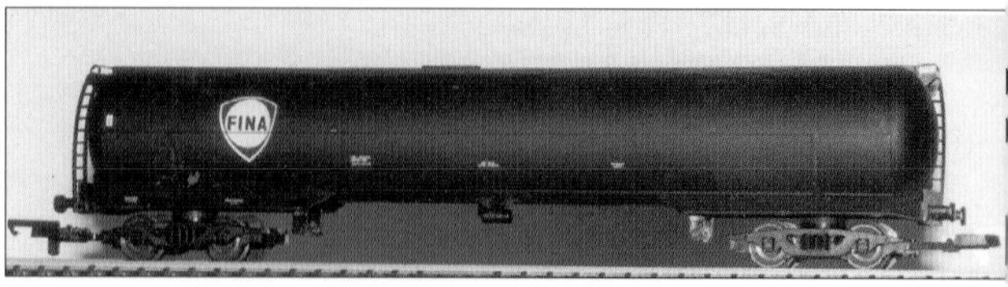

'Fina' bogie tank wagon [W29]

L305643	**'Shell'** PR78537 Ltd Edn (Langdale) - *?*	12	15
L305649	**'Total'** PR82758 silver - *84*	12	15

W30. PDA Bogie Twin Tank Wagon (1991)

L305615	**'Blue Circle'** 20203 light grey - *91*	12	15
L305616	**'Croxton & Garry'** CG9526 white - *91*	12	15
L305618	**'Derbyshire Stone'** CG9536 white - *91*	12	15
L305617	**'Lloyds & Scottish'** 9736 light grey - *91*	12	15

W31. 82T 'Procor' Bogie Pallet Van (1983)

L305661	**'UKF'** LS7008 white+brown - *83*	12	15
L305660	**'Fisons'** LS7020 white+green - *83*	12	15
L305660	**'Fisons'** LS7020 cream+green - *83*	12	15
L305655	**'Kemira Fertilizers'** BRT7105 blue - *94*	12	15
L305659	**'Neill & Brown'** LS7020 blue - *83*	12	15
L305662	**BR** LS7020 brown - *83*	12	15

W32. BHA Hooded Steel Carrier (1990)

L305680	**'Railfreight Metals'** 962001 red - *90*	12	15
L305681	**'Tiphook'** 962001 grey+blue - *91*	12	15

SETS

There have been many train sets over the years as well as some train packs. Special value is applied to these only where they contain models unique to them. To establish which these are, the locomotive list is worth studying. Other sets sell for between £25 and £50.

Lima 0 (British)

HISTORY

It is probably no coincidence that Lima's British outline 0 gauge range was launched in 1973, just as the Tri-ang Big Big system was disappearing from the shops. Indeed, it is understood that Rovex Ltd assisted Lima to get started in this market.

The British range was only a small part of a much larger international 0 gauge system made by Lima, which included 16.5mm track, lineside accessories and train sets. to 1:48 scale.

At present we have only limited information about the dates when the Lima 0 gauge models for the British market were available, but it would seem that they arrived in 1973 and ended in the early 1980s. It would appear that the tools were brought out of the storeroom in 1991 to produce a batch of Class 33 locomotives and Mk1 coaches in Network SouthEast livery for a special order - returning then to the store. Six of the models again featured in the 1999/2000 Lima catalogue, these being the two LMS versions of the 0-6-0 Fowler loco, two LMS Mk1 coaches and two versions of the mineral wagon. We do not know what happened to the tooling after that, it is assumed that they are still with Lima.

We are keen to learn more about Lima's venture into the UK 0 gauge market and would like to hear from anyone who can add to the story.

LMS 0-6-0 [L2] & BR Class 33 Diesel [L4]

LOCOMOTIVES

Although three types of locomotive were made for the British market, only two were based on British prototypes. One of these, the LMS 4F 0-6-0, was also shown in the catalogue in the early 1970s in SNCF green livery.

The locomotives had 12v DC pancake motors and ran on two rails. The motor itself is quite good, relative to the price, but the locos sometimes suffered from poor current collection and the plating wearing off the wheels after a lot of use. The 0 gauge track had a plastic sleeper web with 00 scale rail.

Cat No.	Company, Number, Colour, Dates	£	£
L1.	**LMS Class 4F 0-6-0T** (1987)		
	This was the same as the Class 4F (below) but had a plastic coal bunker added onto the rear of the cab and no tender. 6v battery powered. In each case the second colour was reserved for the coal bunker		
(500156)	**94** red+yellow ex-Safari set - *87*	35	NA
(500157)	**652** black+red ex-Freight set - *87*	35	NA
(500158)	**303** yellow+black, smoke stack ex-Crane set - *87*	40	NA
L2.	**LMS Class 4F 0-6-0** (1975)		
6533	**4547** LMS black - *75-00*	40	55
6534	**4683** LMS red - *75-00*	45	65
6533	**4547** BR black - *made?*	NPG	NPG
6535	**501-C3 + 29-C74** SNCF dark green - *?*	65	80
6536	**347748** DB black, red wheels - *made?*	NPG	NPG
6537	**628** CIE black, 'snail' logo - *made?*	NPG	NPG
(110150)	**4547** black 6v battery driven ex-set - *84*	40	NA
(500155)	red and grey 6v battery smoke stack chimney, no cab roof, ex-Wild West set - *87*	50	NA
L3.	**Diesel Shunter 0-4-0DS** (1973)		
	This was a model made for the US market and is thought to be of a freelance or Continental design. Kits were available, from another source, with which to convert this model into a Sentinel shunter or a Wisbech and Upwell tram engine ('Toby').		
6546	**D2852** BRe blue - *73-80*	25	40
6546	**D9574** BRe blue - *made?*	NPG	NPG
6545	**'Esso'** - *73-?*	NPG	NPG
L4.	**Class 33 Diesel** (1977)		
	Continental bogies.		
6576	**D6514** BRc green - *77-78*	35	50
6576	**D6506** BRc green - *78-82*	35	50
6577	**D6524** BRe blue - *77-82, 91*	35	50
6852	**33050** ***Isle of Grain*** BR Railfreight Construction triple grey - *91*	45	60

COACHES

Only two coach types were made - both BR Mk1s. The Network SouthEast versions of 1991 both had Thames route branding. They had Continental bogies.

Cat No.	Company, Number, Colour, Dates	£	£
C1a.	**BR Mk1 Corridor Composite** (1975)		
6620	**GWR** 5015 choc+cream - *75-82*	20	25
6616	**LMS** 15865 maroon - *75-00*	20	25
6618	**BR** 15218 red+cream - *75-82*	25	30
6617	**BR(SR)** S15865 green - *75-80*	20	25
6619	**BR** 15867 blue+grey - *75-82*	25	30
?	**BR NSE** 7190 blue+red+grey - *91*	25	30
6621	**CIE** green - *75?*	30	NPG

Mk1 Composite Coach No 15867 [C1a]

Cat No.	Company, Number, Colour, Dates	£	£
C1b.	**BR Mk1 Brake End** (1976)		
6646	**GWR** 5103 choc+cream - *76-82*	20	25
6645	**LMS** 5051 maroon - *76-00*	20	25
6644	**BR** 34100 red+cream - *76-82*	25	30
6647	**BR(SR)** S1297 green - *76-80*	25	30
6654	**BR** 35028 blue+grey - *76-82*	25	30
6619	**BR NSE** 35309 blue+red+grey - *91*	25	30
?	**CIE** green - *made?*	NPG	NPG

WAGONS

As with the H0 and N gauge ranges, Lima produced a small number of British wagons, in this case only two, and widened the range by using Continental wagons turned out in liveries that might be acceptable in the UK. It is possible that some of the Continental range of wagons produced for other markets found their way into the UK but these have not been included here as it is thought that they were not made for this purpose.

Cat No.	Company, Number, Colour, Dates	£	£
	Original Continental Style Wagons		
W1.	**Continental LWB Mineral Wagon** (1976)		
6726	**'NCB'** 1879 grey - *76-82*	7	9
?	**BRe** grey - *77?*	7	9
W2.	**Continental Ferry Van** (1975)		
	The NE version was described as a 'box van'.		
6751	**NE** 167349 brown - *77-80*	12	15
6745	**BRe** brown - *75-82*	12	15
W3.	**Continental Refrigerator Van** (1975)		
6710	**'Coca-Cola'** white - *75*	12	15
6710	**'Schweppes'** 24185? cream - *76-80*	12	15
6710	**'Sundries'** (CIE) yellow/orange - *made?*	NPG	NPG
	Also available on the Continent as 'Spatenbrau', 'Ledererbrau' and 'Carlsberg'.		
W4.	**Continental Bogie Tanker** (1973)		
6766	**'BP'** green+grey - *73-82*	12	15

6764	**'Esso'** 521155? silver - *73-76?*	12	15
6768	**'Mobiloil'** white - *73-82*	12	15
6765	**'Shell'** yellow+grey - *73-82*	12	15
6770	**'Texaco'** red+grey - *77-82*	12	15

W5. Freightliner Wagon + 3 x 20' Containers (1973)

6781	**'Danzas'** white, **'K&N'** blue, **'FFSS'** - *73?*	10	12
6781	**'Danzas'** white, **'K&N'** blue, **'CTI'** brown - *75*	10	12
6782?	+ **'ACL'** red, **'Sea Wheel'** grey, **'Carl Tidderman'** light blue - *73?*	10	12
6783	**'Sealand'** white, **'ACL'** red, **'Carl Tidderman'** pale blue - *73?-80*	10	12
6784	**'Seatrain'** white, **'LEP European Container Services'** brown, **'Contrans'** orange - *73?-80*	10	12
6785	**'Irish Ferryways'** red, **'Insulated Container'** (CIE) white, **CIE** red/brown - *75*	15	NPG

British Design Wagons

W6. 16T Mineral Wagon (1975)

-	**Banana** yellow ex-set - *?*	15	NA
6731	**'Caxton'** 32 lime green - *75-82*	7	9
6754	**'Clay Cross'** 1791 brown * - *77-00*	7	9
6738	**'Dearne Valley'** 61 blue * - *77-80*	8	10
6756	**'Evans & Bevan'** 1759 black * - *77-82*	7	9
6755	**'Glasshoughton'** 126 yellow * - *77-82*	7	9
6733	**'Hall & Dean'** 115 yellow - *75-82*	7	9
6730	**'Kendall & Co.'** 26 grey - *75-82*	7	9
6729	**'North Thames Gas'** 357260 brown - *75-80*	8	10
-	**'Ovomaltine'** yellow ex-set - *?*	15	NA
6737	**'Oxford Gas'** 18 lime green * - *77-80*	8	10
?	**'Royal Arsenal'** 144 red - *?*	10	NPG
6739	**GW** 122060 grey * - *77-00*	8	10
6732	**BR** B54884 brown - *73-80*	8	10

7-Plank Wagon 'Dearne Valley Colliery Co.' [W6)

* Pre-production models were 7-plank wagons but the actual production models were steel mineral wagons.

W7. GWR 'Toad' Brake Van (1975)

6746	**GW** 114756 light grey - *75-82*	8	10

Bachmann LMS 'Jubilee' from computer artwork by Robbie McGavin

Lone Star 000

HISTORY

In 1940 Aubrey Robert Mills, known to his friends as Bob, worked in a lockup garage beneath the forecourt of The Bridge Filling Station in Green Lanes, Palmers Green, London, building a die-casting machine. He entered into a partnership with Sidney Ambridge and together they founded Die Casting Machine Tools Ltd (DCMT) to develop the business. Later the River Works at 152 Green Lanes, Palmers Green, became the home of DCMT. For a few years they found themselves involved in war work but, when peace came, they found good trade in supplying the blossoming array of new companies that formed to manufacture for the fast growing post-war market.

Milestones

1940 DCMT formed by A.R. Mills and Sidney Ambridge.
1946 Mills and Ambridge visit Ambrit Industries in California.
1949 DCMT manufacturing for Crescent Toys.
1950 DCMT start their own toy range under the name 'Slikker Toys'.
1955 Tie-up with Harvey's hollow-cast figure business.
1956 Opening of additional factory at Hatfield.
1956 'Road-masters' car series introduced.
1957 Launch of 'Lone Star Locos'.
1960 Introducing 'Treble-O-Lectric'.
1962 American range.
1962 Arrival of blister packaging.
1963 'Gulliver County' launched.
1964 Canadian liveries.
1963 'Impy' cars launched.
1965 Production of Treble-O-Lectric and Lone Star Locos ceases
1967 New range of 'Treble-O-Trains' launched.
1968 Push-along trains renamed 'Impy Treble-0-Trains'
1969 'Tuf-Tots' launched.
1970 Railway range removed from UK market and renamed 'Lone Star Model Trains'
c1973 Model trains withdrawn.
1978/79 Abortive plan to re-launch railway system.
1983 Lone Star/DCMT in liquidation.
1985 Treble-O-Trains Ltd. dissolved
1988 Lone Star sold to Sohni-Esco Group.

One of these new companies was founded by an ex-employee of DCMT, Rodney Smith and his partner Leslie Smith, who pooled their demob money and bought one of the DCMT machines. The company they founded was Lesney and the product range the machine made for them was Matchbox Toys. Another famous ex-employee of DCMT was Jack Odell who worked for Lesney before setting up his own company Lledo to produce the 'Days Gone' and Vanguard' series of diecast vehicles.

With the war over, in 1946 Ambridge and Mills made a lengthy visit to Frank Youssi's diecasting factory (Ambrit Industries) in Glendale, California, to study production there. It was not long before DCMT decided to go into manufacturing themselves and one of the first companies they did diecasting work for was Crescent Toys; a company also remembered for their model railway accessories. When they parted company with Crescent Toys in 1950, they decided to manufacture and market toys themselves.

The craze with children in the early '50s was the 'Wild West' films seen on television and a series particularly popular was 'Riders of the Range'. The writer remembers watching it, half hidden behind the sofa! DCMT cashed in on this craze and produced the first diecast toy revolver and the 'Lone Star' range was born. Lone Star was hugely popular, partly through its links with the television programme, but also through other links it developed with the Eagle boy's comic and a serial on Radio Luxembourg. The company even launched its own Lone Star comic in 1953!

Lone Star's toy range became considerable and diverse in subject matter. In 1954/55 a new factory (now gone) was built for Lone Star production on Birchwood Industrial Estate in Hatfield and they tied up with the Harvey Toy Co. of Wood Green, London, who made, amongst other things, plastic soldiers. By the end of the decade they had a range of 200 figures. Another factory in the DCMT group was AGM Industries, the initial coming from the three principals - Ambridge, Gower and Mills. This factory (also now gone) was in Holloways Lane, Welham Green, near Hatfield. Expansion of the toy business led to the company moving to a new factory at Hatfield and a series of diecast cars called 'Road-masters' followed. Next came the series for which they are best remembered by model train collectors.

While the idea of an N gauge system had been around for a long time, Lone Star were the first company to attempt producing a commercial range for the British market. It started as a push-along system, designed by Stuart Goss in 1957 and called 'Lone Star Locos'. All items were to 000 scale with a track gauge of 8.25 mm (exactly half 00 gauge). Initially all parts, including the track and buildings, were diecast and roughly based on real prototypes.

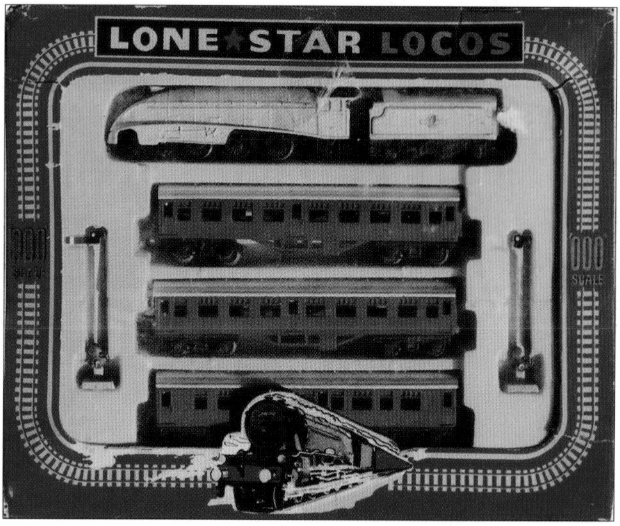

Lone Star Locos train pack No.2 Mainline Passenger Set

At the Harrogate and Brighton toy fairs in 1960, an electric range, known as 'Treble-O-Lectric', was launched which used many of the push-along castings fitted with plastic wheels to run on a finer-scale 9 mm track with 'tension-lock' couplings. In order to fit a motor inside locomotives, two completely new models were tooled-up and these were the Class 23 ('Baby Deltic') and the Class 24 diesels.

1962 saw the introduction of an American range of locos and rolling stock which won DCMT a major contract to supply Montgomery Ward of Chicago. This company had a large mail order business and some 600 retail store outlets across North America. Blister packaging was also introduced in 1962. Vinyl was used the following year in the production of a series of buildings called 'Gulliver County' and with these came a set of diecast 000 scale road vehicles. Encouraged by the good sales across the Atlantic, Canadian liveries followed in 1964.

In 1965 however, following an unsuccessful attempt to interest Lines Bros. (Tri-ang) in purchasing the railway system, production of Lone Star Locos and Treble-0-Lectric ceased.

It is interesting to note that further models had been planned including a 'Warship' diesel hydraulic, a 'Peak' diesel and a DMU. A static crane was going to be made from the superstructure of the crane truck, mounted on a base, and a total of 31 items of track were originally planned. There was also an engine shed proposed, along with oil tanks and an oil pump for a diesel depot.

In 1967, many of the passenger and goods stock items from the Treble-0-Lectric range were reissued in bubble-packs as Treble-0-Trains, using locomotives from the electric system, but without motors, and with a new plastic track produced for the series. In 1968, this system was renamed 'Impy Treble-0-Trains' and new bubble-packs were produced.

In 1970 the train system was designated 'for export only', renamed 'Lone Star Model Trains', the term '000' finally dropped in favour of 'N Gauge' and the bubble-packs were replaced by boxes. It remained available for overseas sales until approximately 1973.

In 1979, Lone Star made plans to re-launch the model railway system. Contemporary subjects, such as the '125 High Speed Train' were mocked up but the system never reached production. Bob Mills had died in the 1960s and Sidney Ambridge died in 1980.

Meanwhile, the mid 1960s had seen the launch of Lone Star's Impy series of small cars to compete with Matchbox and Huskey. Tuf-Tots, Roadmaster Majors, Kings of the Road and many other series followed. In 1988 Lone Star was taken over by Sohni-Esco of Germany and production at Hatfield came to an end. However, DCMT continued as an independent company, still in the business of manufacturing diecasting machines.

Treble-0-Electric set

Plastic copies of Lone Star 000 manufactured in Hong Kong may be found. Some were pirate copies made under the name 'Linda' and were imported into the UK in 1962 by Randall & Wood of Wood Green, London. Others were produced under the well known Hong Kong brand - 'Blue Box'. Later there were bubble-packed copies sold under the names 'Kelly' and 'HoHoHo' but it is not clear whether these are copies or from earlier tooling sold in the Far East.

GEM Models reissued white metal copies of the Lone Star 000 Citroen and the articulated lorry while the Tuf-Tots were reissued as Mokes by Microlink of Swansea.

Some Impy/Treble-O-Trains goods stock was included in a Japanese N gauge set made by Loco-Mate in the early 70s.

Further Reading

A useful book called '*Lone Star: The Toy Company and its Model Cars*' has been written by Andrew Ralston and published by Auto Review Publications (ISBN 1900482142). This provides a useful history of the company but when it comes to describing the models it has a bias towards the car ranges rather than the railway.

A book called *'The Bumper Book of 'Lone Star' Diecast Models & Toys 1948-88'*, has been written by Geoffrey Ambridge whose father was one of the partners who started the whole thing. Geoffrey Ambridge also has a website for the book at www.lone-star-diecast-bk.com which is also a free forum for Star collectors.

There were also two articles by Clive Gehle in the January and February 2000 issues of *Model Railway Collector* which were specifically about the Lone Star railway models.

Dutch collector, Donald Troost, has published a colour catalogue of the entire Lone Star 000 range in three volumes and this is currently the definitive guide to the system. These highly detailed volumes are based on an original concept by American collector Dallas Mallerich and have brought together the knowledge of other leading collectors. They are a 'must' for any serious collector. Details may be obtained from DUTCHCOLL@cs.com.

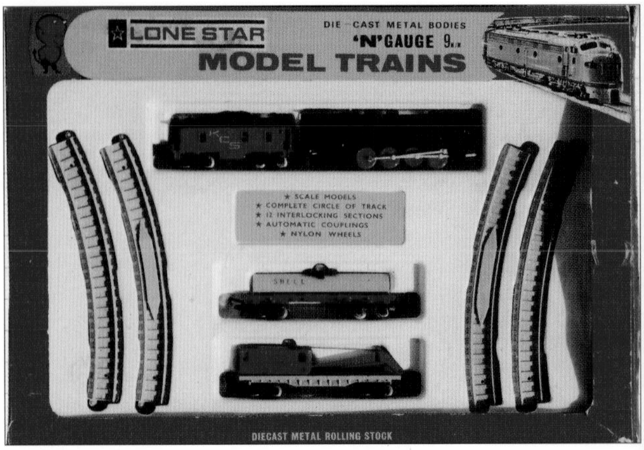

Lone Star Model Trains set [6]

THE MODELS

Numbering - As the various train series overlapped, it is possible to find a particular model with more than one code number. For example, the signal box appeared as 33, 80, EL.152 and 92 and yet only the packaging changed. In order to keep it simple we have listed below the models as they were presented in series, but be aware that if you have an unboxed item you may find it in more than one list.

Colours - Many of the models were produced in a variety of colours and some are rarer than others.

Prices - It is very difficult to give a realistic guide to these as dealers often have little idea of the rarity or otherwise of items they are selling. It is therefore possible to pick up unusual items at bargain prices but it is also possible to find relatively common pieces overpriced. A further consideration is that prices for mint boxed Canadian and US liveries are much higher in North America than they are in the UK. It is UK prices that we have included here.

Cat No.	Company, Number, Colour, Dates	£	£
1.	**'Lone Star Locos' in Boxes** (1957-60)		
1	0-6-0 Class 3F tank loco	5	8

2-6-2T and Lone Star Locos box [1]

2	2-6-2 Class 3 tank loco	5	8
3	open goods wagon (2)	3	5
4	BR Midland Region coach	3	5
5	straight track - metal (3)	2	4
6	curved track - metal (3)	2	4
7	0-6-0 diesel shunting loco	4	7
8	4-6-2 Class A4 Gresley loco	5	8
9	tender for No.8	3	4
10	4-6-2 Class 8P loco 'Princess Royal'	5	8
11	tender for No.10	3	4
12	US diesel loco	5	8
13	brake van	3	4
14	cattle wagon	3	4
15	'UD' tank wagon	3	4
16	'BP' tank wagon	3	4
17	'Shell' tank wagon	3	4
18	goods van (2)	5	6
19	BR Mk1 composite coach	4	5
20	points - metal (1LH, 1RH)	4	5
21	crossovers - metal (2)	3	4
22	sleeper built buffer stops (3)	3	5
23	re-railer track - metal (3)	2	3
24	station and platform	7	10
25	flat wagon (3)	4	6
26	US passenger car	4	5
27	girder bridge with piers	6	8
28	incline piers (6)	3	5
29	trees - plastic (3)	5	6
30	telegraph poles - plastic (12)	5	6
31	fences and gates - plastic (12+2)	5	6
32	semaphore signal	4	5
33	signal box	3	5
34	American flat car	3	5
35	American flat car with cars	17	20
36	American crane car	4	6
37	American tank car	4	6
38	American caboose	3	5
39	American box car	4	6
40	level crossing	4	6
41	automobiles (3)	21	25
42	footbridge	5	8
GS1	goods train set	NA	35
GS2	main line express set	NA	35
GS3	main line goods set	NA	35
GS4	American diesel set	NA	35

2. 'Lone Star Locos' Blister Packs (1962-65)

50	Class 3F tank 0-6-0T with track	5	8
51	Class 3 tank 2-6-2T with track	5	8
52	diesel shunter 0-6-0 with track	4	8
53	Class A4 Gresley loco 4-6-2	5	8
54	'Princess Royal' Class 4-6-2	5	8

'Princess' loco in Lone Star Locos blister pack [2]

55	tender for No.53 with 2 straight tracks	3	5
56	tender for No.54 with 2 straight tracks	3	5
57	Midland Region coach with track	5	5
58	BR Mk1 composite coach	4	5
59	brake van with flat wagon	4	8
60	cattle wagon with open goods wagon	5	8
61	'UD' tanker with straight track	4	5
62	'BP' tanker + flat wagon	4	6
63	'Shell' tanker with re-railer track	4	5
64	goods van + open wagon	5	8
65	100T breakdown crane wagon	4	5
66	US diesel loco	5	6
67	US passenger coach	4	5
68	bogie flat wagon with track	4	6
69	bogie tank wagon	4	6
70	US caboose	3	5
71	US box car	4	6
72	straight track (5)	4	5
73	curved track (5)	4	5
74	points (1LH, 1RH) and track (2)	5	6
75	re-railer track (4)	3	4
76	crossover (1), buffer stops (2) and track (2)	4	6
77	level crossing with re-railer track	4	5
78	girder bridge with piers	6	8
79	incline piers (6)	3	5
80	signal box with signal	5	8
81	signals (3)	6	10
82	plastic trees (5)	5	6
83	telegraph poles, fences and gates	6	8

3. 'Treble-O-Lectric' (1960-65)

Track and spare parts have been excluded from the following list. For set contents, see end of this section.

EL.50	standard goods set	NA	55
EL.51	standard passenger set	NA	55
EL.52	goods set with accessories	NA	60
EL.53	passenger set with accessories	NA	60
EL.54	'Transcontinental' passenger set	NA	65
EL.55	'Transcontinental' goods set	NA	65
EL.56	BR deluxe scenic set	NA	80
EL.60	D5000 diesel loco	10	12
EL.60A	D5000 diesel loco (non-motorised)	5	7
EL.61	D5900 diesel loco	10	12
EL.61A	D5900 diesel loco (non-motorised)	5	7
EL.62	US F7 diesel loco Union Pacific	12	25
EL.62A	US F7 diesel loco Union Pacific (non-motorised)	5	7
EL.63	US F7 diesel loco New Haven	15	30
EL.63A	US F7 diesel loco New Haven (non-motorised) USA & Canada only	20	25
EL.64	US F7 diesel loco Chesapeake & Ohio	15	30
EL.64A	US F7 diesel loco Chesapeake & Ohio (non-motorised) USA & Canada only	20	25
EL.65	US F7 diesel loco Kansas City Southern	15	30
EL.65A	US F7 diesel loco Kansas City Southern (non-motorised) USA & Canada only	20	25
EL.66	US 0-8-0 Baldwin steam loco + tender Union Pacific	18	25
EL.66L	US 0-8-0 Baldwin steam loco + tender Union Pacific with headlight	20	30
EL.67	F7 diesel loco Canadian Pacific	16	20
EL.67A	F7 diesel loco Canadian Pacific (non-motorised) USA & Canada only	20	25
EL.68	F7 diesel loco Canadian National	16	20
EL.68A	F7 diesel loco Canadian National (non-motorised) USA & Canada only	20	25
EL.70	Mk1 composite coach - maroon	4	5
EL.71	Mk1 brake end coach - maroon	4	5
EL.72	US passenger car Union Pacific	4	6
EL.73	US 'Vista Dome' car Union Pacific	4	6
EL.74	Mk1 composite coach - green	5	6
EL.75	Mk1 brake end coach - green	5	6
EL.76	US passenger car New Haven	6	7
EL.77	US 'Vista Dome' car New Haven	6	7
EL.78	US Pullman car	6	7
EL.79	US 'Vista Dome' car Pullman car	6	7
EL.80	brake van	2	3
EL.81	'Shell' tank wagon	3	4

EL.82	'BP' tank wagon	3	4
EL.83	'UD' tank wagon	3	4
EL.84	cattle wagon	3	4
EL.85	open goods wagon	3	4
EL.86	goods van	3	4
EL.87	US box car Union Pacific	4	6
EL.88	100T breakdown crane wagon	7	10
EL.89	bogie Flat wagon with Citroen DS19 and Land Rover	15	20
EL.90	bogie tank wagon 'Mobilgas'	7	9

Canadian Pacific caboose [3]

EL.91	US caboose Union Pacific	4	6
EL.92	US box car Boston & Maine	4	6
EL.93	US box car New Haven	4	6
EL.94	US box car Santa Fe	4	6
EL.95	bogie tank wagon 'Texaco'	7	9
EL.96	bogie flat wagon with 'Austin' articulated lorry	15	25
EL.97	US caboose New Haven	4	6
EL.98	US caboose Chesapeake & Ohio	4	6
EL.99	US caboose Kansas City Southern	4	6
EL.100	straight track - nickel silver (9.2")	1	1
EL.101	half straight track - nickel silver (2.6")	1	1
EL.102	curved track - nickel silver (12" radius)	1	1
EL.103	half curved track - nickel silver (12" radius)	1	1
EL.104	left hand point - nickel silver	3	4
EL.105	right hand point - nickel silver	3	4
EL.106	left hand diamond crossing - nickel silver	3	4
EL.107	right hand diamond crossing - nickel silver	3	4
EL.108	re-railer 9.2" with track - nickel silver	3	4
EL.109	re-railer 4.6"	2	3
EL.110	power feed terminal	1	2
EL.111	uncoupler and straight track - nickel silver	1	2
EL.112	uncoupler	1	2
EL.113	power feed terminal Leads	1	2
EL.114	point operating motor	4	5
EL.115	electric point switch	2	2
EL.116	left hand electric point	7	10
EL.117	right hand electric point	7	10
EL.130	Canadian Pacific passenger car	8	10
EL.131	Canadian Pacific 'Vista Dome' car	8	10
EL.132	Canadian National passenger car	8	10
EL.133	Canadian National 'Vista Dome' car	8	10
EL.140	box car Canadian Pacific	8	10
EL.141	caboose Canadian Pacific	8	10
EL.142	refrigerated box car Canadian Pacific	8	10
EL.143	caboose Canadian National	8	10
EL.150	station and platform	8	12
EL.151	platform extensions with lamp standards	10	12
EL.152	signal box	5	16
EL.153	semaphore signal - home (2)	5	6
EL.154	semaphore signal - distant (2)	5	6
EL.155	rail built buffer stops (3)	2	3

Canadian Pacific F7 diesel [3]

EL.156	girder bridge with piers	6	12
EL.157	incline piers (6)	3	7
EL.158S	incline tray - straight (4)	8	10
EL.158C	incline tray - curved (4)	8	10
EL.159	telegraph poles (28)	4	5
EL.160	fences (24) and gates (4)	4	5
EL.161	trees (plastic) (3)	4	5
EL.162	tunnel	5	10
EL.163	footbridge	5	12
EL.164	level crossing with barriers	4	8
EL.165	loading gauge (3) (not made)	-	-
EL.166	2-colour light signals (3)	9	12
EL.167	set of 12 plastic figures (unpainted)	10	12
EL.168	set of 5 road vehicles (Citroen DS19, Land Rover, Dennis fire engine, Austin articulated flat lorry, AEC Regal IV single deck bus) *	35	50
EL.169A	bridge girder (trade pack)	NPG	12
EL.169B	bridge pier (trade pack)	NPG	12
EL.170	timber yard corner piece	NPG	NPG
EL.171	coal yard corner piece	NPG	NPG
EL.172	sand quarry corner piece	NPG	NPG
EL.173	farm land corner piece	NPG	NPG
EL.174	station centre section	NPG	NPG
EL.175	level crossing centre section	NPG	NPG
EL.176	complete set of 6 pieces - *made?*	NPG	NPG
EL.177	4-piece scenic baseboard (36"x36")	20	25
EL.180	fish plates (12)	2	2
EL.181	spare band drives (5)	4	4
EL.182	battery controller	5	6
EL.183	track clips (10)	4	5
EL.184	variable transformer rectifier controller	4	5
EL.185	Isolating fish plates (12)	3	3
EL.186A	replacement motor for diesels	8	10
EL.186B	replacement motor for the Baldwin 0-8-0	8	10
EL.187A	D5000 chassis and bogies (no wheels)	NPG	5
EL.187B	D5900 chassis and bogies (no wheels)	NPG	5
EL.187C	F7 chassis and bogies (no wheels)	NPG	5
EL.188A	British coach bogie and wheels	NPG	4
EL.188B	US passenger car bogie and wheels	NPG	4
EL.188C	US goods bogie and wheels	NPG	4
EL.189	brass driving wheels for diesels (12)	NPG	5
EL.190A	British coach wheels (12)	NPG	5
EL.190B	US passenger car wheels (12)	NPG	5
EL.191A	British goods rolling stock wheels (12)	NPG	5
EL.191B	US goods rolling stock wheels (12)	NPG	5
EL.192	track fixing screws (20)	NPG	4
EL.193	carbon brushes (2) and springs (2)	NPG	5
EL.197	transformer/rectifier	5	10
EL.198	controller	10	20
EL.199	half amp cutout - *not made*	NA	NA

* This set of vehicles was at one time sold in a Gulliver County box.

4. 'Treble-O-Trains' Blister Packs (1966-68)

74	US diesel loco Union Pacific	10	12
75	D5900 diesel loco	10	12
76	US Baldwin 0-8-0 (tenderless)	10	15
77	BR Mk1 composite coach	4	5
78	US passenger car	4	5
79	US box car New Haven	4	6
80	bogie tank wagon 'Shell'	4	5
81	bogie flat wagon with Citroen DS19 and Land Rover	15	20
82	100T breakdown crane wagon	7	10
83	US caboose New Haven	4	6
84	cattle wagon and brake van	6	8
85	curved track - plastic (6)	4	6
86	straight track - plastic (6)	5	7
87	trees (6)	5	6
88	level crossing with barriers and track	4	8
89	figures, telegraph poles, fences, gates	10	12
90	footbridge	5	10
91	0-6-0 tank loco with open goods wagon	7	12
92	signal box with 2 colour light signals	8	10
93	crossovers - plastic	3	5

94A	right hand point - plastic	4	5
94B	left hand point - plastic	4	5

5. Impy 'Treble-O-Trains' Blister Packs (1968-69)

With the exception of the five items listed below, this was an identical range to Treble-O-Trains in blister packs. They had the same catalogue numbers and values but different package design.

95	'Princess' steam locomotive	10	20
96	D5000 diesel locomotive	10	20

Bogie Shell tanker in Treble-0-Trains blister pack [5]

97	'Vista Dome' car	4	6
8020	Union Pacific goods set	NA	45
8030	Union Pacific passenger set	NA	45
?	'Shell' Bogie Tanker	10	20

6. Lone Star Model Trains

This was the same range shown in 4 and 5 above but packed in boxes with the new name and with a '7' added to the catalogue number.

7. 'Gulliver County' Buildings

These were vinyl moulded buildings, each a single moulding with features picked out with paint.

1320	inn	10	18
1321	church	10	18
1322	fire station	10	20
1323	ranch style bungalow	10	18
1324	shop with car park	10	18
1325	garage service station	10	18

Collection of Gulliver County models (Brian Salter) [7]

1326	pair of shops	10	18
1327	two storey house with garage	10	18
1328	thatched cottage	10	18
1330	town square - *not made*	NA	NA
1331	town hall - *not made*	NA	NA
1332	theatre - *not made*	NA	NA
1333	school - *not made*	NA	NA
1340	Twin Falls station	10	18
	scenic village set*	NPG	200

* The Scenic Village Set consisted of two pieces of hardboard painted green with roads marked out on them, one of each of the Gulliver County buildings, several of the N scale road vehicles, fences, telegraph poles and trees.

SETS

The Lone Star Locos sets were called 'Gift Sets' and were packaged in window boxes with card decking and trays. The following five were made:

No.1 Goods Train Set - 2-6-2T, box van, 'UD' tanker, 'Shell' tanker, brake van, signal box and two signals.

No.2 Main Line Passenger Set - A4 loco and tender, 3 BR composite coaches and 2 signals.

No.3 Main Line Goods Set - 'Princess' loco and tender, box van, goods truck, flat truck, brake van, signal box and 2 signals.

No.4 American Transcontinental Diesel Set - US diesel, 3 US passenger cars and 2 signals.

No.5 American Transcontinental Goods Set - US diesel, US box car, US tank car, US caboose and 2 signals.

The **Treble-O-Lectric** sets had the models still in their individual blue and yellow boxes which was slotted into spaces in the set box decking. The set box had no window but a lift-off lid. They had the following contents:

EL.50 BR Standard Goods Set - D5000 diesel, a brake van, cattle wagon, goods van and an oval of track.

EL.51 BR Standard Passenger Set - D5900 diesel with two coaches and an oval of track

EL.52 BR Goods & Accessories Set - D5000 diesel, brake van, 'Shell' tanker, cattle wagon, open wagon, an oval of track, a point and siding, buffer stop, signal box, signal, station, fences & gates, trees and telegraph poles.

EL.53 BR Passenger & Accessories Set - This was the same as EL.52 but with the train from EL.51.

EL.54 Transcontinental Passenger Set - Union Pacific F7 diesel, 2 matching passenger cars and an oval of track. For USA and Canada only, sets were available in all liveries.

EL.55 Transcontinental Goods Set - Union Pacific diesel, 'Mobilgas' tanker, UP box car, UP caboose and an oval of track. For USA and Canada only, sets were available in all liveries.

There was also a Baldwin Impy set comprising a tender-less push-along Baldwin, bogie 'Shell' tanker, 100T crane and a US caboose. The box had no illustration on it but was labelled 'Durham Industries Inc.' with a New York address.

EL.56 BR De Luxe Scenic Set (2 Levels) - this had an elevated section in the middle and contained 4 vacuum-formed scenic sections which could be bought separately. It included over 90 pieces in all including a diesel passenger train and cost 9 guineas.

EL.57 BR De Luxe Scenic Set (Flat) - this had 4 scenic sections which together made a flat layout with roadways in the middle.

There was also a version exclusive to the USA that appeared in the Montgomery Ward catalogue, featuring a lake and mountain but this was made by Life-Like and not Lone Star.

For the Treble-O-Trains sets, in Impy packaging, the models were unboxed and laid in depressions in a vacuum-formed tray in a window set box. The contents of the Baldwin set were most strange consisting of a tender-less loco, bogie 'Shell' tanker, 100 ton crane wagon, American box van, British brake van, signal box, 2 colour light signals, footbridge, level crossing and an oval of track.

Useful Railway Modelling Books

From the publishers of BRITISH RAILWAY MODELLING

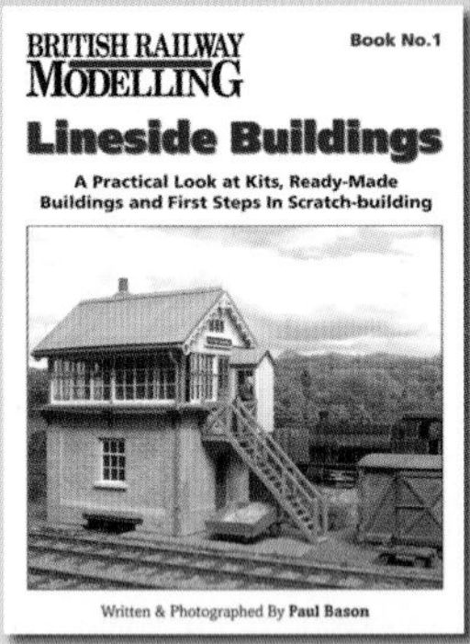

Lineside Buildings - £9.99

Scenic Modelling - £9.99

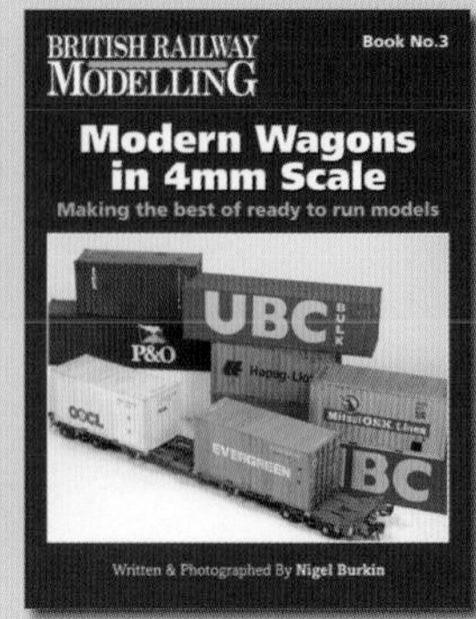

Modern Wagons in 4mm scale - £11.99

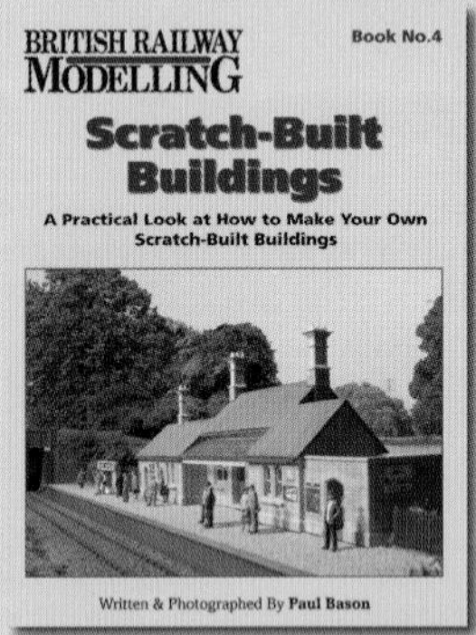

Scratch-Built Buildings - £9.99

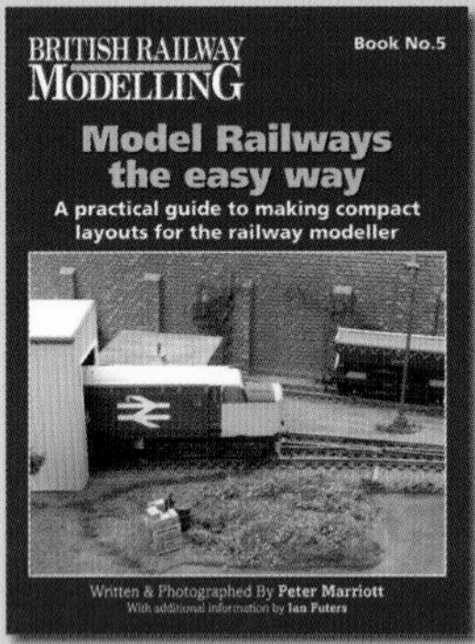

Model Railways the easy way - £9.99

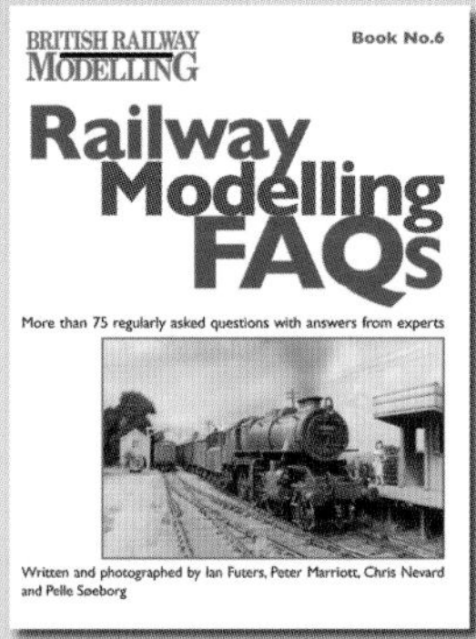

Railway Modelling FAQ's - £14.99

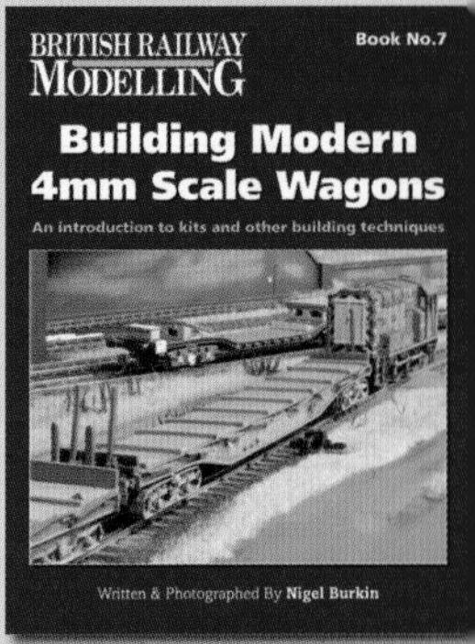

Building modern 4mm scale wagons £11.99

Keep your books in a pristine condition. This BRM Branded book slipcase holds all seven books of the series - £5.64

New wider BRM slipcase, holds 12 issues - £7.69

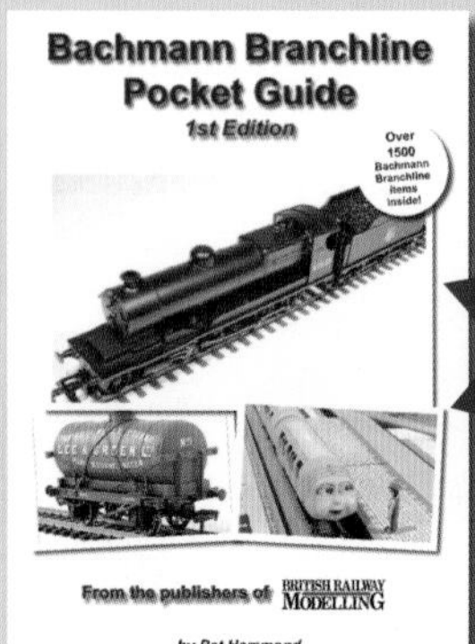

Bachmann Branchline £9.99

See page 92 for details

To order any of the above books call 01778 391180

Note: Above prices are correct at the time of going to press for more up to date prices visit our website

www.model-railways-live.co.uk

Mainline

HISTORY

Palitoy was a division of the General Mills Corporation of America and had previously been in the model railway market when, in the early 1950s, they had made and marketed an S gauge train set. They already used the Kader Industrial Company in Hong Kong to manufacture toys for them and so it was natural for them to go to Kader when, in the mid 1970s, they decided to produce an 00 scale model railway system for the British market.

Milestones

1976 Mainline Railways is launched by Palitoy.
1981 Release of the 'Manor' Class model.
1981 Palitoy acquire Airfix assets.
1983 General Mills decide to pull out of toy production in Europe.
1983 Design Department closes in August
1985 Dapol acquire the intellectual assets of the Mainline range

The new system was launched at the 1976 Harrogate Toy Fair followed by the Brighton Toy Fair. For their stand at Harrogate, Kader supplied the pre-production working chassis of the J72 and Palitoy provided cast resin shells for the bodies - they looked excellent! For the Brighton Fair a number of J72 pre-production models were running and attracted much attention. There were also pre-production wagons and coaches to be seen plus a pair of static 4MTs and a running 'Peak', all with cast resin shells.

LNER Class J72 No.581 [L3]

The new system was called Mainline Railways and the excellent BR Standard 4MT 4-6-0, a Class 45 diesel and some Mk1 coaches quickly followed. The first steam locomotive was to have been a Standard Class 5 (later to be modelled by Bachmann) but, with the release of the Hornby 'Black 5', the marketing department at Palitoy mistakenly thought they were duplicating models and suggested the Class 4 instead. Models they considered as a subject for an 0-6-0 tank before choosing the J72 were an LNER J94, a Southern G6 and an LMS 'Jinty'. The latter was dropped as Hornby retooled their own 'Jinty' at about this time. Development and expansion carried on apace and 1981 saw the release of the model of a 'Manor' Class locomotive which set the highest standards so far.

In 1981 Palitoy took over the rival Airfix GMR system and the Airfix models were gradually absorbed into the Mainline range.

Unlike Airfix, Palitoy did not own the tools with which its models were made. When Mainline models were ordered from Kader it was on the understanding that Kader retained ownership of the tools. When the Palitoy acquired Airfix, it became owners of the Airfix tools and, on the advice of the Palitoy (Far East) office, placed the ex-Airfix wagon tooling with Todco who were the third manufacturing company involved with Airfix tools after Sanda Kan and Cheong Tak. This was to lead to complications and misunderstandings later when the Mainline Railways assets were sold.

In 1983, General Mills decided to withdraw from toy development in Europe. This was not a sign of failure on the part of the Mainline range but rather a sweeping decision made many miles away on the other side of the Atlantic which affected various European toy ranges. The design department at Coalville was officially closed on August 31st 1983 and the research and development facility within the company, for most product ranges, came to an end. The company was acquired by Kenner Parker (later Kenner Parker Tonka) and subsequently the Palitoy name disappeared.

On the 17th of May 1985 the Mainline stock and intellectual assets were sold to Dapol.

Further Reading

A detailed listing of the Airfix and Mainline model railway systems was produced by the late Charles Manship in the 1980s, but this is no longer available. However, there was been a series of articles by Graham Smith-Thompson, in *Model Railway Enthusiast* magazine, profiling the Airfix and Mainline ranges together with other systems that later used the tools. There were six parts devoted specifically to Mainline Railways published in the January-May and July 1999 issues of the magazine.

Couplings - There were three types of coupling used on Mainline stock. The first of these (type A) was based on a concept coupling drawn in Hong Kong as similar dimensions to the Hornby tension lock but with the arm in a sprung socket. This was redrawn by the designer at Palitoy and formed the coupling first seen on models when the system was launched. There were problems with the type A and before bulk production got underway it was redesigned (type B) and is the most common type found on Mainline stock. Type C couplings were made at the Todco factory and came after acquisition of the Airfix range. They had a gravity operated hook and were either push-fitted or screwed on. This design was later used by Dapol.

Ex-LNER Class N2 0-6-2T No.69531 [L5]

Catalogue Numbers - In some cases these were used for more than one item, as in the case of trade packs - e.g. 37067. Later numbers were often prefixed by a '9' when a new computer was installed at Palitoy. From that time, all products carried a six-figure code and it is probable that the '9' prefix indicated that the item was from the Hobbies Division. Because a model is listed here with the '9' prefix it does not mean that it cannot be found boxed or listed in a catalogue without the prefix - and vice-versa. Brackets applied to catalogue numbers indicate that the number applied to more than a solo model, i.e. a train set or trade pack.

'X' Models - models found with an 'X' scratched on the underside were ones rejected by quality control and later sold-off cheaply in the staff shop.

Dates - Those shown in the following lists are based on catalogue and price list appearances and are provided for guidance only. Where it is known that catalogue dates are misleading, they have been altered accordingly.

Listing - The locos are listed in order of size, starting with tank engines, followed by tender locos and ending with diesels, electrics and multiple units. The coaches are listed with pre-Nationalisation stock first, followed by vehicles of later years. Wagons are listed in the order of: flats, open wagons, hoppers, tanks, vans, brake vans and bogie stock.

LOCOMOTIVES

Samples on the Market - Far East manufacturers sent samples to their customers for approval before proceeding with full production. These samples often ended up in collections and today they command a good price. In some cases samples exist of Mainline models that did not reach the production stage and these are of even greater interest to collectors.

Smoke - Some models were advertised 'with smoke' in 1982 but mention of it was immediately dropped after this. It seems that the locomotives described were produced but without smoke generators fitted.

Cat No.	Company, Number, Colour, Dates	£	£

L1. GWR Class 14XX 0-4-2 Tank (ex-Airfix)

937096	**1403** GWR green - *not made*	NA	NA
937097	**1442** BRb black - *not made*	NA	NA

See Dapol D19.

GWR Class 57xx 0-6-0PT No.5764 [L2]

L2. GWR Class 57XX Pannier Tank 0-6-0PT (1982)

Seen at the 1981 Harrogate Toy Fair but not released until 1982.

9/37084	**5764** Great Western green - *82-84*	22	30
9/37084	as above but green number plates, and number missing from rear bufferbeam - *82*	90	100
9/37084	**5764** GWR (button) green - *82*	250	260*
9/37085	**5768** BRb black yellow spots - *82-84*	30	38
9/37085	as above but blue spots, error - *82*	120	130

* The highest recorded price at auction is £300.

L3. LNER Class J72 0-6-0T (1976)

The mechanism was erratic and the plastic axles of early ones have a habit of splitting and allowing the wheels to go out of quarter. These ones were designed so that the wheels screwed into the axle. On later ones the wheels pushed onto the axles. Rpsv = Ross pop safety valves. esv = enclosed safety valves

37054	**581** LNER green lined Rpsv - *76-79*	20	28
937506	? LNER black modified model - *not made*	NA	NA
37067*	**69023 *Joem*** North Eastern green esv as preserved - *80*	20	28
937507	? BR/NER green York Station Pilot - *not made*	NA	NA
37055	**68745** BRa black Rpsv - *76-79*	20	28
37070	**69001** BRb black esv - *80-81*	18	26

* This catalogue number was also used for a trade pack of 6 mixed J72s.

L4. GWR Class 66XX 0-6-2T (1983)

One of two Mainline models with blackened metalwork.

937038	**6697** GWR green - *83-84*	30	35
937038	As above but incorrectly with 'GWR' from the Collett Goods - *83-84*	150	160

Ex-GWR Class 66xx 0-6-2T No.6652 [L4]

937039	**6652** BRb black - *83-84*	30	35
937508	? BRc lined green only 8 samples made - *84*	300	NA

L5. LNER Class N2 Tank 0-6-2T (ex-Airfix) (1982)

The completed models arrived too late to be sold by Airfix and, instead, were marketed by Palitoy. They carried the Airfix logo beneath the keeper plate.

9/54154	**9522** LNER lined green - *82-84*	22	30
954158	**4744** LNER lined black - *83-84*	28	38
9/54155	**69531** BRb lined black - *82-84*	22	30

L6. GWR Class 61XX 2-6-2T (ex-Airfix) (1984)

Unlike the Airfix versions of this model, those made by Palitoy had flanged centre drivers.

937083	**6169** GWR green - *84*	27	35
937086	**6167** BRc lined green - *84*	27	35

L7. LMS Class 2P 4-4-0 (1984)

So late was this model, that some were released only in their polystyrene trays. A large quantity went to Dapol who released them in their own packaging. It had the former 4F tender

937514	**635** LMS lined black - *84*	32	42
937515	**40568** BRb lined black - *84*	30	40

L8. GWR Class 2251 'Collett Goods' 0-6-0 (1978)

37058	**3205** GWR semi-gloss green* - *78-80*	35	40
37058	**3205** GWR matt green sample 6 made - *78*	200	NA
37059	**2213** BRb black lined - *78-80*	30	35
37077	**3210** BRc green lined - *80*	32	40

37059 was demonstrated at the 1981 Harrogate Toy Fair with steam and whistle sound. This was to also be fitted to 37058. * 2205 has also been reported (unconfirmed).

L9. GWR 2301 'Dean Goods' 0-6-0 (ex-Airfix) (1982)

The moulds for the plastic parts of this model were made for Airfix by Heller in France and taken over by Palitoy who shipped them out to Sanda Kan in Hong Kong to make. One of two Mainline models with blackened metalwork.

9/54156	**2516** GWR green - *82-84*	28	38
9/54156	as above but black - *82?*	250	260

Ex-GWR 'Dean Goods' 0-6-0 No.2538 [L9]

9/54157	**2538** BRb black - *82-84*	28	38
9/54157	as above but blue green - *82*	250	260

L10. LMS Class 4F 0-6-0 (ex-Airfix)

This was to have been a revised version from the Airfix tooling.

937512	? LMS black - *not made*	NA	NA
937513	? BR black - *not made*	NA	NA

L11. GWR Class 43XX 'Mogul' 2-6-0 (1981)

BR fitted outside steam pipes to the Class 43XX and so the GWR models were assembled without them and the BR ones with them - however errors did occur.

37090	**5322** Great Western green - *81-82*	32	40
37090	as above but with steam pipes fitted, 3 were found by quality control, later sold - *81*	250	260
937090	**4375** Great Western semi-gloss green, 6 samples made, proposal dropped - *84*	200	210
9/37045	**4358** BRb lined green advertised with smoke - *82-84*	32	40
9/37091	**5328** BRb black - *81-84*	37	45

* 2322 has also been reported (unconfirmed)

L12. GWR Class 78XX 'Manor' 4-6-0 (1980)

9/37078	**7819 *Hinton Manor*** GWR green - *80-84*	32	40
937100	**7808 *Cookham Manor*** GWR green - *83-84*	32	40

GWR 'Manor' Class No.78008 Cookham Manor [L12]

37079	**7812 *Erlestoke Manor*** BRb lined black - *80-81*	42	50
9/37043	**7827 *Lydham Manor*** BRc green advertised with smoke - *82-84*	32	40
-	**7822 *Foxcote Manor*** * BR green** *not made*	NA	NA
-	***Oxford Manor*** BRc green - *82* ***	NPG	NPG

* This was to be the power unit for the 'Cambrian Coast Express' passenger set but production was cancelled. The pre-production sample was sold at auction in 1997 for £340. ** This was shown with 'Cambrian Coast' headboard, 2 white lamps and whitened buffers. *** This model turned up in Lawson's model shop in Plymouth in 1982 but was not officially made. How it came to be in the stock delivered and what happened to it, remain mysteries. Even more mysterious is the fact that there was no member of the class called *Oxford Manor*.

L13. GWR 'Modified Hall' 4-6-0

Planned for 1984 but not made.

L14. LMS Class 6P/7P Rebuilt 'Patriot' 4-6-0 (1980)

37065	**5530 *Sir Frank Ree*** LMS black * - *80*	50	70
37082	same with steam sound - *80*	100	120
37075	**45540 *Sir Robert Turnbull*** BRa experimental green - *80-81*	45	60
37076	**45536 *Private W Wood VC*** BRa black - *80-81*	38	50
37082	same with steam sound * - *80*	70	100
37082	**45530 *Sir Frank Ree*** BR black * with steam sound - *80*	80	100
37066	**45532 *Illustrious*** BRc green - *80-81*	38	50

* not in the catalogue.

L15. LMS Class 5XP 'Jubilee' 4-6-0 (1979)

Finer quality wheels with plastic centres called Dyna-Cast, made in Singapore, were proposed for the 'Jubilee' but due to technical difficulties all models were released with 'Scot' type wheels. In 1981, the 'Jubilee' received a re-profiled chimney with skirt mounting studs and improved wheels. Some had turned brass safety valves fitted. Ffst = Fowler flush sided 3,500 gallon tender. Frt = Fowler riveted 3,500 gallon tender. St = Stanier 4,000 gallon tender

37061	**5690 *Leander*** LMS maroon St small nameplate - *79-80*	32	40
9/37061	same with correct size nameplate - *80-81*	32	40
9/37061	same with improved wheels - *81-83*	38	45
37095	same with Mk2 steam + whistle sound - *81*	60	75
9/37046	**5719 *Glorious*** LMS maroon, fine wheels, Ffst advertised with smoke - *82-84*	42	50
37034	same with steam sound - *82*	NPG	NPG
37074	**5687 *Neptune*** LMS black straw lining St small nameplate and other errors, 3 samples exist - *80*	300	310
37074	**5687 *Neptune*** LMS black straw lining St correct nameplate - *80-81*	32	40
37095	same with Mk2 steam + whistle sound - *81*	75	100

Old (near) & new ex-LMS 'Jubilee' Class loco bodies (note chimney, cab windows & safety value) [L15]

37034	**45698 *Mars*** BRb green Frt advertised with smoke, fine wheels - *82*	38	45
9/37047	same with smoke and steam sound - *82-84*	48	55
936153	**45700 *Amethyst*** BRb black lined Ffst new		

	cab glazing, turned brass safety valves, fine wheels - *83-84*	32	40
37089	**45690 *Leander*** BRc green St - *81-82*	32	40
37062	**45691 *Orion*** BRc green St small nameplate - *79-80*	32	40
9/37062	same with correct size nameplate - *80-81*	32	40
9/37062	same with improved wheels - *81-83*	38	45
37081	same with Mk1 steam sound - *80-81*	38	45
37095	same with Mk2 steam + whistle sound - *81*	NPG	NPG

L16. LMS Original 'Royal Scot' Class 4-6-0 (1981)

Differed from 'Rebuilt Scot' only in the body shell used.

9/37092	**6127 *Old Contemptibles*** LMS maroon - *81-83*	32	40
9/37092	as above with improved finish - *83-84*	40	50
937509	as above without coal rails or smoke deflectors - *not made*	NA	NA
9/37093	**46137 *Prince of Wales's Volunteers, (South Lancashire)*** BRb green - *82-83*	32	40
9/37093	as above with improved finish - *83-84*	40	50

L17. LMS Rebuilt 'Royal Scot' Class 4-6-0 (1977)

All were fitted with the Stanier 4,000 gallon tender.

37060	**6100 *Royal Scot*** LMS maroon as preserved, bell on front, name on smokebox door - *80*	30	38
37080	as above but with Mk1 steam sound - *80*	40	60
37060	as above but all black cab fronts * about 2,000 used mainly in sets - *80*	38	45
37056	**6115 *Scots Guardsman*** LMS black lined straw - *77-79*	30	38
37057	**46100 *Royal Scot*** BRb green - *77-79*	33	40
37057	as above with semi-gloss livery and BRc, fine wheels, just 4 samples received - *81?*	200	210
937088	**46115 *Scots Guardsman*** BRc green new pattern matt silver cadmium plated fine scale driving wheels - *83-84*	35	42

* Due to a production fault, a batch was made with all black cab fronts instead of LMS maroon.

L18. LNER Class B1 4-6-0

Pre-production models were made and finished as listed here ready for the 1984 catalogue which did not materialise. Replica paid for the completion of the tooling and Kader made batches for them. It then passed to Bachmann.

937510	**1000 *Springbok*** LNER apple green - *not made*	NA	NA
937511	**61007 *Klipspringer*** BR lined black - *not made*	NA	NA

L19. BR Standard Class 4 4-6-0 (1976)

37052	**75006** BRb black (small) lined - *76-80*	38	42
37053	**75001** BRc green lined, matt finish - *76-80*	38	42
37053	as above with semi-gloss livery, just 8 samples made - *84?*	200	NA

BR Standard 4 4-6-0 No.75001 [L19]

937052	**75033** BRc black lined, traction tyres fitted, sold in tray only ** - *83-84*	235	NA
937053	**75027** BRc green lined, traction tyres fitted 3 samples made * - *84?*	500	NA
?	BR with B1 tender, planned for 1985 - *not made*	NA	NA

* One of these was sold by auction in 1997 for £500. ** One was sold in 2004 for the price shown.

L20. Class 03 Diesel Shunter 0-6-0DS (1979)

9/37037	**D2179** BRc green - *82-84*	20	30
9/37036	**03382** BRe blue - *82-84*	18	29

L21. Class 42 'Warship' Diesel Hydraulic B-B (1979)

9/37073	**D823 *Hermes*** BRc maroon - *80-84*	25	32
9/37064	**D824 *Highflyer*** BRc green - *79-84*	22	30
37094	same with diesel sound and klaxon - *81*	30	40
37087	**D825 *Intrepid*** BRc green - *81-82*	25	32

9/37063	**827 *Kelly*** BRe blue - *79-84*	20	30
37094	same with diesel sound and klaxon - *81*	30	40

L22. Class 45 Diesel 1Co-Co1 (1976)

-	unpainted grey plastic only 12 made and distributed to the trade for comments. Not all were returned - *76?*	400	NA
	BRc Green		
37050	**D49 *The Manchester Regiment*** early matt, later semi-gloss - *77-79*	25	35
37050	same but grille surrounds painted the same grey as the roof, no BR decals, sample - *77*	200	210
(37068)[1]	**D52 *The Lancashire Fusilier*** - *80*	22	NA

BR Class 45 main line diesel No.D52 The Lancashire Fusilier [L22]

9/37041	**D100 *Sherwood Forester*** split headcode boxes - *82-84*	45	65
(37048)[2]	same with diesel sound and klaxon - *82-83*	45	65
	BRe Blue		
37051	**45039 *The Manchester Regiment*** early matt, later semi-gloss - *76-79*	22	32
37051	same but split diecast motor block, no traction tyres, diecast wheels, no pickups on trailing bogie, 144 made - *76*	80	85
(37068)[1]	**45044 *Royal Inniskilling Fusilier*** - *80*	22	NA
9/37040	**45048 *Royal Marines*** split headcode boxes - *82-84*	34	45
(37048)[2]	same with diesel sound and klaxon - *82-83*	45	65

[1] In 1980, retailers were offered packs of six Class 45s consisting of two each of these two plus two of Cat. No. 37051 (above). [2] Also sold together in a trade pack.

L23. Class 56 Diesel Co-Co (1983)

937035	**56079** BRe blue - *83-84*	25	35
937044	**56084** BReLL blue - *83-84*	22	30

OTHER LOCOMOTIVES PLANNED

1985

SR 'Lord Nelson' Class 4-6-0 [later modelled by Bachmann in 1992]
LMS 8F 2-8-0 (with both Stanier and Fowler tenders) [later modelled by Hornby in 1988]
GWR Class 28XX 2-8-0 [later modelled by Hornby in 1991]
LNER/BR Class A1 4-6-2 [later made by Bachmann in 2001]
LMS/BR Ivatt 2MT 2-6-2T [later made by Bachmann in 1995]
SR Class N 2-6-0 [later modelled by Bachmann in 1998]

1986

BR Class 25 [previously modelled by Hornby and later by Bachmann in 2001]
LMS/BR 'Black 5' 4-6-0 [previously modelled by Hornby]
SR/BR Class Q1 0-6-0 [later made by Hornby in 2003]
LNER/BR Class J94 0-6-0ST [modelled by Dapol in 1985]
GWR Class 8750 0-6-0PT [later modelled by Bachmann in 1999]

COACHES

The first coaches Palitoy produced were BR Mk1s and these were followed by some early LMS panelled stock. With the exception of livery changes, expansion of this range was slow until 1981 when a full brake and some Collett type coaches were announced. After that the coach range was greatly enlarged by the addition of the former Airfix models.

A pair of LNER Gresley coaches was developed but never got to the mould-making stage in the Far East.

Cat No.	Company, Number, Colour, Dates	£	£

C1. GWR Suburban 'B Set' Coach (ex-Airfix) (1983)

'B Set' coaches were brake ends which were always used in pairs.

937320	**GWR** 6396 brown+cream - *83-84*	15	18
937320	**GWR** 6896 brown+cream - *83-84*	15	18
937321	**BR** W6447W lined maroon - *83-84*	12	18

C2a. GWR Collett 60' All 3rd/2nd (1983)

937124	**GWR** 1116 brown+cream - *83-84*	15	18
937124	**GWR** (button) 1137 brown+cream - *83-84*	15	18
937123	**GWR** 6007 brown+cream - *?*	20	25
937309	**BR** W1087W maroon - *83-84*	15	18

C2b. GWR Collett 60' Brake Composite (1983)

937123	**GWR** 6507 brown+cream - *83-84*	15	18
937123	**GWR** 6562 brown+cream - *83-84*	15	18
937124	**GWR** 1007 brown+cream - *?*	20	25
937308	**BR** W7365W maroon - *83-84*	15	18

C3a. GWR 'Centenary' Composite (ex-Airfix) (1983)

937314	**GWR** 6659 brown+cream Cornish Riviera Limited - *83*	8	14

C3b. GWR 'Centenary' Brake 3rd (ex-Airfix) (1983)

937316	**GWR** 4575 brown+cream Cornish Riviera Limited - *83*	8	14

C4. GWR Auto Trailer (ex-Airfix) (1982)

937318	**GWR** 187 brown+cream twin coats of arms - *82-84*	12	18
937319	**BR** W176W red+cream 1956 livery - *83-84*	12	18

EX-GWR autotrailer No.W178W [C4]

937319	**BR** W178W red+cream 1956 livery - *83-84*	12	18

C5a. LMS 57' Panelled Composite (1977)

37109	**LMS** 3621 maroon 1936 livery - *77-81*	10	15
37109	as above but mid grey roof - *?*	50	55
37111	**BR** M3621M red+cream 1949 livery - *78-81*	12	16
37115	**BR** M3542M lined maroon 1956 livery - *80-81*	14	18
37115	**BR** M3542M dull maroon with mid grey roof and gold and black lining - *80*	50	55
37115	**BR** M3542M semi-gloss maroon with mid grey roof and gold and black lining - *80*	50	55

C5b. LMS 57' Panelled Brake 3rd/2nd (1977)

37110	**LMS** 5327 dull maroon, silver-grey roof - *77-81*	10	15
37110	as above but mid grey roof - *?*	50	55
37112	**BR** M5371M red+cream 1949 livery - *78-81*	12	16
37112	**BR** M5321M red+cream 1949 livery - *78-81*	12	16
37116	**BR** M5335M semi-gloss maroon yellow lining and yellow-grey roof - *80-81*	14	18
37116	**BR** M5335M dull maroon with mid grey roof and gold and black lining - *80*	50	55
37116	**BR** M5335M semi-gloss maroon with mid grey roof and gold and black lining - *80*	50	55

C6. LMS 50' Parcels Van Type BG (1983)

937118	**LMS** 30965 maroon - *83-84*	10	15
937336	**BR** M31346 red+cream - *84*	15	18

LMS 50' parcels van No.30965 [C6]

937307	**BR** M31361 red -*83*	12	16
937347	**BR** lined maroon - *84*	15	18
937304	**BR** M31262M blue+grey - *83-84*	10	15
937117	**BR** M31398 blue 1966/67 livery NFV - *83-84*	10	15

C7a. LMS Stanier Composite (ex-Airfix) (1983)

937326	**LMS** 3935 maroon 60' (A) * - *84*	12	20
937327	**BR** M3868M maroon 60' lined improved finish - *83-84*	10	18

*These resulted from a colour correction ordered by Airfix but were kept in store until old stocks were used up. They were inherited by Palitoy who boxed and sold them.

C7b. LMS Stanier Brake End (ex-Airfix) (1983)

937328	**LMS** 5542 maroon 57' (A) * - *84*	12	20
937329	**BR** M3868M maroon 57' lined improved finish - *83-84*	12	20
937329	**BR** M5434M maroon 57' lined improved finish - *83-84*	12	20
937329	**BR** M5648M maroon 57' lined improved finish - *83-84*	12	20

* see note for C7a.

C7c. LMS Stanier Vestibule 3rd/2nd (ex-Airfix)

Palitoy redesigned this Airfix proposal as a one piece moulding, to improve the appearance of the glazing and to fit a new 57' chassis. The conversion was later finished by Replica Railways who sold the model.

937348	**LMS** maroon 57' - *not made*	NA	NA
937349	**BR** maroon 57' - *not made*	NA	NA

C8. LMS 68' Dining Car (12-wheel) (ex-Airfix)

These were in the design stage when Airfix went into receivership and Mainline took up the project. It next fell into the hands of Dapol who actually produced the first batch of models. Their tools, thought to have been damaged in a factory fire, were later sold to Hornby who modified them and now make the model.

937345	**LMS** maroon - *not made*	NA	NA
937346	**BR** maroon - *not made*	NA	NA

C9. LMS 57' Suburban Stock (ex-Airfix)

937332	**LMS** maroon lavatory brake/3rd - *not made*	NA	NA
937334	**LMS** maroon lavatory composite - *not made*	NA	NA
937333	**BR** maroon lavatory brake/2nd - *not made*	NA	NA
937335	**BR** maroon lavatory composite - *not made*	NA	NA

C10. LNER Gresley Stock

These were planned for 1984 but not made.

C11a. BR Mk1 Corridor 2nd (1976)

cb = Commonwealth bogies

37101	**BR** W24720 red+cream - *76-80*	10	15
37121	**BR** S25915 green - *81*	14	17
37105	**BR** W24716 brown+cream - *77-80*	10	15
37107	**BR** M25390 maroon - *77-80*	10	15

BR Mk1 corridor 2nd Class No.W24720 [C11a]

937107	**BR** M25390 semi-gloss maroon cb* - *83*	10	15
937107	as above but yellow-grey roof - *83-84*	18	22
37103	**BR** M1709 blue+grey - *76-80*	9	13
37103	**BR** M25454 matt blue+grey, white line masked and sprayed - *76-?*	9	13
37103	as above but blue semi-gloss and white line printed - *?-80*	9	13

* This and the maroon brake end had the descriptions in the catalogue and on the boxes transposed.

C11b. BR Mk1 1st Open (FO)

cb = Commonwealth bogies

937341	**BR** brown+cream open cb - *not made*	NA	NA
937339	**BR** maroon cb - *not made*	NA	NA
937305	**BR** M34571 blue+grey - *not made*	NA	NA

C11c. BR Mk1 Corridor Brake 2nd (BSK) (1976)

cb = Commonwealth bogies, sb = standard bogies

37102	**BR** W34820 red+cream - *76-80*	10	15
37122	**BR** S34938 green - *81*	14	17
37106	**BR** W34860 brown+cream - *77-81*	10	15
37108	**BR** M35040 matt maroon - *77-81*	10	15
37108	as above but semi-gloss paint sb - *83*	25	30
937108	**BR** M35040 semi-gloss maroon cb* - *83*	15	18
937108	as above but yellow-grey roof sb - *83-84*	25	30
37104	**BR** M34571 matt blue+grey, white line masked and sprayed - *76-?*	9	13
37104	as above but semi-gloss blue, white line printed - *?-80*	9	13

* This and the maroon composite had the descriptions in the catalogue and on the boxes transposed.

C11d. BR Mk1 Corridor Brake Composite (BCK)

cb = Commonwealth bogies

937344	**BR** brown+cream cb - *not made*	NA	NA
937342	**BR** maroon cb - *not made*	NA	NA
937306	**BR** M1708 blue+grey - *not made*	NA	NA

C11e. BR Mk1 Buffet Restaurant Car (1981)

cb = Commonwealth bogies

937337	**BR** green - *84*	14	17
937338	**BR** brown+cream cb - *84*	10	15
937114	**BR** M1713 maroon lined cb - *81-84*	10	15

BR Mk1 buffet restaurant car No.M1713 [C11e]

937114	as above but 'Kitchen' in lower case, only 2 made - *81*	150	160
937113	**BR Inter-City** W24716 blue+grey cb 'Kitchen' in lower case - *81-84*	9	13
937113	**BR Inter-City** M1709 blue+grey - *81-84*	9	13

C12. Mk2D Stock (ex-Airfix) (1983)

937301	**BR Inter-City** E5690 blue+grey open 2nd brake - *83-84*	12	20
937302	**BR Inter-City** E3170 blue+grey open 1st - *not made*	NA	NA
937303	**BR Inter-City** E9479 blue+grey open 2nd - *83-84*	10	14

OTHER COACHES PLANNED

1985

SR/BR Bulleid brake 3rd, composite and semi-open 3rd [later made by Bachmann]
BR Mk1 SO coach [later made by Bachmann in 2000]
LMS 12-wheel 69' sleeping car

1986

LNER Gresley buffet car
SR utility van
BR Mk1 BG full brake [later made by Bachmann in 2000]
GWR Collett 1st [later made by Bachmann in 1990]

WAGONS

A large range of Mainline wagons was made, the later ones coming from Airfix tooling. Typically Mainline were the small hopper, small tank wagon, cattle truck and the coke wagon. Many of the open wagons had private owner liveries and some later ones had loads and these are harder to find.

So as not to place all their eggs in one basket, most of the newly acquired Airfix tools went to a different Hong Kong company for production. This was the Todco Engineering Company.

Some Mainline wagons were reissued with Airfix style chassis. A new 10' chassis was tooled up from the acquired Airfix drawings and improved by the incorporation of such features as small integral 'dummy' hooks on the buffer headstocks and separately attached vacuum cylinder to the underside for 'fitted' wagons, with 3-hole disc wheels on shouldered steel axles. Screw attachment posts were added on the underside and the RCH type buffer shanks, which frequently broke on the Airfix wagons, were slightly thickened up. The chassis had fine in-line brake gear and steel shouldered axles with plastic wheels. The chassis became standard across the range and was later used by Replica Railways and Bachmann Branchline.

In 1984, a completely new, modern style hopper wagon, type HEA, was tooled up, but it did not attain production due to the termination of the range.

Cat No.	Company, Number, Colour, Dates	£	£

W1a. 'Conflat' (ex-Airfix) with AF Container (1984)

After the acquisition of the Airfix tools, those for this model were transferred to the Kader factory in Hong Kong so that they could be modified to take the Palitoy small AF container.

937384	**BR** + blue insulated AF container - *84*	6	10

W1b. 'Conflat' (ex-Airfix) with BD Container (1983)

See note for W1a.

937355	**GW** 39005 dark grey + **GWR** Furniture container - *83-84*	7	12
937364	**GW** 39005 dark grey + **'Pickfords'** container - *83*	8	14
937393	**GW** 39324 dark grey + **'C&G Ayers'** 37 container - *84*	8	14
937352	**BR** B735833 red brown + **BR** maroon container - *83-84*	7	12
937352	**BR** W36507 red brown + **BR** maroon container - *84*	7	12

W2a. 1-plank Open Wagon (1978)

37150	**NE** 221119 red-brown Lowfit - *78-80*	6	10
37149	**BR** B450023 red-brown Lowfit - *78-80*	6	10

W2b. 1-plank Open Wagon + AF Container (1982)

37401	**GW** 70001 dark grey Match Truck + **GWR** white container AF-2102 - *82*	8	12

GWR 1-plank wagon with AF type container (S&D Models) [W26]

937401	as above but new chassis - *83-84*	8	12

W2c. 1-plank Open Wagon + BD Container (1982)

37433	**LMS** 219215 grey + **LMS** container maroon - *83*	8	12
937368	**NE** 221119 red-brown Lowfit + **LNER** container BK1820? blue - *83-84*	8	12
37458	**NE** 221119 red-brown Lowfit + **'Frasers'** container green+white - *83*	8	14
937402	**BR** B450000 red-brown + **'Bird's Eye'** container - *82-84*	8	12
937402	**BR** B450023 red-brown + **'Bird's Eye'** container - *82-84*	8	12

W3. 3-plank Open Wagon (1982)

This model was based on inherited Airfix design work and had a new chassis largely based on the Airfix one. nc = new chassis.

937361	'James **Carter** & Sons' 172 grey nc - *83-84*	6	10
937362	'E **Turner** & Sons' 26 cream nc - *83-84*	6	10
937419	**LMS** 471419 grey nc - *82-84*	6	9
937379	**NE** 535962 grey - *84*	6	10
937420	**BR** M473453 red brown nc - *82-84*	6	9

W4. 5-plank Open Wagon (1976)

37131	**'Ellis & Everard Ltd'** 136 red+black - *76-80*	6	9
937421	**'Timpson'** 5 blue - *82-83*	6	10
37176	**'Wadworths'** 66 black - *80-81*	6	10
37132	**'Warrener'** 3 green - *76-80*	6	9
37130	**LMS** 24361 grey - *77-80*	6	10
37170	**BR** M360241 red-brown - *79-81*	5	9

W5. 5-plank Open Wagon (ex-Airfix) (1983)

937456	**'BAC'** 4253 red brown - *83-84*	6	9
937455	**'Black Rock Quarries'** 46 black - *83-84*	6	9
937455	as above but brown - *83-84*	100	120
937389	**'Webster'** 341 dark brown - *84*	6	10
937382	**LMS** red brown - *84*	6	10
937380	**NE** 214021 red brown - *84*	6	10

W6. 7-plank Open Wagon (1977)

937175	**'Bass'** 65 grey - *80-83*	6	9
37169	**'Cambrian'** 1078 black - *79-81*	6	10
37127	**'Colman's'** 35 yellow - *77-80*	6	9
37151	**'Courtaulds'** 18 green - *78-80*	6	9
37129	**'CWS'** 1941 dark brown Coal * - *77-84*	6	9
37404	**'Diamond'** 34 red - *81-82*	6	10

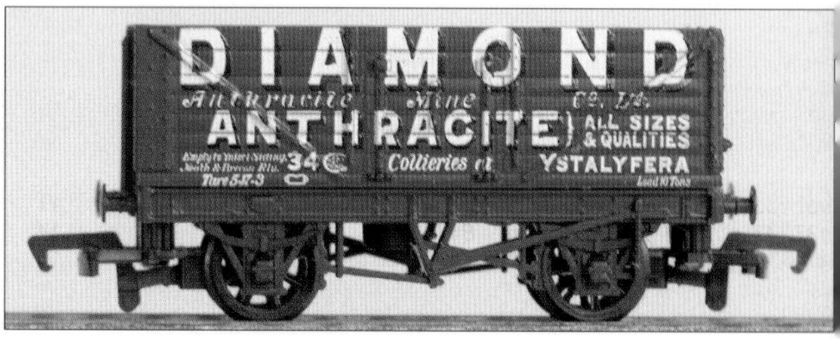

7-plank wagon - 'Diamond' [W6]

37428	**'Emlyn'** 813 dark green - *82-83*	6	10
37168	**'Horlicks'** 1 brown - *79-81*	6	10
37167	**'S J Moreland'** 1 red+black - *79-81*	6	10
937386	**'Parkinson'** 107 dark blue * - *84*	6	10
37406	**'Patent Nut & Bolt Co**.' 658 dark brown - *81-82*	6	10
37457	**'Perfection'** 82 red * - *83-84*	6	10
37128	**'Persil'** 258 dark green - *77-80*	6	9
937405	**GW** 06515 dark grey - *81-82*	6	10
37126	**NE** HB4333 grey Loco - *77-80*	6	9
937126	**NE** HB4333 grey Loco * - *83-84*	6	10
37152	**BR** P99347 grey - *78-80*	5	10
37152	**BR** P99347 early BR grey ex-set - *81*	12	NA

* New chassis.

W7. 7-plank Open Wagon (ex-Airfix) (1984)

937387	**'Brentnall & Cleland'** 3000 black - *84*	6	10
937385	**'David Jones'** 650 red-brown - *84*	6	10

W8. 12T 9-plank Coke Wagon (1978)

937363	**'Arthur H.Stabler'** 21 grey - *83-84*	6	10
37409	**'Baldwin'** 2030 black - *81-83*	6	10
37164	**'Bedwas'** 621 light grey - *79-81*	6	10
37429	**'Carpenter'** 28 red - *82-83*	6	10
37178	**'CCC'** 105 dark red - *80-81*	6	10

Coke wagon - 'Coalite' [W8]

37163	**'Coalite'** 552 black - *79-81*	6	10
937163	**'Coalite'** 552 black new chassis - *83-84*	6	10
937388	**'Dinnington'** 254 red-brown - *84*	6	12
37157	**'MOY'** 1851 red-brown - *78-80*	6	10
37158	**'TCD'** 171 black - *78-80*	6	10
37179	**'TWW'** 1746 brown - *80-81*	6	10

W9. NE 9-plank 20T Mineral Wagon (ex-Airfix) (1983)

37446	**'Charringtons'** 257 brown - *83-84*	7	12
937394	**'Gas Light & Coke'** 794 grey - *84*	7	12

W10. 16T Steel Mineral Wagon (1975)

37145	**'ICI'** 776 dark blue Mond Division - *77-80*	6	9
37133	**BR** B265451 grey - *76-80*	6	9
37133	as above but pale grey, early sample * - *75*	30	35
37133	the same but one stripe at wrong end * - *75*	35	40
37133	**BR** B265451 early BR grey ex-set - *81*	12	NA
37133	**BR** B118301 grey - *81?*	6	9
37403	**BR** B118301 grey + ore load - *81*	6	9
937374	**BR** grey - *made?*	NPG	NPG
37144	**BR** B566728 red-brown - *77-80*	6	9
37144	**BR** B595150 red-brown - *77-80*	6	9
937424	**BR** B595150 red-brown + coal - *82-84*	6	9

* The chassis on these early examples did not have the Mainline logo on the underside and some had spoked wheels.

W11. GWR 20T Steel Mineral Wagon (ex-Airfix) (1983)

37459	**'Avon Tyres'** 1 black - *83-84*	7	11
937437	**'Blaenavon'** 2441 brown - *83-84*	7	11
937438	**'Glenhafod'** 2277 black - *83-84*	7	11
937390	**'PJ&JP'** 3619 black - *84*	7	12
937391	**'SC'** 25503 dark grey - *84*	7	12
937439	**'Stewart & Lloyds'** 3506 grey - *83-84*	7	11
937377	**GW** PO Lease Hire - *84*	8	14
37424	**BR** grey + coal - *84*	7	12

W12. 12T/24T Ore Hopper Wagon (1978)

37160	**'BISC'** 776 dark grey iron ore - *78-80*	6	11
937160	**'BISC'** 776 dark grey iron ore new chassis - *83-84*	7	11
37408	**'Cadbury Bournville'** 156 blue - *81-83*	7	11
37180	**'Clay Cross'** 72 red brown - *80*	7	12

24ton ore hopper wagon - 'Hoare Bros' [W12]

37407	**'Hoare Bros.'** 101 black - *81*	7	12
37161	**'Sheepbridge'** 8251 red brown - *79-80*	7	11
37159	**BR** B433475 grey Ore Hop - *78-80*	6	11
37422	**BR** B437319 grey Sand + sand load - *82, 84*	8	14
37159	**BR** B433475 early BR grey, ex-set - *81*	12	NA
37162	**BR** B435925 red brown - *79-80*	7	11

W13. NE 21T Hopper Wagon (ex-Airfix) (1983)

937443	**'Charringtons'** B421818K grey+orange - *83-84*	7	11
37444	**'House Coal Concentration'** B429816K red brown - *83-84*	7	11
937441	**'MOT'** 1324 black - *83-84*	7	12
937441	as above but in bauxite brown - *83*	100	120
937392	**'Norman Jackson'** 10 black - *84*	7	11
937357	**NE** 193258 grey - *83-84*	7	11
937351	**BR** E252543K grey - *83-84*	7	11

Also referred to as a '20T Hopper'.

W14. HBA Hopper Wagon (1976)

937370	**BR** red brown - *84*	7	11
937372	**BR Railfreight** grey - *84*	7	11

W15. 12T Tank Wagon (1976)

37177	**'Benzole & By-Products'** 1 buff - *80-81*	8	12
37135	**'BP'** 5049 light grey, black solebar - *76-80*	7	11
937135	**'BP'** 5049 light grey, red solebar - *83-84*	8	12
37147	**'Crossfield Chemicals'** 49 dk.green - *77-80*	8	12
37153	**'Esso'** 3066 silver - *78-81*	8	12
37166	**'ICI'** 895 dark blue - *79-81*	7	11
37166	as above but CC symbol missing from yellow square - *79*	45	50
37411	**'National'** 731 silver - *81-82*	8	12
37146	**'National Benzole'** 2006 black - *77-80*	8	12

Tank wagon - 'National' [W15]

37146	**'National Benzole'** 2003 black - *77-80*	8	12
37146	as above but name in white and 6-pointed star, early sample - *77*	50	55
937410	**'Ronuk'** 38 blue - *81-83*	9	13
37134	**'Royal, Daylight'** 1534 black - *76-80*	8	12
37165	**'Shell** 4492 silver - *79-81*	8	12
937396	**'Shell Electrical Oils'** SM2202 brown - *84*	8	12
937396	as above but yellow body with red lettering, original samples - *84*	45	50
37136	**'United Molasses'** 128 red-brown - *76-80*	8	12
937383	**LMS Cresote** 304592 grey - *84*	8	14

W16. 20T Tank Wagon (ex-Airfix) (1983)

937395	**'Crossfield'** 15 dark green - *84*	8	12
937395	semi-gloss green planned but cancelled, only one made - *84*	NA	NA
37453	**'ICI** '499 dark blue - *83-84*	8	12

W17. LMS Cattle Wagon (1977)

37154	**LMS** 12098 grey - *78-80*	6	10
37143	**BR** M12098 red-brown - *77-81*	6	10

W18. GWR 12T Goods Fruit Van (1980)

37174	**GW** 134149 dark grey *80-81*	6	10
937174	**GW** 134149 dark grey new chassis - *83-84*	7	10
37173	**BR** W134251 red-brown - *80-81*	6	10

W19. GWR 12T 'Mogo' Van (1981)

These were vans with double end doors used for transporting motor cars.

37430	**GW** 126342 dark grey Mogo - *82-84*	7	10
37105	**BR** W105682 red-brown Mogo - *81*	6	9

W20. LMS 12T Single Vent Sliding Door Van (1975)

37138	**'Allsopp's'** 4 cream, white roof - *76-80*	7	10
937365	**'ICI'** 2300 maroon Salt fixed doors - *83-84*	8	12
37148	**LMS** 511476 grey, grey roof - *77-80*	7	11
37137	**BR** B753722 red-brown, grey roof - *76-80*	7	11
37137	as above but oxide brown instead of bauxite, one of initial launch batch - *75*	35	40

W21. LMS 12T Single Vent Van (ex-Airfix) (1983)

937371	**LMS** 508587 grey - *83-84*	8	12
937375	**BR** B753722 red-brown - *84*	8	12

937373	**BR** M501083? blue Cell truck - *84*	10	14

W22. GWR 12T Double Vent Van (1981)

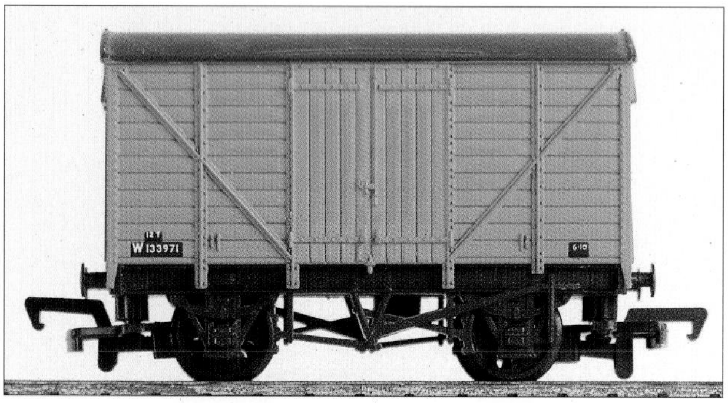

Ex-GWR double vent van [W22]

37413	**'Shepherd Neame'** 3 cream - *81-83*	7	11
37414	**GW** 123507 dark grey - *81*	9	13
937414	**GW** 123507 dark grey, new chassis - *83-84*	9	13
37415	**BR** W141826 red-brown - *82-84*	8	12
37431	**BR** W133971 grey - *82-84*	8	12

W23. SR 12T Box Van (ex-Airfix) (1983)

937449	**BR** S47002 brown - *83-84*	10	14

W24. GWR 20T Brake Van (1978)

37156	**GW** 56684 dark grey Shrewsbury - *78-81*	8	12
37426	**GW** 56590 dark grey Oswestry - *82-84*	8	12
37427	**BR** W68855 light grey - *82-84*	8	12
37155	**BR** W68816 red-brown - *78-80*	8	12

W25. LMS 20T Brake Van (ex-Airfix) (1984)

937381	**LMS** brown - *84*	8	12
937376	**BR** grey - *84*	8	12

W26a. LNER/Standard 16' 20T Brake Van (1976)

937369	**NE** 182922 brown - *83-84*	8	12
37139	**BR** B951480 red-brown - *76-81*	8	12
37139	as above but yellow-brown 2,000 made error used up in sets - *76*	10	NA
937366	**BR** B950880 grey - *83-84*	8	12

W26b. 10' Short Brake Van (1975)

37140	**NE** 178595 red-brown - *76-80*	7	10
37140	as above but chocolate brown, error, few made for launch at Harrogate, then used as rep samples - *75*	50	55

10' short brake van - LNER [W26b]

37140	**NE** 178595 red-brown (on wagon chassis) - *?*	12	15
37140	**NE** 182030 brown - *76-80*	7	10
37142	**BR** E168064 light grey - *77-80*	7	10
37142	**BR** E168064 early BR grey ex-sets - *81*	12	15

W27. GWR 'Macaw B' Bogie Bolster Wagon (1980)

37172	**GW** 84773 dark grey - *80*	8	12
37172	**GW** 107291 dark grey - *81*	8	12
37172	same but underscale numbers - *80*	8	12
37171	**BR** W84922 grey larger numbers - *81-82*	7	10
37171	same but underscale numbers - *80*	8	12
37416	**BR** W84922, W84921 grey + girder load - *81-83*	8	12
37416	same but underscale numbers - *81*	10	15

W28. GWR 'Macaw H' Bogie Bolster (ex-Airfix) (1983)

937378	**GW** dark grey Macaw H - *84*	8	12
937353	**BR** W107364 grey, Bogie Bolster A - *83-84*	8	12

W29. GWR 'Crocodile' H Well Wagon (1980)

37181	**GW** 41973 dark grey - *80-81*	8	12
37181	as above but white printing missing on one side from lower deck side - *?*	20	25
37418	**GW** 41973 dark grey + marine boiler - *81-83*	10	14
37182	**BR** W41947 grey Weltrol WH - *80-83*	9	13

W30. GWR 'Siphon G' Bogie Milk Van (ex-Airfix) (1982)

937322	**GW** 1478 brown - *83-84*	10	15
937323	**BR** W1457 maroon - *82-84*	10	15
54307	**BR** W1452 maroon - *82-84*	10	15

W31. GWR 'Siphon H' Bogie Milk Van (ex-Airfix) (1982)

937324*	**GW** 1437 brown - *82-83*	10	15
937325	**BR** W1429 maroon - *83-84*	10	15

* also found with catalogue number 54308

OTHER WAGONS PLANNED

1985
BR 'Chevron' type PCA tank wagon [later made by Dapol]
'Freightliner' wagon and containers
SR 25T brake van [later made by Bachmann]

1986
GWR cattle wagon
LNER box van
TEA bogie tank wagon
bogie pallet van

ACCESSORIES

Palitoy accepted Peco's offer of their 'Setrack' which was made by Garnet in Austria. Airfix, who used the same source, had chosen black sleeper bases and so, for Mainline, a brown moulded sleeper base was ordered. Both had steel rails. Due to continual production difficulties in Austria, none of the correct specification isolating points was ever delivered to Palitoy. Instead, Peco were compelled to supply their own UK-made ones from the 'Streamline' range, with their nickel silver rails, for the assembly of Mainline train sets at the Coalville factory.

The only other accessories produced were power and circuit controllers, electronic steam sound with whistle and diesel sound with klaxon modules. There was also a series of card building kits, by Gilmour. Palitoy had planned to reintroduce some of the former Airfix plastic lineside kits in 1984 but this was abandoned.

SETS

Sets do not seem to have been too prominent and the Company were not encouraged along this line as they did not sell well. Over the years a total of 20 were made. At present these are not attracting enough attention from collectors to push the prices up and are best valued according to their contents.

Marklin H0 (British)

HISTORY

The firm was founded in Goppingen, Germany, by tinsmith Theodor Fredrich Wilhelm Marklin in 1859, to make dolls house accessories in lacquered tinplate. He died after a fall in 1866 and his widow, Karoline, who was his second wife and effectively the sales manager, was left to carry on alone despite, remarrying in 1868. It was 20 years before her sons were old enough to take over. Wilhelm Marklin's three sons, Eugen, Wilhelm and Karl, took over the company in 1888 and it became known as Marklin Brothers. In 1891 they acquired the famous company of Ludwig Lutz and moved its production to Goppingen. In 1892 they took in another partner, Emil Friz von Plochingen who brought with him much needed capital to allow the company to grow. Richard Safft joined them in 1907. The families Marklin, Plochingen and Safft were still the owners of Marklin at the time of the company's financial crisis in the spring of 2006.

LMS short coach No.342 (Vectis) [C1]

By the time of the 1891 Leipzig Spring Fair, they had perfected the first train set with trains that ran on track and its success lead to the company concentrating on model trains. Many of their models were marketed in Britain through Bassett-Lowke. Over the years they have manufactured models in all the leading gauges including Z gauge.

In 1936 Marklin made their first attempt at breaking into the British 00/H0 market with a number of their German H0 locomotives and coaches produced in LMS and LNER liveries. However, the most interesting development was the production of an LMS Compound which, today, is one of the most sought after of Marklin models. These were not repeated after the war.

H0 scale remains their largest range and in the mid 1960s they again attempted to break into the British market by producing a British diesel hydraulic locomotive. By now, however, British modellers were committed to 4mm scale. A model of in H0 scale is to 3.5mm scale and, however well engineered, looks too small alongside British 00 models. Thus sales were poor and Marklin did not experiment further.

More recently, Marklin have marketed a *Harry Potter* set in Germany but the locomotive is the Hornby model with non-insulated wheels, NEM coupler pocket and the fitting of a Marklin skate under the tender and so is to 00 rather than H0 scale. They also repackaged some of Hornby's Thomas series models.

Prices - The tables show a suggested range of prices for models in very good condition. This assumes no metal fatigue or corrosion and with original paintwork.

LOCOMOTIVE

A review of the model appeared in the October 1967 issue of *Model Railway Constructor*.

Cat No.	Company, Number, Colour, Dates	£	£

British Outline Locomotives

LMS 'Compound' 4-4-0 [L1] (Vectis)

L1. LMS 'Compound' 4-4-0 (1938)

This made use of an existing 4-4-0 mechanism but had specially designed bodies for the locomotive and tender. It carried 'LMS' on the tender and an non-authentic number on the cabsides.

E800.1	**E800** red LMS - *38?*	10000	15000

L2. Class 42 'Warship' Diesel-Hydraulic B-B (1967)

There were 3-rail and 2-rail versions, the latter in Marklin's 'Hamo' series. The model is fitted with traction tyres and has working headlights in the direction of travel. It has a plastic moulded body and fixed buffer beams.

8373	**D830 *Majestic*** green BRc 2-rail - *67-?*	30	40
3073	**D830 *Majestic*** green BRc 3-rail - *67-?*	30	40

Continental Locomotives

These were standard German models released in LMS and LNER liveries for the British market. There is some evidence that the models were taken from storage and repainted in the factory. 'LMS' or 'LNER' were carried on the tender and a non-authentic number on the cabsides.

L3. German 0-4-0 with 4-wheel Tender (1938)

The locomotive had smoke deflectors, twin domes and a riveted tender. The wheels and edge of the footplate and tender chassis were bright red.

R700.1	**R700.1?** red LMS - *38?*	1500	3000
R700.1	**?** green LNER - *made?*	NPG	NPG

L4. Streamlined 0-4-0 with 4-wheel Tender (1938)

The locomotive had twin domes and a riveted 4-wheel tender. The streamlined front was typically German in shape. The wheels were bright red.

SLR700	**?** red LMS - *made?*	NPG	NPG
SLR700	**?** green LNER - *38?*	2500	4000

L5. German 'Pacific' 4-6-2 (1938)

The locomotive had large smoke deflectors, three domes and a riveted 8-wheel tender. The wheels and edge of the footplate and tender chassis were bright red.

Ex-German LNER 4-6-2 [L5]

HR700.1	**?** red LMS - *38?*	4000	6000
HR700.1	**?** green LNER - *38?*	4000	6000

COACHES

These were short bogie coaches of standard German design with British liveries. All had recessed doors.

C1. Standard Short Coach (1938)

Based on the Marklin H0 Mitropa coach 17.5cm long. The recessed doors had glazed rectangular windows.

342E.1	**342** red LMS - *38*	650	750

C2. Pullman Car (1938)

Based on the Marklin H0 Mitropa coach 17.5cm long. The recessed doors had oval representations of windows.

349E.2	**349E** green+cream LNER Pullman - *38?*	650	750

C3. Standard Long Coach (1938)

German style bogie coach 22.5cm long.

?	**352** red LMS - *38*	650	750

S.TODD. barber.

THE BELL

HEAD

Ye Old Smugglers Inn

MASTER
MODELS
MADE IN ENGLAND

MasterModels

HISTORY

The 00 scale lineside accessories, which were to become MasterModels, were started by Don Bowles of Croydon. His first advertisement appeared in July 1950 and referred to 'realistic' models which were 'hand-built to scale and not diecast'. The illustration accompanying the advert showed six lineside accessories ranging from a telegraph pole to a water tower. Bowles advertised on a regular basis until February 1951 when BJ Ward of Grand Buildings, Trafalgar Square, London, advertised that they were now the sole distributors of MasterModels. Don Bowles moved to Angel Hill, Tiverton in July 1951 and reverted to being a model railway retailer.

Hospital (MS/2) flats (MS/3) & office block (MS/1)

BJ Ward was founded by Bertram (Bertie) John Ward and the company's address was soon being given as 130 Westminster Bridge Road. From the time Ward became involved, a cottage industry gave way to mass production by die-casting which was carried out by a company called Kenlow.

The MasterModels series was manufactured until 1962 and during that time more than 100 lineside accessories were introduced including, towards the end, some rather poor looking plastic figures.

Milestones

1950 First MasterModels made by Don Bowles.
1951 Don Bowles hands over to BJ Ward and a new numbering system introduced.
1952 Special value sets released.
1952 Bestseller Smith's bookstall released.
1954 Apparent end of Don Bowles influence.
1954 Tudor building series launched.
1954 Girder bridge released.
1956 Earliest known catalogue.
1957 Major changes to the range.
1958 Building papers.
1958 Last known catalogue and last diecast model introduced.
1962 The year the set of plastic figures is thought to have been released.
1962 MasterModels range peters out.

Several items were dropped from the B J Ward catalogue by 1954 but a number of new models were introduced into the range as well. The range appeared to have reached its peak by 1956 and it seems likely that 1958 was the last year any new models were introduced; with the final release being in October of that year.

The models were initially sold in grey boxes and these were later replaced by the more familiar cream coloured ones. A few, especially when a special size of box was needed, came in plain brown cardboard boxes with a MasterModels label attached. Small translucent paper envelopes were sometimes used, each with a stapled MasterModels card. Box labels were usually off-white or cream but strange colours, such as bright blue, do sometimes turn up.

MasterModels were advertised in the model railway press and in both the Gamages and Bradshaw's catalogues. The Company also produced their own sales leaflet and in 1956, 1957 and 1958 published their *Catalogue and Handbook* which provided good detail of the range and their associated series.

Like all good model ranges, MasterModels had its imitators. A Japanese company called AHI Brand Toys produced 'Tru-Size' metal miniature figures and animals in H0 scale, a series which definitely contained copies of the British range. They had a larger and thicker base than their MasterModels originals but were otherwise identical. As far as we know, two sets were made. One contained the No. 23 track repair party but with the flag waving figure replaced by a cable drum. The other set was a mixture of figures from sets 2, 3, 23 and 67.

Apart from MasterModels, BJ Ward also marketed platform and building series that included Woodside, Rickwood, Clarewood (kits), Hailey and Dudley. Hailey models were made at Goods Depot, Sackville Road, Hove, while Dudley models were apparently made by a couple of joiner/carpenters on Dudley Road in Eastbourne who did a bit of model making when things were slow.

They also sold the 'Wardie' tunnels and road bridge and the 'K' Series garage accessories which were larger than 00 scale. The 'Gilco' sets, which BJ Ward distributed, contained some of the 'Wardie' garage accessories, such as petrol pumps. Puck sponge rubber scenery (made by Grovewell Ltd), Kentoys (presumably made by Kenlow), the Wee World Series and the Anorma range of building kits were all advertised in the MasterModels catalogue and handbook.

Station & platform accessories

Further Reading

The authoritative work, published in 2009, is The Illustrated Kemlows Story by Paul Brooks (ISBN 978 0 9561879 0 1). This includes coloured illustrations of the entire range and was published by Paul Brooks. Also from the same source is a small book called '*MasterModels - Listing of Models for Collectors*'. *Model Railway Enthusiast* magazine had a long running series called 'The MasterModels Gallery' which included coloured photographs of most of the range. This may be found in every issue of the magazine from June 1998 to March 2000.

Identifying MasterModels - There have been a number of makes of 00 scale figures available in Britain and it is not easy to identify them as they rarely carry a maker's mark. The most common are MasterModels and Britains Lilliput. While Britains figures are quite smooth and nicely proportioned, those of MasterModels are a little more rugged. The MasterModels range included many lineside and platform accessories and some of the larger ones carry the tooled-in inscription 'British Made'.

Some figures, such as the wheelbarrow and track repair workmen with tools, turn up in several sets while some castings, such as the telephone kiosk, turn up in a variety of disguises. Very early models were made in brass sheet by modeller Don Bowles and these are quite different from the later cast models and have a 'tinplate' feel about them. At the very end, BJ Ward started using plastic mouldings instead of metal castings for some of its figures but these were quite crude and generally unattractive.

Colours - Colours of many of the items in the sets vary. The colour of the clothes worn by figures were changed from time to time. Seats, lamps, hoardings, signs etc. changed between light green, dark green, red brown, chocolate, grey and cream. We have not recorded these colours here as there is little evidence of when changes occurred and which colour combinations were brought together in sets. No doubt some colours are rarer than others but we have little information on this to offer you.

Packaging - Most items/sets sold in a cream coloured box. Early boxes were printed in black in an oval on a cream, yellow or blue (very rare) label. Later ones were printed in three colours with a 'Master 00 Gauge Models' logo. Some early models were sold in translucent paper envelopes.
Dates - The dates given in the following table are taken from when advertisements for the models appeared in the model railway press or in retailer's catalogues.

No. Column - An additional column has been provided to record the number of items in the box.

MODELS

Cat No.	Company, Number, Colour, Dates	£	£
1.	**Early Lettered Items and Sets**		
	This untidy pattern of codes was used on early models some of which were later added to the numbered series above. DB = thought to be a Don Bowles design		
A	**Set of Track Signs** 3 bar type signs on two posts and base: 'Catch Points', 'Danger', 'Weigh Bridge' - *51-59*	10	15

Set A track signs

Cat No.	Company, Number, Colour, Dates	£	£
B	**Set of Track Signs** 2 squarish signs on single posts: 'Passengers Must Not Cross the Line', 'Beware of the Trains' - *51-61*	6	10
BBS/1	**Bridge End Supports** 2 embankment ends for No.68 in numbered table below, made from wood and cardboard - *56*	NPG	15
BBS/2	**Bridge End Supports** 2 as above but for No.77 double girder bridge - *56*	NPG	15
BC4	**Track Signs** (4) B (above) and C (below) sets of signs combined - *55-60*	10	15
BR/1	**Dog & Partridge Inn** wood block building decorated with printed paper, sign Dog and Partridge Inn - *54*	20	35
BR/2	**Black Horse Inn** wood block building decorated with printed paper, sign Black Horse Inn - *54*	20	35
BR/3	**Tudor House** wood block building decorated with printed paper - *54*	20	35
BR/4	**Blue Anchor Inn** wood block building decorated with printed paper, sign Blue Anchor Inn - *54*	20	35
BR/7	**Transformer Station** these can vary considerably in appearance usually including a brick building, transformer, fence and notices - *53-57*	20	30
BR/8	**House** wood block building decorated with printed paper, also referred to as TS/5 - *54-57*	20	35
BR/9	**Barber Shop** wood block building decorated with printed paper, sign 'S Todd, Barber', possibly the same as TS/4 - *54-55*	20	35
BR/10	**The Rising Sun** wood block building decorated with printed paper, sign 'Rising Sun', also referred to as TS/2 - *54-57*	20	35
BR/11	**The Bell Inn** wood block building decorated with printed paper, sign 'The Bell' - *54-55*	20	35

Tudor series buildings

Cat No.	Company, Number, Colour, Dates	£	£
BR/12	**The Coach Inn** wood block building decorated with printed paper, sign 'The Coach Inn', also referred to as TS/1 - *54-57*	20	35
BR/13	**The Smugglers Inn** wood block building decorated with printed paper, sign 'Ye Old Smugglers Inn', access to coaching yard beneath building - *54-56*	20	35
BR/14	**Hotel Royal** wood block building decorated with printed paper - *54-56*	20	35
BR/15	**Antique Shoppe** wood block building decorated with printed paper, also referred to as TS/3 - *54-57*	20	35
BR/16	**Corner Shop** wood block building decorated with printed paper - *54-56*	20	35
BR/17	**Manor House** wood block building decorated with printed paper - *54-55*	20	35
BS	**Buffer Stop with Buffers** earlier code for BS1 - *50*	4	8
BS1	**Buffer Stop with Buffers** DB, single casting, grey with red buffer beam - *51-57*	4	8
BS2	**Buffer Stop with Lamp** single casting with lamp but no buffers, grey with red buffer beam and lamp - *51-60*	4	8
BS3	**Buffer Stop with Lamp and Buffers** single casting with lamp and buffers, grey with red buffer beam - *52-57*	4	8
C	**Set of Track Signs** 2 square signs on single posts: 'British Railways - Do not Touch Conductor Rails', 'British Railways - Take Care When Crossing' - *51-57*	6	10
C1	**Imitation Coal** small bag of imitation coal - *52?*	NPG	8
C2	**Imitation Coal (double size)** large bag of imitation coal - *52-60*	NPG	10
D1	**Miniature Posters (00)** 50 in packet, including coloured posters and monochrome railway signs - *55-59*	NPG	5
D2	**Miniature Posters (00)** 25 in packet - *55-60*	NPG	5
D3	**Sheet of Miniature Posters (00)** 12 on a sheet by 'Posterstamps' - *55-58*	NPG	5
-	**Miniature Posters (00)** sheet of 60 coloured posters and sheet of 20 monochrome railway signs - *?*	NPG	5
-	**Sheet of Miniature Posters (TT)** two thirds size posters in 2 packets of 50 - *55*	NPG	8
DH/1	**Building Paper** Red Brick, 30"x22" - *58*	NPG	4
DH/2	**Building Paper** Stone, 30"x22" - *58*	NPG	4
DH/3	**Building Paper** Parquet, 30"x22" - *58*	NPG	4

DH/4	**Building Paper** Green Roman Tile, 30"x22" - *58*	NPG	4
DH/5	**Building Paper** Red Roman Tile, 30"x22" - *58*	NPG	4
DS	**Double Signal** earlier code for DS3 below - *50*	5	10
DS3	**Double Signal (Home and Distant)** DB, no further information - *52-53*	5	10
ES	**Electric Signal** no further information - *52*	8	15
F6	**6" Fencing with Base** (6) (see FB6 below) - *51*	12	15
F12	**12" Fencing** 9 post 3-rail flexible fencing made from wire with 5 lengthened posts for fixing into the baseboard - *51-57*	15	20
FB6	**6" Fencing with bases** six 6" lengths of 3-rail flexible fencing made from wire with bases on 3 of the 5 posts - *52*	12	15
H1	**Hoarding (Small)** small hoarding between 2 posts on a base with 1 coloured advert - *51-54*	3	5

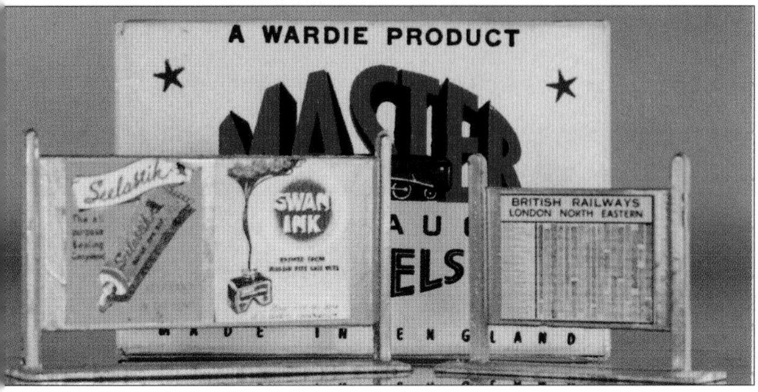

Large hoarding & small timetable

H1/T3	**Small Hoarding/ Large Timetable** set combining H1 (above) and T3 (below) - *55-59*	8	12
H2	**Hoarding** large hoarding between 2 posts on a base with 2 coloured adverts - *51-61*	5	8
H2/T1	**Large Hoarding/ Small Timetable** set combining H2 (above) and T1 (below) - *55-61*	8	12
H3	**Hoarding (Warning Notice)** small hoarding between 2 posts on a base with notice: 'British Railways - Warning - Trespassers Will Be Persecuted - By Order' - *51-53*	3	5
H3/T4	**Warning Notice and Departures Board** set combining H3 (above) and T4 (below) - *55-59*	8	12
LA2	**Lamps with Advertisement Board** 2 modern street lamps with curved tops and an advert board on the standard, square bases, 'Keep Death off the Roads', 'Buy British, Buy Master Models' - *55-61*	8	12
LCG	**Level Crossing Gates** (2) (see 9 in numbered list below) - *51-52*	8	12
LDB	**Double Lamp** no further information - *51*	5	10
LG	**Loading Gauge** DB, (see 80 in numbered list below) - *50-51*	5	10
LSA	**Lamp with Advertisement Board** (2) (see LA2 above) - *51-55*	4	10
LSB	**Single Lamp** no further information - *50-51*	5	10
MP	**Miniature Posters** (see D1, D2, D3 above) - *55-60*	NPG	NPG
MS/1	**Office Building** 5 storey modern building with clock - *57*	20	35
MS/2	**Hospital Building** 2 storey modern building - *57*	20	35
MS/3	**Flats Building** 4 storey modern building - *?*	20	35
00	**Scale Scenic Background** (4) (see 98 in numbered series) *-52-61*	10	15
00	**Bus and Coach Stops** (4) (see 94 in numbered series) - *53-61*	4	10
00	**Posters** (see D1, D2, D3 etc.) - *?*	NPG	NPG
00	**Telegraph Pole** made from steel wire with 2 or 3 arms - *54*	4	6
PL1	**New Universal Plus Point Lever** no further information - *?*	NPG	NPG
Q1	**Imitation Quarry Granite** no further information - *56-61*	NPG	10
RC1	**Rail Cleaner** no further information - *60-61*	NPG	NPG
SA	**Advertisement** small black brass hoarding with coloured advert: 'Chivers Jellies' - *51*	8	12
SG	**Grey Seat** small grey wrought-iron and plank seat - *51-53*	2	4
SG4	**4 Grey Seats** 4 of SG (above) - *55-59*	8	10
SM	**Green Seat** small green wrought-iron and plank seat - *51-53*	2	4

Single green seats

SM4	**4 Green Seats** 4 of SM (above) - *55-59*	8	10
SS	**Single Semaphore Signal** home or distant - *52*	4	6
SS1	**Single Semaphore Signal (Home)** DB, home - *50-53*	4	6
SS2	**Single Semaphore Signal (Distant)** DB, distant - *50-53*	4	6
?	**Signal Arms** upper and lower quadrant - *?*	5	8
ST	**Timetable & Seat** DB, brass sheet and bar seat, GWR timetable on back of seat, later replaced by No.39 - *51*	5	8
T	**Water Tower** DB, a water column of early design - *50*	20	30
T1	**Timetable (Small)** small hoarding between 2 posts on a base with a small timetable, sometimes with 'Arrivals' on label on reverse - *51-55*	3	5
T2	**Timetable** no further information - *51*	8	10
T3	**Timetable (Large)** large hoarding between 2 posts on a base with large timetable - *51-55*	4	8
T4	**Train Departure Board** large hoarding between 2 posts on a base with 2 small timetables, sometimes with 'Train Departures' on label on reverse - *51-55*	4	8
TD6	**Telegraph Pole** DB, double pole structure (joined by cross pieces) with 6 arms, no base, later coded TPD6, listed also as TPD - *50-52*	2	3
TH	**Water Tower** water column - *51*	12	18
TNL	**Water Tower** large water column with 2 moveable hoses and chains and a ladder - *51-52*	18	25
TNS	**Water Tower** small water column with 2 hoses and chains but no ladder - *51-52*	18	25
TP	**Telegraph Pole** DB, pole with 4 arms and no base, later coded TP4 - *50-52*	4	6
	Telegraph Pole, pole 3.75" long with 2 arms - *58-61*	4	6
TP4	**Telegraph Pole** (see TP above) - *52-57*	4	6
TPB	**Telegraph Pole** DB, pole with 4 arms and a base, later called TPB4 - *50-52*	4	6
TPB4	**Telegraph Pole** (see TPB above) - *52-57*	4	6
TPD	**Telegraph Pole** (see TD6 above) - *50-52*	4	6
TPD6	**Telegraph Pole** (see TD6 above) - *52-57*	4	6
TS/1	**The Coach Inn** (see BR/12 above) - *55*	20	35

TS/2	**The Rising Sun** (see BR/10 above) - *55*	20	35
TS/3	**Antique Shoppe** (see BR/15 above) - *55*	20	35
TS/4	(**Tea Shoppe** possibly same as BR/9) - *55*	20	35
TS/5	**House** (see BR/8 above) - *55*	20	35

Large water column with 2 hoses

TT	**Posters** (see D1, D2, D3 etc.) - *?*	20	35
W	**Track Signs** 3 bar type signs on two posts and base: 'Whistle', 'Reduce Speed', '20 mph on Curve' - *51-57*	10	15
WB4	**Wagon Buffers (Round)** 4 brass wagon buffers - *50-53*	NPG	8
WC	**Water Crane** DB, water crane made from wire with hose, chain and a winding handle rising from the base, replaced by No.48 - *50-53*	10	15
WT	**Water Tower** (see WT1 below) - *52-53*	18	25
WT1	**Water Tower** water tank on girder frame, also listed as WT - *51-57*	18	25
WT2	**Water Tower** water tower on wooden block disguised as a building with brick paper, same casting as WT1 - *53-55*	25	30
WT2	**Water Tower** as above but with a lean-to attached to the building - *?*	25	30
	Imitation Grass Mat sheet 12"x22", suede finish - *58-60*	NPG	8

2. Numbered Items and Sets

After a period of haphazard letter codes, a straightforward numbering system was introduced for models in the MasterModels range and these are listed below

1	**Track Accessories** (4) station nameboard (Waterloo, Crewe, Cardiff or Glasgow), telegraph pole, single lamp standard, level post (brown + white) - *51-54*	12	15
1	**Railway Staff** (5) porter with sack barrow, station master, porter with 3 cases, guard with flag, short porter with silver box - *51-57?*	10	15
1	**Railway Staff** (5) porter with sack barrow, porter with 2 cases, porter with 3 cases, guard with flag, guard holding a lamp up high - *57?-60*	10	15
2	**Railway Passengers** (5) lady with coat over her arm, small boy, golfer with clubs, man with rolled brolly, postman - *51-60*	10	15
3	**Assorted Figures** (5) man in top hat and tails, woman in evening dress and cape, boy or girl, woman with handbag, man (green) with brolly and rolled newspaper - *51-60*	10	15
4	**Seated Figures** (5) two soldiers, a Wren, man in suit, woman in coat - *51-60*	10	15
5	**Seated Figures** (4) nun, woman in coat, man in overcoat, lovers - *51-62*	10	15

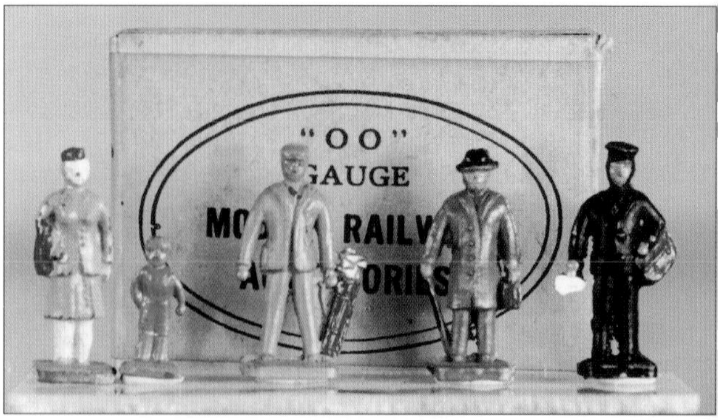

Railway passengers

6	**Double Seats** (2) single casting double sided seats - *51-60*	5	10
7	**Platform Accessories** (7) weighing machine, chocolate machine, hand trolley, 3 churns, cycle - *51-60*	12	15
7	**Platform Accessories** as above but with 4 churns - *55-59*	12	15
8	**Milk Churns** 12 cone shaped with flared top -*51-57*	12	15
8	**Milk Churns** 6 bottle shaped and 6 cone shaped without flare - *58-61*	12	15
9	**Pair of Level Crossing Gates** each mounted on a post with a green base, each with half red disc, originally coded LCG, (see also 76 below) - *52-61*	6	10
10	**Station Equipment** (4) round or oval pillar box, bus or coach stop, telephone kiosk, single or double street lamp - *52-60*	12	15
10	**Station Equipment** (4) round or oval pillar box, bus or coach stop, telephone kiosk, Castrol hoarding - *58-60*	12	15
11	**Gradient Posts** (6) brown posts and bases with white arms - *51-55*	18	20
11	**4 Sheep in Pen** grey wooden base, green and cream metal fence - *56-60*	20	25
12	**Electric Trolley + Trailer** + driver (plugs into trolley), 2 barrels, 2 crates, trolley + trailer usually blue - *52-59*	12	15
14	**'WHSmith's' Bookstall** green (shades), single casting with printed card for back of stall, other detail on printed labels - *52-62*	15	20
15	**Telephone Kiosks** (2) single casting, detail in wrap-round printed label - *52-55*	8	12
16	**Single Station Lamp Standards** (3) round base, cast-iron type standards, curved-over top with modern lamps - *52-57*	9	12
16	**Single Station Lamp Standards** (3) tall, small round base, concrete type standards, curved-over top with tiny modern lamps - *58-61*	9	12
17	**Steel Girders** 6 pieces of unpainted girder shaped metal, also coded 'FI' - *52*	15	20
18	**Cable Drums** (2) single casting, unlagged type, Henley - *52-58*	6	10
18	**Cable Drums** (2) one lagged + one unlagged type, Henley - *58-60*	6	10
19	**Tar Barrels** (6) crude castings, black with yellow ends - *52-57*	9	12
19	**Tar + Oil Barrels** (12) crude castings, 6 black		

	+ 6 grey - *58-61*	12	15
20	**Oil Barrels** (6) crude castings, grey with white ends - *52-57*	9	12
21	**Platform Gardens** (2) island beds, 1 rectangular + 1 diamond, single castings with 1 bush each - *52-57*	6	10
21/22	**Platform Gardens** 1 rectangular + 1 diamond + 2 semicircle - *58-59*	12	15

Tar barrels

22	**Platform Gardens** 2 semicircle border beds, single castings with 2 bushes each - *52-57*	6	10
23	**Track Repair Party** (6) lookout with flags, man with shovel, man with sledge hammer, man with pickaxe, man and a wheelbarrow - *52-60*	12	15
24	**Police Boxes** (2) same casting as telephone kiosk but different wrap-round printed label, dark blue - *52-58*	10	15
25	**Placards** (3) each a casting with a printed label showing posters behind wire - *52-57*	12	15
26	**Sleeper Buffer** - buffer stops built from old railway sleepers filled with sand or ballast, single casting - *52-60*	4	6
27	**Scales with Light Luggage** (5 pieces) green, black and silver scales that turn up in other sets, 2 suitcases, golf bag, basket of fruit - *52-57*	15	20
28	**Signal Ladders** (6) stamped metal ladders mounted on a card and probably sold separately - *53-59*	12	18
29	**Glass Crates** (3) single castings, painted cream and wrapped round with printed wood effect label - *52-57*	12	15
30	**Corrugated Iron Sheets** (3) grey castings - *55-58*	9	12
31	**Enquiry Kiosks** (2) same casting as telephone kiosk but with different printed wrap-round label, green - *52-58*	10	15
32	**Lagged Cable Drums** (2) as in 18 above but both lagged, Henley - *53-57*	6	10
33	**'Esso' Oil Drums** (3) red with white Esso labels, early box has been found with deep blue label - *52-54*	6	10
33	**'Esso' Oil Drums** 3 green and 3 red with white Esso labels - *55-61*	12	15

Watchman's hut

34	**Watchman's Hut** open front covered seat and brazier with red foil fire, man with sledge hammer - *52-60*	6	10
35	**Cable Laying Party** (5) man with sledge hammer, man with pickaxe, man with wheelbarrow, Henley cable drum (either) - *52-62*	10	15
36	**'Finley's' Tobacco Kiosk** same as 14 above but brown and with different printed card and stuck-on labels (these vary) - *52-62*	15	20
37	**'Walton's' Fruit Kiosk** same as 14 above but black and with different printed card and stuck-on labels - *52-62*	15	20
38	**Sand Bin & Fire Buckets** sand bin with red label, red rack and 4 fire buckets, man with shovel - *52-61*	8	12
39	**Seat with Station Name** seat attached to a station nameboard (Westbay, Glasgow, Crewe, Masterhalt, Waterloo, Swansea, Edinburgh) - *52-57*	4	6
40	'**Permanent Way Cabin** 'timber' hut on metal base with barrel and plastic pipe from gutter, man with pickaxe or shovel - *53-60*	8	12
41	**Water Column** cylindrical tank on top of post with round base, ladder and plastic pipe - *53-60*	6	10
42	**Railway Container** 'Don't carry it...send it' by Carter Paterson '** - *53-61?*	6	10
42	**Railway Container** 'Smiths Bluecol the Safe Anti Freeze' - *53-61?*	6	10
42	**Railway Container** yellow plank effect sometimes marked British Railways Furniture - *53?-61*	6	10
43	**Cycle Rack & 4 Cycles** rack (a grey cast slab with grooves in), 4 cast cycles in different colours - *52-60*	10	15
44	**Petrol Pumps** (2) 'Esso' pumps red or blue with plastic pipes, bit too large for 00 - *52-57*	10	15
45	**Coal Office** same as 40 above but sign on roof and no base, water butt or workman - *53-60*	10	15
48	**Water Crane** very like Hornby Dublo water crane but marked 'MasterModels' on the base - *53-61*	6	10
49	**Level Crossing** two pairs of gates on a single cast metal roadway ramp base that goes under the track - *53-57*	18	25

Level crossing

49	**Level Crossing** two pairs of gates on separate cast metal roadway ramps that abut the track - *58-61*	22	30
50	**AA Box & Patrolman** traditional AA box (special casting), motorcycle and AA sidecar, AA patrolman to sit on bike - *53-60*	30	40
51	**Semaphore Ground Signals** (2) black ground signal with grey horizontal arm operated by sprung counterweight, dummy lights - *53-57*	10	15
51/2	**Ground Signal and Disc Shunt Signal** one from set 51 above and one from set 52 below - *58-59*	10	15
52	**Disc Shunt Signals** (2) black shunting signals with grey disc with black bar operated by sprung counterweight, dummy lights - *53-57*	10	15
53	**4-Aspect Searchlight Junction Signals** (2) black searchlight signal with ladder and dummy lights, red light with grey surround - *53-57*	10	15
54	**2-Arm Electric Banner Signals** (2) black		

	banner signal with ladder and 2 round discs (grey with red or green stripe) on horizontal arm - *53-57*	10	15
55	**3-Aspect Colour Light Signals** (2) black colour light signals with ladder and dummy lights in a grey surround - *53-57*	10	15
56	**Aspect Searchlight Signals** (2) black searchlight signal with ladder and dummy green light with grey surround - *53-57*	10	15
57	**Crew Unloading Trucks** (7) 2 men carrying plank between them on their shoulders, man with box on head, man carrying box in front of him, man lifting something down, foreman in suit - *53-60*	12	15
58	**Track Ballast** packet of track ballast - *53-61*	NPG	10
59	**Tarpaulin Covers** (2) black fabric with strings and printed in white with cross and BR317521 - *53-61*	8	12
60	**Station Names** 12 names on gummed paper - *53-57*	NPG	15
61	**AA Boxes** 2 of the traditional AA box No.54 from 50 above - *53-61*	12	20
62	**Police Box with Patrolman** Police box from 24 above, motorbike without sidecar, police rider on bike (ex-AA man) - *53-61*	30	40
63	**Pillar Boxes** 2 oval pillar boxes - *53-57*	6	10
64	**Wicket Gate** kissing type gate set in a short length of fence - *53-60*	6	10
65	**'Charrington's' Coal Bunker** block of three coal bunkers with nameboard across the top, scales, man carrying sack on back - *54-60*	5	10
66	**Station Clocks** 2 double sided bracket clocks with crazed faces - *54-61*	6	10
67	**Street Personnel** (5) woman in coat, man having his shoes cleaned, policeman conducting traffic, news vendor - *54-57*	10	12
67/9	**Street Personnel** (8) sets 67 and 69 combined - *58-62*	16	18
68	**Girder Bridge for Single Track** grey or brown hogs back bridge in cast metal pieces - *54-62*	25	35
69	**Belisha Crossing Set** 2 Belisha beacons and a crossing attendant with a stop board - *54-57*	6	10
70	**Bus Shelter** single casting in shades of green with London Transport posters and map on printed paper - *55-60*	8	12

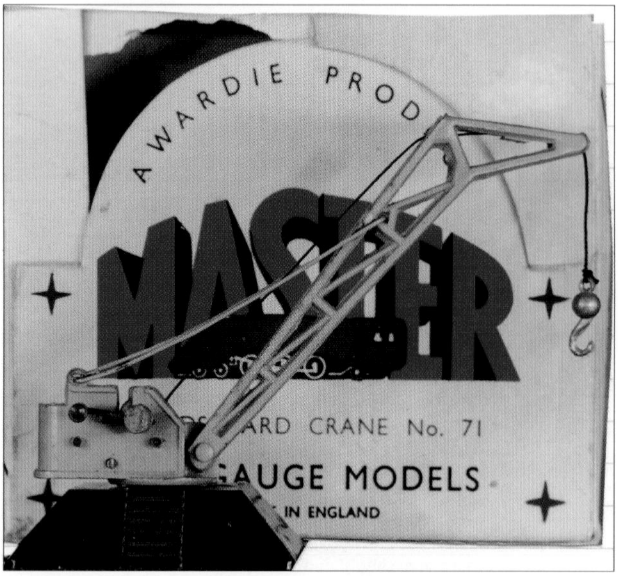

Loading Crane on Base

71	**Loading Crane on Base** grey crane that swivels on a pyramidal stepped base, working jib and hook cable - *55-62*	15	20
72	**Gent's Toilet** 2 castings which together form an outdoors wrought-iron urinal block - *54-61*	10	15
73	**Mine Workers** 5 black workmen with silver kneepads, a wheelbarrow - *55-57*	18	20
74	**6" Paling Fences** supplied 6 or 12 to a box they were sold singly, green single casting fence with top rail and base - *55-60*	12	15
75	**Station Name & Seat with Figures** double seat with nameboard and three seated figures: nun, man in coat, woman in coat - *55-59*	10	15
76	**Level Crossing Gates (Double Track)** pair of long reach gates on posts each with square base (2 sets needed) - *55-61*	8	12
77	**Girder Bridge (Double Track)** same as 68 but extended in width with a second floor section and girder sections to join them - *55-60*	30	40
78	**Sitting Army Figures** (5) 2 WRAC, 2 soldiers with hats, 1 soldier without - *55-57*	10	15
79	**Sitting Naval Figures** (5) 2 WRN, 3 sailors - *55-58*	10	15
80	**Loading Gauge** white with white pedestal fixed to a black base strip, white gauge suspended on short wires, originally coded 'LG' - *52-61*	6	10
81	**Massey Harris Tractor & Roller** red tractor with black wheels, blue or green driver, blue roller with grey wheels, originally coded K49 - *55-61*	35	50
82	**Massey Harris Tractor & Rake** red tractor with black wheels, blue or green driver, blue rake with red wheels, originally coded K50 - *55-61*	35	50
83	**Massey Harris Tractor & Hay Trailer** red tractor with black wheels, blue or green driver, green trailer with black wheels, originally K47 - *55-60*	35	50

Gantry Signal

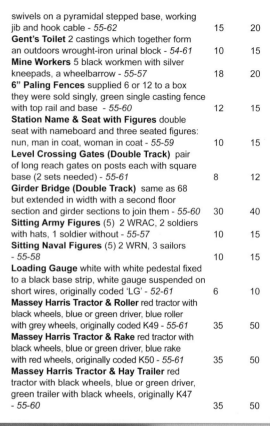

84	**Gantry Signal** dummy colour light signals on black gantry cast in two halves and riveted together *** - *56-62*	15	20
85	**Service Personnel** (5) Wren, seated sailor, army officer, soldier with kit bag, military policeman - *57-62*	10	15
86	**BR Personnel** (7) driver, fireman, porter and broom, coach window cleaner and ladder, Pullman car steward - *57-62*	14	18
87	**Petrol Pumps on Stand** all red with 'Essolube' or 'Shell X100' motor oil on sign between 2 'Esso' pumps, plastic pipes, originally coded K16 - *56-60*	8	12
88	**Roadside Kiosks** (4) RAC, telephone, enquiries and police kiosks, castings are slightly different from earlier ones * - *58-61*	20	25
89	**Footbridge** two sections of 6" paling fence (74 above) welded to cast floor section - *58-62*	8	12
90	**Sheep** (6) from 11 above - *60*	12	18
92	**Four Electric Signals** this consists of one		

	each from 53, 54, 55 and 56 above - *56-59*	20	25
94	**Bus and Coach Stops** (4) London Transport design, 2 single flag bus stops, single flag coach stop with timetable, double flag coach + bus stop, (see 00 or K14 in other tables) - *59-61*	12	15
94	**Bus and Coach Stops** (4) London Transport design, 3 single flag bus stops, single flag coach stop - *?*	12	15
95	**4 Road Signs** round double sided signs: road up, no parking, open/closed, no entry, from K9, K20 and K21 - *55-58*	12	18
96	**Left Luggage Office** long double fronted kiosk with door between, both signs say Left Luggage - *58-61*	20	30
96	**Left Luggage Office** as above but both signs say Parcels Office - *58-61*	20	30
96	**Left Luggage Office** as above but one sign says Left Luggage and the other Parcels Office - *58-61*	20	30
98	**Scale Scenic Background** cardboard tube containing 4 sheets 20"x8", (see also '00' in lettered table above) - *61*	15	20
97	**Oil Storage Tanks** 2 silver tanks mounted on a cradle, 'Shell Petroleum Products' transfer on each tank - *58-62*	15	20

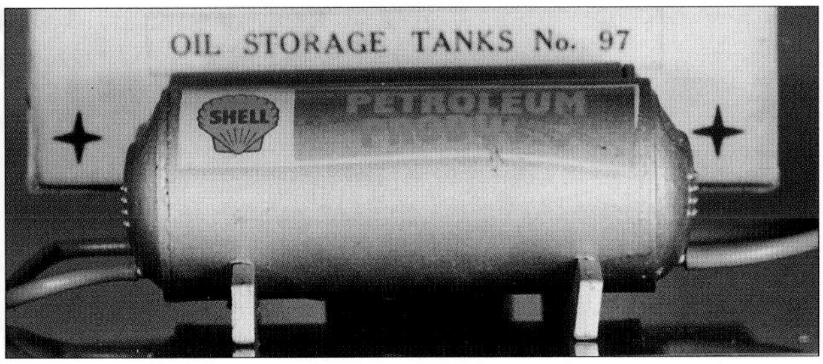

Oil storage tanks

5800	**Single Signal** - *?-61*	10	15

* The police and enquiries boxes now have a light projection on top and the RAC and telephone boxes share a flat topped casting. ** Identical to one sold by Trix and possibly supplied by BJ Ward. *** This appears to have been designed so that an alternative semaphore gantry could be made with the castings.

3. Presentation Sets

1	**Special Value Set** (8) buffer stop, timetable, hoarding, 4 track signs, seat - *52-54*	NPG	40
2	**Special Value Set** (7) siding buffer, 2 track signs, 2 station lamps with adverts, timetable, seat - *52-54*	NPG	40
3	**Special Value Set** (8) 2 timetables, 4 track signs, 2 hoardings - *52-54*	NPG	40
	Plastic Set (11) double lamp standard, 2 Belisha beacons, policeman, red woman, telephone kiosk, motorcycle, motorcyclist, news vendor, pillar box, bus stop - *62?*	NPG	15

The plastic set has been found with some parts in metal.

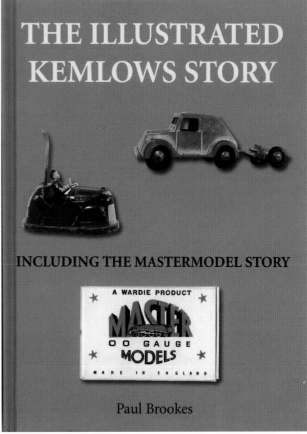

A WARDIE PRODUCT
MASTER
"OO" GAUGE MODELS
MADE IN ENGLAND
CREWE
GLASGOW
EAT MORE FRUIT
CHARRINGTONS
BOOKSTALL

Mathieson

HISTORY

Seeing a gap in the finescale N gauge market, PHF Global limited formed Mathieson Models to market a new range of accurate 2mm scale wagons to sell in Britain. The programme started in April 2009 and much work has already been done by the Autumn, with the first releases in November. The models are made in China.

Collectors Club - In 2009 a collectors club was formed. This is run by the company from Acomb near York.

7-plank coal wagon - 'Cwmgwrach' (Mathieson) [W1]

WAGONS

The prototypes represent small vehicles which would have lost the correct sense of scale proportion, had not the N gauge wheel standards created in the 1960s been retained. The models therefore have NMRA fine wheel profiles giving smaller flange depth and narrower tread. Modern production techniques ensure true running and the wagons are comfortable on most proprietary trackage systems.

The limited space between the solebars dictates the use of shorter axles than most other N gauge stock but conversion to 2mm finescale standards will present no problems. Axle length over pinpoints is only 13.7mm - considerably shorter than any other current manufacturer in British N and the width over solebars is only 14mm. That is almost 1.5mm less than any other current representation of wooden stock from any other manufacturer in ready to run or kit form.

Much thought was given to the coupler style and it was decided to rely upon the Rapido style purely on the basis that, more than any other, it is the current 'industry standard' for British models. To minimise the intrusive nature of these couplers they have been produced in transparent plastic. This minimises their impact in a train of vehicles. Wheels and buffers are chemically blackened and smaller diameter shanks and larger heads feature on the buffing gear.

Only 450 of each are being made.

7-plank coal wagon - 'Haydock' (Mathieson) [W1]

Cat No.	Company, Number, Colour, Dates	£	£
Open Wagons			
W1.	**7-Plank RCH 1908 Coal Wagon** (2010)		
MW0002	'CH **Atkinson'** 8602 black - *10*	6	8
MW0010	**'Bradbury'** 2018 black - *10*	6	8
MW0012	**'Bute'** 129 black - *10*	6	8
MW0005	**'Cory Brothers & Co.'** 3262 black - *10*	6	8
MW0004	**'Cwmgwrach'** 426 black - *10*	6	8
MW0007	**'Duffryn Rhondda'** 698 black - *10*	6	8
MW0009	'GR **Cawood & Co.'** 8602 black - *10*	6	8
MW0011	**'Haydock'** 561 black - *10*	6	8
MW0003	**'Pentrich Colliery Co.'** 109 black - *10*	6	8
MW0008	**'United National Collieries'** 12 black - *10*	6	8
MW0006	**'Ynisarwed'** 296 black - *10*	6	8
MW0001	**'Ystradgynlais & Yniscedwyn Collieries'** 854 black - *10*	6	8

7-plank coal wagon - 'Ynisarwed' (Mathieson) [W1]

Railway modeller, photographer and artist - Robbie McGavin

MILLS·BROS
MODEL MAKERS
SHEFFIELD
Price 6d.
Price 6D.
Season 1933-34.
MILBRO
SCALE MODEL RAILWAYS
SEASON 1935-36
SEASON 1937-38
SEASON 1938-39
MILLS BROS
MODEL MAKERS
ST MARY'S ROAD
SHEFFIELD
MILBRO
TRADE MARK
MILLS BROS. MODEL ENGINEERS LTD.
ST. MARY'S ROAD, SHEFFIELD.
SHEFFIELD & LONDON.
PRICE 6d.
PRICE 9d.
MILLS BROS.
(SHEFFIELD) LIMITED
SCALE MODEL RAILWAYS
ST. MARY'S ROAD · SHEFFIELD 2
ONE SHILLING
Mills Models
MILLS BROTHERS (SHEFFIELD) LTD.
129 ST. MARY'S ROAD, SHEFFIELD.

Milbro 0
(Mills Brothers)

HISTORY

Mills Brothers (Engineers) Ltd was founded in 1919 by three brothers - William, Frank and Herbert Mills. They were based at 129 St. Mary's Road, Sheffield, and were later registered as Mills Brothers (Sheffield) Ltd; another address was Ellesmere Road, Sheffield. They used the trade mark 'Milbro' and had a London showroom at 2 Victoria Colonnade, Victoria House, Southampton Row from the mid 1930s to the 1950s. The Company manufactured good quality, true to scale, 0 gauge railway models of prototypical appearance. While 0 gauge was their main output, they also produced some models in gauge 1. Wooden sleepered track was one of their principal products.

During the second half of the 1920s and throughout the 1930s, their locomotives set a standard higher than that of Bassett-Lowke but, being a small firm with low production runs, limited range and higher prices, they made less of a mark in the history of railway modelling. They did also make some wagons for Bassett-Lowke. As an example of the higher cost of their quality products, in 1936, the Milbro 6-8 volt DC *Princess Royal* cost £22.10.0d (£22.50) while the Hornby 0 gauge 20 volt AC *Princess Elizabeth*, when it was released the following year, was priced just £5.5s.0d (£5.25)!

LMS 4-4-2T No.501 (Vectis) [L1]

Early catalogues produced by Mills Brothers Ltd suggest that they started off by marketing models produced by the Leeds Model Company (LMC) and then used the LMC motors as the power unit for their own models. However, before long, Mills were producing a mechanism of their own, built into the chassis side-frames which stretched the length of the locomotive. As many Milbro products did not carry their trade mark, identifying their locomotives can be problematical and expert advice is recommended.

Like the Leeds Model Company, Mills sold parts for the scratch-builder and these can mislead collectors into thinking that a model was made by Mills. Ultimately, experience is needed for sound identification of a Mills product, but a common fault to look for on scratch-built models is parts out of position such as buffers too far apart, wagon axleguards too near the buffer beams, or wagon strapping poorly applied.

By the end of the 1940s Mills were selling only their track and parts for scratch-builders. After the war this level continued, although they also stocked other manufacturers' products, such as Romford motors and Bilteezi sheets.

In 1962 Mills Bros. decided to stop manufacturing and Edward Exley Ltd took over their remaining stock. The stock was large and Exley declared at the time that it was their intention to continue to produce some of the 0 gauge items and that details would be included in their catalogue for 1962-63. The Milbro name was also to be retained for a while.

LOCOMOTIVES

Cat No.	Company, Number, Colour, Dates	£	£
L1.	**Standard Tank 4-4-2T (Freelance)** (1937)		

The freelance 4-4-2 tank locomotive was produced in the late 1930s. Called the 'Standard Electric Tank Locomotive', it was LNER in character with a straight footplate, fully enclosed cab with two windows each side and a variety of chimneys and domes according to the railway it represented. All versions were 3-rail electric.

-	**601** GWR green - *37-39*	350	450
-	**201, 420, 501** LMS maroon - *37-39*	330	450
-	**347, 456, 701** LNER green - *37-39*	350	450
-	**401** SR - *37-39*	380	500

L2. Standard Tank 0-6-2T (Freelance) (1938)

This was similar to the 4-4-2 tank locomotive (L1 above), with a common cab and the same side tanks, but with a leading driver replacing the front bogie on the former. All versions were 3-rail electric.

-	**?** GWR - *38-40*	330	450
-	**420** LMS maroon - *38-40*	350	450
-	**?** LMS black - *38-40*	350	450
-	**458** LNER green - *38-40*	350	450
-	**?** LNER black - *38-40*	330	450
-	**?** SR green? - *38-40*	380	500

L3. 'Scale' Models (1930)

The company normally produced only electrically powered locomotives built to special order, including its catalogue items which were as follows (the numbers, names and liveries are as shown in the catalogue but almost certainly these would be done according to the customer's choice).

	Pre-Grouping		
-	**35** GNR green Stirling 'Single' - *33-34*	NPG	NPG
-	**373** GC green Robinson 4-6-2T - *?*	750	950
-	**17** Metropolitan brown electric Bo-Bo - *30-34*	NPG	NPG
	GWR		
-	**3232** GWR green 2-4-0 3232 Class - *32-34*	NPG	NPG
-	**6000** ***King George V*** GWR green 4-6-0 - *35-39*	NPG	NPG
	LMS		
-	**7100** LMS black 0-6-0 'Jinty' - *33-39*	280	330
-	**2500** LMS black 2-6-4 Stanier Tank - *34-39*	1400	1600
-	**764** LMS maroon 4-4-0 700 Class Express - *31-39*	NPG	NPG
-	**1102** LMS maroon 4-4-0 'Compound' - *32-39*	NPG	NPG

LMS 'Compound' No.1102 (Andrew Woodfield) [L3]

-	**5363** ***Harrier*** LMS black 4-4-0 'George V' Class - *33-34*	NPG	NPG
-	**13098, 13126** LMS maroon 2-6-0 'Crab' - *32-39*	NPG	NPG
-	**13126** LMS black 2-6-0 'Crab' - *32-39*	NPG	NPG
-	**5945** ***Ingestre*** LMS maroon 4-6-0 'Claughton' Class - *33-34*	NPG	NPG
-	**6100** ***Royal Scot*** LMS maroon 4-6-0 Fowler tender - *32-39*	800	1500
-	**6200** ***Princess Royal*** LMS maroon 4-6-2 Fowler tender - *35-39*	1600	2100
-	**6220** ***Coronation*** LMS blue 4-6-2 streamlined - *c38*	2000	3000
	LNER		
-	LNER green Robinson ex-Great Central 4-6-2T - *?*	NPG	NPG
-	**1448** LNER black 0-6-0 J39 - *37-39*	NPG	NPG
-	**8304** LNER green 0-6-0 J72 - *?*	120	170
-	**4472** ***Flying Scotsman*** LNER light green 4-6-2 A1 - *37-39*	NPG	NPG
-	**2509** ***Silver Link*** LNER silver 4-6-2 A4 - *36-39*	2100	2700
-	**2001** ***Cock O' the North*** LNER lt.green 2-8-2 P2 - *34-39*	NPG	NPG

-	**10000*** LNER lt.green 4-6-4 'Hush-Hush Compound' - *31-34*	NPG	NPG
	SR		
-	**901 *Winchester*** green SR, 4-4-0 'Schools' - *37-39*	850	1300
-	**5068** SR green EMU motor coach - *30-34*	NPG	NPG

* Referred to in early catalogues as *The Flying Scotsman*.

COACHES

The Milbro coaches were particularly attractive and have become very collectable, being made of wood with glass windows. They were available in gauges 0 and 1, as corridor or non-corridor stock and in the liveries of the Big Four. One could also buy the wooden parts, in both scales, with which to build your own and this included dining and Pullman cars. Interiors, including seating, tables and electric lights, could also be supplied. In 1928 they introduced articulated sets with compensating bogies. These were available in twins or triplets.

The LNER teak coaches (teak was actually used in their construction) are everyone's favourites, some of these having nicely detailed interiors with antimacassars on the seats and lamps on the tables. The LNER coaches go especially well with other companies' LNER locomotives, such as Bassett-Lowke, whose contemporary tinplate LNER coaches were very inferior products compared with Milbro.

NB. If you do not find your Milbro coach listed here, there is a good chance that it was made or finished to special order.

C1. Standard Wooden Corridor Coaches (1926)

These 16.5" long coaches had bodies made entirely of seasoned hardwood and were constructed by an interlocking process. They had recessed wooden panels, real glass in the windows and could be supplied as either side or centre corridor stock according to the customer's requirements. The interiors had a mahogany finish and the coaches were fitted will Milbro brass bogies and cast iron wheels. Concertina connectors were fitted to dining saloons and corridor coaches.

Cat No.	Company, Number, Colour, Dates	£	£
-	**GWR** brown+cream 1st/3rd - *c26-40*	170	200
-	**GWR** 3014 brown+cream brake/3rd - *c26-40*	170	200
-	**GWR** brown+cream brake van - *c26-40*	170	200
-	**GWR** brown+cream dining car - *c26-40*	170	200
-	**GWR** brown+cream sleeping car - *35-37*	170	200
-	**GWR** brown+cream kitchen car - *36-40*	170	200
-	**GWR** brown+cream full brake - *36-40*	170	200
-	**LMS** 3762 maroon 1st/3rd - *c26-40*	170	200
-	**LMS** 1267 maroon side-corr. 1st - *c26-40*	170	200
-	**LMS** maroon brake/3rd - *c26-40*	170	200
-	**LMS** 2506 maroon all-3rd - *c26-40*	170	200
-	**LMS** maroon brake van - *c26-40*	170	200
-	**LMS** 3762 maroon dining car - *c26-40*	170	200
-	**LMS** 1267 maroon sleeping car - *34-40*	200	220
-	**LMS** maroon kitchen car - *36-40*	200	220
-	**LMS** maroon full brake van - *36-40*	170	200
-	**LNER** 8173 teak 1st/3rd - *28-40*	220	280

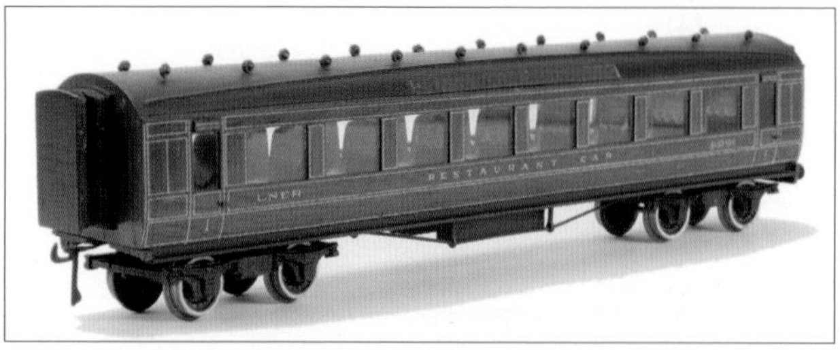

LNER all-1st restaurant (Vectis) [C1]

-	**LNER** 8052, 8173 teak all 1st - *28-40*	220	280
-	**LNER** 8061, 8173 teak brake/3rd - *28-40*	220	280
-	**LNER** 6789, 8052 teak all 3rd - *28-40*	220	280
-	**LNER** teak brake van - *28-40*	220	280
-	**LNER** 8032 teak restaurant car - *28-40*	220	280
-	**LNER** teak sleeping car - *35-40*	250	300
-	**LNER** teak kitchen car - *36-40*	250	300
-	**LNER** 8061 teak full brake - *36-40*	250	300
-	**SR** green 1st/3rd - *28-40*	170	200
-	**SR** green brake/3rd - *28-40*	170	200
-	**SR** green, brake van - *28-40*	170	200
-	**SR** 1739 green, dining car - *28-40*	170	200
-	**SR** green, sleeping car - *35-37*	NPG	NPG
-	**SR** green kitchen car - *36-40*	200	220
-	**SR** green full brake - *36-40*	170	200

C2. Standard Wood Non-Corridor Coaches (1926)

These 15" long coaches had bodies made entirely of seasoned hardwood and were constructed by an interlocking process. They had recessed wooden panels and real glass in the windows. The interiors had a mahogany finish and the coaches were fitted will Milbro brass bogies and cast iron wheels.

-	**GWR** brown+cream 1st/3rd - *c26-40*	140	170
-	**GWR** brown+cream brake/3rd - *c26-40*	140	170
-	**GWR** brown+cream full brake - *c26-40*	140	170
-	**LMS** maroon 1st/3rd - *c26-40*	140	170
-	**LMS** maroon brake/3rd - *c26-40*	140	170

LMS all-3rd No.17004 (Vectis) [C2]

-	**LMS** 17004 maroon all 3rd - *c26-40*	140	170
-	**LMS** maroon full brake - *c26-40*	140	170
-	**LNER** teak 1st/3rd - *28-40*	140	170
-	**LNER** teak brake/3rd - *28-40*	140	170
-	**LNER** teak full brake - *28-40*	140	170
-	**SR** green 1st/3rd - *28-40*	170	200
-	**SR** green brake/3rd - *28-40*	170	200
-	**SR** green full brake - *28-40*	170	200

C3. Pullman Cars (1928)

These were also built in hardwood throughout and had a mahogany interior. They were lined and detailed in gold and fitted with Mansell type cast iron wheels and compensated bogies. They were finished in brown and cream with white roofs.

-	**Pullman** *Princess Helen* brown+cream parlour car - *c28-40*	220	270
-	**Pullman** *Bessborough* brown+cream parlour car - *c28-40*	220	270
-	**Pullman** *Pullman Lady* brown+cream parlour car - *c28-40*	220	270
-	**Pullman** brown+cream brake end - *c28-40*	220	270

C4. Unpainted Wooden Coach Bodies (1926)

These were the bodies of the coaches listed in tables C1 and C2 which could be bought without fittings and unpainted.

-	corridor coach - *c26-40*	NPG	NPG
-	dining car - *c26-40*	NPG	NPG
-	non-corridor coach - *c26-40*	NPG	NPG
-	Pullman car - *c28-40*	NPG	NPG

C5. 6-wheeled Suburban Stock (1928)

-	**GWR** brown+cream - *28-40*	70	90
-	**LMS** maroon - *28-40*	70	90
-	**LNER** 6173 teak - *28-40*	70	90
-	**SR** green - *28-40*	70	90

C6. 4-wheeled Suburban Stock (1928)

-	**GWR** brown+cream - *28-40*	45	70
-	**LMS** maroon - *28-40*	45	70
-	**LNER** teak - *28-40*	45	70
-	**SR** green - *28-40*	45	70

C7. Triplet Articulated Sets (1928)

These were built to the same specification as the coaches in tables C1 and C2 but consisted of three shorter coaches joined in a triple articulated set by shared compensating bogies.

-	**GWR** brown+cream - *28-40*	170	200

-	**LMS** maroon - *28-40*	170	200
-	**LNER** teak - *28-40*	170	200
-	**SR** green - *28-40*	170	200

C8. Twin Articulated Sets (1928)

These were built to the same specification as the coaches in tables C1 and C2 but consisted of two shorter coaches joined in a twin articulated set by shared compensating bogies.

-	**GWR** brown+cream - *28-40*	140	170
-	**LMS** maroon - *28-40*	140	170
-	**LNER** teak - *28-40*	140	170
-	**SR** green - *28-40*	140	170

C9. Mail Vans (1938)

These were built to the same specification as the coaches in tables C1 and C2 but were more modern vehicles.

-	**GWR**, Royal Mail brown+cream - *38-40*	170	200
-	**LMS**, Royal Mail maroon - *38-40*	170	200
-	**LNER**, Royal Mail teak - *38-40*	170	200

C10. Buffet Cars (1938)

These were built to the same specification as the coaches in tables C1 and C2 but were more modern vehicles.

-	**LMS** 1239? maroon Buffet Car - *38-40*	200	220
-	**LNER** teak Buffet Car - *38-40*	200	220

C11. 'Coronation Scot' (1938)

-	**LMS** ? blue 1st brake - *c38*	200	220
-	**LMS** ? blue 3rd brake - *c38*	200	220
-	**LMS** ? blue 1st dining car - *c38*	200	220

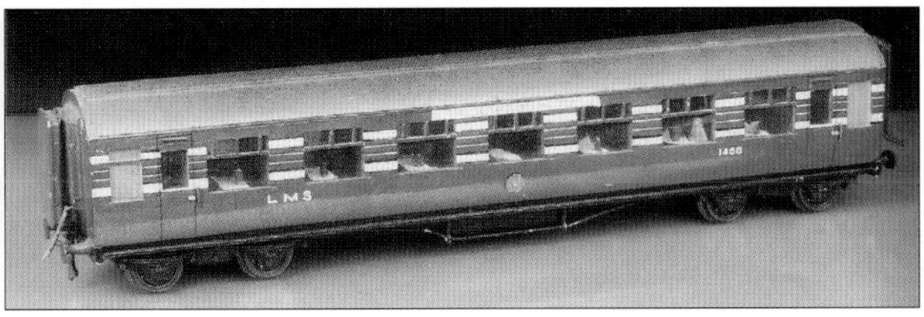

LMS 'Coronation Scot' 3rd diner (Christies) [C11]

-	**LMS** 1468 blue 3rd dining car - *c38*	200	220
-	**LMS** ? blue kitchen car - c38	200	220

WAGONS

There was a wide range of wooden wagons available, in gauges 0, 1 and 2.5". They were made of embossed wood, to represent planking, with embossed metal strapping, corner plates etc. nailed and glued on. Van roofs were fitted with ventilators and brake vans had chimneys, handrails and footboards. Axleboxes were screwed onto the solebars and buffers, in brass, were screwed onto the buffer beams (sprung buffers and axleboxes were used in some larger gauge models). Couplings were of pressed steel or sprung stamped-out nickel-plated brass and the wheels cast iron, although solid brass wheels were available at an additional cost. The wagons were initially finished with enamel paint, but by the 1930s a matt finish was being applied.

The wagons were produced in quantities or made to order, but examples of what could be bought were illustrated in the catalogues and it is on the basis of the catalogues that the following tables have been prepared. As customers could have the wagons made in any livery and, presumably, with any running number, other versions are bound to be found. Nearly all were also available in kit form.

As stated in the introduction, Mills Bros. also made some wagons for Bassett-Lowke, but these had a distinctly Milbro look about them.

Cat No.	Company, Number, Colour, Dates	£	£

__Flat and Open Wagons__

W1. Single Bolster Timber Wagons (1928)

These could be used singly or in pairs to transport long loads. In pairs, the inner facing buffer beams were not fitted with buffers and the wagons were permanently joined by a bar. The bolster swivelled and it came with chains fitted. Also available as a kit.

-	**MR** grey - *28?*	15	25
-	**GW** dark grey - *30-40*	15	25
-	**LMS** grey - *30-40*	15	25
-	**NE** 2573 grey - *30-40*	15	25

NE single bolster wagon (Vectis) [W1]

-	**NE** 32573 black - *30-40*	15	25
-	**SR** 7960 brown - *30-40*	15	25
-	unbranded 79607 grey pair joined - *28?*	20	35

W2. Carriage Wagons (1928)

Fitted with Mansell carriage type cast iron wheels and carriage type axle guards, it had side rails with 2 cross ties but open ends. Also available as a kit.

-	**LNWR** grey? - *28-30?*	25	35
-	**MR** 3501? grey? - *28-30?*	NPG	NPG
-	**GN** brown? - *28-30?*	25	35
-	**GC** grey? - *28-30?*	25	35
-	**GW** dark grey - *28-40*	15	25
-	**LMS** grey - *28-40*	15	25
-	**NE** grey? - *28-40*	15	25
-	**SR** brown - *28-40*	15	25
-	**SR** 2573 light green, yellow lining - *28-40*	100	120

W3. 3-plank Double Bolster Wagon (1930)

Fitted with chains.

-	**GW** 5204 dark grey - *30-40*	25	35

W4. 10T 3-plank Open Wagon (1928)

This was referred to in the Milbro catalogues as an 'Engineering Department ballast and low sided wagon'.

-	**LNWR** grey? - *28?-31?*	25	35
-	**MR** grey? - *28?-31?*	25	35
-	**GN** brown? - *28?-31?*	25	35
-	**GC** grey? - *28?-31?*	25	35
-	**GW** dark grey - *28?-40*	15	25
-	**GW** ED 39817 red-brown - *28?-40*	25	35
-	**LMS** 56705 grey - *28?-40*	15	25
-	**NE** 19107 brown - *28?-40*	15	25
-	**SR** 2573 brown - *28?-40*	15	25

W5. 4-plank Open Fish Wagon (1932)

This was a drop-side wagon inscribed 'Fish'.

-	**LMS** 7960 light grey - *32-40*	25	35
-	**NE** 32573 brown Fish - *32-40*	25	35
-	**NE** 4621 brown Fish - *32-40*	25	35

W5A. 5-plank Open Wagon

-	**LMS** 130769 grey - *?*	25	35

W6. Lithographed 12T Open Wagon (1929)

From 1930 the catalogues contained a short range of open wagons, made in wood but with litho paper finishes on sides and ends. They had diecast wheels, brass buffers, single or 3-link couplings and cast axleboxes on a steel back plate. When first introduced, it had been intended to extend the range but nothing came of this. The trademark 'Milbro' was carried on the end paper

-	**GW** 109451 dark grey 5-plank - *29-40*	25	35
-	**LMS** 56705 brown? 7-plank - *30-40*	25	35
-	**NE** 19107 brown? 6-plank - *30-40*	25	35
-	**SR** 15117 brown 7-plank - *30-40*	25	35

W7. 12T Standard 6-plank Open Wagon (1930)

-	**'Bass'** Great Stuff This 987 green - *36-40*	70	90
-	**'Eveson'** 6504 - *36-40*	70	90
-	**'Hamleys'** red - *36-40*	25	30

6-plank wagon - 'Eveson' (Milbro) [W7]

-	**'OXO'** Beef in Brief 25742 black - *36-40*	70	90
-	**'Virol'** orange 7960 - *36-40*	70	90
-	**'Wagon Repairs Ltd'** 1574 black - *36-40*	70	90
-	**'William Younger's'** Scotch Ale 51367 maroon - *36-40*	70	90
-	**GW** dark grey - *30-40*	20	25
-	**LMS** 2573 grey? - *30-40*	20	25
-	**NE** 19107 grey - *30-40*	20	25
-	**SR** brown - *30-40*	20	25

W8. 20T 6-plank Tube Wagon (1930)

-	**GW** dark grey - *30-40*	25	35
-	**LMS** 2573 grey? - *30-40*	25	35
-	**LMS** 39317 grey - *30-40*	25	35
-	**NE** grey - *30-40*	25	35
-	**SR** brown - *30-40*	25	35

W9. 10T 7-plank Open Wagon

Also available as a kit.

-	**LNWR** grey? - *?-40*	25	35
-	**MR** 397 grey - *?-40*	25	35
-	**GN** brown? - *?-40*	25	35
-	**GC** grey? - *?-40*	25	35
-	**GW** 39817 dark grey - *?-40*	15	25
-	**LMS** 39817, 56705 grey - *?-40*	15	25
-	**NE** grey? - *?-40*	15	25
-	**SR** 3987 brown - *?-40*	15	25

W10. 8T 10-plank Coke Wagon (1930)

-	**GW** dark grey - *30-40*	25	35
-	**LMS** grey? - *30-40*	25	35
-	**NE** 5204, 51367 grey - *30-40*	25	35
-	**SR** brown - *30-40*	25	35

Tank Wagons

W11. Square Tar Tank Wagon (1929)

This was lettered in white, had metal strapping and tie bars.

-	**LMS** 5204 black Tar - *29?-40*	35	45

W12. Tar & Oil Tank Wagons (1928)

The model was illustrated in the catalogue carrying the 'GN' insignia on its solebars. It is not known what other railway company's initials can be found on this model. Also available as a kit.

-	**'Esso'** 1960?, 2373? black, white letters - *36-40*	120	140
-	**'Esso'** un-numbered black, white letters - 36-40	120	140
-	**'Esso'** 73817, cream, blue/red letters - *36-40*	120	140
-	**'Pratt's Spirit'** 7960 greenish grey - *31-35*	120	140
-	**'Pratt's Spirit'** 46213 - *31-35*	120	140
-	**'Royal Daylight'** 46213 black - *31-35*	120	140
-	**'Royal Daylight'** 25742 brown - *31-35*	120	140
-	**GN** 3955? black Tar - *28?-35*	35	45

Esso tank wagon (Vectis) [W12]

Vans

W13. Lime Wagon (1928)

This was the traditional 5-plank wagon and pitched roof type. Also available as a kit.

-	Lime - *28?-40*	25	35

W14. Cattle Wagon (1928)

Also available as a kit.

-	**LNWR** grey? - *28?-31?*	25	35
-	**MR** grey? - *28?-31?*	25	35
-	**GN** brown? - *28?-31?*	25	35
-	**GC** 30121 grey? - *28?-31?*	25	35
-	**GC** 720 grey - *28?*	25	35
-	**GW** dark grey - *28?-40*	15	25
-	**LMS** 9061 grey - *28?-40*	15	25
-	**NE** grey? - *28?-40*	15	25
-	**SR** 25742 brown - *28?-40*	15	25

W15. Gunpowder Van (1928)

The van had white lettering and black metal strapping.

-	**LMS** 431 red Gun Powder Van - *c28-40*	45	70
-	**NE** red Gun Powder Van - *c28-40*	45	70

W16. Horse Box (1929)

These were constructed in the same way as Milbro coaches of the period and had glass in the windows.

-	**LMS** lined maroon - *c29-40*	170	220
-	**SR** lined dark green - *c29-40*	170	220

W17. Fish Van (1932)

-	**LMS** 7214 brown Fish - *32-40*	35	45
-	**NE** 2573 brown Fish - *32-40*	35	45

W18. Cement Van (1936)

-	**'Earle's Cement'** 2573 yellow - *36-40*	120	140

Cement van - 'Earles' (Vectis) [W18]

W19. Ventilated Van (1936)

-	**'Bass'** 2134 green - *36-40*	120	140
-	**'Bovril'** 2573 blue - *36-40*	120	140
-	**'Gaymer's Cider'** 46213 yellow - *36-40*	120	140
-	**'OXO'** 2045 black Beef in Brief - *36-40*	120	140
-	**'Player's'** Please 13625 blue - *36-40*	120	140
-	**'Stephen's'** 98014, 39317 blue - *36-40*	120	140
-	**'Virol'** 2573, 7960 orange - *36-40*	120	140

W20. All-Metal Goods Rolling Stock (1930)

In 1930, Milbro started manufacturing in metal, models of steel prototype wagons. The only example they illustrated in their catalogues was the LNER box van. The models were all built to the customer's specification.

-	**NE** box van - *30-40*	25	35

W21. Box Van (1928)
Also available as a kit.

-	**LNWR** grey? - *28?-31?*	25	35
-	**MR** 1321 grey? - *28?-31?*	25	35
-	**GN** brown? - *28?-31?*	25	35
-	**GC** grey? - *28?-31?*	25	35
-	**GW** dark grey - *28?-40*	15	25
-	**LMS** grey - *28?-40*	15	25
-	**NE** 79607 grey? - *28?-40*	15	25
-	**SR** brown - *28?-40*	15	25
-	**SR** 39817 dark grey - *28?-40*	15	25

W22. Refrigerator & Banana Van (1928)

-	**NE** white black letters Refrigerator Van - *c28-40*	35	45

W23. Meat Van (1933)

-	**LMS** 39817, 46213 grey Meat - *33-40*	45	80

W24. Fruit Van (1933)

-	**NE** 25742 brown Fruit - *33-40*	35	45

W25. Goods Brake Vans (1928)
The Midland Railway and LNER models were also available in kit form in the 1920s.

-	**GW** 46213, 9061 dark grey 10T 1 verandah - *28?-40*	25	35
-	**LNWR** grey? 10T - *28?-30*	35	45
-	**MR** grey? 10T verandah one end and platform at other - *28?-30*	35	45
-	**GN** brown? 10T - *28?-30*	35	45
-	**LMS** 2573 grey 10T verandah one end and platform at other - *28?-40*	20	30
-	**LMS** 46213 grey 4-wheel 2 verandahs 4.5" long - *?*	20	30

GWR goods brake van [W25]

-	**LMS** 39817 grey 6-wheel 2 verandahs - *?*	35	45
-	**LMS** 9061 grey 20T 6-wheel - *31-40*	35	45
-	**NE** 13987 grey? 10T 2 verandahs and duckets - *28?-40*	25	35
-	**NE** no number dark brown 4-wheel - *?*	25	35
-	**SR** 46213 brown 10T 2 verandahs - *28?-40*	25	35

W26. 6-wheel Milk Vans (1929)

-	**GW** 1794 brown - *c29-40*	70	90
-	**LMS** 1239 maroon - *c29-40*	70	90
-	**LNER** - *c29-40*	70	90
-	**SR** green? - *c29-40*	70	90

Bogie Wagons

W27. 30T Bogie Bolster Wagon (1932)
Fitted with brass compensating bogies and two bolsters with chains.

-	**NE** 5756 brown? - *32-40*	90	120
-	**NE** 9061 grey + timber load - *32-40*	90	120

W28. Bogie Carriage/Theatre Wagon (1928)
This was like a a long bogie version of the Carriage Wagon in table W2, made to go with passenger stock. In 1930, the title of the wagon in the catalogue was extended with '...or Theatrical Property Wagon'.

-	1367 - *28?-40*	90	120
-	854 brown - *28?-40*	90	120

W29. Bar & Rail Bogie Bolster Wagon (1928)
This was a bogie bolster wagon with 6 bolsters, their pins linked across in pairs by fine chains. It was fitted with brass compensating bogies. Also available as a kit.

-	**LMS** 12314, 79607 Steel Bars - *28-40*	90	120
-	**NE** - *28-40*	90	120

W30. 30T Bogie Plate Wagon (1932)
This model seems to have been based on a drawing in the April 1929 issue of *Model Railway News* which had the same running number. It had 3 planks.

-	**GW** dark grey - *32-40*	90	120
-	**LMS** grey? - *32-40*	90	120
-	**NE** 139422 grey Plate - *32-40*	90	120
-	**SR** brown - *32-40*	90	120

W31. 50T Bogie Brick Wagon (1932)
This model was fitted with a diamond frame, brass bogies and cast iron wheels. This model seems to have been based on a drawing in the April 1929 issue of *Model Railway News* which had the same running number. This has 6 planks.

-	**NE** 451001, 98014 red-brown Brick - *32-40*	90	120

W32. High Capacity Bogie Wagon (1930)
Also available as a kit.

-	**MR** 37410? grey - *?*	NPG	NPG
-	**NER** 5054 black? - *?*	90	120
-	**GW** 2593 dark grey - *30-40*	90	120
-	**LMS** 32573? grey - *30-40*	90	120
-	**NE** grey? - *30-40*	90	120
-	**SR** 720 brown - *30-40*	90	120

W33. Bogie Oil Tank Wagon (1928)
This was fitted with compensating bogies, cast iron wheels and tensioning wires.

-	Oil 840? black - *28?-*	140	170
-	**'Esso'** 2360 cream blue/red letters - *36?-40*	170	220
-	**'Pratt's'** 4932 geenish grey - *30-35?*	170	220

W34. High Capacity Box Wagons (1928)
This was fitted with 4 sliding doors, compensating brass bogies and cast iron wheels.

-	**LNWR** 720 dark grey - *28?-31?*	140	170
-	**MR** grey? - *28?-31?*	140	170
-	**GN** brown? - *28?-31?*	140	170
-	**GC** grey? - *28?-31?*	140	170

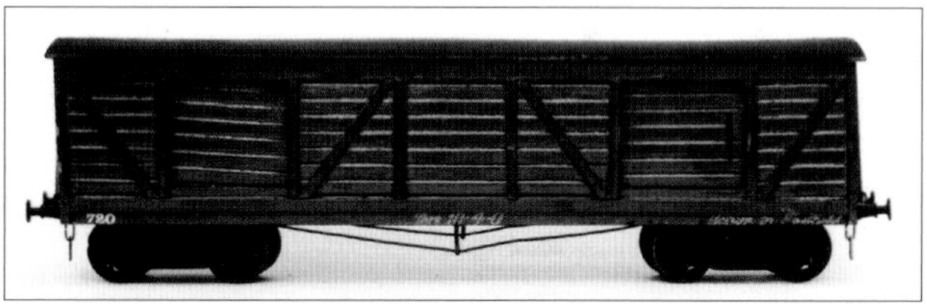

High capacity box van [W34]

-	**GW** 51367 dark grey - *28?-40*	140	170
-	**LMS** 2070 grey - *28?-40*	140	170
-	**NE** grey? - *28?-40*	140	170
-	**SR** 13989 brown - *28?-40*	140	180
-	**SR** 13987 dark grey - *28?-40*	140	180

ACCESSORIES
There was an interesting range of buildings and accessories all of which were made of wood including stations, low overbridges, tunnel mouths, signal cabins and platelayers huts. It seems that some of these, at least, were made for Milbro by outside manufacturers such as Hailey. Other accessories included buffer stops, level crossings, loading gauges, field sign posts, coal stacks, turntables and gradient posts. These were also made in both scales.

4498
L N E R

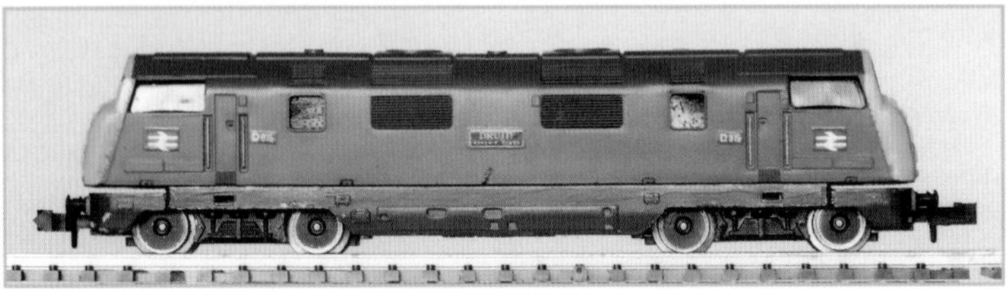

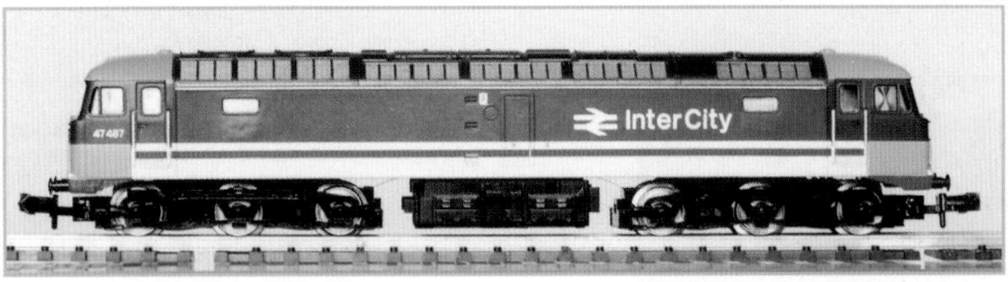
InterCity

GUARD
M 21240

M 16171

NATIONAL BENZOLE

ALKALINE
DURACELL

Minitrix (British)
including Hornby Minitrix

HISTORY

Minitrix Electric first appeared in Germany in 1964, although the Minitrix name had previously been used on a push-along range of trains since 1959. The Wrexham based British Trix company, by then part of the Courtaulds Group, marketed Minitrix in the UK from 1965. It was decided that there was a market for models based on British prototypes and permission to go ahead with these was given by Trix. The plastic parts for the new British range were tooled and made in the Trix factory in Wrexham.

Ex-LMS Ivatt 2-6-2T 753 No.41234 [L3]

In 1967, British Trix was sold to Trix in Germany and a company called Thernglade Ltd was established to take over production in the UK. Ernst Rozsa, who had been with the British Trix company since 1961, was made a Director of Thernglade and was responsible for Minitrix development at that time. Now in financial difficulty themselves, in 1971 the German owners decided to pull out of train production in the UK and production ceased in November that year. As the Minitrix market had been expanding quite nicely in Britain, the Minitrix tooling and stocks were moved to Germany for further use.

In 1972, the German Trix company merged with George Adam Mangold Gmbh to form Trix-Mangold Gmbh and they invited Rovex, the former Tri-ang company and now part of Dunbee Combex Marx (DCM), to market their British range of Minitrix models in the UK. These were sold under the name Hornby Minitrix and the agreement ran from January 1st 1973.

Rovex had been making the Tri-ang Hornby 00 system and had been skirting around the perimeter of N gauge without wishing to commit themselves to manufacturing an N gauge range as well. As a stopgap they had marketed the Lima N gauge system during the 1960s through their subsidiary G&R Wrenn. Wrenn had become an independent company again with the break-up of the Tri-ang empire in 1971 and the agreement that Rovex had with Lima was at an end. This left Rovex (whose 00 system was now called Hornby Railways) free to transfer their loyalty to another N gauge brand and the result was a very satisfactory partnership with Trix-Mangold that lasted until the end of 1986.

Ex-LMS Ivatt 2-6-0 No.46406 [L4]

The British Minitrix models were now well marketed and with help from Rovex (later known as Hornby Hobbies Ltd) the range was steadily expanded. Rovex found it a good and trouble free system and they got on well with the manufacturers. They had a quality inspector who had previously worked for Rolls Royce and when the first Minitrix locomotives arrived he started unpacking them to test them. Surprised that the man should think this necessary, he was sent over to Nuremberg, to the Trix factory, to see how well they were tested there.

Trix had produced a model of a Warship diesel for the British market but Rovex said if they were going to handle Minitrix sales in the UK they wanted more steam locomotives. The model of the 'Britannia' was already in production by 1971 and therefore not suggested by Rovex but, instead, they found locomotives that suited the Minitrix chassis and supplied drawings so that Trix could make them. Trix always needed some persuasion to make new models of British outline locomotives because of the high cost involved and the small size of the market. The use of existing German chassis meant compromise but helped to convince the Germans that the models were worth doing.

The series of N scale lineside buildings were not made in Germany. They were based on Hornby 00 scale railway buildings and were made in Hong Kong probably from drawings prepared at Margate. It is possible that the DCM owned Louis Marx Inc. factory in Hong Kong, known as the ELM Tooling Company, produced them. The white plasticard mock-ups of these models have survived at Margate.

Hornby Minitrix was never big business and they were made in fairly small quantities, but it ticked over nicely for several years. In their peak year Rovex sold £150,000 worth of Minitrix. £75,000 of that would probably have gone to Minitrix to tool up another loco. The models had superb pulling power and were always seen as the quality end of the N gauge market.

Despite being sold as Hornby Minitrix in the UK, some of the British models were included in the German catalogue, just as 'Minitrix'.

On 1st January 1987, Euro Models & Toys became the importers of the whole of the Minitrix range and the name 'Hornby' was dropped from the packaging. Although the range continued to expand, rising prices and the fast expansion of the Graham Farish range took their toll. Principal casualties were the low volume British models and from 1990 these were available only on occasions when batches had recently passed through the factory. The shortage of new models had the effect of driving up the price of second-hand ones.

Ex-LNER Class A3 No.60103 Flying Scotsman [L5]

From 1993, distribution of Minitrix in Britain was in the hands of Bachmann, while the models were available. Trix were in financial difficulty again and on 1st January 1997 Trix-Mangold was taken over by Marklin. At this point, Gaugemaster became the importer but it was not until the Summer of 2000 that Bachmann cleared the last of their stock. This, strangely enough, coincided with their purchase of Graham Farish. With Bachmann upgrading the Graham Farish N gauge range, the future of the British Minitrix range does not look good!

Catalogue Numbers - Some models have appeared under several different catalogue numbers which causes confusion. Trix, British Trix and Rovex/Hornby Hobbies all had their own numbers for the same model. Alternative catalogue numbers are shown in brackets ().

LOCOMOTIVES

All Minitrix locomotives used existing chassis from German models, even those made in the UK. This made it necessary to make many compromises with the locomotive bodies.

Cat No.	Company, Number, Colour, Dates	£	£

L1. Fowler Class 2F (Dock Tank) 0-6-0T (1973)

This model was solely made in Germany and may also be found in an East German livery.

N201	**47160** BRc black (12052) - *73*	30	40

L2. LNER Class J63 0-6-0T (1967)

A white metal body kit made in the UK, subsequently marketed by Beaver as kit N452 and fitted to the German T3 locomotive chassis. The Minitrix instructions suggested that it be finished as shown in this table. W&H also advertised the German T3 finished in LNER green livery.

2991	**E8210** LNER black - *67*	NA	60

L3. LMS Ivatt Class 2MT 2-6-2T (1974)

N205	**41234** BRc black (12040) - *74*	45	55

L4. LMS Ivatt Class 2MT 2-6-0 (1973)

N213	**46406** BRc green (12038) - *82*	55	65
12038	**46402** BRc green - *85*	75	85
N202	**46400** BRc black (12039) - *73*	45	55

L5. LNER Class A3 4-6-2 (1988)

N216	**4472 *Flying Scotsman*** LNER green - *not made*	NA	NA
N218	**2500 *Windsor Lad*** LNER green - *not made*	NA	NA
12950	**4472 *Flying Scotsman*** LNER light green - *88*	85	95
N215	**60101 *Cicero*** BRc green - *not made*	NA	NA
12949	**60103 *Flying Scotsman*** BRc green - *88*	90	100

L6. LNER Class A4 4-6-2 (1980)

N214	**4498 *Sir Nigel Gresley*** LNER blue (12946) - *83*	85	95

Ex-LNER Class A4 No.60022 Mallard [L6]

N211	**60022 *Mallard*** BRc green (12947) - *80*	100	110

L7. BR 'Britannia' Class 4-6-2 (1971)

The model was originally advertised under the catalogue number '2906' but, by the time it was assembled in the UK and released, it had changed to '2037'.

2037	**70000 *Britannia*** BRc green (12037, N203) - *71*	70	80
N217	**70036 *Boadicea*** BRc green (12042) - *85*	85	95

L8. BR Class 9F 2-10-0 (1975)

BR Class 9F 2-10-0 No.92018 [L8]

N209	**92220 *Evening Star*** BRc green (12041) - *79*	80	90
N207	**92018** BRc black (12058) - *75*	75	85

L9. Class 27 Diesel Bo-Bo (1967)

2902	**D5370** BRe blue - *67*	60	70
2901	**D5379** BRc green (N204, 12940) - *67*	40	50
N212	**27014** BRe blue (12969) - *80*	45	55

L10. Class 42 'Warship' Diesel B-B (1970)

The Warship chassis came in three versions. The original one, assembled in the UK and used between 1970 and 1972 in the UK and Germany, had a completely cast base. The 2nd style, used from 1974 (on the introduction of N206), was made in Germany and had a full length insert base. The 3rd style, made from 1979 (on the introduction of N208) had a revised rigid chassis with bogie frame detail.

2035	**D805 *Benbow*** BRc green - *70*	60	70
2905	**D815 *Druid*** BRe blue - *70*	60	70
2904	**D816 *Eclipse*** BRc green - *70*	60	70
2905	**D816 *Eclipse*** BRe blue - *71*	65	75
2034	**D823 *Hermes*** BRe blue (N206, 12942) - *70*	40	50
N208	**D825 *Intrepid*** BRc green (12943) - *79*	45	55
2036	**D838 *Rapid*** BRc maroon - *71*	110	120
2906	**D866 *Zebra*** BRc maroon - *71*	85	100
2904	**D866 *Zebra*** BRc green (2035) - *71*	65	75
2905	**D866 *Zebra*** BRe blue (2034) - *72*	65	75

L11. Class 47 Diesel Co-Co (1982)

N210	**47170 *County of Norfolk*** BReLL blue (12966) - *82*	55	65

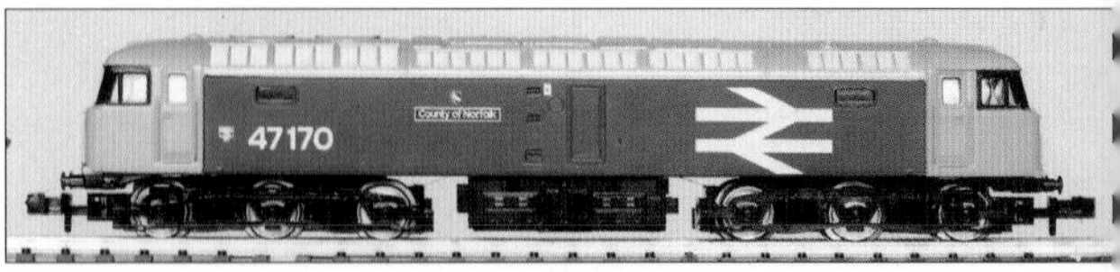

BR Class 47 No.47170 County of Norfolk [L11]

N220	**47378** BReLL Railfreight grey - *not made*	NA	NA
12024	**47378** BReLL Railfreight grey - *87*	60	70
N221	**47487** BR IC grey - *not made*	NA	NA
12025	**47487** BR IC grey - *87*	60	70
N219	**47541 *The Queen Mother*** BRe blue (12958) - *85*	55	65

COACHES

The first Minitrix coaches for the British market were suggested by Sydney Pritchard, head of Peco, and the earliest ones were sold in Peco packaging during 1967 and 1968. These were the BR Mk1s. Numbers appeared on the coaches from the start as indicated in the following tables but sometimes numbers turn up on the wrong coach.

The first two Mk1 coaches (2921 and 2929) were described as having a moulded chassis and superstructure, nylon bogies, turned metal wheels, provision for interior lighting and printed sides. They were five and three eighths inches in length over the buffers.

The Mini Coachbuilder kits were available in 1970 and numbered 3921-3928. They were UK made and unmade kits are very rare.

Cat No.	Company, Number, Colour, Dates	£	£

C1a. LNER Gresley Corridor 3rd (1988)

LNER Gresley teak corridor 3rd No.4237 [C1a]

13014	**LNER** 4237 teak - *88*	17	22
13116	**BR** E12451E maroon - *91*	25	30

C1b. LNER Gresley Brake Composite (1988)

13013	**LNER** 4173 teak - *88*	17	22
13115	**BR** E10076E maroon - *91*	25	30

C2a. BR Mk1 Corridor Composite CK (1967)

2943	**GWR** 2018 brown+cream - *72*	12	15
2941	**LMS** 1671 maroon - *72*	12	15
13065	**BR** M4330 red+cream - *87*	12	15
2925	**BR** S15900 green - *67*	12	15
-	above as a Mini Coachbuilder kit - *70*	NPG	NPG
2923	**BR** W16198 brown+cream (13004, N301) - *67*	8	11
-	above as a Mini Coachbuilder kit - *70*	NPG	NPG
2921	**BR** M16171 maroon (13005, N305) - *67*	8	11
-	above as a Mini Coachbuilder kit - *70*	NPG	NPG
2927	**BR** M16171 blue+grey (13003, N303) - *67*	7	10
-	above as a Mini Coachbuilder kit - *70*	NPG	NPG
2933	**BR** S15900 blue - *70*	14	17
2934	**BR** W16198 blue+grey (13003, N303) - *70*	7	10

C2b. BR Mk1 Corridor 2nd SK (1968)

2925/2	**BR** S15902 green (2931) - *68*	14	17
2930	**BR** ? Brown+cream - *68*	22	27
2929	**BR** M16752 maroon - *68*	12	15
2927/2	**BR** M16171 blue+grey (2932) - *68*	12	15

C2c.	**BR Mk1 Brake Composite BCK** (1967)		
2944	**GWR** 3146 brown+cream- *72*	12	15
2942	**LMS** 5540 maroon - *72*	12	15
13066	**BR** M26546 red+cream - *87*	12	15
2926	**BR** S2301 green - *67*	12	15
-	above as a Mini Coachbuilder kit - *70*	NPG	NPG
2924	**BR** W21194 brown+cream (13007, N302, N307) - *67*	8	11
-	above as a Mini Coachbuilder kit - *70*	NPG	NPG
2922	**BR** M21240 maroon (13008, N308) - *67*	8	11
-	above as a Mini Coachbuilder kit - *70*	NPG	NPG
2928	**BR** M21240 blue+grey (13006, N306) - *67*	7	10
-	above as a Mini Coachbuilder kit - *70*	NPG	NPG
2935	**BR** ? blue+grey - *70*	22	27
2936	**BR** S2301 blue - *70*	14	17

C2d. BR Mk1 Brake 2nd BSK (1968)

BR Mk1 BSK in green livery No.S2301 [C2d]

2926/2	**BR** S2301 green - *68*	14	17
2922/2	**BR** M21240 maroon - *68*	12	15
2928/2	**BR** M21240 blue+grey - *68*	12	15

C2e.	**BR Mk1 Full Brake BG** (1971)		
2937	**BR** 80555 maroon - *71*	12	15
2938	**BR** 81304 blue+grey - *71*	15	18

C2f.	**BR Mk1 Sleeping Car SLE** (1937)		
2939	**BR** maroon - *not made*	NA	NA
2940	**BR** blue+grey - *not made*	NA	NA

WAGONS

The first wagons issued were models of BP tanks using 15' wheelbase chassis. These moulds passed to Peco who altered the moulds to carry their own name. The rest of the early wagons were based on items from the British Trix 00 range. They used a common 10' wheelbase chassis and some were sold in pairs. A few wagons were actually from the German range but produced in British liveries.

Cat No.	Company, Number, Colour, Dates	£	£

Continental Style Wagons

W1. LWB Barrel Wagon (1973)

The barrels and mounting plate can be a combination of red, blue, yellow or grey.

N504	**BRe** B740387 brown + 5 barrels (13573) - *73*	5	7

W2. Side-tipping Hoppers (pair) (1984)

Standard German item.

N524	both red+green - *84*	7	10

W3. LWB Van ('CovAB') (1973)

N505	**BRe** 200424 brown (13574) - *73*	4	7

W4. Car Transporter (1973)

The cars were various colours. Standard German item.

N510	**DB** 869014 brown + 4 cars - *73*	6	9

W4A. Bogie Container Wagon (1991)

Bogie container flat with three 20ft containers [W4a]

13635	black + **'P&O'** blue, **'Metal Box'** grey, **'Royal Mail Parcels'** red - *91*	11	14

W5. Bogie Ballast Hopper (1973)

N506	**BRe** B413161 grey (13575) - *73*	6	9

W6. Bogie Covered Wagon (1973)

Standard German item.

N509	**'Ford'** 0554178 blue (13519) - *73*	6	9

British Style Wagons

W7. 8-plank Open Wagon (1971)

N523	**'Arnolds Sands'** red-brown (13284) - *84*	4	7
13833	'FS **Brightmore'** 113 grey - *92*	5	7
13633	**'British Steel'** 20 blue* - *91*	5	10
3271	**'Chubb'** 101 red-brown - *71*	8	11
N515	'E **Foster & Co.'** 2009 grey (13579) - *80*	4	7
3272	**'Wm Gordon Jameson's'** 51 yellow (3 yellow shades recorded) (13577, N507) - *71*	4	7
N511	**'Ilkeston & Heanor Water Board'** 14 blue (13583) - *74*	4	7
3268	**'Isaac Wilkinson'** 35 red - *71*	15	20
13832	**'Lilleshall'** 1641 red-brown - 92	5	8
N512	**'Millom Co-op'** green (13584) - *74*	4	7
3275	**'Nicholsons' Brewers'** 1 black - *71*	8	11
3273	**'Roberts Jenks'** 100 black (13580, N508) - *71*	4	7
3259	'AJ **Salter'** 122 red-brown - *not made*	NA	NA
N522	**'Scarwood'** light grey (13581) - *84*	4	7
N514	**'Sheepbridge'** 8234 brown (13578) - *80*	4	7

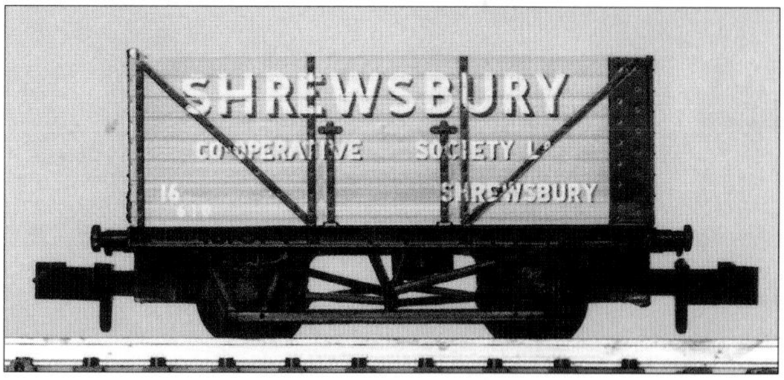

8-plank open wagon - 'Shrewsbury' [W7]

13834	**'Shrewsbury'** 16 grey - *92*	5	8
3274	**'Sutton Manor'** 1075 grey - *71*	8	11
3209	**GWR** 109432 grey - *72*	9	12
3208	**LMS** 299471 brown - *72*	9	12
3211	**LNER** 87365 brown - *72*	9	12
3210	**SR** 36327 grey - *72*	9	12

* Often found in a 13833 box.

W8. 16T Mineral Wagon (1971)

3206	**BR** B239021 grey (N513, 13571) - *79*	5	8
3207	**BR** B586537 brown (N502, 13576) - *71*	4	7

In the 1984/85 catalogue the catalogue numbers for these two wagons were swapped round.

W9. HAA MGR Hoppers (1982)

Prices of these were around the £18-£20 mark until Bachmann released their models in the Graham Farish range.

N517	**BR** 351540 aluminium+brown (13277) - *82*	6	9
N529	**BR Railfreight** B352556 aluminium+red - *not made*	NA	NA

HHA coal hopper wagon [W9]

13632	**BR Railfreight** B352556 aluminium+red - *87*	7	10
13637	**BR Coal** 351556 - *91*	7	10

W10. 10' Tank Wagon (1982)

13634	**'Duracell'** black+copper - *91*	5	8
N518	**'Esso'** 1800 silver (13273) - *83*	6	9
N519	**'National Benzole'** P93 buff (13274) - *83*	6	9
N516	**'Shell BP'** A5066 silver (13272) - *82*	6	9

W11. 15' Modern Tank Wagon (1967)

These tanks were designed, tooled up and produced by Trix but the tooling was later taken over by Peco who tooled a replacement chassis which could also be used on other wagons.

2955	**'BP'** 1350, 9675, 9682, 9689 white - *67*	15	20
2956	**'BP'** green - *not made* *	NA	NA
2957	**'BP'** silver - *not made* *	NA	NA
2958	**'BP'** black - *not made* *	NA	NA

* These were later made by Peco using the same tools.

W12. BR Ventilated Van (1973)

Planned but not made in the UK.

3213	**BR** grey - *not made*	NA	NA
3214	**BR** brown - *not made*	NA	NA
N503	**BR** B852193 grey VAN - *not made*	NA	NA
N503	**BR** B852193 grey shock van (13572) - *73*	4	7
13572	**BR** B852193 brown shock van - *?*	10	13
N525	**BR Rft** 230002 grey+red - *not made*	NA	NA
13631	**BR Rft** 230002 grey+red - *87*	6	9

W13. BR Standard Brake Van (1973)

Planned but not made in the UK.

3221	**BR** brown - *not made*	NA	NA
N501	**BR** B952698 brown (13570) - *73*	5	8
N526	**BR Rft** B954817 grey+red - *not made*	NA	NA
13630	**BR Rft** B954817 grey+red - *87*	6	9
13636	**BR Sector** B972163 - *91*	6	9

BR standard brake van [W13]

Hornby Class N15 Sir Meliagrance from computer artwork by Robbie McGavin

OO Works

Please note that the table numbers have been changed in this chapter to accomodate new models.

HISTORY

This Robertsbridge based company, build 4mm scale/16.5mm gauge limited run batches of ready-to-run models of prototypes that are uneconomical for major model railway manufacturers to produce. The company is run by Roderick Bruce and the products, until recently, all had a Southern bias. His first model was of a 'King Arthur' Class locomotive which was available in six different versions.

LOCOMOTIVES

The models are of white metal construction, giving them weight, and excellent pulling power. They come ready-to-run and ready finished.

Cat No.	Company, Number, Colour, Dates	£	£

L1. Adams 'Radial' 0415 Class 4-4-2T (2004)

This was OO Works fourth locomotive, following the previous two in having a resin body with metal details and a custom-built chassis. Famous for their use on Dorset's Lyme Regis branch this proved a most popular model, with the majority produced in the BR black livery.

-	LSWR Pea green - *04-05*	100	185
-	**5** EKR green - *04-05*	100	185
-	SR olive green - *04-05*	100	185

Adams 'Radial' tank Class 0415 4-4-2T [L1] (OO Works)

-	SR black with 'Sunshine' lettering - *04-05*	100	185
-	**30582** BR lined black - *04-05*	100	185
-	**30584** BR lined black - *04-05*	100	185

L2. SE&CR Wainwright Class H 0-4-4T (2009)

S001	**1016** SR olive green - *09*	110	195
S002	**1326** SR olive green - *09*	110	195
S003	**1552** SR black 'Sunshine' - *09*	110	185
S004	**31305** BRc lined black - *09*	110	190
S005	**31263** BRc lined black - *09*	110	190

L3. L&Y Class 23 0-6-0ST (2008)

Aspinall's conversion of the Barton Wright 0-6-0 tender locos.

M001	**11532** LMS grey - *08*	95	173
M002	**11320** LMS grey - *09*	95	173
M003	**51404** BRb black - *08*	95	173
M004	**51446** BRc black - *08*	95	173
M005	**11305** BRc black - *09*	95	173

L4. SR Billinton E4 Class 0-6-2T (2006)

The Billinton 'E4' class locomotive is a popular model

-	**2485** SR olive green - *06-07*	85	155
-	SR black with 'Sunshine' lettering - *06-07*	85	155
-	**32503** BRb lined black - *06-07*	85	155
-	**32468** BRc lined black - *06-07*	85	155

L5. SECR Wainwright L Class 4-4-0 (2003)

This model was OO Works third production. It followed the now established practice of a resin body with metal details on a custom-built chassis.

-	SECR grey - *03-04*	100	180
-	**1765** SR olive green - *03-04*	100	180
-	**1762** SR Malachite green - *03-04*	100	180
-	**31778*** BR liner black - *03-04*	100	180

*31776 featured above left was produced as a special order without a number in BR lined black livery for numbering and detailing by the client.

L6. LSWR Drummond 700 Class 0-6-0 (2007)

Nicknamed 'Black Motor'. This model features a cast metal body with a solid brass milled chassis.

-	SR plain black choice of numbers - *07*	100	185
-	SR lined green choice of numbers - *07*	100	190
-	**30315** BRb black - *07*	100	185
-	**30315** BRc black - *07*	100	185
-	**30700** BRb black - *07*	100	185
-	**30700** BRc black - *07*	100	185

L7. SECR Wainwright C Class 0-6-0 (2002)

This was OO Works second model. It featured a resin body with metal details on OO Works' first custom-built chassis.

-	SECR grey - *02-03*	95	165
-	**513** SR plain black - *02-03*	95	165
-	**513** SR lined black - *02-03*	95	165
-	SR Malachite green 'Sunshine' lettering - *02-03*	95	165
-	**31692** BR black - *02-03*	95	165

L8. SR Maunsell N15 Class 4-6-0 (2001)

This was OO Works' first model. It was made of a resin body with metal details on a modified Bachmann 'Royal Scot' chassis. By using a ready-to-run chassis some compromises were required with dimensions.

-	SR olive green - *01-03*	100	175
-	SR pre-war light green - *01-03*	100	175
-	**767 *Sir Valence*** SR Malachite green - *01-03*	100	175
-	SR wartime black - *01-03*	100	175
-	**30782 *Sir Brian*** BRb green - *01-03*	100	175
-	**30770 *Sir Prianius*** BRc - *01-03*	100	175

COACHES

Cat No.	Company, Number, Colour, Dates	£	£

C1. Pullman Observation Car

This was OO Work's first and to date only coach model. It was constructed using a resin body with metal floor and metal details. This proved to be a very popular model. Because of the price it was also offered as a kit, however the overwhelming majority of purchasers opted for the ready-to-run versions.

-	**14** 'Devon Belle' white roof - *?*	90	123
-	**14** 'Devon Belle' grey/white roof - *?*	90	123
-	**14** 'Devon Belle' grey roof - *?*	90	123
-	**15** 'Devon Belle' white roof - *?*	90	123
-	**15** 'Devon Belle' grey/white roof - *?*	90	123

Devon Belle Pullman observation car [C1] (Vectis)

-	**15** 'Devon Belle' grey roof - *?*	90	123
-	**Sc280M** lined maroon - *?*	90	123
-	**Sc281** maroon - *?*	90	123

After their use on the 'Devon Belle' cars no. 14 and 15 were transferred to the London Midland Region finding use on the Land Cruise Train in Wales before being moved up to Scotland. Both of these versions were only available as a special order and only a handful were produced. Sc 280M appeared in lined maroon livery on the Kyle Line. Sc281 ran in unlined maroon livery on the Oban Line.

UK TOY & MODEL AUCTIONS

Specialist Auctioneers of Toys and Models

THINKING OF SELLING YOUR COLLECTION?

TOYS & MODELS WANTED

FOR OUR FORTHCOMING AUCTIONS

We are able to give help if selling as part of an estate etc. Send your lists or contact

46 Wirral Gardens, Bebington, Wirral, Merseyside CH63 3BH
Telephone Barry Stockton 0151-334 3362
or Tony Oakes 01270 841558

www.uktoyauctions.com

AMC • AMC • AMC • AMC • AMC • AMC • AMC • AMC • AMC • AMC • AMC

MasterCard VISA VISA

ALTON MODEL CENTRE

7a NORMANDY ST, ALTON, HANTS GU34 1DD
Tel: 01420 542244 Fax: 01420 544463
Email: AltonModelCentre@hotmail.co.uk
MON-SAT 9am-5.30pm
SUN 10am - 4pm inc Bank Holidays

Hampshire's Largest Model Shop - probably!

N Gauge from Dapol, Grafar, Ratio, PECO.
OO Gauge from Hornby, Bachmann, ViTrains, Heljan, PECO, Lima, Replica, Dapol, Wills. Knightwing, Gaugemaster, Parkside, Slaters, Coopercraft, Mailcoach, etc.
Loco Kits from DJH, South Eastern Finecast, Nu-cast, Craftsman, etc.
O Gauge from PECO, Parkside, Slaters, Coopercraft, etc.

All this plus magazines, books and DVD's plus diecast models from EFE, Corgi, OOC, CMNL, Oxford, Classix & Britbus.

SECONDHAND MODEL RAILWAYS BOUGHT, SOLD & PART EXCHANGED

HORNBY BACHMANN BRANCH-LINE CORGI

AMC • AMC • AMC • AMC • AMC • AMC • AMC • AMC • AMC • AMC • AMC

LACY SCOTT & KNIGHT

The largest one-day model railway, diecast, tinplate, lead and steam model auctions in the country.

• Four major sales per year of 1,500 lots • Refreshments on sale and viewing days • Payment to vendors within 10 working days • Free on-site parking

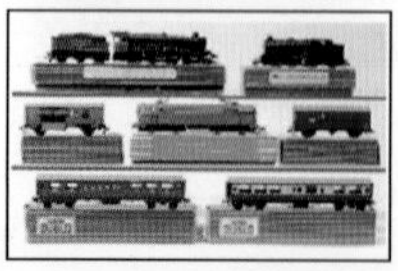

Examples of items which have successfully passed through our auctions

Auction Centre, 10 Risbygate Street, Bury St Edmunds, Suffolk, IP33 3AA
Telephone: 01284 748623 Fax: 01284 748620
Email: fineart@lsk.co.uk Catalogue website: www.lsk.co.uk

Peco N

Please note that the table numbers have been changed in this chapter to accomodate new models.

HISTORY

Peco is the trademark of the Pritchard Patent Product Company which was established in April 1946 by Mr and Mrs S C Pritchard. It started operations in a small cottage in Devon at Branscombe with just one employee.Over the years that followed, Peco became the leading company in the production of model railway track.

In need of more room, the company moved to a church hall in Sidmouth in 1947 and later acquired a separate office in town. They also acquired premises for a workshop in a yard off what was then Sidmouth railway station.The next move came in January 1951 when a head office, showroom and stores were established in Seaton (this showroom was the birthplace of the writer's own interest in railway modelling, as opposed to toy trains, following a visit there at the age of 12 while on holiday in Devon!).

GWR 'Collett Goods' 0-6-0 [L1] (Peco)

Although track has always been the best known Peco product, and is today sold all over the world, the company has repeatedly looked for gaps in the market and set about filling them. So it was, in the mid 1960s, that the need for British outline N gauge models was realised and, initially in association with Trix, the company became involved in the production of N gauge wagons.The first of these were made in the production unit in Seaton.

By the late 1960s, the Peco business had grown to such an extent that a new factory was required. After some difficulty in obtaining planning permission to build in this beautiful part of South Devon, a site in Beer, the next village along the coast, was purchased from Axminster Rural District Council in 1970. Here a brand new factory and exhibition complex was built to the company's own specification and opened for production the following year. It is here that Peco products are made today.

Dates - The listing of Peco products has not been an easy task and while we have a good idea when models first appeared there is little or no evidence of when production ceased. Only dates of introduction are given, therefore.

LOCOMOTIVES

The Stanier 'Jubilee' model was developed in conjunction with Rivarossi in Italy. All the new tooling, which excluded the bogie truck and the motor, was paid for by Peco and the tools were later transferred to Beer. The 1969 model was made in Italy by Rivarossi and Peco granted them permission to sell it there. Later models, which consisted of *Silver Jubilee* and maroon versions were entirely produced by Peco at Beer where the tooling is currently stored.

White metal locomotive body kits, thought to have been made by Wills, were also available from 1973 for fitting to Arnold chassis. These included a 'Hymek', Class 4 diesel (made by Anbrico), a Fairburn 2-6-2 tank, an 0-6-0 dock tank, Peckett 0-4-0ST, 0-4-0T and a Manning Wardle type 0-4-0ST. Painting and detailing was left to the modeller. Briefly, a complete kit for a Collett 0-6-0 was available.

Cat No.	Company, Number, Colour, Dates	£	£

L1. GWR 2251 Class 'Collett Goods' 0-6-0 (2007)

The model is ready fitted with a decoder and fitted with a Mashima motor. It has a finely detailed moulded plastic body and fine cab and boiler handrails. The wheel profiles are to a fine standard and fully spoked. Rear tender handrails, front coupling, brake handle and water gauge are supplied separately for fitting. Two drawbars are also supplied and the loco is fully DCC equipped.

NL24A	**3206** GWR green - *07*	100	126
NL27J	**2235** BRc black - *09?*	100	126
NL24B	**2238** GWR green - *07*	100	126
NL25D	**2252** GWR (button) green - *07*	100	126
NL25F	**2284** GWR (button) green - *07*	100	126
NL24G	**2281** GWR green - *08*	100	126
NL25H	**2291** GWR (button) green - *08*	100	126
NL27K	**3203** BRc black - *09?*	100	126
NL27	**3208** BRc black - *not made*	100	126
NL27C	**2274** BRc black - *07*	100	126
NL27E	**3216** BRc black - *07*	100	126
NL27I	**3208** BRc black - *07*	100	126

L2. LMS 'Jubilee' Class 4-6-0 (by Rivarossi) (1977)

NL22 was supplied unnamed and with a sheet of transfers for all six names and numbers. *Silver Jubilee* also had its transfers provided and this and NL22 also had an alternative double chimney supplied in the box.

NL22	**5593 *Kolhapur*** LMS maroon - *85*	70	85

Ex-LMS 'Jubilee' Class No.45593 Kolhapur [L2] (Vectis)

NL22	**5690 *Leander*** LMS maroon - *85*	70	85
NL22	**5691 *Orion*** LMS maroon - *85*	70	85
NL22	**5696 *Bahamas*** LMS maroon - *85*	70	85
NL22	**5729 *Furious*** LMS maroon - *85*	70	85
NL22	**5738 *Samson*** LMS maroon - *85*	70	85
NL21	**5713 *Renown*** LMS black - *69*	60	75
?	**5572 *Silver Jubilee*** LMS black - *77*	75	90

COACHES

Coaches were initially produced in conjunction with Minitrix who also sold them. They were made in the Trix factory at Wrexham but Peco sold them as 'Wonderful Coaches'.

Cat No.	Company, Number, Colour, Dates	£	£

C1a. BR Mk1 Corridor Composite CK (by Minitrix) (1967)

NR70	**BR** S15900 green - *67*	10	15
NR60	**BR** W16198 brown+cream - *67*	10	15
NR50	**BR** M16171 maroon - *67*	10	15

BR Mk1 CK in blue & grey [C1a]

NR80	**BR** M16171 blue+grey - *67*	10	15

C1b. BR Mk1 Brake Composite BCK (by Minitrix) (1967)

NR71	**BR** S2301 green - *67*	10	15
NR61	**BR** W21194 brown+cream - *67*	10	15
NR61	**BR** W21060 brown+cream - *68*	NPG	NPG
NR51	**BR** M21240 maroon - *67*	10	15
NR81	**BR** M21240 blue+grey - *67*	10	15

C1c. BR Mk1 All 2nd SK (by Minitrix) (1968)

NR72	**BR** S15902 green - *68*	10	15
NR62	**BR** ? brown+cream - *68*	10	15
NR52	**BR** M16752 maroon - *68*	10	15
NR82	**BR** M16171 blue+grey - *68*	10	15

WAGONS

The first wagon was the modern tank wagon which was produced initially in conjunction with Minitrix and jointly sold by them. It was designed, tooled and made in the Trix factory. This arrangement did not last long.

The ready to run wagons were introduced as 'Wonderful Wagons' and were on either a 10' or a 15' wheelbase chassis. Peco also made wagon kits of the standard range as well as some additional subjects. These included an SR brake van and on a 9' chassis a pig iron wagon, tippler wagon and a mineral wagon. The catalogue numbers of kits were prefixed with 'KNR' and the kit-built models had no printing on them and so needed finishing. A good range of wagon chassis could be bought separately.

From 1973, loads for wagons were also available separately, if required, and eventually included the full container range (as listed below in table W3a), coal, planks, bricks, barrels, crates and sand. The plastic mouldings for open wagon loads were made in such a way that they could be cut in half so that one and a half loads could be used in the long wheelbase wagons. Coal rails were also available for the open wagons.

It would appear that around 1968, Atlas negotiated with Peco to supply them with at least three of their wagons for use in the Atlas range. They went as far as illustrating them in the 1968/69 Atlas catalogue but in subsequent catalogues these had been replaced by other wagons using the same allocated catalogue numbers.

Cat No.	Company, Number, Colour, Dates	£	£

W1. 'Lowmac'

This was to be a 22' wheelbase vehicle, proposed and illustrated in the catalogue in 1983.

NR-35B	**BR** B904662 brown - *not made*	NA	NA

W2a. 'Conflat' & Container (1981)

NR-P32	**BR** B73570 grey + **'LEP'** red - *83*	4	6
NR-P31	**BR** B73570 grey + **'Lyons Tea'** blue - *81*	4	6

BR 'Conflat' and container [W2a]

NR-P30	**BR** B73570 grey + **'Raleigh Cycles'** green - *81*	4	6
NR-20	**BR** B73570 grey + **GWR** Furniture BK-1869 brown - *81*	4	6
NR-21	**BR** B73570 light grey + **LMS** Furniture K1 maroon - *81*	4	6
NR-22	**BR** B73570 brown + **BR** Furniture BK1872 brown - *83*	4	6

W2b. Containers (only) (1982)

These were sold in pairs of different designs e.g. GWR + LMS, BR + LEP, Raleigh + Lyons (recommended value - £5 per pack).

NR-208	**'LEP'** red - *83*	2	NA
NR-209	**'Lyons Tea'** blue - *82*	2	NA
NR-209	**'Raleigh Cycles'** green - *82*	2	NA
NR-207	**GWR** Furniture BK-1869 brown - *82*	2	NA
NR-207	**LMS** Furniture K1 maroon - *82*	2	NA
NR-208	**BR** Furniture BK1872 red-brown - *83*	2	NA

W3. Bolster Wagon (1973)

Sold in pairs (at £8 per pair).

NR-39M	**LMS** 14555 light grey - *82*	3	NA
NR-39E	**NE** 231331 brown - *not made*	NA	NA
NR-39E	**NE** 23255 brown - *73*	3	NA

W4a. Plate Wagon (lwb) (1974)

NR-5W	**GW** 32637 dark grey - *74*	3	4
NR-5B	**BR** B932968 grey - *68*	3	4
NR-5R	**BR Railfreight** red - *not made*	NA	NA

This wagon briefly appeared in the 1968/69 Atlas catalogue but probably did not materialise in the Atlas range.

W4b. Double Bolster Wagon (lwb) (1974)

NR-4M	**LMS** 14565? light grey - *made?*	NPG	NPG
NR-4E	**NE** 231331 brown - *74*	3	4

W5a. 5-plank Open Wagon (1971)

NR-P88	'John **Allbutt'** 1 grey - *99*	3	5
-	**'Burgess & Penfold'** 55 grey Sp Edn (Scale Rail) - *96*	4	5
NR-481	**'Burgess & Penfold'** 55 grey - *09*	4	6
NR-P86	**'Constable Hart'** 127 dark grey - *98*	3	5
NR-P85	**'Cranmore Granite'** 367 light grey - *98*	3	5
NR-P87	**'Cumberland Granite'** 22 dark grey - *99*	3	5
NR-P111	**'Dowlow Lime'** 141 red-brown ** - *00?*	3	4
NR-P83	'Charles **Dunsdon'** 21 dark green - *72*	3	5
NR-P80	**'Garswood'** blue - *72*	4	6
NR-P82	'A **Gresley'** 7 red-brown - *72*	3	5
NR-P84	**'Hopton Wood'** 2 grey+red - *97*	3	5
NR-P480	**'Logan & Son'** 564 black - *08*	5	6
NR-P81	**'Mendip Mountain'** 238 grey - *75?*	4	6
NR-P441	'A F **Moodey'** ? ? - *09*	4	6

5-plank open wagon - 'Teign Valley Granite Co' [W5a]

NR-P89	'E A **Stevenson'** 10 blue *96*	3	5
NR-P440	**'Teign Valley Granite Co.'** 735 red-brown - *07*	6	7
NR-40W	**GW** 109458 dark grey - *75?*	3	5
NW-40BW	**GW** dark grey weathered * - *81*	NPG	NPG
NR-40M	**LMS** 345699 light grey - *71*	3	5
NR-40E	**LNER** 628494 red-brown - *99*	3	5
NR-40S	**SR** 5095 dark brown - *71*	3	5
NW-40BS	**SR** dark brown weathered * - *81*	NPG	NPG

* Proposed weathered and repaired wagons which were included in a late supplement to the 1981 catalogue. **This was originally sold with a roof but the Dowlow family told Peco that they generally ran without a roof as it was more trouble than it was worth. Thus, Peco produced it without a roof (see Lime Wagon below for earlier version).

W5b. 5-plank China Clay Hoods (2001)

MMR01	**BR** B743000 brown + hood blue Sp Edn (Mevagissey) - *01*	4	6

W5c. Lime Wagon (5-plank with roof) (1973)

NR-P112	**'Crawshay Bros.'** 136 cream - *73*	3	4
NR-P111	**'Dowlow Lime'** 141 red-brown * - *75?*	3	4

NR-P113	**'SLB'** 702 grey - *75?*	3	4

*This were originally sold in this form but the Dowlow family told Peco that they generally ran without a roof as it was more trouble than it was worth. Thus, Peco produced it without a roof (see 5-plank Wagon above for later version).

W6. 6-plank Tube Wagon (lwb) (1968)

NR-7W	**GW** 94856 dark grey - *74*	3	4
NR-7B	**BR** B731490 red-brown - *68*	3	4
NR-7R	**BR Railfreight** 140279 red - *82*	3	4

W7a. 7-plank Coal Open Wagon (1971)

Some wagons are sold with a coal load.

NR-P98	**'Ammanford Colliery'** 48 brown - *96*	3	4
NR-P110a	**'Birmingham Co-operative'** 31 black - *08*	5	6
NR-P110b	**'Birmingham Co-operative'** 39 black - *08*	5	6
NR-P110c	**'Birmingham Co-operative'** 45 black - *08*	5	6
NR-P106	**'Bradford & Sons'** 3 brown Sp Edn 500+ (Howe & Davies ***) - *00*	4	5
NR-P108	**'Chatterley Whitfield'** 1822 grey** - *99*	3	5
NR-P99	**'Crigglestone Collieries'** 222 red - *96*	3	4
-	**'Edinburgh Collieries Company Ltd'** 558 grey Sp Edn (Harburn) - *97*	4	5
NR-P105	**'Edward Eastwood'** 2 green - *97*	3	4
-	**'Fife Coal'** 963 brown Sp Edn (Harburn) - *02*	4	5
NR-404a	'W **Fowler'** 301 red - *09*	4	6

7-plank open wagon 'W.Fowler' [W7a]

NR-404b	'W **Fowler'** 305 red - *09*	4	6
NR-404c	'W **Fowler'** 310 red - *09*	4	6
-	**'Glasgow Iron & Steel Co.'** 963 red-brown Sp Edn (Harburn) - *97*	4	5
NR-P401a	**'Glynea & Castle'** 178 ? - *09*	4	6
NR-P401b	**'Glynea & Castle'** 191 ? - *09*	4	6
NR-P401c	**'Glynea & Castle'** 197 ? - *09*	4	6
NR-104a	'D **Hampton'** 1 red - *09*	4	6
NR-104b	'D **Hampton'** 2 red - *09*	4	6
NR-P93	**'Hood & Sons'** 3 green - *77*	4	5
NR-102a	**'ICI'** 326 red - *09*	4	6
NR-102b	**'ICI'** 330 red - *09*	4	6
NR-102c	**'ICI'** 341 red - *09*	4	6
NR-P114	**'ICI Lime Ltd'** 9395 grey - *97*	3	4
NR-P405	**'Jones, Ferguson & Co.'** 1038 black - *10*	5	6
NR-P92	**'Kingsbury'** 710 green - *75?*	4	5
NR-P95	**'Lydney Coal Co.'** 9 green-grey - *92*	3	4
NR-P94	**'Norchard'** 13 black - *92*	3	4
NR-P91	**'Parkend'** 330 black - *73*	3	4
NR-P97	**'Peco Golden Jubilee 1946-1996'** blue+gold Ltd Edn (Peco) - *96*	5	6
NR-P96	**'Princess Royal'** 250 bright red - *92*	3	4

7-plank open wagon 'Redgrave' [W7a]

NR-P109	**'Redgrave & Co.'** 1386 grey - *08*	4	5
NR-P?	**'Shaw & Son'** - *not made*	NA	NA
NR-P406	**'Tipentwys'** 767 black - *10*	5	6
NR-P107	**'Tredegar'** 5100 red - *99*	3	4
NR-P403	**'Upyon'** 1872 black - *10*	5	6
NR-P90	**'Ward & Sons'** 12 red-brown - *75?*	4	5
NR-P400	**'Wemyss'** 12 red-brown - *not made*	NA	NA
NR-P400	**'Wemyss'** 1072 red-brown - *07*	4	5
NR-P400	**'Wemyss'** 1364 red-brown - *07*	4	5
NR-P400	**'Wemyss'** 1072 grey Sp Edn (Harburn Hobbies) - *07*	4	5
NR-P103	**'White & Beeny'** 304 black - *97*	3	4
NR-P103	**'White & Beeny'** 304 black - *09*	5	6
NR-P402A	'Richard **White' & Sons** 109 blue - *10*	4	5
NR-P402B	'Richard **White' & Sons** 110 blue - *10*	4	5
NR-41W	**GW** 29617 dark grey - *77*	3	4
NW-41BW	**GW** 24572 grey weathered * - *81*	NPG	NPG
NR-41M	**LMS** 313159 light grey - *81?*	3	4
NW-41BM	**LMS** light grey weathered * - *81*	NPG	NPG
NR-41E	**LNER** 603436 grey - *99*	3	4
NR-41S	**SR** 5095 dark brown - *71*	3	4
NR-41S	**SR** (no number) dark brown - *71?*	4	5

* Proposed weathered and repaired wagons which were included in a late supplement to the 1981 catalogue. ** Shown as a 5-plank wagon in the 2000 catalogue. *** initially sold only through Pecorama at Beer, Devon.

W7b. Salt Van (7-plank with roof) (1973)

NR-P122A	**'Chance & Hunt'** 311 brown - *10*	4	6
NR-P122B	**'Chance & Hunt'** 312 brown - *10*	4	6
NR-P122C	**'Chance & Hunt'** 314 brown - *10*	4	6

Salt van 'Chance & Hunt' [W7b] (Peco)

NR-P120	**'Saxa Salt'** 251 yellow - *73*	3	4
NR-P121	**'Shaka Salt'** 166 bright blue - *75?*	3	4

W8a. 9-plank Wagon with High Bar (lwb) (1968)

NR-10S	**SR** 6241 dark brown - *75?*	3	4
NR-10B	**BR** B715010 brown - *68*	3	4

W8b. OBA 9-plank Wagon (lwb) (1982)

NR-11R	**BR Railfreight** 110264 red+grey OBA no bar - *82*	3	4

This wagon briefly appeared in the 1968/69 Atlas catalogue but probably did not materialise in the Atlas range.

W9. 'Butterley' Steel Type Coal Wagon (1971)

NR-P100	**'Charringtons'** 7190 orange-red - *75?*	3	4
NR-P101	**'Denaby'** 950 black - *75?*	4	5
NR-44W	**GW** 23301 dark grey - *75?*	3	4
NR-44E	**NE** 131450 brown - *71*	3	4
NR-44B	**BR** B288543 grey - *84*	3	4

W10a. HAA MGR Hopper Wagon (2004)

The numbers were released in a haphazard order and could not be ordered from Peco individually. Coal loads are available (NR-210) as too are canopies for the HAAs (NR-211).

NR-300	**BR** B350246, B350397, B350427, B350782, B350954, B350973 silver+brown HOP-AB - *04*	8	11
NR-301	**Railfreight** 357421, 358853, 356158, 357933, 358314, 356837 silver+red - *04*	8	11
NR-302	**Railfreight Coal** 355656, 355159, 355898, 355473, 355072, 355012 silver+yellow - *05*	8	11

NR-303	**EWS** B357016 silver+maroon - *06*	NPG	NPG
NR-303A	**EWS** 357012 silver+maroon - *06*	NPG	NPG

W10b. HBA/HCA MGR Hopper Hood & Load (2006)

NR-211	hood and load only - *06*	NPG	11

W10c. CDA China Clay Hopper Wagon (2006)

NR-305	**'ECC International'** 375070 silver+blue - *not made*	NA	NA
NR-305	**'ECC International'** 375073 silver+blue - *06*	8	11
NR-305A	**'ECC International'** ? silver+blue - *06*	8	11
NR-305B	**'ECC International'** 375070 silver+blue - *06*	8	11

CDA china clay hopper 'ECC' weathered [W10c] (Peco)

NR-305C	**'ECC International'** 375067 silver+blue - *06*	8	11
NR-305W	**'ECC International'** silver+blue w - *10*	12	14
NR-306	**EWS** 375046 sliver + maroon - *not made*	NA	NA
NR-306	**EWS** ? sliver + maroon - *06*	8	11
NR-306A	**EWS** 375046 sliver + maroon - *06*	8	11
NR-306B	**EWS** 375066 sliver + maroon - *06*	8	11
NR-60J	**'Peco 1946-2006'** 606060 sliver + blue - *06*	9	12

W11. BRT Bulk Grain Wagon (1969)

NR-11AC	**'Abbot's Choice'** - blue (NR-P67) - *69*	4	5
NR-P65	**'Dewar's'** blue - *?*	4	5
NR-66	**'Grain'** 7586 red-brown - *90?*	4	5
NR-P64	**'Grant's'** blue - *95*	4	5
NR-11JH	**'Haig'** blue (NR-P68) - *69*	4	5
NR-P63	**'Johnnie Walker'** blue - *05*	4	6
NR-P70	**'The Malsters Association of Great Britain'** yellow - *79*	4	5
NR-11WH	**'White Horse'** blue (NR-P69) - *69*	4	5

W12a. 14T Small Tank Wagon (1981)

NR-?	**'Berry Wiggins'** silver Sp Edn (N Gauge Society 35th Anniversary) - *02*	5	6
NR-P174A	**'Burmah'** 101 black - *09*	6	7
NR-P174B	**'Burmah'** 118 black - *09*	6	7
NR-P174C	**'Burmah'** 494 black - *not made*	NA	NA
NR-P174C	**'Burmah'** 111 black - *09*	6	7
NR-P173	**'Chemical & Metallurgical Corporation'** 36 maroon - *08*	6	8
NR-P161	**'Esso'** silver - *81*	5	6
NR-P176A	**'Highland Bitumens'** 1 black - *09*	6	7
NR-P176B	**'Highland Bitumens'** 2 black - *09*	6	7
NR-P176C	**'Highland Bitumens'** 4 black - *09*	6	7
NR-P162	**'National Benzole'** 256 buff - *84*	4	5
NR-P163	**'Royal Daylight'** red - *84*	4	5
NR-P170	**'Scottish Oil Agency'** * 462 red - *07*	5	7
NR-P170	**'Scottish Oil Agency'** * 474 red - *07?*	5	7
NR-P160	**'Shell/BP'** black - *81*	4	5
NR-P162	**'Shell/BP'** - *not made*	NA	NA
NR-P169	**'United Molasses'** 55, 61, 62, 68, 75 brown - *82*	4	5

* Based on a Hurst Nelson prototype.

W12b. Small Tank Wagon (with ladders) (1982)

With ladders either side.

Tank wagon 'Briggs' [W12b]

NR-P175A	**'Briggs Dundee'** 38 black - *09*	6	7
NR-P175B	**'Briggs Dundee'** 42 black - *09*	6	7
NR-P175C	**'Briggs Dundee'** 48 black - *09*	6	7
NR-P161	**'Esso'** 3060, 3061, 3064, 3067, 3069 silver - *03* *	6	7
NR-P168	**'Express Dairies'** dark blue or black Milk - *82* *	4	5
NR-P171	**'Shell Electrical Oils'** 2443 maroon - *07*	6	7
NR-P172	**'Shell Electrical Oils'** 2443 yellow - *07*	6	7
NR-P171	**'Shell Electrical Oils'** 2441 yellow - *07*	6	7
NR-P167	**'United Dairies'** white Milk - *82* **	4	5

* This model seems to have been released as '3061' in 2003 but had alternative numbers available by 2005. ** These were originally listed in 1981 as NR-162 and NR-163.

W13a. 15' Modern Tanker (end ladders) (ex-Minitrix) (1967)

These tanks were designed, tooled up and produced by Trix but the tooling was later taken over by Peco who tooled a replacement chassis which could also be used on other wagons.

NR-P75	**'Albright & Wilson'** MD22 light blue - *83*	4	6
NR1	**'BP'** 9675 white (NR-P50) - *67*	5	7
NR-P50	**'BP'** 9678 white - *81*	4	6
NR2	**'BP'** 1354 silver grey (NR-P51) - *67*	5	7
NR2	**'BP'** 9685 silver grey (NR-P51) - *67*	5	7
NR3	**'BP'** 1336 green (NR-P52) - *67*	5	7
NR-P52	**'BP'** 9685 green - *81*	4	6
NR-P4/52	**'BP'** 1348 green - *81*	4	6
NR-P4/52	**'BP'** 1354 green - *81*	4	6
NR-P4/52	**'BP'** 9689 green - *81*	4	6
NR4	**'BP'** 9678 black (NR-P53) - *67*	5	7
NR4/53	**'BP'** 9675 black (NR-P53) - *67*	5	7
NR-P4/53	**'BP'** 9689 black (NR-P53) - *67*	5	7
NR-P53	**'BP'** 9685 black - *81*	4	6
NR-P?	**'BP Chemicals/STS Leasing'** ? ? - *not made*	NA	NA
NR-P78A	**'Ciba Geigy'** ?? - *10*	NPG	NPG
NR-P78B	**'Ciba Geigy'** ?? - *10*	NPG	NPG
NR-P78C	**'Ciba Geigy'** ?? - *10*	NPG	NPG
NR-P76	**'Fina'** 2 silver - *03*	6	8
NR-P76	**'Fina'** 2,3, 4, 5 silver - *04*	6	8
NR-P74	**'Rugby Cement'** PR9435 grey - *83*	4	6

This wagon briefly appeared in the 1968/69 Atlas catalogue but probably did not materialise in the Atlas range.

W13b. 15' Modern Tanker (side ladders) (1982)

NR-P71	**'ICI Mond Div'** ICI M70801 dark grey - *82*	4	6

W13c. 15' Modern Tanker (no ladders) (1983)

NR-P79	**'Mobil LP Gas'** 57882 white - *83*	4	6

W14. Cattle Wagon (1971)

NR-45W	**GW** 13865 dark grey - *77*	3	4
NR-46A	**GW** 38622 dark grey Ale Wagon * - *09*	5	6
NR-46B	**GW** 38659 dark grey Ale Wagon * - *09*	5	6
NR-46C	**GW** 186461 dark grey Ale Wagon * - *09*	5	6
NR-45M	**LMS** 294528 light grey - *71*	3	4
NR-45E	**LNER** 4125111 red-brown - *99*	3	4
NR-45S	**SR** 53710 dark brown - *75?*	3	4
NR-45BA	**BR** B892080 brown - *08*	5	6
NR-45BB	**BR** B893778 brown - *08*	5	6
NR-45BC	**BR** B892109 brown - *08*	5	6

* Supplied with barrels.

W15. BR Yellow Spot Banana Van (2010)

NR-P50a	**BR 'Fyffes'** B881234? brown - *10*	4	6
NR-P50b	**BR 'Fyffes'** B881061 brown - *10*	4	6
NR-P50c	**BR 'Fyffes'** B881234? brown - *10*	4	6

W16. BR Pallet Van (lwb) (1968)

NR-8A	**'Army'** 41000 dull green - *68*	3	4
NR-P54	'Army' 41000 dull green - *76?*	6	8
NR-8F	**'Ford'** blue - *69*	4	5
NR-P55	**'Ford'** dark blue revised livery - *76*	3	4
NR-P56	**'Izal'** B782357 bright green - *79*	3	4
NR-8B	**BR** B787067 brown - *68*	4	5

This wagon briefly appeared in the 1968/69 Atlas catalogue but probably did not materialise in the Atlas range.

W17. Twin Ventilated Box Van (1971)

NR-P131	**'Bass'** 13 dark grey - *75*	3	4
NR-P135C	**'BPCM'** 112 orange-brown - *09*	5	6
NR-P135A	**'BPCM'** 124 orange-brown - *09*	5	6
NR-P135B	**'BPCM'** 143 orange-brown - *09*	5	6
NR-P133	**'Express Dairy Eggs'** 153398 black - *08*	5	6
NR-P134	**'ICI Salt'** 2300 red - *08*	5	6
NR-P136N	'JW **Stuart'** ? brown - *10*	5	6

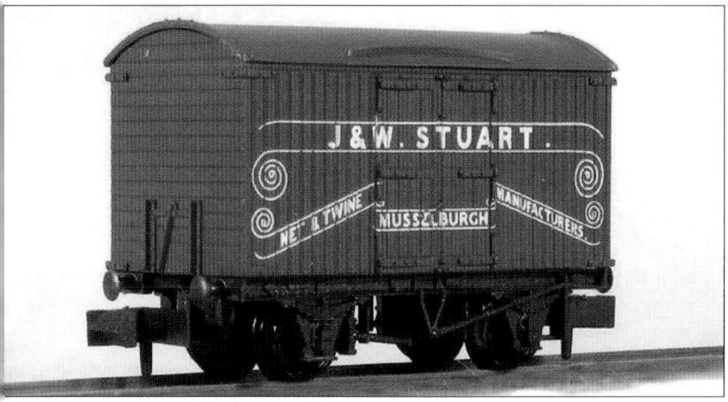

Ventilated van - 'J.W.Stuart' [W17] (Peco)

NR-P130	**'Worthington'** 3 red-brown - *72*	3	4
NR-43W	**GW** 100418 dark grey - *71*	3	4
NR-43M	**LMS** 291859 light grey - *77*	3	4
NR-43E	**NE** 15216 brown - *71*	3	4
NR-43B	**BR** W11275 brown - *84*	3	4

W18. BR Fish/Parcels Van (lwb) (1968)

NR-6	**BR** E87000 white Fish (NR-6B) - *68*	3	4
NR-9	**BR** E87641 light blue Express Parcels (NR-9B) - *68*	3	4
NR-12R	**BR Railfreight** 200278 red+grey - *82*	3	4

This wagon briefly appeared in the 1968/69 Atlas catalogue but probably did not materialise in the Atlas range.

W19. Refrigerator Box Van (1971)

NR-P141	**'Colman's Mustard'** yellow - *73*	3	4
NR-P140	**'Fyffes Bananas'** yellow - *74*	3	4
NR-?	**'N Gauge Society'** white - *77*	5	8
NR-42E	**NE**151275 white - *71*	3	4
NR-42S	**SR** 50680 cream Banana Van - *73*	3	4
NR-42R	**BR Rft** 230307 red+grey VEA - *83*	3	4

* Early models are marked 'Refrigerator' while newer models are marked 'Ventilated Refrigerator'.

W20. LNER 10ft Brake Van (1972)

NR-49E	**NE** 157691 brown - *72*	3	4
NR-49E	**NE** 178595 brown - *not made?*	3	4

W21. LMS 10ft Brake Van (1972)

NR-48M	**LMS** 1675, 1875 grey - *72*	3	4

W22. MR 10ft Brake Van (1977)

Veranda one end and open platform the other.

NR-47	**MR** M521 grey - *77*	3	4

W23. BR(ER) 20T Brake Van (lwb) (1973)

NR-28E	**NE** 157691 brown - *73*	4	5
NR-28B	**BR** B952116 brown - *73*	4	5

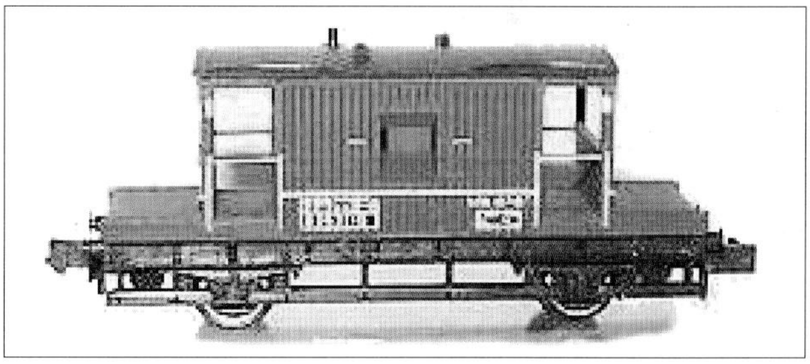

BR brake van [W23]

NR-28R	**BR Rft** B954673 red+grey CAR - *91*	4	5
NR-28C	**BR Eng.** DB953053 grey+yellow - *07*	6	7

W24. Freightliner Container Flat

This was illustrated in April 1968 but no further information about it has been found.

NR-?	**BR** flat with 3 20' BRe Freightliner containers - *made?*	NPG	NPG

Peco Wonderful Wagons 00 & TT

HISTORY

These were first advertised in 1954 with a review in the May 1954 issue of the *Railway Modeller*. The first batches used wooden sides and later ones had a full diecast body, with moulded plastic additions, to which the embossed cardboard sides are glued.

Apart from the later tank wagons, Peco Wonderful Wagons were available only as kits. One of the real attractions at the time they were first available was that the assembled models had sprung axleboxes. Although the idea is not considered sufficiently authentic for today's highly detailed models, at the time it was a good selling point. They also had pin point axles and were originally available with Dublo type finescale or the coarser Trix wheels. Peco couplings, as used on Dublo stock, were standard, although it is common to find wagons fitted with scale three link couplings.

1st series 7-plank wagon 'C&G Ayres' [W2]

The kits are no longer sold, but Peco are still selling off the stock of embossed sides. So, if you have a damaged, grubby or tatty wagon, it is possible to get a new side. However, it will be from a later printing and may not be exactly the same as that of the original wagon.

The wagons were produced in both 4mm and 3mm scale with 12 types in 00 and five types in TT. The wagons were mostly produced with private owner finishes and made a colourful train. At the time there was little in the way of private owner wagons produced in 4mm by the proprietary toy train and model makers and this was largely the reason for Peco's success. Indeed, it was to be many years before private owner wagons started to make their presence felt in the mainstream 00 market and that was with the arrival of pad-printing and Airfix and Mainline Railways in the mid 1970s.

The TT range of Wonderful Wagons was produced in response to Tri-ang's venture into the 3mm market. In addition to producing their own range, Peco bought-in moulded Tri-ang TT plastic wagon bodies from Rovex to fit to their own more detailed chassis.

Beware Of - It is easy to stick other wagon-side papers onto a Peco wagon and there are a number in circulation which are causing confusion. The non-authentic 'Charles and Diana' wagon was produced by Peco but some very attractive ones carrying printed paper sides, such as 'Dorchester Gas', 'Dutton Massey' and 'Wadworths', were produced by Collett in the early 1970s.

00 WAGONS

'W' after the colour means 'weathered' but in this case the printing often includes signs of wagon repairs.

Cat No.	Company, Number, Colour, Dates	£	£

1st Series Wagons

These kits had wooden body sides on a diecast floor.

W1. 5-plank Open Wagon (1957)

R60/1B	**'Beswicks'** 191 white - *57-61*	5	10
R60/1R	**'Black Rock Quarries'** 47 black - *57-61*	5	10

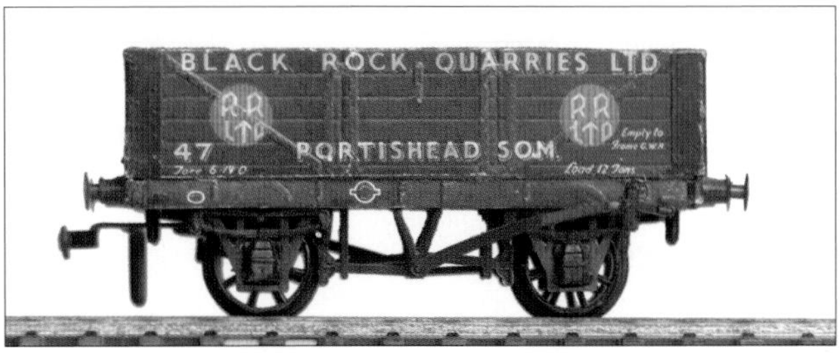

1st series 5-plank - 'Black Rock Quarries' [W1]

R60/1E	**'Ellis & Everard'** 220 yellow - *57-61*	5	10
R60/1C	**'English Clays'** 303 red-brown - *57-61*	5	10
R60/1F	**'Forest Rock'** 71 light grey - *57-61*	5	10
R60/1S	**'Sussex Brick'** 4 red-brown - *57-61*	5	10

W2. 7-plank Coal Open Wagon (end door) (1954)

R50/4 with Dublo wheels and R51/3 with Tri-ang wheels.

R50/1A	**'C&G Ayres'** 555 green+yellow - *54-60*	4	9
R54/5A	'C&G **Ayres'** 555 green+yellow W - *54-60*	5	10
R50/1C	'W **Craven Llewelyn'** 105 red-brown - *54-61*	4	9
R50/1D	**'Devlins'** 14 light green - *54-60*	4	9
R50/1H	**'Hickling**' 2824 buff - *54-61*	4	9
R50/1P	**'Parkend**' 330 black - *54-61*	4	9

W3. 7-plank Coal Open Wagon (side doors only) (1954)

Wooden body sides on a diecast floor. R52/6 with Dublo wheels and R53/7 with Tri-ang wheels.

R52/3J	'Frank **Jackman'** red-brown - *54-61*	4	9
R52/7J	'Frank **Jackman'** red-brown W - *54-60*	5	10
R52/3P	**'Peterborough Co-op'** 137 grey - *54-61*	4	9
R52/3S	**'Shelley'** 21 light yellow - *54-61*	4	9
R52/3T	'Wm **Tickle'** light green - *54-61*	4	9
R52/3W	'Richard **White'** blue - *54-61*	4	9

W4. Salt Van (1956)

Card roof. R58 with Dublo wheels and R59 with Tri-ang wheels.

R58/9C	**'Chance & Hunt'** 171 red-brown * - *56-61*	6	12
R58/9M	**'Mangers'** 181 green - *56-60*	5	10

1st series salt van 'Sifta Salt' [W4]

R58/9A	**'Saxa Salt'** 251 yellow - *56-61*	5	10
R58/9F	**'Sifta Salt'** 110 bright blue - *57-60*	5	10
R58/9S	**'Stafford Salt Works'** C25 red - *56-61*	5	10

* hard to find in original condition as the brown fades to orange with time.

2nd Series Wagons

Introduced in 1960, these had an all diecast body.

W5. 'Conflat' (1963)

R64	**BR** B735770 brown - *63-86?*	4	8

W6. Private Owner Containers (1963)

Card kits. All had grey roofs.

R66C	**'Cross & Blackwell'** brown - *63-89?*	2	4
R66F	'IC **Fuzzey**' brown+cream - *63-86?*	2	4
R66(J)L	**'Lyons Tea'** dark blue - *63-*	2	3
R66R	**'Raleigh'** bright green - *63-*	2	3
R66SC	**'Silver Cross'** deep blue - *68-*	2	3
R66BR	**BR** brown - *68-*	2	3

W7. 3-plank Wagon (1960)

10' wheelbase underframe and all diecast body (early examples has a folded card body). R62/3 with Dublo wheels and R63 with Tri-ang wheels.

R62/3BC	**'Blarnavon Company'** 502 brown - *64-78*	3	7
R62BQ	**'BQC'** 333 red - *63-86?*	3	7
R62FM	**'Field & MacKay'** 4 brown - *69-86?*	4	8
R62PG	**'Pwllheli Granite Co.'** black - *64-86?*	3	7
R62/3W	**GWR** 109458 dark grey - *60-78*	4	8
R62/3M	**LMS** 296254 light grey - *60-78*	4	8
R62/3E	**LNER** 103693 brown - *60-78*	4	8
R62/3S	**SR** 39010 dark brown - *60-78*	4	8
R62/3BF	**BR** M29337 red-brown - *60-78*	4	8

2nd series SR 3-plank wagon [W7]

R62/3BU	**BR** W109446 grey - *60-78*	4	8

W8. 5-plank Mineral Wagon (1962)

R70B	**'Bibbington'** 214 buff - *77-85*	3	7
R70C	'Joseph **Cole**' 5 chrome yellow - *62-78*	3	7
R70DS	**'Derbyshire Stone'** 2100 black - *69-85*	3	6
R70DN	**'Dixon'** 210 red-brown - *76-85*	3	7
RW70D	**'Dixon'** 210 red-brown W - *79-85*	3	7
R70D	**'Charles Dunsdon'** 21 dark green - *63-85*	3	6
R70G(W)	**'Garswood'** blue X259 - *66-85*	3	6
RW70G(W)	**'Garswood'** blue X259 W - *79-85*	4	8
R70?	**'General Refractories** - *not made*	NA	NA
R70AG	'A **Gresley & Co.**' 7 red-brown - *64-78*	3	7
R70L	**'Logan Sons & Co.'** 295 maroon - *66-78*	3	7
R70M	**'Mendip Mountain Quarries'** 238 grey - *62-85*	3	6
R70T	**'Tarmac'** black - *65-85*	3	6

W9. 7-plank Coal Open Wagon (1962)

Plastic side extensions.

RW54A	**'Anderson & Co.'** brown W - *81-85*	5	9
R54B	**'Baddesley'** 1311 black - *62-85*	3	6
R54C	**'Cliffe Hill Granite Co. Ltd.**' 530 red - *62-78*	3	7
R54DV	**'Dearne Valley'** 64 blue - *65-78*	3	7
R54E	**'Emlyn'** 941 dark green - *69-78*	3	7
RW54E	**'Emlyn'** 941 dark green W - *77-85*	3	7
R54H	**'Hood & Son'** 3 deep green - *79-85*	3	7
R54K	**'Kingsbury'** 710 green - *63-85*	3	6
R54M	'S **Moseley & Son'** 57 light grey - *69-78*	3	7

2nd series 7-plank wagon [W9]

RW54M	'S **Moseley & Son'** 57 light grey W - *79-85*	3	7
R54N	**'Newbattle'** 37 black - *76-85*	3	7
R54P	**'Pinxton'** 921 black - *74-85*	3	7
R54TJ	'T **Jenkinson & Sons'** black - *64-78*	3	7
R54W	**'Ward & Son'** 12 brown - *66-78*	3	7

W10. Lime Wagon (1963)

Grey plastic roof moulding with side extensions

R68C	**'Crawshay Bros.'** 136 buff - *63-85*	3	6
R68D	**'Dowlow Lime'** 141 red-brown - *63-80*	3	7
RW68D	**'Dowlow Lime'** 141 red-brown W - *81-85*	4	8
R68S	**'SLB'** 702 grey - *72-85*	3	7

2nd series lime wagon - 'South Wales Lime & Portland Cement Co' [W10]

R68SW	**'South Wales Lime & Portland Cement Co.'** 60 white - *66-85*	3	6

W11. Salt & Grain Wagon (1968)

Plastic roof moulding and side extensions. Dark grey roof.

R58ICI	**'ICI Salt Division'** 3784 blue - *68-85*	3	7
R58LW	**'Leith General Warehousing'** 97 brown - *76-85*	5	9
R58SX	**'Saxa Salt'** 251 yellow - *69-85*	3	6
R58H	**'Shaka Salt'** 166 bright blue - *72-85*	3	7
RW58SH	**'Shaka Salt'** 166 bright blue W - *81-85*	5	9
R58SS	**'Stafford Salt Works'** C25 red - *69-85*	3	7
R58US	**'Union Salt'** 2714 light grey - *68-85*	3	6

W12. Box Van (1966)

Plastic roofs with plastic body side extensions..

R72B	**'Bass'** 13 grey - *69-85*	3	6
R72BC	**'Blue Circle Portland Cement'** 177 yellow - *69-85*	3	7
RW72BC	**'Blue Circle Portland Cement'** yellow W - *79-85*	4	8
R72C	**'Colmans Mustard'** yellow - *66-85*	3	6
R72CK	**'Carricks'** 181 black - *72?-85*	3	7
R72F	**'Fyffes Bananas'** yellow - *68-85*	3	6
R72Z	**'Izal'** green - *66-78*	3	6
R72S	'J&W **Stuart**' brown - *69-85*	3	6

2nd series van - 'Worthington' [W12]

R72W	**'Worthington'** 3 brown - *69-85*	3	6

3rd Series Wagons

W13.	**Petrol Tank Wagon** (1968)		
R74BP	**'BP'** 6507 grey - *68-85*	4	7
R74E	**'Esso'** 2060 silver - *68-85*	4	7
R74S	**'Shell/BP'** silver - *not made*	NA	NA
R74S	**'Shell'** grey - *68-85*	4	7
W14.	**Milk Tank Wagon** (with ladders) (1990)		
With ladders either side.			
R74E	**'Express Dairies'** black - *90-*	4	5
R74U	**'United Dairies** black' - *90-*	4	5

4th Series Wagons

W15.	**Tank Wagon** (with ladders) (1989)		
R75RD	**'Royal Daylight'** red - *89-*	4	5
R75S	**'Shell BP'** black - *89-*	4	5

Scalecraft Kits

W16.	**Roadrailer** (1960)		
Manufactured by Scalecraft but distributed by Peco.			
R101	Kit No.1 - road tractor, adapter bogie and box van - *60-76*	20	35
R102	Kit No.2 - box van only - *60-86?*	12	25
R103	Kit No.3 - road tractor and adapter bogie only - *60-76*	12	25

TT WAGONS

Cat No.	Company, Number, Colour, Dates	£	£
W17.	**'Conflat'** (1968)		
S74	**BR** brown - *68-75*	4	8
W18.	**Private Owner Containers** (1968)		
S75	**BR** brown - *68-75*	2	4
W19	**3-plank Wagon** (1962)		
S62G	**GWR** dark grey - *62-75*	5	9
S62L	**LMS** light grey - *62-75*	5	9
S62NE	**LNER** red-brown - *62-75*	5	9
S62S	**SR** dark brown - *62-75*	5	9
S62BG	**BR** grey - *62-75*	5	9
S62BR	**BR** red - *62-75*	5	9
W20	**5-plank Open Wagon** (1st Series) (1958)		
S60B	**'Beswick Lime Works'** white - *58-63*	5	9
S60R	**'Black Rock Quarries'** black - *58-63*	5	9
S60E	**'Ellis & Everard'** yellow - *58-63*	5	9
S60C	**'English Clays'** red-brown - *58-63*	5	9
S60F	**'Forest Rock Granite'** light grey - *58-63*	5	9
S60S	**'Sussex Brick Co.'** red-brown - *58-63*	5	9
W21.	**5-plank Open Wagon** (2nd Series) (1964)		
S70C	'Joseph **Cole & Sons Ltd'** chrome yellow - *64-75*	5	9
S70AG	'A **Gresley & Co.'** red-brown - *69-75*	5	9
S70M	**'Mendip Mountain Quarries'** dark grey - *64-73*	5	9
W22.	**7-plank Coal Open Wagon** (1962)		
S54B	**'Baddesley'** black - *62-72*	5	9
S54CH	**'Cliffe Hill Granite Co. Ltd'** bright red - *62-75*	5	9
S54K	**'Kingsbury'** green - *63-75*	5	9

Tri-ang TT Plastic Wagon Bodies on Peco Chassis

W23.	**Lime Wagon**		
S?	**'Crawshay'** buff - *not made*	NA	NA
W24.	**Steel Low-Sided Wagon** (1959)		
S67	grey - *59-74*	5	7
W25.	**Steel Mineral Wagon** (1959)		
S65	grey - *59-74*	5	7
W26.	**Cattle Van** (1959)		
S66	brown - *59-74*	5	7
W27.	**Goods Van** (1959)		
S64	grey - *59-74*	5	7

Bachmann Class A2 Bachelors Button from computer artwork by Robbie McGavin

Playcraft Car Carriers

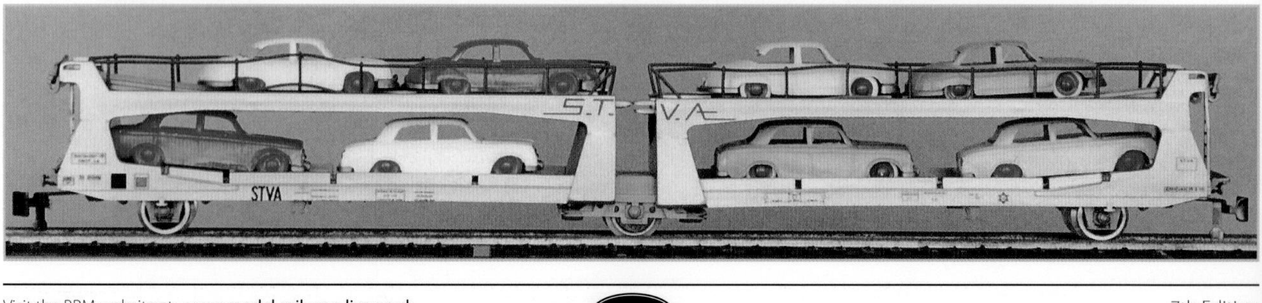

Playcraft

HISTORY

The Playcraft trademark was owned by Mettoy of Northampton, who also owned Corgi Cars and distributed Canadian Aurora plastic kits in the UK.

Although never developed into a major British range, the appearance of this 12 volt 2-rail system in the market in 1961 worried Britain's major model railway manufacturers at the time. The reason: its price! Advertised as 'Build that Big Layout for a Small Price', Playcraft was the cheapest mass-produced electric railway system yet seen.

Milestones

1961 Launch by Mettoy of Jouef models under the Playcraft label at the 1961 Toy Fair.
1961 First sets available for Christmas.
1961 Class 29 released.
1963 Playcraft sets with track-mats are advertised.
1963 Diesel shunter released.
1963 TPO released.
1967 Release of the Kangourou.
1968 The year of the last catalogue.
1969 Last UK price list.
1970 Only French models available.
c1975 A late batch of Class 29 diesels is available.
1995 Jouef bought by the Rivarossi/ Lima Group.
2004 Hornby acquire the Jouef brand name and tooling.
2008 Hornby acquire the Mettoy name with the purchase of Corgi Classics.

Throughout the 1950s, the competitive British market, led by Tri-ang Railways, offered comprehensive model railway systems at very attractive prices, but from 1961 the new Playcraft range cut the cost of 'getting started' even further.

BR Class 21 diesel [L3]

Sold mainly through FW Woolworths, Mettoy were clearly interested in the beginner's market and offered starter sets at £1 each. As a result, two of the major players at the time responded with cheap starter sets of their own and Playcraft's expansion of British models was contained.

Playcraft was first used on a re-badged version of the Aurora model highways systems, but was quickly applied to the new railway range and the Aurora kits. Most of the railway models were made in France by Jouef, although elements were also produced by Brawa, Pola, Aurora and at the Mettoy plant at Forest Fach in Wales. To give maximum flexibility, the range was scaled at 3.5mm/ft, H0 scale. Some British outline wagons were nearer to 4mm/ft, as were the British designed accessories such as an excellent signals kit. It is also true that many of the models were based on French and other Continental prototypes.

Playcraft Railways was launched at the 1961 Toy Fair with the first sets being available by the following Christmas. Throughout their life a mixture of Playcraft Railways and Jouef boxes were used. Larger sets such as the Kangarou and Cockerill crane used standard Jouef packaging with English instructions on a card insert. Production of the British models continued quite actively up until the end of 1968, after which there seems to have been a general run-down so that, by the end of the decade, only models of French prototypes were being offered.

This, however, was not the end of the British range. In the early 1970s an unattractive clockwork version of the Class 29 diesel, fitted to a rigid 4-wheel chassis was produced.

in the 1990s, Jouef fell on hard financial times and went into liquidation. It was bought by the Rivarossi/Lima Group in 1995 and when that group went into liquidation in 2004, the name and tooling was acquired by Hornby. Four years later the Jouef and Mettoy names were reunited when Hornby purchased the intellectual assets of Corgi Classics.

The Playcraft name lived on into recent times with a cheap plastic push-along train sets marketed by Child Guidance Toys of Mettoy-Playcraft (Sales) Ltd of London. This must have been well priced as it sold very well, particularly through mail order catalogues.

Further Reading

We know of no books specifically about the Playcraft range but there was a series of articles in *Model Railway Collector*: Volume 7 Nos. 3 and 4 (March and April 2000).

Playcraft packaging

Couplings - Playcraft models may be found with three types of coupling. The earliest type, known as 'Lanal', were original Jouef couplings, similar to a type used by Tri-ang. From around 1963/64, the Peco design, used for Hornby-Dublo and Trix models, were fitted to Playcraft stock. After 1968, stock began to appear with European lifting bar couplings as fitted to Jouef items. Despite this, Jouef were using Lanal couplings on starter sets as late as the 1980s.

Numbering - Early models were numbered with a 'PR' prefix which, by 1964, had been reduced to just 'P'. For simplicity, we have dropped the 'R' and given all the models a 'P' prefix.

Dates - These are the dates that the models first appeared in British catalogues.

Listing - The locos are listed in order of size, starting with tank engines' followed by tender locos and ending with diesels, electrics and multiple units. The coaches are listed with pre-Nationalisation stock first followed by vehicles of later years. Wagons are listed in the order of: flats, open wagons, hoppers, tanks, vans, brake vans and bogie stock.

LOCOMOTIVES

Cat No.	Company, Number, Colour, Dates	£	£
L1.	**Continental Tank 0-4-0** (1961)		
Early models had silver wheels and later ones had red ones.			
P535	**708** BRc green clockwork - *61*	5	10
P535	**708** BRc green electric - *61*	7	15
P535	**708** BRc black clockwork - *61*	5	10
P831	**708** BRc black electric - *61*	7	15
-	**708** BRe red clockwork from a set - *69*	10	NA

L2. Diesel Shunter 0-4-0 (1964)

Based on a North British diesel hydraulic shunter of 1953 design.

P838	**D2705** green no decals hazard stripes - *64*	25	30
P8381	**D2705** BRe blue hazard stripes - *68*	35	40

BR 0-4-0 diesel shunter [L2]

P536	**D2705** green clockwork no decals - *64*	12	22
P?	**D2705** brown no decals - *?*	75	NPG

L3. Classes 21/29 Diesel Bo-Bo (1961)

Based on a North British diesel electric locomotive. It had 8-wheel drive from a centrally mounted motor and was powerful. The Class 21s did not make it into blue livery but the identical looking Class 29 locomotives did.

P837	**D6100** BRc green - *61*	10	30
P8371	**D6100** BRe blue - *68*	12	35
-	**D6100** BRe blue from sets clockwork with 4 wheels only * - *70*	10	NA
J8911	**D6100** BRe blue raised detail 4-wheel drive in new chassis Sp Edn (Tonbridge Wells Model Shop) ** - *75*	15	NA

* Partnered with SNCF day cars re-branded as BR buffet and composite coaches, it was sold as a starter set. Similar treatment befell the SNCF BB66150 diesel, this time matched with bright red ex-SNCF coaching stock. ** The 1976 Jouef catalogue shows the Class 29 (D6100) but now fitted with Continental couplings. This was a retooled version using a later Jouef M20 motor driving one bogie only. The bogies were from a German Bo-Bo electric model. All exterior detail was on raised mouldings, including numbers and BR arrows. Re-branded ex-SNCF day cars were matched with it, given correct BR Mk1 numbers for a buffet, brake 2nd and Composite!

L4. Continental Locos sold as Playcraft

cc = closed cab. oc = open cab.

P828	**SNCF** 2-8-0 green - *68*	20	40
P828	**SNCF** 2-8-0 black - *68*	20	40
P829	**SNCF** 0-8-0 tank green cc - *67*	20	35
P829	**SNCF** 0-8-0 tank black cc - *67*	20	35
P830	**SNCF** 0-8-0 tank green oc - *67*	20	35
P830	**SNCF** 0-8-0 tank black oc - *67*	20	35
P836	**Nord** Type 231C green Pacific' - *63*	20	35
P836	**Nord** Type 231C black 'Pacific' - *63*	20	35
P836	**Nord** Type 231C brown 'Pacific' tender drive - *63*	40	55
P840	**SNCF** 0-4-0 diesel shunter - *65*	15	25
P841	**SNCF** BB67001 Class diesel - *65*	12	28
P842	**SNCF** BB13001 Class electric - *65*	20	45
P843	**TEE** CC40101 electric - *65*	20	40
P852	**SNCF** 'Panoramic' railcar - *66*	15	35
P853	**SNCF** BB 66150 Class diesel - *66*	15	30
P854	**SNCF** CC 7107 Class electric - *66*	20	40
P855	**Dutch** 1308 electric - *67*	60	70
P856	**SNCF** CC70000 Class diesel-electric - *67*	15	35
P761	**Budd** stainless steel 2-car EMU - *67*	15	35

COACHES

The British coaches were rather short for Mk1s but a special feature was the early fitting of interiors. These were correctly a light timber colour and the restaurant car even had its kitchen detailed with printed self-adhesive stickers. Thus, the interiors were much better than those of Tri-ang Hornby, the main competitor at the time. By October 1963, a Royal Mail travelling post office set was being offered; the coach from the set also being available separately as well as a non-operating version. The four British Mk1s were issued in blue and grey livery during 1967 together with teak versions.

There were several Continental coaches sold in Playcraft packaging. These initial models had Lanal couplings but soon changed to the Peco type. The demand for the Continental stock in Britain is quite low, although the rare ones command premium prices. The 1969 price list shows two 'vintage' SNCF coaches. These would be rare if ever released in Playcraft boxes.

Cat No.	Company, Number, Colour, Dates	£	£

C1. Travelling Post Office (1963)

The model may be found with black or brown nets.

P454	**Royal Mail** W80300 operating TPO set red - *63*	10	15

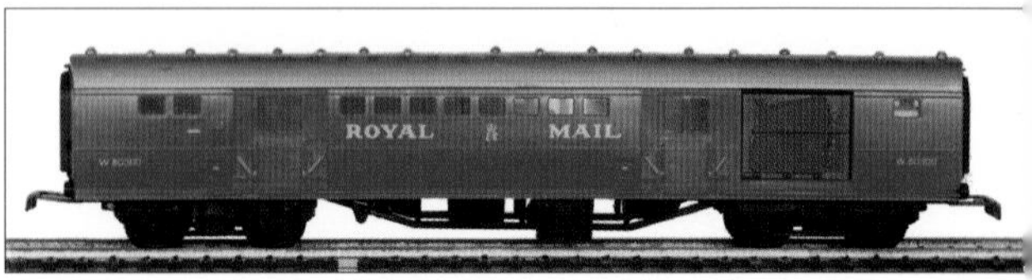

Royal Mail TPO sorting coach [C1]

P459	**Royal Mail** W80300 non-operating coach red - *63*	8	12

C2a. BR Mk1 Composite (1961)

?	teak - *67*	15	20
P337	**BR** S15021 green - *62*	5	7
P347	**BR** W15772 brown+cream - *62*	5	7
P457	**BR** 15100 maroon - *61*	4	6
P4571	**BR** S15021 blue+grey - *67*	10	15

C2b. BR Mk1 2nd Class Open (1962)

?	teak - *67*	15	20
P336	**BR** S4010 green - *62*	5	7
P346	**BR** W476?? brown+cream - *62*	5	7
P456	**BR** M6372 maroon - *62*	4	6
P4561	**BR** S4010? blue+grey - *67*	10	15

C2c. BR Mk1 2nd Brake Corridor (1961)

?	teak - *67*	15	20
P338	**BR** S35010 green - *62*	5	7
P348	**BR** W34060? brown+cream - *62*	5	7

BR Mk1 brake 2nd [C2c]

P458	**BR** 34060 maroon - *61*	4	6
P4581	**BR** S35010 blue+grey - *67*	10	15

C2d. BR Mk1 Restaurant Kitchen Car (1962)

?	teak - *67*	15	20
P335	**BR** S1720 green - *62*	5	7
P345	**BR** W172?? brown+cream - *62*	5	7
P455	**BR** 1701 maroon - *62*	4	6
P4551	**BR** S1720? blue+grey - *67*	10	15

C3. Continental Coaches sold as Playcraft

P866	**Budd** EMU centre car - *67*	8	12
P451	**SNCF** 1st class stainless steel - *63*	5	7
P452	**SNCF** standard 1st green - *63*	5	7
P453	**SNCF** standard composite green - *62*	5	7
P850	**SNCF** post office van brown - *63*	7	10
P4500	**STM** green vintage double deck French		

	suburban - *69*	20	30
P4501	**STM** green vintage French suburban - *69*	20	30
P864	**TEE** passenger coach - *64*	7	10
P865	**TEE** luggage/generator car - *64*	7	10
P8651	**TEE** luggage/generator car + lights - *64*	15	20
P460	**Wagon-Lits** luggage van blue - *63*	8	12
P860	**Wagon-Lits** dining car blue - *62*	7	10
P861	**Wagon-Lits** 1st class Pullman car - *62*	7	10
P862	**Wagon-Lits** 3933 sleeping car blue - *63*	7	10
P863	**Wagon-Lits** Channel ferry sleeper - *63*	7	10
P868	**Wagon-Lits** dining car red - *68*	15	20
P467	heating generator van blue - *68*	15	20

WAGONS

Although we tend to think of certain Playcraft wagons as being British, they were, in fact, based largely on French vehicles. The bogie wagons ran on American type diamond bogies typical of the TP stock supplied to France by the USA after the First World War. An attractive feature of those wagons that were supposed to represent British prototypes was the use of British Railways names for them such as 'Boplate', 'Weltrol' and 'Walrus' which were on printed data panel labels but later printed directly onto the side of the wagon. Look out for errors where wrong labels were applied.

The Continental wagons have limited appeal in Britain although the Kangourou set has tempted a number of British Railways stalwarts!

Cat No.	Company, Number, Colour, Dates	£	£

W1. Open Goods Wagon (1966)

This wagon had the name 'Tube' moulded into it. It also had brake gear. Versions made from 1969 were in Jouef boxes and had Continental couplings.

P631	**BR** B731490 bright yellow - *66*	10	12
P631	**BR** B731490 grey - *66*	4	6
P631	**BR** B731490 very pale grey - *66*	5	8
P631	**BR** B731490 red-brown - *69*	5	8
P631	**BR** B731490 dark brown - *69*	5	8
P631	**BR** B731490 grey - *69*	5	8

W2. Coal Wagon with Load (1961)

This was a Continental body and not the same as W1. Without brake gear.

P632	**SNCF** bright green - *61?*	5	NPG
P632	**SNCF** maroon + black load - *61?*	5	7
P632	**SNCF** maroon + grey load - *62*	7	9
P632	**SNCF** maroon + brown load - *62*	8	10

W3. 24.5T Open Mineral Wagon (1962)

P633	**BR** B280650 brown - *63*	10	12
P633	**BR** B280650 grey - *63*	4	6
P633	**BR** B280650 very pale grey - *63*	4	6
P632	**BR** B280650 yellow - *67?*	10	12
P632	**BR** B280650 yellow (Jouef) - *69*	10	12
P633	**BR** B280650 red-brown (Jouef) - *69*	8	10
P633	as above but green chassis - *69*	10	12

W4. Drop-side Goods Wagon (1962)

P634	grey - *62*	6	8
P634A	grey + ballast - *61*	6	8

W5. 13T Drop-side Wagon (1964)

These were also marked SNCF as crane riding wagons and were sold two to a set.

P644	**BR** B468400 or.brown + 3 tubes - *64*	5	7
P645	**BR** B468400 choc-brown with lugs + 2 maroon **BR** containers - *64*	7	9
P646	**BR** B468400 brown with lugs - *64*	4	6
P646	**BR** B468400 olive green with lugs - *64*	4	6

W6. European Open Goods Wagon (1965)

P623	**SNCF** green - *65*	8	10
P623	**SNCF** brown - *69*	8	10

W7. Twin Silo Bulk Cement Wagon (1964)

P642	**'Blue Circle'** B24 grey - *64*	4	6

'Blue Circle' twin silo bulk cement wagon [W7]

W8. Cereal Hopper (1965)

P647	**'Algeco'** SNCF 502134 grey - *65*	5	8

W9. Twin Barrel Wagon (1964)

P643	E762100 Wines from France red - *64*	5	7
P643	E762100 Wines light maroon - *?*	8	10

W10. Small Tank (1964)

P637	**'Butagaz'** - *?*	10	20
J639	**'Primagaz'** - *69*	10	20
P640	**'Shell BP'** 1608 silver - *made?*	NPG	NPG
P640	**'Shell BP'** 6010 silver - *64*	5	7
P636	**'Solonia'** - *?*	10	20

W11. Goods Van (with Sliding Doors) (1961)

P635A	bright green - *61?*	10	12
P635	maroon - *62*	4	6
P635	dark brown - *c67*	4	6

W12. French Mineral Water/Beer Van (1965)

P625	**'Evian'/'Badoit'** SNCF 506013 silv - *65*	6	8
P625	**'Evian'/'Evian'** SNCF 506013 silver - *?*	15	20

French van - 'Badoit' [W12]

P627	**'Heineken'** Nederland NS280785 - *67*	12	15
P626	**'Kronenbourg'** SNCF 506015 red - *65*	6	8

* Variations include two sizes of the name 'Kronenbourg' and different data panels.

W13. European Goods Van (1967)

P624	**SNCF** 337557 brown * - *67*	8	10
P6241	**SNCF** 337557 brown with lights - *67*	10	12

* This was also used as a 'conversion' van with an Peco type coupling on one end and a Tri-ang type on the other end.

W14. European Goods Wagon (with Sliding Roof) (1965)

P622	**SNCF** grey - *65*	8	10

W15. BR 20T Standard Brake Van (1961)

P630	**BR** B951718 green ex sets - *61?*	10	12
P630	**BR** B951718 brown - *62*	4	6

W16. 30T Bogie Bolster Wagon (1962)

P655	**BR** B922768 dark grey + 3 logs - *62*	5	7
P659	**BR** B922768 dark grey + 3 cars - *63*	6	10

W17. 35T 'Weltrol' Well Wagon (1962)

P658	**BR** B900923 grey - *62*	4	6
P658.2	**BR** B900923 grey + brown transformer - *64*	5	7

W18. 12.5T 'Tierwag' Car Carrier (1962)

Both BR and SNCF versions exist.

P654	**BR** B909204 blue-grey + 6 cars - *64*	6	10

'Tierwag' car carrier [W18]

P654	**BR** B909204 black + 6 cars - *62*	6	10
P654	**BR** B909204 powder blue + 6 cars - *67*	12	15

W19. French STVA Artic Car Transporter (1967)

P6571	**SNCF** 2087 grey + 8 cars - *67*	15	20

W20. French 'Kangourou' Road Rail (1967)

P664	**SNCF** CIMT Algeco + CIMT Segi wagons + **'Calberson'** and **'Bailly'** trailers + Lorraine tractor - *67*	35	50
P665	Kangourou wagon + semi-trailer - *67*	10	15
-	**'TNTE'** trailer grey+green - *?*	NPG	NPG

W21. 42T 'Boplate' Bogie 3-plank Open Wagon (1962)

P652	**BR** B947147 dark grey - *62*	5	7

W22. 50T Bogie Open Wagon (1962)

P650	**BR** E451023 green - *62*	5	7
P650	maroon - *c65?*	5	7

W23. 40T 'Walrus' Bogie Hopper Wagon (1962)

Labels varied in their inscriptions. The two common ones are 'WALRUS 40 TONS DE992500' and 'TARE 25-3'

P657	**BR** DB992500 brown non-operating - *62*	4	6
P657	**BR** DB992500 grey non-operating - *62*	4	6
P660	**BR** DB992500 operating set - *64*	10	12
P661	**BR** DB992500 brown operating - *64*	4	6
P661	**BR** DB992500 grey operating - *64*	4	6

BR 'Walrus' bogie hopper wagon [W23]

P661	**BR** Tare 25-3 brown operating - *c67?*	4	6
P661	**BR** Tare 25-3 grey operating - *c67?*	4	6

W24. Short Bogie Tanker (1962)

P651	**'Shell'** 1608 silver - *62*	5	7

W25. Long Wheelbase Bogie Tanker (1969)

P6511	**'Butagaz'** 00744756 silver - *69*	15	25

W26. Long Wheelbase Bogie Cattle Van (1969)

P6531	**SNCF** 1900144 brown - *69*	15	25

W27. 10T Bogie Goods Van (with Sliding Doors) (1962)

P653	green - *62*	5	7
P653	brown - *64*	5	7
P653	**BR** 86512 green GUV - *c69?*	5	7

W28. 7T Bogie Refrigerator Van (1962)

P656	**'Stef'** white - *64*	6	8
P6564	**'Traffic Services Ltd'** 3880 white - *78-80*	6	8
P656	**BR** GUV 86512 white - *62*	5	7

W29. 85T 'Cockerill' Large Crane (1966)

P663	**SNCF** 559 grey Operating set - *66*	20	30

ACCESSORIES

There was a good range of accessories with the goods depot and engine shed being particularly popular. The shed was very similar to that offered in the Hornby Dublo range, but was bright red, and also had an extension set. Curiously it was described as having operating smoke vents! The girder bridge set was modelled on the Great Central Railway overbridge at Rugby and designed in the UK.

TRAIN SETS

There was quite a large range of train sets which took the names of famous stations and goods depots according to whether they were passenger or freight sets. In nice condition the more common sets (Clapham, Stratford, Broad Street and Snow Hill) sell for between £25 and £40. The sought after sets are, of course, the London-Paris Night Ferry in its original picture box, the operating crane train set and, interestingly, some of the later starter sets with vehicles in odd colours. Expect to pay around £70 for an early Night Ferry set with a black Nord Pacific. The prestigious Lakeside sets in good boxed condition can command a price of £200 or more.

Replica Railways

HISTORY

When General Mills decided to cease toy production in Europe, Dapol acquired the stock, intellectual assets and the former Airfix tooling from Palitoy. The tools for Palitoy's own Mainline Railways belonged to Kader of Hong Kong, their manufacturer.

Milestones

1984 Hayes approaches Kader regarding the use of the Mainline tools.
1985 Hayes goes to Hong Kong to visit Kader and work out a production plan.
1987 First catalogue released.
1987 B1 model is released.
1987 Kader buys Bachmann.
1989 Bachmann Industries Europe Ltd is formed.
1990 The 'Modified Hall' is released.
1990 Bachmann Branchlines launched in UK and, with tools no longer available, Hayes withdraws from production in China.
1995 Replica Railways start producing injection moulded spares in the UK.
2003 Replica explore possibilities of UK manufacture of R-T-R coaches.

Godfrey Hayes of Replica Railways discovered that the former Mainline tools belonged to Kader and approached them in 1984 with a view to taking over the distribution of models made by them. In May 1985 Hayes was invited to Hong Kong to discuss the project.

A production plan was worked out and, in the autumn of 1985, the first sample wagons arrived. Advertisements were placed in the model railway press to launch the new range. Dapol, who owned the intellectual assets of the Mainline system were unhappy with the arrangement and a court case followed. Replica, however, weathered the storm, and more wagons and some coaches were available by Christmas. A steady stream of models appeared over the next few years.

Ex-GWR 'Hall' Class No.7911 Lady Margaret Hall [L3]

Godfrey Hayes set very high quality standards and every item brought in from the Far East was unpacked and inspected. After testing for running qualities and finish the models were repackaged in the green Replica boxes and rejects were returned to Kader.

In 1987, Kader took over the American toy company of Bachmann, for whom they were a primary manufacturer and this effectively signalled the end of the Replica range. In order to expand into Europe, Kader formed Bachmann Industries Europe and the former Mainline range became the core of their products for the British market. Kader could not manufacture for their new European company while at the same time produce models for a rival and so further access to the Mainline tools was denied Replica.

Following their the departure from manufacturing in China, Replica Railways concentrated on their range of spares, transfers and other miscellaneous accessories. The decision to produce ready-to-run models in the UK came about in 2003. They explored the cost and feasibility of producing a small production run of vehicles made from modifying their 'Chinese' Mk1 coach tools which they had brought back to the UK in 1998. The result of this experiment was a PCV. The success of the PCV was encouragement enough to look at what else they could produce.

At the time they identified a demand for Southern Region rolling stock and luckily had already researched what they thought were ideal subjects. The 63' BR suburban coach stock had actually been drawn-up ready to manufacture as early as 1992. With a little updating of the plans with currently demanded features, such as flush glazing, three different coaches were put into production.

The Class 419 motorised luggage van' (MLV) is another item they have in development. The motive power for the MLV is produced in the Far East but the bodies are moulded and tampo printed in the UK. They are assembled by Replica Railways in Swindon.

Further Reading

There has been a series of articles by Graham Smith-Thompson, in *Model Railway Collector* magazine (formerly *Model Railway Enthusiast*), profiling the Airfix and Mainline ranges and other systems that later used the tools. There were three parts devoted specifically to Replica Railways published in the December 1999 and January and February 2000 issues of the magazine.

Dates - As there were only two Replica catalogues, we have depended on press advertising to determine when models reached the shops. A single date has been given because Replica models were produced in batches. Generally there was only an initial batch of models which, when sold-out, was not repeated.

Listing - The locos are listed in order of size starting with tank engines followed by tender locos and ending with diesels. The coaches are listed with pre-Nationalisation stock first followed by vehicles of later years. Wagons are listed in the order of: timber open wagons, steel open wagons, hoppers, tanks, vans and brake vans.

Numbers - the running numbers were usually changed when a new batch of models was made.

LOCOMOTIVES

Cat No.	Company, Number, Colour, Dates	£	£
L1.	**GWR Class 57XX 0-6-0PT** (ex-Mainline) (1986)		
11001	**7768** GWR shirt button logo green - *86*	27	38
11003	**7752** GWR green - *88*	27	38

GWR Class 57xx 0-6-0PT No. 7752 [L1]

Cat No.	Company, Number, Colour, Dates	£	£
11002	**7843** BRc black - *88*	27	38
11002	**8743** BRc black - *88*	27	38
L2.	**GWR 'Collett Goods' 0-6-0** (ex-Mainline) (1989)		
	With a 'Manor' tender.		
11041	**2244** GWR green - *89*	30	40
11042	**2203** BRb black - *89*	30	40
L3.	**GWR 'Modified Hall' 4-6-0** (Mainline/Replica) (1990)		
	Production had reached the test-shot stage when Replica took it over. It was much improved by Replica and the tender completely retooled.		
11151	**6976 *Graythwaite Hall*** G()W green - *90*	43	48
11153	**6998 *Burton Agnes Hall*** G()W green as preserved - *90*	43	48
11152	**7911 *Lady Margaret Hall*** BRc green - *90*	43	48

L4. LNER Class B1 4-6-0 (partly ex-Mainline) (1987)

This was in an advanced stage of tooling when Mainline closed down and so the Replica models were the first to be produced from these tools. The resulting model reflected original Mainline quality and style rather than later production under the Bachmann label

11011U	as 11011 but no name or number - *88*	NPG	NPG
11012	**1000 *Springbok*** LNER green - *87*	44	50
11013	**1059** LNER lined black - *90*	42	50
11011	**61026 *Ourebi*** BRb black - *87*	44	50
11014	**61132** BRb lined black - *90*	42	50
11???	**61174** BRb lined black - *?*	42	50
11014A	**61264** BR lined black Sp Edn 300 (Steam World Magazine) - *93*	70	100
11014	**61132** BRc lined black - *90*	42	50

L5. BR 'Standard' Class 4 4-6-0 (ex-Mainline) (1990)

This has a separate chimney moulding and finer printing than the Mainline model. It also had a completely redesigned chassis with a can motor.

11031	**75019** BRb black lined Ltd Edn 750 - *90*	60	75
11032A	**75027** BR black? lined 2 mockups done then dropped - *92?*	NPG	400
11031	**75019** BRc black lined Ltd Edn 750 - *90*	60	75
11033	**75037** BRc black lined Ltd Edn 750 - *90*	60	75
11032	**75024** BRc green lined Ltd Edn 24 only - *90*	200	250

L6. Class 03 Diesel 0-6-0DS (ex-Mainline) (1987)

11021	**D2083** BRc green - *87*	26	36

BR Class 03 diesel shunter No.03189 [L6] (Replica)

11022	**03189** BRe blue - *87*	26	36

L7. Class 45/1 Diesel 1Co-Co1 (ex-Mainline) (1989)

Manufacture of the Replica model reflected original Mainline quality and style rather than later production under the Bachmann label.

-	unpainted grey, unnamed, unnumbered - *?*	45	60
11501U	blue unnamed, unnumbered * - *?*	45	60
11502	**45106** BRc green full yellow ends Tinsley plaque - *89*	27	38
11501	**45128** BRe blue - *89*	27	38

* Included was a Replica Railways sealed pack of alternative names, including *Zephyr*, *Apollo* and *Wyvern*, which were all unofficial names put on by Tinsley. Also included were Tinsley shed plates and a Tinsley motif in the form of transfers.

L8. Class 419 Motor Luggage Van (MLV) (2008)

The drive is being imported from the Far East but the body moulding and assembly is undertaken in the UK..

-	**BR(SR)** 680?? green - *08*	NPG	NPG

COACHES

Initially these reflected Mainline types but with different liveries and Commonwealth bogies on Mk1s. There were reruns of Collett and LMS 57' and 50' types but all had different fleet/stock numbers. New types produced included Mk1 corridor composite brakes, first opens and full brakes in various liveries. Most were developments of existing Mainline tools but the full brake was an entirely Replica model. The prices vary but the higher quality of Replica coaches is respected and they generally sell at higher prices than those from the Airfix and Mainline ranges. The appearance of the 'Bachmann' name on the underneath of the model can cause confusion.

Cat No.	Company, Number, Colour, Dates	£	£

C1a. GWR Collett Brake Comp (ex-Mainline) (1989)

This is the ex-Mainline model of a Collett 60' E159 brake composite coach.

12041	**GWR** 6356, 6544 brown+cream 1st/3rd brake - *89?*	12	18
12043	**BR** W6543? red+cream 1st/2nd - *91?*	12	18
12042	**BR** W6487W maroon 1st/3rd - *91?*	12	20

C1b. GWR Collett 3rd (2nd) (ex-Mainline) (1987)

This is the ex-Mainline model of a Collett 60' C77 all-third corridor coach.

12051	**GWR** 1087, 1116, 1137 brown+cream all 3rd - *87?*	12	18

Ex-GWR Collett 3rd class coach [C1b] (Replica)

12053	**BR** W1139 red+cream all 3rd - *89*	12	18
12052	**BR** W1098W maroon all 2nd - *89*	12	20
12053	**BR** W1087W maroon all 3rd - *89*	12	18

C2a. LMS Composite (ex-Mainline) (1989)

Based on a 1920s LMS 57' coach. Although the ex-Mainline, the roof was retooled to take separate vents. They also had rubber corridor connectors in place of the plastic ones.

12201	**LMS** 3621 maroon silver roof - *89*	12	18
12202	**BR** M3541M maroon, grey roof - *89*	12	18

C2b. LMS Brake 3rd (2nd) (ex-Mainline) (1989)

Based on a 1920s LMS 57' coach. Although the ex-Mainline, the roof was retooled to take separate vents. They also had rubber corridor connectors in place of the plastic ones.

12211	**LMS** 5270 maroon, silver roof - *89*	12	18
12212	**BR** M5334M maroon, grey roof - *89*	12	18

C3a. LMS Vestibule 3rd (mixed origin) (1990)

Stanier 1930s coach designed by Airfix and re-drawn by Palitoy and tooled by Kader but not produced. Replica re-drew the roof and Kader made it for them.

12221	**LMS** 9174 maroon all 3rd, silver roof - *90?*	15	20

C3b. LMS Open 2nd (1990)

Stanier 1930s coach.

12222	**BR** M9088M maroon 2nd, grey roof - *90?*	12	18

C4. LMS 50' Parcel Van (ex-Mainline) (1989)

12251	**LMS** 31239 maroon - *89*	10	15
12253	**BR** M31262M? red+cream - *89*	10	15
12252	**BR** M31293M maroon - *89*	10	15

Mk1 Stock

C5a. BR Mk1 Corridor 2nd (SK) (ex-Mainline) (1986)

12111	**BR** S25942 green - *86?*	12	18

BR Mk1 SK green No.SZ5942 [C5a]

12112	**BR I-C** M18753 Executive grey - *86?*	12	18
12113	**NSE** 18955 blue - *87?*	12	18

C5b. BR Mk1 Brake End (BCK) (mixed origin) (1990)

Developed by Palitoy for Mainline but not made. Altered by Replica and made for them by Kader. Replica purchased the tooling from Kader.

12147	**BR** M21076 red+cream - *90*	15	20
12141	**BR** S21263 green - *90?*	15	20
12144	**BR** W21243 brown+cream - *90?*	15	20
12146	**BR** E21086 maroon - *90?*	15	20
12145	**BR** M21268 blue+grey - *90*	15	20
12142	**BR IC** 21266? Executive grey - *90?*	15	20

C5c. BR Mk1 1st Open (FO) (mixed origin) (1990)

Developed by Palitoy for Mainline but not made. Altered by Replica and made for them by Kader. Replica purchased the tooling from Kader.

12137	**BR** M3024 crimson+cream - *90?*	15	20
12131	**BR** S3067 green - *90?*	15	20
12134	**BR** W3101 brown+cream - *90?*	15	20
12136	**BR** Sc3102 maroon - *90?*	15	20
12135	**BR** M3119 blue grey - *90?*	15	20
12132	**BR IC** 3114 Executive grey - *90?*	15	20

C5d. BR Mk1 Brake 2nd (BSK) (ex-Mainline) (1986)

12121	**BR** S34642 green - *86?*	12	18
12122	**BR I-C** M35454 Executive grey - *86?*	12	18
12123	**NSE** 35193, 35464 blue - *87?*	12	18

C5e. BR Mk1 Buffet/Rest't (RB) (ex-Mainline) (1986)

12101	**BR** S1717 green - *86*	12	18
12104	**BR** W1732 brown+cream - *89?*	12	18
12106	**BRc** M1646, M1714 maroon - *90?*	12	18
12106	**BR** M1676 maroon - *90?*	12	18
12102	**BR I-C** E1868 Executive grey - *86?*	12	18
12102A	**BR IC Charter** 1659 grey - *90?*	12	18

C5f. BR Mk1 Gangwayed Full Brake (BG) (1994)

Based on a 57' coach, designed by Replica and tooled by Kader. The are owned by Replica.

BR Mk1 BG No.M80725 [C5f] (Replica)

12167	**BR** M80725 red+cream - *94*	15	20
12173	**BR** E80654 red - *94*	15	20
12161	**BR** S80875 green - *94*	15	20
12164	**BR** W80664 brown+cream - *94*	15	20
12166	**BR** M80855 maroon - *94*	15	20
12167	**BR** M80725 maroon - *94*	15	20
12168	**BR** blue - *94*	15	20
12165	**BR** blue+grey - *94*	15	20
12169	**BR ScotRail** 92061, 92086, 92088, 92091, 92128 transfers grey+blue B4 bogies - *94*	15	20
12162	**BR** 92034, 92008, 92193, 92131, 92004 transfers **IC** Executive grey B4 bogies - *94*	15	20
12163	**NSE** blue - *94*	15	20
12171	**BR Provincial** Services 92317 blue+buff - *94*	15	20
12172	**RES** 92234, 92332, 92381, 95204 transfers red+dark grey plated windows - *94*	15	20
12170	**Post Office** 92207 92112 92124 92361 92220 92139 92179 transfers NEX red - *94*	15	20

C6. BR Propelling Control Vehicle PCV (2003)

UK production.

15002	**RES** (blue flash) supplied as transfers red+black - *03*	20	27

BR PCV in RES livery [C6] (Replica)

15001	**Post Office** 94303, 94338, 94322, 94332 supplied as transfers red+black - *03*	20	27
15000K	unpainted kit - *04*	20	25
15150	**EWS** maroon+yellow Ltd Edn pair 150 - *05*	50	65

C7a. BR Mk1 Suburban 3-Car Sets (2005)

The real 63' coaches were built at Swindon in 1956 and turned out in carmine livery. Later they were repainted green.

-	**BR(SR)** S41062 1st/2nd green	18	NA
-	**BR(SR)** S43379 brake 2nd green	18	NA
-	**BR(SR)** S43378 brake 2nd green	18	NA
12593	above three coaches as set 154 - *05*	NA	53
-	**BR(SR)** S41060 1st/2nd green	18	NA
-	**BR(SR)** S43374 brake 2nd green	18	NA

BR suburban 3-car set [C7a] (Replica)

-	**BR(SR)** S43375 brake 2nd green	18	NA
12591	above three coaches as set 152 - *05*	NA	53
-	**BR(SR)** S41061 1st/3rd crimson red	18	NA
-	**BR(SR)** S43376 brake 2nd crimson red	18	NA
-	**BR(SR)** S43377 brake 2nd crimson red	18	NA
12592	above three coaches as set 153 - *08*	NA	64

C7b. BR Mk1 Suburban Coaches (2005)

The real 63' coaches were built at Swindon in 1956 and turned out in carmine livery. Later they were repainted green.

12596A	**BR(SR)** S46280 1st/2nd green - *05*	18	20
12596B	**BR(SR)** S46283 1st/2nd green - *05*	18	20
12596C	**BR(SR)** S46297 1st/2nd green - *05*	18	20
12596D	**BR(SR)** S46298 1st/2nd green - *05*	18	20
12596D	**BR(SR)** S46298 1st/2nd green - *05*	18	20
?	**BR(WR)** W? 1st/3rd crimson red - *09*	18	22
?	**BR(WR)** W? brake 3rd crimson red - *09*	18	22
?	**BR(WR)** W? 1st/2nd maroon - *09*	18	22
?	**BR(WR)** W? brake 2nd maroon - *09*	18	22

WAGONS

Without a catalogue or check list, these are going to cause confusion in future years when they turn up unboxed. Chassis are to Airfix style with brakes in-line with the wheels and often carry the name Bachmann on their underside.

Cat No.	Company, Number, Colour, Dates	£	£
W1.	**1-plank Wagon** (ex-Mainline) (1990)		
13051	**LMS** grey + B container - *not made*	NA	NA
13101	**LMS** 13101 grey + brown container **'Pimm & Son'** - *90?*	7	9

LMS 1-plank wagon with 'William Whitely' container [W1]

13103	**LMS** 210401 grey + maroon container **'William Whiteley'** - *90?*	7	9
13052	**LNER** brown + B container - *not made*	NA	NA
13053	**LNER** brown + B container '**Frasers**' - *not made*	NA	NA
13101	**LNER** 203175 red-brown + dark brown container **'Pimm & Son'** - *90?*	7	9
13102	**LNER** 221104 red-brown + dark brown container '**H Timson & Sons**' - *90?*	7	9
-	**LNER** brown + yellow+blue container Sp.Edn. (**'Bristol Show'** - 25th Anniversary) - *93*	12	15

W2. 3-plank Wagon (ex-Mainline) (1989)

13301	**'Bath & Corsham Freestone Quarries'** 14 light grey - *89*	6	8
13302	'William **Neave & Son'** 6 grey - *89*	6	8
13303	**'Trimsaran'** 51 dark red - *89*	7	9

W3. 7-plank Wagon (ex-Mainline) (1985)

13204	'C & G **Ayres'** 530 green+yellow - *87*	6	8
13206	**'Bognor Coal & Transport** ' 4 red - *87*	7	9
13203	**'Diamond'** 34 red - *85?*	6	8
13207	**'Lambert & Cox'** 19 red-brown - *88*	6	8
13210	**'Llewellyn Brothers'** 203 dark brown - *90*	6	8
13211	'Thomas **Lockwood'** 108 grey - *90*	6	8
13202	**'Patent Nut and Bolt**' 658 brown - *85?*	6	8
13205	'F & E **Poole'** 200 light blue - *87*	8	10
13208	**'Renwick Wilton'** 658 black - *88*	6	8
13208	**'Renwick Wilton'** 521 maroon - *88*	6	8
13209	'Hugh **Wood**' 50 grey - *88*	7	9
13212	**'Stanton'** 9988 orange - *90*	7	9
-	**'Warley MRS 21st Exhibition'** yellow Sp Edn (Warley MRC) - *88*	12	15
13201	**GWR** 6515 grey - *85?*	4	6

W4. 9-plank Coke Wagon (ex-Mainline) (1989)

13351	**'Abbott'** 3606 black - *89*	6	8

9-plank coke wagon - 'Smokeless Fuels' [W4]

13353	**'Smokeless Fuels'** 232 black - *89*	6	8
13352	**'Suncole'** 5060 black - *89*	6	8

W5. 16T Steel Mineral Wagon (ex-Mainline) (1989)

13401	**BR** M621988 grey - *89*	4	6
13402	**BR** B569425 MCV brown - *89*	4	6

W6. 24T Hopper Wagon (ex-Mainline) (1989)

13411	**BR** B436872 1960s grey Iron Ore - *89*	5	7
13412	**BR** B437398 1970s grey Ore Hop - *89*	5	7

W7. 46T HEA/HBA Hopper (ex-Mainline) (1986)

14101	**BR** 360364 bauxite - *86*	6	8
14102	**BRe Railfreight** 360694 red+grey - *86*	6	8
14102	**BRe Railfreight** 361874 red+grey - *?*	6	8

HEA hopper wagon in Railfreight Distribution livery [W7]

14103	**Railfreight** revised livery - *86*	6	8
14103B	**Railfreight** - *88?*	6	8
14103C	**Railfreight** (**Coal**) 360711 black+yellow - *90?*	6	8
14103D	**Railfreight Distribution** 361579 black+yellow - *90?*	6	8

W8. 12T Tank Wagon (ex-Mainline) (1988)

13802	**'Esso Petroleum'** 3060 silver - *88*	8	10
13801	**'Shell Electrical Oils**' 3102 yellow - *88*	8	10
13801	**'Shell Electrical Oils'** 2443 yellow - *88*	8	10

W9. GWR 12T Fruit Van (ex-Mainline) (1989)

13601	**GWR** 134287 dark grey - *89*	6	8
13602	**BR** W134281 brown - *89*	6	8

W10. GWR 12T Ventilated Van (ex-Mainline) (1989)

13611	**GWR** 134065 dark grey - *89*	6	8
13612	**BR** W142051 brown - *89*	6	8

W11. GWR 20T 'Toad' Brake Van (ex-Mainline) (1989)

13551	**GWR** 58759 dark grey Worcester - *89*	6	8

W12. BR 20T 'Standard' Brake (ex-Mainline) (1987)

13502	**BR** DB951968 Departmental grey+yellow - *87?*	5	7
13503	**BR** B954603 brown+yellow air-piped - *87?*	5	7
13501	**BR Railfreight** B954978 grey+red - *87?*	5	7
13504	**BR Railfreight** B954835 grey+red air-piped yellow flash - *87?*	5	7

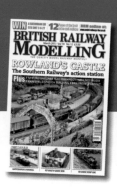

Rivarossi H0 (British)

HISTORY

Rivarossi, an Italian company, was started in 1945, later becoming part of the Lima Group.They had a good reputation for the quality of their models, which found a large market in America.

Along with a number of other Continental manufacturers, in 1977 Rivarossi decided to attempt a break into the British market. Failing to understand the importance of the scale difference, they produced their launch models in a scale somewhere between 00 and H0. The British market was almost completely 00 and so the models appeared too small alongside their British equivalents. Had they chosen 00 scale from the outset, they could have caused quite an upset. Instead, they withdrew and their stock of British models took many years to clear. Some were still in their catalogue in 1988.

Rivarossi is now part of Hornby International.

LMS 'Royal Scot' Class No.6140 Hector [L1] (Rivavossi)

LOCOMOTIVES

The one and only loco was announced at the 1977 Nuremberg Fair, but did not arrive until two years later.

It was made to mixed scales. The height and width were 1:80 scale and the length was 1:84 scale. However, the diameter of the wheels was 1:87 scale.

Cat No.	Company, Number, Colour, Dates	£	£
L1.	**'Royal Scot' Class 4-6-0** (1978)		
These were parallel boiler 'Scots'. Only *Hector* had smoke deflectors.			
1348	**6100 *Royal Scot*** maroon LMS - *78-80?*	30	50
1350	**6140 *Hector*** maroon LMS - *79?-80?*	40	60

COACHES

The coaches announced at the 1977 Nuremberg Fair were of a later Stanier design, looking like Hornby Dublo coaches, but the coaches that arrived in 1979 were earlier Reid panelled stock. All were stated to be used in the 'Royal Scot' train formation.

The 1st class coach was identified as being of 1928 build and we know that only 16 of that seating arrangement were made and not all were identical to the model.

The coaches came with two clip-in corridor end boards and replacement plug-in tension-lock couplings.

Cat No.	Company, Number, Colour, Dates	£	£
C1.	**Corridor Vestibule 1st** (1979)		
2932	**LMS** 15604 maroon - *79-80?*	NPG	NPG
2933	**LMS** 15933 maroon - *79-80?*	15	25
C2.	**Brake Corridor 3rd** (1979)		
2934	**LMS** 16100 maroon - *79-80?*	15	25
C3.	**Corridor 3rd** (1979)		
2931	**LMS** 14289 maroon - *79-80?*	15	25
2935	**LMS** 14299 maroon - *79-80?*	15	25
2935	**LMS** 14250 maroon - *79-80?*	15	25
2936	**LMS** 14520 maroon - *79-80?*	15	25

LMS panelled brake 3rd No.16100 [C2] (Rivarossi)

SETS

Only one set was made and this is a hard item to find. It consequently fetches as much as £230 in unused condition. The set contained *Royal Scot* and four LMS coaches.

Alessandro Rossi the founder of Rivarossi (died 2010)

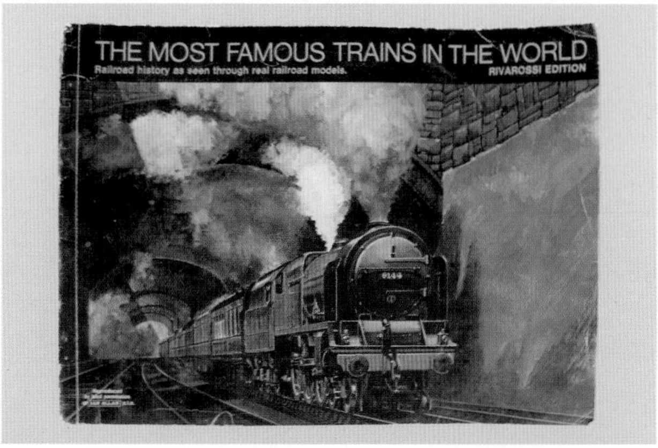
THE MOST FAMOUS TRAINS IN THE WORLD
Railroad history as seen through real railroad models.
RIVAROSSI EDITION

HORNBY®
DIGITAL
Hornby 'Elite' Digital Control
Attractive hand held or free standing unit
Connect up to 8 Walkabout 'Select' units for additional individual loco control
Multi-Function keyboard providing programming and functions for up to 254 locomotives and 255 accessories including points
Large no nonser LCD screen
The 'Elite' supp Short (1-127) Extended (128-9 Addressing
Simple to us press and rot controls
THIS PRODUCT CONFORMS T APPLICABLE NMRA STAND
The digital unit that puts you in control without the need for an electronics degree!
For more information visit: www.hornby.com
R1076 Virgin Trains Pendolino
R1097 East Coast Pullman
R1126 Mixed Freight
If you can use a TV remote then you can use the Elite.

Rovex Tri-ang Hornby

This section includes the model railway range started by **Rovex** in 1950, renamed **Tri-ang Railways** in 1952, again renamed in 1965 as **Tri-ang Hornby**, becoming **Hornby Railways** in 1972 and finally just **Hornby** in 1997. While the name changed several times, it remained one continuous system being made first at Richmond, then at Margate and now in China. It does not include Hornby Trains (0 gauge) or Hornby Dublo both of which were made in Liverpool by Meccano Ltd until train production there ceased in 1964.

Please note that the table numbers have been changed in this chapter to accommodate many new models.

HISTORY

Rovex Plastics Ltd was founded in 1946 by Alexander Venetzian who made toys for Marks & Spencers. Venetzian was asked to produce an electric train set based on the LMS express locomotive *Princess Elizabeth*. Needing more space for this project the company was moved from Chelsea to a disused brewery in Richmond. The train set was delivered in time for Christmas 1950 but financial limitations prevented further development. Meanwhile, the giant toy manufacturer Lines Bros. Ltd, who traded under the name 'Tri-ang', wanted to get into the post war model railway market. In 1951, Rovex Plastics Ltd. became a wholly owned member of the Lines Bros. Group. The trains would now be called Tri-ang Railways and the company renamed Rovex Scale Models Ltd. To aid development of the system, a brand new factory was built at Margate, in Kent, and production moved there in the Summer of 1954.

Demand from the public for new models was so great that in 1951 Rovex bought the tools of a goods train set made by Pyramid Toys Ltd. which they were selling under the name Trackmaster. This gave them an 0-6-2 tank engine, with a diecast body, and two wagons.

By farming out work to outside designers and tool makers, progress was made. The 'Jinty' 0-6-0T and a range of station buildings came in 1952 and a guards van and other wagons in 1953.

Almost immediately there was pressure on the young firm to produce for the export market and the first of a range of Transcontinental models, primarily for North America, was released in 1954.

Under constant pressure, the system expanded fast. 1955 saw the first real Tri-ang Railways retail catalogue which soon became the best in the UK. By 1956 there were 10 locomotives available and a good range of rolling stock and lineside buildings, etc. As if the existing pressure was not enough, in 1957 Rovex were pressed by Lines Bros. to start a TT gauge model railway system. A completely new 00 track system called Series 3 also arrived that year.

At around this time, in order to overcome trade tariffs, Lines Bros. Ltd. were expanding toy production overseas and Tri-ang Railways were soon being made for local markets in South Africa, Australia and New Zealand, creating interesting variations for future collectors.

1962 was a high water mark in the development of Tri-ang Railways. That year another new track system called 'Super 4' was introduced and along with it an extensive new series of station buildings.

There were now 25 locomotives to choose from (including two historical subjects), an extensive range of British and Transcontinental rolling stock, new scale length coaches had just been added, there was a catenary system, locos had Magnadhesion and smoke and the famous railway artist, Terence Cuneo, had been engaged to show how you could 'weather' your Tri-ang models.

Much of this growth was at the expense of other manufacturers and the two main rival systems, Trix and Hornby-Dublo, were feeling the draught. The former had already changed hands twice and, in 1964, Meccano Ltd, the manufacturers of Hornby-Dublo invited Lines Bros. Ltd to buy them out. Meccano Ltd. joined the Lines Bros. Group.

Hornby's Alfred the Great pulling the Bournemouth Belle from a computer artwork by Robbie McGavin

Milestones

1946 Venetzian founds Rovex Plastics Ltd.
1949 Pyramid Toys launch Trackmaster set.
1950 First Rovex train set in an M&S store.
1951 Lines Bros. buy Rovex Plastics Ltd.
1951 Trackmaster tools purchased by Lines.
1952 Tri-ang Railways launched in May.
1953 Renamed Rovex Scale Models Ltd.
1954 Move to purpose-built factory in Margate.
1954 Launch of Transcontinental Series.
1955 Production starts up in South Africa.
1956 First New Zealand made models in shops.
1956 Polystyrene replaces cellulose acetate.
1957 Australian production starts at Moldex Ltd.
1957 Launch of Tri-ang TT.
1959 Tension-lock couplings introduced.
1961 Tri-ang factory opens in Calais.
1961 Walter Lines retires.
1962 Major expansion of range including introduction of 'Super 4' track.
1963 Rovex absorb Real Estate kits and re-launch as Model-Land.
1964 Lines Bros. take-over Meccano Ltd.
1964 Lines turn down Lone Star buyout invite.
1965 Tri-ang Railways becomes Tri-ang Hornby.
1966 Lines Bros. turn down Trix buyout invite.
1966 Tri-ang Big Big 0 gauge trains launched.
1966 Rovex absorb Frog kit production.
1967 First models made for ATT of USA.
1967 Internal mergers form Rovex Industries Ltd.
1967 Rovex absorb Minic Motorway.
1969 Name changed again to Rovex Tri-ang Ltd.
1970 Finer scale adopted for track and wheels.
1971 Lines Bros. in receivership.
1972 Rovex bought by Dunbee-Combex-Marx.
1972 Tri-ang Hornby becomes Hornby Railways
1972 Death of Walter Lines.
1974 Tampo printing starts at Margate.
1976 Rovex International formed to export.
1976 Hornby Hobbies name first used.
1976 Hornby face Airfix/Mainline challenge.
1977 Frog and Big Big tools sent to Russia.
1979 H&M purchased and later absorbed.
1979 Hornby live-steam 'Rocket' in shops.
1980 DCM liquidates. Rovex in receivership.
1980 Paint finish adopted throughout range.
1980 Renamed Hornby Hobbies Ltd.
1981 Management buyout by Wiltminster Ltd.
1986 Hornby Group plc floatation.
1995 First model made by Sanda Kan in China.
1996 Hornby buy tools from Dapol Ltd.
1997 First former Airfix/Dapol model in shops.
1997 Hornby Collectors Club formed.
1998 Hornby Collectors Centres established.
1999 Last model made in the Margate factory.
2000 Hornby plc. invite buyers; later withdrawn.
2000 Rebuilt Merchant Navy released.
2001 Hogwarts Express released.
2003 Hornby announce record profits.
2003 Live Steam and the Skaledale range arrive.
2004 Special 50th Edition Catalogue released.
2004 Hornby buy Electrotren.
2004 Hornby buy the Lima Group.
2004 Hornby Italia formed.
2005 Lima Group and Electrotren production moved to China.
2005 Hornby France formed to buy MKD.
2006 Hornby buy Heico and form Hornby Deutschland.
2006 First former Lima models appear in Hornby range.
2006 Lyddle End range launched.
2007 Hornby buy Humbrol and Airfix.
2007 The 'RailRoad' budget range is launched.
2008 'SkaleAutos', 'SkaleScenics' and 'SkaleLighting' are launched.
2008 Hornby buy Corgi Classics, adding Bassett-Lowke to their portfolio.
2008 Hornby's principal manufacturer, Sanda Kan, is taken-over by Kader.
2009 Hornby look for alternative manufacturers in China to spread risk.
2009 Bassett-Lowke joins the Hornby catalogue.
2010 The first Corgi Lineside models appear in the Hornby SkaleAutos range.

By this time, production of Hornby-Dublo had already ceased but there were large stocks to clear. Under public pressure it was agreed to retain the Hornby name by renaming Tri-ang Railways, 'Tri-ang Hornby'. This was presented at the time as an amalgamation of the two systems, but the only additions this brought to the Tri-ang system were the E3000 (after extensive modification) and, for a brief period, the terminus station kit.

It is interesting to note that Lines Bros. were also invited to buy both Trix and Lone Star Treble-O-Lectric! On both occasions they declined.

Another subsidiary of Lines Bros., G&R Wrenn Ltd., put in a bid for the Hornby-Dublo tools and these were used to launch Tri-ang Wrenn in 1967. They also took over remaining stocks of Hornby-Dublo and Tri-ang Railways TT. Lines Bros. Ltd were under pressure to get into N gauge but chose instead to import the Lima system which they marketed through G&R Wrenn Ltd.

Trackmaster 0-6-2T [L18a] (Vectis)

The Tri-ang Hornby period will be best remembered for the change to blue liveries for modern stock, the introduction of pre-Nationalisation liveries for steam locomotives, the disappearance of the Transcontinental range, the appearance of 'Battle Space' and the introduction of exhaust noise. Memorable locomotives of this period include E3000, 'Hymek', Class 37, M7, 'Hall', *Flying Scotsman*, *Coronation* and, of course, *Evening Star*. Around 1970 Tri-ang Hornby went 'finescale' with a new track system and re-profiled wheels.

In 1967, Rovex Scale Models Ltd. had become the core of Rovex Industries Ltd. which was called the 'model division' and included Minic Ltd., Minimodels Ltd., Spot-On Ltd., Pedigree Dolls Ltd. and IMA Ltd. (Frog). It also had under its wing G&R Wrenn Ltd which was not a fully owned company. The division was renamed Rovex Tri-ang Ltd. in 1969.

Amongst other things, losses overseas saw the giant Lines Bros. Group in trouble. At their peak they had 40 companies world-wide. In 1971 the crash came when Lines Bros. Ltd called in the Receiver. The Group was broken up and sold off. The profitable Rovex Tri-ang Ltd was for a brief period called Pocket Money Toys Ltd and then sold as Rovex Ltd, with its factories at Margate and Canterbury, to Dunbee Combex Marx Ltd. (DCM). At this point it parted company with G&R Wrenn which had bought itself free and renamed its system Wrenn Railways. The name Tri-ang had been sold with one of the other companies and so a new name was required for the Tri-ang Hornby system. Hornby Railways was chosen and this took effect from January 1972.

The Princess Elizabeth of 1950 with 'Plunger' pick-ups [L54a]

The 1970s saw new challenges come from Airfix and Palitoy who both launched model railway systems which offered finer scale models. This, and pressure from Lima, forced Rovex Ltd to raise its standards. There was steady development of new locomotives (over 20 in all) including the A4, 'Footballer', 'King', 'Patriot' and 'Duchess'. New diesels included the HST which was to become a major money spinner. There was also a new range of regional coaches as well as BR Mk3s and these would serve the system for many years.

In 1980 DCM were in trouble and the ball was in the air once again. Hornby Hobbies Ltd., as it was now called, became an independent company through a management buyout, with the help of venture capital. On 29 October 1986, Hornby Group plc was floated on the Unlisted Securities Market and became a public company. By now both the GMR (Airfix) and Mainline (Palitoy) systems had ceased to be produced and this led to a new player, Dapol, entering the field and Lima getting a stronger toehold.

Changes taking place on British Railways brought new liveries thus offering more subjects to model. The demand for higher standards of modelling lead to a number of models being retooled and a search for ways to improve printing on models. In 1996, Hornby Hobbies purchased a number of tools from Dapol including several formerly used for the Airfix GMR system and a very small number of Mainline Railways origin. About this time, Hornby moved all their production to China and a company called Sanda Kan who are based at Kwai Chung in the Hong Kong New Territories.

In 2004, Hornby published the 50th edition of their model railway catalogue with a 16 page look back at previous editions by guest writer Pat Hammond. 2004 also saw a major expansion of the group which gave it greater international status. This started with a friendly take-over of Spain's leading model railway manufacturer, Electrotren, and the transfer of its production to China.

By the end of the year they had also bought the tools and intellectual assets of the Lima Group, giving Hornby ownership of the leading model railway brands in Britain, Italy, Spain and France as well as part of the German business and another important export line to America. The Lima assets included Lima, Rivarossi, Arnold, Pocher and Jouef.

Ex-SE&CR Class S Saddle Tank [L16]

While British outline models from the former Lima range were absorbed into the Hornby catalogue, reintroduced Continental models carry the original Lima, Rivarossi, Arnold and Jouef brand names; however, they are all now made in China. Hornby International was established to be the umbrella for these brands and Hornby Italia, Hornby France and Hornby Deutschland were formed to handle retailing in Italy, France and Germany. Through its Continental purchases, Hornby moved from being a model maker solely in 00 scale to one producing H0 and N scale models as well.

Two other smaller companies, MKD in France and Heico in Germany were acquired and became part of Hornby International. These were followed in Britain by the acquisition of Humbrol and its important subsidiary Airfix. The Hornby empire was further expanded in 2008 with the purchase of Corgi Classics which added more brand names such as Corgi, Lledo and Vanguard but also that of the great early model manufacturer - Bassett-Lowke.

Prior to this purchase, Hornby had entered into an agreement with Oxford Diecast who now supply Hornby with their own range of 00 scale diecast road vehicles branded SkaleAutos. With the purchase of Corgi Classics, Hornby now own the former Lledo Trackside and the Corgi OOC bus ranges, both of which are also compatible with Hornby Railways. In 2010, exclusive versions of some of the Corgi Trackside models started to appear in the Hornby SkaleAutos series, as well as one from the Lledo range. It will be interesting to see how these will be developed and what Hornby have in mind for Bassett-Lowke, which adds 0 gauge to the scales made by Hornby.

Since 1996, the privatised railways have brought a continuously changing selection of new liveries. Hornby Hobbies now has most of its models made by Sanda Kan which, following financial difficulties, became part of the Kader Group in 2008. The resin buildings are made elsewhere. Hornby are gradually upgrading their range.

With persistent criticism, by some model enthusiasts, of its cheaper low detail models produced for the toy market, in 2007, Hornby separated off most of these under the brand name Hornby RailRoad. This created an inexpensive range to encourage beginners into the market and made it clear that they were not intended to be finescale models.

For its British outline models, competition comes from Bachmann, using upgraded Mainline tools as well as new high quality tooling, and from Heljan of Denmark who more recently entered the UK 00 model diesel market. Another newcomer is ViTrains, a company formed in Italy by former Lima employees.

Hornby Hobbies recognises the important collectors' market and have established the Hornby Collectors Club and a chain of Collectors Centres. Since 1997 the product has been called just 'Hornby' and it justifiably retains the position it has held for the last 45 years as Britain's most popular model railway system.

The new 'Schools' Class Model Cheltenham [L33b]

Further Reading

If you are interested in further study of this model railway system, we recommend that you read *The Rovex Story* by Pat Hammond. So far, three volumes have been published by New Cavendish Books. These are *Volume 1 - Tri-ang Railways* (ISBN 0904568571), which covers the story from the birth of the system in 1950 to 1965, *Volume 2 - Tri-ang Hornby* (ISBN 1872727581) which covers the period 1965 to 1971 and *Volume 3 - Hornby Railways* (ISBN 1904562000) which takes the story from 1972 up to 1996. A briefer history of the Hornby name from 1920 to the present day will be found in Ian Harrison's book *Hornby - The Official Illustrated History* published by Harper Collins (ISBN 000715173X).

Collectors Clubs

The Tri-ang Society caters for collectors of a wide range of Tri-ang toy products. The Society has a regular newsletter, called *Tri-ang Telegraph*, which contains a number of original articles by well known collectors. Details of the Tri-ang Society may be obtained from the Miles Rowland Tel: 0161 9765059. Tri-ang Railways and Tri-ang Hornby are also usually well covered in *Train Collector*, the magazine of the Train Collectors Society (details at the front of this book).

As indicated above, Hornby Hobbies sponsor their own Collectors Club which publishes a full colour bimonthly magazine, called *The Collector*, which includes news of latest releases and regular profiles of models from the past. There is also the occasional release of *The Collector Plus* which is aimed at the more serious collector. Further information about this organisation may be obtained from the Hornby website at http//www.hornby.com.

Overseas Models - Many Tri-ang models were made in Australia, New Zealand and a few in South Africa, for local distribution but only British made models are listed here.

Trancontinental - This range is included as it was made in Britain and is reputed to have sold better in the UK than in North America, for which it was designed. Transcontinental models appear at the end of each section.

Class A4 Merlin in BR 'purple' livery [L59d]

'R' Numbers - These are catalogue numbers. Where two 'R' numbers are provided alongside a locomotive model, the additional one is for the tender (steam engines) or dummy unit (multiple units) when sold separately. In the early 1970s, with the introduction of computers, it became necessary to bring 'R' numbers up to three digits and this was done by adding one or two noughts in front of the one or two figure numbers. Thus, R52 became R052. From January 1997, all new 'R' numbers had 4 digits.

'R' Numbers in Brackets - These are used where the correct part number for a model from a train set or pack is not known. The number in the brackets is that for the set or pack from which the model comes.

'W' Weathered - a 'W' after the colour in the following tables indicates that the model has a 'weathered' finish.

'HCC' = Hornby Collectors Centre.
'HCClub' = Hornby Collectors Club.

Dates - Wherever possible, in this chapter, with models made after 1971, we have given you the years in which we understand that the models were actually made and it should be remembered that models often appeared in the catalogue after production had ceased in order to clear slow moving stock. Where production dates were unavailable (post 1999) we have provided the years when the model appeared in the catalogue. By this time it was usual for only one batch to be made and if, for example, the dates given are 01-03 then the models would almost certainly have been made in 2001 but remained in the catalogue a further two years to clear stocks.

The Year of Introduction - This has been added to the title to each table and refers to the year that the model was first released in the Hornby (or Tri-ang) range.

Dating Models by Couplings

IIa - old Tri-ang large hook and bar type 52-54.
IIb - as IIa but skid at bottom of uncoupling bar 54-58.
IIIa - modern tension lock coupling with black stud hinge and hole at back of coupling 58-62?
IIIb - as IIIa but no hole 59-62.
IIIc - as IIIb but eyelet instead of stud 62-69.
IIId - as IIIc but larger hook 67-79.
IIIe - re-profiled hook to effect closer coupling 79-85
IIIf - plastic coupling bar with profiled hook 86 -95
IIIg - as IIIf but hook stem straight again 95-
Note that on some later models, the plastic coupling bar is an extension of the chassis or bogie moulding.
The most recent models from Hornby have a new small coupling some of which are clipped into a NEM socket.

Packaging - The very early Tri-ang Railways were sold in a much darker red boxes and these are popular with collectors adding about 30%-50% to the value of boxed items.

Couplings - Couplings provide a useful way of dating stock. The original rolling stock consisted of a pair of coaches made by Rovex Plastics Ltd for the *Princess Elizabeth* train set and some 7-plank open wagons and closed vans acquired from Trackmaster. These both had their own type of non-universal hook and loop couplings (a hook at one end and a loop at the other). The first Tri-ang couplings were a universal automatic coupler which had a large triangular hook and a bar (MkIIa). A vertical bar attached to the

A pair of Tri-ang dock shunters [L68]

hook could be forced up by a ramp set in the track to effect an automatic uncoupling. In 1954 a skid-like lump was put on the bottom of this vertical bar to add weight to the hook to stop it sticking. This altered design is known as the MkIIb. In 1959 this coupling was replaced by the tension-lock coupling (MkIII) which had the bar fixed at both ends and a finer hook which actually gripped the bar of the adjoining coupling. This became the standard British design, adopted by other manufacturers, but during its production in the Margate factory it underwent evolution resulting in a number of minor variations which can be used to date rolling stock.

Rolling Stock Wheels - These changed over the years roughly according to the following order: split plastic sleeve axle with open axle boxes (1952-63), plastic wheels on steel pinpoint axles (1963-1974) and all plastic axles and wheels (1974-present day). White rims first appeared in 1971 and have been used at various times, on certain items. Metal tyres (originally known as Silver Seal wheels) were introduced in 1974 and became standard for many years. Models, when transferred to the Silver Seal range were given a new 'R' number although only the wheels were different (when considering these as another variation, bear in mind that wheels are easily exchanged). There is currently a move back to steel axles and bushed darkened metal wheels.

LOCOMOTIVES

'Noise' - refers to a tender fitted device which creates a 'chuff-chuff' sound as the wheels turn.

DCC Sound System - This is a sound system which was developed by ESU and first used in Electrotren models made by Hornby for the Spanish market.

Smoke - From the early 1960s some models were released fitted with smoke units. These carried an 'S' suffix to the catalogue number (e.g. R52S) and sometimes an 'S' on the underneath of the loco. Other locos carry the mark 'SS' which stood for Synkrosmoke and these were fitted with a piston device which pushed out the smoke in puffs. Later use of smoke in the first 4-4-0 locomotives of 1981 and the later Class 28XX 2-8-0 engines, was not identified by a suffix to the catalogue number.

Ex-Lima Class 59 in DB Schenker livery [L89]

Code 3 Models - There are a number of excellently renumbered and renamed Hornby models which have been done for shops, in batches, professionally, outside the factory. These normally have etched metal nameplates but have not been included in this catalogue.

X Suffix Models - From 2007, brand new locomotives were offered in two versions - with only a DCC decoder socket fitted ('DCC ready') or with the decoder also fitted ('DCC fitted'). The latter models have an 'X' suffix to their catalogue number and are restricted to a production of 200 plus in each case. To save space only the 'DCC ready' versions are listed and an extra £10-£15 should be added to the quoted value of 'DCC fitted' models.

Cat No.	Company, Number, Colour, Dates	£	£

Tank Locomotives

L1. L&Y Class 0F 'Pug' 0-4-0ST (ex-Dapol) (1998)

Aspinall designed this tiny locomotive and the first of the 57 built started work in 1891. They were usually found in dock areas where the short wheelbase was essential for the tight curves.

Lancashire & Yorkshire Railway 0-4-0ST [L1]

R2065	**11232** LMS plain black - *98-99*	25	30
R2065A	**11250** LMS plain black - *00-02*	25	32
R2927	**51235** BRa plain black - *11*	45	57
R2093A	**51218** BRb plain black - *99*	25	30
R2093B	**51222** BRb plain black - *99*	25	30
R2093C	**51235** BRb plain black - *00-02*	25	32
R2335	**51231** BRb plain black W - *03*	25	35
R2335A	**51232** BRb plain black W - *04*	25	35
R2335B	**51218** BRb plain black W - *05*	25	35
R3024	**51240** BRb plain black - *11*	45	62
R2453	**51218** BRc plain black W - *05*	25	35
R2453A	**51235** BRc plain black W - *06*	27	38

L2. CR Class 0F 'Pug' 0-4-0ST (1980)

Based on Drummond's design of 1885.

R752	**205** 'Stewart & Lloyds' brown - *83-85*	20	28
R750	**205** 'Stewart & Lloyds' brown Sp Edn 260 (Grattans) - *83*	NPG	NPG
R174	**4** 'Huntley & Palmer' brown - *85*	25	30
R162	**112** 'NCB' yellow - *84*	20	28
R161	**3** 'William Mansfield' blue - *86-87*	20	NA
R214	**7** 'Powergen' light blue - *94-97*	15	20
R779	**7** ***Desmond*** red - *81-83*	18	25

Caledonian Railway 0-4-0ST [L2]

R159	**313** ***Robbie Burns*** MR maroon ex-set - *86-87*	18	NA
X10207	**885** MR maroon ex-R1115 MO set - *08*	20	NA
R057	**270** CR blue - *80-81*	15	25
R2361	**270** CR deep blue Sp Edn (HCClub) - *03*	15	25
R2672	**272** CR blue (Railroad) - *07-11*	15	23
(R1151)	**314** CR blue ex-'Caledonian Belle' train set - *11*	28	NA
(R1127)	**33** maroon FR ex-City Industrial MO set - *09*	28	NA
(R1130K)	**57075** ***Blue Thistle*** blue ex-'Highland Rover' MO set Sp Edn (Argos) - *09*	20	NA
R255	**8** ***Loch Ness*** HR blue - *88-93*	15	22
R072	**6** ***Ben-Y-Gloe*** HR blue - *94-00*	15	22
R150	**627** LYR black - *86-92*	18	25
R300	**16023** LMS black - *92-98*	15	20
R770	**16032** LMS black Sp Edn 480 (Beatties) - *83*	30	45
R266	**16020** ***Monty*** LMS black - *90*	22	28
R337	**16030** LMS black - *95-98*	17	22
R152	**16031** LMS maroon ex-set - *90-94*	20	NA
(R1051)	**16037** LMS red ex-MO set - *04*	20	NA
R?	**51200** BRb black Sp Edn (HCClub) - *10*	18	30
R782	**56025** ***Smokey Joe*** BR black - *83-10*	18	25
R3064	**56025** ***Smokey Joe*** BR black (RailRoad) - *11*	18	25
R2049	**56038** BRa black Sp Edn (HCClub) - *98*	18	30
R2132W	**56010** BRc black in R1017 set - *99-02*	15	NA
R?	**1** 'Hornby USM Debut December 1986' red Sp Edn 34? (Hornby Share Launch Debut) - *86*	400	NPG
R2150	**H2000** maroon Ltd Edn (HCClub) - *00*	15	25
R2597	**80** ***Queen Elizabeth II*** black Ltd Edn (HCClub) - *06*	20	NA

* a blue bodied version has also turned up.

L3. GWR Class 101 Holden 0-4-0T (1978)

Only one member of the class was made and it was never to leave the yard. A blue 'Forest of Pendle MRS' Holden 0-4-0T is Code 3, the transfers having been put on an R796 tank by the society (150 were made). pf = paint finish. npf = non-paint finish.

R2263	'Lynne & Co. Collieries' blue - *02-04*	15	26
R153	**1** 'Tolgus Tin Co.' grey - *86-88*	20	25
R796	**2** 'Crewe & District' blue - *91-92*	20	25
R796	**30** 'Pendle Forest MRS' blue (Code 3 150 made) - *94*	40	45
R794	**4** 'H.A.R.Wood' green - *91-92*	20	25
R795	**6** 'Lion Works' black - *91-92*	25	28
R155	**21** 'Colman's' yellow, npf - *84-85*	18	NA
R155	**21** 'Colman's' yellow, pf - *84-85*	25	NA
R163	**45** 'Ford' white - *84-85*	20	30
R2878	**856** 'Portnoy Collieries' red (RailRoad) - *09-11*	18	23
R164	***Iron Horse*** green - *84*	35	NPG
R766	**1** ***Super S*** red - *83-85*	20	NA
R758	**6** ***Northern Nellie*** blue *-83*	20	25
R759	**7** ***Southern Connie*** yellow - *84*	18	25
R760	**7** ***Connie*** yellow - *84*	20	25
R760	**8** ***Polly*** red - *83*	18	25
R854	**23** ***Sentinel*** maroon - *96-98*	15	25
R781	**34** ***Terry*** orange - *83*	15	22
R336	**36** ***Roger*** red - *82-84*	20	NA
R2129	**105** red - *99-02*	15	22
(R1121)	**2009** ***Blue Diamond*** blue ex-Devon Flyer set - *09-11*	20	NA
R2430	***Hornby*** red - *04-06*	18	25
X5018	as above but ex-MO R1046 Christmas set - *08*	18	NA
X5785	***Little Giant*** green ex-sets - *06-08*	20	NA
X10193	***Little Giant*** GWR green ex-MO R1109 set - *08*	20	NA
(R1035)	**709** LSWR lined light brown ex set - *03-05*	18	NA
R2451	**710** LSWR lined light brown - *05-07*	20	28
R2451A	**726** LSWR lined light brown - *06-07*	20	28
R077	**101** Great Western green, npf - *78-80*	10	18
R333	**101** Great Western green, pf - *80-81*	15	25
R173	**101** (GWR 150) 1985 green - *85*	25	35
R2304	**101** GWR green Sp Edn (HCClub) - *02*	20	30
R2431	**101** GWR green - *05-06*	20	28
(R2670)	**104** GWR green (RailRoad) ex-pack - *07-11*	18	NA
(R1050)	**101** GWR green ex-Sp Edn set (Toys-R-Us) - *05*	25	NA
R2957	**101** GWR plain green GWR 1835-2010 Ltd Edn 1835 - *10*	20	25
R2665	**328** BRb green Ltd Edn (HCClub) - *07*	20	30
R2130	**9** CIE green - *99-02*	18	22

GWR Class 101 Commemorating 175th Anniversary of the GWR [L3]

R099	**99** CIE green, npf - *79*	40	NA

L4. **Industrial 0-4-0T** (Freelance) (1960)

The body has characteristics which suggest that the designer was influenced by the SR Class C14, a Urie rebuild of the 1906 Drummond design for the LSWR.

R?	black (no decals) - *?*	20	NA
R355B	**6 *Connie*** deeper blue ex-set - *72-73*	35	NA
R355B	**6, 7 *Nellie*** blue both early and late lining - *60-68*	20	48
R?	**7 *Nellie*** yellow - *?*	65	NPG
R355B	**7 *Nellie*** deeper blue - *71-72*	30	60
R355B	**9 *Nellie*** deeper blue - *70*	30	60
R355	**6 or 9 *Connie*** blue - *60-62?*	35	65
R355Y	**6 or 8 *Connie*** yellow - *63-65*	50	80
R355R	**6 or 9 *Polly*** red - *63-70*	25	55

0-4-0 industrial tank Connie [L4]

R355R	**7 or 9 *Polly*** blue - *?*	25	55
R355G	**27** shades of green - *70-72*	20	60
R455	**25550** red, chrome dome - *73-75*	25	40
R455	**25550** red, no chrome dome - *73-75*	30	45
R255	**7178** blue with gold or yellow lining - *76-78*	20	40
R255	**7178** blue with white lining - *76*	60	NPG
R?	BRb black - *61-62*	40	60
R?	BRc black - *c65*	40	60

L5. **Class D Industrial 0-4-0T** (1991)

This is based on a steelworks locomotive found in South Wales.

R531	**40 *King George V*** red - *91-92*	12	18
R368	**40 *King George V*** green - *95-96*	12	18
R863	**43 *Queen Mary*** red - *92-97*	10	NA
R2452	**1** 'Lion Works Collieries' maroon - *05-07*	20	28
(R1061)	**1** 'Eddie Stobart Ltd' green ex-set - *05-06*	20	NA
R2507	**2 *Monica Pitman*** green Sp Edn 500 (Eddie Stobart Ltd) - *05*	32	38
R2673	**2** 'Morse Collieries' blue (RailRoad) - *07-09*	15	23

D Class industrial tank [L5]

R2507A	**3 *Joan Etheridge*** green Sp Edn 500 (Eddie Stobart Ltd) - *05*	30	35
R2507B	**4 *Harry Parsons*** green Sp Edn 500 (Eddie Stobart Ltd) - *05*	30	35
R2940	**4** 'Trewavas Aggregates' red (RailRoad) - *10-11*	20	25
R068	**5** 'NCB' grey - *93-94*	15	20
R153	**5** 'ER' red - *94-99*	15	20
R069	**23** 'Hensall Sand' blue - *93*	15	20
R2131	**1203** CR blue - *99-02*	15	20
R2131W	as above in MO set R1028K - *08*	15	NA
(R1068)	**4** MSLR lined red ex-set - *06*	20	NA
R2189	**?** LMS maroon ex-sets - *02-04*	15	NA
X4550	**2606** LNER black ex-set - *02-03*	15	NA
R2671	**5** LNER green (RailRoad) - *07-09*	15	23
X10191	**6** LNER green ex-MO R1120M set - *08*	20	NA
R2264	**09** Southern black - *02-04*	15	26
X10228	**63** Southern green ex-R1111KM MO set - *08*	20	NA
R2439	**7** SR bright green Sp Edn (HCClub) - *05*	20	35
R2245	**4** BRa black Ltd Edn (HCClub) - *01*	18	35
R856	**9** BRa green - *96-97*	10	NA
R2058	**7** BRb blue - *98*	20	25
R2773	**07** BRc green (RailRoad) - *08-09*	15	23
R063	'British Toy & Hobby Association 50th Anniversary' blue Sp Edn 300 - *94*	45	60
R058	***Hornby*** red - *93-97*	10	NA
R066	***Hornby*** yellow - *93-98*	10	15
R066	***Hornby*** grey - *93*	20	NA
(R1147)	grey-green W ex-'Codename Strike Force' set - *10-11*	9	NA

L6. **Freelance 0-4-0T** (2009)

This is based on the earlier short wheelbase Thomas the Tank Engine model with the face replaced by a smokebox door.

R?	**43209** BRb lined black (HCClub 2009 issue) - *09*	25	35

Freelance 0-4-0T in LB&SCR livery [L6]

R2941	**629** LBSC brown (RailRoad) - *10-11*	20	25

More 0-4-0 tanks will be found under 'PLAY LOCOMOTIVES' later on in this section.

L7. **GWR Class 14xx 0-4-2T** (ex-Airfix) (1997)

Collett design of 1932 for branch lines. Some Hornby Class 14XXs have been renumbered after leaving the factory.

R2026	**1458** GWR green - *97-98*	25	35
R2026A	**1472** GWR green - *98*	25	35
R2026B	**1427** GWR green - *00-01*	30	42
R2026C	**1444** GWR green - *00-01*	30	42
R2026D	**1410** GWR green - *03*	30	42
R2778	**4869** GWR (button) green - *08-09*	42	57
R2381A	**1436** BRb plain green - *05*	30	46
R2381	**1419** BRb plain green - *04*	30	46
R3027	**1444** BRb lined green - *11*	50	70
R2539	**1464** BRc plain green - *06-07*	38	50
R2095A	**1421** BRc green - *99-01*	30	42
R2095B	**1470** BRc green - *99-01*	30	42
R2095C	**1445** BRc green - *01-02*	30	42
R2173	**1432** BRc green, train pack with 2 coaches Ltd + Sp Edn 1,250 - *00*	NA	65
(R2173)	**1432** BRc green - *00*	40	NA
R9070	**11** (*Oliver*) GWR roundel green with face - *see Thomas section*	35	49

L8a. LSWR Class M7 Tank 0-4-4T (1967)

Designed by Drummond for the LSWR in 1897, over 100 were built and became an important part of the Southern Railway's fleet. G = firebox glow.

R868	**245** Southern dark green, npf - *72-75*	35	65
R103	**249** Southern olive - *85-86*	55	75
R868	**328** Southern bright green, npf, G - *69-70*	35	65
R868	**328** Southern bright green, npf - *71*	35	65
R754	**30027** BRc lined black G - *67-70*	50	75
R862	**30111** BRc lined black - *87-88*	50	75

L8b. LSWR Class M7 0-4-4T (2006)

Completely retooled to super-detail standard. Two different lengths of footplate and with our without push-pull gear. Both 'DCC ready' and 'DCC fitted' (has X suffix) versions of each general release loco were made. Add £10-£15 for X models.

R2678	**252** LSWR lime green Sp Edn (Hattons) - *07*	70	90
R2840	**E42** SR olive green - *09*	70	100
R2924	**51** SR olive green - *10-11*	75	100
R2625	**111** SR olive green - *06-07*	60	80
R2503	**357** SR olive green - *06*	60	80

Ex-LSWR Class M7 0-4-0T in SR livery [L8b]

R2923	**242** SR malachite green - *10-11*	75	100
R2733	**676** SR malachite green - *08-09*	70	85
R2504	**30479** BRb lined black - *not made*	NA	NA
R2504	**30051** BRb lined black - *06*	60	80
R2734	**30056** BRb lined black - *08-09*	70	91
R2505	**30031** BRc lined black - *06-07*	60	80
R2506	**30108** BRc lined black W - *06-07*	60	80
R2626	**30023** BRc lined black - *07-08*	60	80
R2735	**30036** BRc lined black - *08-09*	70	91

L9. GWR Class 2721 0-6-0PT (open cab) (1981)

A Dean design. Versions of this model made from 2001 onwards had much improved detail. chip = DCC decoder fitted

R59	**2744** Great Western green - *81-84*	20	28
R165	**2783** Great Western green - *89-96*	20	28
R760	**2776** Great Western green - *96-98*	20	28
R760A	**2783** Great Western green - *99*	25	30
R760B	**2730** Great Western green - *00*	25	30
R2006	**2788** Great Western green ex-set - *96-02*	20	NA
R2534	**2738** Great Western green - *06-07*	28	39
R2534A	**2748** Great Western green - *09-10*	30	45
(R1077)	**2728** Great Western green chip ex-set - *06-07*	30	NA
R158	**2747** Great Western black - *85-88*	35	50
R2198	**2771** GWR green - *01*	30	35
R2198A	**2759** GWR green - *02*	25	36
R2328	**2799** GWR green - *03*	25	36
R2328A	**2759** GWR green - *04*	25	36
R2328B	**2771** GWR green - *05-06*	28	39
(R1037)	**2761** GWR green, ex-R1037 set - *03-04*	25	NA
R2739	**2764** GWR green - *08-09*	30	45
R3066	**2765** GWR green (RailRoad) - *11*	20	30
R073	**5** red with a coat of arms - *93*	25	35

L10. GWR Class 57xx Pannier 0-6-0PT (1971)

A Collett design of 1929. npf = non-painted finish.

R51S/R051	**8751** GWR green gloss, npf, smoke - *71-74*	18	30
R041	**8751** GWR green, npf, no smoke - *75-80*	18	30
R300	**8773** GWR green - *80-81*	22	35

GWR Class 57xx 0-6-0PT [L10]

R048	**L90** London Transport ex-set red - *78*	30	NA
R382	**8** GWR bright green with face - *see Thomas section*	-	-

L11a. LMS Class 3F 'Jinty' 0-6-0T (1953)

A Fowler design. This model was also made in New Zealand and Australia from a different body tool and usually has a lamp mounted on the smokebox. s-tw = see-through wheels (gaps between spokes)

R377S	GN&SR brown, s-tw, ex-Ltd Edn RS615 *Railway Children* set - *70-72*	60	NA
R757	**2021** LMS lined black s-tw - *73*	25	NA
R52RS	**7606** LMS maroon, s-tw, smoke unit (also R52AS)- *70-73*	25	35
R452	**7606** LMS maroon, s-tw - *73-74*	25	35
R52	BRa unlined black - *53*	100	150
R52	**47606** BRb unlined black - *53-57*	10	30
R52	**47606** BRb lined black - *57-59*	20	45
R52	**47606** BRc lined black - *59-64*	15	40
R52/R52S	**47606** BRc lined black s-tw - *64-74*	20	40
R52/R52S	**47606** BRc lined black, cream backed transfers, s-tw - *72*	30	50
R558S	'Battle Space' khaki, s-tw - *66-67*	50	NA

L11b. LMS Class 3F 'Jinty' 0-6-0T (1978)

New model with cab interior and wire handrails. npf = non-paint finish. T7 = type 7 motor fitted. chip = DCC decoder fitted

R2882	**24** SDJR dark blue (RailRoad) - *09-11*	22	27
(R1125)	**24** SDJR dark blue ex-'Somerset Belle' set DCC- *09-11*	35	NA
R2658	**7412** LMS black - *07*	35	40
(R1144)	**7413** LMS plain maroon, ex-'The Night Mail' set - *not made*	NA	NA
(R1144)	**7414** LMS maroon ex-'LMS Night Mail 'train set - *10*	25	NA
R052	**16440** LMS maroon npf - *78-79*	25	30
R301	**16440** LMS maroon - *80-89*	30	35
R2942	**16440** LMS maroon (RaiRoad) - *10-11*	22	27
R2674	**7413** LMS maroon (RailRoad) - *07-11*	22	27
R2469	**16624** LMS plain black W T7 - *05-08*	30	42
R2469A	**16700** LMS plain black W T7 - *06*	30	42
R130	**8400** LNER green - *88-89*	30	NA
R2468	**47281** BRb plain black W T7 - *05-07*	30	42
R2468A	**47294** BRb plain black W T7 - *06*	30	42
R058	**47458** BRc black - *78-79*	25	30
R302	**47480** BRc black - *80-86*	30	35
R053	**47556** BRc black - *88-91*	35	40
(R1075)	**47646** BRc black chip ex-set - *06-09*	30	NA
R2657	**47427** BRc black - *07*	35	40

L12. GNR Class J13/J52 0-6-0ST (1981)

Under the GNR these were classified as J13 but were reclassified as J52 when taken over by the LNER.

R396	**1247** GNR green - *81-82*	30	45
R2186A	**1241** GNR green - *00-03*	28	33
R2186B	**1226** GNR green - *00-03*	28	35
R2971	**1250** GNR green - *10*	38	45
R861	**3980** LNER black - *87-88*	35	55
R504	**3111** LNER black - *92-93*	35	50
R2400	**3975** LNER plain black - *04*	28	38
R2400A	**3970** LNER plain black - *05-06*	30	42
(R1097)	**3972** LNER plain black ex-'East Coast Pullman' set - *08-10*	32	NA
R2401	**No.2** BRb plain black W - *04-05*	30	38

Ex-GNR Class J13 0-6-0ST [L12]

R2546	**68878** BRb plain black W - *06-08*	30	42
R186	**68846** BRc black - *92-94*	30	45
R2274	**68846** BRc black - *02-03*	35	45

L13. NBR Class J83 0-6-0T (1976)

A Holmes tank engine design of 1900 frequently seen as station pilots. DC = decoder fitted.

(R1069)	**8469** LNER green W ex-set - *07-08*	25	NA
R252	**8477** LNER gloss green no lines - *76-77*	18	25
R252	**8477** LNER matt green no lines - *77-78*	18	25
R316	**8473** LNER green no red lining - *94-98*	25	35
R2164B	**8477** LNER lined green - *00-02*	22	30
X4549	**8474** LNER green ex-R1030 - *02-03*	25	NA
R2164A	**8481** LNER lined green - *00-02,07*	22	30
R2970	**8905** LNER plain black - *10*	33	40
R2325	**9832** LNER lined black - *03*	25	35
R2325A	**9828** LNER lined black - *04-05*	25	35
R2325B	**9819** LNER lined black - *05-07*	28	39
R722	**68472** BRa green - *95-96*	23	NA
R2541	**68472** BRa lined light green - *06.08*	28	39
R2155A	**68474** BRb black - *00-01*	22	30
R2155B	**68463** BRb black - *00-01*	22	30
R2155C	**68478** BRb black - *01-02*	22	30
(R1126)	**68478** BRb black DC ex-'Mixed Freight' set - *09-11*	30	NA
R2324	**68450** BRb lined black W - *03*	28	35
R2384A	**68474** BRb lined black - *04*	25	35
R2384	**68481** BRb lined black - *made?*	NPG	NPG
R2540	**68480** BRc lined black W - *06-08*	28	39

L14. LBSCR Class A1X 0-6-0T (ex-Dapol) (1998)

Stroudley's 'Terrier' tank engine of 1872 as redeveloped by Marsh in 1911.

R9069	**55 *Stepney*** LBSC orange-yellow with face - *see Thomas section*	38	49
R2483	**41 *Piccadilly*** LBSC orange-yellow - *05-10*	38	57
R2177	**54 *Waddon*** LBSC orange-yellow Ltd Edn 1000 (HCC) - *00*	40	55
R2190	**83 *Earlswood*** LBSC orange-yellow - *01*	35	45
R2605	**44 *Fulham*** LBSC orange-yellow Sp Edn 1200 (HCC) - *06*	45	58
R2679	**5 *Portishead*** GWR green * - *07-08*	40	55

Ex-LB&SCR 'Terrier' 0-6-0T in K&ESR livery as Bodiam [L14]

R2216	**3 *Bodiam*** Kent & East Sussex Railway dark blue - *01-02*	40	55
R2063	**W2 *Freshwater*** SR green - *98*	35	45
R2100	**W11** SR green - *99-01*	35	45
R2100B	**W12** SR green - *00-02*	35	45
R3022	**2662** SR olive green - *11*	45	61
R2407	**13 *Carisbrooke*** SR malachite - *04*	35	45
R2443	**12 *Ventnor*** SR malachite - *05*	35	45
R2406	**32635 *Brighton Works*** BR orange-yellow - *04-05*	35	45
R2627	**32640** BRb lined black - *07*	35	45
R2165A	**32670** BRc lined black - *00-03*	32	40
R2165B	**32636** BRc lined black - *00-04*	32	45
R2165C	**32640** BRc lined black - *01*	32	42
R2550	**32678** BRc lined black - *06*	38	49
R2741	**32662** BRc lined black - *08-09*	40	57
R2891	**55** black lined in red + Maunsell BCK Sp Edn 1000 (Bluebell) 50th Anniversary train pack - *09*	NA	150
(R2891)	above loco only - *09*	45	NA

* in 2007 available only in Hornby Collector Centres but joined the main catalogue in 2008.

L15. LBSCR Class E2 Tank 0-6-0T (1979)

Billinton designed tank engine of 1913. npf = non paint finish.

R353	**100** LBSC brown npf - *79*	30	45
R315	**100** LBSC brown - *80*	30	45
R261	**104** Southern olive, alternative number transfers **101, 102, 103** - *82-84*	40	50
R157	**103** Southern black - *85*	50	60

An example in SR green has been found with the number '2106' printed on.

L16 SE&CR Class S Saddle Tank 0-6-0ST (1956)

Roughly based on Maunsell's SE&CR design of saddle tank of 1917.

R153	**748** BRb black - *56-58*	30	50
R151	**748** BRb black c/w - *57-58*	35	75
R153	**748** BRc black - *59-61*	25	50
R255	TR black+green c/w - *59-58*	30	75

L17. WD Class J94 0-6-0ST (ex-Dapol) (1998)

A Riddles design which was mass produced during the Second World War. J94 was applied as a class code to those locomotives bought by the LNER after the war and were later absorbed by BR. The model is fitted with a type 7 motor. Some Hornby Class J94s have been renumbered after leaving the factory.

R2062	**8006** LNER black - *98*	35	45
R2145	**68075** BRb black Sp Edn 500 (HCClub) - *00*	35	45
R2326	**68074** BRb black - *03-05*	35	45
R2380	**68071** BRb plain black W - *04*	35	45
R2380A	**68020** BRb plain black W - *05-06*	38	49
R2094A	**68049** BRc plain black - *99*	35	45
R2094B	**68062** BRc plain black - *99*	35	45
R2094C	**68080** BRc plain black - *00-02*	35	45
R2533	**68035** BRc plain black W - *06-08*	38	49
R2855	**68010** BRc plain black - *09-10*	40	64
R3023	**68006** BRc plain black - *11*	50	70
	Longmoor Military Railway		
R2151	**157** LMR blue Sp Edn (HCC) - *99-00*	35	45
R2151A	**196** LMR blue - *01-02*	35	45
R2151B	**156 *McMurdo*** LMR blue - *02-03*	35	45
	Industrial Tanks		
R2454	***Cadley Hill No.1*** NCB? green - *05-06*	38	49
R2096	***Harry*** NCB red - *99-01*	35	45
R2281	***Joseph*** NCB light green - *02-04*	35	45
R2327	***Peter*** NCB light green - *03*	35	45
R2556	***Stanley*** NCB? - *not made*	NA	NA
R2212	***Whiston*** NCB Bold Colliery green - *01*	35	45

'Austerity' 0-6-0T in National Coal Board livery as Wimblebury [L17]

R2556	**7 *Wimblebury*** NCB violet - *07*	40	50
R2740	**18** WPR black - *not made*	NA	NA
R2740	**16** WPR (Wemyss Private Railway) brown - *08-09*	40	57
R2399	**49** NCB bright green - *04*	35	45

L18a. GNR Class N2 0-6-2T (ex-Trackmaster) (1949)

The original clockwork Trackmaster model was sold in its own packaging by Pyramid Toys. The tools were bought by Rovex in 1951.

-	**69561** BRa black (Trackmaster) c/w - *49-51*	35	95
R51	**69561** BRa black c/w - *51-53*	45	110
R51	**69561** BRb black c/w - *53-54*	55	125

L18b. GNR Class N2 Tank 0-6-2T (ex-Airfix) (2000)

Gresley design of suburban tank of 1920. 5-pole skew wound motor.

R2214A	**1763** GNR green - *01-03*	35	45
R2214B	**1730** GNR green - *01-05*	35	45
R2251	**4744** LNER lined black W - *02-04*	35	45
R2251	**4749** LNER lined black W - *not made*	NA	NA
R2269	**4753** LNER lined black - *02-04*	35	45
R2981	**69563** BRa plain black + 2 Gresley coaches Ltd Edn 1948 'London 1948' train pack * - *11*	NA	205
(R2981)	above loco on its own - *11*	70	NA
(R1029)	**69522** BRb lined black ex-set - *02-03*	35	NA
R2178A	**69546** BRc lined black - *00-01*	35	45
R2178B	**69506** BRc lined black - *00-02*	35	45

* This commemorates the Olympic Games held in London in 1948 and forms part of the London 2012 package.

L19. GWR Class 61xx 2-6-2T (ex-Airfix) (1999)

A Collett Prairie tank design of 1931. Type HP motor.

R2928	**5108** GWR (shirt button) plain green - *10*	35	45
R2098	**6113** Great Western green - *99*	35	45
R2098A	**6147** Great Western green - *00-01*	35	45
R2098B	**6105** Great Western green - *02*	35	46
R2098C	**6120** Great Western green - *02-03*	35	46
R2098D	**6121** Great Western green - *03*	35	46
R2098E	**6119** Great Western green - *04-05*	35	54
R2143	**6150** Great Western green Ltd Edn 1000 - *99*	40	46
R2213A	**6156** BRb black - *01*	40	50
R2213B	**6134** BRb black - *01-03*	40	50
R2624	**5157** BRb black W - *07-08*	40	50
R2737	**4134** BRb green - *08-09*	50	94
R2357	**6167** BRc lined green - *04*	35	50
R2357A	**6132** BRc lined green - *03-06*	35	50
R2357B	**6167** BRc lined green - *04*	35	50

L20. BR Class 3MT Standard Tank 2-6-2T (1956)

Riddles's design of lighter large tank for restricted routes, dating from 1952. s-tw = see-through wheels (gaps between spokes)

R59	**82004** BRb lined black - *56-58*	30	75
R59	**82004** BRc lined black - *59*	30	75
R59	**82004** BRc green - *60*	30	75

BR 3MT Standard 2-6-2T [L20]

R59	**82004** BRc green, s-tw - *61-66, 69-72*	25	65
R59	**82004** BRc green, nickel tyres, s-tw - *72*	50	100

L21a. LMS Fowler Class 4P Tank 2-6-4T (1980)

Fowler's large tank design of 1927. The chassis was modified in 1992.

R055	**2300** LMS maroon - *80-81*	35	44
R505	**2312** LMS maroon - *92-95*	35	44
R261	**2301** LMS maroon - *94-95*	35	44
R299	**2309** LMS maroon - *96-98*	35	48
R088	**2345** LMS lined black - *84-85*	50	65
R239	**42363** BRb lined black - *92-95*	35	45
R062	**42308** BRc lined black + alt. nos. **42305, 42310, 42319** - *82-84*	35	50

L21b. LMS Fowler Class 4P Tank 2-6-4T (2002)

Super detailed model with a new chassis and 5-pole skew wound motor. DCC Ready.

R2224	**2305** LMS maroon - *not made*	NA	NA
R2224	**2311** LMS maroon - *03-04*	45	60
R2397	**2341** LMS plain black - *not made*	NA	NA
R2397	**2341** LMS lined black - *04-05*	52	64
R2397A	**2321** LMS lined black - *05-07*	55	70
R2398	**42322** BRa plain black - *04-05*	52	64
R2223	**42356** BRb black - *not made*	NA	NA
R2223	**42355** BRb lined black - *03-04*	45	60
R2223A	**42301** BRb lined black - *04-05*	45	60
R2287	**42322** BRb lined black W - *03-04*	45	60
R2738	**42315** BRb lined black - *08-09*	45	80
R2529	**42327** BRc lined black - *06-07*	55	70

L22. LMS Stanier Class 4P Tank 2-6-4T (2007)

Stanier's large 2-cylinder tank design of 1935. DCC fitted 5-pole skew wound motor. Both 'DCC ready' and 'DCC fitted' (has X suffix) versions of each general release loco were made. Add £10-£15 for X models.

R2635	**2546** LMS lined black - *07-08*	60	75
R2730	**2484** LMS lined black - *08-09*	65	85
R2636	**42468** BRb lined black - *07-09*	60	75
R2731	**42587** BRb lined black - *08-09*	65	85
R2637	**42437** BRc lined black - *07-09*	60	75
R2732	**42616** BRc lined black - *08-09*	65	85
R3021	**42613** BRc lined black W - *11*	75	100

L23. LNER Thompson Class L1 Tank 2-6-4T (2010)

This is Thompson's large mixed traffic tank design of 1945 which was intended to be the railway's standad large tank. Coming late, they saw very little LNER service and were taken new into British Railways' stud. They were seen around London, East Anglia and in the Hull district. The models are powered by a 5-pole skew wound motor and have extensive cab interior detail.

R2912	**9011** LNER lined light green - *10-11*	75	90
R2959	**67717** BRa lined light green - *10-11*	75	90

LNER Class L1 2-6-4T [L23]

R2913	**67772** BRb lined black - *10-11*	75	90
R2914	**67722** BRc lined black - *10-11*	75	90
R3007	**67759** BRc lined black W - *11*	77	107

Tender Locomotives

L24. L&MR *Rocket* 0-2-2 (1963)

The locomotive comes with two crew in period costume. These are sometimes missing and, if so, this greatly reduces the value of the model. Loco drive.

L&MR yellow

R651S/R652	***Rocket*** + smoke - *63*	45	130
R346	***Rocket*** + smoke + 1 coach - *64-66*	60	135
R346C	***Rocket*** no smoke + 3 coaches - *68-69*	65	150
R796	***Rocket*** + 3 coaches train pack - *82-84*	NA	150
(R796)	***Rocket*** ex-train pack nickel tyres - *82-84*	60	NA
R771	***Rocket*** + 3 coaches train pack (packaged for sale in France with Hornby Acho) - *83-84*	NA	200

L25. GWR Class 3031 'Dean Single' 4-2-2 (1961)

This was also known as the 'Achilles' Class and consisted of 80 locomotives built at Swindon from 1891. Loco drive and in 2007 received a new chassis.

Great()Western Green

R2956	**3012** ***Great Western*** matt + 2 scale clerestory coaches Ltd Edn 1000 (GWR 1835-2010) - *10*	NA	120
(R2956)	above loco only - *10*	70	NA
R354+R37	**3046** ***Lord of the Isles*** matt - *61-65, 67*	25	85
R354S+R37	**3046** ***Lord of the Isles*** matt with smoke unit fitted - *61-62*	30	95
R354	**3046** ***Lord of the Isles*** gloss - *70-74*	30	85
R795	**3046** ***Lord of the Isles*** tampo printed splasher + 3 coaches - *81-82*	NA	135
(R049)	above loco only - *81-82*	65	NA

R2560	**3046 *Lord of the Isles*** + 3 short clerestory coaches Ltd Edn 2500 - *07*	NA	120
(R2560)	above loco only - *07*	65	NA
R2614	**3047 *Lorna Doone*** Ltd Edn 2000 - *07*	65	95
R2706	**3050 *Royal Sovereign*** + 3 clerestories Ltd Edn 2000 - *08*	NA	125
R2828	**3064 *Duke of Edinburgh*** Ltd Edn 2000 - *09-10*	70	96

GWR 'Achilles' Class 4-2-2 as Duke of Edinburgh [L25]

R9231	***Emily*** with face and no dome - see *Thomas section*	-	-

L26. CR 'Caledonian Single' 4-2-2 (1963)

A solitary locomotive built in 1886 by Neilson & Co. Loco drive. The chassis was improved in 2007.

R553+R554	**123** CR matt blue - *63-66*	55	100
R553	**123** CR gloss blue - *71-74*	60	85
R2610	**123** CR matt blue + 3 CR coaches train pack - *07*	NA	120
(R2610)	above loco only - *07*	60	NA
R763	**14010** LMS maroon in presentation box- *83*	40	65
R2806	**14010** LMS maroon + 3 CR coaches in LMS livery train pack Ltd Edn 2000 - *09-11*	NA	130
(R2806)	above loco only - *09*	70	NA
R2683	**14010** LMS lined black Ltd Edn 2000 - *08-09*	40	85
R765	as above Sp Edn 400 (Grattans) - *83*	40	90

L27. GWR 'County' Class 38xx 4-4-0 (1981)

County Class introduced by Churchward. Ringfield tender drive. From 2011 the motor was fitted in the locomotive.

Great()Western Green

R392	**3821 *County of Bedford*** smoke - *81-84*	45	55
R3061	**3821 County of *Bedford*** (RailRoad) - *11*	55	70

GWR 'County' Class 4-4-0 as County of Bedford [L27]

R390	**3830 *County of Oxford*** - *84-85*	60	70
R584	**3825 *County of Denbigh*** - *91*	60	70
R298	**3828 *County of Hereford*** Ltd Edn 2000 - *91*	60	70
R125	**3824 *County of Cornwall*** - *94-95*	60	70
R2980	**3818 County of Radnor** + 2 'scale' clerestory coaches Ltd Edn 1908 'London 1908' train pack * - *11*	NA	164
(R2980)	above loco on its own - *11*	60	NA

* This commemorates the Olympic Games held in London in 1908 and forms part of the London 2012 package.

L28a. LMS Class 2P 4-4-0 (ex-Tri-ang L1) (1973)

This was an overscale model developed from the Tri-ang L1 with loco drive.

R450	**690** LMS lined black - *73-74*	45	65

L28b. LMS Class 2P 4-4-0 (ex-Mainline) (1999)

Fowler's 1928 version of a 2P. Ringfield tender drive. From 2011 the motor was fitted in the locomotive.

R3029	**25** S&DJR very dark blue - *11*	65	90
R2217	**44** S&DJR very dark blue - *01*	50	64
R2217A	**46** S&DJR very dark blue - *02-04*	50	64
R2099A	**579** LMS lined black - *99-01*	40	54
R2099B	**645** LMS lined black - *99*	40	40
R2099C	**644** LMS lined black - *00-05*	40	54
R2172	**634** LMS black + 3 coaches train pack Sp Edn 1250 (Kays) - *00*	NA	85
(R2172)	above loco only - *00*	45	NA

R2183A	**40610** BRa lined black - *00-05*	40	54
R2183B	**40634** BRa lined black - *00-04*	40	54
R2527	**40604** BRb lined black W - *06-08*	50	64
R3028	**40663** BRc lined black - *11*	65	90

L29. MR Class 4P Compound 4-4-0 (1981)

Deeley designed locomotive of 1905. Ringfield tender drive. From 2011 the motor was fitted in the locomotive.

R355	**1000** MR maroon - *83-85*	40	60
R3063	**1000** LMS maroon (RailRoad) - *11*	55	70
R376	**1000** LMS maroon smoke - *81-82*	40	60
R755	as above Sp Edn 300 - *82*	40	80
R175	**41043** BRa black - *86-87*	40	68

L30. LNER Class D49/1 'Shire/Hunt' 4-4-0 (1981)

A Gresley design of 1927. Ringfield tender drive. From 2011 the motor was fitted in the locomotive.

LNER Green

R378	**2753 *Cheshire*** smoke - *81-82*	45	60
R859	**359 *The Fitzwilliam*** - *88-89*	50	64

LNER Shire Class - Cheshire [L30]

R123	**222 *The Berkeley*** - *94-95*	50	64
R3062	**222 *The Berkeley*** (RailRoad) - *11*	55	70

BR Black

R259	**62700 *Yorkshire*** BRb - *82-84*	55	70
R860	**62750 *The Pytchley*** BRb - *88-89*	50	65
R2021	**62758 *The Cattistock*** BRc - *97-98*	50	65

L31. LSWR Class T9 4-4-0 (2008)

Dugald Drummond's successful 'Greyhound' express locomotive of 1899. Super-detailed model with narrow and wide cab versions. Decoder socket in tender and metal boiler to add weight. Both 'DCC ready' and 'DCC fitted' (has X suffix) versions of each general release loco were made. Add £10-£15 for X models. Ncab = narrow cab. Wcab = wide cab. Wcart = water cart tender. 6-w = 6-wheel tender.

R2892	**120** LSWR bright green Wcart Ncab Ltd Edn (HCClub) - *09*	70	91
R2690	**120** SR olive green Wcart Ncab NRM model - *08-09*	70	91
R2813	**312** SR olive green + 3 Maunsell coaches Ltd Edn 2500 (coach set 329) 6-w train pack- *09-11*	NA	180
(R2813)	above loco only - *09-11*	75	NA
R2952	**338** SR 8-w olive green + Maunsell coach + Pullman car + baggage car 'Imperial Airways' Ltd Edn 1500 train pack - *10-11*	NA	180
(R2952)	above loco only - *10-11*	75	NA
R2711	**729** SR olive green 6-w Ncab - *08-09*	70	91
R2829	**314** SR plain black - *09*	70	100
R2889	**30119** BRa SR green (Royal Train) Ltd Edn 1200 (HCC) - *09*	70	100
R2712	**30724** BR lined black Wcart Ncab - *08-09*	70	91
R2830	**30285** BRb lined black Wcart - *09*	70	100
R2713	**30310** BRb lined black Wcart Wcab - *08*	70	91
R2831	**30726** BRc lined black 6-w - *09*	70	100

L32. SR Class L1 4-4-0 (1960)

Maunsell's successful design of 1926. The original Tri-ang model with loco drive.

R350+R36	**31757** BRc green - *60-67*	55	80
350	**1757** Southern dark green - *71-72*	45	70

The Tri-ang Class L1 4-4-0 of 1960 [L32]

L33a. SR Class V 'Schools' 4-4-0 (1981)

Maunsell's design of 1930 and Britain's most powerful 4-4-0. Ringfield tender drive. RD = presentation pack with Royal Doulton plate.

	Southern		
R683	**926 *Repton*** olive - *83-84*	50	65
R817	**900 *Eton*** olive, sometimes without smoke deflectors - *86-87*	45	60
R057	**903 *Charterhouse*** olive - *89-90*	40	60
R533	**934 *St. Lawrence*** olive Ltd Edn 2000 - *92*	55	70
R132	**936 *Cranleigh*** olive - *94-95*	40	60
R380	**928 *Stowe*** malachite smoke - *81-82*	50	70
R583	**921 *Shrewsbury*** malachite - *91-92*	40	60
R648	**905 *Tonbridge*** malachite RD Ltd Edn 3000 - *96*	60	90
R2018	**930 *Radley*** malachite - *97-98*	45	60
R2124	**907 *Dulwich*** malachite - *99-00*	45	60
R2144	**914 *Eastbourne*** malachite Sp Edn 1000 (Collectors Centre) - *00*	45	60
	British Railways		
R084	**30927 *Clifton*** BRb black - *84-85*	70	85
R2039	**30925 *Cheltenham*** BRb black Sp Edn 1000 (Cheltenham MC) - *97*	45	60
R2079	**30912 *Downside*** BRc black + 3 Pullman train pack Ltd Edn 2000 - *98*	NA	120
(R2079)	above loco only - *98*	70	NA
R257	**30911 *Dover*** BRc green - *82-83*	85	105
R317	**30908 *Westminster*** BRc green - *96*	45	60
R2082	**30902 *Wellington*** BRc green + 3 coaches pack Sp Edn 1500 (Kays) - *98*	NA	110
(R2082)	above loco only - *98*	60	NA
R2181	**30935 *Sevenoaks*** BRc green - *00-01*	55	70

L33b. SR Class V 'Schools' 4-4-0 (2008)

Maunsell's express passenger design of 1930 and Britain's most powerful 4-4-0. Super-detailed model with 5-pole skew wound motor in the locomotive. Decoder socket in tender. Extensice cab interior detail. Both 'DCC ready' and 'DCC fitted' (has X suffix) versions of each general release loco were made. Add £10-£15 for X models. NYMR=National Collection model Xsc= no smoke deflectors.

R2742	**903 *Charterhouse*** SR olive green Xsd - *09-11*	80	108
R2843	**907 *Dulwich*** SR olive green Xsd - *09-10*	80	120
R2745	**902 *Wellington*** SR malachite green - *09-10*	80	108
R2827	**925 *Cheltenham*** SR malachite green NRM - *09*	80	120
R2898XS	**30909 *St Pauls*** BRb black DS - *10*	190	235
R2815	**30924 *Haileybury*** BRb black std tender + 3 Maunsell coaches train pack Ltd Edn 2500 - *09-11*	NA	200

The interior of the cab of the new 'schools' Class loco [L33b]

(R2744)	above loco only - *09-11*	85	NA
R2844	**30934 *St Lawrence*** BRb black std tender - *09-11*	80	120
R2744	**30932 *Blundell's*** BRb black std tender - *08-09*	80	108
R2845	**30901 *Winchester*** BRc green std tender - *10-11*	80	120
R2743	**30915 *Brighton*** BRc green - *09*	80	108

L34. GWR Class 2301 0-6-0 (ex-Airfix) (1998)

Dean's standard 0-6-0 goods locomotive of 1883. Ringfield tender drive.

R2064	**2468** Great Western green - *98-00*	40	55
R2064A	**2322** Great Western green - *99*	40	55
R2064B	**2526** Great Western green Ltd Edn 500 (HCClub) - *99*	55	75
R2064C	**2579** Great Western green - *00-01*	38	50
R2210	**2579** BRb lined black - *01*	40	50
R2275	**2322** BRb plain black - *02-04*	40	50
R2275A	**2538** BRb plain black - *05-06*	40	50

L35. MR Class 3F 0-6-0 (1958)

Original Tri-ang model with loco drive. A Johnson design of 1885 later modified by Deeley.

R251	**3775** MR maroon - *66-67*	40	70
R251	**43620** BRc maroon - *not made*	NA	NA
R251+R33	**43775** BRc black - *58-63*	40	75
R251S	**43775** BRc black with smoke unit - *64-65*	45	80
R661S	**43775** BRc black W ex-set - *65*	80	NA

L36. MR/LMS Class 4F 0-6-0 (ex-Airfix) (1998)

A Fowler design of 1911. Later batches were made for the LMS and the S&DJR. Ringfield tender drive. From 2011 the moter was fitted in the locomotive.

R2148	**60** S&DJR dark blue Ltd Edn 1000 (Collectors Centres) - *00*	50	65
R3030	**4312** LMS lined black - *11*	75	100
R2193	**4418** LMS plain black - *01*	40	45
R2396	**43924** BRa plain black W - *04-05*	40	50

Ex-LMS Class 4F 0-6-0 [L36]

R2276	**44447** BRb plain black - *02-04*	40	50
R2276A	**44454** BRb plain black - *03-04*	40	50
R2138	**44523** BRb black + 6 wagons 'The Colliery Set' train pack Sp Edn 1000 (AB Gee) - *99*	NA	80
(R2138)	above loco only - *99*	45	NA
R2066	**44331** BRc black - *98*	30	35
R3031	**44331** BRc plain black - *11*	75	100
R2135M	**44313** BRc black, yellow stripe Ltd Edn 1500 - *99-00*	45	60
R2545	**43990** BRc black W - *not made*	NA	NA
R2545	**44218** BRc black W - *06*	45	59

L37. SR Class Q1 0-6-0 (2003)

Bulleid austerity design of 1942. A super-detailed model with a 5-pole skew wound motor in the loco. 'DCC Ready'. The BR versions are fitted with working mechanical lubricators.

R2343	**C8** SR plain black - *03-04*	45	60
R2343A	**C9** SR plain black - *04-05*	45	60
R2343B	**C21** SR plain black - *04-05?*	45	60
R2355	**33037** BRb black W - *not made*	NA	NA
R2355	**33037** BRb plain black - *03-04*	45	60
R2355A	**33017** BRb plain black - *04-07*	55	70
R2355B	**33013** BRb plain black - *05-07*	55	70
R2538	**33002** BRb plain black W - *06-07*	55	70
R2344	**33009** BRc plain black - *not made*	NA	NA
R2344	**33009** BRc black W - *03-04*	40	55
R2344A	**33006** BRc black W - *04-06*	55	70
R2344B	**33020** BRc black W - *05-06*	55	70
R2537	**33023** BRc black - *06-07*	55	70
R3011	**33005** BRc plain black - *11*	75	106

L38. LMS Class 2F 2-6-0 (1975)

An Ivatt design of 1946. Loco drive.

R857	**46400** BRc black - *75-77*	30	45

Proposed but the only one made - an LMS version of the Class 2F [L38]

R852	**46521** BRc green - *78-79*	30	50

Ex-GWR Earl Cairns from computer artwork by Robbie McGavin

L39. GWR Class 68xx 'Grange' 4-6-0 (2005)

Collett's design of 1936. 5-pole skew wound loco mounted motor. DCC ready, NEM coupling pockets.

R2402	**6818 *Hardwick Grange*** GWR (roundel) green, small tender - *05*	70	85
R2547	**6877 *Llanfair Grange*** GWR (roundel) green, small tender- *06-06*	70	85
R2403	**6862 *Derwent Grange*** BRb black - *05*	60	75
R2548	**6816 *Frankton Grange*** BRb black W - *06-09*	70	114
R2404	**6869 *Resolven Grange*** BRc green W - *05-07*	55	70
R2502	**6879 *Overton Grange*** BRc green - *05-07*	65	80
R2786	**6825 *Llanvair Grange*** BRc green - *not made*	NA	NA

L40. GWR Class 49xx 'Hall' 4-6-0 (1966)

Collett's 1928 design. Loco drive with X04 motor. Chuff-chuff noise was added from 1971, nickel tyres from 1972 and the alternative names were included up until the end of 1972.

	Great()Western Green		
R759G	**4983 *Albert Hall*** gloss - *70-71*	35	50
R759N	as above with sound added - *71-72*	30	45
R759A	as above with nickel tyres added - *72*	30	45
-	**4916 *Crumlin Hall*** - *70-72* *	55	NA
-	**6922 *Burton Hall*** - *70-72* *	55	NA
-	**5955 *Garth Hall*** - *70-72* *	55	NA
R759	**4983 *Albert Hall*** gloss - *73-76*	30	45
R759	**4983 *Albert Hall*** waxy appearance - *77*	30	45
R761	**5934 *Kneller Hall*** - *78-79*	35	50
R313	**4930 *Hagley Hall*** - *80-83*	35	50
R759	**4983 *Albert Hall*** BRc green - *66-69*	35	60
R765	**25555 *Lord Westwood*** red - *73-75*	25	55
R?	**25555 *Lord White*** red - *not made*	NA	NA

* Renamed/renumbered using transfers supplied with R759G, R759N and R759A.

L41. GWR Class 29xx 'Saint' 4-6-0 (1988)

Churchward's 1902 design. Adapted from the Tri-ang Hornby Hall. Ringfield tender drive.

R380	**2937 *Clevedon Court*** BRb black - *88-91*	45	60
R830	**2920 *Saint David*** Great()Western green - *86-87*	50	65
R141	**2918 *Saint Catherine*** Great()Western green - *94-95*	50	65
R2019	**2927 *Saint Patrick*** G()W green - *97-98*	45	60

L42a. GWR 'Castle' Class 4-6-0 (ex-Airfix/Dapol) (1997)

Collett's 4073 Class. Some models have the Hawksworth flat-sided tender (ht) while others have Collett's step-sided tender (st). Ringfield loco drive but a new 5-pole skew wound motor was fitted in 2007. dc = double chimney. hb = headboard. From 2005, these were 'DCC Ready' (DCC). chip = DCC decoder fitted.

	Great()Western Green		
R2232	**4097 *Kenilworth Castle*** st - *01-02*	50	70
(R1160)	**4097 *Kenilworth Castle*** st ex-'The Cornishman' train set DCC - *11*	NPG	NA
R2317	**4093 *Dunster Castle*** st - *03*	50	70
R2389	**4086 *Builth Castle*** st - *03-05*	50	70
(R1077)	**4082 *Windsor Castle*** st chip ex-set - *06-07*	75	NA
(R1077)	**5021 *Whittington Castle*** chip ex-set - *not made*	NA	NA
	GWR (shirt-button) Green		
R2196M	**5029 *Nunney Castle*** GWR, st, train pack with 3 coaches Sp Edn 1500 - *01*	NA	100
(R2196)	above loco only - *01*	50	NA
R2459	**5075 *Wellington*** GWR st - *05*	65	85
X5979	**4087 *Cardigan Castle*** GWR ex-Cornish Riviera R1102 MO set DC 2000 made- *07*	90	NA
	BR Green		
R2088	**5097 *Sarum Castle*** BRb ht Sp Edn 1000 (Beatties) - *98*	50	70
R2024	**5042 *Winchester Castle*** BRb ht train pack with 3 coaches - *97-98*	NA	90
R2028	above loco only - *97-98*	50	NA
R2086	**5053 *Earl Cairns*** BRb ht - *98-01*	50	70
R2822	**5053 *Earl Cairns*** BRb ht Pete Waterman Collection - *09-11*	90	120
R2090	**5004 *Llanstephen Castle*** BRb ht train pack with 3 coaches Ltd Edn 2000 - *99*	NA	90
(R2090)	above loco only - *99*	50	NA
R2133M	**7025 *Sudeley Castle*** BRb ht train pack + 3 Mk1s Sp Edn 1500 (Kays) - *99*	NA	100
(R2133)	above loco only - *99*	50	NA
R2141	**5069 *Isambard Kingdom Brunel*** BRb ht Sp Edn 1000 (A.B.Gee) - *99*	60	80
R2455	**4079 *Pendennis Castle*** BRb st - *05*	65	85
R2498	**7036 *Taunton Castle*** BRb ht W Ltd Edn 500 ** (HCClub) - *05*	70	90
R2543	**4081 *Warwick Castle*** BRb ht - *06-08*	70	90
R2551	**5077 *Fairey Battle*** BRb st - *06-07*	70	90
R2280	**5073 *Blenheim*** BRc, dc, st - *02*	50	70
R2318	**5071 *Spitfire*** BRc dc st - *03*	40	70
R2364M	**5038 *Morlais Castle*** BRb, hb, st Torbay Express Ltd Edn 1500 train pack with 3 brown+cream Mk1s - *03*	NA	120
(R2364)	above loco only - *03*	50	NA
R2372M	**5020 *Trematon Castle*** BRc train pack with 3 brown+cream Mk1s - *03*	NA	120
(R2372)	above loco only - *03*	50	NA
(R1048)	**7028 *Cadbury Castle*** BRc ht ex-set - *04-05*	50	NA
R2424	**5074 *Hampden*** BRc st dc - *04-05*	50	70
R2432	**7005 *Sir Edward Elgar*** BRc + 3 brown+cream Mk1 coaches + 'Cathedrals Express' headboard + 112 reporting number Sp Edn 1,000 (Hereford Models) - *04*	NA	120
(R2432)	above loco only - *04*	50	NA
R2736	**7013 *Bristol Castle*** BRc dc - *08*	80	99
R27??	**5007 *Rougemont Castle*** BRc + 3 maroon +cream Collett coaches Red Dragon Ltd Edn 1500 mail order train pack - *08*	NA	165
(R27??)	above loco only ex-mail order train pack - *08*	90	NA
	'Hogwarts Express'*		
R2284	**5972 *Hogwarts Castle*** red, hb, st in Philosopher's Stone packaging - *01-02*	60	70

R2337	5972 ***Hogwarts Castle*** as above but Chamber of Secrets packaging - *03*	60	70
R2378	5972 ***Hogwarts Castle*** as above but Prisoner of Azkaban packaging - *04*	60	70
R2491	5972 ***Hogwarts Castle*** as above but Goblet of Fire packaging - *05-06*	60	70
R2662	5972 ***Hogwarts Castle*** as above but Order of the Phoenix packaging, with headlight, DCC - *07-08*	60	70
R2885	5972 ***Hogwarts Castle*** as above but Half Blood Prince packaging, with headlight, DCC - *09*	65	90
R2301	5972 ***Hogwarts Castle*** red as above but gold plated metal, st - *01*	90	120

* The Hornby 'Hogwarts Express' train set was also sold in Germany by Marklin in special packaging. ** Due to an error, early in 2006, a quantity of the models was supplied to Rails of Sheffield and 88 were sold before they were withdrawn. These were sold without certificates and reduces the certificated models to 412. *** Released at 'Steam 2009' at the Swindon GWR railway museum.

L42b. GWR 'Castle' Class 4-6-0 (2010)

Collett's 4073 Class completely retooled as a super-detail model. Some models have the Hawksworth flat-sided tender (ht) while others have Collett's step-sided tender (st). 5-pole skew wound motor. dc = double chimney. 'DCC Ready' or 'DCC fitted' (X suffix). Allow £5-£10 extra for a 'DCC fitted' model. DS = DCC sound chip fitted.

R2848*	5011 ***Tintagel Castle*** GWR green st - *11*	90	120

Close up detail on the new 'Castle' Class model [L42b]

R2897XS	4098 ***Kidwelly Castle*** BRb green ht DS - *10*	190	235
R2849	5068 ***Beverston Castle*** BRb green st - *10-11*	90	120
R2958	7007 ***Great Western*** BRb green ht (GWR 1835-2010) Ltd Edn 1000 - *10*	90	120
R2986	7036 ***Taunton Castle*** BRb green st + 3 Mk1 chocolate+cream The Royal Duchy coaches Ltd Edn 1000 'A Date with the Duchy' train pack - *11*	NA	230
(R2986)	above loco on its own - *11*	90	NA
R2850	7034 ***Ince Castle*** BRc green st dc - *10*	90	120
R2852	7037 ***Swindon*** **BRc green (Sp Edn (Steam Museum, Swindon) - *10*	70	90
R2994XS	7029 ***Clun Castle*** BRc green dc st DS - *11*	200	266

* Before this could be made,the tooling broke and new tooling had to be made. ** A mockup was displayed at 'Steam 2009' at the Swindon GWR railway museum but the actual production model was not available until the following year.

L43. GWR 'County' Class 10xx 4-6-0 (ex-Dapol) (1997)

Hawksworth's County Class of 1945. Ringfield loco drive. From 2005, these were 'DCC Ready'. dc = double chimney. The models have the Hawksworth flat sided tender.

	GWR Green		
R2025	1004 ***County of Somerset*** G()W train pack with 3 coaches - *97-98*	NA	110
R2029	above loco only - *97-98*	40	NA
R2937	1006 ***County of Cornwall*** G()W (RailRoad) - *10-11*	50	60
R2085	1029 ***County of Worcester*** G()W - *98*	50	70
R2391	1010 ***County of Carnarvon*** G()W - *04-05*	50	70
	BR Black		
R2097	1015 ***County of Gloucester*** BRb - *99-00*	50	70
R2174	1022 ***County of Northampton*** BRb Sp Edn 1500 (Kays) - *00*	60	80
R2558	1007 ***County of Brecknock*** BRb - *06-07*	70	93
	BR Green		
R2461	1005 ***County of Devon*** BRb - *05-07*	70	93
R2166	1006 ***County of Cornwall*** BRc + 3 coaches train pack Ltd Edn 2000 - *00*	NA	100
(R2166)	above loco only - *00*	50	NA
R2211	1020 ***County of Monmouth*** BRc, dc - *01*	50	70
R2392	1026 ***County of Salop*** BRc dc - *04*	55	75

L44a. GWR 'King' Class 60xx 4-6-0 (1978)

Collett's express class of 1927. On this model, the boiler was not undercut. Ringfield tender drive.

R78	6024 ***King Edward I*** Great()Western green, npf - *78-80*	25	40

L44b. GWR 'King' Class 60xx 4-6-0 (1980)

The boiler was now undercut. Ringfield tender drive. npf = non paint finish. dc = double chimney. RD = presentation pack with Royal Doulton plate.

	Great () Western Green		
R349	6013 ***King Henry VIII*** - *80-83*	30	40
R070	6000 ***King George V*** ex-set - *85*	35	NA
R292	6027 ***King Richard I*** - *88-91*	40	55
R082	6008 ***King James II*** - *93-94*	40	55
R650	6018 ***King Henry VI*** RD Ltd Edn 3000 - *96*	60	75
R2022	6006 ***King George I*** - *97-98*	40	55
R2119	6014 ***King Henry VII*** - *99-01*	40	55

Ex-GWR 'King' Class - King George V in 'Express Blue' [L44b]

	BR Blue		
R737	6000 ***King George V*** BRb, bell on front - *96-97*	45	60
	BR Green		
R2084M	6009 ***King Charles II*** BRa train pack Sp Edn 1500 (Kays) - *98*	NA	100
R303	6005 ***King George II*** BRc dc - *95-96*	40	55
R845	6010 ***King Charles I*** BRc ex-set dc - *96-98*	45	NA
R2077	6026 ***King John*** BRc + 3 coaches train pack Ltd Edn 2000 - *98*	NA	90

L44c. GWR 'King' Class 60xx 4-6-0 (2003)

This is the super-detail model, tooled-up in China with a 5-pole skew wound motor in the loco. All have had blackened metalwork. From 2005, these were 'DCC ready'. sc = single chimney, dc = double chimney

R2233	6029 ***King Stephen*** Great () Western green sc - *03*	70	83
R2390	6028 ***King Henry II*** Great () Western green sc - *04*	70	85
R2460	6008 ***King James II*** Great()Western green sc - *05*	70	90
R3074	6002 ***King William iV*** Great () Western green Ltd Edn 1200 + Royal Mail first day cover - *11*	105	143
R2544	6006 ***King George I*** GWR (roundel) green sc - *06-07*	75	93
R2309	6028 ***King George VI*** BRb blue Ltd Edn 1000 (Collectors Centres) - *03*	70	85
R2234	6002 ***King William IV*** BRc green dc - *03-05*	70	83
R2530	6007 ***King William III*** BRc green dc - *06-07*	75	93

L45a. LMS 'Black 5' Class 4-6-0 (1973)

Ringfield tender drive. Body has top feed but no dome. ovg = old valve gear (from the 'Britannia' model).

R061	**5112** LMS black, ovg, + alternative numbers and names * - *76*	30	42
-	**5158 *Glasgow Yeomanry*, 5156 *Ayrshire Yeomanry*** alternative numbers and names for R061 - *76*	30	NA
R840	**5112** LMS black, + alternative numbers and names - *77-78*	30	40
-	**5158 *Glasgow Yeomanry*, 5156 *Ayrshire Yeomanry*** alternative numbers and names for R840 - *77-78*	35	NA
R320	**5138** LMS black - *81-84*	30	40
R842	**4657** LMS maroon - *78-79*	30	45
R859	**45192** BRc black, ovg, + alternative numbers and names * - *73-75*	35	48
-	**45158 *Glasgow Yeomanry*, 45156 *Ayrshire Yeomanry*** alternative numbers and names for R859 - *73-75*	30	NA
R068	**45021** BRc black Ltd Edn 2500 - *84*	45	60

*Early models of the 'Black Five' had tender wheels both sides fitted with rubber tyres and the tender was permanently attached to the loco. Later ones had tyres on one side only and the loco and tender were separate.

L45b. LMS 'Black 5' Class 4-6-0 (1987)

Ringfield tender drive. New body with dome and a new scale Stanier metal chassis (except R858 which had the old chassis).

R2881	**5112** LMS lined black (RailRoad) - *09-11*	50	65
R858	**5241** LMS black - *87-89*	35	45
R2083M	**5379** LMS black Sp Edn 1500 (Kays) - *98*	40	50
R2081	**45292** BRa lined black Ltd Edn 1500 (Littlewoods) - *98*	40	50

Railroad 'Black 5' LMS No.5112 [L45b]

R314	**44808, 44871, 44932** BRc black - *90-91*	30	40
R292	**45422** BRc black - *96-97*	35	45
R347	**44932** BRc green Sp Edn 1500 (Kays) - *92*	40	50
R9049	**3** green with face - *see Thomas section*	-	-

L45c. LMS 'Black 5' Class 4-6-0 (2002)

Stanier's most successful mixed traffic development of 1934. Retooled super-detail model. DCC ready and 5-pole skew wound motor. db = domed boiler. dlb = domeless boiler. ff = forward topfeed. All are DCC Ready. DS= digital sound

R2257	**5055** LMS lined black dlb - *02*	55	75
R2323	**5000** LMS lined black, NRM series dlb - *03*	65	85
R2561	**5036** LMS lined black dlb - *06-08*	55	75
R2887M	**5026** LMS lined black + 3 LMS coaches Thames-Forth Express train pack Sp Edn 1200 (Argos + Shop Direct) - *09*	NA	120
R2250	**45253** BRb black W - *not made*	NA	NA
R2250	**45253** BRb lined black db - *02*	55	75
R2359	**44908** BRb black - *02*	55	75
R2322	**44668** BRb lined black db ff - *03-05*	65	86
R2804XS	**44875** BRb lined black db DS - *09-10*	190	235
R2450	**45069** BRb lined black W db - *not made*	NA	NA
R2895XS	**45377** BRc lined black db DS - *10*	190	235
R2450	**45393** BRb lined black W db - *05-07*	70	93
R2525	**45270** BR? lined black? W - *06 made?*	NPG	NPG
R2258	**44781** BRc black - *not made*	NA	NA
R2258	**44781** BRc black db ff W - *02*	55	75
R2360	**44762** BRc black W - *02*	55	75
R2321	**45455** BRc plain black db - *03-04*	65	86
R2857	**45458** BRc lined black db ff - *09-10*	70	122
R2382	**44666** BRc lined black W db ff - *04-05*	65	86
R2449	**45157 *The Glasgow Highlander*** BRc lined black dlb - *05*	70	88
R2555	**45156 *Ayrshire Yeomanry*** BRc lined black dlb - *06-07*	70	93
R2686A	**44781** BRc black riveted tender Ltd Edn 1004 40th Anniversary last steam run - *08*	85	110
R2686B	**44871** BRc black welded tender Ltd Edn 1004 40th Anniversary last steam run - *08*	85	110
R2904	**45190** BRc lined black Pete Waterman Collection - *10-11*	80	106
R2979	**44932** BRc lined black db + 3 WCR Mk2d Pullman cars 'West Coast Railway Pullman' Train pack - *11*	NA	205
(R2979)	above loco on its own - *11*	80	NA
R2995XS	**45010** BRc lined black W DS – *11*	200	266

L46. LMS 'Patriot' Class 4-6-0 (1979)

Fowler's 1930 development of a 5XP Express locomotive. From 2000 this model had blackened metalwork. Ringfield tender drive.

R357	**5541 *Duke of Sutherland*** LMS maroon, non paint finish - *79*	30	40
R311	**5541 *Duke of Sutherland*** LMS maroon - *80*	35	45
R2936	**5532 *Illustrious*** LMS maroon (RailRoad) - *10-11*	50	60
R308	**5533 *Lord Rathmore*** LMS maroon - *95-97*	35	50
R2182A	**5539 *EC Trench*** LMS maroon - *00-02*	45	60
R2182B	**5514 *Holyhead*** LMS maroon - *00-02*	45	60
R324	**45519 *Lady Godiva*** BRa black - *83*	50	65
R578	**45537 *Private Sykes VC*** BRb green - *91*	55	70
R2456	**45543 *Home Guard*** BRb green W - *05-07*	60	75
R2347	**45515 *Caernarvon*** BR green + 3 Mk1s The Manxman Ltd Edn train pack - *02*	NA	120
R2208	**45515 *Caernarvon*** BRc green - *01-02*	50	65

L47. LMS Rebuilt 'Patriot' Class 4-6-0 (2007)

An express passenger class of 1930. Some of the class were rebuilt with tapered boilers between 1946 and 1948. 5-pole skew wound motor in the loco. Both 'DCC ready' and 'DCC fitted' (has X suffix) versions of each general release loco were made. Add £10-£15 for X models.

R2632	**45531 *Sir Fredrick Harrison*** BRb green - *07-08*	75	90
R2726	**45536 *Private W Woods VC*** BRb green - *08-09*	80	102

Rebuilt 'Patriot' Class - Sir Fredrick Harrison [L47]

R2633	**45545 *Planet*** BRc green - *07*	75	90
R2634	**45512 *Bunsen*** BRc green W - *07*	75	90
R2727	**45528 *REME*** BRc green - *08-09*	80	102

L48. LMS Rebuilt 'Royal Scot' Class 4-6-0 (2007)

An express passenger class of 1943. 5-pole skew wound motor in the loco. Double chimney. Both 'DCC ready' and 'DCC fitted' (has X suffix) versions of each general release loco were made. Add £10-£15 for X models.

R2631	**6133 *The Green Howards*** LMS black - *07-08*	75	90
R2664	**6100 *Royal Scot*** LMS maroon bell no smoke deflectors Ltd Edn (HCC) - *07*	75	90
R2628	**46102 *The Black Watch*** BRb green - *07*	75	90
R2629	**46140 *The King's Royal Rifle Corps*** BRb green W - *07-08*	75	90
R2630	**46146 *The Rifle Brigade*** BRc green - *07-08*	75	90
R2728	**46120 *Royal Inniskilling Fusiliers*** BRc green - *08-09*	80	100
R2729	**46144 *Honourable Artillery Company*** BRc green - *08-09*	80	100
R27??	**46127 *Old Contemptibles*** BRc green + 3 Mk1 maroon coaches Irish Mail Ltd Edn 1500 pack - *08*	NA	165
(R27??)	above loco only ex-mail order train pack - *08*	90	NA
R2824	**46100 *Royal Scot*** BRc green Pete Waterman Collection - *09*	85	112
R3018	**46115** Scots Guardsman BRc green - *11*	95	123

L49. LNER Class B1 4-6-0 (2011)

This model will be able to use parts from the B17.

R2998	**1040 *Roedeer*** LNER lined black - *11*	90	119

R2999	**61138** BRb lined black - *11*	90	119
R3000	**61243 *Sir Harold Mitchell*** BRc lined black - *11*	90	119

L50. GER Class B12 4-6-0 (1963)

Holden's 1911 design which was later redeveloped by Gresley in 1932. Loco driven. It became the first loco model to be 'upgraded' in China. smoke = smoke generator fitted. N = chuff-chuff sound fitted.

R150	**8504** LNER matt green - *?*	55	65
R866	**8509** LNER matt green - *?*	30	55
R866S	**8509** LNER gloss green, smoke - *70*	30	55
R389G	**8509** LNER matt green, smoke, kit - *70*	NA	140
R389S	**8509** LNER gloss green, smoke, kit - *70-71*	NA	140
R866NS/ R866AS	**8509** LNER green, smoke + N - *71-74*	25	40

Ex-GER Class B12 in LNER green [L50]

R866	**8509** LNER matt green + N - *78-79*	25	40
R284	**8579** LNER fully lined green + N - *96-00*	30	40
R?	**8572** LNER fully lined green + N - *?*	30	40
R2156A	**8537** LNER fully lined green + N - *00-02*	40	50
R2156B	**8578** LNER fully lined green + N - *00-03*	40	50
R2156C	**8546** LNER fully lined green + N - *01-02*	40	50
X4647	**8544** LNER fully lined green + N Sp Edn ex-MO set R1032K - *03-04, 08*	40	NA
(R1097)	**8544** LNER matt green + N ex-'East Coast Pullman' set - *08-11*	40	NA
(R1122)	**8537** LNER fully lined green ex-set - *not made*	NA	NA
(R1122)	**8528** LNER fully lined green ex-'Eastern Valleys Express' set - *09-10*	45	NA
R150	**7476** NE black + N - *76-78*	30	45
X5763/4	**61525** BRb blue + N ex-MO R1089 set - *06*	45	NA
R2102A	**61520** BRb lined black + N - *99*	37	45
R2102B	**61553** BRb lined black + N - *99*	37	45
R2320	**61520** BRb lined black + N - *03-04*	45	55
R150	**61572** BRc black - *63-69*	25	40
R150S	**61572** BRc black, smoke - *64-69*	30	45
R150SF	**61572** BRc black, smoke Acho couplings - *67-70*	70	150
R389	**61572** BRc black, smoke, kit - *68-69*	NA	120
R150NS	**61572** BRc black, smoke + N - *70-71*	30	50
R2134M	**61565** BRc black + 3 coaches, Sp Edn 1500 (Kays) train pack - *99*	NA	100

L51a. LNER Class B17/4 4-6-0 (1980)

Gresley's 1928 design. Ringfield tender drive. 5-p = 5-pole motor.

	LNER Light Green		
R053	**2862 *Manchester United*** + sheet alt. names - *80-81*	45	60
	2864 *Liverpool* * - *80-81*	40	NA
	2848 *Arsenal* * - *80-81*	40	NA
	2866 *Nottingham Forest* * - *80-81*	40	NA
R188	**2848 *Arsenal*** - *92*	45	60
R2017	**2862 *Manchester United***, green cylinders Sp Ed 1500 (Kays) - *97*	40	NA
R2056	**2857 *Doncaster Rovers*** - *98*	45	60
R2185	**2859 *Norwich City*** - *00-04*	55	70
	BR Green		
R2319	**61661 *Sheffield Wednesday*** BRa light green 5-p - *03-05*	65	80
R060	**61656 *Leeds United*** BRb + sheet alt. names - *82-83*	55	70
	61663 *Everton* ** BRb - *82-85*	40	NA
	61665 *Leicester City* ** BRb - *82-85*	40	NA
	61672 *West Ham United* ** BRb - *82-85*	40	NA
R2038A	**61650 *Grimsby Town*** BRb Sp Edn 250 (Rails) - *97*	80	100
R2038B	**61654 *Sunderland*** BRb Sp Edn 250 (Rails) - *97*	80	100
R2038C	**61651 *Derby County*** BRb Sp Edn 250 (Rails) - *97*	80	100
R2038D	**61649 *Sheffield United*** BRb Sp Edn 250 (Rails) - *97*	80	100
R2209	**61652 *Darlington*** BRb - *01*	60	80
R2532	**61648 *Arsenal*** BRb 5-p - *06-07*	68	89

Ex-LNER Class B17 - Arsenal [L51a]

R133	**61663 *Everton*** BRc - *94-95*	40	50
R2273	**61663 *Everton*** BRc - *02-05*	50	70
R315	**61662 *Manchester United*** BRc - *96-97*	35	50
R2014	**61664 *Liverpool*** BRc Ltd Edn 1000 - *97*	45	55
	BRa Black		
R2044	**E1664 *Liverpool*** + 3 coaches train pack Sp Edn 1500 (Kays) - *97*	NA	90
(R2044)	above loco only - *97*	75	NA

* Alternative name and number transfers supplied with R053. ** Alternative name and number transfers supplied with R060.

L51b. LNER Class B17/1 4-6-0 (2011)

In 2010 the B17 model was completely retooled enabling Hornby to model the various subclasses. They have a loco mounted 5-pole skew wound motor. The B17/1s were built by the North British Locomotive Company and introduced in 1928 with the small Great Eastern type 3,500 gallon tenders.

R2920	**61600 Sandringham** LNER green - *11*	90	120

L51c. LNER Class B17/2 4-6-0 (2011)

The B17/2s were built by the LNER at Darlington and fitted with Great Eastern 3,700 gallon tenders.

R2921	**61637 *Thorpe Hall*** BRb green - *11*	90	120
R3004	**61631** Selby Hall BRb green W - *11*	90	120

L51d. LNER Class B17/4 4-6-0 (2011)

These were built by the LNER and Robert Stephenson & Company and were paired with LNER group standard tenders. They were also named after football clubs.

R2922	**61650 *Grimsby Town*** BRc green - *11*	90	120
R3003	**61669** Barnsley BRc green - *11*	90	120

L52a. SR Class N15 'King Arthur' 4-6-0 (1976)

This short lived model was not up to the new standards being introduced in the late 1970s and was dropped. It was loco driven.

R154	**795 *Sir Dinadan*** Southern gloss green - *76-77*	40	65
R154	**795 *Sir Dinadan*** Southern matt green - *78*	45	70

L52b. LSWR Class N15 'King Arthur' 4-6-0 (2007)

Based on Urie's 1918 design, the class was later much extended by Maunsell. This is a completely new model with the motor in the engine. Two styles of cab were modelled and 6-wheel (6) and 8-wheel (8) tenders. Those paired with the 6-wheel tender have a higher cab floor and so a shallower cabside. NRM = one of Hornby's National Railway Museum Collection. Both 'DCC ready' and 'DCC fitted' (has X suffix) versions of each general release loco were made. Add £10-£15 for X models.

R2580	**736 *Excalibur*** SR green (8) - *07*	75	95

Ex-LSWR 'King Arthur' Class - Sir Valence [L52b]

R2836	**767 *Sir Valence*** SR olive green (8) - *09*	75	117
R2638	**777 *Sir Lamiel*** SR green (NRM) (8) - *07*	75	95
R2620	**746 *Pendragon*** SR malachite green - *07*	75	95
R26??	**E773 *Sir Lavaine*** SR olive green 'White Pullman EXCL Limited' + 3 Pullman cars Ltd Edn 1500 MO train set - *08*	NA	140
(R26??)	above loco only - *08*	75	NA
R2723	**751 *Etarre*** SR olive green (8) - *08*	75	99

R3075	**785 *Sir Mador de la Port*** SR olive green Ltd Edn 1200 + Royal Mail first day cover - *11*	105	143
X10252	**797 *Sir Blamor de Ganis*** SR olive green (8) ex-MO R1118 set Ltd Edn 2000- *08*	80	NA
R2???	**797 *Sir Blamor de Ganis*** SR olive green (8) + 3 Pullman cars, Sp Edn 2000 'Southern Belle' MO train pack - *08*	NA	140
(R2???)	above loco only - *08*	85	NA
R2581	**30764 *Sir Gawain*** BRb green W (8) - *07*	75	95
R2582	**30803 *Sir Harry le Fise Lake*** BRb green (6) - *07*	75	95
R2623	**30755 *The Red Knight*** BRb green - *not made*	NA	NA
R2623	**30737 *King Uther*** BRb green (8) - *07-09*	75	95
R2621	**30799 *Sir Ironside*** BRb green W (6) - *07-09*	75	95
R2622	**30778 *Sir Pelleas*** BRb green (8) - *07*	75	95
R2724	**30800 *Sir Meleaus de Lile*** BRb green (6) - *08-09*	80	106
R2905	**30452 *Sir Meliagrance*** BRb green (8) Pete Waterman Collection - *10-11*	80	106
R2583	**30453 *King Arthur*** BRc green (8) - *07*	75	95
R2725	**30450 *Sir Kay*** BRc green (8) - *08-09*	80	106

L53. BR Class 75000 4MT 4-6-0 (2009)

Riddles mixed traffic design of 1951. A super-detailed model from the start with DCC ready and fitted versions. Decoder socket in tender. Both 'DCC ready' and 'DCC fitted' (has X suffix) versions of each.

R2714	**75005** BRb black BR2 tender - *09-10*	80	108
R2715	**75062** BRc black BR2A tender - *09-10*	80	108

BR Class 4MT showing cab interior detail [L53]

R2716	**75070** BRc black W BR1B tender - *09-11*	80	108
R3016	**75072** BRc lined black - *11*	98	131

L54a. LMS 'Princess' Class 4-6-2 (1950)

This is the original Rovex model of 1950 which was later driven by a loco mounted X04 motor. It remained in production until the mid 1970s when the tools wore out. It was also made in New Zealand and Australia using the earliest tools. gold = gold BRb logo on tender.

	46201 *Princess Elizabeth*		
R50+R30	BRb black, gold, roller pickups - *50*	2000	NA
R50+R30	BRb black, gold, plunger pickups - *50-52*	20	50
R50+R30	BRb black, gold - *52-55*	15	50
R50+R30	BRb black, transfer logo - *55*	30	65
R50+R30	BRb black, transfers + lining - *55-58*	20	45
R50+R30	BRb black, transfer logo, red letters on black nameplate - *58*	80	95
R53+R31	BRb olive green, gold - *53*	30	50
R53+R31	BRb olive green, transfer logo - *54*	45	65
R53+R31	BRb olive green, transfers + lining - *54-56*	30	50
R53+R31	BRb green, transfers + lining - *56-57*	20	45
R53+R31	BRc green, transfers + lining, lacquered finish - *58-61*	25	60
R386	BRc green, CKD kit - *62-69*	NA	180
	46205 *Princess Victoria*		
R050	BRb black, gold, mail order model - *74*	25	65
R053	BRb green, gold, mail order model - *74*	25	65
R048	BRb maroon, gold, mail order - *74*	100	NPG
-	BRb blue, gold - *not made*	NA	NA
R50+R30	BRc black, transfers + lining - *59-62*	20	35
	Maroon Models		
R258	**6201 *Princess Elizabeth*** LMS - *70*	25	35
R258NS	**6201 *Princess Elizabeth*** LMS - *71-74*	25	35
-	**6204 *Princess Louise*** * LMS - *70-72*	40	NA
-	**6210 *Lady Patricia*** * LMS - *70-72*	40	NA
-	**6212 *Duchess of Kent*** * LMS - *70-72*	40	NA
R386	**6201 *Princess Elizabeth*** LMS kit - *70?*	25	300
R386?	**6200 *The Princess Royal*** LMS kit - *70*	NA	300
R260	details unknown Sp Edn 200 - *73*	NPG	NPG
R258+R34	**46200 *The Princess Royal*** BRc - *59-64,69*	25	65
-	**46213 *Princess*** BRc blue - *not made*	NA	NA

* Renamed/renumbered using transfers supplied with R158 and R258NS.

L54b. LMS 'Princess' Class 4-6-2 (1984)

The Princess Royal Class was Stanier's first development of Pacific locomotives for the LMS. This original scale model was a great improvement on the original Rovex Princess but was limited to dome-less examples thus preventing its use for Princesses in BR maroon livery. Some Hornby Princesses have been renumbered and renamed after leaving the factory.

R832	**6201 *Princess Elizabeth*** LMS maroon, maroon tender chassis * - *86-87*	40	55
R084	**6201 *Princess Elizabeth*** LMS maroon, black tender chassis - *93-94*	40	55
R050	**6200 *The Princess Royal*** LMS maroon, Fowler tender * - *84-85*	45	60
R2033	**6208 *Princess Helena Victoria*** LMS maroon + 3 coaches Ltd Edn 3000 train pack - *97*	NA	90
(R2033)	above loco only - *97*	40	NA
R2052	**6211 *Queen Maud*** LMS maroon Sp Edn 1000 (A.B.Gee) - *98*	50	65
R375	**6210 *Lady Patricia*** LMS maroon Sp Edn 1000 (Kays) - *90*	50	65
R2051	**6206 *Princess Marie Louise*** LMS black Sp Edn 1000 (A.B.Gee) - *98*	50	65
R138	**46208 *Princess Helena Victoria*** BRb blue - *94-95*	50	65
R037	**46210 *Lady Patricia*** BRb blue - *89-91*	55	80
R080	**46201 *Princess Elizabeth*** BRb green * - *84-85*	40	60
R2070	**46204 *Princess Louise*** BRb green Sp Edn 1000 (A.B.Gee) - *98*	50	75
R196	**46209 *Princess Beatrice*** BRb green - *92-93*	45	65

* This had the same basic tender as the 'Black Five' (i.e. underscale plastic chassis) but from R037 (1989) onwards, models were given the metal Stanier chassis.

L54c. LMS 'Princess' Class 4-6-2 (2001)

This is the super-detail model tooled-up in China and used the chassis from the scale length 'Coronation' of 2000. A changeable top mould allowed both domed and dome-less examples to be modelled. It is fitted with a loco mounted 5-pole skew wound motor. From 2005, these were 'DCC Ready'.

R2225	**6207 *Princess Arthur of Connaught*** LMS maroon - *01-02*	65	85
R2215	**6201 *Princess Elizabeth*** maroon LMS gold plated Ltd Edn 5000 - *02*	100	140
R2313	**6204 *Princess Louise*** LMS maroon - *03-05*	70	89
(R1045)	**6201 *Princess Elizabeth*** LMS maroon ex-R1045 Sp Edn (M&S) - *03*	75	NA
X4625/X4627	**6201 *Princess Elizabeth?*** LMS maroon ex-MO set R1057 - *08*	75	NA
R2426	**46201 *Princess Elizabeth*** BRb black Ltd Edn 2004 - *04*	70	90
R2448	**46210 *Lady Patricia*** BRb blue W - *05-06*	85	105
R2226	**46203 *Princess Margaret Rose*** BRb green, domed boiler - *01-02*	65	85
R2616	**46211 *Queen Maud*** BRb green - *07-09*	65	85

Ex-LMS Princess Elizabeth [L54c] (Tony Wright)

R2823	**46201 *Princess Elizabeth*** BRc green Pete Waterman Collection - *09*	85	124
R2314	**46212 *Duchess of Kent*** BRc green - *03*	70	89
R2447	**46207 *Princess Arthur of Connaught*** BRc maroon - *05*	75	95
R3015	**46207 *Princess Arthur of Connaught*** BRc maroon DS - *11*	98	131
R2990XS	**46208 *Princess Helena Victoria*** BRc maroon DS - *11*	200	266
R2559	**46203 *Princess Margaret Rose*** BRc maroon as preserved - *06-07*	85	105
R2559W	**46203 *Princess Margaret Rose*** BRc maroon as preserved ex-R1106K set - *08*	85	NA

L55a. LMS 'Duchess' Class 4-6-2 (1977)

Seen by many as the peak of Stanier's locomotive development, the 'Duchesses' first appeared in 1937. This is the original 'Duchess' model of 1977 which had a Ringfield tender drive. npf = non paint finish. RD = presentation pack with Royal Doulton plate.

R066	**6233 *Duchess of Sutherland*** LMS maroon, npf * - *77-80*	35	50
R305	**6234 *Duchess of Abercorn*** LMS maroon * - *80-81*	50	65
R459	**6253 *City of St Albans*** LMS black RD Ltd Edn 3,000 - *96*	65	80
R372	**46231 *Duchess of Atholl*** BRb blue Sp Edn 1,500 (Kays) - *92*	50	65
R208	**46239 *City of Chester*** BRb blue ex-R775 'The Caledonian' set - *94-95*	50	NA
R262	**46231 *Duchess of Atholl*** BRb green * - *82-84*	50	65
-	**46232 *Duchess of Montrose*** - *82-84* **	35	NA
-	**46230 *Duchess of Buccleugh*** - *82-84* **	35	NA
R2015	**46255 *City of Hereford*** BRb green - *97*	60	75
R379	**46250 *City of Lichfield*** BRc green Sp Edn 2000 (Kays) - *91*	55	70
R221	**46252 *City of Leicester*** BRc green - *92-93*	60	75
R2112	**46237 *City of Bristol*** BRc green + 3 coaches, train pack Ltd Edn 2000 - *99*	NA	100
(R2112)	above loco only - *99*	40	NA
R2015W	**46236 *City of Bradford*** BRc green first with dark metalwork R1004 'The Duchess' set - *99*	50	NA
R2176M	**46221 *Queen Elizabeth*** BRc green train pack with 3 coaches, Sp Edn 1500 (Kays) - *00-01*	NA	100
(R2176)	above loco only - *00-01*	40	NA
R?	***Queen Elizabeth*** gold plated metalwork - *02*	110	150
R577	**46251 *City of Nottingham*** BRc maroon - *91-94*	45	60
R194	**46247 *City of Liverpool*** BRc maroon Sp Edn 1500 (Kays) - *94*	60	75
R2041	**46247 *City of Liverpool*** BRc maroon, red nameplates Sp Edn 1000 (Hattons) - *97*	60	75
R134	**46226 *Duchess of Norfolk*** BRc maroon - *94-95*	55	70
R2023	**46225 *Duchess of Gloucester*** BRc maroon - *97-98*	55	70
R2078	**46248 *City of Leeds*** BRc maroon + 3 coaches train pack Ltd Edn 2000 - *98*	NA	100
(R2078)	above loco only - *98*	40	NA

* These had the same tender chassis as the early 'Princess' but from 1991 onwards the new scale metal tender chassis was used. ** Renamed/renumbered using transfers supplied with R262.

Proposed model which failed to make it into production in this livery [L55a]

L55b. LMS 'Duchess' Class 4-6-2 (2002)

This was the completely retooled super-detail model released in 2002 based on the fine detailed chassis from the Coronation Class model of 2001. It has a loco mounted 5-pole skew wound motor. SST = sloping smokebox top. HB = head board. From 2005, these were 'DCC ready'. DS = digital sound.

R2989XS	**6232 *Duchess of Montrose*** LMS maroon (no smoke deflectors) DS - *11*	200	266
R2230	**6230 *Duchess of Buccleuch*** LMS maroon - *02-03*	60	80
R2370	**6233 *Duchess of Sutherland*** LMS maroon + 3 royal coaches - *04*	NA	115
(R2370)	above loco only - *04*	60	NA
R2659M	**6233 *Duchess of Sutherland*** LMS maroon + 3 Stanier coaches Sp Edn 'The Royal Highlander' train pack - *07*	NA	130
R2985	**6233 *Duchess of Sutherland*** LMS maroon + 3 Stanier maroon coaches Ltd Edn 1000 'A Duchess at Carlisle' train pack - *11*	NA	230
(R2985)	above loco on its own - *11*	98	NA
R3014	**6233 *Duchess of Sutherland*** LMS lined black - *11*	98	131
R2311	**6242 *City of Glasgow*** LMS black SST - *03-04*	70	89
R2856	**6246 *City of Manchester*** LMS black SST - *09*	85	134
R2722	**46252 *City of Leicester*** BRa black - *08-09*	90	120
R2386	**46225 *Duchess of Gloucester*** BRb blue SST - *04*	60	90
R2553	**46237 *City of Bristol*** BRb blue SST - *06-07*	85	105
(R1094)	**46237 *City of Bristol*** BRb blue with red nameplates ex-set - *07*	85	NA
R2303M	**46224 *Princess Alexandra*** BRb blue SST HB + 3 coaches 'The Royal Scot' MO train pack Ltd Edn 1,500 - *02*	NA	120
(R2303)	above loco only - *02*	60	NA
R2231	**46228 *Duchess of Rutland*** BRb green, SST - *02-04*	60	75
R2930	**46243 *City of Lancaster*** BRc maroon - *10*	100	124
R2306	**46244 *King George V1*** BRb green + 3 Mk1s Ltd Edn 3,000 'The Caledonian' train pack - *03-04*	NA	120
(R2306)	above loco only - *03-04*	60	NA
R2446	**46232 *Duchess of Montrose*** BRc green W - *05*	70	90
R2312	**46239 *City of Chester*** BRc green, red nameplates - *03-04*	70	90
R2782XS	**46249 *City of Sheffield*** BRc green DS - *08-10*	140	193
R2444	**46238 *City of Carlisle*** BRc maroon - *05*	80	100
R2894XS	**46240 *City of Coventry*** BRc maroon DS - *10*	140	193

Ex-LMS 'Duchess' - City of Coventry [L55b]

R2383	**46251 *City of Nottingham*** BRc maroon W - *04-05*	65	80
R2262	**46245 *City of London*** BRc maroon Sp Edn 1,000 (Collector Centres) - *02*	80	100
R2552	**46248 *City of Leeds*** BRc maroon - *06*	85	105

* This is a sound system developed by ESU and used in Electrotren models made by Hornby for the Spanish market.

L56a. LMS 'Coronation' Class 4-6-2 (1970)

This is the underscale original model. It had an X04 loco mounted motor until the 1980s when this was replaced by a Ringfield tender drive. The 1970s models had a gloss finish while all those from 1983 and with a tender drive had a matt finish.

	LMS Blue		
R864	**6220 *Coronation*** gloss - *70-72*	55	75
-	**6221 *Queen Elizabeth*** ** gloss - *70-72*	65	NA
-	**6222 *Queen Mary*** ** gloss - *70-72*	65	NA
-	**6224 *Princess Alexandra*** ** gloss - *70-72*	65	NA
R685	**6220 *Coronation'*** matt * - *83-85, 92-94*	45	60
R175	as above Special 325 (B/P) - *94*	NA	70
R752	as above Special 30 (QVC) - *94*	NA	120
R834	**6222 *Queen Mary*** matt * - *85-86*	60	75
R2068	**6221 *Queen Elizabeth*** 1999 - *not made*	NA	NA
	LMS Maroon		
R871	**6244 *King George VI*** gloss - *71-74*	50	65
-	**6228 *Duchess of Rutland*** *** gloss - *71-72*	65	NA
-	**6221 *Queen Elizabeth*** *** gloss - *71-72*	65	NA
-	**6241 *City of Edinburgh*** *** gloss - *71-72*	65	NA
R767	**6244 *King George VI*** matt * Sp Edn 500 (Beatties) - *83*	65	80
R072	**6237 *City of Bristol*** matt * - *85-86*	70	90
-	**6237 *The Stock Exchange*** matt * Sp Edn for Hornby USM Debut December 1986 - *86*	700	800
R2087	**6221 *Queen Elizabeth*** 1999 - *not made*	NA	NA
	LMS Black		
R2092	**6245 *City of London*** LMS matt black, * Ltd		

	Edn 1000 - *98*	75	90
R2050	**6221 *Queen Elizabeth*** 1999 - *not made*	NA	NA

* The motor is in the tender. ** With alternative numbers and names supplied with R864. *** With alternative numbers and names supplied with R871.

L56b. LMS 'Coronation' Class 4-6-2 (2001)

The controversial streamlined version of Stanier's Princess Coronation (Duchess) Class. This was a completely new model introduced in 2001. It has a loco mounted 5-pole skew wound motor. DCC = 'DCC Ready'.

	LMS Blue		
R2206	**6220 *Coronation*** - *01-02*	65	80
R2271	**6223 *Princess Alice*** - *02-05*	65	80
R2285	**6221 *Queen Elizabeth*** Sp Edn 500 (HCClub) - *02*	70	85
(2371M)	**6224 *Princess Alexandra*** ex- R2371M Coronation Scot train pack Ltd Edn 2000 - *04, 08*	70	NA
	LMS Maroon		
R2179	**6229 *Duchess of Hamilton*** - *not made*	NA	NA
R2689	**6229 *Duchess of Hamilton*** Ltd Edn - *08*	80	100
R2179	**6225 *Duchess of Gloucester*** - *01*	65	80
R2205	**6235 *City of Birmingham*** - *01-04*	65	80
(R2199)	**6220 *Coronation*** in R2199M train pack - *01*	65	NA
R2531	**6226 *Duchess of Norfolk*** W - *06*	80	100
(R1065)	**6233 *Duchess of Sutherland*** ex-set - *06*	85	NA
R2907	**6239 *City of Chester*** + LMS maroon + 3 Stanier coaches Ltd Edn 1000 'Days of Red and Gold' from Barry J Freeman Collection - *10*	NA	200
(R2907)	above loco only - *10*	85	NA
	LMS Black		
R2270	**6241 *City of Edinburgh*** - *02-04*	65	80
(R1060)	**6224 *City of Lancaster*** W ex- R1060 VE Day Ltd Edn 1000 MO set - *05*	85	NA

L57a. LNER Class A3 4-6-2 (1968)

This was the original Tri-ang Hornby model with the body as a single moulding and a banjo dome. Driven by an X04 motor in the loco. ct = corridor tender. nct = non-corridor tender. npf = non-paint finish. N = chuff-chuff sound from tender. fsw = fine scale wheels. G = firebox glow.

	LNER 4472 Flying Scotsman		
R855	light green, ct, npf, G - *68-70*	18	35
R855N	light green, N, ct, npf, G - *71-77*	20	35
R845	light green improved lining, ct, fsw, npf - *78-79*	30	40
R322	light green, ct, fsw, crew - *80*	30	40
	BRc 60103 Flying Scotsman		
R850	green, nct, npf, red nameplate G - *68*	30	45
R850	green, nct, npf, black nameplate G - *69-70*	25	40
R850	green, ct, npf G - *69-70*	30	45

L57b. GNR/LNER Class A1/A3 4-6-2 (1981)

The model was virtually completely redesigned in time for release in 1981. This gave it wire handrails, daylight under the boiler, reshaped cab and (from 1993) a choice of domes, tenders, chimneys and the option of smoke deflectors. GN = Great Northern style tender (with rails round top). Ringfield tender drive. ct = corridor tender. nct = non-corridor tender. gsd = German smoke deflectors. rd = early round dome (all others have a banjo dome). dc = double chimney

	LNER 4472 *Flying Scotsman*		
R398	light green, ct, rd - *81-95*	25	40
R398	light green, ct, rd, silver hinges + handles - *96-06*	30	45
R387	light green, simplified lining **, rd - *82-84*	65	85
R074	light green, GN, rd - *93-94*	40	55
R075	light green, 2 tenders (both green), rd, Ltd Edn 2800 * - *93*	110	150
R114	light green, 2 tenders (both green), rd, Sp Edn 2000 (GUS) * - *93*	110	150
R098	light green, 2 tenders (one blue/grey) Ltd Edn 5000 - *95*	95	120
	BR 60103 *Flying Scotsman*		
R078	BRc green, nct, gsd, dc - *93-96*	45	60
R080	BRc green, nct, gsd, dc, Sp Edn 200 (BCA) - *93*	NA	120
R2020	BRb green, nct - *97-98*	60	75
R375	**61 *Pretty Polly*** LNER light green, GN, Sp Edn 1000 (Beatties) - *95*	65	80
R042	**4476 *Royal Lancer*** LNER light green, ct, rd - *89-90*	40	55
R140	**60071 *Tranquil*** BRa purple, GN, Sp Edn 1500 (Littlewoods) - *96*	60	75
R2036	**60075 *St Frusquin*** BRa purple, GN, Sp Edn 2000 (Kays) - *97*	55	70

Ex-LNER Class A3 in BR 'Express Blue' - Pretty Polly [L57b]

R129	**60061 *Pretty Polly*** BRb blue, GN, Sp Edn 1000 (Beatties) - *95*	60	75
R146	**60052 *Prince Palatine*** BRb blue, GN - *94-95*	45	60
R295	**60080 *Dick Turpin*** BRb green, GN - *95-97*	50	65
R059	**60061 *Pretty Polly*** BRc green, GN, gsd, dc, Sp Edn 1000 (Beatties) - *94*	75	95
R383	**4** blue with face - *see Thomas section*	-	-

* These were the same product but the GUS version had an extra outer protective box. They shared a number sequence for the certificates. While the certificates in the box

LMS 'Coronation' - Duchess of Devonshire from computer artwork by Robbie McGavin [L56b]

indicated that 5,000 were made, the true production figures are those shown here. ** The loco had no gold printing on the buffer beam, no boiler band next to the cab and no pen-line handrails on cab or tender. It was mostly used in the R547 and R548 train sets.

L57c. GNR/LNER Class A1/A3 4-6-2 (1998)

This was the super-detail version tooled-up in China and can be identified by a join-line along each side of the boiler and a finely detailed chassis. It came with a separate front coupling and dust shield and doors for the cab. Brake rods and brake pipes were already fitted. Wheels and rods were of a finer profile. GN = Great Northern style tender (with rails round top). ct = corridor tender. nct = non-corridor tender. gsd = German smoke deflectors. rd = early round dome (all others have a banjo dome). dc = double chimney. hb = headboard. Ringfield tender drive. From late 2002, the A3 models (identifiable in having a grey gear fitted to the rear of the driven tender wheels) had 5-pole armatures.

	LNER Light Green		
R2146	**103 *Flying Scotsman*** rd, nct, gold metalwork, Ltd Edn 2000 - *99-00*	80	155
R2147	**4472 *Flying Scotsman*** dc, ct, Ltd Edn 500 (HCClub) - *00*	55	75
R2261	**4472 *Flying Scotsman*** ct, Pegler Edition - *02-03*	65	85
R9098	**4472 *Flying Scotsman*** with face - *see Thomas section*	55	73
R2103	**2505 *Cameronian*** GN - *99-00*	45	70
R2191	**94 *Colorado*** GN, Ltd Edn 500 (HCClub) - *01*	55	70
R2265	**2751 *Humorist*** GN, dc, rd - *02-03*	50	60
	Various Liveries		
R2168	**E112 *St Simon*** BRa light green, GN, 'The Yorkshire Pullman' train pack with 3 Pullman cars Ltd Edn 2000 - *00*	NA	100
(R2168)	above loco only - *00*	50	NA
R2363M	**60092 *Fairway*** BRa green hb + 3 Gresley coaches Ltd Edn 1500 The Northumbrian train pack - *03*	NA	120
(R2363)	above loco only - *03*	50	NA
R2201	**60110 *Robert the Devil*** BRb blue, GN - *01*	65	80
(R1034)	**1760 *Hamleys Express*** red ex-set Sp Edn (Hamleys) - *02-04*	60	NA
	BR Brunswick Green		
R2140	**60048 *Doncaster*** BRb GN, Sp Edn 1000 (A.B.Gee) - *99*	65	80
(R1100)	**60073 *St Gatien*** BRb GN ex MO set - *08*	65	NA
R2054	**60103 *Flying Scotsman*** BRc nct, dc - *98-01*	50	60
R2126	**60046 *Diamond Jubilee*** BRc nct, dc, Ltd Edn 500 - *99*	65	80
R2152	**60085 *Manna*** BRc GN, gsd, nct, dc - *00*	50	60
R2195M	**60106 *Flying Fox*** BRc GN, Sp Edn 1500 train pack with 3 coaches - *01*	NA	100
(R2195)	above loco only - *01*	50	NA
R2365M	**60051 *Blink Bonny*** BRc + 3 Pullman cars Sp Edn 1500 'The Queen of Scots' MO train pack - *04*	NA	120
(R2365)	above loco only - *04*	50	NA

L57d. GNR Class A1 4-6-2 (RailRoad) (2007)

As above but now with the motor in the locomotive. This model was produced for the RailRoad budget range..

R2675	**4472 *Flying Scotsman*** LNER green A1 ct rd (Railroad) - *07-11*	45	56
(R1072)	**4472 *Flying Scotsman*** ct, rd ex-set - *07-10*	45	NA
(R1152)	**4472 *Flying Scotsman*** ex-set - *11*	50	NA

L57e. GNR Class A1 4-6-2 (2005)

This is Gresley's original design of Pacific locomotive for the GNR dating from 1922. Here we have the ultimate super-detailed model released in 2005 with a 5-pole skew wound motor in the loco. It also has a fixed rear pony truck with roller wheels, thus eliminating daylight under the cab. Alternative pony truck wheels were supplied in the box. It came 'DCC ready', 5-pole motor and fitted with NEM coupling sockets. GN = GNR style tender.

R2405	**4472 *Flying Scotsman*** LNER green - *not made*	NA	NA
R2549	**4475 *Flying Fox*** LNER green GN - *06-07*	85	105
R3073	**4476 *Royal Lancer*** LNER green Ltd Edn 1200 + Royal Mail first day cover - *11*	115	154
R2598M	**2569 *Gladiateur*** LNER green GN + 3 Pullmans train pack Sp Edn - *07*	NA	120
(R2598M)	above loco only - *07*	85	NA
R2405	**1470N *Great Northern*** LNER green GN - *05-07*	75	95

L57f. LNER Class A3 4-6-2 (2005)

Gresley's 1927 redevelopment of his A1 class. This is the ultimate super-detailed model (as above) released in 2005 with a 5-pole skew wound motor in the loco. It also has a fixed rear pony truck with roller wheels, thus eliminating daylight under the cab. Alternative pony truck wheels were supplied in the box. It came DCC ready with a 5-pole motor and was fitted with NEM coupling sockets. GN = GNR tender, dc = double chimney, sc = single chimney. rd = round dome.

R2441	**4472 *Flying Scotsman*** LNER green (as at June 2004) smoke deflectors, NRM headboard - *05-10*	85	105

Flying Scotsman as seen during the 1988 visit to Australia [L57f]

R2687	**4472 *Flying Scotsman*** LNER green Ltd Edn 1000 (as at 1988 visit to Australia) special headboard - *08*	90	110
R2953	**4472 *Flying Scotsman*** LNER green as preserved with 2 tenders + Pullman observation car, US 1969 Tour Ltd Edn 1500 - *11*	90	110
(R2953)	above loco only - *11*	85	NA
(R1074)	**60052 *Prince Palatine*** BRb blue sc GN ex-'The Master Cutler' set - *06*	85	NA
(R1082)	**60103 *Flying Scotsman*** BRb blue ex-set - *06*	85	NA
(R1082A)	**60103 *Flying Scotsman*** BRb blue ex-HM2000 set Sp Edn Marks & Spencers, 'DONCASTER' on front bufferbeam - *06*	95	NA
R2341	**60035 *Windsor Lad*** BRb green - *05-07*	75	95
R2536	**60073 *St. Gatien*** BRb green sc GN - *06-07*	85	105
R2617	**60067 *Ladas*** BRb green sc rd - *07*	85	105
R2342	**60077 *The White Knight*** BRc green dc - *05-06*	75	95
R2569	**60039 *Sandwich*** BRc green GN dc + 3 maroon Mk1s - *06-07*	NA	120
(R2569)	above loco only - *06*	85	NA
R2720	**60049 *Galtee More*** BRc grn dc GN - *08*	85	105
R2966	**60043 *Brown Jack*** BRc green dc GN - *11*	100	120
R3013	**60093 *Coronarch*** BRc green dc GN - *11*	98	131

L57g. LNER Class A3 4-6-2 (Live Steam) (2005)

This is the Live Steam model, with a boiler in the tender which generates steam to drive the cylinders and operate the whistle. The body is moulded in a special heat-resistant plastic.

R2485	**4472 *Flying Scotsman*** LNER green - *05-10*	180	226
R2566	**4472 *Flying Scotsman*** LNER green 2 tenders Ltd Edn 1000 - *08-10*	190	236
R2492	**60096 *Papyrus*** BRb green - *05-08*	180	210

L58. A1 Trust Tornado 4-6-2 (2011)

This is a RailRoad model, produced in response to the great interest that the real locomotive has generated amongst children. It is a sector of the market that has kept *Flying Scotsman* train sets in the order books. This is a completely new model of *Tornado*, as built, with new tooling that includes acurate details that were not in the original LNER/BR A1 Class designed by A.H.Peppercorn.

R3060	**60163 *Tornado*** BRa light green (RailRoad) - *11*	56	75
R3070	as above special edition - *11*	70	93

'New Build' Class A1 Tornado in BR 'Apple Green' [L58] (Hornby)

R3059	**60163 *Tornado*** BRb green + 3 Mk1 maroon coaches train pack - *11*	NA	164
(R3059)	above loco on its own - *11*	70	NA

L59a. LNER Class A4 4-6-2 (1979)

Gresley's ultimate express engine development of 1935. This is the original model before it went out to China for detailing. Ringfield tender drive. ct = corridor tender. nct = non-corridor tender. v = with valances down over the wheels (all others non-valanced). pq = with plaque. npf = non-paint finish. dc = double chimney. RD = presentation pack with Royal Doulton plate.

R099	**2512 *Silver Fox*** LNER silver ct v - *85-89*	60	85
R312	**2509 *Silver Link*** LNER silver ct v - *90-94*	55	75
R313	**4482 *Golden Eagle*** LNER green ct v - *90-91*	45	70
R077	**4468 *Mallard*** LNER blue ct pq v dc - *84-85, 91-92*	40	50
R327	**4468 *Mallard*** LNER blue ct v dc - *88-89*	35	48
R304	**4468 *Mallard*** LNER blue nct pq v dc - *93-98*	40	55
R328 *	**4469 *Sir Ralph Wedgwood*** LNER blue nct v Ltd Edn 3000 - *94*	50	80
R372	**4902 *Seagull*** LNER blue ct v dc - *81-82*	45	60
R888	**4498 *Sir Nigel Gresley*** LNER blue ct v - *87-89*	55	70
R528	**4498 *Sir Nigel Gresley*** LNER blue ct Ltd Edn 2000 - *92*	75	95
R376	**4469 *Gadwall*** LNER blue nct v Sp Edn 1500 (Kays) - *95*	100	115
R649	**1 *Sir Ronald Matthews*** LNER blue nct RD Ltd Edn 3000 - *96*	65	80
R099	**4466 *Herring Gull*** LNER black nct Sp Edn 985 (Littlewoods) - *95*	150	170
R341 *	**4466 *Sir Ralph Wedgwood*** NE black nct Ltd Edn 3000 - *94*	65	80
R2040	**60026 *Miles Beevor*** BRa? deep blue? Sp Edn (BCA) - *not made*	NA	NA
R376	**60022 *Mallard*** BRa blue ct pq dc Sp Edn 1000 (Kays) - *90*	95	120
R294	**60028 *Walter K. Whigham*** BRa purple ct - *95*	60	75
R2037	**60029 *Woodcock*** BRa purple ct Sp Edn 1000 (Beatties) - *97*	70	90
(R1040)	**60022 *Mallard*** BRb exp. blue ex-'The Mallard' train set Sp Edn (Toys-R-Us) - *03*	80	NA
R204	**60019 *Bittern*** BRb green nct ex-R770 'The Tees Tyne Pullman' set - *94-95*	45	NA
R350	**60022 *Mallard*** BRc green ct pq dc npf - *79-81*	40	50
R309	**60022 *Mallard*** BRc green ct pq dc - *80-83, 89-93*	30	40
R353 *	**60006 *Sir Ralph Wedgwood*** BRc green nct dc Ltd Edn 3000 - *94*	65	80
R144	**60010 *Dominion of Canada*** BRc green ct dc - *94-95*	55	70
R286	**60009 *Union of South Africa*** BRc green planned for 1996 - *not made*	NA	NA
R286	**60021 *Wild Swan*** BRc green ct dc Ltd Edn 1000 - *96-97*	50	65

The 1979 model of an Ex-LNER Class A4 - Wild Swan [L59a]

R2032	**60020 *Guillemot*** BRc green nct + 3 coaches train pack Ltd Edn 3000 - *97*	NA	100
(R2032)	above loco only - *97*	50	NA
- *	3 'Wedgwood' locos in wooden box - *94*	NA	250

* In 1994, Sir Ralph Wedgewood was released at intivals in three different liveries. The last one was sold with a wooden presentation box that would hold all three locomotives.

L59b. LNER Class A4 4-6-2 (1998)

This was the super-detail model tooled-up in China with a much finer chassis. Ringfield tender drive. ct = corridor tender. nct = non-corridor tender. v = with valances down over the wheels (all others non-valanced). pq = with plaque. dc = double chimney. sc = single chimney.

R2246	**2510 *Quicksilver*** LNER silver-grey ct v Sp Edn (Collectors Centres) - *01*	70	85
(R2278M)	**2511 *Silver King*** LNER silver-grey ct v Sp Edn ex-mail order train pack - *02*	NA	110
(R2278)	above loco only - *02*	60	NA
R2059	**4468 *Mallard*** LNER blue nct v dc Ltd Edn box 1500 - *98*	60	80
R2059	**4468 *Mallard*** LNER blue nct v dc - *99-03*	60	80
R2127	**4903 *Peregrine*** LNER blue nct v dc Ltd Edn 500 - *98-99*	95	120
R2154	**4485 *Kestrel*** LNER blue ct v sc - *00-01*	60	80
R2167	**60034 *Lord Faringdon*** BRa garter blue ct dc + 3 coaches 'The Royal Scot' pack Ltd Edn 2000 - *00*	NA	110
(R2167)	above loco only - *00*	50	NA
R2149	**60007 *Sir Nigel Gresley*** BRa garter blue ct Ltd Edn 500 (HCClub) - *00*	60	80
(R1040)	**60022 *Mallard*** BRb blue ex-Sp Edn (Toys-R-Us) - *04-05*	75	NA
R2089	**60014 *Silver Link*** BRb green ct + 3 coaches 'The Flying Scotsman' train pack Ltd Edn 2000 - *99*	NA	90
(R2089)	above loco only - *99*	50	NA
R2136	**60012 *Commonwealth of Australia*** BRb green ct etched brass nameplate Sp Edn 500 - *99*	120	160
R2101	**60030 *Golden Fleece*** BRc green ct dc - *99*	60	75
(R1024)	**60031 *Golden Plover*** BRc green ct dc - *01-02*	75	NA
R2203	**60024 *Kingfisher*** BRc green ct dc - *01*	60	75
R2302	**60009 *Union of South Africa*** BRc* green ct dc Ltd Edn 500 (HCClub) - *02*	95	120
R2247	**60019 *Bittern*** BRc green Sp Edn 500 - *02*	70	85
R2266	**60017 *Silver Fox*** BRc green - *02*	70	85

* The model carried a special emblem on one side only.

L59c. LNER Class A4 4-6-2 (Live Steam) (2003)

This is the Live Steam model launched in 2003, with a boiler in the tender which generates steam to drive the cylinders and operate the whistle. The body is moulded in a special heat-resistant plastic. sc = single chimney. dc = double chimney.

R2367	**2509 *Silver Link*** LNER silver-grey sc - *04-10*	175	226
(R1041)	**4468 *Mallard*** LNER blue ex-set dc - *03-09*	240	NA
R2259	**4902 *Seagull*** LNER blue dc - *04-09*	250	325
R2368	**4495 *Golden Fleece*** NE black sc - *04-09*	175	226
R2277	**60008 *Dwight D Eisenhower*** BRb green sc - *04-09*	175	226

L59d. LNER Class A4 4-6-2 (2004)

This is the ultimate super-detailed model released in 2004 with a 5-pole skew wound motor in the loco. It came 'DCC ready', has a 5-pole motor and was fitted with NEM coupling sockets. It also has a fixed rear pony truck with roller wheels, thus eliminating daylight under the cab. Alternative pony truck wheels were supplied in the box. sc = single chimney. dc = double chimney. ct = corridor tender. nct = non-corridor tender. v = valances. en = etched nameplates. CC= Commonwealth Collection. DS = DCC sound chip fitted.

R2965	**2509 *Silver Link*** LNER light & dark grey - *11*	90	120
R2373	**2512 *Silver Fox*** LNER silver-grey + 3 Gresley teak coaches Ltd Edn - *04*	NA	120
(R2373)	above loco only - *04*	75	NA
R2445	**2510 *Quicksilver*** LNER silver-grey + 3 silver Stanier coaches Ltd Edn 2000 - *05*	NA	120
R2339	**4468 *Mallard*** LNER blue dc, nct, v - *04-11*	90	132
R2684	**4468 *Mallard*** LNER blue dc, nct, v, Ltd Edn 5000 70th anniversary speed record, 18ct gold plated parts and plush box - *08-09*	100	148
R2888M	**4489 *Kingfisher*** LNER blue + 3 teak Gresley coaches 'Flying Scotsman' train pack Sp Edn 1200 (Argos + Shop Direct) - *09*	NA	200

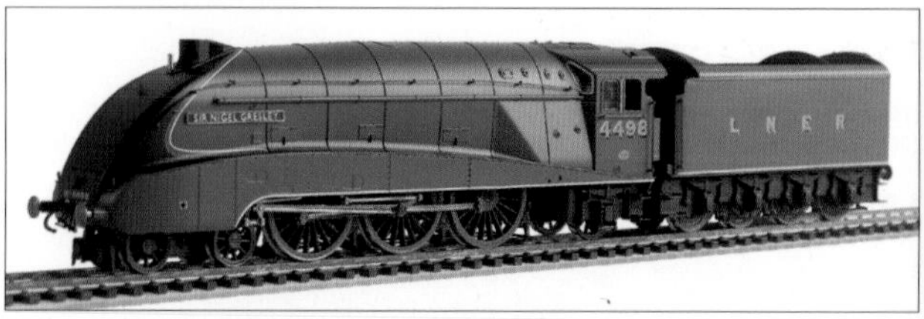

The 2004 model of an A4 - Sir Nigel Gresley [L59d]

R2688	**4498 *Sir Nigel Gresley*** LNER blue sc, v, Ltd Edn 2008 70th Anniv. Hornby Dublo, in Hornby Dublo style box - *08*	80	100
R2805XS	**4466 *Herring Gull*** LNER blue v sc nct DS - *09-10*	190	235
R2338	**4901 *Charles H Newton*** NE black dc - *not made*	NA	NA
R2338	**4901 *Sir Charles Newton*** NE black dc, nct - *04-07*	70	95
R2896XS	**60001 *Sir Ronald Matthews*** BRc green sc nct DS - *10*	190	235
R2798	**60027 *Merlin*** BRa purple sc, ct, en Sp Edn 1000 (Modelfair.com) - *08*	90	119

R2906	**60024** ***Kingfisher*** BR Express blue + 3 BR teak Gresley coaches Ltd Edn 1000 'Rare Bird' from Barry J Freeman Collection - *11*	NA	220
(R2906)	above loco only - *11*	85	NA
R2991XS	**60018** ***Sparrow Hawk*** BRb Express Blue DS sc nct - *11*	200	266
R2494	**60020** ***Guillemot*** BRb green sc, nct - *05-06*	85	105
R2435	**60003** ***Andrew K McCosh*** BRb green sc, ct + 3 red+cream Gresley coaches 'The Northumbrian' train pack Ltd Edn 3000 - *05*	NA	150
(R2435)	above loco only - *05*	70	NA
(R1064)	**60022** ***Mallard*** BRb green 1928 rebuilt ct Sp Edn (Boogaloo) ex-'The Mallard Express' set - *05*	70	NA
R2826	**60013** ***Dominion of New Zealand*** BRb green nct sc Ltd Edn CC 1000 - 09	100	130
R2825	**60012** ***Commonwealth of Australia*** BRc green ct sc Ltd Edn CC 1000 - 09	100	130
R2910	**60010** ***Dominion of Canada*** BRc green sc Ltd Edn CC 1000 - *10*	100	130
R2909	**60009** ***Union of South Africa*** BRc green ct sc Ltd Edn CC 1000 - *10*	100	130
R3008	**60011** ***Empire of India*** BRc green sc ct - *11*	108	145
R2615	**60021** ***Wild Swan*** BRb green sc nct - *07-08*	85	105
R2340	**60031** ***Golden Plover*** BRc green dc, ct - *04-05*	70	95
R2535	**60029** ***Woodcock*** BRc green dc ct* - *06-08*	85	105
R2721	**60018** ***Sparrow Hawk*** BRc green dc nct - *08*	90	120
R3012	**60027** ***Merlin*** BRc green sc ct - *11*	108	145
R27??	**60025** ***Falcon*** BRc green + 3 Mk1 maroon+ cream coaches Heart of Midlothian Ltd Edn 1500 pk - *08*	NA	165
(R27??)	above loco only ex-mail order train pack - *08*	90	NA

* should have had cut-down tender. This model was also sold in the mail order 'Heart of Midlothian' train set in 2008.

L59e. LNER Class A4 4-6-2 (RailRoad) (2008)

This version of the model has been produced for the RailRoad range and has a new body specially developed for it and has loco drive. It has the 1998 A4 chassis but with a fixed pony truck. 'DCC ready' or X = 'DCC fitted'. ct = corridor tender. nct = non-corridor tender. v = valances.

R2779	**4484** ***Falcon*** LNER blue with valances nct (RailRoad) - *08-11*	45	67
(R1126)	**4903** ***Peregrine*** LNER blue v dc ex-'Blue Streak' MO set Sp Edn (Argos) - *09*	60	NA
(R2888M)	above loco only	60	NA
R2784X	**60022** ***Mallard*** BRc green (RailRoad) X ct - *08-11*	55	77
(R1136)	**60015** ***Quicksilver*** BR green Sp Edn 2000 (BVG) ex-Yorkshire Pullman set - *09*	55	NA
R9257	***Spencer*** lt. grey ct with face (*see Thomas section*)	55	72

L60a. SR WC/BB Class 4-6-2 (1961)

Bulleid's light Pacific design of 1945. Loco mounted X04 motor.

	SR Green		
R869S	**21C151** ***Winston Churchill*** bright green with black shading - *69*	80	NPG
R869S	**21C151** ***Winston Churchill*** bright gloss green, red shading - *69-72*	55	85
R869S	**21C151** ***Winston Churchill*** dark green - *71*	120	NPG
-	**21C157** ***Biggin Hill**** - *69-72*	40	NA
-	**21C164** ***Fighter Command**** - *69-72*	40	NA
-	**21C165** ***Hurricane**** - *69-72*	40	NA

The original BB Class model of 1961, seen here as Spitfire, released in 1981 [L60a]

R374	**21C166** ***Spitfire*** malachite - *81-83*	50	70
-	**21C155** ***Fighter Pilot*** ** - *81-83*	50	NA
-	**21C165** ***Hurricane*** ** - *81-83*	50	NA
-	**21C170** ***Manston*** ** - *81-83*	50	NA
R866	**21C155** ***Fighter Pilot*** malachite - *87?*	50	60
R866	**21C155** ***Fighter Pilot*** SR malachite, 'Golden Arrow' - *88-89*	45	55
R320	**21C101** ***Exeter*** SR malachite Ltd Edn 4000 - *95*	50	80
R265	**21C119** ***Bideford*** SR malachite - *96-97*	45	55
	BR Green		
R074	**34076** ***41 Squadron*** BRb - *85-86*	80	110
R646	**34085** ***501 Squadron*** BRb 'Golden Arrow' Sp Edn 1000 (Beatties) - *96*	100	130
R356+38	**34051** ***Winston Churchill*** BRc - *62-63*	45	75
R356S+R38	**34051** ***Winston Churchill*** BRc with smoke - *61-69*	45	75
R310	**34054** ***Lord Beaverbrook*** BRc - *95-97*	45	60

* Renamed/numbered with transfer provided with R869S. ** Renamed/renumbered with transfer provided with R374.

L60b. SR BB/WC Class 4-6-2 (2001)

Completely new super-detail model released in 2001 with a 5-pole skew wound motor. Up until the end of 2004, all models had a sprung rear driving axle but from 2005 the spring had gone. ht = high tender, lt = cut-down tender, ssd = short smoke deflectors. wc = wide cab, nc = narrow cab. From 2005, these were 'DCC Ready'.

	SR Malachite Green		
R2219	**21C110** ***Sidmouth*** - *not made*	NA	NA
R2219	**21C123** ***Blackmore Vale*** ht, ssd, nc - *01-04*	60	75
R2283	**21C155** ***Fighter Pilot*** ht nc - *02-05*	60	75
R2286	**21C164** ***Fighter Command*** SR grey, nc, ht, Sp Edn 1000 (Much Ado) - *02*	120	140

The 2001 model of Class BB/WC in 'Photographic Grey' [L60b]

	BR Malachite Green		
R2279M	**21C157** ***Biggin Hill*** BRa ht, nc, + 3 Pullmans Ltd Edn 3000 - *02*	NA	120
(R2279)	above loco only - *02*	65	NA
R2661M	**21C159** Ltd Edn 1500 + 3 Pullman cars MO 'Bournemouth Belle' train pack - *07*	NA	130
X5921	above loco only - *07*	65	NA
R2369	**34074** ***46 Squadron*** BRa ht, wc, 'Golden Arrow' + 3 Pullman cars - *04*	NA	130
(R2369)	above loco only - *04*	65	NA
R2685	**34006** ***Bude*** BRa Stanier 4,000 gall. black tender, extended smoke deflectors, Ltd Edn 2008 60th Anniversary exchange trials - *08-10*	90	119
R2691	**34031** ***Torrington*** no insignia - *08-10*	90	119
R2315	**34037** ***Clovelly*** no BR decals, ht, nc - *03*	75	95
R2220	**34081** ***92 Squadron*** BRa ht, wc - *01-04*	60	75
R2692	**34090** ***Sir Eustace Missenden*** BRa - *08-10*	90	119
	BR Brunswick Green		
R2817	**34007** ***Wadebridge*** BRb + 2 Pullman cars + the 'Devon Belle' observation car train pack - *09*	NA	200
(R2817)	above loco only - *09*	90	NA
R2568	**34026** ***Yes Tor*** BRb + 3 Pullman cars 'The Devon Belle' boards - *not made*	NA	NA
R2568	**34030** ***Watersmeet*** BRb + 3 Pullman cars 'The Devon Belle' boards - *06*	NA	150
(R2568)	above loco only - *06*	85	NA
R2908	**34042** ***Dorchester*** BRb green + 3 BR Stanier coaches Ltd Edn 1000 'Fireworks at Chilcompton' from Barry J Freeman Collection - *10*	NA	200
(R2908)	above loco only - *10*	90	NA
R2316	**34061** ***73 Squadron*** BRb, ht - *03*	75	95
R2221	**34067** ***Tangmere*** BRb, wc - *01-04*	80	95
R2388	**34083** ***605 Squadron*** BRb ht, wc - *04-06*	NA	95
R2542	**34092** ***City of Wells*** BRb - *06-07*	85	105
(R1119)	**34039** ***Boscastle*** BRb ex-'Golden Arrow' MO set Sp Edn 2000 - *08*	85	NA
R2218	**34041** ***Wilton*** BRc lt, nc - *01-04*	60	75
R2436	**34043** ***Combe Martin*** BRc + 3 maroon Mk1s train pack Ltd Edn 3000 - *05*	NA	115
(R2436)	above loco only - *05*	85	NA
R2385	**34051** ***Winston Churchill*** BRc lt, nc, NRM series - *04*	75	95
R2308M	**34067** ***Tangmere*** BRc wc with 3 coaches		

	'Excalibur Express' Sp Edn 1500 MO pack with headboard - *04*	NA	120
(R2308)	above loco only - *04*	65	NA
R2260	34070 ***Manston*** BRc lt, nc, Sp Edn 500 (HCClub) - *02*	100	125
R2458	34078 ***222 Squadron*** BRc ht wc - *05-07*	80	95
R2282	34091 ***Weymouth*** BRc lt, wc - *02*	70	85
R2926	34107 ***Blandford Forum*** BRc lt, wc - *10*	100	120

L61. BR Rebuilt BB/WC Class 4-6-2 (2006)

Bulleid's Light Pacific design of 1945 as some were rebuilt in BR days. Completely new super-detail model with a 5-pole skew wound motor. ht = high tender, lt = low tender. These were all 'DCC Ready'.

R2584	34003 ***Plymouth*** BRc green W ht - *06-08*	85	105
R2708	34008 ***Padstow*** BRc green lt - *08-10*	95	123
R2608	34026 ***Yes Tor*** BRc green ht - *07-09*	85	108
R2609	34036 ***Westward Ho*** BRc green lt - *07-09*	85	116
R2585	34045 ***Ottery St. Mary*** BRc green ht - *07-09*	85	113

Rebuilt BB/WC Class as Sir Keith Park [L61]

R2586	34053 ***Sir Keith Park*** BRc green ht - *07*	85	105
R2709	34058 ***Sir Fredrick Pile*** BRc green - *08-10*	95	123
R2587	34062 ***17 Squadron*** BRc green ht - *07*	85	105
R2607	34088 ***213 Squadron*** BRc green lt - *07*	85	108
R2886M	34088 ***213 Squadron*** BRc green 'The Cunarder' train pack + 3 Pullman cars Ltd Edn 1200 (Argos + Shop Direct) - *09*	NA	140
R2606	34109 ***Sir Trafford Mallory*** BRc green - *07-09*	85	108

L62. BR 'Merchant Navy' (Rebuilt) 4-6-2 (2000)

Bulleid's 'Heavy Pacific' design of 1941 as they were after being rebuilt in BR days. This super-detail model has a loco mounted 5-pole skew wound motor. Up to the start of 2003, models had a sprung rear driving axle. hb - headboard. 5100 = 5100 gallon tender From 2004, these were 'DCC Ready'.

R2171	35005 ***Canadian Pacific*** BRb blue - *00-03*	65	80
	BR Green		
R2170	35023 ***Holland-Afrika Line*** BRb - *00*	65	80
R2204	35020 ***Bibby Line*** BRb - *01-05*	70	85
R2267	35025 ***Brocklebank Line*** BRb - *02-05*	70	85
R2300	35021 ***New Zealand Line*** BRb hb + 3 Pullman cars 'Bournemouth Belle' train pack - *02*	NA	130
(R2300)	above loco only - *02*	70	NA
R2710	35010 ***Blue Star*** BRc green - *08-10*	90	119
R2466	35011 ***General Steam Navigation*** BRc 5100 - *05*	75	95
(R1038)	35012 ***United States Lines*** BRc 5100 ex-R1038 set - *03-06*	75	NA
R2310	35016 ***Elders Fyffes*** BRc 5100 - *03-04*	75	95
R2528	35019 ***French Line CGT*** BRc - *06*	85	105

Rebuilt MN Class as French Line CGT [L62]

R2204	35020 ***Bibby Line*** BRc - *made?*	NPG	NPG
R2194	35022 ***Holland-America Line*** BRc 'Atlantic Coast Express' hb + 3 SR Mk1s train pack Ltd Edn 2000 - *01*	NA	140
(R2194)	above loco only - *01*	70	NA
R2599	35026 ***Lamport & Holt Line*** BRb + 3 Mk1 coaches train pack Sp Edn 1500 - *06*	NA	149
(R2599)	above loco only - *06*	80	NA
R2967	35026 ***Lamport & Holt Line*** BRc - *11*	100	120
R2268	35027 ***Port Line*** BRc - *02-03*	70	85
R2169	35028 ***Clan Line*** BRc - *00*	60	75
R2169	35028 ***Clan Line*** BRc flatter smokebox door - *01-02*	60	75
(R1073)	35028 ***Clan Line*** BRc ex-'VSOE' set - *07-11*	80	NA
R?	35028 ***Clan Line*** BRc with 'Express for Children' headboards and special code disks + 3 Pullman cars Sp Edn 2 (Save the Children Fund) - *06*	NA	250
R2294	35029 ***Ellerman Lines*** BRc NRM series - *02*	85	100

L63. BR 'Clan' Class 7P6F 4-6-2 (2009)

Based on the Riddles designed small boiler 'Pacifics', this is a super-detailed model to the highest standard of the time. It has the 5-pole skew-wound motor in the locomotive. Both 'DCC ready' and 'DCC fitted' (has X suffix) versions of each general release loco were made. Add £10-£15 for X models.

BR Brunswick Green

'Clan Class' as Clan Macgregor [L63]

R2846	72000 ***Clan Buchanan*** BRc - *09*	100	131
R2925	72005 ***Clan Macgregor*** BRc - *10-11*	100	131
R2847	72008 ***Clan Macleod*** BRb - *09-11*	100	131

L64a. BR 'Britannia' Class 7P6F 4-6-2 (1960)

Riddles's standard Express locomotive of 1951. This model was loco driven. From 1971 the models had sticker nameplates.

BR Brunswick Green

R259+R35	70000 ***Britannia*** BRc metal nameplates - *60-70*	25	75
R259SF	70000 ***Britannia*** BRc Acho couplings - *67-70*	90	180
R259NS	70000 ***Britannia*** BRc - *71-72*	35	60
-	70006 ***Robert Burns*** * BRc - *71-72*	55	NA
-	70013 ***Oliver Cromwell*** * BRc - *71-72*	55	NA
-	70010 ***Owen Glendower*** * BRc - *71-72*	55	NA

* Renamed/renumbered using transfers supplied with R259NS.

L64b. BR 'Britannia' Class 7P6F 4-6-2 (1973)

The models had sticker nameplates. nsd = no smoke deflectors. ul = no lining on loco or tender. td = Ringfield motor tender driven.

BR Brunswick Green

R056	70047 ***Iron Duke*** * BRb, ul, nsd - *75?*	120	NA
R056	70047 ***Iron Duke*** * BRc, ul, nsd - *75-77*	35	NA
R056	70014 ***Iron Duke*** * BRc, ul, nsd - *75-76*	40	NA
R056	70014 ***Iron Duke*** * BRc, ul, smoke deflectors (c50 made) - *76?*	120	NA
R057	mail order model for sets for '75 - *not made*	NA	NA
R552	70013 ***Oliver Cromwell*** BRc, td, loco and tender attached ** - *73-75*	35	50
R063	70000 ***Britannia*** BRc, td ** - *76-79*	35	50

* Cheap mail order model. ** Made with the same chassis (with overlong wheelbase) as the 1981 model and was in no way similar to the 1960 model. However, unlike the 1981 model, it used the old valve gear.

L64c. BR 'Britannia' Class 7P6F 4-6-2 (1981)

Ringfield tender drive. Wire handrails. After *Morning Star*, the models were fitted with the 9F slide bars and valve gear. The nameplates were printed directly onto the smoke deflector.

BR Brunswick Green

R033	70021 ***Morning Star*** BRc - *81-82*	50	65
-	70028 ***Royal Star*** * - *81-82*	50	NA
-	70034 ***Thomas Hardy*** * - *81-82*	50	NA
-	70038 ***Robin Hood*** * - *81-82*	50	NA
R329	70004 ***William Shakespeare*** BRc - *90-91*	40	55
R190	70000 ***Britannia*** BRb - *92*	50	65
R507	70000 ***Britannia*** BRb Ltd Edn 2000, Royal Duties (white cab roof) - *92*	60	85
R378	70032 ***Tennyson*** BRc Sp Edn 2000 (Kays) - *91*	70	85
R242	70006 ***Robert Burns*** BRb Sp Edn 2000 (Kays) - *96*	70	85
R2031	70023 ***Venus*** BRb, 'The Bristolian' train pack with 3 coaches Ltd Edn 3000 - *97*	NA	110
R2010	70042 ***Lord Roberts*** BRb Ltd Edn 1000 - *98*	65	85
R2091	70028 ***Royal Star*** BRb green - *99*	75	90
(R1021)	70012 ***John of Gaunt*** BRc, ex-R1021 Kays		

	set - *99*	55	NA
R2104	**70050 *Firth of Clyde*** BRc, late tender - *99*	60	75
R2142	**70038 *Robin Hood*** BRb Sp Edn 1000 (A.B.Gee) - *99*	55	70
R2192	**70046 *ANZAC*** BRc, late tender Ltd Edn 1000 (Collectors Centres) - *00*	55	70
R2175	**70052 *Firth of Tay*** BRc, late tender Sp Edn 1500 (Kays) - *00*	50	65

* Alternative transfer names and numbers provided with R033.

L64d. BR 'Britannia' Class 7P6F 4-6-2 (2000)

This is the upgraded model which is similar to the 1981 model (above) but had a finely detailed chassis and later style smoke deflectors with cut-out handholds instead of handrails on some of the models. Ringfield tender drive. Some models were fitted with the BR1 tender with its pinched top and some with the high sided BR1D tender fitted to the last 10 members of the class. hb = headboard. 5-p = 5-pole motor. From 2005 the locos were DCC ready.

	BR Brunswick Green		
R2207	**70000 *Britannia*** BRb - *01-02*	50	75
(R1086M)	**70000 *Britannia*** BR? ex-MO Premier set R1086 - *08*	80	NA
R2484	**70036 *Bodicea*** BRb 5-p - *05*	75	95
R2387	**70018 *Flying Dutchman*** BRb 5-p - *04*	75	95
R2180	**70040 *Clive of India*** BRc - *00-01*	50	75
R2272	**70025 *Western Star*** BRc - *02-03*	50	75
R2329M	**70054 *Dornoch Firth*** BRc W BR1D hb + 3 coaches Ltd Edn 1500 'Thames-Clyde' train pack - *03*	NA	120
(R2329)	above loco only - *03*	60	NA
R2457	**70046 *ANZAC*** BRc W BR1d 5-p - *05*	75	95
(R1099K)	**70046 *ANZAC*** BRc BR1d 5-p ex-MO set - *08*	80	NA
	BR Black		
R2975	**70000 *Britannia*** no decals, lining on boiler only - *10*	100	120

L64e. BR 'Britannia' Class 7P6F 4-6-2 (2006)

This is a completely retooled super-detailed model to the highest standard of the time. It has the 5-pole skew-wound motor in the locomotive. Both 'DCC ready' and 'DCC fitted' (has X suffix) versions of each general release loco were made. Add £10-£15 for X models.

	BR Brunswick Green		
R2562	**70000 *Britannia*** BRb - *06*	85	105
R2819	**70009 *Alfred the Great*** BRb + 3 Pullman cars 'Bournemouth Belle' train pack - *09*	NA	200
(R2819)	above loco only - *09*	95	NA
R2835	**70010 *Owen Glendower*** BRc - *10-11*	100	131
R2717	**70015 *Apollo*** BRb - *08-09*	90	119
R2619	**70037 *Hereward the Wake*** BRb - *07*	85	105
R2719	**70038 *Robin Hood*** BRc - *08-09*	90	119
R2618	**70045 *Lord Rowallan*** BRb - *07*	85	105
R2718	**70050 *Firth of Clyde*** BRb - *08-09*	90	119
R2563	**70030 *William Wordsworth*** BRc - *06*	85	105
R2564	**70052 *Firth of Tay*** BRc - *06-07*	85	105
R2565	**70013 *Oliver Cromwell*** BRc (preserved) - *06*	85	105
R2660M	**70008 *Black Prince*** BR Ltd Edn MO pack with 3 Mk1 coaches - *07*	NA	130
X5913	above loco only - *07*	90	NA

L65a. LMS Class 8F 2-8-0 (1988)

Stanier's standard heavy freight locomotive of 1935. Ringfield tender drive. G = Firebox glow

R315	**8193** LMS black G (also R325) - *88-91*	45	60
R325	**8027** LMS black G - *90-91*	50	65
R325	**8118** LMS black G - *90-91*	50	65
R325	**8233** LMS black G - *90-91*	50	65
R297	**8035** LMS black G - *96-97*	45	60
R322	**48758** BRb black G - *89*	45	60
R324	**48774** BRb black G - *90-91*	50	65
R324	**48141** BRb black G - *90-91*	50	65
R324	**48278** BRb black G - *90-91*	50	65
R2055	**48705** BRc black G - *98*	40	65
R2043	**300** WD grey Sp Edn 500 (Much Ado About Toys) G - *97*	130	160

L65b. LMS Class 8F/O6 2-8-0 (2002)

The super-detail model has a 5-pole skew wound loco mounted motor. All are 'DCC Ready'.

R2227	**7675** LNER plain black - *03-07*	60	80
R2228	**8510** LMS plain black - *03-05*	60	80
R2249	**8042** LMS plain black W - *03-05*	60	80
R2394	**8453** LMS plain black - *04*	65	85
R2394A	**8493** LMS plain black - *04*	65	85
R2394B	**8400** LMS plain black - *04-06* *	70	93
R2229	**48154** BRb plain black - *03*	60	80
R2395	**48119** BRb plain black W - *04*	65	85
R2395A	**48062** BRb plain black W - *05-07*	70	93
R2393	**48773** BRc plain black - *04*	65	85

Ex-LMS Class 8F No.48151 [L65b]

R2462	**48151** BRc plain black - *05-07*	70	93
R2463	**48739** BRc plain black W - *05-06*	70	93
R3026	**48723** BRc plain black W - *11*	100	134

* not yet seen - was this made?

'Britannia' Class Firth of Clyde from a computer artwork by Robbie McGavin [L64e]

L66a. GWR Class 28xx 2-8-0 (1991)

Churchward's heavy long distance freight locomotive of 1903. Ringfield tender drive. Models have a firebox and a smoke unit.

R532	**2859** Great Western green G S - *91-93*	55	70
R2153	**2869** GWR plain green G S - *not made*	NA	NA
R2053	**2844** GWR (roundel) plain green G S - *98*	55	70
R2153A	**2821** GWR plain green G S - *00-01*	55	70
R2153B	**2839** GWR plain green G S - *00-01*	55	70
R2153C	**2835** GWR plain green G S - *?*	55	70
R2464	**2828** GWR plain green G S - *not made?*	NPG	NPG
R2464	**2847** GWR plain green G S - *05-07*	65	80
R2202	**2861** BRb plain black G S - *01*	60	75
R2202A	**2865** BRb plain black G S - *02-04*	70	85
R143	**2857** BRc plain black G S - *94-96*	60	75
R2465	**2836** BRc plain black W G S - *05-07*	75	93

L66b. GWR Class 28xx 2-8-0 (2010)

This is the model as retooled in 2010. with the 5-pole skew wound motor in the locomotive.

R2915	**2818** Great Western plain green - *10-11*	100	130
R2916	**2812** GWR (shirt button) plain green - *10-11*	100	130

The new model of GWR Class 38xx [L66c]

R2917	**2810** BRc plain black - *10-11*	100	130
R3005	**2845** BRc plain black W - *11*	100	130

L66c. GWR Class 38xx 2-8-0 (2010)

Built in 1904, this is very similar to the 28xx Class but has windows in the cab sides and continuous covers over the two back paits of driving wheels.

R2918	**3803** GWR plain green - *10-11*	100	130
R3006	**3864** BRb plain black W - *11*	100	130
R2919	**2891** BRc plain black - *10-11*	100	130

L67a. BR Class 9F 2-10-0 (1971)

This was the original *Evening Star* model which can be easily identified by its handrails being part of the body moulding. When originally designed, only the handrails on the back edge of the cab had daylight behind them but this left them prone to breaking and so the gap was soon filled in. Ringfield tender drive. npf = non-paint finish.

R264	**92166?** BRb black - *72*	35	50
R550	**92166** BRb black * - *73*	35	50
R264	**92200** BRc black alt nos. - *82-83*	35	50
-	**92183** ** - *82-83*	35	NA
-	**92215** ** - *82-83*	35	NA
-	**92239** ** - *82-83*	35	NA
	92220 *Evening Star*		
R301	BRb green Sp Edn (NRM) - *?*	80	100
R861	BRc gloss green, npf, separate cab handrails * - *71*	55	70
R861	BRc gloss green, npf * - *71-74*	40	55
R065	BRc matt green, npf, - *77-79*	35	50
R303	BRc green - *80-82*	30	45
R330	BRc green, Sp Edn 125 (NRM) - *83*	80	100

* Loco and tender permanently joined together. ** Alternative number for R264.

L67b. BR Class 9F 2-10-0 (1988)

Riddles's large class of heavy freight locomotives of 1954. This was similar to the last model but now had wire handrails. Tender drive.

R330	**92207, 92231, 92222** BRc black - *90-91*	40	55
R864	**92241** BRc black - *96*	40	55
R2016	**92001** BRc black - *97*	40	55
R2057	**92212** BRc black - *98*	40	55
R373	**92220 *Evening Star*** BRc green - *88-91*	45	60

L67c. BR Class 9F 2-10-0 (1999)

This third model had a much improved chassis, blackened metalwork and a choice of tenders. Ringfield tender drive. It was the upgraded model and the tooling work was done in China. lt = large tender.

R2105A	**92108** BRc black, lt - *99*	55	70
R2105B	**92139** BRc black, lt - *99*	55	70
R2105C	**92158** BRc black, lt - *00-01*	60	75
R2105D	**92156** BRc black, lt - *02-04*	60	75
R2139	**92099** BRc black + 5 vans train pack Sp Edn 1000 (A.B.Gee) - *00*	NA	140
R2244	above loco repackaged - *00*	70	90
R2200	**92151** BRc black W lt - *01*	60	75
R2200A	**92134** BRc black W lt - *01-03*	60	75
R2248	**92239** BRc black W - *02-04*	60	75
R2137	**92203 *Black Prince*** BRc black Sp Edn 500 - *99*	80	100
R2187	**92220 *Evening Star*** BRc green - *00-01*	60	75

L67d. BR Class 9F 2-10-0 (RailRoad) (2008)

This fourth model now has loco drive and was developed for the RailRoad range. DCC ready.

R2785	**92220 *Evening Star*** BRc green RailRoad - *08-11*	50	65

Railroad version of the BR Class 9F No.92221 [L67d]

R2880	**92221** BRc black (RailRoad) - *09-11*	50	65
	Thomas Series		
R9684	***Murdoch*** gold - *11*	70	92

Diesel Locomotives

L68. Dock Shunter/ Switcher (Freelance) (1957)

Some bodies were printed in New Zealand and these include ones with 'TR' but no shield.

R253	**3** Dock Authority black - *72-78*	20	35
R253	**3** Dock Authority red - *64-71*	20	35
R253	**5** Dock Authority black, early coupling - *57-61*	30	65
R253	**5** Dock Authority red - *62-63*	30	65
R353	Tri-ang Railways yellow, no buffers - *60-62*	25	48
R353	**TR20071** TR yellow, no buffers - *60-62*	25	48
R353	**TR20071** TR red, no buffers - *63-65*	20	NA
R655	TR red, no buffers - *64*	35	NA

L69. Freelance/North British Diesel 0-4-0DS (2011)

This was produced exclusively for the Thomas series in 2011. It features similar to a North British design of 1957.

R9683	**(Dart)** Vicarstown Dieselworks red+yellow - *11*	30	41

L70. North British Diesel 0-4-0DS (1962)

R?	'Battle Space' red - *66-67*	35	NA
R557?	violet c/w - *68?*	40	NA
R?	black c/w - *65*	40	NA

North British diesel shunter No.D2907 [L70]

R557	BRc blue c/w - *62-65*	15	75
R557?	BRc green c/w - *68?*	95	125
R756	BRc red c/w - *66*	30	NA
R654	BRc blue - *64-65*	25	NA
R559	**D2907** BRc green - *63-67*	25	75

L71. Class 06 Barclay Diesel 0-4-0DS (1988)

Type HP motor.

R234	**A5** 'Robert Horne' cream - *95-97*	20	30
R2188	**D2412** BRc green Sp Edn (HCClub) - *00*	25	35
R136	**D2424** BRc green - *95*	25	35
R875	**D2428** BRc green - *88-91*	25	35

R799	**4** 'CEGB' grey - *91-92*	22	30
R051	**6** 'Redland' green - *93-94*	25	35
R2009	**8** 'ECC' blue - *97-98*	22	30
R801	**302** 'Tilbury Refineries' yellow - *91-94*	22	30
X5531	**06002** BRe blue ex-MO set R1063 - *08*	22	NA
R2184	**06003** Rft Distribution grey - *00-01*	22	27
R2470	**06003** BRe blue - *05-07*	22	31
R2676	**06003** BRe blue (RailRoad) - *07-10*	20	23
R874	**06005** BRe blue - *88-91*	20	35
(R1070)	**06008** BRe blue ex-'Goods Master' set - *07-10*	20	NA
R3065	**06008** BRe (railroad) blue - *11*	20	25
R2003	**06008** BRe Departmental grey Set R1003 - *97-98*	28	NA
R2783	**06008** Pullman blue+white (HCClub) - *08*	25	30
R2375	Virgin red+silver Sp Edn (HCClub) - *04*	25	30

Class 06 diesel shunter in Bartellos Circus livery [L7l]

(R1107)	'Bartellos' Big Top Circus' red+yellow (RailRoad) ex-set - *08-09*	20	NA
R061	Hornby Railways yellow - *93*	15	25

L72a. Class 08 Diesel Shunter 0-6-0DS (1956)

This model was also made in New Zealand and Australia with a different body tool. This has a higher cab roof.

R256	TR black c/w - *57?*	80	100
R256	TR maroon c/w - *57-58*	40	75
R316	VR blue, made for Australia - *74-75*	60	80
R152	**D3035** BRe blue - *69-75*	25	35
R152	**D3035** BRe green - *62-?*	45	50
R1520	**1520** bright blue made for Canada - *71*	60	95
R152	**13002** BRb black - *56*	50	65
R152	**13002** BRb green - *59?*	75	100
R152	**13005** BRb black - *56-58*	20	40
R154	**13005** BRb black c/w - *57-58*	80	100
R152	**13005** BRb olive - *56?*	50	65
R152	**13035** BRb green - *58-68*	25	40
R317	black with face - *see Thomas section*	-	-
R9066/ R9067	green+yellow Sodor Iron Works with face *-see Thomas section*	-	-

L72b. Class 08 Diesel Shunter 0-6-0DS (1976)

arc = automatic rear coupling. ladders = metal ladders up sides of radiator. chip = DCC decoder fitted

R339	**17** WD green, arc, ladders - *82-84*	25	50
R2334	**3973** ***Concorde*** LMS (BRML) lined dark maroon - *03*	25	40
R156	**13012** BRc green, arc, ladders - *76-79*	20	25
R354	**D3010** BRc green paint finish, arc, ladders - *80-81*	25	37
(R1075)	**D4093** BRc green chip ex-set - *06-09*	35	NA
(R1126)	**D4174** BRc green chip ex-'Mixed Freight' set - *09-10*	35	NA
R2157B	**08096** BRc green - *00-03*	30	37
R780	**08201** BRe blue, arc, ladders - *81-88*	25	30
R780	**08201** BRe blue, red wheels, ladders - *87-88*	20	25
R2123	**08500** ***Thomas 1*** York Wagon Depot red - *99-01*	25	30
R2774	**08500** ***Thomas 1*** York Wagon Depot red (RailRoad) - *08-11*	25	31
R2669	**08513** Virgin red+black (RailRoad) ex-pack - *07-11*	34	NA
(R2669)	above loco only - *07-11*	25	NA
R2007	**08523** Mainline blue ex-R1002 set - *97-98*	25	NA
R2157A	**08531** BRc green - *00-02*	30	37
R2425	**08568** ***St Rollox*** black+v.pale grey - *04*	32	41
R050	**08633** ***The Sorter*** Express Parcels red+black - *93-94*	30	45

Class 08 diesel shunter in Virgin Trains livery [L72b]

R2008	**08661** ***Europa*** Railfreight Distribution grey - *97-98*	30	38
R054	**08673** ***Piccadilly*** BRe IC grey - *88-92*	30	38
R2239	**08810** Anglia blue - *01-02*	30	38
R2163	**08828** EWS maroon - *00-02*	30	38
R2256	**08830** BRe blue W - *02*	28	35
R2111	**08896** ***Stephen Dent*** EWS maroon - *99*	25	30
R272	**08933** BRe Railfreight grey - *95-96*	25	38
R803	**08938** ED grey, ladders - *86-88*	25	38
R2333	**08642** BRML Eastleigh Works lined black - *03*	25	40
R165	NSWR maroon (Australia) arc, ladders - *77-78*	40	65
(T1500)	'Dinosafari' buff ex-T1500 set - *00-02*	25	NA
(T1501)	'Battle Zone' dark green ex-T1501 set - *00-02*	25	NA

L72c. Class 08/09 Diesel Shunter 0-6-0DS (2005)

Super-detail model from new tooling. 'DCC ready'. Cab interior detail, opening doors, sprung buffers. el = extra lights on outriggers. DS = DCC sound chip fitted.

R2903XS	**D3105** BRc green DS - *10-11*	140	170
R2417	**3256** BRc green - *05-07*	45	55
R2589	**D3200** BRc green - *06-08*	45	58
R2933	**D3509** BRc green - *10*	55	75
R2977XS	**D3511** BRc green DS - *11*	140	170
R2872	**D3721** BRc green - *09-11*	55	75
R3037XS	**D3963** BRc green DS - *11*	150	205
R2438	**D3986** BRc green Ltd Edn 1100 (Hornby Collector Centres) - *05*	45	65
R2418	**08402** BRe blue - *05*	45	55
R3049	**08417** Serco red+grey - *11*	60	83
R2591	**08419** BRe blue W - *06-08*	45	58
R2590	**08528** BRe blue - *06-07*	45	58
R2592	**08530** Freightliner green - *06-08*	45	58
R2595	**08630** EWS maroon - *06-07*	45	58
R3036XS	**08661** ***Europa*** Railfreight Distribution grey DS - *11*	150	205
R3048	**08673** ***Piccadilly*** BRe IC dark grey+beige - *11*	60	83
R2871	**08676** ***Dave 2*** EWS maroon - *09-10*	55	75
R2777	**08799** EWS maroon - *08*	45	58
R2902XS	**08844** EWS maroon+yellow DS - *10-11*	140	170
R2593	**08847** Cotswold Rail light grey el - *06-08*	45	58
R2934	**08865** EWS maroon+yellow - *10-11*	45	60
R2594	**08871** Cotswold Rail light grey - *06-08*	45	58
R2419	**09012** ***Dick Hardy*** EWS Departmental grey el - *05-07*	45	58

L73. Class 20 Diesel Bo-Bo (ex-Lima) (2008)

Introduced by Lima in 1985. 'DCC ready' and a new 5-pole skew wound bogie fitted motor. Now with NEM pockets and separate handrails.

R2762	**D8098** BRc green - *08-09*	45	62
R2763	**20128** BRT grey+red - *08-10*	45	62

Ex-Lima Class 20 in BR Railfreight livery [L73]

R2760	**20227** BReLL Railfreight grey - *08-09*	45	62
R2761	**20035** BRe blue - *08-09*	45	62

L74. Class 25 Diesel Bo-Bo (1977)

npf = non paint finish. wbl = with blue line. wgl = with grey line

	BR Green		
R878	BRc green, wbl, **D5177, D5200, D5206, D7568, D7597** alt. number transfers - *87-88*	NA	40
-	**D5177** * BRc - *87-88*	25	NA
-	**D5200** * BRc - *87-88*	25	NA
-	**D5206** * BRc - *87-88*	25	NA
R253	**D5206** BRc, wbl - *95-96*	30	40
-	**D7568** * BRc - *87-88*	25	NA
R327	**D7571** BRc, wbl - *80-81*	20	30
R2121A	**D7581** BRc, wgl - *00-02*	35	40
R072	**D7596** BRc, wbl, npf - *77-79*	20	30
R2121	**D7596** BRc, wgl - *99*	35	40
-	**D7597** * BRc - *87-88*	25	NA
	BR blue		
R877	BRe blue, **25218, 25071, 25078, 25052, 25054** alt. number transfers - *87-89*	NA	40
R2237B	**25033** BRe - *01*	32	38
-	**25052** ** BRe - *87-88*	25	NA
-	**25054** ** BRe - *87-88*	25	NA
R2237A	**25056** BRe - *01*	32	38
-	**25071** ** BRe - *87-88*	25	NA
-	**25078** ** BRe - *87-88*	25	NA
-	**25218** ** BRe - *87-88*	25	NA
R326	**25241** BRe - *80-84*	20	30
R068	**25247** BRe - *77-79*	20	30

* Alternative transfer numbers for R878. ** Alternative transfer numbers for R877.

L75. Class 29 Diesel Bo-Bo (1978)

npf = non-paint finish.

R084	**6124** BRe blue - *78-80*	15	25
R337	**6142** BRe blue - *80-82*	20	27

Class 29 diesel in BR blue as No.6124 [L75]

R318	**6142** BRe blue, Zero 1 chip fitted Sp Edn (Beatties) - *82*	50	70
R338	**D6103** BRc green - *80-81*	22	30
R080	**D6110** BRc green, npf - 78-79	20	35
R2122A	**D6119** BRc 2-tone green - *00-01*	35	50
R2238A	**D6129** BRe blue - *01*	30	37
R2122	**D6130** BRc 2-tone green - *99*	30	48
R2238B	**D6137** BRe blue - *01*	30	37

L76a. Class 31 Diesel A1A-A1A (1962)

Brush Type 2.

R357(G)	**D5572** BRc dull green - *63-67*	15	25
R357	**D5572** BRc gloss green - *72-76*	15	25
R357	**D5572** BRc electric blue - *68*	20	30
R357	**D5572** BRe rail blue - *69-71*	15	25
R357(G)	**D5578** BRc dull green - *63-67*	55	70
R357	**D5578** BRc experimental blue, pale blue window surrounds - *62*	50	95
R357B	**D5578** BRc experimental blue, with white lines and roof - *65-66*	30	65
R307	**42202** NSWR maroon (Australia) - *74-76*	50	85

L76b. Class 31 Diesel A1A-A1A (2005)

Brush Type 2. Super-detail model with 5-pole skew wound motor. Twin bogie drive. Pickups on all wheels. 'DCC ready'. NEM coupling sockets fitted. DS= DCC sound chip fitted.

R2572	**D5640** BRc green - *06-07*	75	95
R2526	**31130** ***Calder Hall Power Station*** Railfreight Coal grey Sp Edn 1000 (*Rail Express*) - *05*	75	90
R2649	**31165** BR blue - *07-08*	75	90
R2413A	**31174** BRe blue W - *05-07*	65	85
R2803XS	**31233** Railfreight Petroleum triple grey DS - *09*	170	210
R3044	**31233** Network Rail yellow - *11*	100	133
R2413B	**31268** BRe blue W - *10-11*	80	103
R2900XS	**31247** Railfreight red stripe DS - *11*	170	210
R2413	**31270** BRe blue W * - *not made*	NA	NA
R2753	**31296** Railfreight Construction triple grey - *08*	80	108
R2803XS	**31302** Rft Petroleum triple grey DS - *not made*	NA	NA
R2963	**31439** North Yorkshire Moors Railway Regional Railways blue+grey - *11*	80	103

Class 31 diesel Minotaur in Fragonset black livery [L76b]

R2573	**31452** ***Minotaur*** Fragonset black - *06-07*	75	95

* missing body-side beading - replaced by 31174 in June 2005.

L76c. Class 31 'Skin-head' A1A-A1A (2005)

As above but with no code boxes on the cab roofs. 5-pole skew wound motor. Twin bogie drive. Pickup on all wheels. 'DCC ready'. NEM coupling sockets fitted.

R2420	**D5512** BRc green - *05*	65	85
R2420A	**D5511** BRc green - *10*	80	103
R2754	**31105** Rft red stripe grey - *08-10*	80	108
R2421	**31110** BR Civil Engineer's grey+yellow - *05-07*	65	85
R2571	**31111** BRe blue - *06-07*	75	95

L76d. Class 31 A1A-A1A (ex-Lima) (2011)

R3067	**31256** BRe blue (RailRoad) - *11*	40	52

L77. Class 33 Bo-Bo (ex-Lima) (2010)

Reintroduced for the RailRoad range.

R2939	**D6537** BRc green (RailRoad) - *10-11*	35	44

L78. Class 35 'Hymek' Diesel B-B (1967)

Western Region diesel hydraulic. Two different motor bogies were used, the Ringfield not being used until 1977 or 1978. Later models have better detail. npf = non-paint finish. 5-p = 5-pole motor.

R758	**D6830** BRe blue numbering error - *66-67*	40	65
R2410	**D7046** BRc green 5-p - *04-05*	45	54
R758	**D7063** BRc green, npf - *67*	15	45
R074	**D7063** BRc green, npf - *77-78*	15	35
R758	**D7063** BRe electric blue, npf - *68*	12	35
R396	**D7063** BRe electric blue, npf, kit - *68*	NA	200
R758	**D7063** BRe blue, npf - *70-76*	10	25
R396	**D7063** BRe blue, npf, kit - *69-70*	NA	120
R2423	**D7067** BRe blue W 5-p - *04-06*	45	59
R2570	**D7092** BRc green W - *06-08*	45	59
R122	**D7093** BRe blue, white window frames - *94-96*	25	45
R335	**D7097** BRc green - *79-82*	25	35
R9097	**D7101** BRe blue with face - *see Thomas section*	-	-

Class 35 'Hymek' in Irish CIE livery [L78]

R768	CIE orange - *77, 81*	55	90

L79a. Class 37 Diesel Co-Co (1966)

English Electric Type 3. Two different motor bogies were used. scb = split code box on cab front. npf = non-painted finish Fitted with 5-pole motor from 2004.

R9064	**D261** green with face on one end - *see Thomas series*	-	-
R2471A	**D6700** BRc green scb - *05-07*	42	59
R2471B	**D6704** BRc green scb - *05-06*	42	59
R284	**D6713, D6721, D6796** BRc green, scb, alternative numbers - *88-90*	NA	40
-	**D6713** * BRc green scb - *88-90*	20	NA
-	**D6721** * BRc green scb - *88-90*	20	NA
R347	**D6736** BRc green, scb - *86-87*	20	30

-	**D6796** * BRc green scb - *88-90*	20	NA
R751	**D6830** BRc green, npf - *66-67*	15	50
R751	**D6830** BRe blue, npf R751A - *68-76*	12	22
R2128	'Eddie Stobart' green Sp Edn 1000 (Eddie Stobart Club/Trafford Model Centre) - *99*	40	80
(R1026)	**37001 *Norman Bell*** 'Eddie Stobart Ltd.' green Sp Edn 1000 (Eddie Stobart Club/ Trafford Model Centre) ex-R1026 set - *02*	40	NA
R2574	**37038** DRS dark blue - *06-07*	42	59
(R1054)	**37040** EW&S maroon+yellow ex-Sp Edn set (Toys-R-Us) - *05*	40	NA
R2027	**37042** EWS maroon, scb - *97-98*	35	NA
R2255	**37057+37042** (dummy) EWS maroon W pair - *02*	55	70
R348	**37063** BReLL Railfreight grey, scb - *86-89*	25	40
R359	**37071** BReLL bright blue - *82-85*	18	NA
R365	**37072** BReLL bright green - *84*	18	30
R369	**37073** BRe blue - *80-83*	18	30
R751	**37130** BRe blue, npf - *77-79*	15	25
R285	**37166, 37187, 37202** BRe blue, alternative numbers - *88-90*	NA	35
-	**37166** ** BRe blue - *88-90*	20	NA
R2255A	**37174+37298** (dummy) EWS maroon W pair - *03-05*	55	75
-	**37187** ** BRe blue - *88-90*	20	NA
R2012C	**37198** Mainline blue - *97*	30	45
-	**37202** ** BRe blue - *88-90*	20	NA
R2012B	**37203** Mainline blue - *97*	30	45
R402	**37207 *William Cookworthy*** BRe blue - *84-86*	20	35
R2412	**37216+37248 *Midland Railway Centre*** (dummy) Mainline blue W pair - *04-05*	NA	75
-	**37248** *(see 37216)*	-	-
R2472A	**37260 *Radio Highland*** BReLL blue W - *05-07*	42	59

Class 37 diesel in BR large logo blue as No.37261 Caithness [L79a]

R2472B	**37261 *Caithness*** BReLL blue W - *05-06*	42	59
	37298 *(see 37174)*	-	-
R2012A	**37371** Mainline blue - *97*	30	45
R2255	**37405+37416** EWS maroon W coupled pair - *not made*	NA	NA
R2409	**37410 *Aluminium 100*** grey Transrail - *04-05*	45	54
R2060C	**37415** EW&S maroon - *98*	30	40
R327	**37424** BR Transrail grey - *96-97*	25	40
R2060A	**37427** EW&S maroon - *98*	30	40
R286	**37518, 37677, 37688** BReLL Railfreight red-stripe grey, alternative numbers - *88-89*	NA	45
-	**37518** *** BReLL Railfreight grey - *88-89*	20	NA
-	**37677** *** BReLL Railfreight grey - *88-89*	20	NA
-	**37688** *** BReLL Railfreight grey - *88-89*	20	NA
R2060B	**37688** EW&S maroon - *98*	30	40
R243	**37885** BRe Railfreight Metals grey - *95*	25	45
R871	**37937** BRe blue, number choice - *96*	20	40

* Alternative transfer numbers for R284. ** Alternative transfer numbers for R285. *** Alternative transfer numbers for R286.

L79b. Class 37 Diesel Co-Co (ex-Lima) (2008)

Introduced by Lima in 1986. Now fitted with a 5-pole skew wound bogie mounted motor and new couplings. 'DCC ready'.

R2775	**37414** Regional Railways blue (RailRoad) - *08-10*	35	44

L80. Class 40 1Co-Co1 (ex-Lima) (2010)

Reintroduced for the RailRoad range.

R2938	**D40152** BRe blue (RailRoad) - *10-11*	NPG	NPG

Ex-Lima Class 40 in BR blue as No.40152 [L80]

L81. Class 42 'Warship' B-B (ex-Lima) (2011)

Reintroduced for the RailRoad range.

R3068	**D802** Formidable BRc green (RailRoad) - *11*	40	52

L82a. Class 43 'HST 125' (1978)

Ringfield motor. 5-pole motors were fitted from 2004. The Hornby model is of the early DMB unit and so has guard's compartment windows. Models made from 1988 onwards had the exhaust baffle on cab roof. In 2008 this model was retired in favour of the former Lima model and the super-detailed version tooled up by Hornby.

	Inter-City 125 Blue		
R069/070	**253 001 (W43002+W43003)** 2-car - *78-80*	20	35
R332	**253 005 (43010+43011)** 3-car (R370/371) - *80-84*	NA	45
R2296	**253036 (W43142+W43141)** 4-car - *02-04*	NA	85
(R541)	**43010/43011** BRe I-C ex-set - *80-81*	25	NA
	Inter-City 125 Executive Grey		
R401	**253 028 (34125+42251+43126)** 3-car (R708/709) + sheet of numbers - *83-91*	NA	45
(R556)	as above but ex-set - *83-85*	30	NA
	Inter-City Swallow Grey		
R2613	**43040 *Granite City*+12116+12117+43041 *City of Discovery*** 4-car - *07*	NA	100
R336	**43046+43080+43066+43050** 3-car pack (R706/707) - *90-97*	NA	40
R?	**43050+43119** black roof - *?*	NPG	NPG
R?	**43051 *Armada 400*+43072** Sp Edn 3-car pack - *88-89?*	NA	130
R397	**43072+43051** 3-car pack (R797/798)- *88-91*	NA	40
(R901)	**43102+43086** ex-4-car set - *96-97*	50	NA
R897	**43154 *Intercity*/43193** Ltd Edn. 5000 ex-5-car set (R3392/R3393) - *96*	35	NA
	Great Western Green & Ivory		
R2115	**43002+43124** 4-car pack - *99-01*	NA	60
	FGW purple		
R2299	**43042+43029** 4-car pack - *02-05*	NA	85
R2500	**43185 *Great Western*+43192 *City of Truro*** revised livery 4-car pack - *05-07*	NA	85
	Midland Mainline Jade Green		
R2046	**43058 *Midland Pride*+43059** 4-car pack - *97-98*	NA	60
	Midland Mainline Blue & White		
R2376	**43070+43069** + 2 coaches 4-car pack - *04*	NA	90
R2376A	**43197+43196** + 2 coaches 4-car pack - *05-07*	NA	90
	Virgin Red & Black		
R2045	**43063 *Maiden Voyager*+43093 *Lady in Red*** 4-car pack, also in R1023 set - *97-05*	NA	60
R2298A	**43065+43080** 4-car pack - *04-06*	NA	90

Class 43 No.43087 in Hornby livery [L82a]

R2298	**43068 *The Red Arrows*+43062** 4-car pack - *02-03*	NA	85
(R1080)	**43087+43155** Hornby ex-set - *06*	50	NA
R2114	**43092 *Institution of Mechanical Engineers 150th Anniversary 1847- 1997*+43090** 4-car pack - *99-01*	NA	60
R2298B	**43193+43103** 4-car pack - *04-05*	NA	90
	GNER Navy Blue		
R2116	**43116+43095** 4-car pack - *99-00*	NA	60
R2000	**43117+43118** 4-car pack - *97-98*	NA	60
R2612	**43118 *City of Kingston Upon Hull* +42192+ 42193+43115 *Aberdeenshire*** 4-car - *07*	NA	100
R696	Intercity XPT silver 3-car pack * (R741/742) - *83-84*	NA	100

* Examples may be found with either a power car and 2 coaches or with one of the coaches replaced by a dummy power car.

L82b. Class 43 'HST 125' (ex-Lima) (2008)

This former Lima model was originally added to the Lima range in 1982. Hornby planned to replace their own model with it in 2007 but on testing the body tool it was found to be badly damaged. Their own tool was therefore used instead for the 2007 releases. 5-pole ringfield motor.

R2707	**43101+43100** Virgin red+black (RailRoad) - *08-10*	45	50
R2612	**43118 *City of Kingston Upon Hull* +42192+ 42193+43115 *Aberdeenshire*** GNER 125 navy 4-car - *not made*	NA	NA
R2613	**43040 *Granite City*+12116+12117+43041 *City of Discovery*** ICs grey 4-car - *not made*	NA	NA

L82c. Class 43 'HST 125' (2008)

This is a completely retooled model to super-detail standards. Centrally mounted 5-pole skew wound motor connected to both bogies. Fitted with lights. Both 'DCC ready' and 'DCC fitted' (has X suffix) versions of each general release loco were made. Add £10-£15 for X models.

R2701	**253 027(W43054+W43055)** Intercity 125 blue+yellow+grey 2-car train pack - *08-10*	115	148
R2702	**254007 (43103 *John Wesley*+43194)** IC Exec grey 2-car train pack - *08-11*	115	148

New Class 43 model as No.43103 John Wesley [L82c]

R2984	**43103+43014** Network Rail yellow Measurement train - *11*	135	184
R2703	**43015 *City of Inverness*+43113 *The Highlands*** GNER navy 2-car train pack - *08-09*	115	148
R2704	**43196 *The Newspaper Society Founded 1836* + 43162** Virgin red+black 2-car train pack - *08-10*	115	148
R2964	**43300 *Craigentinny*+43310** East Coast silver+ white 2-car train pack - *10*	115	148
R2812	**43017+43162** FGW Purple 2-car train pack - *09-11*	115	148
R2705	**43080+43068** Grand Central black 2-car train pack - *09-11*	115	148
R2948	**43055+43048 *TCB Miller MBE*** East Midlands deep violet 2-car train pack - *10-11*	115	148
R2949	**43321+43285** Cross Country purple+grey 2-car train pack - *10-11*	115	148

L83a. Class 47 Diesel Co-Co (1975)

Ringfield motor. npf = non-paint finish. 5-p = 5-pole motor.

R2433	'Eddie Stobart' green Sp Edn (Eddie Stobart Club) - *04*	NA	50
R245	BRe Rft Distribution grey, choice of names/ numbers - *89-90,96*	NA	50
R287	BRe blue choice of names/ numbers - *88-89*	NA	50
R219	BRe NSE bright blue, choice of numbers / names - *89-93*	NA	50
R288	BRe InterCity grey, choice of names/ numbers - *88-90*	NA	50
R060	**D1520** BRc green npf - *76*	15	35
R073	**D1670 *Mammoth*** BRc green npf - *79-80*	18	40
R328	**D1670 *Mammoth*** BRc green - *80-81*	20	35
R863	**D1738** BRc gloss green npf - *75*	25	35
R2481	**47054** West Coast Railways maroon - *05*	40	50
R342	**47079** BRe Railfreight Construction grey - *90-92*	30	NA
R416	**47085 *REPTA 1893-1993*** Railfreight Distribution grey - *94?*	30	35
R2254	**47120** BReLL blue W - *02*	35	50
-	**47124** BRe blue see R287 above - *88-89*	25	30
R416	**47156 *REPTA 1893-1993*** Railfreight Distribution grey - *94?*	40	50
R307	**47170 *County of Norfolk*** BReLL blue - *82-83*	25	35
R2479A	**47200 *The Fosse Way*** Cotswold Rail pale grey - *05-06*	40	59

Class 47 No.47207 Bulmers of Hereford in Railfreight Distribution livery [L83a]

-	**47207 *Bulmers of Hereford*** BRe Railfreight Distribution grey see R245 above - *89-90,96*	20	NA
-	**47231 *The Silcock Express*** BRe Railfreight Distribution grey see R245 above - *89-90,96*	20	NA
R116	**47234** Railfreight Distribution grey - *94*	28	45
R2353	**47237** DRS dark blue 5-p - *not made*	NA	NA
R2013B	**47270** Freightliner grey - *97*	25	30
R2013C	**47301** Freightliner grey - *97*	25	30
-	**47311 *Warrington Yard*** BRe Railfreight Distribution grey, see R245 above - *89-90, 96*	20	NA
R2479B	**47316 *Cam Peak*** Cotswold Rail pale grey - *05-07*	40	59
R2080	**47345** Freightliner grey train pack with 3 wagons - *98*	NA	85
(R2080)	above loco only - *98*	35	NA
-	**47353** BRe blue see R287 above - *88-89*	25	30
R2013A	**47376 *Freightliner 1995*** Freightliner grey - *97*	25	30
R898	**47378** BReLL Railfreight General grey - *87-88*	25	40
R354	**47406 *Rail Riders*** BRe blue - *85*	30	40
-	**47409** BRe blue see R287 above - *88-89*	25	30
R075	**47421** BRe blue npf - *77-78*	15	25
R2254A	**47432** BReLL W blue - *03-04*	30	54
R2254B	**47473** BReLL W blue - *04*	45	54
R769	**47480 *Robin Hood*** BRe blue Sp Edn 480 (Beatties) - *83*	35	60
R802	**47487** BRe InterCity grey - *86-87*	30	40
R2353	**47501** DRS dark blue 5-p - *04*	45	54
R319	**47541 *The Queen Mother*** BRe blue - *83-85*	30	40
R329	**47541 *The Queen Mother*** BRe blue Sp Edn 187 (Grattans) - *83*	NA	50
-	**47549 *Royal Mail*** BRe InterCity grey see R288 above - *88-90*	20	NA
R404	**47568** BRe blue - *84-87*	25	30
R876	**47573 *The London Standard*** BRe NSE bright blue - *87-88*	30	40
-	**47576 *King's Lynn*** BRe NSE bright blue see R219 above - *89-93*	20	NA
-	**47579 *James Nightingale GC*** BRe NSE bright blue see R219 above - *89-93*	20	NA
-	**47583 *County of Hertfordshire*** BRe NSE bright blue see R219 above - *89-93*	20	NA
R587	**47586 *Northamptonshire*** InterCity Swallow grey - *91-92*	30	35
-	**47613 *North Star*** BRe InterCity grey see R288 above - *88-90*	20	NA
-	**47620 *Windsor Castle*** BRe InterCity grey see R288 above - *88-90*	20	NA
R886	**47711 *Greyfrier's Bobby*** BRe ScotRail grey - *87-88*	30	45
R316	**47712 *Lady Diana Spencer*** BReLL blue - *81*	30	35
R887	**47716 *The Duke of Edinburgh's Award*** BRe ScotRail grey - *87-88*	30	45
R2289C	**47722 *The Queen Mother*** Virgin red+black - *03*	35	52
R2289D	**47741 *Resilient*** Virgin red+black - *03*	35	52
R2437	**47781 *Isle of Iona*** RES + VDA + 2xMk2A Serco test train pack - *05-07*	NA	100
(R2437)	above loco only - *05-07*	45	NA
R2480	**47784** One Anglia blue+black - *not made*	NA	NA
R2289E	**47805 *Pride of Toton*** Virgin red+black - *04*	35	54
R2289A	**47807 *Lion of Vienna*** Virgin red+black - *02*	35	50
R717	**47808** BRe Parcels red ex-R346 set - *95-96*	35	NA
R2061B	**47814 *Totnes Castle*** Virgin red+black - *98*	35	40
R2352	**47816 *Bristol Bath Road*** FGW green gold stripe - *04*	35	54
R2480	**47818** One Anglia light blue+black - *05*	40	50
X3857	**47822 *Pride of Shrewsbury*** Virgin red+black R1022 set (Kays) - *99-00*	35	NA
R2351	**47839** Riviera Trains navy blue 5-p - *04*	35	54
R2351W	**47???** Riviera Trains blue ex-MO set R1083L- *08*	22	NA

R2289B	**47841 *Spirit of Chester*** Virgin red+black - *02*	35	50
R2061A	**47844** Virgin red+black - *98*	30	40
R2677	**47844** Virgin red+black (RailRoad) - *07-10*	35	44
R2061C	**47845 *County of Kent*** Virgin red+black - *98*	30	40
R2422	**47853 *Rail Express* /D1733** Riviera Trains BRe XP64 light blue 5-p - *04*	35	54
R2289G	**47854 *Womens Royal Voluntary Service*** Virgin red+black 5-p - *04-06*	35	55

L83b. Class 47 Diesel Co-Co (ex-Lima) (2007)

This model joined from the Lima range in 1987. Hornby altered the bogie frames to take their own motor.

Ex-Lima Class 47 'Blue Pullman' livery No.47709 Dionysos [L83b]

(R1093)	**47709 *Dionysos*** Nanking blue ex-set - *07-08*	55	NA

L84. Class 50 Diesel Co-Co (2004)

Super-detail model. 'DCC ready', drive to both bogies and pickups on all wheels. DS = DCC sound chip fitted.

R2474	**D421** BRe blue - *05-07*	75	95
R2749	**50001 *Dreadnought*** NSE blue - *not made*	NA	NA
R2429	**50002 *Superb*** NSE Revised bright blue W - *04-06*	75	95
R2487	**50004 *St Vincent*** BReLL blue - *05-06*	75	95
R2408	**50007 *Sir Edward Elgar*** BRe heritage green - *04*	70	85
R2499	**50007 *Sir Edward Elgar*** BRe heritage green W Ltd Edn 500* (HCClub) - *05*	70	90
R3054	**50008 *Thunderer*** BRe blue - *11*	80	119
R2748	**50011 *Centurion*** BReLL blue - *08-09*	80	108

Class 50 No.50011 Centurion in BR large logo blue [L84]

R2486	**50013 *Agincourt*** BRe blue - *05-07*	75	95
R2802XS	**50015 *Valiant*** BRe Depart grey+yellow DS - *09-11*	170	210
R2348	**50018 *Resolution*** BRe blue - *03-04*	70	85
R2641	**50020 *Revenge*** BReLL blue - *07-09*	70	85
R2575	**50027 *Lion*** NSE bright blue - *06-07*	75	95
R2374	**50031 *Hood*** BReLL blue Ltd Edn (HCC) - *04*	70	85
R2349	**50035 *Ark Royal*** BReLL blue - *03-04*	70	85
R2428	**50037 *Illustrious*** BRe blue - *04-06*	75	95
R2901XS	**50037 *Illustrious*** BReLL blue DS - *10-11*	170	210
R2350	**50045 *Achilles*** NSE Revised bright blue W - *03-04*	70	85
R2749	**50048 *Dauntless*** NSE blue - *08-09*	80	100
R2434	**50149 *Defiance*** Railfreight General grey Sp Edn 1,000 (Rail Express) - *03-04*	75	89

Due to an error, early in 2006, a quantity of the models was supplied to Rails of Sheffield and 121 were sold before they were withdrawn. These were sold without certificates and reduces the certificated models to 379.

L85. Class 52 'Western' Diesel C-C (1981)

Western Region diesel hydraulic. Ringfield motor. 5-p = 5-pole motor. npf = non paint finish.

R778	**D1008 *Western Harrier*** BRe blue - *81-82*	30	40
R2475	**D1009 *Western Invader*** maroon W 5-p - *05-07*	40	59
R2158	**D1012 *Western Firebrand*** BRe blue - *?*	30	40
R2158	**D1013 *Western Ranger*** BRe blue - *00-03*	30	40
R319	**D1035 *Western Yeoman*** BRc green - *92-93*	30	40
R101	**D1039 *Western King*** BRc maroon - *94-95*	30	40
R348	**D1058 *Western Nobleman*** BRe blue - *96-97*	30	40
R352	**D1062 *Western Courier*** BRc maroon, npf - *79*	20	30
R368	**D1062 *Western Courier*** BRc maroon - *80-81*	25	35

L86. Class 55 'Deltic' Co-Co (ex-Lima) (2007)

Former Lima model first introduced to the Lima range in 1977.

(R1092)	**D9014 *The Duke of Wellington's Regiment*** BRc green ex-set - *07-08*	40	NA
R2879	**55001 *St Paddy*** BRe blue RailRoad - *09-11*	40	44

L87a. Class 56 Diesel Co-Co (ex-Mainline) (1998)

Heavy freight locomotive. Ringfield motor. 5-p = 5-pole motor.

R2288B	**56038** EW&S maroon - *02*	35	48
R2106A	**56047** Transrail Dutch grey+yellow - *00-01*	30	48
R2235C	**56048** BReLL blue - *02*	35	48
R2106	**56049** Transrail Dutch grey+yellow - *99*	30	48
R2075	**56058** EW&S maroon+yellow - *98*	30	45
R2288D	**56058** EW&S maroon+yellow 5-p - *04*	35	50
R2288A	**56059** EWS maroon+yellow - *02*	35	48
R2576	**56063** Railfreight Trainload grey W - *06-07*	40	52
R2107D	**56066** BRe Transrail grey - *00-01*	30	48
R2288A	**56068** EW&S maroon+yellow - *not made*	NA	NA
R2416B	**56083** Loadhaul black+orange 5-p - *06-07*	40	55
R2288C	**56088** EW&S maroon+yellow - *03*	35	48
R2476B	**56088** BReLL Railfreight red stripe 5-p - *05-07*	40	52
R2476A	**56090** BReLL Railfreight red stripe 5-p - *05-07*	40	52
R2235E	**56098** BReLL blue - *03-04*	35	52
R2235D	**56099** BReLL blue - *02*	35	48
R2074	**56100** Loadhaul black - *98, 00*	30	50
R2235A	**56101** BReLL blue - *01*	30	48
R2075A	**56105** EW&S maroon Ltd Edn 500 - *98*	50	70
R2253A	**56105** BReLL blue W - *03*	35	48
R2416A	**56107** Loadhaul black+orange 5-p - *04-06*	40	55
R2074B	**56109** Loadhaul black - *98, 00-01*	30	50
R2235B	**56113** BReLL blue - *01*	30	48
R2477A	**56113** BRe Coal triple grey W 5-p - *05-07*	40	55
R2074A	**56118** Loadhaul black Ltd Edn 500 - *98*	50	70
R2107A	**56119** BRe Transrail grey - *99*	30	50
R2107C	**56123 *Drax Power Station*** BRe Transrail grey - *99*	30	50
R2253	**56123** BReLL blue W - *02*	35	48
R2477B	**56125** BRe Coal triple grey W 5-p - *06-07*	40	59
R2107B	**56127** BRe Transrail grey - *99*	30	50
R2235G	**56131 *Ellington Colliery*** BReLL blue 5-p - *04*	35	52

L87b. Class 56 Diesel Co-Co (2007)

Main line Type 5 heavy freight locomotive. This is an entirely retooled model to a high specification. Romanian, Doncaster and Crewe variations. See-through grilles, opening doors and directional lights. Initially released with both decoder fitted and non-fitted versions of each. DS = digital sound. Both 'DCC ready' and 'DCC fitted' (has X suffix) versions of each general release loco were made. Add £10-£15 for X models.

R3033XS	**56001 *Whatley*** Rft coal triple grey - *11*	160	231
R2751	**56003** LoadHaul black+orange - *08*	95	116
R2645	**56013** BRe blue - *07-09*	80	95

Class 56 No.56003 in LoadHaul livery [L87b]

R3052	**56031 *Merehead*** Rft Construction triple grey - *11*	90	128
R2752	**56032 *Sir De Morgannwg/County of South Glamorgan*** Railfreight Metals tripe grey - *08-09*	85	108
R2961	**56040 *Oystermouth*** BReLL Railfreight red-stripe grey - *11*	80	102
R2646	**56049** BReLL Railfreight red-stripe grey - *07-09*	80	102
R2648	**56059** EWS maroon - *07-10*	80	95
R3050	**56082** BRe blue - *11*	90	128
R3033XS	**56095 *Harworth Colliery*** Rft Coal triple grey - *11?*	160	231
R2750	**56103 *Stora*** EWS maroon - *08*	95	116
R2781XS	**56125** BRe Railfreight Coal DS - *not made*	NA	NA
R2781XS	**56127** BRe Railfreight Coal DS - *08-09*	120	193
R2647	**56128 *West Burton Power Station*** BRe Railfreight Coal - *07-08*	80	95
R2776	**56302 *Wilson Walshe*** Fastline Sp Edn *(Rail Express) - 07*	95	110

L88. Class 58 Diesel Co-Co (1982)

Heavy freight locomotive. Type 7 motor.

R250	**58001** Railfreight red stripe - *84-87*	20	30
R2336	**58002** ***Daw Mill Colliery*** **+ 58005** ***Ironbridge Power Station*** (dummy) Mainline blue W - *03-06*	60	80
-	**58005** ***Ironbridge Power Station*** (*see above*)	-	-
R332	**58006** Railfreight Coal grey - *90-91*	30	45
R250	**58007** BRe grey, number both ends - *82*	30	40
R250	**58007** Railfreight red stripe number one end - *83*	25	35
R2071	**58008** Mainline blue - *not made*	NA	NA
R2011B	**58021** ***Hither Green Depot*** Mainline blue - *97*	40	48
R2011A	**58023** ***Peterborough Depot*** Mainline blue - *97-98*	35	45
R2411	**58024** EW&S + **58037** ***Worksop Depot*** EWS maroon W pair - *04*	NA	70
R332	**58025** Railfreight Coal grey - *90-91*	30	45
R250?	**58027** Railfreight red stripe - *83?*	40	48
R2125A	**58030** EWS maroon - *99*	35	45
R2346	**58033** EW&S early maroon - *03-04*	35	50
R283	**58034** ***Bassetlaw*** Railfreight red stripe - *88-89*	35	48
R2034	**58037** EWS maroon - *97-98*	35	45
-	**58037** ***Worksop Depot*** EWS maroon W - *see 58024*	-	-
R2125B	**58039** EWS maroon - *99*	35	45
R2252A	**58041** ***Ratcliffe Power Station*** Coal grey W - *03-04*	35	50
R2011C	**58042** ***Petrolea*** Mainline blue - *97*	40	48
R332	**58044** Railfreight Coal grey - *90-91*	30	45
R2345	**58046** ***Thoresby Colliery*** Coal grey - *03-04*	35	50
R2252B	**58047** ***Manton Colliery*** Coal grey - *not made*	NA	NA

Class 58 EWS No.58047 [L88]

R2125C	**58047** EWS maroon - *00, 02*	30	40
R262	**58048** Railfreight red stripe ex-R887 set - *94*	30	NA
R2072	**58048** EW&S maroon - *not made*	NA	NA
R705	**58050** ***Toton Traction Depot*** Coal grey - *89*	30	42
R2252	**58050** Railfreight Coal grey W - *02*	30	42
R358	**58050** ***Toton Traction Depot*** Mainline blue - *96*	40	48

L89. Class 59 Diesel Co-Co (ex-Lima) (2006)

From their introduction all of the class were privately owned and not a part of the BR fleet. Re-motored and wheeled and 'DCC ready'. The original Lima model was released in 1994.

R2861	**59001** ***Yeoman Endeavour*** Aggregate Industries blue+green - *09-11*	50	77
R2519	**59005** ***Kenneth J Painter*** Foster Yeoman silver+blue - *06-07*	45	60
R3041	**59005** ***Kenneth J Painter*** Foster Yeoman silver+blue - *11*	40	55
R2521	**59102** ***Village of Chantry*** ARC yellow+ grey - *06-07*	45	60
R2520	**59201** ***Vale of York*** EWS maroon - *06-09*	45	60
R2935	**59206** ***John F Yeoman*** DB Schenker red - *10*	40	50

L90. Class 60 Diesel Co-Co (2005)

Super-detail model. Twin bogie drive, all round current contacts, 5-pole skew wound motor, 'DCC ready'. DS = digital sound.

R2489	**60007** Loadhaul black+orange - *06-07*	75	90
R2639	**60014** ***Alexander Fleming*** EWS triple grey - *07*	75	90
R2488	**60026** EW&S maroon - *05-06*	75	90
R2746	**60029** ***Clitheroe Castle*** EWS maroon - *08-09*	80	108
R3051	**60033** ***Tees Steel Express*** EWS blue - *11*	90	128

Class 60 DB Schenker No.60040 The Territorial Army Centenary [L90]

R2883	**60040** ***The Territorial Army Centenary*** DB Schenker maroon - *09*	85	118
R2899XS	**60042** ***The Hundred of Hoo*** EWS maroon DS - *10-11*	140	210
R2780XS	**60048** ***Eastern*** EWS maroon DS - *08-09*	120	193
R2747	**60062 Samuel Johnson** Railfreight Petroleum triple grey - *08-09*	80	108
R2640	**60066** ***John Logie Baird*** Transrail triple grey Coal Load - *07*	75	90
R26??	**60074** ***Teenage Spirit*** DB Schenker light blue Teenage Cancer Trust Sp Edn 1000 (*Rail Express Modeller*) - *08*	75	90
R2577	**60077** ***Canisp*** Rft Trainload grey - *06-07*	75	95
R2490	**60078** Mainline blue - *06-07*	75	90
R2604	**60081** ***Isambard Kingdom Brunel*** EWS green Sp Edn (*Rail Express*) - *06*	75	90

L91. Class 66 Diesel Co-Co (ex-Lima) (2007)

Post BR introduction. The original Lima model was released in 1999.

R2651	**66042** ***Lafage Buddoy Wood*** EWS maroon - *07-08*	55	70
R2652	**66702** ***Blue Lightning*** GBRf blue - *07-08*	55	70
R2650	**66709** ***Joseph Arnold Davies*** GBRf Medite black - *07-09*	55	74
R3076	**66723** ***Chinook*** GBRf violet - *11*	45	60
R2934	**66842** Advenza Freight dark blue - *10*	40	50

Ex-Lima Class 66 Advenza No.66842 [L91]

R3042	**66843** Colas Rail orange+yellow - *11*	45	60

L92. Class 67 Diesel Bo-Bo (ex-Lima) (2006)

Post BR introduction. The original Lima model was released in 2002.

R2523	**67005** ***Queen's Messenger*** EWS Royal dark purple - *06-09*	60	80
R2951	**67014** ***Thomas Telford*** Wrexham & Shropshire grey+silver + grey+silver Mk3 DVT train pack - *10-11*	NA	130
(R2951)	above loco only - *10-11*	65	NA
R2764	**67018** ***Rapid*** EWS maroon - *08-09*	60	80
R2522	**67027** ***Rising Star*** EWS maroon - *06-07*	55	70
R2890	**67029** ***Royal Diamond*** EWS silver train pack with silver DVT + Mk3 1st + Mk3 sleeper in EWS maroon 'EWS Managers' train pack - *09-10*	NA	184
(R2890)	above loco only - *09-10*	65	NA

Electro-Diesel Locomotives

L93. Class 73 Bo-Bo (ex-Lima) (2006)

The first 6 locomotives were built in 1962 and form subclass 73/0. The remainder were built in 1965 and form subclass 73/1. The original Lima model was released in 1986 and was one of their better models. 5-pole skew-wound motor. NEM coupling pockets fitted in 2008.

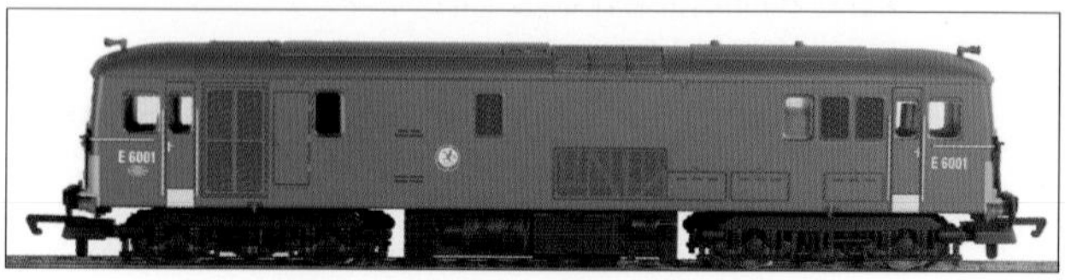

Ex-Lima Class 73 No.E6001 in BR green [L93]

R2656	**E6001** BRc green 73/0 - *07-08*	45	60
R2517	**E6003** BRc green, grey stripe 73/0 - *06-08*	45	60
R2516	**73101** ***The Royal Alex*** Pullman brown+cream 73/1 - *06-08*	45	60
R2518	**73107** ***Spitfire*** Fragonset black 73/1 - *06-08*	45	60
R2765	**73108** BRe Engineers grey+yellow - *08-10*	50	70
R2766	**73129** ***City of Winchester*** NSE blue - *08-09*	50	70
R3045	**73202** ***Dave Berry*** *Gatwick Express* white+red - *11*	40	55

R2767	**73204 *Stewarts Lane 1960-1985*** BReLL IC dark grey+beige - *08*	50	66
R2654	**73204 *Janice*** GBRf blue+yellow 73/1 - *07-09*	45	70
R2655	**73235** SWT blue+yellow+red 73/1 - *07-09*	45	70

Electric Locomotives

L94. Steeple Cab Electric 0-4-0 (Freelance) (1959)

R254	BRc green - *59-64*	35	75
R254	TR green - *61-63*	65	75
R252	TR maroon dummy pantograph - *59-62*	40	75

L95. Class EM2 Electric Co-Co (1961)

R351	**27000 *Electra*** BRc green - *61-65*	55	120
R388	**27000 *Electra*, 27002 *Aurora*, 27006 *Pandora*** BRc green CKD kit with choice of names - *65*	NA	120
R351	**27000 *Electra*** BRc electric blue - *66-68*	50	135
R388	**27000 *Electra*, 27002 *Aurora*, 27006 *Pandora*** BRc electric blue CKD kit with choice of names - *66-67*	NA	250
R388	**27000 *Electra*, 27002 *Aurora*, 27006 *Pandora*** BR electric blue kit with name choice - *68*	NA	240

Class EM2 No.27000 Electra [L95]

R351	**27000 *Electra*** BRe rail blue - *69-71*	60	120
R388	**27000 *Electra*, 27002 *Aurora*, 27006 *Pandora*** BRe rail blue, kit with name choice - *69-70*	NA	240
R351	**E27000 *Electra*** BRe rail blue - *71*	75	120

L96. Class 81 (AL1) AC Electric (1966)

R753	**E3001** BRd electric blue 2 pantographs - *66*	120	160
R753	**E3001** BRd electric blue 1 pantograph - *67*	90	130
R753	**E3001** BRe electric blue 1 pantograph - *68*	70	100
R753	**E3001** BRe rail blue 1 pantograph - *69-70*	60	85

L97. Class 86/2 Electric (1981)

Ringfield motor with a 5-pole motor fitted from 2004. Some have non-functioning pantographs.

R289	BRe I-C grey alternative names - *88*	NA	50
R289	**86102 *Robert A Riddles*** BRe I-C grey Sp Edn 950 (IWPA) - *89*	50	75
R301	**86210 *C.I.T 75th Anniversary*** BRe RES red Sp Edn 1000 (CIT) - *96*	35	45
R289	**86213 *Lancashire Witch*** BRe I-C grey Sp Edn? - *89?*	55	75
R2160A	**86215 *The Round Tabler*** Anglia blue - *04*	45	54
R2120	**86218 *NHS 50*** Anglia blue - *99*	35	50
R360	**86219 *Phoenix*** BRe blue - *81-83*	30	45
R2290B	**86225 *Hardwick*** Virgin red+black - *02*	35	50
R2362	**86227 *Golden Jubilee*** Anglia blue, Union Jacks - *03*	35	47
-	**86228 *Vulcan Heritage*** BRe I-C grey - *see R289 at top*	35	NA
R2414	**86233 *Alstom Heritage* E3172** BRd electric blue - *04*	45	54
R2415	**86235 *Novelty*** ICs grey - *04*	45	54
R2160	**86235 *Crown Point*** Anglia blue - *00-02*	35	50
R2290C	**86236 *Josiah Wedgwood*** Virgin red+black - *03*	40	47
R2243	**86237 *University of East Anglia*** Anglia blue - *not made*	NA	NA
R2331	**86241 *Glenfiddich*** RES red - *03*	40	47
R2290A	**86242 *James Kennedy*** Virgin red+black - *02*	40	50
R367	**86243 *The Boy's Brigade*** BRe blue - *83-84*	40	55
R2242	**86245 *Caledonian*** Virgin blue - *01*	45	60
R800	**86246 *Royal Anglian Regiment* BRe** I-C grey - *86-87*	35	45
R2290D	**86248 *Sir Clwyd/County of Clwyd*** Virgin red+black - *05*	40	55
-	**86255 *Penrith Beacon*** BRe I-C grey - *see R289 at top*	35	NA
R2755	**86259 *Les Ross*** BRd electric blue - *08-09*	50	68

Class 86 No.86259 Les Ross in heritage 'Electric Blue' livery [L97]

R2159	**86261 *The Rail Charter Partnership*** EWS maroon - *00-02*	35	45
R2159A	**86401 *Hertfordshire Rail Tours*** EWS maroon+yellow - *03*	35	47
R368	**86401** BRe NSE bright blue - *88-89*	35	50
R333	**86405** I-C grey - *90-91*	30	45
R388	**86414 *Frank Hornby*** BRe I-C grey Ltd Edn 1750 - *88-89*	35	45
R322	**86417** BRe RES red - *96-97*	35	50
-	**86417 *The Kingsman*** BRe I-C grey - *see R289 at top*	35	NA
R333	**86419** I-C grey - *90-91*	30	45
R589	**86419 *Post Haste*** BRe Parcels red - *91-92*	30	50
R2240	**86426** EWS maroon - *01*	35	45
R333	**86431** I-C grey - *90-91*	30	45
R335	**86504 *Halley's Comet*** BRe Railfreight General grey - *90-91*	30	45
R2241B	**86602** Freightliner green - *01*	50	65
R2241A	**86631** Freightliner green - *00-01*	50	65
R3058	**86637** Freightliner green+yellow - *11*	40	55
R2596	**86901 *Chief Engineer*** NetworkRail yellow - *06-09*	45	59

L98. Class 87 AC Electric (ex-Lima) (2009)

36 locos built in 1973. Model introduced by Lima in 1979. 5-pole skew wound bogie mounted motor. Now fitted with NEM coupling pockets. 'DCC ready'. Non-working pantograph.

R2772	**87004 *Britannia*** BRe blue - *09-10*	50	68
R2787	**87010 *King Arthur*** IC Swallow dark grey+white - *09-10*	50	68

L99. Class 90 Electric (1988)

From 2004 5-pole motors were being fitted.

R242	**90001** Intercity Swallow grey - *88-90*	35	45
R2048	**90002 *Mission Impossible*** Virgin red+ black Sp Edn 525 (Model Rail) - *97*	60	85
R2473	**90003 *Raewald of East Anglia*** One Anglia blue - *05*	35	50
R2588	**90005 *Vice Admiral Lord Nelson*** One Anglia blue - *06-07*	40	59
R2067	**90012 *British Transport Police*** Virgin red+ black - *98*	35	45
R2109A	**90014** Virgin red+black - *99-00*	35	45

Class 90 FirstScotRail No.90019 [L99]

R2109B	**90015** ***The International Brigade Spain 1936-1939*** Virgin red+black - *99-00*	35	45
R062	**90018** BRe RES red - *93-94*	40	50
R2663A	**90019** First ScotRail violet + Mk3 Caledonian sleepers - *08-09*	NA	116
(R2663A)	above loco only - *08*	55	NA
R595	**90020** BRe Parcels red, dummy pantograph - *91-93*	45	NA
R2110	**90020** ***Sir Michael Heron*** EWS maroon - *99-00*	35	45
R2663A	**90021?** First Scotrail violet + 3 Mk3 Caledonian sleepers - *08-09*	NA	125
(R2663A)	above loco only - *08-09*	50	NA
R3053	**90021** First (EWS) violet - *11*	45	58
R2236	**90024** GNER navy blue - *01*	38	50
R2663	**90024** First Scotrail violet + 3 Mk3 Caledonian sleepers - *07*	NA	116
(R2663)	above loco only - *07*	50	NA
R471	**90028** BRe I-C grey dummy pant - *92*	50	60
R2330	**90029** ***FrachtVerbindungen*** BR/DB red - *03*	40	52
R2955	**90029** ***The Institution of Civil Engineers*** EWS maroon+yellow+ Virgin Mk3 DVT Charter Relief train pack - *11*	NA	130
(R2955)	above loco only - *11*	50	NA
R593	**90030** BRe main line grey - *91*	40	50
R593	**90033** BRe main line grey - *91*	40	50
R593	**90034** BRe main line grey - *91*	40	50
R2291B	**90037** Railfreight Distribution grey - *02-05*	40	52
R586	**90037** BRe Railfreight Distribution grey - *91*	40	50
R2291A	**90039** Railfreight Distribution grey - *02-04*	40	52
R586	**90040** BRe Railfreight Distribution grey - *91*	40	50
R847	**90040?** BRe Railfreight Distribution grey Sp Edn 30 (QVC) - *94*	NA	60
R2482	**90041** Freightliner green - *05-06*	50	65
R586	**90042** BRe Railfreight Distribution grey - *91*	40	50
R3077	**90046** Freightliner green - *11*	57	77
R2292	**90128** ***Vrachtverbinding*** BR/SNCB blue - *02*	50	65
R2358	**90130** ***Fretconnection*** Sibic SNCF grey+ yellow - *04*	50	65
R270	**90131** Railfreight Distribution grey - *95-96*	35	45
R2005	**90135** Railfreight Distribution grey - *97*	35	45
R?	**DC230 ST** ***Connectivity*** red+black Sp Edn 60 (Xerox) metallic nameplates* - *98*	120	150

* Possibly a Code 3 model. It was given as prizes on a series of training courses run by the Xerox Corporation and had numbered certificates.

L100. Class 91 Electric (1990)

ICs = InterCity Swallow grey livery

R240	**91001** ICs - *90-91*	30	40
R585	**91001** ***Swallow*** ICs - *91-94*	45	60
R356	**91003** ***The Scotsman*** ICs - *94*	40	50
R736	**91003** ***The Scotsman?*** ICs Sp Edn 30 (QVC) - *94*	NA	60
(R1012)	**91003** GNER navy blue ex-set - *98*	35	45
R585	**91004** ***The Red Arrows*** ICs - *91-94*	45	60
R240	**91008** ICs - *90-91*	30	40
R293	**91009** ***Saint Nicholas*** ICs - *95*	40	50
R240	**91010** ICs - *90-91*	30	40
R585	**91011** ***Terence Cuneo*** ICs - *91-94*	45	60
R269	**91014** ICs, dummy pant - *94-99*	30	NA

Class 91 No.91014 in BR Inter-City livery [L100]

R2002	**91019** ***Scottish Enterprise*** navy blue GNER 4-car pack - *98-00*	NA	75
(R2002)	above loco only - *98-00*	40	NA
R2002A	**91023** ***Scottish Enterprise*** navy blue GNER 4-car pack - *02-04*	NA	75
(R2002A)	above loco only - *02-04*	40	NA
R2069	**91022** ***Robert Adley*** ICs - *98-99*	35	45
R392	**91025** ***BBC Radio One FM*** ICs - *93*	45	60
R392	**91025** ***BBC Radio 1 FM*** ICs - *93*	45	60
R2002	**91030** GNER navy blue 4-car pack - *97*	NA	75
(R2002)	above loco only - *97*	40	NA
R367	**91031** ***Henry Royce*** ICs - *96*	35	45
R2427A	**91110** ***David Livingstone*** navy blue GNER + DVT + 2 Mk4s train pack - *05-06*	NA	100
(R2427A)	above loco only - *05-07*	40	NA
R2602	**91122** ***Tam The Gun*** navy blue GNER Mallard + DVT + 2 Mk4s pack - *06*	NA	100
(R2602)	above loco only - *06*	40	NA
R2427	**91129** ***Queen Elizabeth II*** navy blue GNER Mallard 4-car pack - *04*	NA	90
(R2427)	above loco only - *04*	40	NA
R392	**919799** ***BBC Radio One FM*** ICs Sp Edn 71 (BBC Radio 1) - *92*	90	120

L101. Class 92 Electric (1995)

Many have non-functioning pantographs.

R2354A	**92001** ***Victor Hugo*** EWS Tunnel maroon+ yellow - *03-06*	45	59
R289	**92009** ***Elgar*** BRe Tunnel Railfreight Distribution grey - *95-96*	35	NA
R3057	**92017** ***Bart the Engine*** Stobart Rail blue - *11*	57	77
R374	**92020** ***Milton*** EPS Tunnel grey - *96*	45	60
R855	**92022** ***Charles Dickens*** BRe Railfreight Distrib. Tunnel grey ex-R825 set - *96-98*	35	NA
R2004	**92026** ***Britten*** BRe Tunnel grey - *97-98*	40	55
R2354B	**92031** ***The Institute of Logistics and Transport*** EWS Tunnel maroon - *03-04*	35	55
R2035	**92045** ***Chaucer*** EPS Tunnel grey - *97*	45	60

Multiple Units & Railcars

L102a. Class 101 DMU (1958)

R157+R158	**M79079+M79632** BRc green from 66 with yellow panels 2-car - *62-67*	25	65
R157+R158	**M79628+M79629** BRb green 2-car - *58*	30	70

Tri-ang Class 101 DMU as revised in 1974 [L102a]

R157+R158	**M79628+M79629** BRc green 2-car - *59-61*	20	60
R157	**M79079+M79632** BRc green illuminated headcode 2-car - *74-78*	35	45
R157C	**M79079+M79632** BRe blue with yellow panel 2-car - *70-71*	50	75

L102b. Class 101 DMU (ex-Lima) (2006)

Former Lima model, released in 1997. Now with new 5-pole skew wound motor and wheels. 'DCC ready'.

R2578	**M30304+M59115+M50322** BRc green - *06-07*	60	76
R2578A	**M50309+M59120+M50327** BRc green - *07*	60	76
R2579	**M30319+M59130+M50337** BRe blue - *06-07*	60	76
R2579A	**M50314+M59125+M50332** BRe blue - *07-10*	60	76
R2696	**53753+53170** SPT blue - *08-10*	70	91
R2697	**M50320+M59131+M50338** BRc green - *08-09*	70	91
R2698	**W50304+W59122+W50239?** BRe blue+grey - *08-10*	70	91

L103. 'Blue Pullman' DMU (1963)

Up until 1969 the white window panel in the sides of the cars was a separate moulding and the glazing was flush. For the new livery of 1969 the body tool was modified and the window panel was painted on. The glazing was now no longer flush. The 1974 model had the white window band painted through to the end of the side of the car.

R555+R556	BR Pullman blue+white, front crest - *63-67*	25	65
R555+R556	BR Pullman blue+white, yellow front - *68*	35	60
R555+R556	BR Pullman Rail blue +white, yell front - *68*	50	80
R538	BR Pullman blue+white crest on sides - *74*	40	NA

R555C	**W60095**+**W60747** BR Pull grey+blue - *69-72*	30	65

Tri-ang 'Blue Pullman' of 1963 [L103]

R555C	**W60095**+**W60745** BR Pullman grey+blue - *?*	40	75

L104. Class 110 DMU (1982)

nos = a sheet with two sets of alternative numbers was provided in the pack. A choice of three destination blinds was provided.

	Green		
R687	**E51824**+**E59708**+**E51844** BRc 3-car- *83-84*	40	55
R689	**E51824** power car BRc - *83-84*	20	NA
R690	**E51844** dummy car BRc - *83-84*	12	NA
R369	**E51829**+**E59695**+**E51812** BRc 3-car - *92-97*	40	55
R340	**E51829** power car BRc - *92-97*	20	NA
R349	**E51812** dummy car BRc - *92-97*	12	NA
R369A	**E51840**+**E59701**+**E51815** BRc 3-car - *98*	35	50
R340	**E51840** power car BRc - *98*	20	NA
R349	**E51815** dummy car BRc - *98*	12	NA
R2297A	**E51841**+**E59710**+**E51819** BRc 3-car - *02-03*	45	65
R2297B	**E51834**+**E59703**+**E51827** BRc 3-car - *03-04*	40	60
R2297C	**E51823**+**E59707**+**E51843** BRc 3-car - *05*	50	70
R2297D	**E51838**+**E59700?**+**E51817** BRc 3-car - *06*	55	76
	Blue		
R267	**E51819**+**E51846** BRe 2-car, alt. nos. - *89-91*	30	40
R209	**E51819** power car BRe - *89-91*	20	NA
R210	**E51846** dummy car BRe - *89-91*	12	NA
	White		
R698	**E51816**+**E59707**+**E51832** BRe 3-car nos - *82-83*	35	50
R700	**E51816** power car BRe - *82-83*	20	NA
R701	**E51832** dummy car BRe - *82-83*	12	NA
R377	**E52073**+**E59816**+**E51846** BRe 3-car - *96-97*	35	50
R340A	**E52073** power car BRe - *96-97*	20	NA
R349A	**E51846** dummy car BRe - *96-97*	12	NA
	Blue & Grey		
R2073	**E51827**+**E59808**+**E52080** BRe 3-car - *98*	40	60
R403	**E51815**+**E59814**+**E52078** BRe 3-car nos - *84*	40	60
R064	**E51815** power car BRe - *84*	20	NA
R065	**E52078** dummy car BRe - *84*	12	NA
R2073A	**E52066**+**E59696**+**E52085** BRe 3-car - *99-00*	40	60

L105. Class 121 Railcar (ex-Lima) (2006)

Former Lima model, released in 1998. Now with new 5-pole skew wound motor and new wheels. NEM coupling pockets fitted in 2008.

R2644	**W55020** BRc dark brown+cream - *07-08*	45	60
R2769	**121020** (**55020**) Chiltern Railways blue - *08-09*	50	70
R2510	**W55021** BRe blue (yellow cab doors) - *06*	45	60

Ex-Lima Class 121 in BR blue & grey [L105]

R2668	**W55024 L124** BRe blue - *07*	45	60
R2508A	**121025** (**W55025**) BR NSE dark blue Thames - *07-08*	45	60
R2770	**W55026** BRe blue+grey - *08-09*	50	70
R2509	**W55027** BRc green - *06*	45	60
R2771	**W55028** BRc green - *08-10*	50	66
R2508	**55031** BR NSE dark blue Thames - *06*	45	60
R2509A	**W55032** BRc green - *07-09*	45	70

L106. Class 142 'Pacer' DMU (1987)

R297	**142013** (**55554+55604**) BRe Manchester PTE orange - *89*	45	65
R326	**142015** (**55556+55606**) BRe Western England brown+cream - *92-93*	50	70
(R346)	**142020** (**55561+55611**) BRe Regional Railways Tyne & Wear PTE yellow - *95-96*	40	NA
R103	**142023** (**55564+55614**) BRe Regional Railways grey - *94-95*	35	55
R2611	**142045** (**55636+55586**) Merseyrail Northern yellow - *07-08*	45	60
R867	**142048** (**55589+55639**) BRe Provincial Sector blue - *87-92*	28	45
(R1022)	**142065** (**55715+55761**) Northern Spirit blue Sp Edn (Kays) - *99*	30	NA
R451	**142069** (**55719+55765**) BRe Regional Railways GMPTE grey - *96-97*	35	55
R2161	**142074** (**55724+55770**) Northern Spirit blue - *00-02*	40	55
R2700	**142090** (**55786+55740**) Arriva light blue - *08-09*	45	68
R2809	**142068** (**55718+55764**) FGW violet 'gold star' livery - *10-11*	55	75

L107. Class 153 'Super Sprinter' Railcar (2008)

Converted from 155 2-car units built from Leyland National bus parts on bogied underframes. 5-pole skew wound motor bogie with all wheel pick-up and working lights. DCC ready.

R2756	**153333** (**52333**) Central Trains green - *08-09*	50	68
R2757	**153324** (**52324**) Northern Rail violet + purple - *08-09*	50	68
R2758	**153359** (**57359**) Arriva Trains Northern purple + gold - *08*	50	68
R2759	Arriva Trains Wales ? - *not made*	NA	NA
R2759	**153303** (**52303**) Regional Railways deep blue + grey - *09-10*	50	68
R2792	Wessex Trains ? - *not made*	NA	NA

Class 153 'Super Sprinter' in Wessex Railways livery [L107]

R2866	**153382** (**57382**) Wessex Trains 'golden knot' livery black+gold - *09-10*	50	68
R2792	**153374** (**57374**) East Midlands Trains ? - *08-10*	50	68

R2931	**153334** (**52334**) London Midland green - *10-11*	50	68
R2932	**153367** (**57367**) Arriva Trains Wales light blue - *10-11*	50	68

L108. Class 155 'Super Sprinter '(ex-Dapol) (1999)

R2162B	**155317** (**57317+52317**) Provincial grey+blue 2-car - *00-06*	50	65
R2162A	**155325** (**57325+52325**) Provincial grey+blue 2-car - *00-04*	45	60
R2108	**155344** (**57344+52344**) Metro maroon 2-car - *99-04*	45	60

L109. Class 156 DMU (ex-Lima) (2006)

Former Lima model, released in 1992, with new 5-pole skew wound motor and wheels. 2-car set.

R2511	**156401** Central Trains green - *06-07*	60	77
R2513	**156425** NorthernRail violet+white - *06-07*	60	77
R2512	**156430** Strathclyde PTE (new) maroon+cream - *06-07*	60	77
R2693	**156416** (**57416+52416** ***St Edmund***) One grey-blue * - *08-10*	70	90
R2694	**156465** (**57465+52465**) First ScotRail violet - *08-09*	70	90
R2950	**156433** (**57433+52433**) First ScotRail violet - *10-11*	70	90

Ex-Lima Class 156 in new ScotRail livery [L109]

R2695	**156484** (**57484+52484**) Northern Rail (Settle & Carlisle) dark blue - *08-10*	70	90

* The wrong inscription appeared on the box which described the contents as 'R2396 Northwest Regional Railways Class 156416'.

L110a. GWR AEC Railcar (ex-Lima) (2006)

Former Lima model, released in 1980, with new motor and wheels. 'DCC ready'.

R2653	**W22W** BRc green - *07*	45	60
R2869	**W23W** BRc maroon+cream - *09-11*	55	75
R2524A	**26** GWR (roundel) dark brown+crm - *07-08*	45	60
R2524	**29** GWR (roundel) dark brown+crm - *06-07*	45	60

L110b. GWR AEC Parcels Railcar (ex-Lima) (2008)

Former Lima model, released in 1982, with new motor and wheels. 'DCC ready'.

R2876	**34** GWR Express Parcels brown+cream - *09-11*	55	75
R2768	**34** GWR (button) Express Parcels brown+cream - *08*	50	63

L111. Class 4-SUB EMU (1957)

Most of the British sets are a blue-green but those produced towards the end were a yellow-green. Tools went to New Zealand in 1965 where a slightly different model was made. New Zealand made examples have a light grey roof.

R156/R225	**S1052S+S1057S** no decals green 2-car - *57*	55	110
R156/R225	**S1052S+S1057S** BRb green 2-car - *57-58*	55	110

Tri-ang 4-SUB EMU [L111]

R156/R225	**S1052S+S1057S** BRc green 2-car - *59-62*	45	110
R156/R225	**S1052S+S1057S** BRc yellow-green 2-car - *62-64*	75	130

A single car in Victorian Railways blue but unmarked has turned up. It is not known whether this was a released model or a factory-escape. This had been painted green, suggesting that its rarity value was not recognised by a previous owner. It appears to have originated in Britain rather than New Zealand.

L112. Class 5-BEL 'Brighton Belle' EMU (2011)

After the success of Hornby's 8-wheel and 12-wheel Pullman cars, the Brighton Belle Pullman EMU seemed the next logical step. The brown and blue versions have different bogies.

R2987	**?** 2 x PulDMBT motor brake Pullman 3rd cars brown+cream - 11	135	184
R2988	**?** 2 x PulDMBT motor brake Pullman 3rd cars blue+grey - 11	135	184

The trailer 1st with kitchen (PulTFK) and trailer 3rd (PulTTL) will be found at the end of the tables on Pullman cars later in this chapter.

L113. Class 370 'APT' (1980)

R543	**370001+370002** ***City of Derby*** BRe I-C APT grey, all yell front, 5-car set R702, R703, R704, R707 and R706 - *80*	NA	150
R794	**370001+370002** ***City of Derby*** BRe I-C APT grey, yell + black front, 5-car R702, R703, R704, R707 and R706 train pack - *81-84*	NA	140

L114a. Class 373 'Eurostar' (Jouef) (H0 scale model) (1995)

R543	**3211/3212** 'Eurostar' grey (Jouef on under side) - *95-96*	30	50

L114b. Class 373 'Eurostar' (Hornby) (1996)

	'Eurostar' grey		
Eur3003X	**3003** power car - *99*	18	NA
Eur3004X	**3004** dummy car - *99*	12	NA
R665A	**3003+3004** train pack - *99*	NA	50
Eur3015X	**3015** power car - *96-98*	18	NA
Eur3016X	**3016** dummy car - *96-98*	12	NA
R665	**3015+3016** train pack - *96-98*	NA	50
Eur3019X	**3019** power car - *96-97*	18	NA
Eur3020X	**3020** dummy car - *96-97*	12	NA
R647	**3019+3020** train pack - *96-97*	NA	50

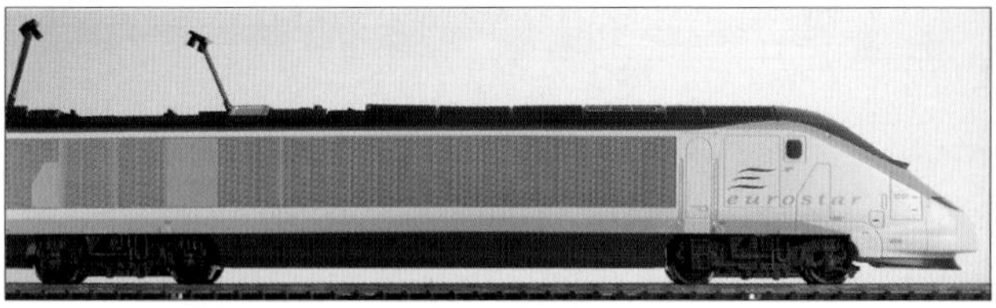

Class 373 'Eurostar' [L114b]

Eur3021X	**3021** power car - *96-97*	18	NA
Eur3022X	**3022** dummy car - *96-97*	12	NA
R816	**3021+3022** ex-set - *96-97*	35	NA
(R1013)	**3219+3220** ex-set - *99-08*	35	NA
R2379	**3106+3107** 6-car train pack - *04-07*	NA	80
R2379A*	**3007+3008** 6-car train pack - *08-10*	NA	148
(R1071)	**3219+3106** ex-'Eurostar' set - *07-11*	35	NA
	GNER navy blue		
R2197	**3301+3302** + 2 coaches train pack - *01-03*	NA	80
R2197A	**3306** ***Golden Jubilee*** **/3305** + 2 coaches train pack - *04-05*	NA	120

* This has 'R2379' on the packaging but 'R2379A' on the small white sticker on the box and on the instruction sheet. It is 'DCC ready'.

L115. Class 390 'Pendolino' EMU (2007)

Built for Virgin Trains for the West Coast Main Line. Both 'DCC ready' and 'DCC fitted' (has X suffix) versions of each general release loco were made. Add £10-£15 for X models.

R2467+(R1076)	**390012** (**69112+69512+69612** ***Virgin Star*** **+69212**) * Virgin silver+red 4-car pack - *07-10*	NA	114
(R1134)	**390045** (**69145+69545+69645** ***101 Squadron*** **+69245**) * Virgin silver+red 4-car pack Sp Edn (concessions) - *09*	NA	116
(R1155)	**390???** (**691??+695??+696??+692??**) * Virgin/ Alstom livery silver+red+black ex-4-car analogue set - *11*	NA	138

* The Pendolinos are 9 car units of which cars 1, 3, 4 and 9 are included in this train pack and the R1076 train set. These are: DMRFO, PTFO, MFO and DMSO.

L116a. Class 395 HS1 'Javelin' EMU (2009)

Built by Hitachi as a high speed commuter train for the CTRL through Kent to London the units run in 6-car sets. Hornby sell theirs as a 4-car set but with the possibility of buying the additional two cars to add on. Both 'DCC ready' and 'DCC fitted' (has X suffix) versions of each general release loco made. Add £10-£15 for X models.

R2821	**395001** (**39011+39012+39013+39016**) Southeastern High Speed, deep violet 4-car train pack - *09-10*	110	140

Class 395 'Javelin' EMU 'London 2012' [L116a]

R2972	**395003** ***Sir Steve Redgrave*** (**39031+39032+ 39033+39036**) Southeastern High Speed, deep violet 4-car train pack - *10-11*	NA	154
(R1148)	all cars numbered **2010** 'London 2012' white 4-car ex-train set Ltd Edn 2012 - *10*	110	NA
R2961	all cars numbered **2010** 'London 2012' white 4-car train pack Ltd Edn 2012 - *10*	110	140

L116b. Class 395 'Javelin' EMU (train set version) (2010)

This is a simplified version of the Javelin model which is a lot cheaper to manufacture and was developed for use in train sets.

(R1139)	**395001** (**39011+39012+39016**) Southeastern High Speed, deep violet 4-car 'Blue Rapier' train set - *09-11*	NA	90
(R1153)	'London 2012' deep violet 3-car train set - *10-11*	NA	100

L117. Class 423 4VEP EMU (2011)

A 'slam-door' commuter train built by BR at York from 1967 until 1974. 194 units were made. They were refurbished in 1988-1990, they were reclassified Class 423/1.

R2946	**7733** (**S76442+S62217+S70907+S76441**) BR blue 4-car train pack - *11*	120	150

Class 423 4-VEP EMU [L117] (Hornby)

R2947	**3185** (**76923+62466+71146+76923**) NSE bright blue 432/1 4-car train pack - *11*	120	150

L118. Class 466 'Networker' 2-Car EMU (1997)

R2001A	**466016** (**64875+78327**) NSE white KentLink Networker - *99-01*	45	65
R2307A	**466020** (**64879+78331**) Connex white - *03-04*	55	80
R2307B	**466035** (**64894+78346**) Connex white - *03-04*	55	80
R2001	**466040** (**64899+78351**) NSE white KentLink Networker - *97-98*	50	70
R2603	**466023** (**64882+78334**) South Eastern, white with SET logos Sp Edn 1000 (Modelzone) - *06*	55	75
R2893	**466031** (**64890+78342**) Original NSE, KentLink bright blue Sp Edn 1000 (Modelzone) - *09*	80	95

BATTLE SPACE

There were three items of motive power in the 'Battle Space' series, two of them, the 'Jinty' 0-6-0T and North British shunter 0-4-0DS, are included in the main part of the locomotive section above, under their model types. The third item was exclusive to 'Battle Space' and is detailed here.

Cat No.	Company, Number, Colour, Dates	£	£

LB1. Turbo Car (1967)

The electric motor drove a fan at the rear of the vehicle which propelled it.

R752	red with yellow plastic spike - *67*	100	150
R752	red with yellow plastic spike - *68-70*	85	125

PLAY LOCOMOTIVES

These are freelance 0-4-0 locomotives produced exclusively for 'starter' sets and not produced as authentic models. They were not based on known prototypes. Some authentic 0-4-0T models, such as the Holden tank and CR Pug, were also produced in non-authentic liveries for use in 'starter' sets but are listed under their model type earlier in this chapter.

Cat No.	Company, Number, Colour, Dates	£	£

LP1. 'Top Tank' 0-4-0T (1964)

This has a small square tank mounted on top of the boiler. Both clockwork and electric models exist.

R657	black clockwork - *64-67*	3	8
R659	black electric - *64-67*	3	8

'Top Tank' 0-4-0T [LP1]

R660	bright blue - *66?*	4	10
R660	mid blue - *66?*	8	15
R660	yellow - *67*	4	10
R660	dark green - *68*	5	12

0-4-0 Diesel Shunter

(see L67. North British Shunter 0-4-0DS)

LP2. Barclay 0-4-0DS (1969)

R858	blue - *69-71?*	25	NA
R858	red - *?*	35	NA

LP3. 'Continental' Tank 0-4-0T (1968)

c/w = clockwork.

R852	**7744** blue - *68-74*	12	NA
R852	**7744** black - *?-68*	10	15
R852T	**7744** black NMRA couplings - *?-68*	10	15
R852CN	***Chugga*** yellow - *69-71*	40	80
R854	red c/w - *69?-79*	5	NA
R854	**1863** red c/w - *71?*	25	NA
R854	maroon c/w - *69?-79*	8	NA
R854	green c/w - *71*	10	NA
R852?	blue with red chassis electric - *?*	10	NA
R854	**7321** bright green c/w - *71-72*	12	NA
R854	**7321** dark green c/w - *?*	8	NA
R854	**7321** red c/w - *?*	10	NA
R854	**7321** black c/w - *73-82*	10	15
R854T	with NMRA couplings - *?*	30	60
R762	black sold in a temporary box - *73*	15	20
R755	**6042** black, can motor - *73-75*	10	NA
R755	**6042** black, X04 motor - *73-75*	10	18
(R168)	**6042** black, can motor, nickle-plated wheels - *75*	12	20
R854	***Timmy*** red c/w - *83-87*	12	NA
T121	***Peter*** yellow c/w - *83-85*	12	NA
T118	***Adam, Michael, Simon, Robert, William*** red c/w - *84-90?*	12	NA
T118	***Edward, Douglas*** blue c/w - *84-90?*	12	NA
T118	***Henry*** green c/w - *84-90?*	12	NA
T118	***Ivor*** red c/w - *91-?*	14	NA
T774	***Postman Pat*** **1** red c/w T107 set - *84-87*	20	NA
T774	***Mr Puffer*** light blue c/w - *?*	20	NA
T868	**2571** red c/w - *88-94*	7	10
T113	***Pound Puppies*** yellow c/w ex-T113 set - *not made*	NA	NA

LP4. Swedish Diesel 0-4-0 (1969)

R853	blue - *69*	25	NA
R853	**5771** yellow - *69-71*	20	NA
R853	**4718** red - *69-71*	20	NA

'Swedish' diesel 0-4-0 [LP4]

LP5. 'Wild West' 0-4-0 (1971)

R873	**1863** red ex-Wild West set - *71-72*	80	NA*
-	grey loco only no markings - *?*	20	NA

* the set sells for about £180.

LP6. 'International' Tank 0-4-0T (1975)

R254	**254** black - *75-76*	15	20
R256	**256** black - *76-77*	12	17
R256	**256** red - *77*	12	17
R257	**256** green - *76*	15	20
R256	**7 *Bulldog*** green - *83*	20	25
R164	**1 *Iron Horse*** grey - *84-85*	20	25

LP7. Push-Along Models 0-4-0T (1983)

T123	***Gordon*** blue push along - *84*	4	NA
T123	***Percy*** green push along - *84*	4	NA
T123	***Thomas*** blue push along - *84*	4	NA
T123	***James*** red push along - *84*	4	NA
T119	**4 *Dixie*** red push along - *83-85*	4	NA
T120	**2 *Pixie*** blue push along - *83-87*	4	NA
T116	***My First Train*** red push along - *87-91*	5	NA
T106	**5 *Postman Pat*** red push along - *84*	5	NA

THOMAS THE TANK ENGINE AND FRIENDS

Some of the locomotives released in the Thomas & Friends series, such as Percy, Bill & Ben and Toby, were purpose built and have not appeared in any other guise. Others, such as Henry, Gordon, James and Edward, are adapted versions of models found elsewhere in the locomotive section and have been recycled, often with alterations, for the Thomas & Friends series when no longer required for their original purpose. You may also find reference to these 'Thomas' series versions above under their model types.

Cat No.	Company, Number, Colour, Dates	£	£

LM1. Various Models

Names in brackets are not actually carried by the locomotive.

R251	**1** (*Thomas*) blue 0-6-0T push along - *88-92 95-?*	6	NA
R352	**1** (*Thomas*) blue 0-4-0T c/w - *86-98*	8	12
R9005	**1** (*Thomas*) blue 0-4-0T c/w - *98-99*	8	25
R9034	**1** (*Thomas*) blue 0-6-0T c/w - *99-02*	10	15
R354	**1** (*Thomas*) blue 0-4-0T elec - *95-98*	18	NA
R351	**1** (*Thomas*) blue 0-6-0T elec - *85-10*	30	43
(R9260)	**1** (*Thomas*) blue 0-6-0T elec (new face with red cheeks) W ex-set - *08-10*	30	NA
R9232	**2** (*Edward*) blue 4-4-0T elec - *06-10*	65	84
R9049	**3** (*Henry*) green 4-6-0 elec - *02-10*	65	86
R383	**4** (*Gordon*) blue 4-6-2 elec - *86-92, 95-10*	75	100
R852	**5** (*James*) red 2-6-0 elec - *88-10*	65	86
R810	**6** (*Percy*) green 0-4-0ST c/w - *87-98*	10	18
R9004	**6** (*Percy*) green 0-4-0ST c/w - *98-99*	10	18
R9035	**6** (*Percy*) green 0-4-0ST c/w - *99-02*	10	18
R350	**6** (*Percy*) green 0-4-0ST elec - *85-10*	20	30
R9025	**7** (*Toby*) brown 0-4-0 Tram c/w - *99*	10	18
R9046	**7** (*Toby*) brown 0-6-0 Tram elec - *01-10*	25	35
R382	**8** (*Duck*) green 0-6-0PT elec - *86-91, 95-10*	30	42
R9070	**11** (*Oliver*) GWR roundel grn 0-4-2T - *05-10*	45	63
R9024	***Bill*** yellow 0-4-0ST c/w - *99*	10	18
R9026	***Ben*** yellow 0-4-0ST c/w - *99*	10	18
R9047	***Bill*** yellow 0-4-0ST elec - *01-10*	18	29
R9048	***Ben*** yellow 0-4-0ST elec - *01-10*	18	29
R9231	***Emily* 3046** green 4-2-2 - *07-10*	60	82
R9098	***Flying Scotsman* 4472** LNER green - *05-07*	60	80

9F Murdoch newly added to the 'Thomas' range [LM1]

R9684	***Murdoch*** gold 2-10-0 - *11*	70	92
R9257	***Spencer*** grey 4-6-2 (A4) - *08-10*	65	86
R9069	***Stepney* 55** LBSC or-yell 0-6-0T - *05-10*	45	63
R9683	***(Dart)*** Vicarstown Dieselworks 0-4-0DS yellow +red - *11*	30	41
R317	(*Devious Diesel*) black 0-6-0DS elec - *87-88*	30	44
R9050	(*Devious Diesel*) black 0-6-0DS elec - *02-10*	30	44
R9066	'Sodor Ironworks' green+yellow, face with open mouth (*Bert*) 0-6-0DS - *03-09*	28	44
R9067	'Sodor Ironworks' green+yellow, face with closed mouth ('*Arry*) 0-6-0DS - *03-09*	28	44
R9097	**D7101** (*Hymek*) BRe blue Bo-Bo - *05-10*	40	59
R9064	**D261** (*Diesel*) green Co-Co - *03-10*	40	59
R90	(*Bertie the Bus*) maroon battery - *88-92, 95-98*	10	NA
R9096	(*Bertie the Bus*) maroon battery - *05-09*	10	14

TRANSCONTINENTAL

This range was produced with overseas markets in mind but sold in greater volume in Britain.

Cat No.	Company, Number, Colour, Dates	£	£

LT1. Class 23 TC 'Pacific' (*Hiawatha*) 4-6-2 (1954)

The model was also sent out to Australia and New Zealand for finishing and sale in local packaging. 8wt = 4+4 wheel tender. 6wt = A3 6+2 wheel tender.

R54+R32	**2335** black 8wt - *54-61*	20	50
R54+R32	**2335 *Hiawatha*** black 8wt - *62-69*	30	60
R54+R32	**2335 *Hiawatha*** black 8wt no. in yell - *?*	40	70
R54S	**2335 *Hiawatha*** black 8wt + smoke - *68*	40	60
R54S	**2335 *Hiawatha*** black Acho couplings - *68*	50	100
R54S +R32L	**2335 *Hiawatha*** black Lima couplings, grey and red Lima box as cat. no. 8100 - *68*	90	150
R?	**2335 *Hiawatha*** black 6wt - *70?*	40	60
various	**1542** black 6wt - *70-73*	30	65
various	**2335** Canadian Pacific black - *69-73*	70	120

LT2. Class Wab 'Baltic' Tank 4-6-4T (1955)

The tank was fitted with lamps front and back but these are sometimes missing on used models. The model was also made in Australia, New Zealand and South Africa.

R56	**4830** Tri-ang Railways black - *55-60*	20	70
R56	**4830** Tri-ang Railways maroon - *61*	100	200

TransContinental 'Baltic' tank 4-6-4T [LT2]

R56	**4830** TR shield logo maroon - *61*	120	180

LT3. Class F7 A+B Units Diesel (1955)

The model was also sent out to Australia and New Zealand for finishing and sale in local packaging. TR = Tri-ang Railways. TC = Transcontinental. TA = TransAustralia. CN = Canadian National. CP (and CPRail) = Canadian Pacific.

R55	**4008** (A unit) TR silver+red, silver cabs - *55-57*	15	40
R57	**4008** (dummy A unit) TR silver+red, silver cabs - *55-57*	10	30

R56	**4008** (B unit) TR silver+red no cabs - *56-60*	15	40
R56	**4008** (B unit) TR silver+red, no cabs, number both ends - *56*	30	50
R56	**4009** (B unit) TR silver+red no cabs - *?*	50	90
R55	**4008** (A unit) TR silver+red, red cabs - *58-61*	12	40
R57	**4008** (dummy A unit) TR silver+red, red cabs - *58-61*	8	30
R55	**4008** (A unit) TC silver+red - *62-64*	20	55
R55	**4008** (A unit) TC silver+red 2 motors - *63*	50	90
R55	**4008** (A unit) TA silver+red - *66-66,70*	90	120
R0551	**4008** (A unit) CN black+red - *65-66, 69-73*	12	40
R0552*	**4008** (A unit) CP grey+maroon - *67-69*	80	120
R0553*	**1404** (A unit) CPRail red - *70-73*	20	30
R0550*	**1404** (A unit) TC red - *72-73*	15	NA

* Also found with other 'R' numbers

LT4. RS2 Switcher Bo-Bo (1957)

TR = Tri-ang Railways. CN = Canadian National. CPRail = Canadian Pacific. NSWR = New South Wales Railway. VR = Victorian Railways.

R155	**5007** TR maroon - *57*	100	200
R155	**5007** TR green - *57*	100	250
R155	**5007** TR yellow - *57*	80	170
R155	**5007** TR yellow, dazzle stripes - *58-60*	25	45
R155	**7005** TR yellow, dazzle stripes - *61*	30	50
R155	**7005** Transcontinental yellow - *62-64*	30	50
R1550	**7005** TransAustralia yellow - *65-67*	70	100
R1551	**3000** CN black - *65-72*	35	50
R1552	**3000** Canadian Pacific grey - *69*	120	150
R1553	**1553** CPRail orange-red - *71-73*	30	50
R308	**48142** NSWR maroon - *made?*	NPG	NPG
R308	**34051** NSWR maroon - *74-76*	65	85
R763	**T336** VR blue - *76*	55	75

LT5. B-60 'Double Ended Diesel' (1958)

The model was also made in Australia and New Zealand and in different liveries. TR = Tri-ang Railways.

R159	**5007** TR blue+yellow - *58-61*	20	30
R250	**5007** TR blue+yellow dummy unit - *58-61*	20	30
R159	**5007** TR shield blue+yellow - *62-69*	25	40

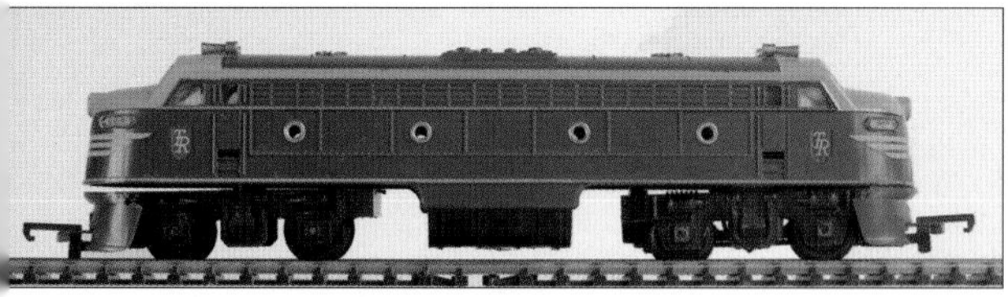

TransContinental 'Double Ended' diesel [LT5]

R159	**5007** TR shield green-blue+yellow - *68, 70*	30	50
R159	**5007** TR or VR on front bright blue+yellow, no name or shield on sides - *71-78*	40	60
R?	**5007** TR green+yellow - *60?*	110	150

LT6. TC Electric Loco (1959)

This was made from the same body tool as 'Double Ended Diesel'.

R257	**7503** Tri-ang Railways green+orange - *59-60*	90	120
R257	**7503** Tri-ang Railways 2 -tone green - *61*	145	175
R257	**7503** TR shield 2 -tone green - *62-64*	130	160

Yard Switcher (see L58. Dock Shunter 0-4-0DS)

LT7. Budd RDC-2 (1961)

TC = Transcontinental.

R352	**31018** TC silver+red - *61-67*	80	110
R232	**31018** TC silver+red, dummy - *61-67*	110	150
R232	**31027** TC silver+red, dummy - *61-67*	110	150
R352CN	**101** CN silver+black - *65-71*	80	110
R232CN	**101** CN silver+black, dummy - *65-71*	50	80
R829	**303** Northern Pacific silver - *68*	85	110
R825	**303** Northern Pacific silver dummy - *68*	55	80
R830	**3400, 3403** Santa Fe silver - *68*	85	110
R826	**3400, 3403** Santa Fe silver dummy - *68*	55	80
R831	**9003** C&O silver - *68*	85	110
R827	**9003** C&O silver, dummy - *68*	55	80
R832	**501, 503** Reading Lines silver - *68*	85	110
R828	**501, 503** Reading Lines silver dummy - *68*	55	80
R352A	**31018** TransAustralia silver+red - *65-67*	120	165

LT8. *Davy Crockett* 2-6-0 (1962)

R358/ R233	**1863 *Davy Crockett*** red+yellow (also R358S) TTR - *62-65*	50	125
R358SL	**1863 *Davy Crockett*** red+yellow Lima couplings, TTR, grey and red Lima box as cat. no. 8102 - *62-65*	90	150

LT9. Continental 'Prairie' 2-6-2T (1963)

R653	black single dome - *63-65*	70	125

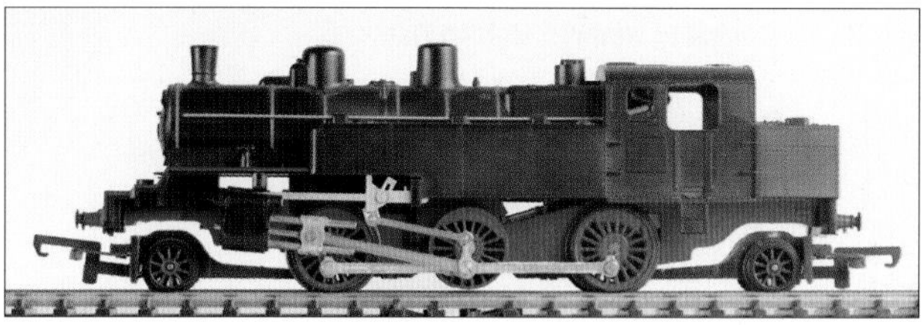

Continental 'Prairie' tank engine [LT9]

R653	black+red double dome - *69*	90	140

NSWR Suburban Electric

(made only in Australia and so not included here)

LT10. S Class GM Co-Co (1977)

VR = Victorian Railways.

R317	**S311** VR blue+yellow - *77-78*	35	65
R317	***Sir Ferdinand Muller*** VR blue+yellow - *77-78*	60	75
R317	***Sir Charles Gavin Duffy*** VR blue+yellow - *77-78*	60	75
R318	**GM12** Commonwealth Railways maroon - *77-78*	50	70
R318	**S311** Commonwealth Railways maroon - *77-78*	50	70

COACHES

Standard British Passenger Stock

Tri-ang Railways, Tri-ang Hornby and Hornby Railways coaches are always plastic and marked on the underside with 'Tri-ang', 'Tri-ang Hornby', 'Hornby Railways' or 'Hornby'. On some, the name 'Tri-ang' has been erased on the mould but the words 'Built in Britain' remain.

Coach Finder

4-wheel coaches - C16
6" coaches - C1
7" coaches - C2
9" coaches - C4-C6
12-wheel diner - C28
Airfix (ex) coaches - C19-C21 & C40
BR DMU centre cars - C12-C14
BR DVT - C43 & C45
BR Mk1 coaches - C37 & C38
BR Mk2 coaches - C39 & C40
BR Mk3 coaches – C41-C43
BR Mk4 coaches - C44 & C45
BR Standard GUV - C38
Caledonian coaches - C24
Clerestory coaches - C17 & C18
Coach Packs – C50
'Eurostar' stock - C46
Gresley coaches - C29-C32
GWR coaches - C17-C23 & C27
Hawksworth coaches - C23
Hitachi - C48 & C49
Lima (ex) coaches - C13b, C38, C42d & C42e
LMS coaches - C25-C28
LNER coaches - C29-C32
Maunsell coaches and Van - C35 & C36
'Pendolino' Stock - C47

'Play' coaches - CP1
Pullman cars - C6-C11
Rocket coaches - C15
SR coaches - C33-C36
Stanier coaches - C25-C28
Suburban coaches - C5, C19 & C29
Thompson coaches - C32
TPOs - C3, C27, CT2
'Transcontinental' cars - CT1-CT4
Utility Van (bogie)/SR Luggage Van - C34

Cat No.	Company, Number, Colour, Dates	£	£

Tri-ang Short Coaches of the 1950s

C1. LMS 6" Coach (1950)

Rovex	**LMS** 7573, 27424 maroon, hook+loop couplings - *50-52*	8	15
R20	**LMS** 7573, 27424 maroon, Tri-ang transfers on underside - *52?*	15	20

Tri-ang original 6" coach [C1]

R20	**LMS** 7573, 27424 maroon, hook+bar coupling (Mk2) - *52?-56*	4	10

C2. BR 7" Coach + 'Primary' Coach (1952)

R21	**BR** M7071 red+cream Tri-ang transfers on underside - *52*	10	15
R21	**BR** M7071 red+cream - *52-56*	5	8
R22	**BR** S17035 green - *53-56*	8	15

Tri-ang - 7" coach [C2]

R230	no number maroon Primary - *59-62*	4	10
R231	no number green Primary - *59-61*	4	10

C3. BR 7" Travelling Post Office (1955)
(see also C23 & CT2 below)

The car was sold as part of an operating accessory which included pick-up and put-down trackside apparatus. The 'R' number and values refer to the complete set.

R23	**Royal Mail** M30224 brown, transfers - *55*	40	50
R23	**Royal Mail** M30224 maroon, transfers - *55-56*	10	18
R23	**Royal Mail** M30224 maroon - *57-68*	5	16
R402M	**Royal Mail** M30224 blue+grey - *69-72*	7	18

C4a. BR 9" Composite (1956)

The tools for the composite were later used in New Zealand for green coaches. Models with closed axle boxes sometimes sell for more than those with open axle boxes.

R29	**BR** M24001 red+cream - *56-57*	8	11
R29	**BR** M24001 maroon+cream - *58-62*	7	10
R29	**BR** 24010 maroon+cream - *58-62*	7	10
R221	**BR** S15033 blue-green - *57-61*	10	12
R221	**BR** S15034 blue-green - *57-61*	10	12
R221	**BR** S15033 blue-green - *57-61*	10	12
R221	**BR** S15034 blue-green - *57-61*	10	12
R221	**BR** S15034 yellow-green - *61-62*	15	17
R330	**BR** W15771 dark brown+cream - *60-62*	12	15

Tri-ang 9" composite coach [C4a]

R321	**BR** M24001 maroon - *59-61*	8	10
R321	**BR** 24010 maroon - *59-61*	8	10
R720	bright red+cream also R724 - *63-67*	5	NA
R?	red with or without buffers - *66?*	5	NA

C4b. BR 9" Brake 3rd (1956)

The tools for body of the brake 3rd were later used in New Zealand for green coaches. Models with closed axle boxes sometimes sell for more than those with open axle boxes.

R28	**BR** M34000 red+cream - *56-57*	8	11
R28	**BR** M34000 maroon+cream - *58-62*	7	10
R28	**BR** 34002 maroon+cream - *58-62*	7	10
R220	**BR** S34243 blue-green - *57-61*	10	12
R220	**BR** S34245 blue-green - *57-61*	10	12
R220	**BR** S34245 yellow-green - *61-62*	15	17
R329	**BR** W34302 dark brown+cream - *60-62*	12	15
R320	**BR** M34001 maroon - *59-61*	8	10
R320	**BR** 34002 maroon - *59-61*	8	10

C4c. BR 9" Restaurant Car (1957)

The tools for the restaurant car were later used in New Zealand for green coaches. Models with closed axle boxes sometimes sell for more than those with open axle boxes. O = orange curtains. B = blue curtains.

R224	**BR** M2001 maroon+cream O or B - *57-62*	8	15
R224	**BR** 2401 maroon+cream O or B - *57-62*	8	15
R229	**BR** S1007 blue-green O or B - *58-61*	12	15
R229	**BR** S1007 yellow-green O - *61-62*	15	17
R331	**BR** W301 dark brown+cream O - *60-62*	12	18
R322	**BR** M2001 maroon O - *59-61*	8	15
R322	**BR** 2401 maroon O - *59-61*	8	15

C5a. BR 9" Suburban Composite (1956)

ca - closed axle boxes.

R223	**BR** S3152S * blue-green - *57-61*	10	15
R223	**BR** S3155S blue-green - *57-61*	10	15
R223	**BR** S3153S * blue-green - *57-61*	10	15

Tri-ang 9" suburban coach [C5a]

R223	**BR** S3153S yell-green ca - *61-63,67*	15	18
R121	**BR** M41006 maroon - *56-61*	10	12
R121	**BR** 41007 maroon - *56-61*	10	12
R121	**BR** 41007 maroon ca - *61-62,67*	12	14

* large or small numbers may be found.

C5b. BR 9" Suburban Brake 3rd (1956)

The tools for the brake 3rd were later used in New Zealand for green coaches. ca - closed axle boxes.

R222	**BR** S4717S blue-green - *57-61*	10	12
R222	**BR** S4718S * blue-green - *57-61*	10	12
R222	**BR** S4718S yellow-green ca - *61-63,67*	15	18
R120	**BR** M43171 maroon - *56-61*	10	12
R120	**BR** 53171 maroon - *56-61*	10	12
R120	**BR** 53171 maroon ca - *61-62,67*	12	14

* large or small numbers may be found.

Utility Van - *see* **SR 9" Utility/Luggage Van** *under 'Pre-Nationalisation Stock'*

1st Series Pullman Cars

C6a. 9" Pullman/Continental Sleeper (1958)

The 9" Pullman cars sometimes had plain brass lampshades and sometimes they were painted pink. At one stage lampshades were reduced to a narrow spike. A rarer version has a cream coloured roof and late models had white rim wheels. The Golden Arrow stickers were supplied in a separate packet in 1962 together with a locomotive headboard.

R228	**Pullman** *Anne, Jane *, Ruth* or *Mary* dark brown+cream - *58-73*	8	15
R228	as above with white wheel rims - *70*	10	15

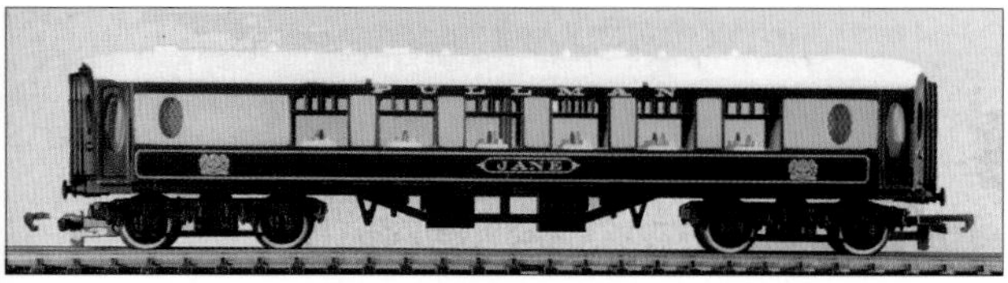

1st series Pullman Parlour car [C6a]

R228	as above with deep cream roof - *?*	13	18
R228	with 'Golden Arrow' stickers - *62-63*	18	20
R625	Continental Sleeping Car blue - *63-65*	20	40

* An example of *Jane* has been found with blue (instead of pink) lampshades and is considered to be very rare.

C6b. 9" Pullman Brake Car (1960)

See note with 6a (above) re-lampshades, roof colour and 'Golden Arrow' stickers.

R328	**Pullman** *Car No.79* dark brown+cream - *60-73*	8	14
R328	with white wheel rims - *70*	10	15
R328	with deep cream roof - *?*	13	15
R328	with 'Golden Arrow' stickers - *62-63*	18	20

2nd Series Pullman Cars

C7a. Pullman Parlour Car (1975)

npf = non-paint finish ie: the main body colour is provided by the colour of the plastic.

	Dark Brown & Yellow (or Cream)		
R229	**Pullman** npf *Lucille - 75-76*	8	13
R229	**Pullman** *Lucille, Agatha, Ursula, Sheila* transfers detailed arms npf - *77-79*	10	14
R223	**Pullman** *Lucille, Agatha, Ursula, Sheila* crude coat-of-arms - *80-93*	10	14
R223	**Pullman** *Lucille, Agatha, Ursula, Sheila* design change - *94-01*	10	14
R4312	**Pullman** (RailRoad) - *07-10*	10	16
	'Tees Tyne Pullman'		
R241	**Pullman** *Ansonia* also ex-set - *94-96*	12	NA
R217	**Pullman** *Rosemary* also ex-set - *94-96*	10	NA
	'The Kentish Belle'		
R4037	**Pullman** *Adrian* ex-R2079 pack - *98*	12	NA
R4038	**Pullman** *Lydia* ex-R2079 pack - *98*	12	NA
	'Yorkshire Pullman'		
(R2168)	**Pullman** *Zena* ex-pack - *00*	12	NA
(R2168)	**Pullman** *Eunice* ex-pack - *00*	12	NA
(R1136)	**Pullman** *Minerva* ex-MO set - *09*	15	NA
(R1136)	**Pullman** *Niobe* ex-MO set - *09*	15	NA
	'Torquay Pullman Limited' *		
(R1077)	**Pullman** *Zena* ex-pack - *06-07*	12	NA
(R1077)	**Pullman** *Eunice* ex-pack - *not mad*	NA	NA
(R1077)	**Pullman** *Evadne* ex-pack - *06-07*	12	NA
(R1077)	**Pullman** *Juana* ex-pack - *06-07*	12	NA
	'Queen of Scots'		
(R1024)	**Pullman** *Juana* ex-set - *01-02*	12	NA
(R1024)	**Pullman** *Sheila* ex-set - *01-02*	12	NA
(R2598M)	**Pullman** *Thelma* ex-pack - *07*	12	NA
(R2598M)	**Pullman** *Car No 73* ex-pack - *07*	12	NA
	'Thanet Belle'		
(R2279M)	**Pullman** *Coral* ex-MO pack - *02*	12	NA
(R2279M)	**Pullman** *Maid of Kent* ex-MO pack - *02*	12	NA
	'Western Pullman'		
(R1048)	**Pullman** *Aurelia* ex-set - *04-05*	12	NA
(R1048)	**Pullman** *Chloria* ex-set - *04-05*	12	NA
	M&S 'Orient Express'		
(R1062)	**Pullman** *Lucille* ex-set - *05*	12	NA
(R1062)	**Pullman** *Agatha* ex-set - *05*	12	NA
	'East Coast Pullman'		
(R1097)	**Pullman** *Lucille* ex-set - *08-11*	12	NA
(R1097)	**Pullman** *Agatha* ex-set - *08-11*	12	NA
	'East Coast Express'		
X5573	**Pullman** *Lucille* ex-MO R1099 set - 08	12	NA
X5572	**Pullman** *Agatha* ex-MO R1099 set - 08	12	NA
	'Southern Belle'		
X5153	**Pullman** *Aurelia* ex-MO R1118 set - *08*	14	NA
X4971	**Pullman** *Leona* ex-MO R1118 set - *08*	14	NA
	'Golden Arrow'		
X4993	**Pullman** *Cygnus* ex-MO R1119 set - *08*	14	NA
X10256	**Pullman** *Hercules* ex-MO R1119 set - *08*	14	NA
X10257	**Pullman** *Phoenix* ex-MO R1119 set - *08*	14	NA
	'The White Pullman'		
(R26??)	**Pullman** ? ex-MO train pack - *09*	15	NA
(R26??)	**Pullman** ? ex-MO train pack - *09*	15	NA
	'The Cunarder'		
(R2886M)	**Pullman** *Octavia* ex-MO train pack - *09*	15	NA
(R2886M)	**Pullman** *Noble* ex-MO train pack - *09*	15	NA
	'The Cornishman'		
(R1160)	**Pullman** *Rosemary* ex DCC train set – *11*	16	NA
(R1160)	**Pullman** ? ex DCC train set - *11*	16	NA
	Dark Brown & Yellow (white roof)		
R469	**Pullman** 'Orient Express' 8 names choice as transfers - *84-87*	10	15
R491	**Pullman** 'Orient Express' *Cygnus - 84-85*	12	18
R492	**Pullman** 'Orient Express' *Perseus, - 84-85*	12	18
R493	**Pullman** 'Orient Express' *Phoenix, - 84-85*	12	18
R586	**Pullman** 'Orient Express' *Phoenix, Perseus* or *Cygnus*, plinth mounted track, a brass plaque and 2 bufferstops, in grey box - *84*	70	200
	Blue + Grey		
R230	**Golden Arrow** S309S (large) SS - *75-76*	18	23

2nd series Pullman parlour car in BR blue & grey [C7a]

R230	**Golden Arrow** S309S (small) SS - *76-78*	15	20

* These coaches have cream coloured panels above the windows and stuck-on coachboards.

C7b. Pullman Brake Car (1980)

Based on 1928 all steel stock.

	Dark Brown & Yellow (or Cream)		
R233	**Pullman** *Car No.77, 78, 79, 80 - 80-01*	10	14
R4313	**Pullman** (RailRoad) - *07-11*	10	16
R236	**Pullman** *Car No.77* also ex-R770 'Tees Tyne Pullman' set - *94-95*	12	NA
R4039	**Pullman** *Car No.68* ex-R2079 ex-'The Kentish Belle' pack - *98*	12	NA
(R2168)	**Pullman** *Car No.65* ex-'Yorkshire Pullman' pack - *00*	12	NA
(R1136)	**Pullman** *Car No.62* ex-'Yorkshire Pullman' MO set - *09*	15	NA
(R1024)	**Pullman** *Car No.78* ex-'Queen of Scots' set - *01-02*	12	NA
(R2598M)	**Pullman** *Car No 77* ex-'Queen of Scots' train pack - *07*	12	NA
(R2279M)	**Pullman** *Car No.11* ex-'Thanet Belle' pack - *02*	12	NA
(R1048)	**Pullman** *Car No.54* ex-'Western Pullman' set - *04-05*	12	NA
(R1048)	**Pullman** *Car No.27* ex-'Western Pullman' set - *04-05*	12	NA
(R1062)	**Pullman** *Car No.88* ex-M&S 'Orient Express' set - *05*	12	NA
(R1097)	**Pullman** *Car No.? ex-*'East Coast Pullman' set - *08-11*	12	NA
X5574	**Pullman** *Car No.68* ex-'East Coast Express' MO R1099 set - *08*	12	NA
X10255	**Pullman** *Car No.58* ex-'Southern Belle' MO R1118 set - *08*	12	NA
(R26??)	**Pullman** ? ex-'The White Pullman' MO train pack - *09*	15	NA

(R2886M)	**Pullman** *Car No.54* ex-'The Cunarder' MO train pack - *09*	15	NA
(R1160)	**Pullman** ? ex-'The Cornishman' train set - *11*	16	NA

2nd series Pullman brake car in umber and cream [C7b]

3rd Series Pullman Cars

C8a. Pullman K Class 1st Parlour Car (2003)

These 2003 released Pullman cars are based on K type cars. M = matchboard sides. S = smooth sides.

Dark Brown & Cream

R4143	**Pullman** *Leona* M - *03*	20	25
R4478	**Pullman** *Leona* M - *11*	35	47
R4143A	**Pullman** *Niobe* M - *03-05*	20	25
R4143B	**Pullman** *Rosemary* M - *07-09*	28	40
R4162	**Pullman** *Minerva* S - *03-06*	20	33
R4162A	**Pullman** *Leona* S - *07-08*	25	35
R4421	**Pullman** *Octavia* M - *10-11*	30	42
R4426	**Pullman** *Rosemary* S - *10-11*	30	42
(R2300)	**Pullman** *Rosemary* S ex-'Bournemouth Belle' train pack - *03*	20	NA
(R1038)	**Pullman** *Cygnus* S ex-'VSOE' set - *03-06*	20	NA
(R1038)	**Pullman** *Ibis* S ex-'VSOE' set - *03-06*	20	NA
(R1073)	**Pullman** *Cygnus* S ex-'VSOE' set - *07-11*	30	NA
(R1073)	**Pullman** *Ibis* S ex-'VSOE' set - *07-11*	30	NA
(R4254)	**Pullman** *Lucille* S ex-'VSOE' coach pk - *06-08*	20	NA
(R4254)	**Pullman** *Perseus* S ex-'VSOE' coach pack - *06-08*	25	NA
(R4254)	**Pullman** *Zena* S ex-'VSOE' coach pack - *06-08*	25	NA
(R2369)	**Pullman** *Niobe* M ex-'Golden Arrow' train pk - *04*	20	NA
(R4196)	**Pullman** *Onyx* M ex-'Golden Arrow' coach pk - *04*	20	NA
R4482	**Pullman** *Onyx* S - *11*	35	47
(R4251)	**Pullman** *Minerva* M ex-'Devon Belle' coach pack - *06-08*	25	NA
X5922	**Pullman** *Rosemary* M ex-MO 'Bournemouth Belle' train pack Ltd 1500 - *07*	23	NA

C8b. Pullman K Class 3rd/2nd Parlour Car (2003)

M = matchboard sides. S = smooth sides.

Dark Brown & Cream

R4144	**Pullman** *Car No.35* M - *03*	20	25
R4144A	**Pullman** *Car No.34* M - *03-07*	23	25
R4479	**Pullman** *Car No.34* M - *11*	35	47
R4144B	**Pullman** *Car No.36* M - *08-09*	28	40

3rd series Pullman 3rd class parlour car [C8b]

R4163	**Pullman** *Car No.64* S - *03-07*	23	33
R4484	**Pullman** *Car No.64* S - *11*	35	47
R4422	**Pullman** *Car No.85* M - *10-11*	30	42
R4427	**Pullman** *Car No.66* S - *10-11*	30	42
(R4169)	**Pullman** *Car No.66* S ex-'Bournemouth Belle' coach pack - *03*	20	NA
(R2365M)	**Pullman** *Car No.61* Sp Edn 1500 'Queen of Scots' MO pack with coach boards - *03-04*	25	NA
(R2568)	**Pullman** *Car No.36* M ex-'Devon Belle' train pack - *06-08*	20	NA
(R4380)	**Pullman** *Car No.208* M ex-'Devon Belle' coach pack - *09*	30	NA

C8c. Pullman K Class 1st Kitchen Car (2003)

M = matchboard sides. S = smooth sides.

Dark Brown & Cream

R4145	**Pullman** *Minerva - not made*	NA	NA
R4480	**Pullman** *Minerva* M - *11*	35	47
R4145	**Pullman** *Cynthia* M - *03*	20	25
R4145A	**Pullman** *Sappho* M - *03-07*	23	25
R4145B	**Pullman** *Medusa* M - *08*	25	35
R4164	**Pullman** *Argus* S - *03-07*	23	33
R4164A	**Pullman** *Octavia'* S - *07-08*	25	35
R4164B	**Pullman** *Cecilia* S - *08*	25	35
R4423	**Pullman** *Aurelia* dark M - *10-11*	30	42
R4428	**Pullman** *Zenobia* S - *10-11*	30	42
(R4169)	**Pullman** *Fingall* S ex-'Bournemouth Belle' coach pack - *03*	20	NA
(R1038)	**Pullman** *Minerva* S ex-'VSOE' set - *03-06*	20	NA
(R1073)	**Pullman** *Minerva* S ex-'VSOE' set - *07-11*	30	NA

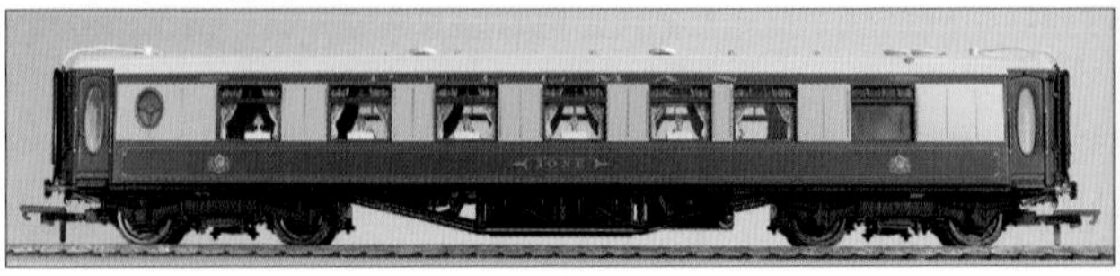

3rd series Pullman 1st kitchen car [C8c]

(R4254)	**Pullman** *Ione* S ex-'VSOE' coach pack - *06-08*	20	NA
(R2369)	**Pullman** *Cecilia* M ex-'Golden Arrow' train pk - *04*	20	NA
(R2369)	**Pullman** *Chloria* M ex-'Golden Arrow' train pack - *04*	20	NA
(R4196)	**Pullman** *Adrian* M ex-'Golden Arrow' coach pack - *04*	20	NA
R4485	**Pullman** *Adrian* S - *11*	35	47
(R4196)	**Pullman** *Zenobia* M ex-'Golden Arrow' coach pack - *04*	20	NA
(R2365M)	**Pullman** *Rosamond* S Sp Edn 1500 'Queen of Scots' MO pack with coach boards - *03-04*	25	NA
(R2568)	**Pullman** *Iolanthe* M ex-'Devon Belle' train pack - *06-08*	20	NA
(R4251)	**Pullman** *Fingall* M ex-'Devon Belle' coach pack - *06-08*	25	NA
(R2817)	**Pullman** Geraldine M ex-'Devon Belle' train pack - *09*	30	NA
(R4380)	**Pullman** *Argus* M ex-'Devon Belle' coach pack - *09*	30	NA
(R2952)	**Pullman** *Ibis* M 'Imperial Airways Empire Service' ex-train pack Ltd Edn 1500 - *10-11*	30	NA

C8d. Pullman K Class 3rd/2nd Kitchen Car (2003)

M = matchboard sides. S = smooth sides.

Dark Brown & Cream

R4146	**Pullman** *Car No.59 - not made*	NA	NA
R4146	**Pullman** *Car No.171* M - *03*	20	25
R4146A	**Pullman** *Car No.166* M - *03-07*	23	33
R4165	**Pullman** *Car No.167* S - *03-08*	25	35
R4424	**Pullman** *Car No.169* M - *10-11*	30	42
R4429	**Pullman** *Car No.171* S - *10-11*	30	42
(R2300)	**Pullman** *Car No.169* S ex-'Bournemouth Belle' train pack - *03*	20	NA
(R2568)	**Pullman** *Car No.61* M ex-'Devon Belle' train pack - *06-08*	25	NA
R4486	**Pullman** *Car No.61* S - *11*	35	47
X5923	**Pullman** *Car No.31* M ex-MO 'Bournemouth Belle' train pack Ltd Edn 1500 - *07*	23	NA
R4481	**Pullman** *Car No.60* M - *11*	35	47

C8e. Pullman K Class Brake 3rd/2nd Car (2003)

M = matchboard sides. S = smooth sides.

Dark Brown & Cream

R4150	**Pullman** *Car No.54 - not made*	NA	NA
R4150	**Pullman** *Car No.65* M - *03*	20	25
R4482	**Pullman** *Car No.65* M - *11*	35	47
R4150A	**Pullman** *Car No.161* M - *03-05*	20	25
R4166	**Pullman** *Car No.248* S - *03-07*	23	33
R4150B	**Pullman** *Car No.209* M - *06-07*	23	30
R4166A	**Pullman** *Car No.54* S - *06-09*	28	40
R4150C	**Pullman** *Car No.162* M - *08*	25	35

R4425	**Pullman** *Car No.55* M - *10-11*	30	42
R4430	**Pullman** *Car No.27* S - *10*	30	42

3rd series brake 3rd car [C8e]

(R2365M)	**Pullman** *Car No.161* S Sp Edn 1500 'Queen of Scots' MO pack, roof and end boards - *03-04*	25	NA
(R2300)	**Pullman** *Car No.62* S ex-'Bournemouth Belle' train pack - *03*	20	NA
(R4169)	**Pullman** *Car No.63* S ex-'Bournemouth Belle' coach pack - *03*	20	NA
R4487	**Pullman** *Car No.63* S - *11*	35	47
X5924	**Pullman** *Car No.154* M ex MO 'Bournmouth Belle' train pack Ltd Edn 1500 - *07*	23	NA
(R4251)	**Pullman** *Car No.65* M ex-'Devon Belle' coach pack - *06-08*	25	NA
(R2817)	**Pullman** *Car No.27* M ex-'Devon Belle' train pack - *09*	30	NA
(R4380)	**Pullman** *Car No.54* M ex-'Devon Belle' coach pack - *09*	30	NA

C8f. Pullman Bar Car (2009)

Dark Brown & Cream

R4387	**Pullman** *'Daffodil Bar' Diamond - 09-11*	30	42

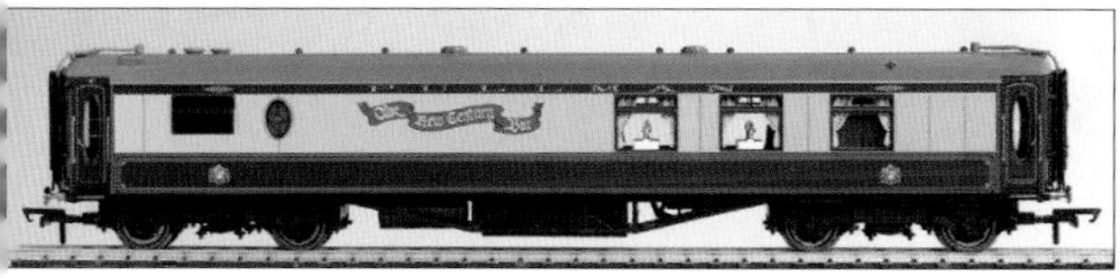

3rd series Pullman bar car [C8f]

R4418	**Pullman** *'The New Century Bar'* S - *10-11*	30	42

C9a. Pullman H Class 12-wheel 1st Class Parlour (2009)

R4384	**Pullman** *Monaco* dark brown+cream - *09-10*	32	42
(R2819)	**Pullman** *Malaga* dark brown+cream ex-'Bournemouth Belle' train pack - *09*	32	NA
(R4381)	**Pullman** *Sunbeam* dark brown+cream ex-'Bournemouth Belle' coach pack - *09*	32	NA

12-wheel Pullman 1st class parlour car [C9a]

C9b. Pullman H Class 12-wheel 3rd Class Parlour (2009)

R4385	**Pullman** *Car No.98* dark brown+cream - *09*	32	42
(R2819)	**Pullman** *Car No.96* dark brown+cream ex-'Bournemouth Belle' train pack - *09*	32	NA
R4419	**Pullman** *Car No.294* dark brown+cream - *10-11*	32	42
R4475	**Pullman** *Car No.97* dark brown+cream - *11*	35	47

C9c. Pullman H Class 12-wheel 3rd Class Kitchen Car (2009)

(R4381)	**Pullman** *Car No.45* dark brown+cream ex-'Bournemouth Belle' coach pack - *09*	32	NA

C9d. Pullman H Class 12-wheel 3rd Class Brake (2009)

(R2819)	**Pullman** *Car No.94* dark brown+cream ex-'Bournemouth Belle' train pack - *09*	32	NA
(R4381)	**Pullman** *Car No.95* dark brown+cream ex-'Bournemouth Belle' coach pack - *09*	32	NA
R4477	**Pullman** *Car No.95* dark brown+cream - *11*	35	47

C9e. Pullman H Class 12-wheel 1st Class Kitchen Car (2009)

R4420	**Pullman** car *Neptune* dark brown+cream - *10-11*	32	42
R4476	**Pullman** car *Portia* dark brown+cream - *11*	35	47

C10. Pullman Devon Belle Observation Car (2009)

R4377	**Pullman** 'Devon Belle' M dark brown+cream - *09*	35	48
R4436	**Pullman** 'Devon Belle' M dark brown+cream (1947) - *10*	30	42
(R2953)	**Pullman** 'Devon Belle' Sc281 M dark brown+cream ex-'*Flying Scotsman* USA Tour' train pack Lt Edn 2000 - *11*	35	NA
R4473	**Observation Car** Sc281 maroon - *11*	35	47

C11a. 'Brighton Belle' Trailer 1st Kitchen (2011)

After the success of Hornby's 8-wheel and 12-wheel Pullman cars, the 'Brighton Belle' Pullman EMU seemed the next logical step.

R4528	**Pullman ?** PulTFK brown+cream - *11*	35	46
R4529	**Pullman ?** PulTFK brown+cream - *11*	35	46
R?	**Pullman ?** PulTFK blue+grey - *11*	35	46
R?	**Pullman ?** PulTFK blue+grey - *11*	35	46

C11b. 'Brighton Belle' Trailer 3rd (2011)

R4527	**Pullman ?** PulTTL brown+cream - *11*	35	46
R?	**Pullman ?** PulTTL blue+grey - *11*	35	46

DMU Centre Cars

C12. 'Blue Pullman' DMU Centre Car (1963)

R426	**Pullman** W60745 (or none) blue+white crests on window panel - *63-68*	35	50
R426	**Pullman** W60745 grey+blue - *69-70*	25	40
R426	**Pullman** W60745 blue+white crest below window panel ex-R538 set- *74*	26	NA
R426	**Pullman** W60747 blue+white, error - *69-70*	40	55

C13a. Class 101 DMU Centre Car (1961)

R334	**BR** M59120 green - *61-67*	15	20
R334	**BR** M59120 small number green - *77*	15	20

C13b. Class 101 DMU Centre Car (ex-Lima) (2006)

(R2578)	**BR** M59115 green - *06*	18	NA
(R2578A)	**BR** M59120 green - *07*	18	NA
(R2697)	**BR** M59131 green - *08-10*	18	NA
(R2579)	**BR** M59130 blue - *06*	18	NA
(R2579A)	**BR** M59125 blue - *07-09*	18	NA
(R2698)	**BR** W50122 blue+grey - *08-10*	18	NA

C14. Class 110 DMU Centre Car (1982)

This is a trailer second.

Green

R688	**BR** E59708 2nd - *83-85*	18	20
R491	**BR** E59695 2nd - *92-98*	15	17
(R2297A)	**BR** E59710 ex-R2297A - *02-03*	15	NA
(R2297B)	**BR** E59703 ex-R2297B - *03-04*	15	NA
(R2297C)	**BR** E59707 ex-R2297C - *05*	15	NA
(R2297D)	**BR** E59700 ex-R2297D - *06*	15	NA

Centre car for Class 110 DMU [C14]

Blue & Grey

R428	**BR** E59814 2nd - *84-85*	12	15
X3655	**BR** E59808 2nd ex-R2073 pack - *98-99*	12	NA
X3655A	**BR** E59696 2nd ex-R2073A pack - *00*	12	NA

White

R699	**BR** E59707 2nd - *82-83*	15	20
X3320	**BR** E59816 2nd ex-R377 pack - *96*	15	NA

Pre-Nationalisation Stock

C15. *Rocket* Coach (1963)

The coaches were produced with a choice of 3 names, in equal quantities, *Times, Dispatch, Experience*.

R621	**Liverpool Manchester** yellow 'Railway Company' - *63-65*	12	25
R621	**Liverpool Manchester** yellow - *64-66*	12	25
R?	**Liverpool Manchester** yellow ex-R796 pack, few sold solo, metal tyres - *82*	15	35

C16. 4-wheeled Coach (1976)

R219	**CR** 12 maroon+white - *80-82*	7	12
R4107W	**CR** blue ex-MO R1028K set - *08*	10	NA
(R1130K)	**CR** blue ex-'Highland Rover' MO set - *09*	12	NA
(R1151)	**CR** blue ex-'Caledonian Belle' train set - *11*	12	NA
(R1127)	**FR** blue ex-'City Industrial' MO set - *09*	12	NA
R095w	**HR** 12 red ex-Toys-R-Us set - *94*	7	NA
X10208	**MR** ? maroon ex-MO R1115 set - *08*	10	NA
(R1068)	**MSLR** 8 maroon ex-set - *06*	7	NA
R213	**GWR** 12 dark brown+yellow - *78-81*	6	8
R213	**GWR** 12 dark brown+yellow - *82-83*	6	8
R213	**GWR** 12 dark brown+yellow + crest - *?*	10	20
R446	**GWR** 12 dark brown+yellow - *87-?*	6	8
R446	**GWR** 12 dark brown+yellow fine printing -*?-07-10*	10	12
X10194	**GWR** ? dk.brown+yellow ex-MO R1116M set - *08*	10	NA
R468	**LMS** 12 maroon - *84-11*	7	10
R?	**LMS** 3 maroon - *?*	6	NA
(R1131M)	**LMS** maroon ex-'Midland Belle' MO set - *not made*	NA	NA
R498	**LNER** 12 teak ex-set - *87-88*	8	NA
X4554	**LNER** 137 teak ex-set - *02-03*	8	NA
X4555	**LNER** 138 teak ex-set - *02-03*	8	NA
X10192	**LNER** ? teak ex-MO R1120M set - *08*	10	NA
R4121	**SR** 100 malachite green - *00-01*	6	9

4-wheeled coach in SR olive green livery [C16]

R4135	**SR** 350 olive green - *01-09*	7	10
X10229	**SR** ? olive green ex-MO R1111KF set - *08*	10	NA
R296	**BR** 12 yellow track cleaner - *82-11*	12	15
R212	12 blue yellow line - *76-78*	6	10
R199	12 blue gold line - *86-87*	6	10
(R1016)	12 bright blue ex-set - *99-01*	6	NA
R176	12 blue+red ex-'Stationmaster' - *93-96*	5	NA
R176	12 red+blue ex-'Stationmaster' - *93-96*	5	NA
(R1031)	maroon ex-set - *02-03*	6	NA
(R1046)	green with red roof ex-set - *04*	6	NA
X5021	green with red roof ex- MO R1046 set - *08*	7	NA
	Thomas Series		
R110	*Annie* teak - *85-10*	8	10
R112	*Clarabel* teak - *85-10*	8	10
R252	*Annie* teak motorised ex-Thomas set - *88-?*	7	NA

C17a. Short Clerestory All 3rd (1961)

W = weathered. No interior unit.

	Dark Brown + Cream Coaches		
R332	**GWR** 5017 - *61-70*	10	15
R332	**GWR** 5017 white wheel rims - *71-72*	12	17
R332	**GWR** 5017 with crests ex-pack - *71-72*	20	25
R024	**GWR** 5017 paint finish ex-R795 pack - *81*	15	NA
(R2560)	**GWR** Ex- train pack - *06*	15	NA
	Miscellaneous		
R384	**LMS** 4863 maroon composite - *86-89*	25	28
R024	**LNER** 61456 teak composite - *72-73*	22	25
R391	**LNER** 2247 teak composite - *88-95*	12	15
(R1032)	**LNER** 4103 teak ex-Woolworths set - *03*	12	NA
X4648	**LNER** 4103 teak ex-MO R1032K set - *08*	15	NA
(R1122)	**LNER** 4103 teak lined ex-set - *09-10*	15	NA

LNER short clerestory all 3rd [C17a]

(R1069)	**LNER** 4104 teak W ex-set - *07-08*	12	NA
R379	**GN&SR** maroon+white ex-R615 & R795 Railway Children sets - *71-72*	45	NA
X5765	**BR** red+cream ex-MO R1089 set - *06*	15	NA
R760	bright red, white roof ex-R505 set - *73?*	20	NA

C17b. Short Clerestory Brake 3rd (1961)

W = weathered. No interior unit.

	Dark Brown + Cream		
R333	**GWR** 2316 - *61-70*	10	15
R333	**GWR** 2316 white wheel rims - *71-72*	12	17
R333	**GWR** 2316 with crests - *72*	20	25
R025	**GWR** 2316 paint finish ex-R795 pack - *81*	15	NA
(R2560)	**GWR** ex- train pack - *06*	15	NA
R9201	No markings and with a face at one end (*Old Slow Coach*) from Thomas series - *05-10*	15	20
	Miscellaneous		
R385	**LMS** 6438 maroon - *86-89, 94-95*	25	28
R025	**LNER** 62420 teak - *72-73*	22	25
R449	**LNER** 1475 teak - *88-95*	12	15
(R1032)	**LNER** 3857 teak ex-Woolworths set - *03*	12	NA
X4649	**LNER** 3857 teak ex-MO R1032K set - *08*	15	NA
(R1122)	**LNER** 3857 teak lined ex-set - *09-10*	15	NA
(R1069)	**LNER** 3858 teak W ex-set - *07-08*	13	NA
R620	**BR** 20 black Engineer's Dept. - *63-65*	25	30
R620	**BR** 20 dark green Engineer's Dept. - *66-67*	25	30
X5766	**BR** red+cream ex-MO R1089 set - *06*	15	NA
R761	bright red, white roof, no buffers ex-R505 set - *73*	8	NA

C18a. GWR Clerestory Comp/All 3rd (1982)

R452	**MR** 2913 maroon - *84-85*	25	35
R122	**GWR** 1602 dark brown+yellow - *82-85*	15	20
R435	**GWR** 3162 dark brown+cream - *85-87*	15	20
R484	**GWR** 3162 dark brown+cream - *92-96*	15	20
R4119A	**GWR** 945 cream+dark brown - *00-01*	15	20
R4119B	**GWR** 950 cream+dark brown - *00-01*	15	20
R4119C	**GWR** 947 * cream+dark brown - *02*	15	20
R4119C	**GWR** 948 ** cream+dark brown - *not made*	NA	NA
R4119D	**GWR** 951 * cream+dark brown - *02*	15	20
R4119D	**GWR** 954 ** cream+dark brown - *not made*	NA	NA
R4119E	**GWR** 948 cream+dark brown - *02-03*	15	20
R4119F	**GWR** 954 cream+dark brown - *02-03*	15	20
(R2956)	**GWR** 949? cream+dark brown ex- train pack - *10*	18	NA
R4198	**GWR** 3162 cream+dark brown - *04-05*	15	20

GWR all-3rd clerestory coach [C18a]

(R2706)	**GWR** 1895 dark brown+cream ex-set - *08*	16	NA
(R2706)	**GWR** 1896 dark brown+cream ex-set - *08*	16	NA
R4222	**GWR** 3165 cream+dark brown unlined - *05*	15	20
R4222A	**GWR** 3163 cream+dark brown unlined - *06-07*	15	20
R4364	**GWR** 3242 dark brown+cream - 09	18	24
(R2980)	**GWR** ? dark brown+cream Ltd Edn 1908 ex-'London 1908' train pack - *11*	20	NA

* As per 2002 catalogue. ** As per Oct/Nov 2002 Hornby magazine *The Collector*.

C18b. GWR Clerestory Brake 3rd (1982)

R453	**MR** 1490 maroon - *84-85*	18	25
R123	**GWR** 3371 dark brown+yellow - *82-85*	15	20
R436	**GWR** 3371 dark brown+cream - *85-87*	15	20
R488	**GWR** 3371 dark brown+cream - *92-96*	15	20
(R2706)	**GWR** 2085 dark brown+cream ex-set - *08*	16	NA
R4120A	**GWR** 3380 cream+dark brown - *00-01*	15	20
R4120B	**GWR** 3375 cream+dark brown - *00-01*	15	20
R4120C	**GWR** 3371 cream+dark brown - *02-03*	15	20
R4199	**GWR** 3321 cream+dark brown - *04-05*	15	20
R4223	**GWR** 3325 cream+dk.brown - *05-06*	15	20
R4223A	**GWR** 3380 cream+dark brown - *not made*	NA	NA
R4223A	**GWR** 3336 cream+dark brown - *06-07*	15	20
R4223A	**GWR** 5636 cream+dark brown - *not made*	NA	NA
R4365	**GWR** 3423 dark brown+cream - *09*	18	24
(R2956)	**GWR** 3477? cream+dark brown ex- train pack - *10*	18	NA
(R2980)	**GWR** ? dark brown+cream Ltd Edn 1908 ex-'London 1908' train pack - *11*	20	NA

C19. GWR Suburban 'B Set' (ex-Airfix) (1997)

These are made from Airfix tooling purchased from Dapol in 1996. 'B Set' coaches were brake ends which were always used in pairs.

R4030A	**GWR** 6904 dark brown+cream - *97-98*	15	20
R4030B	**GWR** 6900 dark brown+cream - *97*	15	20
R4030C	**GWR** 6762 dark brown+cream - *00-03*	15	20
R4030D	**GWR** 6763 dark brown+cream - *00-04*	15	20

GWR 'B set' suburban coach [C19]

R4319A	**GWR** 6381 dark brown+cream - *08-09*	18	24
R4319B	**GWR** 6382 dark brown+cream - *08-09*	18	24
R4099A	**BR** W6381W maroon - *99-02*	15	20
R4099B	**BR** W6382W maroon - *99-03*	15	20
R4293A	**BR** W6534W maroon - *07*	15	20
R4293B	**BR** W6535W maroon - *07-09*	18	24

C20. GWR Autocoach (ex-Airfix) (1997)

These are made from Airfix tooling purchased from Dapol in 1996.

R4025	**GWR** 190 dark brown+cream - *97-98*	15	20
R4025A	**GWR** 189 dark brown+cream - *00-01*	15	20
R4025B	**GWR** 192 dark brown+cream - *00-02*	15	20
R4186	**GWR** roundel W194W dark brown+cream - *03*	15	20
R4186A	**GWR** roundel W189W dark brown+cream - *03*	15	20
R4187	**BR** W195W red+cream - *03*	15	20
R4187A	**BR** W192W red+cream - *04-05*	15	20
R4100A	**BR** W188W maroon - *99*	15	20
R4100B	**BR** W196W maroon - *99*	15	20
R4100C	**BR** W187W maroon - *02-05*	15	20
R4100D	**BR** W196W maroon - *not made (see R4100B)*	NA	NA
R4100D	**BR** W188W maroon - *06*	15	20
R4100E	**BR** W194W maroon - *07-09*	15	30
(R2173M)	**BR** W194W maroon ex pack - *00*	16	NA
(R2173M)	**BR** W195W maroon ex pack - *00*	16	NA
R4335	**BR** Test Car 1 ADW150375 red+dark blue Sp Edn 1000 (ModelZone) - *09*	18	22

C21a. GWR 'Centenary' Composite (ex-Airfix) (1997)

These are made from Airfix tooling purchased from Dapol in 1996.

	GWR Paddington-Swansea Cars		
R4026	6658 dark brown+cream - *97-99, 02-03*	15	20
R4026A	6859 dark brown+cream - *04*	15	20
R4026B	6660 dark brown+cream - *05-06*	15	20
R4035	6659 dark brown+cream ex-R2025 pack - *97-98*	16	NA
R4034	6660 dark brown+cream ex-R2025 pack - *97-98*	16	NA
R4126	6661 dark brown+cream - *01*	15	20
	BR Paddington-Weston Cars		
R4028	W6660W red+cream - *97-98*	15	20
R4031	W6658W red+cream ex-R2024 pack - *97-98*	16	NA
R4032	W6661W red+cream ex-R2024 pack - *97-98*	16	NA
	GWR 'Cornish Riviera Express'		
X5981	6660 dark brown+cream ex MO R1102 set - *08*	16	NA
X5982	6661 dark brown+cream ex-MO R1102 set - *08*	16	NA
	(no roof boards)		
R4289	W6661W maroon - *07-08*	16	21

Ex-GWR 'Centenary' composite coach [C21a]

C21b. GWR 'Centenary' Brake (ex-Airfix) (1997)

These are made from Airfix tooling purchased from Dapol in 1996.

	GWR Paddington-Swansea Cars		
R4027	4576 dark brown+cream - *97-00*	15	20
R4036	4577 dark brown+cream ex-R2025 pack - *97-98*	16	NA
R4139	4576 dark brown+cream - *01-04*	15	20
R4139A	4580 dark brown+cream - *02-04*	15	20
R4139B	4575 dark brown+cream - *05-06*	15	20
	BR Paddington-Weston Cars		
R4029	W4578W red+cream - *97-98*	15	20
R4033	W4580W red+cream ex-R2024 pack - *97-98*	16	NA
	GWR 'Cornish Riviera Express'		
X5983	4579 dark brown+cream ex MO R1102 set - *08*	16	NA
	(no roof boards)		
R4290	W4578W maroon - *07-08*	16	21

C22a. GWR Collett Composite (1977)

npf = non-paint finish ie: the main body colour is provided by the colour of the plastic. Until 1982 the coaches had BR bogies and then, from that year, scale 7' Collett ones were fitted.

	Dark Brown & Cream		
R429	**GWR** 6024 glossy BR bogies npf - *77-78*	12	14
R456	**GWR** 6024 satin finish - *79-80*	12	14
R159	**GWR** 6050 crest - *94-97*	12	15
R4065	**GWR** 6099 crest - *98-99*	12	15
R4065A	**GWR** 6068 crest - *00-02*	12	15
R4065B	**GWR** 6030 crest - *03*	12	14
R4065C	**GWR** 6105 crest - *04-05*	12	14
R4065D	**GWR** 6519 crest - *05-06*	12	14
X3733	**GWR** 6105 black roof ex-R2084 pack - *98*	13	NA
X3734	**GWR** 6181 black roof ex-R2084 pack - *98*	13	NA
(R2196M)	**GWR** 6201 Paddington Aberystwyth + Pwllheli ex-R2196M Sp Edn 1500 - *01*	13	NA
(R2196M)	**GWR** 6203 Paddington Aberystwyth and Pwllheli ex-R2196M Sp Edn 1500 - *01*	13	NA
R4291	**GWR** (roundel) 6135 - *07-08*	15	18
R4523	**GWR** (roundel) 6135 (RailRoad) - *11*	14	17
R4242	**BR** W6181W red+cream - *05-08*	14	18
R4242A	**BR** W6187W red+cream - *06*	14	18
R121	**Gordon's** green+yellow - *86-10*	15	20
R091	**James's** red+white - *89-91, 02-03*	15	20
R9051	**James's** bright red+white - *02-10*	15	20

C22b. GWR Collett Brake End (1977)

npf = non-paint finish ie: the main body colour is provided by the colour of the plastic. Until 1982 the coaches had BR bogies and then, from that year, scale 7' Collett ones were fitted.

	Dark Brown & Cream		
R430	**GWR** 4913 glossy BR bogies npf - *77-78*	12	14
R457	**GWR** 4913 satin finish - *79-80*	12	14

GWR Collett brake 3rd [C22b]

R161	**GWR** 4913 crest - *94-97*	12	14
R4066	**GWR** 4944 crest - *98-99*	12	15
R4066A	**GWR** 4930 crest - *00-01*	12	15
R4066B	**GWR** 4940 crest - *02-03*	12	14

R4066C	**GWR** 4932 crest - *04*	12	14
R4066D	**GWR** 5087 crest - *05-06*	12	14
X3735	**GWR** 4924 black roof ex-R2084 pack - *98*	13	NA
(R2196M)	**GWR** 4920 Paddington Aberystwyth + Pwllheli ex-R2196M Sp Edn 1500 - *01*	13	17
R4292	**GWR** (roundel) 5121 - *07-09*	16	20
R4524	**GWR** (roundel) 5121 (RailRoad) - *11*	14	17
R4243	**BR** W5131W red+cream - *05-08*	14	18
R4243A	**BR** W5109W red+cream - *06-08*	14	18
R120	**Gordon's** green+yellow - *86-10*	15	20
R094	**James's** red+white - *89-91*	15	20
R9052	**James's** bright red+white - *02-10*	15	20

C22c. GWR Collett Restaurant Car (1978)

Based on a design of 1925 of which only four were made. Until 1982 the coaches had BR bogies and then, from that year, scale 7' Collett ones were fitted.

R454	**GWR** (roundel) 9578 dark brown+cream shiny dark BR bogies - *78*	12	14
R458	as above but satin finish - *79-80*	12	14
R157	**GWR** 9578 dark brown+cream crest - *94-96*	12	14
R4151	**GWR** 9578 dark brown+cream crest - *02-03*	12	14
R4151A	**GWR** 9579 dark brown+cream crest - *04-06*	12	14
R4151B	**GWR** 9578 dark brown+cream crest - *05-07*	12	14
R4525	**GWR** ? dark brown+cream crest (RailRoad) - *11*	14	17
R4244	**BR** W9579W red+cream - *05-08*	14	18
R4244A	**BR** W9581W red+cream - *06-08*	14	18

C23a. GWR/BR Hawksworth All 3rd (2010)

Although designed by the GWR during Hawksworths time as CME, it is thought that they did not see full service until after nationalisation of the railways in January 1948. The side corridor 3rds had eight compartments and would seat 64 passengers.

R4501	**GWR** 382 dark brown+cream - *11*	27	36
R4405	**BR** W782W red+cream - *10-11*	25	33
R4405A	**BR** W856W red+cream - *11*	27	36

Hawksworth all-3rd coach in BR crimson and cream [C23a]

R4410	**BR** W1717W maroon - *10*	25	33
R4410A	**BR** W2107W maroon - *11*	27	36

C23b. GWR/BR Hawksworth Composite (2010)

Although designed by the GWR during Hawksworths time as CME, it is thought that they did not see full service until after nationalisation of the railways in January 1948. The Hawksworth coaches were built to a new length of 64 feet. The side corridor composite had four 1st class compartments and three 3rd class ones.

R4503	**GWR** 7253 dark brown+cream - *11*	27	36
R4407	**BR** W7821W red+cream - *10-11*	25	33
R4407A	**BR** W7261W red+cream - *11*	27	36
R4412	**BR** W7799W maroon - *10-11*	25	33
R4412A	**BR** W7252W maroon - *11*	27	36

C23c. GWR/BR Hawksworth Composite Brake (2010)

Although designed by the GWR during Hawksworths time as CME, it is thought that they did not see full service until after nationalisation of the railways in January 1948. The corridor passenger section had two 1st class compartments and four 3rd class.

R4504	**GWR** 7372 dark brown+cream - *11*	27	36
R4408	**BR** W7839W red+cream - *10-11*	25	33
R4408A	**BR** W7373W red+cream - *11*	27	36
R4413	**BR** W7849W maroon - *10*	25	33
R4413A	**BR** W7853W maroon - *11*	27	36

C23d. GWR/BR Hawksworth Brake 3rd (2010)

Although designed by the GWR during Hawksworths time as CME, it is thought that they did not see full service until after nationalisation of the railways in January 1948. The coach contained four 3rd class compartments off a side corridor.

R4502	**GWR** 1763 dark brown+cream - *11*	27	36
R4406	**BR** W1773W red+cream - *10-11*	25	33
R4406A	**BR** W2138W red+cream - *11*	27	36
R4411	**BR** W2246W maroon - *10-11*	25	33
R4411A	**BR** W2185W maroon - *11*	27	36

C23e. GWR/BR Hawksworth Full Brake (2010)

Although designed by the GWR during Hawksworths time as CME, it is thought that they did not see full service until after nationalisation of the railways in January 1948.

R4500	**GWR** 316 dark brown+cream - *11*	27	36
R4404	**BR** W298W red+cream - *10-11*	25	33

Hawksworth full brake in BR maroon [C23e]

R4404A	**BR** W?W red+cream - *11*	27	36
R4409	**BR** W322W maroon - *10*	25	33
R4409A	**BR** W325W maroon - *11*	27	36

C23f. GWR/BR Hawksworth 1st Class (2011)

R4505	**GWR** 8001 dark brown+cream - *11*	27	36
R4493	**BR** W8114W red+cream - *11*	27	36
R4499	**BR** W8054W maroon - *11*	27	36

C24a. 'Caledonian' Composite (1962)

R427	**CR** 7511 maroon+white, roof white - *62-67*	15	20
R427	as above with roof grey - *72-73*	14	18
(R2610)	**CR** 460 maroon+white, roof grey ex-set - *07*	18	NA
(R2610)	**CR** 461 maroon+white, roof grey ex-set - *07*	18	NA
R26	**GWR** dark brown+cream - *72-73*	14	20
R747	**LMS** 2643 maroon - *71-73*	10	12
(R2806)	**LMS** 3546 dark maroon ex-Ltd Edn set - *09-11*	20	NA
(R2806)	**LMS** 3547 dark maroon ex-Ltd Edn set - *09-11*	20	NA
R749	**SR** S1750 olive green - *71-73*	12	15

C24b. 'Caledonian' Brake (1962)

R428	**CR** 7501 maroon+white, roof white - *62-67*	15	20
R428	as above with roof grey - *72-73*	14	18
(R2610)	**CR** 143 maroon+white, roof grey ex-set - *07*	18	NA

Caledonian Railway brake composite in LMS livery [C24b]

R27	**GWR** 8176, 8178 dark brown+cream - *72-73*	14	20
R748	**LMS** 2640 maroon - *71-73*	10	12
(R2806)	**LMS** 6618 dark maroon ex-Ltd Edn set - *09-11*	20	NA
R750	**SR** S1774 olive green - *71-73*	12	15

C25a. LMS Stanier Composite (1977)

npf = non-paint finish ie: the main body colour is provided by the colour of the plastic. Unless otherwise stared the maroon coaches has silver roofs.

Maroon

R433	**LMS** 3934 npf - *77-79*	10	13
R474	**LMS** 4120 LMS - *80-85*	10	13
R474	**LMS** 4120 L M S - *86-97*	10	13
R4041	**LMS** 4069 ex-R2033 pack - *97*	12	NA
R4040	**LMS** 4075 ex-R2033 pack - *97*	12	NA
R4061	**LMS** 4183 - *98-99*	10	NA
R4388	**LMS** 4183 (RailRoad) silver roof - *09-11*	12	15
R4061A	**LMS** 4113 - *00-01*	10	13
(R2167)	**LMS** 4028 ex-R2167 pack - *00*	12	NA
(R2167)	**LMS** 4024 ex-R2167 pack - *00*	12	NA
(R2172M)	**LMS** 4114 ex-R2172M pack - *00*	12	NA
(R2172M)	**LMS** 4115 ex-R2172M pack - *00*	12	NA
R4130A	**LMS** 4000 grey roof - *01-02*	10	13
R4130B	**LMS** 4001 grey roof - *01-03*	10	13
R4130C	**LMS** 4020 grey roof - *02-03*	10	13
R4130D	**LMS** 3954 grey roof - *04*	10	13
(R1060)	**LMS** 4256 W ex-R1060 VE Day Ltd Edn		

	1000 MO set - *05*	15	NA
(R1060)	**LMS** 4263 W ex-R1060 VE Day Ltd Edn 1000 MO set - *05*	15	NA
(R2887M)	**LMS** 4069 ex-'The Thames-Forth' MO train pack - *09*	15	NA
(R2887M)	**LMS** 4070 ex-'The Thames-Forth' MO train pack - *09*	15	NA
	The 'Coronation Scot' Coaches		
R422	**LMS** 1070 blue - *84-87, 92-96*	15	20
R4128A	**LMS** 1069 blue - *01, 04-05*	15	20
R4128B	**LMS** 1070 blue - *01-02*	16	22
R4128C	**LMS** 1071 blue - *02-03*	16	22
(R2199M)	**LMS** 3934 maroon ex-R2199M pack - *01*	17	NA
(R2199M)	**LMS** 3935 maroon ex-R2199M pack - *01*	17	NA
R4141	**LMS** 3936 maroon - *01*	20	25
R4141A	**LMS** 3937 maroon - *02*	20	25
	LNER 'Silver Jubilee' Coaches		
R872w	**LNER** 1582 silver Gresley bogies ex-R837 set - *92-93*	20	NA
(R2278M)	**LNER** 1586 [G] 3rd silver BR bogies ex-pack - *02*	20	NA
(R2445)	**LNER** 1586 [G] Ltd Edn MO ex-pack - *05*	20	NA
(R4168)	**LNER** 1582 [B] 1st silver BR bogies ex-R4168 coach pack - *02*	20	NA
	BR Red & Cream		
R437	**BR** M4329 - *77-79*	12	15
R421	**BR** M4329 - *80-83*	12	15
R442	**BR** M4330 - *85-97*	12	15
R355	**BR** ? ex-R775 set - *94*	13	NA
(R1004)	**BR** ? ex-R1004 set - *96*	13	NA
(R2303M)	**BR** M4070M 'The Royal Scot' ex-pack - *02*	13	NA
(R2303M)	**BR** M4071M London Glasgow ex-pack - *02*	13	NA
(R1094)	**BR** M4300 ex-'The Royal Scot' set - *07-09*	13	NA
(R1094)	**BR** M4326 ex-'The Royal Scot' set - *07-09*	13	NA
	BR Maroon		
R429	**BR** M4316 - *91-93*	14	16

1st series Stanier composite in BR maroon [C25a]

(R2176M)	**BR** M15387 ex-R2176M pack Euston Keswick Windermere - *00-01*	15	NA

C25b. LMS Stanier Brake End (1977)

npf = non-paint finish, ie: the main body colour is provided by the colour of the plastic.

	Maroon		
R434	**LMS** 5644 npf - *77-79*	9	12
R475	**LMS** 5714 LMS - *80-85*	9	12
R475	**LMS** 5714 LMS - *86-97*	9	12
R4042	**LMS** 5708 ex-R2033 pack - *97*	11	NA
R4060	**LMS** 5200 - *98-99*	9	12
R4389	**LMS** 5200 (RailRoad) silver roof - *09-11*	12	15
R4060A	**LMS** 5215 - *00-01*	9	12
(R2167)	**LMS** 5619 ex-pack - *00*	11	NA
(R2172M)	**LMS** 5220 ex-pack - *00*	11	NA
R4129A	**LMS** 5205 grey roof - *01-02*	9	12
R4129B	**LMS** 5206 grey roof - *01-03*	9	12
R4129C	**LMS** 5214 grey roof - *02-03*	9	12
R4129D	**LMS** 5456 grey roof - *04*	9	12
(R1060)	**LMS** 5526 W ex-VE Day L/Edn 1000 MO set - *05*	15	NA
(R2887M)	**LMS** 5709 ex-'The Thames-Forth' MO train pack - *09*	15	NA
(R1144)	**LMS** 5710 ex-'LMS Night Mail' train set - *10-11*	15	NA
	The 'Coronation Scot' Coaches		
R423	**LMS** 5792 blue - *84-87, 92-96*	14	18
R4127A	**LMS** 5812 blue - *01*	15	20
R4127B	**LMS** 5814 blue - *01*	15	20
R4127C	**LMS** 5792 blue - *02-03*	15	20
R4218	**LMS** 5052 blue - *04-05*	15	20
(R2199M)	**LMS** 5447 maroon ex-R2199M - *01*	17	NA
R4142	**LMS** 5448 maroon - *01*	20	25
R4142A	**LMS** 5449 maroon - *02*	20	25

	LNER 'Silver Jubilee' Coaches		
R873	**LNER** 1587 Gresley bogies ex-set - *92-93*	20	NA
(R2278M)	**LNER** 1581 [A] 1st BR bogies ex-train pack - *02*	20	NA

1st series Stanier brake coach in LNER 'Silver Jubilee' livery [C25b]

(R2445)	**LNER** 1581 [A] MO ex-Ltd Edn 2000 pack - *05*	20	NA
(R4168)	**LNER** 1587 [F] 3rd BR bogies ex-R4168 coach pack - *02*	20	NA
	BR Red & Cream		
R438	**BR** M26545 - *77-79*	11	14
R424	**BR** M26545 - *80-83*	11	14
R443	**BR** M26546 - *85-97*	11	14
R357	**BR** ex-R775 set - *94*	12	NA
(R1004)	**BR** M5709 ex-R1004 set - *97*	12	NA
(R2303M)	**BR** M5218M 'The Royal Scot' ex-R2303M pack - *02*	12	NA
(R1094)	**BR** M5646 ex-'The Royal Scot' set - *07-09*	12	NA
(R1094)	**BR** M5819 ex-'The Royal Scot' set - *07-09*	12	NA
	BR Maroon		
R447	**BR** M5750 - *91-93*	13	15
(R2176M)	**BR** M34285 Euston Keswick Windermere ex-pack - *00-01*	14	NA
(R2176M)	**BR** M34358 Euston Keswick Windermere ex-pack - *00-01*	14	NA
R592	**Royal Mail** 80868 bright red - *90-93*	14	18

C26a. LMS Period 3 Corridor 1st (2005)

R4230	**LMS** 1043 maroon - *05-07*	23	30
R4230A	**LMS** 1062 maroon - *08-09*	23	30
(R2659M)	**LMS** 1047 maroon ex-train pack - *07*	23	NA
(R2985)	**LMS** ? ex-'A Duchess at Carlisle' train pack - *11*	25	NA

2nd series Stanier LMS corridor 1st [C26a]

R4447	**BR** M1063M red+cream - *10*	25	32
R4234	**BR** M1050M maroon - *05-07*	23	30
R4234A	**BR** M1073M maroon - *08*	23	30
R4234A	**BR** M1040M maroon - *09-10*	25	38

C26b. LMS Period 3 Corridor 3rd (2005)

R4231	**LMS** 1637 maroon - *05-07*	23	32
R4231A	**LMS** 1573 maroon - *08-09*	23	32
(R2659M)	**LMS** 1761 maroon ex-train pack - *07*	23	NA
(R2659M)	**LMS** 1773 maroon ex-train pack - *07*	23	NA
(R2907)	**LMS** 1952 ex-'Days of Red & Gold' train pack Ltd Edn 1000 - *10*	25	NA
(R2907)	**LMS** 1953 ex-'Days of Red & Gold' train pack Ltd Edn 1000 - *10*	25	NA
(R2985)	**LMS** ? ex-'A Duchess at Carlisle' train pack - *11*	25	NA
R4448	**BR** M2001M red+cream - *10-11*	25	32
R4235	**BR** M1668M maroon - *05-07*	23	32
R4235A	**BR** M1832M maroon - *08*	23	32
R4235B	**BR** M1883M maroon - *09-10*	25	38
(R2908)	**BR** M2041 ex-'Fireworks at Chilcompton' train pack Ltd Edn 1000 - *10*	25	NA
(R2908)	**BR** M2042 ex-'Fireworks at Chilcompton' train pack Ltd Edn 1000 - *10*	25	NA

C26c. LMS 'Period 3' Corridor Brake 3rd (2005)

R4232	**LMS** 5620 maroon - *05-07*	23	32
R4232A	**LMS** 5541 maroon - *08-09*	23	32

(R2907)	**LMS** 5817 ex-'Days of Red & Gold' train pack Ltd Edn 1000 - *10*	25	NA
(R2985)	**LMS** ? ex-'A Duchess at Carlisle' train pack - *11*	25	NA
R4449	**BR** M5769M red+cream - *10*	25	32
R4236	**BR** M5593M maroon - *05-07*	23	32
R4236A	**BR** M5842M maroon - *08-09*	23	32
R4236B	**BR** M5629M maroon - *09-10*	25	38
(R2908)	**BR** M5710 ex-'Fireworks at Chilcompton' train pack Ltd Edn 1000 - *10*	25	NA

C26d. LMS 'Period 3' Parcels Van (2005)

R4233	**LMS** 30972 maroon - *05-09*	23	32
R4233A	**LMS** 31109 maroon - *06?* *	23	30

LMS period 3 parcels van [C26d]

R4450	**BR** M3101M red - *10-11*	25	32
R4237	**BR** M31004M maroon - *05-07*	23	32
R4237A	**BR** M31060M maroon - *08-10*	23	32

* not yet seen - was this made?

C27. Travelling Post Office (1978)

npf = non-paint finish ie: the main roof colour is provided by the colour of the plastic. The right-hand price column shows the value of a boxed set while the left column shows the value of an unboxed coach without lineside apparatus.

	GWR Dark Brown & Cream		
R440	**GWR** 848 TPO set - *85-87*	25	35
R4108	**GWR** 848 TPO set - *00-02*	25	35
R4526	**GWR** 30248 Night Mail coach (RailRoad) - *11*	16	20
	LMS Maroon		
R413	**LMS** 30250 TPO set, npf - *78-79*	15	25
R412	**LMS** 30250 TPO set - *83-85*	15	25
R461	**LMS** 30250 TPO set ex-R542 set - *80*	15	NA
R164	**LMS** 30249 TPO set - *94-99*	15	25
R4155	**LMS** 30246 TPO set - *02-10*	28	41
(R1144)	**LMS** 30247 Night Mail ex-'LMS Night Mail' train set - *10-11*	15	NA
R416	**BR** M80328 blue+grey SS - *80-82*	22	30
R416	as above with white rims - *80-82*	22	30
R597w	**BR** M30250M maroon ex-R758 set - *91-93*	16	NA
R416	**Royal Mail** NSX80363 bright-red TPO set - *88-93*	15	25
	Thomas Series		
(R9682)	**Sodor Mail** maroon ex-'Percy & the Mail Train' set - *11*	16	NA

C28. LMS 12-wheel Diner (ex-Dapol) (1999)

	LMS Maroon		
R4095	**LMS** 235 Dining Car - *99-00*	12	15
R4095A	**LMS** 228 Dining Car - *01-02*	12	15
R4095B	**LMS** 230 Dining Car - *02-04*	14	18
R4095C	**LMS** 232 Dining Car - *06-07*	14	19
R4095D	**LMS** 234 Dining Car - *07-09*	16	24
	BR Red + Cream		
R4188	**BR** M234M Restaurant Car - *03*	13	17
R4188A	**BR** M235M Restaurant Car - *03-06*	14	19

Ex-LMS 12-wheel diner in BR crimson and cream [C28]

R4188B	**BR** M233M Restaurant Car - *07-09*	16	24
	BR Maroon		
R4131A	**BR** M230M Restaurant Car - *01-02*	12	15
R4131B	**BR** M239M Restaurant Car - *02-05*	14	18
(R4177)	**BR** M229M ex-R4177 coach pack - *03*	14	NA

C29a. LNER Gresley Suburban Composite (2011)

Gresley introduced his non-gangwayed stock in the 1920s and Hornby have tooled four types of carriage.

R4517	**LNER** ? teak - *11*	32	44
R4521	**BR** E88245E maroon - *11*	32	44

C29b. LNER Gresley Suburban 1st (2011)

R4515	**LNER** ? teak - *11*	32	44
R4519	**BR** ? maroon - *11*	32	44

C29c. LNER Gresley Suburban Brake 3rd (2011)

R4518	**LNER** ? teak - *11*	32	44
R4522	**BR** ? maroon - *11*	32	44

C29d. LNER Gresley Suburban 3rd (2011)

R4516	**LNER** 3234 teak - *11*	32	44
R4520	**BR** ? maroon - *11*	32	44

C30a. LNER Gresley Composite (1977)

npf = non-paint finish, ie: the main roof colour is provided by the colour of the plastic. BlkE = black coach ends (the rest have teak ends). Until 1979 the coaches had BR bogies and then, from 1979, Gresley ones were fitted.

	LNER Teak		
R435	**LNER** 22357 BlkE BR bogie npf -*77-78*	10	13
R435	**LNER** 22357 BlkE npf - *79*	10	13
R477	**LNER** 22357 - *80-97*	10	13
R477	**LNER** 22357 - *99-02*	10	NA
(R1039)*	**LNER** 22356 ex-set - *03-06*	12	NA
(R1039)*	**LNER** 22357 ex-set - *03-06*	12	NA
(R1072)*	**LNER** 22356 ex-set - *07-10*	12	NA

1st series Gresley LNER teak composite coach [C30a]

(R1072)*	**LNER** 22357 ex-set - *07-10*	12	NA
(R1126)	**LNER** 24510 ex-'Blue Streak' MO set - *09*	12	NA
R4332*	**LNER** 22357 (RailRoad) - *08-11*	12	15
R4062	**LNER** 22287 - *98-99*	10	13
R4062A	**LNER** 24386 - *00*	10	13
R4062B	**LNER** 32441 - *01*	10	13
R4062C	**LNER** 32275 - *02-03*	10	13
R4047	**LNER** 24337 ex-Kays R2036 pack - *97*	12	NA
R4046	**LNER** 24367 ex-Kays R2036 pack - *97*	12	NA
	BR Red + Cream		
R409	**BR** E18276 - *88-93*	12	15
R4043	**BR** E18299 ex-Kays R2044 pack - *97*	13	NA
R4044	**BR** E18301 ex-Kays R2044 pack - *97*	13	NA
R4189	**BR** E18236E - *03-08*	12	15
(R2363M)	**BR** E18274E ex-R2363M pack - *03*	13	NA
(R2363M)	**BR** E18269E ex-R2363M pack - *03*	13	NA
(R1040)	**BR** E18281E ex-R1040 Toys-R-Us set - *03*	13	NA
(R1064)	**BR** E18170E ex-Boogaloo MO set - *05*	13	NA
(R1064)	**BR** E18171E ex-Boogaloo MO set - *05*	13	NA
	BR Maroon		
R483	**BR** E11002E - *83-85*	14	16
R400	**BR** E11029E - *92-97*	14	16
R4055	**BR** E18271E - *98-99*	14	16
R4055A	**BR** E18249E - *00-02*	14	16
R4055B	**BR** E18207E - *02-03*	14	16
X3905	**BR** E11000E ex-R2134M pack - *99*	15	NA
(R103)	***Hamleys*** 1760 maroon (all 1st) ex-set - *02-03*	20	NA

1st series Gresley coaches from the Hamley's train set [C30a]

*These versions had blackened metal wheels.

C30b. LNER Gresley Brake End (1977)

npf = non-paint finish, ie: the main roof colour is provided by the colour of the plastic. BlkE = black coach ends (the rest have teak ends). Until 1979 the coaches had BR bogies and then, from 1979, Gresley ones were fitted.

	LNER Teak		
R436	**LNER** 4237 BlkE BR bogies npf - *77-78*	9	12
R436	**LNER** 4237 BlkE - *79*	9	12
R478	**LNER** 4237 - *80-91*	9	12
R4063	**LNER** 5547 - *98-99*	9	12
R4063A	**LNER** 7913 - *00-01*	9	12
R4063B	**LNER** 5550 - *02-03*	9	12
R478 *	**LNER** 4237 ex-R1001 set - *97-02*	11	NA
(R2017)	**LNER** 1076 ex-Kays R2017 pack - *97*	11	NA
(R1039)**	**LNER** 4236 ex-R1039 set - *03-06*	11	NA
(R1039)**	**LNER** 4237 ex-R1039 set - *03-06*	11	NA
R4048	**LNER** 32557 ex-Kays R2036 pack - *97*	12	NA
(R1072)**	**LNER** 4236 ex-set - *07-10*	11	NA
(R1126)	**LNER** 42892 ex-'Blue Streak' MO set - *09*	12	NA
R4333	**LNER** 4237 (RailRoad) - *08-11*	12	15
	BR Red + Cream		
R410	**BR** E10066 - *88-93*	12	14
R4045	**BR** E10098 ex-Kays R2044 pack - *97*	12	NA
R4190	**BR** E10066 - *03-04*	12	14
(R2363M)	**BR** E10066E ex-R2363M pack - *03*	12	NA
(R1040)	**BR** E10097E ex-R1040 Toys-R-Us set - *03*	12	NA
(R1064)	**BR** E10050E ex-Boogaloo MO set - *05*	12	NA
(R1064)	**BR** E10051E ex-Boogaloo MO set - *05*	12	NA
	BR Maroon		
R484	**BR** E16769E - *83-85*	13	15
R448	**BR** E10076E - *92-97*	13	15
R4054	**BR** E10073E - *98-01*	13	15
R4054A	**BR** E10108E - *00-02*	13	15
(R1021M)	**BR** E10065E ex-R1021M set - *99*	14	NA
X3906	**BR** E10058E ex-R2134M pack - *99*	14	NA
X3907	**BR** E10064E ex-R2134M pack - *99*	14	NA
(R103)	***Hamleys*** 1760 maroon (brake 1st) ex-set - *02-03*	20	NA
(R1029)	**BR** DB10074 red ex-R1029 set *-02-03*	15	NA

* See also catalogue picture. ** These versions had blackened metal wheels.

C30c. LNER Gresley Sleeping Car (1978)

npf = non-paint finish, ie: the main roof colour is provided by the colour of the plastic. BkE = black coach ends (the rest have teak ends).

	LNER Teak		
R448	**LNER** 1316 BkE BR bogies npf - *78*	9	12
R448	**LNER** 1316 BkE npf - *79*	9	12
R479	**LNER** 1316 - *82-85*	10	12
R413	**LNER** 1316 - *88-90*	10	12
R430	**LNER** 1237 - *96-97*	10	12
R4064	**LNER** 1147 - *98-99*	10	12
R4064A	**LNER** 1261 - *00-03*	10	12
	BR		
R419	**BR** E1237 red+cream - *88-91*	12	14
R4191	**BR** E1209E red+cream - *03-04*	12	14
R485	**BR** E1237E maroon - *82-83*	14	16

1st series Gresley sleeping car in BR crimson and cream [C30c]

C31a. LNER Gresley Corridor 1st (2004)

The teak grain on the doors of early releases ran in the wrong direction but this had been corrected by the time the 2006 issues were released (this also applies to the other four teak coaches in this series).

	LNER		
R4171	**LNER** 31940 teak - *04-08*	28	36
R4171	**LNER** 22356 teak - *?*	32	40
R4171A	**LNER** 31879 teak - *05-07*	28	36
R2888M	**LNER** 31880 teak ex-'Flying Scotsman' train pack Sp Edn 1200 (Argos + Shop Direct) - *09*	30	NA
R4171B	**LNER** 6467 teak - *not made?*	NPG	NPG
R4171C	**LNER** 441 teak - *11*	40	54
	BR		
R4179	**BR** E11018E red+cream - *04-08*	25	32
R4179A	**BR** E11020E red+cream - *05-08*	25	32
(R2435)	**BR** E11019E red+cream ex-train pack - *05*	25	NA
(R1074)	**BR** E11011E red+cream ex-set - *06*	25	NA
(R4255)	**BR** E11012E red+cream ex-coach pack - *06*	25	NA
R4261A	**BR** Sc11026E maroon - *06-09*	28	38
R4261B	**BR** E11025E maroon - *06-09*	28	38

C31b. LNER Gresley Corridor 3rd (2004)

	LNER		
R4172	**LNER** 1435 teak - *04-07*	28	36
R4172A	**LNER** 364 teak - *05-07*	28	36
R4172B	**LNER** 1463 teak - *08-09*	28	38
R4172C	**LNER** 60654 teak - *10*	28	38
R4172D	**LNER** ? teak - *11*	40	54
	BR Teak		
(R2906)	**BR** E12350 ex-'Rare Bird' train pack Ltd Edn 1000 - *11*	30	NA
(R2906)	**BR** E12351 ex-'Rare Bird' train pack Ltd Edn 1000 - *11*	30	NA
(R2981)	**BR** E1435 ex-'London 1948' train pack - *11*	30	NA
	BR		
R4180	**BR** E12506E red+cream - *04-06*	20	30
R4180A	**BR** E12279E red+cream - *05-08*	25	32
(R2435)	**BR** E12690E red+cream ex-train pack - *05*	20	NA
(R4228)	**BR** E12688E red+cream ex-coach pack - *05*	20	NA
(R1074)	**BR** E12612E red+cream ex-set - *06*	20	NA
(R4255)	**BR** E12620E red+cream ex-coach pack - *06*	20	NA
R4262A	**BR** E12699E maroon - *06-08*	25	32
R4262B	**BR** E12704E maroon - *06-08*	25	32

2nd series Gresley corridor 3rd [C31b]

C31c. LNER Gresley Brake 1st/3rd (2004)

	LNER		
R4170	**LNER** 24387 teak - *04-05*	28	35
R4170A	**LNER** 32558 teak - *05-06*	28	36
R2888M	**LNER** 32558 teak ex-'Flying Scotsman' train pack Sp Edn 1200 (Argos + Shop Direct) - *09*	30	NA
R4170B	**LNER** 42872 teak - *06-07*	28	35
R4170C	**LNER** 42884 teak - *08-09*	28	38
R4170D	**LNER** 24067 teak - *10*	28	38
R4170E	**LNER** ? teak - *11*	40	54
	BR Teak		
(R2906)	**BR** E10104 ex-'Rare Bird' train pack Ltd Edn 1000 - *11*	30	NA
(R2981)	**BR** E24387 ex-'London 1948' train pack - *11*	30	NA
	BR		
R4178	**BR** E10092E red+cream - *04-05*	20	28
R4178A	**BR** E10103E red+cream - *05-08*	25	32
R4178B	**BR** E10077E red+cream - *06-08*	25	32
(R2435)	**BR** E10138E red+cream ex-train pack - *05*	20	NA

(R4228)	**BR** E10134E red+cream ex-coach pack - *05*	20	NA

2nd series Gresley brake composite in BR crimson and cream [C31c]

(R1074)	**BR** E10097E red+cream ex-set - *06*	20	NA
(R4255)	**BR** E10099E red+cream ex-coach pack - *06*	20	NA
R4260A	**BR** E10101E maroon - *06-08*	25	32
R4260B	**BR** E10080E maroon - *06-09*	28	38

C31d. LNER Gresley Buffet Car (2004)

	LNER		
R4173	**LNER** 21608 teak - *04-07*	28	36
R2888M	**LNER** 21609 teak ex-'Flying Scotsman' train pack Sp Edn 1200 (Argos + Shop Direct) - *09*	30	NA
R4173A	**LNER** 32372 teak - *05-06*	28	36
R4173B	**LNER** 24080 teak - *08-09*	28	36
R4173C	**LNER** 24276 teak - *10*	28	38
R4173D	**LNER** ? teak - *11*	40	54
	BR		
R4181	**BR** E9133E red+cream - *04-07*	25	32
R4181A	**BR** E9112E red+cream - *05-07*	25	32
(R4228)	**BR** E9115E red+cream ex-coach pack - *05*	20	NA
(R4255)	**BR** E9144E red+cream ex-coach pack - *06*	20	NA
R4263A	**BR** E9127E maroon - *06-09*	25	32
R4263B	**BR** E9132E maroon - *06-09*	25	32
R4468	**BR** E9193E blue+grey - *11*	40	54

C31e. LNER Gresley 1st Sleeper (2004)

	LNER		
R4174	**LNER** 1208 teak - *04-08*	28	36
R4174A	**LNER** 1149 teak - *05-09*	28	38
R4174B	**LNER** 1317 teak - *10*	28	38
	BR		
R4182	**BR** E1268E red+cream - *04-10*	28	38
R4182A	**BR** E1261E red+cream - *05-09*	28	38
R4264A	**BR** E1235E maroon - *06-09*	28	38
R4264B	**BR** E1237E maroon - *06-10*	28	38

C31f. LNER Gresley Full Brake (2011)

R4530	**LNER** 4067 teak - *11*	33	44
R4530A	**LNER** ? teak - *11*	33	44
R4531	**BR** E70516E maroon - *11*	33	44
R4531A	**BR** ? maroon - *11*	33	44

C32a. LNER Thompson Full 3rd (1970)

R745	**LNER** 1010 teak white rims - *70-75*	8	12

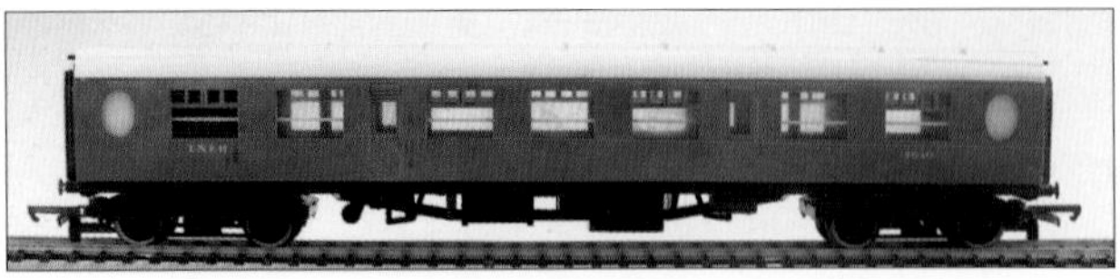

Thompson LNER brown full 3rd coach [C32a]

R937	**LNER** 1010 teak steel rimmed wheels- *76-77*	8	12

C32b. LNER Thompson Brake End (1970)

R746	**LNER** 1870 teak white rims - *70-75*	8	12
R938	**LNER** 1870 teak steel rimmed wheels- *76-77*	8	12
R740	**BR** bright red Breakdown Train Unit (Riding) - *71-73*	20	25

C33a. SR Maunsell Type Composite (1977)

npf = non-paint finish ie: the main body colour is provided by the colour of the plastic.

	SR		
-	**SR** 1384 maroon - *90?*	45	NPG
R431	**SR** 1384 dark green npf - *77-79*	9	11
R441	**SR** 1384 dark green npf - *80-81*	9	11
R441	**SR** 1384 olive green - *84-90*	10	12
R162	**SR** 5544 olive green - *94-97*	10	12
R4059	**SR** 5523 olive green - *98-01*	10	12
R486	**SR** 5117 malachite green - *81-83*	10	12
R424	**SR** 5585 malachite green - *91-93*	10	12
R4009	**SR** 5530 malachite green - *97-98*	10	12
R4009A	**SR** 5540 malachite green - *99-01*	10	12
R4009B	**SR** ???? malachite green - *?*	10	12
R4009C	**SR** 5505 malachite green - *00-02*	10	12
R4009D	**SR** 5512 malachite green - *02-03*	10	12
R4009E	**SR** 5508 malachite green - *04-05*	10	12
R4009G	**SR** 5521 malachite green - *06*	10	12
	BR		
R4269	**BR** S5540S red+cream - *06-07*	18	22
R437	**BR** S5162S green - *85-86*	14	18
R4125A	**BR** S5505S green - *01-02*	14	18
R4125B	**BR** S5520S green - *01-02*	14	18
R4125C	**BR** S5515S green - *03-04*	14	18
R4125D	**BR** S5516S green - *03-06*	14	18
R4125E	**BR** S5511S green - *04-07*	14	18

C33b. SR Maunsell Type Brake End (1977)

npf = non-paint finish ie: the main body colour is provided by the colour of the plastic.

	SR		
-	**SR** 1405 maroon - *90?*	45	NPG
R432	**SR** 1405 dark green npf - *77-79*	9	11
R445	**SR** 1405 dark green npf - *80*	9	11
R445	**SR** 1405 olive green - *84-90*	10	12
R163	**SR** 3562 olive green - *94-97*	10	12
R4058	**SR** 3566 olive green - *98-00*	10	12
R487	**SR** 6564 malachite green - *81-83*	10	12
R425	**SR** 6564 malachite green - *91-93*	10	12

1st series Maunsell brake 3rd in SR malachite green [C33b)

R4008	**SR** 3572 malachite green - *97-98*	10	12
R4008A	**SR** 3570 malachite green - *99-01*	10	12
R4008B	**SR** 3566 malachite green - *99-01*	10	12
R4008C	**SR** 3582 malachite green - *00-02*	10	12
R4008D	**SR** 3563 malachite green - *03*	10	12
R4008E	**SR** 3575 malachite green - *03-05*	10	12
R4008G	**SR** 3576 malachite green - *06*	10	12
	BR		
R4270	**BR** S3573S red+cream - *06-07*	18	22
R438	**BR** S4070S green - *85-86*	14	18
R4124A	**BR** S3579S green - *01*	14	18
R4124B	**BR** S3568S green - *01*	14	18
R4124C	**BR** S3569S green - *03*	14	18
R4124D	**BR** S3577S green - *03-08*	14	18
R4124E	**BR** S3571S green - *04-07*	14	18

C34. SR GBL/PMV Utility/Luggage Van (1958)

Green utility vans were also finished in New Zealand for use there but these were made in the UK.

	SR		
R178	**SR** 2300 malachite-green - *94-96*	12	14
R4057	**SR** 2330 malachite-green - *98-00*	12	14
R4057A	**SR** 2315 malachite-green - *02-04*	10	18
R4057B	**SR** 2299 malachite-green - *04-05*	14	18
R4057C	**SR** 2326 malachite-green - *05-07*	14	19

SR luggage vans [C34]

R174	**SR** 2355 olive-green - *94-96*	12	14
R4056	**SR** 2281 olive-green - *98-00*	12	14
(R2952)	**SR** 2291 olive-green ex-Imperial Airways train pack Ltd Edn 1500 - *10-11*	18	NA
	BR		
R4451	**BR** brown+cream (Churchill's funeral vehicle) - *11*	18	25
R227	**BR** S2357S maroon - *58-61*	12	15
R227	**BR** S2355S maroon - *58-61*	15	18
R226	**BR** S2355S blue-green - *58-61*	12	15
R226	**BR** S2357S blue-green - *58-61*	15	18
R226	**BR** S2355S yellow-green - *62-63*	15	20
R226	**BR** S2357S yellow-green - *67*	15	20
R226	**BR** S2355S electric-blue light grey roof - *68*	20	25
R226	**BR** S2357S electric-blue light grey roof - *68*	20	25
R226	**BR** S2355S rail-blue, dark grey roof - *69-70*	18	22
R4122	**BR** S2390S blue - *00-03*	10	12
R726	**BR** red+green from RS61 set - *64-65*	50	NA

C35a. SR Maunsell Corridor 3rd (2007)

A super-detail model. HW= high windows LW= low windows

	SR Olive Green		
R4297A	**SR** 2349 olive green LW - *07*	20	26
R4297B	**SR** 2350 olive green LW - *07*	20	26
R4297C	**SR** 2354 olive green LW - *08*	20	26
R4297D	**SR** 2355 olive green LW - *08*	20	26
R4297E	**SR** 2361 olive green LW - *08-10*	20	27
(R2813)	**SR** 1225 olive green HW - *09-11*	22	NA
(R2813)	**SR** 1226 olive green HW - *09-11*	22	NA
(R4378)	**SR** 1227 olive green HW - *09-10*	22	NA
	SR Malachite Green		
R4336A	**SR** 1197 green HW - *09-11*	20	27
R4336B	**SR** 1127 green HW - *09*	20	27
R4338C	**SR** 1218 green HW - *09-11*	20	27
	BR Red & Cream		
R4343A	**BR** S1803S red+cream HW - *09-11*	20	27
R4343B	**BR** S838S red+cream HW - *09-11*	20	27
R4343C	**BR** S1130S red+cream HW - *09-11*	20	27
	BR Green		
R4302A	**BR** S1122S green HW- *07*	20	26
R4302B	**BR** S1123S green HW- *07*	20	26
R4302C	**BR** S1186S green HW - *08*	20	26

2nd series Maunsell corridor 3rd in BR green [C35a]

R4302D	**BR** S1121S green HW - *08*	20	26
(R2815)	**BR** S771S green - *09-11*	22	NA
(R4379)	**BR** ? green - *09*	22	NA

C35b. SR Maunsell Corridor 1st (2007)

A super-detail model. HW= high windows LW= low windows

	SR Olive Green		
R4298A	**SR** 7665 olive green LW - *07*	20	26
R4298B	**SR** 7666 olive green LW - *07*	20	26
R4298C	**SR** 7671 olive green LW - *08*	20	26
R4298D	**SR** 7672 olive green LW - *08*	20	26
R4298E	**SR** 7667? olive green LW - *08-09*	20	27
R4298F	**SR** ? olive green LW - *08*	20	27
R4298G	**SR** 7667? olive green LW - *08-10*	20	27
(R4378)	**SR** 7230 olive green HW - *09*	22	NA
	BR Malachite Green		
R4390	**SR** 7211 green LW - *09-11*	20	27
R4390A	**SR** ? green LW - *10-11*	20	27
R4337	**SR** 7411 green HW - *09-11*	20	27
	BR Red & Cream		
R4344A	**BR** S7675S red+cream HW - *09-11*	20	27
R4344B	**BR** S7408S red+cream HW - *09-11*	20	27
R4344C	**BR** S7232S red+cream HW - *11*	20	27
	BR Green		
R4303A	**BR** S7228S green HW- *07*	20	26
R4303B	**BR** S7229S green HW - *07*	20	26
R4303C	**BR** S7406S green HW - *08*	20	26
R4303D	**BR** S7411S green HW - *08*	20	26
R4303E	**BR** S7407S green HW - *08-10*	20	27

C35c. SR Maunsell Composite (2007)

A super-detail model. HW= high windows LW= low windows

	SR Olive Green		
R4299A	**SR** 5138 olive green LW - *07*	20	26
R4299B	**SR** 5141 olive green LW - *07*	20	26
R4299C	**SR** 5146 olive green LW - *08*	20	26
R4299D	**SR** 5150 olive green LW - *08*	20	26
R4299E	**SR** 5137 olive green LW - *08-10*	20	27
	SR Malachite Green		
R4338A	**SR** 5688 green HW - *11*	20	27
R4338B	**SR** 5689 green HW - *11*	20	27

2nd series Maunsell composite in SR malachite green [C35c]

R4338C	**SR** 5686 green HW - *09-11*	20	27
	BR Red & Cream		
R4345A	**BR** S5635S red+cream HW - *09-10*	20	27
R4345B	**BR** S5663S red+cream HW - *09*	20	27
R4345C	**BR** S5676S red+cream HW - *10*	20	27
	BR Green		
R4304A	**BR** S5682S green HW - *07*	20	26
R4304B	**BR** S5683S green HW - *07*	20	26
R4304C	**BR** S5646S green HW - *08*	20	26
R4304D	**BR** S5647S green HW - *08*	20	26
(R2815)	**BR** S5636S green - *09-11*	22	NA
(R4379)	**BR** S5634S green - *09*	22	NA
(R4458)	**BR** S5138S green LW ex-S&D coach pack - *11*	27	NA

R4304A&B have two toilet vents each but R4304C&D have only one.

C35d. SR Maunsell 6-compartment Brake 3rd/2nd (2007)

A super-detail model. HW= high windows LW= low windows

	SR Olive Green		
R4300A	**SR** 4048 olive green LW - *07*	20	26
R4300B	**SR** 4049 olive green LW - *07*	20	26

2nd series Maunsell 6-compartment brake 3rd in SR olive green [35d]

R4300C	**SR** 4050 olive green LW - *08*	20	26
R4300D	**SR** 4051 olive green LW - *08*	20	26
(R2813)	**SR** 3792 olive green HW - *09-11*	22	NA
(R4378)	**SR** 3793 olive green HW - *09*	22	NA
	SR Malachite Green		
R4339A	**SR** 2802 set 239 green HW - *09-11*	20	27
R4339B	**SR** 2803 green HW - *09-11*	20	27
R4339C	**SR** 2803 green HW - *10-11*	20	27
	BR Red & Cream		
R4346A	**BR** S3790S set 242 red+cream HW - *09-11*	20	27
R4346B	**BR** S3791S set 242 red+cream HW - *09-11*	20	27
R4346C	**BR** S2769S set 242 red+cream HW - *09-11*	20	27
	BR Green		
R4305A	**BR** S2796S green HW - *07*	20	26
R4305B	**BR** S2797S green HW - *07*	20	26
R4305C	**BR** S3744S green HW - *08*	20	26
R4305D	**BR** S3745S green HW - *08*	20	26

R4305A&B have two toilet vents each but R4305C&D have only one.

C35e. SR Maunsell 6-compartment Brake Comp. (2008)

A super-detail model. HW= high windows LW= low windows

	SR Olive Green		
R4318A	**SR** 6571 olive green LW- *08*	20	26

R4318B	**SR** 6574 olive green LW - *08*	20	26
R4318C	**SR** ? olive LW green - *08-11*	20	27
(R2952)	**SR** 6583 olive green ex-Imperial Airways train pack Ltd Edn 1500 - *10-11*	25	NA
	SR Malachite Green		
R4341A	**SR** 6592 green HW - *09-11*	20	27
R4341B	**SR** 6593 green HW - *09-11*	20	27
R4341C	**SR** 6596 green HW - *10-11*	20	27
	BR Red & Cream		
R4348A	**BR** S6643S red+cream HW - *09-11*	20	27
R4348B	**BR** S6644S red+cream HW - *09-11*	20	27
R4348C	**BR** S6646S red+cream HW - *10-11*	20	27
	BR Green		
R4320A	**BR** S6600S green HW - *08*	20	26
R4320B	**BR** S6647S green HW - *08*	20	26
R4320C	**BR** S????S green HW - *08-09*	20	27
(R2815)	**BR** S6571S green - *09-11*	22	NA
(R4379)	**BR** ? green - *09*	22	NA
	BR Blue		
(R2891)	plain BR blue, ex-Bluebell Railway 50th Anniversary pack - *09*	20	NA

C35f. SR Maunsell 4-compartment Brake Comp. (2009)

A super-detail model. HW = high windows. LW = low windows.

	SR Olive Green		
R4394A	**SR** 3218 olive green LW - *09-10*	20	27
R4394B	**SR** 3219 olive green LW - *09-11*	20	27
	SR Malachite Green		
R4342A	**SR** 3722 green HW - *09-11*	20	27
R4342B	**SR** 3723 green HW - *09-11*	20	27
	BR Red & Cream		
R4349A	**BR** S3790S red+cream HW - *09-11*	20	27

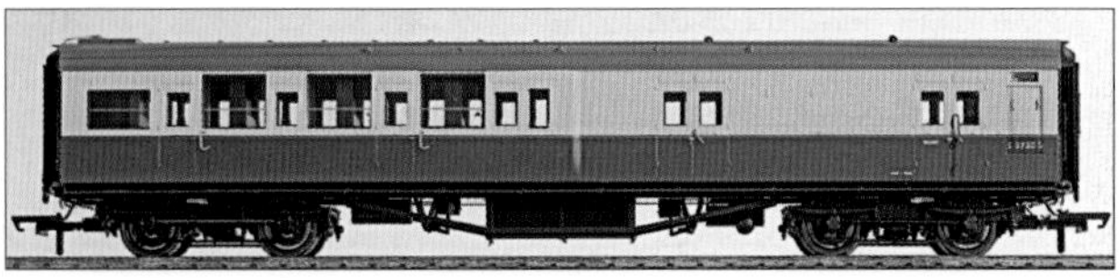

2nd series Maunsell 4-compartment brake composite in BR crimson and cream [C35f]

R4349B	**BR** S3731S red+cream HW - *09-11*	20	27
	BR Green		
R4395A	**BR** S3720S green LW - *09-10*	20	27
R4395B	**BR** S3721S green LW - *09-10*	20	27
(R4458)	**BR** S3214S green LW ex-S&D coach pack - *11*	27	NA
(R4458)	**BR** S?S green LW ex-S&D coach pack - *11*	27	NA
	BR Blue		
(R2891)	**Bluebell** 6575 blue + Sp Edn 1000 (Bluebell) 50th Anniversary ex-train pack - *09*	25	NA

C35g. SR Maunsell Coach Pack (2011)

Following suggestions from the publick that Maunsell coaches should be released as authentic sets, Hornby released their first Maunsell train pack in 2011. HW = high windows. LW = low windows

	BR Green		
R4458	Somerset & Dorset set – composite LW S5138S & 2 x 4-compartment 3rd brake LW S3214S + S?S - *11*	NA	105
R4395B	**BR** S3721S green LW - *09-10*	20	27

C36. SR Maunsell Brake 'Van C' (2007)

A super-detail model. Built as luggage vans with a central guard's compartment they were initially used on milk and parcels trains from 1937. Later they appeared on passenger trains. 250 were built.

	SR Olive Green		
R4301A	**SR** 753 olive green - *07*	16	20
R4301B	**SR** 721 olive green - *07*	16	20
R4301C	**SR** 437 olive green - *08*	16	20
R4301D	**SR** 441 olive green - *08*	16	20
	SR Malachite Green		
R4340A	**SR** 763 green - *09*	20	23
R4340B	**SR** 739 green - *09*	20	23
R4340C	**SR** 772 green - *09-11*	20	23
	BR Red		
R4347A	**BR** S657S dark red - *09*	20	23

Maunsell brake van C in BR red [C36]

R4347B	**BR** S689S dark red - *09*	20	23
R4347C	**BR** S657S dark red - *not made*	NA	NA
R4347C	**BR** S663S dark red - *10*	20	23
	BR Green		
R4306A	**BR** S664S green - *07*	16	20
R4306B	**BR** S652S green - *07*	16	20
R4306C	**BR** S774S green - *08*	16	20
R4306D	**BR** S793S green - *08*	16	20
	BR Blue		
R4467	**BR** S751 blue NAV - *11*	20	26

BR Mk1 Coaching Stock

C37a. BR Mk1 Composite CK (1962)

'Hogwarts Express' coaches made use of the maroon BR Mk1s and were first issued with *Philosopher's Stone* packaging ('PS box') but 'CS Box' refers to *Chamber of Secrets* packaging, 'PA box' refers to *Prisoner of Azkaban* packaging, 'GF box' refers to *Goblet of Fire* packaging 'OP box' to *Order of the Phoenix* packaging *and 'HBP box' to Half Blood Prince packaging.* npf = non-paint finish ie: the main body colour is provided by the colour of the plastic. SS= Silver Seal steel rimmed wheels.

	Bright Red & Yellow		
R626	**BR** 15210 lines npf - *73-75*	8	12
R890	**BR** 15210 no lines * npf - *74*	8	12
R928	**BR** 15210 no lines * SS npf - *76-77*	8	12
R626	**BR** M15210 lines npf - *72*	8	12
R890	**BR** M15210 no lines* npf - *72*	8	12
	Maroon/Red & Cream		
R626	**BR** 15918, 15865 npf - *63-65*	10	14
R727	**BR** 15865 npf - *69-71*	10	14
R730	**BR** 15865 ex-kit npf - *69*	NA	50
R4017	**BR** W15100 ex-R2031 pack - *97*	14	NA
R4018	**BR** W15597 ex-R2031 pack - *97*	14	NA
(R2090)	**BR** W15059 ex-pack - *99*	14	NA
(R2090)	**BR** W15064 ex-pack - *99*	14	NA
(R2133M)	**BR** W15583 ex-pack -*99*	14	NA
(R2133M)	**BR** W15584 ex-pack - *99*	14	NA
R445	**BR** E15769 - *96-97*	12	16
R4068	**BR** E15695 - *98-99*	12	16
X3843	**BR** E15406 ex-R2089 pack - *99*	14	NA
X3842	**BR** E15400 ex-R2089 pack - *99*	14	NA
R4206	**BR** E15331 - *04*	12	16
R4206A	**BR** E15513 - *05-06*	12	16
R4206B	**BR** E15282 - *06-08*	12	16
R4256	**BR** S15042 - *06-08*	12	16

BR Mk1 composite coach in maroon and cream [C37a]

	Green		
R622	**SR** 5015 yellow-green grey roof npf - *69-70*	14	16
R622	**SR** 5015 yellow-green white roof npf - *71*	14	16
R622	**SR** 5015 dark green npf - *74*	10	12
R933	**SR** 5015 dark green SS npf - *76-77*	10	12
R933	**SR** 5740 dark green SS npf - *76-77*	10	12
R622	**BR** S15873 npf - *63-69*	10	14
R4007	**BR** S15042 - *97-98*	12	16
R4115	**BR** S15021 - *00-01*	12	16
R4115A	**BR** S15035 - *02-03*	12	16

R4115B	**BR** S15049 - *04-05*	12	16
R4115C	**BR** S15907 - *04-07*	12	16
R4115D	**BR** S15872 - *07-09*	12	22
X3730	**BR** S15043 rake 885 ex-R2082 pack *-98*	14	NA
(R2194)	**BR** S15915 ex-pack - *01*	14	NA
(R2194)	**BR** S15567 ex-pack - *01*	14	NA
(R4140)	**BR** S15568 ex-coach pack - *01*	14	NA

Dark Brown & Cream

R743	**GWR** 5015 npf - *69-71, 74-75*	10	12
R931	**GWR** 5015 SS npf - *76-77*	10	12
R438	**BR** W15533 - *96-97*	12	16
R848	**BR** W15861 ex-R826 set - *96-98*	14	NA
R858	**BR** W15771 ex-R826 set - *96-98*	14	NA
R4051	**BR** W15542 - *98-99*	12	16
R4089	**BR** W15425 ex-R2077 pack - *98*	14	NA
R4090	**BR** W15428 ex-R2077 pack - *98*	14	NA
(R2166)	**BR** W15584 ex-pack - *00*	14	NA
(R2166)	**BR** W15583 ex-pack - *00*	14	NA
(R2364M)	**BR** W15059 ex-pack - *00*	14	NA

BR (WR) Mk1 composite coach in chocolate and cream [C37a]

(R2364M)	**BR** W15063 ex-pack - *00*	14	NA
R4209	**BR** W15334 - *04*	12	16
R4209A	**BR** W15098 - *05-06*	12	16
R4209B	**BR** W15066 - *07-09*	12	22
(R2432)	**BR** W15128 ex-'Cathedrals Express' pack Sp Edn 1000 (Hereford Models) - *04*	14	NA
(R2432)	**BR** W15129 ex-'Cathedrals Express' pack Sp Edn 1000 (Hereford Models) - *04*	14	NA
(R2986)	**BR** W15060? The Royal Duchy coach boards ex-'A Date with the Duchy' train pack - *11*	14	NA
(R2986)	as above but numbered W15062? - *11*	14	NA

Maroon

R422	**LMS** 2257 3rd npf - *69-75*	8	12
R935	**LMS** 2257 3rd npf SS - *76-77*	8	12
R422	**BR** 15918 npf - *62-69*	8	12
R382	**BR** 15917, 15918, 15863, 15865 kit of 2 npf - *62-66*	NA	80
R4092	**BR** M15350 ex-R2078 pack - *98*	14	NA
R4093	**BR** M15443 ex-R2078 pack - *98*	14	NA
X3849	**BR** M15050 ex-R2112 pack - *99*	14	NA
X3850	**BR** M15181 ex-R2112 pack - *99*	14	NA
(R2176M)	**BR** M15287 ex-pack - *00*	14	NA
R4133A	**BR** M15311 - *01-02*	12	16
R4133B	**BR** M15824 - *02-03*	12	16
R4133C	**BR** M15821 - *04-05*	12	16
R4201	**BR** M15625 W - *04-05*	14	18
R4201A	**BR** M16101 W - *05-07*	14	18
(R2306)	**BR** M15993 ex-train pack - *03-04*	14	NA
(R2306)	**BR** M15986 ex-train pack - *03-04*	14	NA
(R4177)	**BR** M16005 ex-coach pack - *03*	14	NA
(R2329M)	**BR** M15987 W ex-pack - *03*	16	NA
(R2329M)	**BR** M15917 W ex-pack - *03*	16	NA
(R2436)	**BR** M16006 ex-'The Pines Express' pack - *05*	14	NA
(R2436)	**BR** M16007 ex-'The Pines Express' pack - *05*	14	NA
(R4229)	**BR** M16109 ex-'The Pines Express' coach pack - *05*	14	NA
R4005	**BR** E15692 - *97-99*	12	16
R4019	**BR** E15700 ex-R2032 pack - *97*	14	NA
R4020	**BR** E15770 ex-R2032 pack - *97*	14	NA
(R1007)	**BR** E15398 ex-set - *97?*	14	NA
(R1021M)	**BR** E15399 ex-set - *99*	14	NA
(R1021M)	**BR** E15398 ex-set - *99*	14	NA
(R2195)	**BR** E16008 Marylebone Rugby Sheffield Sp Edn 1500 - *01*	14	NA
(R2195)	**BR** E16009 Marylebone Rugby Sheffield Sp Edn 1500 - *01*	14	NA
(R2569)	**BR** E15692 ex-'The Talisman' train-pack - *06-07*	14	NA
(R2569)	**BR** E15693 ex-'The Talisman' train-pack - *06-07*	14	NA
(R4252)	**BR** E156?? ex-'The Talisman' coach-pack - *06-07*	14	NA
(R4252)	**BR** E156?? ex-'The Talisman' coach-pack - *06-07*	14	NA
X5914	**BR** E15133 ex- 'Norfolkman' train-pack - *07*	14	NA
X5915	**BR** E15134 ex- 'Norfolkman' train-pack - *07*	14	NA
(R3059)	**BR** E15452 ex-'Tornado Express' train pack - *11*	14	NA
(R3059)	**BR** E15667 ex-'Tornado Express' train pack - *11*	14	NA

Maroon - Hogwarts **

R4148A	99716 in PS box - *02*	12	17
R4175A	as above but CS box - *03*	12	18
R4219A	as above but PA box - *04*	12	18
R4238A	as above but GF box - *05-06*	12	18

Hogwarts Mk1 maroon composite coach [C37a]

R4308A	as above but OP box - *08*	12	20
R4391A	as above but HBP box - *10*	13	20
R4148B	99718 in PS box - *02*	12	18
R4175B	as above but CS box - *03*	12	18
R4219B	as above but PA box - *04*	12	18
R4238B	as above but GF box - *05-06*	12	18
R4308	as above but OP box - *07*	12	18
R4308B	as above but OP box - *08*	12	18
R4391B	as above but HBP box - 10	13	20

Blue & Grey

R727	**BR** 15865 electric blue npf - *65-68*	14	18
R730	**BR** 15865 electric blue ex-kit npf - *67-68*	NA	50
R4110	**BR** W15599 - *00-01*	12	16
R4110A	**BR** W16201 - *02-04*	12	16
R4110B	**BR** W16220 - *05-07*	12	16

*Mail order models had no black line above and below window band. ** The Hornby 'Hogwarts Express' train set was also sold in Germany by Marklin and so unboxed examples found there may be from that set.

C37b. BR Mk1 Brake BSK (1962)

'Hogwarts Express' coaches made use of the maroon BR Mk1s and were first issued with *Philosopher's Stone* packaging ('PS box') but 'CS Box' refers to *Chamber of Secrets* packaging, 'PA box' refers to *Prisoner of Azkaban* packaging, 'GF box' refers to *Goblet of Fire* packaging and 'OP box' to *Order of the Phoenix* packaging. npf = non-paint finish ie: the main body colour is provided by the colour of the plastic. SS= Silver Seal steel rimmed wheels.

Bright Red & Yellow

R891	**BR** 34100 no lines * npf - *74*	7	11
R627	**BR** 34100 no lines * npf - *73-75*	7	11
R929	**BR** 34100 lines SS npf - *76-77*	7	11
R891	**BR** M34100 no lines* npf - *72*	7	11

Maroon/Red & Cream

R627	**BR** 35115, 35024 npf - *63-65*	9	13
R4022	**BR** W34154 ex-R2031 pack - *97*	13	NA
(R2090)	**BR** W34302 ex-pack - *99*	13	NA
(R2133M)	**BR** W34301 ex-pack - *99*	13	NA
R450	**BR** E34600 - *96-97*	11	15
R4069	**BR** E34010 - *98-99*	11	15
X3844	**BR** E34232 ex-R2089 pack - *99*	13	NA
R4205	**BR** E34412 - *04*	11	15
R4205A	**BR** E34166 - *05-08*	11	20
R4257	**BR** S34269 - *06-09*	11	20

Green

R623	**SR** 4351 yellow-green grey roof npf - *69-70*	12	15
R623	**SR** 4351 yell-green white roof npf - *71*	12	15
R623	**SR** 4351 dark green npf - *74*	9	11
R934	**SR** 4351 dark green SS npf - *76-77*	9	11

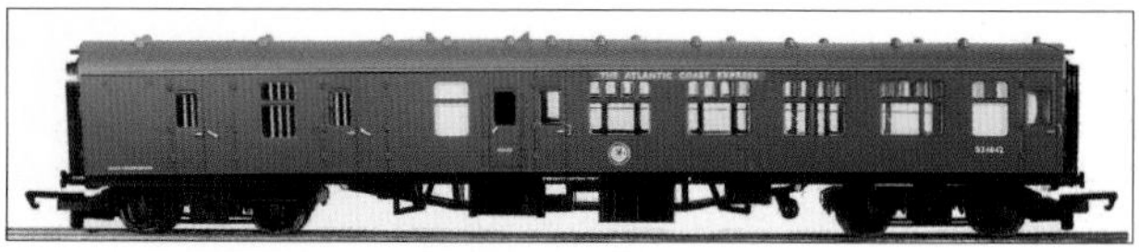

BR (SR) Mk1 brake 2nd from the Atlantic Coast Express set [C37b]

R623	**BR** S34936 npf - *63-69*	9	11
R4006	**BR** S34269 - *97-98*	11	15
R4114	**BR** S34284 - *00-02*	11	15

R4114A	**BR** S34158 - *03-04*	11	15
R4114B	**BR** S34248 - *04-06*	11	15
R4114C	**BR** S34632 - *07-09*	11	20
X3729	**BR** S34271 rake 885 ex-R2082 pack - *98*	13	NA
X3728	**BR** S34272 rake 885 ex-R2082 pack - *98*	13	NA
(R2194)	**BR** S34641 ex-pack - *01*	13	NA
(R4140)	**BR** S34642 ex-coach pack - *01*	13	NA
	Dark Brown & Cream		
R744	**GWR** 5104 npf - *69-71, 74-75*	9	11
R932	**GWR** 5104 SS npf - *76-77*	9	11
R437	**BR** W34149 - *96-97*	11	15
R850	**BR** W34154 ex-R826 set - *96-98*	13	NA
R4050	**BR** W34151 - *98-99*	11	15
R4091	**BR** W34300 ex-R2077 pack - *98*	13	NA
(R2166)	**BR** W34315 ex-pack - *00*	13	NA
(R2364M)	**BR** W34312 ex-pack - *00*	13	NA
R4208	**BR** W34800 - *04*	11	15
R4208A	**BR** W34303 - *05-08*	11	20
(R2432)	**BR** W34292 ex-'Cathedrals Express' pack Sp Edn 1000 (Hereford Models) - *04*	15	NA
(R2986)	**BR** W34249? The Royal Duchy coach boards ex-'A Date with the Duchy' train pack - *11*	14	NA
	Maroon		
R423	**LMS** 5051 npf - *69-75*	7	11
R936	**LMS** 5051 SS npf - *76-77*	7	11
R423	**BR** 35115 npf - *62-69*	9	13
R383	**BR** 35115, 35116, 35024, 35025 kit of 2 npf - *62-66*	NA	80

BR Mk1 maroon corridor brake 3rd [C37b]

R4094W	**BR** M34100 ex-R2078 - *98*	13	NA
X3851	**BR** M34389 ex-R2112 - *99*	13	NA
(R2176M)	**BR** M34285 ex-pack - *00*	13	NA
(R2176M)	**BR** M34358 ex-pack - *00*	13	NA
R4132A	**BR** M34288 - *01-02*	11	15
R4132B	**BR** M34106 - *02-04*	11	15
(R2306)	**BR** M35099 ex-train pack - *03-04*	13	NA
(R4177)	**BR** M35110 ex-coach pack - *03*	13	NA
(R2329M)	**BR** M34286 W ex-pack - *03*	15	NA
R4200	**BR** M34399 W - *04-05*	13	17
R4200A	**BR** M35114 W - *05-09*	13	20
R4200B	**BR** M34399 W - *08*	13	20
(R2436)	**BR** M34706 ex-'The Pines Express' pack - *05*	13	NA
(R4229)	**BR** M34370 ex-'The Pines Express' coach pack 'Sheffield-Bournemouth' - *05*	13	NA
(R4229)	**BR** M34363 ex-'The Pines Express' coach pack 'Liverpool-Bournemouth' - *05*	13	NA
(R2195)	**BR** E34413 'Marylebone Rugby Sheffield' Sp Edn 1500 - *01*	13	NA
R4004	**BR** E34007 - *97-99*	11	15
R4021	**BR** E34225 ex-R2032 - *97*	13	NA
(R1007)	**BR** E34160 ex-set - *97?*	13	NA
(R2569)	**BR** E35162 ex-'The Talisman' train pack - *06-07*	13	NA
(R4252)	**BR** E156?? ex-'The Talisman' coach pack - *06-07*	13	NA
X5916	**BR** E34226 ex-'Norfolkman' train pack - *07*	13	NA
(R3059)	**BR** E34393? ex-'Tornado Express' train pack - *11*	14	NA
	Maroon - Hogwarts **		
X?	99723 ex-various Harry Potter sets - *01-05*	11	NA
R4149A	99723 in PS box - *02*	11	17
R4176A	as above but CS box - *03*	11	17
R4220A	as above but PA box - *04*	11	17
R4239A	as above but GF box - *05-06*	11	17
R4309A	as above but OP box - *08*	11	17
R4392A	as above but HBP box - *10*	11	18
R4149B	99312 in PS box - *02*	11	17
R4176B	as above but CS box - *03*	11	17
R4239B	as above but GF box - *05-06*	11	17
R4309A	as above but OP box - *07*	11	17
R4309B	as above but OP box - *07*	11	17
R4309B	as above but OP box - *08*	11	17
R4392B	as above but HBP box - *10*	11	18
	Blue & Grey		
R4109	**BR** W34809 - *00-01*	9	13
R4109A	**BR** W34917 - *02-06*	9	13

BR Mk1 corridor brake 3rd in blue and grey livery [C37b]

R4109B	**BR** W34812 - *03-09*	9	13
R728	**BR** 35024 electric blue npf - *65-68*	13	17
R731	**BR** 35024 electric blue ex-kit npf - *67-68*	NA	50
R728	**BR** 35024 npf - *69-71*	9	13
R731	**BR** 35024 ex-kit npf - *69*	NA	50
	Blue & White		
(R4310)	**Pullman** ? blue+white ex-coach pack - *07*	22	NA

* Mail order models had no black line above and below window band. ** The Hornby 'Hogwarts Express' train set was also sold in Germany by Marklin and so unboxed examples found there may be from that set.

C37c. BR Mk1 Buffet (1962)

npf = non-paint finish ie: the main body colour is provided by the colour of the plastic. rwe = raised window frames (from 1974 onwards) unpainted (mail order). chrm = chrome raised window frames. alum = aluminium raised window frames. SS = Silver Seal (metal rimmed) wheels.

	Bright Red & Yellow		
R628	**BR** 1805 line npf - *72-74*	7	11
R892	**BR** 1805 no line * npf - *74*	7	11
	Maroon/Red & Cream		
R628	**BR** 1825 npf - *63-65*	9	13

	Green		
R624	**BR** S1851 npf - *63-67*	9	13
R4072	**BR** S1849 - *98-99*	11	15
R4117	**BR** S1852 - *00-01*	11	15
R4117A	**BR** S1850 - *02-03*	11	15
R4117B	**BR** S1857 - *04-06*	11	15
R4117C	**BR** S1851 - *06-08*	11	19
(R4140)	**BR** S1850 ex-coach pack - *01*	13	NA
	Dark Brown & Cream		
R455	**BR** W1814 - *96-97*	11	15
R4052	**BR** W1816 - *98-99*	11	15
R4211	**BR** W1813 - *04-06*	11	15
R4211A	**BR** W1815 - *05-09*	11	19
	Maroon		
R424	**BR** 1807 npf - *62-67*	10	14
R384	**BR** 1805, 1807, 1823, 1825 kit of 2 npf - *62-65*	NA	80
R4203	**BR** M1817 W - *04*	13	17
R4203A	**BR** M1820 W - *05-09*	13	17
R441	**BR** E1821 - *96-97*	11	15
R4067	**BR** E1853 - *98-99*	11	15
	Blue & Grey		
R4112	**BR** W1846 - *00-02*	11	15
R4112A	**BR** W1849 - *00-02*	11	15
R729	**BR** 1825 electric blue npf - *67-68*	13	17
R732	**BR** 1825 electric blue ex-kit npf - *67-68*	NA	50
R729	**BR** 1825 npf - *69-71*	9	13
R732	**BR** 1825 ex-kit npf - *69*	NA	50
R844	**BR** 1805 npf chrm - *74-75*	9	13
R897	**BR** 1805 npf rwe * - *74*	9	13
R897	**BR** 1807 npf rwe - *74?*	9	13
R923	**BR** 1805 npf chrm SS - *76-78*	9	13
R923	**BR** 1805 npf alum - *79*	9	13
R419	**BR** 1805 paint finish - *80-82*	9	13
	Blue		
(R4310)	**BR** 1657 ex-Blue Pullman coach pack - *07-08*	22	NA
	Grey & Beige		
R4138A	**BR IC (Anglia)** 1850 - *01-03*	13	16

BR Mk1 buffet car in 'Blue Pullman' livery [C37c]

*Mail order models had no black line above and below window band.

C37d. BR Mk1 Sleeping Car (1961)

npf = non-paint finish ie: the main body colour is provided by the colour of the plastic. chrome = chrome raised window frames. alum = aluminium raised window frames.

	Maroon		
R339	**BR** 2510 npf - *61-67*	10	14
R381	**BR** 2510, 2511 kit of 2 npf - *62-65*	NA	80
R339	**BR** 80658 npf - *61-67*	10	14
R433	**BR** W2105 - *96-97*	12	16

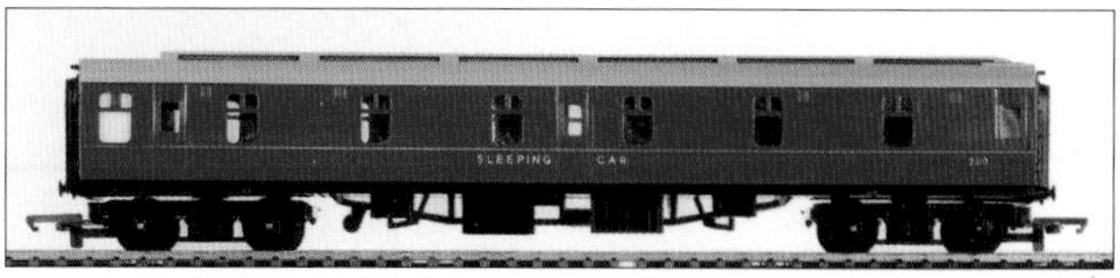

BR Mk1 sleeping car in BR maroon (as released in 1961) [C37d]

R4049	**BR** W2005 - *98-99*	12	16
R4210	**BR** W2104 - *04-05*	12	16
R4210A	**BR** W2127 - *05-07*	12	16
R4134A	**BR** M2003 - *01-02*	12	16
R4134B	**BR** M2064 - *02-04*	12	16
R4202	**BR** M2008 W - *04*	14	18
R4202A	**BR** M2020 W - *05-09*	14	20
R461	**BR** E2510 - *96-97*	12	16
R4070	**BR** E2121 - *98-99*	12	16
	Blue & Grey		
R339	**BR** 2510 electric blue npf - *68*	12	16
R339	**BR** 2510 npf - *69-72*	10	14
R339	**BR** 2510 rail chrome npf - *74-75*	10	14
R924	**BR I-C** 2510 chrome npf - *76-78*	10	14
R924	**BR I-C** 2510 alum npf - *79*	10	14
R420	**BR I-C** 2510 paint finish alum - *80-82*	10	14
R4113	**BR** W2574 - *00-02*	12	15

C37e. BR Mk1 Full Parcels Brake (1962)

npf = non-paint finish ie: the main body colour is provided by the colour of the plastic.

	Maroon/Red & Cream		
R440	**BR** E80533 - *96-97*	12	16
R4073	**BR** E80535 - *98-99*	12	16

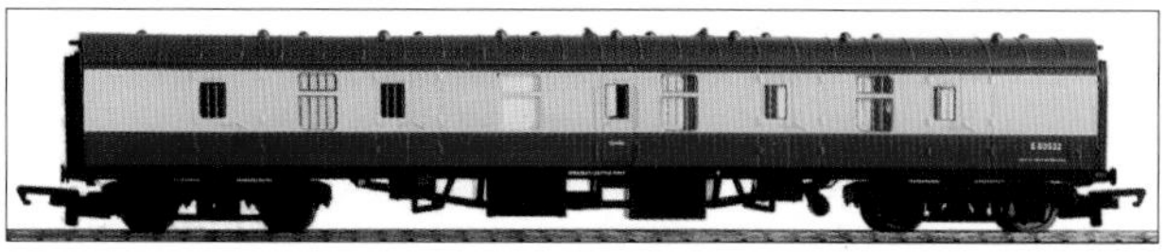

BR Mk1 full brake in maroon and cream [C37e]

R4207	**BR** E80532 - *04-05*	12	16
R4207A	**BR** E80617 - *05-09*	12	20
	Green		
R4071	**BR** S81510 - *98-99*	12	16
R4116	**BR** S81542 - *00-02*	12	16
R4116A	**BR** S81292 green - *03-05*	12	16
R4116B	**BR** S81542 green - *06-09*	12	20
	Dark Brown & Cream		
R436	**BR** W81021 - *96-97*	12	16
R4053	**BR** W81259 - *98-99*	12	16
R4212	**BR** W80705 - *04-07*	12	16
R4212A	**BR** W81206 - *05-07*	12	16
	Maroon		
R425	**BR** 80531, 80657 npf - *62-67*	10	14
R387	**BR** 80531, 80532, 80657, 80658 CKD kit of 2 npf - *62-65*	NA	80

R4204	**BR** M80532 W - *04*	14	18
R4204A	**BR** M80855 W - *05-08*	14	18
(R1007)	**BR** E80617 ex-set - *97?*	14	NA

Blue & Grey

R4111	**BR** W80660 - *00-03*	12	16
R4111A	**BR** W80650 - *03*	12	16
R425	**BR** 80657 electric blue npf - *68*	14	18
R425	**BR** 80657 npf - *69-71*	10	14

C38. BR Standard GUV (ex-Lima) (2007)

R6354	**BR IC** 94312 grey 'Motorail' - *07-10*	15	19

BR Standard gangwayed utility van in RES livery [C38]

R6355	**RES** 94138 red+black Royal Mail NKA - *07-10*	15	19

BR Mk2 Coaching Stock

C39a. BR Mk2 TSO Open Coach (1968)

npf = non-paint finish ie: the main body colour is provided by the colour of the plastic. MO = mail order. chrome = chrome window frames. alum = aluminium window frames. plain = plain window frames. SS = Silver Seal (metal rimmed) wheels.

Blue & Grey

R722	**BR** M5120 interior lights npf - *68-72*	15	18
R722	**BR** M5121 interior lights npf - *?*	18	20
R724	**BR** M5120 IC chrome npf - *73-75*	10	14

BR Mk2 tourist open coach in blue and grey [C39a]

R895	**BR** M5120 IC plain MO npf - *74*	10	14
R921	**BR** M5120 IC chrome SS npf - *76-78*	10	14
R968	**BR** M? IC plain MO npf - *c78*	10	14
R921	**BR** M5120 IC alum SS npf - *79*	10	14
R417	**BR** M5232 IC alum SS - *80-83*	10	14
R417	**BR** M5108 IC alum SS - *80-83*	10	14
X3299	**BR** E5305 ex-R089 'Flying Scotsman' coach pack - *95-96*	25	40
X3296	**BR** E5293 ex-R089 'Flying Scotsman' coach pack - *95-96*	25	40

Miscellaneous Liveries

R432	**Regional Railways** 5267 - *96-97*	15	20
R428	**Regional Railways** 5221 ScotRail - *96*	16	22
R395	**Regional Railways** 5157 ScotRail - *96*	16	22
R439	**NSE** 5381 bright blue - *87-91*	15	20
R4153	**NSE** 5261 blue W - *04*	18	24
R4153A	**NSE** 5265 blue W - *05-09*	18	24
(R2308M)	**Wessex Trains** 5239 *The Red Knight* dark brown + cream ex R2308M 'Excalibur Express' Sp Edn 1500 MO pack - *04*	22	NA
(R2308M)	**Wessex Trains** 5229 *The Green Knight* dark brown + cream ex R2308M 'Excalibur Express' Sp Edn 1500 MO pack - *04*	22	NA
(R2437)	**Serco** RDB977470 grey+red ex R2437 pack - *05-07*	20	NA
(R1093)	**Pullman** 3313 blue+white ex-set - *07-08*	22	NA
(R1093)	**Pullman** 3352 blue+white ex-set - *07-08*	22	NA
(R4310)	**Pullman** 3326 blue+white ex-coach pack - *07-08*	22	NA
(R4310)	**Pullman** 3431 blue+white ex-coach pack - *07-08*	22	NA
R720	**CIE** orange+black SS - *76*	35	45

C39b. BR Mk2 BFK Brake (1968)

npf = non-paint finish ie: the main body colour is provided by the colour of the plastic. MO = mail order. chrome = chrome window frames. alum = aluminium window frames. SS = Silver Seal (metal rimmed) wheels.

Blue & Grey

R969	**BR** W5449 IC plain frames MO npf - *c78*	9	13
R723	**BR** M14052 brake 1st npf with lights - *68-72*	15	18
R726	**BR** M14052 IC chrome frames npf - *73-75*	9	13
R896	**BR** M14052 IC plain frames MO npf - *74*	9	13
R922	**BR** M14052 IC chrome npf SS - *76-78*	9	13
R929	**BR** M14052 IC chrome npf SS - *76-78*	9	13
R969	**BR** M9439 IC plain frames MO npf SS - *c78*	9	13
R922	**BR** M14052 IC alum paint npf SS - *79*	9	13
R418	**BR** M9439 IC alum paint frames SS - *80-83*	9	13
X3297	**BR** E14090 blue+grey ex-R089 'Flying Scotsman' coach pack - *95-96*	25	40

Deep Purple

R459	**Royal Train** 2905 sleeper/power car - *84-85*	15	25
X4981	**Royal Train** 2905? sleeper/power car ex-MO R1057 set - *08*	20	NA

Royal train household couchett [C39b]

(R1045)	**Royal Train** 2921 Royal Household couchette ex-R1045 M&S set Sp Edn + R2370 train pack - *03-04*	20	NA
(R4197)	**Royal Train** 2920 Royal Household couchette ex-R4197 coach pack - *04*	20	NA

Miscellaneous Liveries

R098	**QPV** ADB975468 yellow breakdown crew coach - *87-90*	20	24
R431	**Regional Railways** 17118 1st - *96-97*	15	20
R435	**ScotRail** 17099 brake 1st - *96*	16	22
R444	**NSE** 17086 bright blue brake 1st - *87-90*	15	20
R4154	**NSE** 17057 blue W - *04-06*	18	24
R4154A	**NSE** 17058 blue W - *06-09*	18	24
(R2308M)	**Wessex Trains** 9391 *Pendragon* dark brown + cream ex-R2308M 'Excalibur Express' Sp Edn 1500 MO pack - *04*	22	NA
(R2437)	**Serco** DB977338 grey+red ex R2437 pack - *05-07*	20	NA
(R1093)	**Pullman** 9513 blue+white ex-set - *07-08*	22	NA
R721	**CIE** orange+black SS - *76*	35	45

C40a. BR Mk2d TSO Coach (ex-Airfix) (1998)

This has 8 windows each side. These are made from Airfix tooling purchased from Dapol in 1996.

Blue & Grey

R4216	**BR** W5619 - *04*	14	18
R4216A	**BR** W5627 - *05-07*	14	18

Dark Grey & Beige

R4463	**BR** IC Executive 5430 - *11*	20	27

Red & Black

R4086	**Virgin** 5744 - *98*	12	15
(R1022)	**Virgin** 6165 ex-set - *99*	14	NA
R4086A	**Virgin** 6149 - *99-01*	12	15
R4086B	**Virgin** 6059 [E] - *02*	12	15

Ex-BR Mk2d tourist open coach in Virgin Trains livery [C40a]

R4086C	**Virgin** 5948 [E] - *03*	12	15
R4086D	**Virgin** 5955 [E] - *04*	12	15
R4086E	**Virgin** 5932 [F] - *05-06*	12	15
R4086F	**Virgin** ? [?] - *made?*	NPG	NPG

R4086G	**Virgin** 6180 [E] - *07-08*	12	15
R4086H	**Virgin** 6063 [E] - *08-10*	12	20
	Light Blue		
R4136	**Anglia** 5874 high density - *?*	12	17
R4136A	**Anglia** 6800 high density - *01*	12	17
R4136B	**Anglia** 5836 high density - *02-04*	12	17
	Green & Yellow ('Fag Packet')		
R4225	**FGW** 6202 open class - *05*	14	18
R4225A	**FGW** 6219 open class - *06*	14	18
R4225B	**FGW** 6212 open class - *07-08*	14	18
	Brown & Cream		
(R1065)	'**Northern Belle**' 3174 *Glamis* ex-MO set - *05*	22	NA
(R1065)	'**Northern Belle**' 3182 *Warwick* ex-MO set - *05*	22	NA
	Pullman Dark Brown & Cream		
(R2979)	**West Coast Railway** *Bassenthwaite* ex-'West Coast Railway Pullman' train set - *11*	22	NA
(R2979)	as above but named *Buttermere* - *11*	22	NA
(R2979)	as above but named *Rydal Water* - *11*	22	NA
-	**West Coast Railway** *Crummock Water*	22	NA
-	as above but named *Grasmere*	22	NA
-	as above but named *Ennerdale Water*	22	NA
R?	above three coaches in the 'West Coast Railway Pullman' coach pack - *11*	NA	NPG

C40b. BR Mk2d FO Coach (ex-Airfix) (1998)

This has 7 windows each side. These are made from Airfix tooling purchased from Dapol in 1996.

	Blue & Grey		
R4215	**BR** W3172 - *04-05*	13	17
R4215A	**BR** W3239 - *06-08*	13	27
	Dark Grey & Beige		
R4462	**BR** IC Executive 3186 - *11*	20	27
	Red & Black		
R4088	**Virgin** 3293 - *98-01*	11	14
R4088A	**Virgin** 3345 - *99-01*	11	14
R4088B	**Virgin** 3397 [C] - *not made*	NA	NA
R4088B	**Virgin** 3350 [D] - *02-03*	11	14
R4088B	**Virgin** 3345 [D] - *not made*	NA	NA
R4088C	**Virgin** 3382 [F] - *03*	11	14
R4088D	**Virgin** 3362 [D] - *04*	11	14
R4088E	**Virgin** 3363 [D] - *04-07*	11	14
	Light Blue		
R4137	**Anglia** 3375 - *?*	12	17
R4137A	**Anglia** 3368 - *01*	12	17
R4137B	**Anglia** 3358 - *02-03*	12	17
R4137C	**Anglia** 3290 [K] - *03-05*	12	17
	Green & Yellow ('Fag Packet')		
R4224	**FGW** 5632 - *05*	14	18
R4224A	**FGW** 5636 - *06-07*	14	18

C40c. BR Mk2d BSO Brake (ex-Airfix) (1998)

These are made from Airfix tooling purchased from Dapol in 1996.

	Dark Grey & Beige		
R4464	**BR** IC Executive 9479 - *11*	20	27
	Red & Black		
R4087	**Virgin** 9496 - *98*	11	14
R4087A	**Virgin** 9523 - *99-00*	11	14
R4087B	**Virgin** 9538 [A] - *02*	11	14
R4087C	**Virgin** 9525 [A] - *03*	11	14
R4087D	**Virgin** 9513 [A] - *04*	11	14
R4087E	**Virgin** 9537 [A] - *05-06*	11	14
(R1022)	**Virgin** 9531 ex-set - *99*	14	NA

Ex-BR Mk2d brake car of the 'Northern Belle' [C40c]

R4087F	**Virgin** ? [?] - *made?*	NPG	NPG
R4087G	**Virgin** 9527 [A] - *07-10*	11	20
R4087H	**Virgin** 9526 [A] - *08-10*	11	24
	Green & Yellow ('Fag Packet')		
R4240	**FGW** 9481 - *05-10*	14	24

(R1065)	'**Northern Belle**' Car No.17167 brown+cream ex-MO set - *05*	22	NA

BR Mk3 Coaching Stock

C41a. BR Mk3 Open (7 windows) (1977)

Window strip with raised window frames was printed with the window surrounds. *A sheet of number transfers was provided.

R439	**I-C** * blue+grey Mk2 bogies 2nd - *77-79*	8	12
R439	**I-C** * blue+grey 2nd - *78-79*	8	12
R428	**I-C** * blue+grey 1st - *79*	8	12
R426	**I-C** * blue+grey 2nd - *80-85*	8	12
R425	**I-C** * blue+grey 1st - *80-84*	8	12
R489	**I-C 125** 42251 stone/grey 2nd - *84*	10	14
R488	**I-C 125** 41121 stone/grey 1st - *84*	10	14
R743	XPT trailer silver - *83*	15	NA

*These contained six pairs of numbers on a sheet. For 2nd class HST stock there were W42003, W42004 and W42005 and for loco hauled stock there were M12004, M12005 and M12006. For 1st class HST stock there were W41003, W41004 and W41005 and for loco hauled stock there were M11007, M11008 and M11009.

C41b. BR Mk3 Queen's Saloon (1984)

This was the same as the Mk3 tourist open coach (below) but had double doors at one end of each side.

R451	**Royal Train** 2903 deep purple - *84-85*	10	20

C41c. BR Mk3 Tourist Open (8 windows) (1984)

The window strip was a clear plastic strip, without raised window frames, onto which window surrounds were printed.

R432	**I-C** * blue+grey - *85-88*	8	12
R434	**I-C 125** 42251 beige+grey - *85-87*	8	12
R434	as above but beige and dark grey	8	12
R420	**IC** 42+++ choice of 42191, 42192 or 42193 beige+grey/black - *88-91*	8	12
R704	**IC** 42+++ choice of 42191, 42192, 42193, 42197, 42220 beige+grey/black - *90-98*	8	12

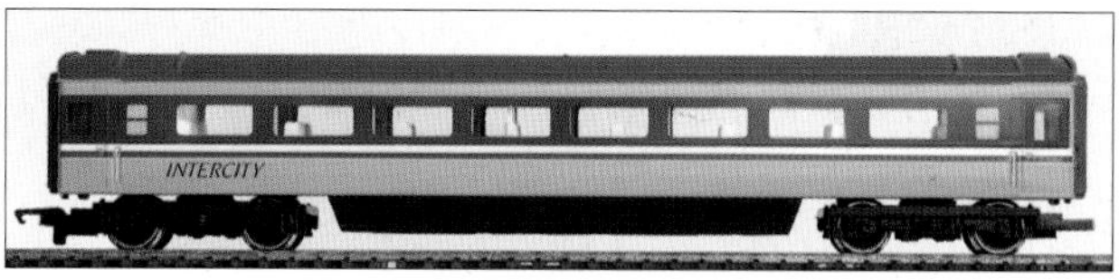

Early model of BR Mk3 tourist class open InterCity livery [C41c]

X3397	**IC** 42220 ex-R897 set -*96*	10	NA
X3394	**IC** 42230 ex-R897 set - *96*	10	NA
X3407	**IC** 42090 ex-R901 set - *96-97*	10	NA
X3412	**IC** 42095 ex-R901 set - *96-97*	10	NA
R454	**Hoverspeed** blue+red - *86-87*	16	20
R426	**Dept M&EE** ADB975814 red+blue Test Coach 10- *91-92*	16	20
R896	**ScotRail** 12030 blue - *88-89*	14	17
X3552	**GNER** 42191 navy blue ex-R2000 set - *97-98*	12	12
X3553	**GNER** 42192 navy blue ex-R2000 set - *97-98*	12	12
R4011	**GNER** 42158 navy blue - *97*	8	10
R4078	**GNER** 42092 [F] navy blue - *98*	10	15
X3604	**Virgin** 42090 [E] red+black ex-R2045 pack - *97*	12	NA
X3605	**Virgin** 42103 [F] red+black ex-R2045 pack - *97*	12	NA
R4081	**Virgin** 42116 [D] - *98*	9	15
X3605	**MM** 42121 [B] jade ex-R2046 pack *97*	12	NA
X3604	**MM** 42120 [C] jade ex-R2046 pack -*97*	12	NA
R4084	**MM** 42119 [D] jade green - *98*	9	15

* A sheet of number transfers was provided. For 2nd class HST stock there were W42003, W42004 and W42005 and for loco hauled stock there were M12004, M12005 and M12006.

C41d. BR Mk3 1st Open (8 windows) (1984)

The window strip was a clear plastic strip, without raised window frames, onto which window surrounds were printed. Thus, different window arrangements, such as those on the Duke's Saloon, can appear on what was structurally a standard coach design.

R431	**I-C** * blue+grey - *85-88*	8	12
R433	**I-C 125** 41121 beige+grey - *85-87*	8	12
R433	as above but beige and dark grey	8	12
R395	**IC** 41+++ choice of numbers 41098, 41098 or 41117 beige+grey/black - *88-89*	8	12

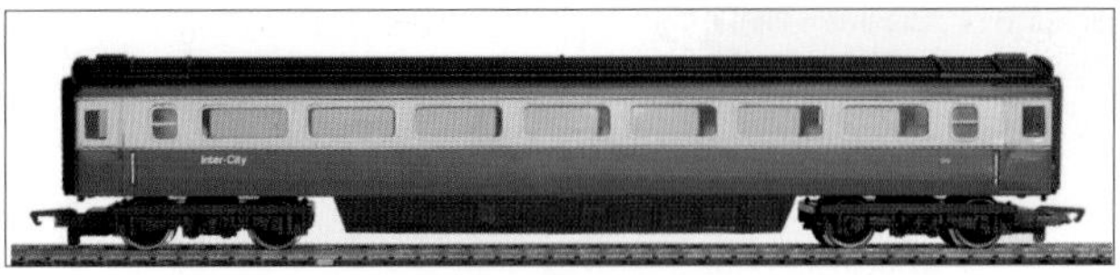

Early model of BR Mk3 open 1st coach in Inter-City blue and grey [C41d]

R719	**IC** 41+++ choice of numbers 41097, 41098, 41117, 41067 beige+grey/black - *91-92*	8	12
R455	**Royal Train** 2904 deep purple Duke's Saloon - *84-85*	15	20
R895	**ScotRail** 1909 blue composite - *88-89*	14	17
R4010	**GNER** 41097 navy blue - *97*	8	10
R4077	**GNER** 41098 [H] navy blue - *98*	10	15
R4080	**Virgin** 41081 [H] red+black - *98*	9	15
R4083	**MM** 41061 [G] jade green - *98*	12	15

* A sheet of number transfers was provided. For 2nd class HST stock there were W42003, W42004 and W42005 and for loco hauled stock there were M12004, M12005 and M12006.

C41e. BR Mk3 Buffet Car (1980)

This was basically the same model as the open coach (31c) but with different windows printed onto the window strip and a different roof moulding.

R427	**BR** W40307 blue+grey Restaurant Buffet 125 - *80-81*	8	10
R427	**BR** 40307 blue+grey Restaurant Buffet 125 - *82-87*	8	10
R490	**BR** 40322 beige+grey Restaurant Buffet 125 - *84-87*	8	12
R430	**IC** 40+++, choice of nos. 40097, 40098 or 40117 beige+grey - *88-89*	8	12
R713	as above but beige+black - *90-92*	9	12
X3395	**IC** 40754 beige+black ex-R897 set - *96*	9	NA
R4012	**GNER** 40750 navy blue - *97*	8	10
R4079	**GNER** 40740 [G] navy blue - *98*	10	15
R4082	**Virgin** 40401 [G] red+black - *98*	9	15
R4085	**MM** 40729 [F] jade - *98*	12	15

C41f. BR Mk3a Brake (1977)

R467	**I-C** 125 blue+grey - *not made*	NA	NA

C42a. BR Mk3 Standard Open (1999)

BR Inter-City Blue & Grey

R4158A	**BR I-C** W42285 - *02-03*	14	17
(R2296)	**BR I-C** W42283 ex-pack - *02-04*	14	NA
(R2296)	**BR I-C** W42284 ex-pack - *02-04*	14	NA
R4367	**BR I-C** W42081 - *09*	16	24
R4445	**BR I-C**125 W42082 - *10-11*	18	24
(R4399)	**Wrexham & Shropshire** M12053 blue+grey ex-W&S coach pack - *10*	16	NA

Ex-BR Mk3 standard open in Wrexham & Shropshire livery [C42a]

BR *INTERCITY* Buff & Black

R4295	**BR ICs** 12143 - *07*	15	18
R4295A	**BR ICs** 12132 - *08-09*	16	24
(R2613)	**BR** ? [?] ex-pack - *07*	15	NA
(R2613)	**BR** ? [?] ex-pack - *07*	15	NA

GNER Navy Blue

R4105	**GNER** 42104 [E] - *99-00*	14	17
(R2116)	**GNER** 42171 [C] ex-pack - *99*	14	NA
(R2116)	**GNER** 42172 [D] ex-pack - *99*	14	NA
(R2612)	**GNER** 42192 [G] ex-pack - *07*	15	NA
(R2612)	**GNER** 42193 [H] ex-pack - *07*	15	NA
R4323	**GNER** 42191 [E] red doors - *08-09*	16	24

Virgin Red & Black

(R2114)	**Virgin** 42230 [E] ex-pack - *99-01*	14	NA
(R2114)	**Virgin** 42237 [D] ex-pack - *99-01*	14	NA
(R1023)	**Virgin** ?2??? ex-set - *99-05*	14	NA
(R1023)	**Virgin** ?2??? ex-set - *99-05*	14	NA
R4097	**Virgin** 12083 [F] - *99-01*	14	17
R4097A	**Virgin** 12125 [F] - *00-03*	14	17
R4097B	**Virgin** 12154 [F] - *03-05*	14	18
R4097C	**Virgin** 12104 [F] - *06*	14	18
R4097D	**Virgin** 42322 [F] - *07-09*	16	24
(R2298)	**Virgin** 42217 [D] ex-pack - *02-05*	14	NA
(R2298)	**Virgin** 42216 [E] ex-pack - *02-05*	14	NA
(R2298A)	**Virgin** 42109 [D] ex-pack - *04-06*	14	NA
(R2298A)	**Virgin** 42108 [E] ex-pack - *04-06*	14	NA
(R2298B)	**Virgin** ? [?] ex-pack - *04-05*	14	NA
(R2298B)	**Virgin** ? [?] ex-pack - *04-05*	14	NA
(R1080)	**Virgin** 42230 [E] red+black ex-set - *06*	14	NA
(R1080)	**Virgin** 42251 [F] red+black ex-set - *06*	14	NA
(R4431)	**Virgin** ? silver+red ex-Virgin Charter Relief coach pack - *11*	18	NA

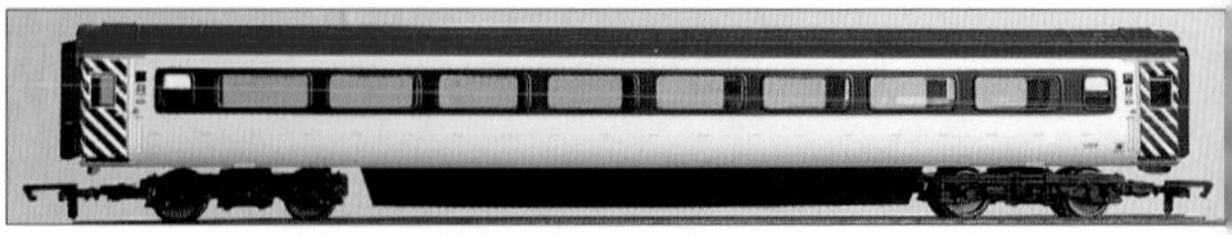

Ex-BR Mk3 standard Virgin Charter Relief coach [C42a]

R4433	**Virgin** 12078 silver+red Virgin Charter Relief - *10-11*	18	24

GWT Ivory & Green

(R2115)	**GWT** 42081 [C] ex-pack - *99*	14	NA
(R2115)	**GWT** 42082 [D] ex-pack - *99*	14	NA
R4102	**GWT** 42089 [E] - *99-03*	14	17
R4102A	**GWT** 42083 - *00*	14	17

FGW Violet

R4161A	**FGW** 42083 [E] - *02-07*	14	18
R4161B	**FGW** 42071 [D] - *02-08*	14	18
R4161C	**FGW** 42118 - *02-03*	14	18
(R2299)	**FGW** 42069 [C] ex-pack - *02-05*	14	NA
(R2299)	**FGW** 42070 [B] ex-pack - *02-05*	14	NA
(R2500)	**FGW** 42042 [B] ex-pack - *06-07*	15	NA
(R2500)	**FGW** 42043 [C] ex-pack - *06-07*	15	NA
R?	**FGW** 'Neon' livery [C] Sp Edn 200 (FGW) * - *06*	20	30
R4370	**FGW** 'Neon' livery 42296 [C] - *09-11*	16	24

MM White, Grey, Blue & Orange

R4214	**MM** 42229 [B] - *04-05*	14	18
R4214A	**MM** 42097 [C] - *06-07*	15	20
(R2376)	**MM** 42227 [C] ex-pack - *04*	15	NA
(R2376)	**MM** 42228 [D] ex-pack - *04*	15	NA
(R2376A)	**MM** 42052 [C] ex-pack - *05-07*	15	NA
(R2376A)	**MM** 42053 [D] ex-pack - *05-07*	15	NA

One Metallic Blue

R4227A	**One Anglia** 12068 - *05-06*	14	19
R4227B	**One Anglia** 12082 - *05-08*	14	19
R4330	**Grand Central** 42401 [B] black - *08-09*	16	21
R4330A	**Grand Central** 42405 [B] black - *10-11*	18	24
R4374A	**Arriva CrossCountry** 42366 [G] grey - *10-11*	18	24
R4374B	**Arriva CrossCountry** 42372[F] grey - *10-11*	18	24
R4374C	**Arriva CrossCountry** 42369 [E] grey - *10-11*	18	24
R4415A	**East Midlands** 42151 [B] white+blue - *10-11*	18	24

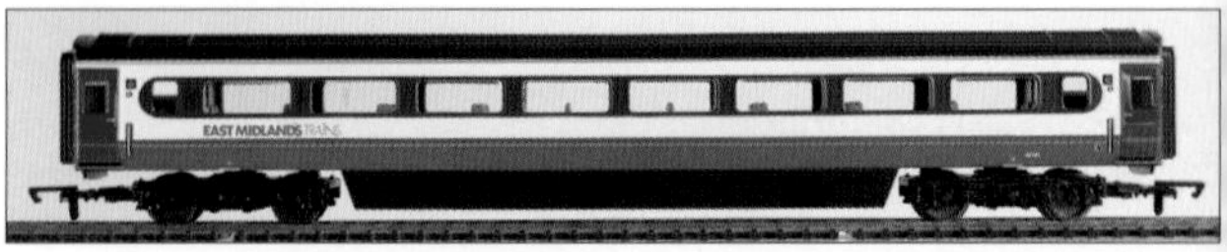

Ex-BR Mk3 East Midlands standard coach [C42a]

R4415B	**East Midlands** 42164 [D] white+blue - *10-11*	18	24
R4441	**East Coast** 42215 [G] white+silver - *10*	18	24
R4441?	**East Coast** ? [?] white+silver Sp Edn (ModelZone) - *10*	18	24

* To celebrate their winning the new franchise, First Great Western commissioned a limited edition of the HST coach from Hornby in the new wavy line livery. It is unnumbered but carries the dedication of coach C. It came with a certificate.

C42b. BR Mk3 Open 1st (1999)

BR Inter-City Blue & Grey

R4157A	**BR I-C** W41137 - *02-04*	13	18

R4366	**BR I-C** W41055 - *09*	16	24
R4444	**BR I-C125** W41056 - *10-11*	18	24
(R4399)	**Wrexham & Shropshire** W11071 blue+grey ex-W&S coach pack - *10*	16	NA
	BR *INTERCITY* Buff & Black		
R4294	**BR ICs** 11021 - *07*	15	20
R4294A	**BR ICs** 11036 - *08-10*	16	21
	GNER Navy Blue		
R4104	**GNER** 41088 [G] - *99-00*	13	16
R4104A	**GNER** 41086 [G] - *?*	13	16
R4322	**GNER** 41098 [L] red doors - *08-09*	16	21
	Virgin Red & Black		
R4096	**Virgin** 11011 [H] - *99-01*	13	16
R4096A	**Virgin** 41168 [H] - *00*	13	16
R4096B	**Virgin** 11042 [H] - *02-03*	13	16
R4096C	**Virgin** 11026 [H] - *03-05*	14	18
R4096D	**Virgin** 11040 [H] - *06-07*	15	20
R4096E	**Virgin** 11042 [H] - *07-08*	16	21
R4096F	**Virgin** ? [?] - *08?*	15	22
R4096G	**Virgin** 11028 [H] - *09-11*	15	24
(R4431)	**Virgin** 110?? silver+red ex-Virgin Charter Relief coach pack - *11*	18	NA
R4432	**Virgin** 11018 silver+red Virgin Charter Relief - *10-11*	18	24
	GWT Ivory & Green		
R4101	**GWT** 41003 [G] - *99-01*	13	16
R4101A	**GWT** 41004 [?] - *00*	13	16
	FGW Violet		
R4160A	**FGW** 41005 [G] - *02-03*	13	16
R4160B	**FGW** 41006 [H] - *02*	13	16
R4160C	**FGW** 41055 [G] - *04-07*	15	20
R4369	**FGW** 'Neon' livery 41144 [G] - *09-11*	16	24
	MM White, Grey, Blue & Orange		
R4213	**MM** 41064 [G] - *04-05*	14	18
R4213A	**MM** 41026 [H] - *06-07*	15	20
	Metallic Blue		
R4226A	**One Anglia** 11037 - *05-07*	15	20

Ex-BR Mk3 open 1st in One Anglia livery [C42b]

R4226B	**One Anglia** 11023 - *05-08*	16	21
	Royal Train - Deep Purple		
(R2370)	2903 Queen's parlour car ex-R1045 set Sp Edn (M&S) ex-set - *03-04*	20	NA
X4979	2903? Queen's parlour car ex-MO R1057 & R1106K sets - *08*	20	NA
(R2370)	2904 Duke's parlour car ex-R1045 set Sp Edn (M&S) ex-set - *03-04*	20	NA
X4980	2904? Duke's parlour car ex-MO R1057 & R1106K sets - *08*	20	NA
(R4197)	2918 Royal Household car ex-coach pack - *03-04*	20	NA
(R4197)	2919 Royal Household car ex-coach pack - *03-04*	20	NA
X10033	2919 Royal Household car ex-MO R1106K set - *08*	20	NA
R4400	2903 HM the Queen's Saloon - *10-11*	20	24
R4401	2904 The Duke of Edinburgh's Saloon - *10-11*	20	24
R4329	**Grand Central** 41205 [F] black - *08-09*	16	21
R4329A	**Grand Central** 41204 [F] black - *10-11*	16	21
(R2890)	**EWS** 11039 maroon ex-EWS Manager's train pack - *09*	20	NA
R4373	**Arriva CrossCountry** 41193 [A] grey - *10-11*	18	24
R4414	**East Midlands** 41077 [G] white+blue - *10-11*	18	24
R4440?	**East Coast** ? [?] white+silver Sp Edn ModelZone) - *10*	18	24
(R4457)	**Network Rail** yellow (some blanked out windows) ex-measurement train coach pack - *11*	20	NA

C42c. BR Mk3 Buffet Car (1999)

R4159A	**BR** W40330 blue+grey - *02-04*	14	18
R4393	**BR** IC W40326 blue+grey Restaurant-Buffet 125 - *10*	18	24
(R4399)	**Wrexham & Shropshire** M10224 blue+grey ex-W&S coach pack - *10*	16	NA
R4296	**BR ICs** 10209 buff+black - *07*	15	20
R4296A	**BR ICs** 10225 buff+black - *08-10*	16	21
R4106	**GNER** 40706 [F] navy - *99-00*	13	16

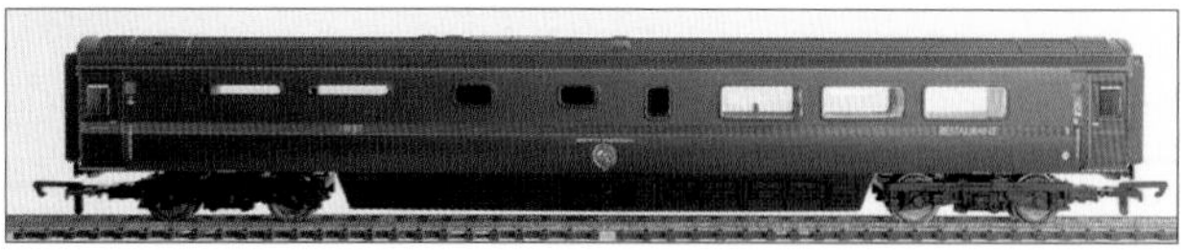

Ex-BR Mk3 GNER buffet car [C42c]

R4106A	**GNER** 40711 [F] navy - *99-00*	13	16
R4324	**GNER** 40711 [J] red doors - *08-10*	16	21
R4098	**Virgin** 10217 [G] red+black - *99*	13	16
R4098A	**Virgin** 10219 [?] red+black - *00-01*	13	16
R4098B	**Virgin** 10253 [G] red+black - *02*	13	17
R4098C	**Virgin** 10205 [G] red+black - *03*	13	16
R4098D	**Virgin** 10220 [G] red+black - *03-05*	14	18
R4098E	**Virgin** 10236 [G] red+black - *06-07*	15	20
(R4431)	**Virgin** ? silver+red ex-Virgin Charter Relief coach pack - *11*	18	NA
R4103	**GWT** 40703 [F] ivory+green - *99*	13	16
R4103A	**GWT** 40707 [F] ivory+green - *00-01*	13	16
R4183A	**FGW** 40703 [F] violet - *03-06*	14	19
R4183B	**FGW** 40712 [F] violet - *03*	13	16
R4183C	**FGW** 41005 [G] violet - 04-*07*	15	20
R4371	**FGW** 'Neon' livery 40733 [F] violet - *09-11*	16	24
R4247	**MM** 40753 [F] white+grey+blue - *06-08*	16	21
R4331	**Grand Central** 40424 [E] black Route 26 - *08-09*	16	21
R4439	**Grand Central** 40426 [E] black Route 26 - *10-11*	16	21
R4434	**EWS** Managers Train 10211 maroon - *10*	18	24
R4403	**Royal Train** 2917 dark purple - *10*	18	24
R4417	**East Midlands** 40749 [F] white+blue - *10*	18	24
R4443	**East Coast** 40748 [J] white+silver - *10-11*	18	24
R4443?	**East Coast** ? [?] white+silver Sp Edn (ModelZone) - *10*	18	24
(R4457)	**Network Rail** yellow ex-measurement train coach pack - *11*	20	NA

C42d. BR Mk3 TGS (ex-Lima) (2006)

This is HST stock with a guards compartment in one end of a standard class coach.

R4275	**BR I-C125** W44005 blue+grey - *06-08*	16	21
R4368	**BR I-C 125** W44034 blue+grey - *09-10*	16	24
R4446	**BR I-C125** blue+grey W44039 - *10-11*	18	24
R4314	**BR ICs** 44057 grey - *07*	15	20
R4314A	**BR ICs** 44024 grey - *08-09*	16	21
R4315	**GNER** 44056 [A] red doors - *07-09*	16	21
R4315A	**GNER** 44063 [A] red doors - *08-10*	16	21
R4278	**Virgin** 44065 red+black - *06-09*	16	21

Ex-BR Mk3 TGS in First Great Western livery [C42d]

R4276	**FGW** 44018 [A] violet - *06-08*	16	21
R4372	**FGW** 44039 [A] 'Neon' livery violet - *09-10*	16	24

R4326	**FGW** 44093 green+white+gold (Fag Packet) - *08-09*	16	21
R4277	**MM** 44069 [A] white+grey+blue - *06-08*	16	21
R4328	**Grand Central** ? [?] black - *not made*	NA	NA
R4376	**Arriva CrossCountry** 44021 [H] grey - *10-11*	18	24
R4416	**East Midlands** 44047 [A] white+blue - *10-11*	18	24
R4442	**East Coast** 44095 [B] white+silver - *10*	18	24
R4442?	**East Coast** ? [?] white+silver Sp Edn (ModelZone) - *10*	18	24

C42e. BR Mk3 SLE (ex-Lima) (2006)

R4282	**BR I-C** E10543 blue+grey - *06-08*	16	21
R4282A	**BR I-C** E10543 blue+grey - *09*	16	21
R4466	**BR I-C** Executive 10713 dark grey+beige - *11*	20	27
R4284	**Royal Household** 10734 deep purple - *06-11*	16	21
R4285	**Northern Belle** 10729 *Crewe* brown+cream - *06-07*	15	20
R4311	**FGW** 10584 green+white+yellow (Fag Packet) - *07-08*	16	21
(R2890)	**EWS** 10546 maroon ex-EWS Manager's train pack - *09*	20	NA
	ScotRail Caledonian		
R4283	10605 2 shades of violet - *06*	15	20
R4283A	10529 2 shades of violet - *07*	15	20
R4307	10523 violet - *07*	15	NA
(R2663)	10613 violet - *07*	15	NA
(R2663)	10680 violet - *07*	15	NA
(R2663)	10607 violet - *07*	15	NA
(R2663A)	10683 violet - *08*	16	NA
(R2663A)	10648 violet - *08*	16	NA
(R2663A)	10693 violet - *08*	16	NA

C43. BR Mk3 Driving Van Trailer (DVT) (2010)

R4435	**BR ICs** 82123 dark grey+beige - *10*	42	50
R4397	**Virgin** 82150 red+black - *10*	42	50
(R2955)	**Virgin** 82126 silver+red ex-Virgin Charter Relief train pack - *11*	42	NA

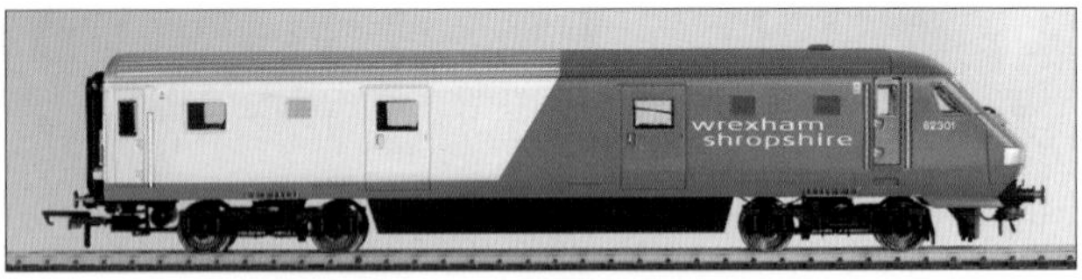

Ex-BR Mk3 driving van trailer in W&S livery [C43]

R4396	**One** 82119 metallic blue - *10-11*	42	50
(R2890)	**EWS** 82146 silver ex-EWS Manager's train pack - *10*	42	NA
(R2951)	**Wrexham & Shropshire** 82301 silver+grey ex-W&S train pack - *10*	42	NA

BR Mk4 Coaching Stock

C44a. BR Mk4 Tourist Open (1990)

R407	**IC** 12401 beige+black - *90-96*	12	14
R407	**IC** 12406 beige+black - *90-96*	12	14
R407	**IC** 12414 beige+black - *90-96*	12	14
R452	**IC** 12410 beige+black ex-R696 set - *91-96*	12	NA
R453	**IC** 12408 beige+black ex-R696 set - *91-96*	12	NA
R4002	**GNER** 12514 navy blue - *97*	12	15
X3556	**GNER** 12405 navy ex-R2002 pack - *97-00*	14	NA
X3557	**GNER** 12406 navy ex-R2002 pack - *97-00*	14	NA
(R1012)	**GNER** 12488 navy blue ex-set - *98-99*	14	NA
(R1012)	**GNER** 12487 navy blue ex-set - *98-99*	14	NA
(R2002A)	**GNER** M12452 [D] navy ex-pack - *02-04*	14	NA
(R2002A)	**GNER** M12453 [C] navy ex-pack - *02-04*	14	NA
R4075	**GNER** 12330 [F] navy blue - *98-00*	12	15
R4075A	**GNER** 12308 [F] navy blue - *02-04*	14	18
R4075B	**GNER** 12315 [?] navy blue - *02-06*	14	19
(R2427)	**GNER** 12400 [C] navy + red doors - *04*	14	NA
(R2427)	**GNER** 12459 [D] navy + red doors - *04*	14	NA
(R2427A)	**GNER** 12407 [C] navy + red doors - *05-07*	15	NA
(R2427A)	**GNER** 12481 [D] navy + red doors - *05-07*	15	NA
R4287	**GNER** 12409 [B] navy + red doors - *06-07*	15	19
(R2602)	**GNER** 11401 [C] navy + red doors - *06*	14	NA
(R2602)	**GNER** 11417 [D] navy + red doors - *06*	14	NA

Ex-BR Mk4 GNER tourist open coach [C44a]

C44b. BR Mk4 Open 1st (1990)

R405	**IC** 11203 beige+black - *90-96*	12	14
R405	**IC** 11208 beige+black - *90-96*	12	14
R405	**IC** 11214 beige+black - *90-96*	12	14
R4001	**GNER** 11229 navy blue - *97*	12	15
R4074	**GNER** 11262 [H] navy blue - *98-00*	12	15
R4074A	**GNER** 11239 [H] navy blue - *02-05*	14	18
R4074B	**GNER** 11206 [?] navy blue - *02-04*	14	18
R4286	**GNER** 11201 [L] navy + red doors - *06-07*	15	20

C44c. BR Mk4 Catering Car (1990)

R408	**IC** 10303 beige+black - *90-96*	12	14
R408	**IC** 10305 beige+black - *90-96*	12	14

BR Mk4 catering car in InterCity livery [C44c]

R408	**IC** 10308 beige+black - *90-96*	12	14
R4003	**GNER** 10304 navy blue - *97*	12	15
R4076	**GNER** 10333 [G] navy blue - *98-00*	12	15
R4076A	**GNER** 10322 [G] navy blue - *02-05*	14	18
R4076B	**GNER** 10308 [?] navy blue - *02-04*	14	18
R4288	**GNER** 10315 [J] navy + red doors - *06-07*	15	20

C45. BR Mk4 Driving Van Trailer (DVT) (1991)

R472	**ICs** 82205 beige+black - *91-97?*	15	NA
R268	**ICs** 82201 beige+black - *91-97*	14	18
R268	**ICs** 82207 beige+black - *93-97*	14	18
R268	**ICs** 82204 beige+black - *93-97*	14	18
X3555	**GNER** 82204 navy ex-R2002 pack - *97-00*	12	NA
(R2002A)	**GNER** 82230 navy blue ex-R2002A - *02-03*	12	NA
X3708	**GNER** navy blue ex-R1012 set - *98*	12	NA
(R2427)	**GNER** 82219 *Duke of Edinburgh* navy ex-Mallard train pack - *04*	14	NA
(R2427A)	**GNER** 82212 navy ex-Mallard train pack - *05*	12	NA
(R2602)	**GNER** 82207 navy ex-Mallard train pack - *06*	14	NA
R4147A	**Virgin** 82110 red+black - *02-03*	15	20
R4147B	**Virgin** 82141 red+black - *02-04*	15	20
R4245	**One Anglia** 82119 metallic blue - *06-07*	22	30

C46. Eurostar Passenger Saloon (1996)

	Eurostar Grey		
Eur3021/1X	37**3021** ex-set R816 - *96-97*	12	NA
Eur3022/1X	37**3022** ex-set R816 - *96-97*	12	NA
Eur3015/1X	37**3015** ex-pack R665 - *97*	12	NA
Eur3016/1X	37**3016** ex-pack R665 - *97*	12	NA
Eur3003/1X	37**3003** ex-pack R665A - *97*	12	NA
Eur3004/1X	37**3004** ex-pack R665A - *97*	12	NA
R4013	37**3015**, 37**3016** 2 x saloons - *97-98*	20	25

Eurostar articulated passenger saloons [C46]

R4013A	37**3003**, 37**3004** 2 x saloons - *99-00*	20	25
R4013B	37**3021**, 37**3022** 2x centre saloons - 00	20	25
R4013C	37**3219**, 37**3220** 2x saloons - *06-10*	25	33
Eur3219/1X	37**3219** ex-R1013 set - *98-08*	14	NA
Eur2220/1X	37**3220**/1X ex-R1013 set - *98-08*	14	NA
(R2379)	37**31061**+9 2x saloons ex-pack - *04-07*	20	NA

(R2379)	373**1071**+9 2x saloons ex-pack - *04-07*	20	NA
(R2379A)	373**0071**+9 2x saloons ex-pack - *08*	25	NA
R2379A)	373**0081**+9 2x saloons ex-pack - *08*	25	NA
	GNER Navy Blue		
(R2197)	373**301** ex-pack - *01-03*	12	NA
(R2197)	373**302** ex-pack - *01-03*	12	NA
(R2197A)	373**305** ex-pack - *04-05*	12	NA
(R2197A)	373**306** ex-pack - *04-05*	12	NA
R4152A	373**303**+373**304** 2 x saloons - *02-04*	25	30
R4152B	373**309**+373**310** 2 x saloons - *02-04*	25	33
(R1071)	37?+37? 2x saloons ex-set - *07*	25	NA

Virgin Pendolino Coaching Stock

C47a. Intermediate Motor 1st Open (MFOD) (2007)

Real coach had seating for disabled passengers. Referred to in the catalogue as 'Pendolino 1st Class Open Coach'.

R4273	**Virgin** 69412 silver+red - *07-08*	20	26
R4273A	**Virgin** 69445 silver+red - *09-11*	20	31

C47b. Intermediate Trailer with Pantograph 1st Open (PTFO) (2007)

Referred to in the catalogue as 'Pendolino Class 390 Trailer Standard Buffet Coach'. Non-working pantograph on model used in train sets and train packs.

(R2467)	**Virgin** 69512 silver+red ex-train pack/set - *07-09*	20	NA
(R1134)	**Virgin** 69545 silver+red ex-MO train pack - *09*	20	NA
(R1155)	**Virgin/Alstom** ? silver+red+black ex-set - *11*	28	NA

C47c. Intermediate Motor 1st Open (MFO) (2007)

Referred to in the catalogue as 'Pendolino 1st Class Open Coach'.

(R4271	**Virgin** 69812 silver+red - *07*	25	35
R4271A	**Virgin** 69845 silver+red - *10-11*	25	35
(R2467)	**Virgin** 69612 'Virgin Star' silver+red ex-train pack and set - *07-08*	25	NA
(R1134)	**Virgin** 69645 '101 Squadron' silver+red ex-MO train pack - *09*	25	NA
(R1155)	**Virgin/Alstom** ? silver+red+black ex-set - *11*	28	NA

C47d. Intermed. Trailer Standard Open (TSO) (2007)

Referred to in the catalogue as 'Pendolino Trailer Standard Open Coach'.

R4272	**Virgin** 68812 silver+red - *07-10*	20	26
R4272A	**Virgin** 68845 silver+red - *09-11*	20	31

C47e. Intermed. Motor Standard Open (MSO) (2007)

Real coach had seating for disabled passengers. Referred to in the catalogue as 'Pendolino Trailer Standard Open Coach'.

R4274A	**Virgin** 69712 silver+red - *07-08*	20	26
R4274B	**Virgin** 69912 silver+red - *07-09*	20	26
R4274C	**Virgin** 69745 silver+red - *08-11*	25	31
R4274D	**Virgin** 69945 silver+red - *09-11*	25	31

C47f. Intermediate Trailer with Pantograph Standard Buffet (PTSRMB) (2007)

Referred to in the catalogue as 'Pendolino 1st Class Open Coach'. Non-working pantograph.

R4271	**Virgin** 69812 silver+red - *07-10*	25	32
R4271A	**Virgin** 69645? silver+red - *10*	25	35

Hitachi Class 395 Passenger Stock

C48a. Standard Coach (2009)

R4382	**SouthEastern High Speed** 39014 deep violet - *09-10*	25	31
R4452	**SouthEastern High Speed** 39034 deep violet - *11*	25	34

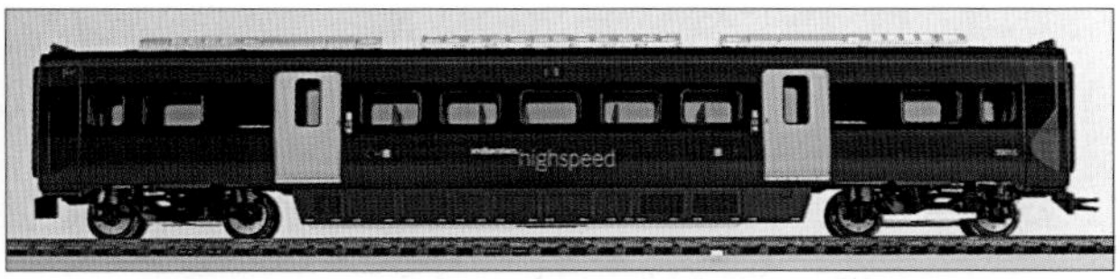

Class 395 open coach [C48b]

R4453	**SouthEastern High Speed** 39035 deep violet - *11*	25	34

C48b. Open Coach (2009)

R4383	**SouthEastern High Speed** 39015 deep violet - *09-10*	25	31

C49. 'Blue Rapier' Open Coach (2010)

R4438	**SouthEastern High Speed** 39012 deep violet - *10-11*	25	31

COACH PACKS

Cat No.	Company, Number, Colour, Dates	£	£

C50. Various

The coaches in the following packs are also insividually listed within the appropriate tables and with greater detail.

R4140	**BR** 3 green Mk1s for 'ACE' - *01*	NA	45
R4168	**LNER** 3 silver Staniers - *02*	NA	50
R4169	**Pullman** 'The Thanet Belle' - *not made*	NA	NA
R4169	**Pullman** 3 cars for 'The Bournemouth Belle' - *03*	NA	75
R4177	**BR** 2 maroon Mk1s + ex-LMS restaurant car for 'The Caledonian' - *03*	NA	45
R4197	**Royal Train** 3 cars - *04*	NA	50
R4196	**Pullman** 3 cars for 'Golden Arrow' - *04*	NA	80
R4228	**BR** - 3 red+cream Gresleys for 'The Northumbrian' train pack - *05*	NA	80
R4229	**BR** - 3 maroon Mk1s for 'Pines Express' train pack - *05*	NA	52
R4255	**BR** - 3 x 2nd series red+cream Gresleys for 'Master Cutler' train pack - *06*	NA	100
R4254	**Pullman** - 3 x 3rd series cars for the 'Venice Simplon-Orient Express' train set - *06*	NA	110
R4252	**BR** - 3 x maroon Mk1s for the 'Talisman' train pack - *06*	NA	55
R4251	**Pullman** - 3 x 3rd series cars for the 'Devon Belle' train pack - *06*	NA	110
R4310	**Blue Pullman** - 2 x Mk2 + 1 x Mk1 - *07*	NA	70
R4378	**SR** - 3 x Maunsell olive green coaches for the 'Southern Suburban 1938' train pack - *09*	NA	70
R4379	**BR(SR)** - 3 x Maunsell BR green coaches for the 'Southern Suburban 1957' train pack - *09*	NA	70
R4380	**Pullman** - 3 x 3rd series cars for the 'Devon Belle' train pack - *09*	NA	110
R4381	**Pullman** - 3 cars for the 'Bournemouth Belle' - *09*	NA	110
R4431	**Virgin** - 3 x Mk3s for Virgin Charter Relief train pack - *10*	NA	75
R4399	**Wrexham & Shropshire** - 3 Mk3s for W&S train pack - *10*	NA	75
R4457	**NetworkRail** measurement train pack 2 MK3s - *11*	NA	54

STARTER SET COACHES

Cat No.	Company, Number, Colour, Dates	£	£

CP1. 4-wheel 'Starter' Set Coach (1969)

R733	yellow + end verandas - *69-71*	4	NA

TRANSCONTINENTAL PASSENGER STOCK

In addition to the British range of coaches, there were two series of Transcontinental passenger cars plus an American style mail car and an old time coach.The coaches in the first series were shorter, toy-like and all carried the inscription 'Tri-ang Railways'. The second series consisted of four attractive models which were available from 1962.Early examples of the second series also carried the inscription 'Tri-ang Railways' but that was soon changed to 'Transcontinental'.This same distinction also applies to the mail car where the earlier wording is most common.

The blue used for Victorian Railways stock was a muddy dark blue but in 1970, the stock of this colour plastic ran out and some VR stock was made in rail blue, much to the consternation of the Australian factory.

The series was principally made for Canada where Canadian

liveries were later used, but it was also sold in Australia where 'TransAustralia' versions were also available. In the late '60s they were exported to America and sold by ATT. These had American railroad names and were made in the UK but packaged in the States. The American range also turns up in Australia where residue stock was sent when the stores were cleared.

Cat No.	Company, Number, Colour, Dates	£	£

CT1. First Series Passenger Cars (1954)

The name and other printed detail was originally applied by transfers but this gave way to heat printing at quite an early stage. TR = Tri-ang Railways

	TR All Silver Cars		
R24	10724, 20425 passenger car - *54-57*	6	10
R25	20425, 10724 vista dome top seating area yellow, dark blue and red - *54-57*	8	12
R25	20425, 10724 vista dome top seating area white, light blue and red - *54-57*	8	12
R25	20425, 10724 vista dome top seating area green, red and yellow - *56-57*	6	10

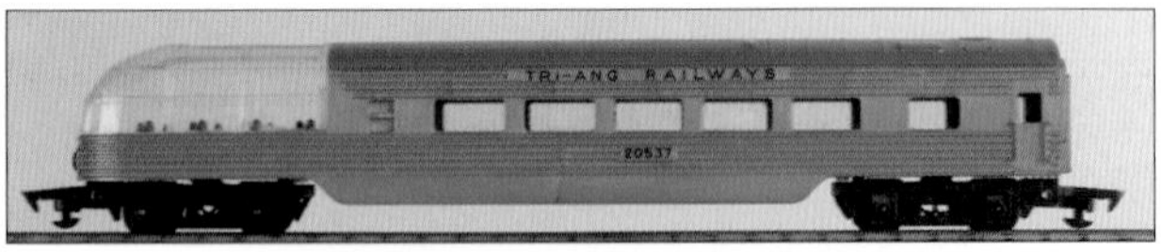

1st version of the 1st series observation car [CT1]

R125	20537 observation car - *57*	10	15
R130	baggage car - *57*	10	15
	TR Silver & Red Cars		
R24	10724, 20425 passenger car - *58-61*	5	10
R25	20425, 10724 vista dome - *58-61*	5	10
R125	20537 observation car- *58-61*	5	10
R130	baggage car- *58-61*	5	10
R324	diner - *60-61*	10	15
	TR Blue Cars		
R131	10724 passenger car blue roof - *58-60*	5	10
R131	10724 passenger car grey roof - *60-61*	5	10
R132	20425 vista dome blue roof - *58-60*	5	10
R132	20425 vista dome grey roof - *60-61*	5	10
R133	20537 observation car blue roof - *58-60*	5	10
R133	20537 observation car grey roof - *60-61*	5	10
R134	baggage car blue roof - *58-60*	5	10
R134	baggage car grey roof - *60-61*	5	10
R325	diner grey roof - *60-61*	10	15

CT2. Mail Car (1956)

The car was sold as part of an operating accessory which included pickup and put-down trackside apparatus. The 'R' number and values refer to the complete set. The name and other printed detail was originally applied by transfers but this gave way to heat printing at quite an early stage. As the transferred version commands a higher price if the transfers are in good condition, it is listed separately here. TR = Tri-ang Railways. TC = Transcontinental.

R119	**TR** 3609 maroon Mail Express transfers - *56-57*	15	20
R119	**TR** 3609 maroon Mail Express heat printing -*58-61*	10	15
R400	**TC** 3609, 3606 red Mail Express - *62-63*	15	20
R401	**TC** 3606, 3609 blue Mail Express - *62-63*	15	20
R?	**Mail** red ex-RS101A Overlander set - *72*	10	NA
R401	**BR Royal Mail** M30224 blue+grey - *74-77*	10	25
R725	**Battle Space** Command Car D-778 khaki green + commandos- *67-71*	20	50

CT3. Second Series Passenger Cars (1962)

The colour of underframes on these passenger cars varied between black, grey and silver. Initially, the silver was self coloured plastic but this never looked good. Consequently the factory resorted to spraying the coaches silver and these are the ones described below as 'bright silver'. Those in American liveries were fitted with NMRA couplings and sold in ATT boxes or sets but the few sent to Australia had normal tension lock couplings and Tri-ang Hornby boxes. TR = Tri-ang Railways. TC = Transcontinental. TA = TransAustralia. CN = Canadian National. CP = Canadian Pacific. CPRail = Canadian Pacific.

2nd series observation car in blue [CT3]

	Green Tri-ang Railways		
R335	70831 passenger car - *62*	35	50
R336	91119 observation car - *62*	35	50
R337	baggage/kitchen car - *62*	35	50
R338	diner - *62*	35	50
	Green Transcontinental		
R335	70831 passenger car - *62-63*	20	45
R336	91119 observation car - *62-63*	20	45
R337	baggage/kitchen car - *62-63*	20	45
R338	diner - *62-63*	20	45
	Blue Transcontinental		
R444	70831 passenger car - *62-66*	10	18
R445	91119 observation car - *62-66*	10	18
R446	baggage/kitchen car - *62-66*	10	18
R447	diner - *62-66*	10	18
	Silver & Red Transcontinental		
R440	70831 passenger car - *62-63*	15	23
R441	91119 observation car - *62-63*	15	30
R442	baggage/kitchen car - *62-63*	15	30
R443	diner - *62-63*	15	25
	Bright Silver & Red Transcontinental		
R4400	70831 pass car silver roof - *70-73*	12	NA
R4410	91119 observation car silver roof - *70-73*	12	NA
R4430	70831 diner silver roof - *70-73*	12	NA
	White & Green Ambulance		
R248	**R A M C** (ex-baggage car) - *63-67,71*	10	30
R248	**R A M C** (ex-baggage car), crosses on sides heat printed * - *?*	12	30
	Blue TransAustralia		
R444A	70831, 31027, 61116 passenger car - *62-64, 68-70*	20	30
R445A	91119 observation car - *62-64, 69-70*	20	30
R446A	baggage/kitchen car - *62-64*	20	30
R447A	diner - *62-64*	20	30
R444A	70831 rail blue passenger car - *70*	30	40
R445A	91119 rail blue observation car - *70*	30	40
	Silver & Red TransAustralia		
R440A	70831, 31027, 31018 passenger car - *62-67,70*	25	35
R441A	9119 observation car - *62-64,70*	25	35
R442A	baggage/kitchen car - *62-64*	25	35
R443A	diner - *62-64,70*	25	35
	Silver NSWR		
R440	passenger car First - *74-78*	18	30
R442	baggage car - *74-78*	18	30
R443	dining car - *74-78*	18	30
	Blue VR		
R444	passenger car First - *76-78*	18	30
R446	baggage car - *76-78*	18	30
R447	dining car - *76-78*	18	30
	Silver & Black Canadian National		
R444CN	300, 303 passenger car - *65-69*	18	25
R445CN	304 observation car - *65-69*	18	25
R446CN	304 baggage/kitchen car - *65-69*	18	25
R447CN	303, 300 diner - *65-69*	18	25
	Bright Silver & Black Canadian National		
R4441	73831, 91119 passenger car - *70-71*	20	25
R4451	91119, 73831 observation car - *70-71*	20	25
R4461	baggage/kitchen car - *70-71*	20	25
R4471	diner - *70-71*	20	25
	Grey & Maroon Canadian Pacific		
R444CP	7752 passenger car yellow lining - *67*	25	30
R444CP	7752 passenger car - *68*	23	30
R445CP	7420 observation car yellow lining - *67*	25	30

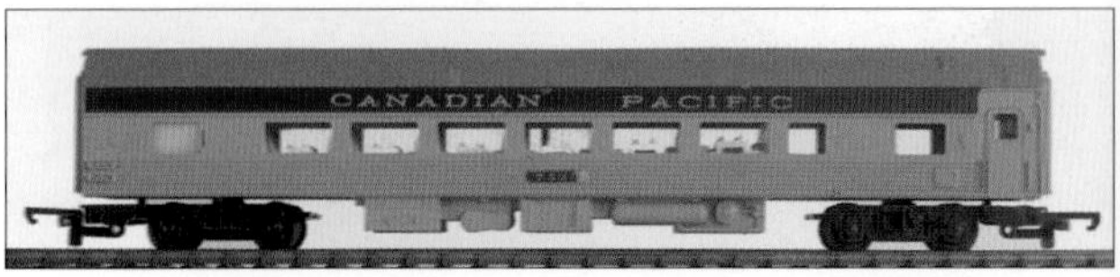

2nd series passenger car in Canadian Pacific livery [CT3]

R445CP	7420 observation car - *68*	23	30

R446CP	7914 baggage/kitchen car yellow lining - *67*	25	30
R446CP	7914 baggage/kitchen car - *68*	23	30
R447CP	7525 diner yellow lining - *67*	25	30
R447CP	7525 diner - *68*	23	30
	Silver & Red CPRail		
R4403	passenger car Danff - *70*	20	25
R4403	passenger car Banff - *71*	20	25
R4413	observation car Danff - *70*	20	25
R4413	observation car Banff - *71*	20	25
R4423	baggage/kitchen car Danff - *70*	20	25
R4423	baggage/kitchen car Banff - *71*	20	25
R4433	diner Danff - *70*	20	25
R4433	diner Banff - *71*	20	25
	Silver & Maroon Pennsylvania		
R803	7752, 1580 passenger car - *67*	30	45
R807	7525 diner - *67*	30	45
R811	3101 baggage/kitchen car - *67*	30	45
R815	3102 observation car - *67*	30	45
	Silver Burlington		
R804	3100 passenger car - *67*	30	35
R808	diner - *67*	30	35
R812	3101 baggage/kitchen car - *67*	30	35
R816	3102 observation car - *67*	30	35
	Silver Santa Fe		
R805	3100 passenger car - *67*	30	35
R809	diner - *67*	30	35
R813	3101 baggage/kitchen car - *67*	30	35
R817	3102 observation car - *67*	30	35
	Silver & Blue Baltimore and Ohio		
R806	3100 passenger car - *67*	30	35
R810	diner - *67*	30	35
R814	3101 baggage/kitchen car - *67*	30	35
R818	3102 observation car - *67*	30	35

*These were usually stickers.

CT4. Old Time Coach (1962)

R448	Smoking Car 257 yellow black lining - *62-65*	15	25
R448	Smoking Car 257 yellow no lining - *?*	18	25

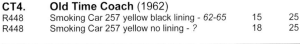

Old time coach [CT4]

R802	**Central Pacific** 257 yellow - *67*	30	35
R801	**Pullman** 250 green - *67*	30	35
R378	teak from Railway Children set - *72*	23	NA

WAGONS

If the range of coaches was large, that of wagons is huge. Like coaches, the range is divided here into Standard British Goods Stock, Starter Set Wagons and Transcontinental Freight Stock but we have also included the Battle Space and Military Wagons in a subsection of their own.

Wagon Packs - For mixed packs of wagons see W24.

British Goods Wagons - The tools for the first two wagons were bought from Pyramid Toys, who had made wagons with cellulose acetate bodies and metal chassis from 1949 until 1951 and sold them under the name 'Trackmaster'. These were purchased in 1951, along with tools for their 0-6-2 tank which was also absorbed into the Tri-ang range.

Some strange colours may be found among Trackmaster wagons due to sunlight discoloration of the brown pigments, turning them to lime green!

Cat No.	Company, Number, Colour, Dates	£	£

W0a. Trackmaster Open Wagon (1949)

These were wagons made by Pyramid Toys before they sold their tools to Tri-ang. The wagons were either used in the Trackmaster train set or were sold singly in cream coloured boxes with a picture of the wagon on them. Later the open wagons were available with a coal load moulding and the boxes stamped 'COAL' and later still they were available with Hornby Dublo couplings in which case the box was stamped 'HD'. They are inscribed 'Trackmaster' underneath and had metal non-insulated wheels.

	GW Blue Grey Wagons		
-	10836 open - *49-51*	7	12

Trackmaster GWR 7-plank coal wagons [W0a]

-	10836 open HD couplings - *51*	12	18
-	10836 open + coal - *50-51*	8	15
-	10836 open + coal HD couplings - *51*	13	20
	NE Brown Wagons		
-	83610 open - *49-51*	7	12
-	83610 open H D couplings - *51*	12	18
-	83610 open + coal - *50-51*	8	15
-	83610 open + coal HD couplings - *51*	13	20
-	86301 open - *?*	25	30

W0b. Trackmaster Closed Van (1949)

These were wagons made by Pyramid Toys before they sold their tools to Tri-ang. The wagons were either used in the Trackmaster train set or were sold singly in cream coloured boxes with a picture of the wagon on them. Later they were available with Hornby Dublo couplings, in which case the box was stamped 'HD'. They are inscribed 'Trackmaster' underneath and had metal non-insulated wheels.

-	**GW** 62134 blue-grey - *49-51*	7	12
-	**GW** 62134 blue-gry HD couplings - *51*	12	18

Trackmaster NE Vans [W0b]

-	**GW** 62314 blue-grey - *?*	25	30
-	**NE** 86203 brown - *49-51*	7	12
-	**NE** 86203 brown HD couplings - *51*	12	18

The development of wheels on Rovex/Tri-ang/Hornby wagons followed that of the coaches, and the wagons, too, are usually well marked with the manufacturer's name, except for those from the late 1960s. Early wagons had diecast chassis (the 10' chassis having been developed from the Trackmaster one) which underwent constant development and, consequently, provided a rich assortment of variations to collect.

Chassis were metal until 1963, after which nearly all were plastic. Exceptions were made where extra weight was required, as in the case of cranes and the unloading hopper wagon. A few wagon bogies remained metal until quite late for the same reason e.g. the rocket launcher and helicopter car. As chassis types do not usually affect value, we have not detailed them here unless relevant to do so.

Other changes that help to identify wagons, especially early ones, are the colour of plastic used and the running number carried. Many different colours and shades of plastic were used in the 1950s, as small batches of unspecified colours of plastic granules could be bought cheaply. In those days it did not seem to matter whether a van was red or white or a well wagon bright orange or blue. Initially, the plastic used was Cellulose-Acetate which had a glossy finish and warped slightly. Around 1956 Rovex changed to using Polystyrene which was more rigid and showed no signs of warping.

Running numbers were applied by heat printing (much akin to branding with a hot iron) and the heat printing tool sometimes broke or got misplaced. The result was changing running numbers on wagons and occasionally numbers used on the wrong wagon. It was not until the mid 1970s that tampo printing was introduced to the factory and much more intricate detail could be carried on rolling stock.

Over the years there have been about 100 wagon types and in the case of the 7-plank open wagon there have been over 100 variations (many not worth listing here)!

Flat Wagons

W1. 'Lowmac MS' (ex-Airfix) (1999)

R6075	**BR** B904685 grey + **'Blaney'** crate - *99-00*	5	7
(R1054)	**BR** E260856 brown + **'DRCL'** crate ochre ex-SP Edn set (Toys R Us) - *05*	6	NA
(R1037)	**BR** E280996 brown + **'DWS'** crate red ex-set - *03-04*	6	NA
R6240	**BR** E662048 brown + **'EJB'** crate - *04-05*	5	7
R6240A	**BR** E260863 brown + **'EJB'** crate - *05-07*	6	8
R6240W	**BR** E260863 brown + **'EJB'** crate ex MO R1063 set - *08*	7	NA
R6130	**BR** E260864 brown + **'ESG'** crate - *01-02*	5	7
(R1127)	**BR** E260864 brown + grey **'Furness Railway'** crate ex- 'City Industrial' MO set - *09*	10	NA
(R1130K)	**BR** E260864 brown + **'NDS Engineering'** crate ex- 'Highland Rover' MO set - *09*	10	NA
R6130A	**BR** E260855 brown + **'ESG'** crate - *03-04*	5	7
R6130B	**BR** E260848 brown + **'ESG'** crate - *05-06*	6	8
R6130W	**BR** ? brown + **'ESG'** crate ex-various MO sets - *08*	6	NA

Lowmac with Morris 1000 Van [W1]

(R1054)	**BR** E260855 brown + **'JLP'** crate grey ex-SP Edn set (Toys R Us) - *05*	6	NA
(R1036)	**BR** E280869 brown + **'JPC'** crate ex-set - *03-05*	6	NA
(R1036)	**BR** ? Brown + **'JPC'** crate cream ex-set - *03-06*	6	NA
R6399	**BR** B904567 brown + Morris 1000 van - *08-09*	7	10
(R1061)	red + **'EPS'** (Eddie Stobart) crate ex-set - *05-06*	10	NA
R6293	red + **'EPS'** crate 201 Sp Edn 500 (Eddie Stobart) - *05*	10	12
R6293A	as above but crate numbered 203 * - *05*	10	12
R6293B	as above but crate numbered 205 * - *05*	10	12
(T1500)	buff ex-set - *00-02*	5	NA
(T1501)	dark green ex-set - *00-02*	5	NA
(R1147)	grey green with pallet + military tank load ex- 'Codename Strike Force' set - *10*	9	NA
(R1147)	grey green with pallet + military van load - ex- 'Codename Strike Force' set - *10*	9	NA
X10232	? ex-MO R1111KF set - *08*	6	NA
-	crate - **'AMR** Pyrotechnics'	1	NA
-	crate - **'Blaney** Machine Tools'	1	NA
-	crate - **'ESG** Machinery'	1	NA
-	crate - **'NDS** Engineering'	1	NA
R6176	above set of 4 crates - *02-08*	NA	6

* 500 were made for Eddie Stobart Ltd. with each number.

W2a. Bolster Wagon (1st Type) (1953)

This had a flat floor with holes in it into which bolsters or loads could be plugged. The bolsters were squeeze fitted, two per wagon, and were black plastic mouldings each with two bright metal pins protruding from beneath.

R17	**BR** 10836 * grey - *53*	10	12
R17	**BR** 58698 grey - *53*	10	12
R17	**BR** 43726 grey '10T' - *53*	7	10
R17	**BR** 43726 grey '1OT' - *53-54*	7	10
R17	**BR** 43726 grey '1' in '1OT' inverted - *54-55*	7	10
R17	**BR** 3726 grey '1' in '1OT' inverted - *55*	8	11
R17	**BR** 3726 grey - *55*	8	11
R17	**BR** 7893 grey - *55-56*	7	10
R17	**BR** 7893 orange-brown - *56*	15	17
R17	**BR** M59015 grey (11.5 mm) - *56-58*	5	10
R17	**BR** M59015 grey (9 mm) - *59-61*	5	10
R17	**BR** M59015 light grey (9 mm) - *61*	7	12
R17	**BR** M59034 grey (11 mm) - *59*	5	10
R17	**BR** M59034 grey (10 mm) - *59-61*	5	10

* Ex-Trackmaster open wagon tool.

W2b. Cable Drum Wagon (1st Type) (1953)

This used the 1st type bolster wagon (above) without the bolsters but with two plastic cable drums which plugged into the wagon base. Values quoted are for the more common wagon variations. Early drums were open with thick plastic tube wound on **(type 1).** These were replaced by open drums with a moulding to represent finer cable **(type 2)** and these, in turn, were replaced by closed drums **(type 3).** Cable and drums both varied in colour as indicated in this table. As drums could easily be swapped around, it is impossible to say which version of the bolster wagon was used in each case. There were four colours for the cables on the types 1 and 2 drums - red, yellow, green or silver and a white cable has been found on a J&P type 1 drum.

R18	**'J&P Cables'** type 3 green - *60-61*	7	10
R18	**'J&P Cables'** type 3 maroon - *60-61*	8	11
R18	as above but orange labels - *?*	20	25
R18	**'J&P Cables'** type 3 brown - *60-61*	9	12
R18	**'Johnson & Philips'** type 1 black * - *53-55*	10	13
R18	**'Johnson & Philips'** type 1 black ** - *53-55*	15	20
R18	**'Johnson & Philips'** type 2 black - *56-57*	8	11

Tri-ang cable drum wagons [W2b]

R18	**'Johnson & Philips'** type 3 green - *58-60*	7	10
R18	**'Johnson & Philips'** type 3 maroon- *58-60*	7	10
R18	**'Johnson & Philips'** type 3 brown - *58-60*	8	11
R18	**'Liverpool Cables'** type 1 black - *53-55*	10	13
R18	**'Liverpool Cables'** type 2 black - *56-57*	8	11
R18	**'Liverpool Cables'** type 3 green - *58-61*	7	10
R18	**'Liverpool Cables'** type 3 maroon - *58-61*	7	10
R18	**'Liverpool Cables'** type 3 brown - *58-61*	8	11
R18	**'Pirelli General'** type 1 black - *53-55*	9	12
R18	**'Pirelli General'** type 2 black - *56-57*	7	10
R18	**'Pirelli General'** type 3 green - *58-61*	7	10
R18	**'Pirelli General'** type 3 maroon - *58-61*	7	10
R18	**'Pirelli General'** type 3 brown - *58-61*	7	11

* red or green or yellow cable. ** white cable.

W2c. Tarpaulin Wagon (1953)

This used the bogie bolster wagon (above) with a single moulding of a tarpaulined load replacing the two bolsters. The loads were supplied by Minic Ltd who used it with some of their 'Push-and-Go' vehicles. As loads could easily be swapped around it is impossible to say which version of the bolster wagon was used in each case. Values quoted are for the more common wagon variations. Sometimes the moulding was heat printed each side with 'Tri-ang' in silver and sometime the silver has disappeared leaving only the impression. Others had no printing on them.

R19	grey tarpaulin - *53-59*	5	10
R19	dark green tarpaulin - *53-59*	6	10
R19	violet-grey tarpaulin - *53-59*	5	10
R19	grey-green tarpaulin - *53-59*	5	10
R19	red-brown tarpaulin - *53-59*	6	10
R19	red tarpaulin - *53-59*	8	10

W3a. Bolster Wagon (2nd Type) + Loads (1962)

This had a flat floor with a central bolster moulded into it which had two black pins protruding from it.

R17	**BR** B913011 light grey - *62*	8	10

2nd series bolster wagons [W3a]

R17	**BR** B913011 red-brown '3' with flat top - *62-63*	5	10
R17	**BR** B913011 red-brown '3' with round top - *63-65*	5	10
R17	**BR** B913011 orange-brown - *?*	14	16
R17	**BR** B41429 red-brown * - *?*	10	12
R17	**BR** 17351 red-brown - *63-64?*	10	12
R17	**BR** B913011 red-brown Minix car, no pins (also R17C) - *66-73*	12	15
R676	**BR** B913011 green - *71-74*	6	10
R17CNP	red-brown no printing ex-starter sets, Minix car - *c68*	8	NA
R17CNP	green no printing ex-starter sets, Minix car - *c68*	8	NA

* This wagon was found with a black Tri-ang Toys etc. container numbered B890B.

W3b. Cable Drum Wagon (2nd Type) (1962)

This used the 2nd type bolster wagon (above) without the pins but with two plastic cable drums which had flat bottoms and were held to the wagon with rubber bands hooked over the buffers.

R18	**'AEI'** B913011 green - *62-71*	7	10
R18	**'AEI'** B913011 brown - *62-71*	7	10
R18	**'J & P'** B913011 green - *62-71*	6	10
R18	**'J & P'** B913011 brown - *62-71*	7	10
R18	**'Pirelli General'** B913011 green - *62-71*	6	10
R18	**'Pirelli General'** B913011 brown - *62-71*	7	10

W3c. Flat Wagon with Container (1962)

This model, which used the 2nd type bolster wagon without the bolster pins, was based on actual containers in this livery used for transporting Tri-ang products from their factories. The inscription 'Return to Wimbledon SR' suggests the Merton factory in particular.

R561NP	blue-black container no printing ex-starter sets - *c68*	10	NA
R561NP	orange container no printing ex-starter sets - *c68*	10	NA

Flat wagons with two rare containers [W3c]

R574	**'Kellogg's Rice Krispies'** BK8900 blue-black container - *68*	25	NA
R?	**'Lyons Maid Ice Cream'** white container - *c68*	30	NA
	'Tri-ang Toys Pedigree Prams'		
R561	BK8900B blue-black - *62-64?*	8	10
R561	BK8900 blue-black - *65?-68?*	7	8
R561	BK8900 black - *?*	12	14
R561	BK890B black - *?*	12	14
R561	BK890B blue-black - *69?-71*	8	10

W4. 'Conflat A' (1982)

This was a one-off wagon presumably made just to take a 20' container.

R017	**BR** 'Conflat A' B727734 brown + **Freightliner** container 09L91 - *82-83*	12	18

W5. 'Conflat' and Container (ex-Airfix) (1997)

R6014	**GW** 39326 dark grey + **GWR** container BC-1710 dark brown - *97-99*	6	8
R6082	**GW** 39026 dark grey + **GWR** container BK-1835 dark brown - *99-00*	6	8
R6131	**GW** 39030 dark grey + **GWR** container K-1704 dark brown - *01-03*	6	8
(R1037)	**GW** 39238 dark grey + **GWR** container BK-1924 dark brown ex-set - *03*	8	NA
R6346	**GWR** 39317 dark grey + **GWR** container BC-1710 dark brown - *not made*	NA	NA
R6346	**GWR** 39317 dark grey + **GWR** container BC-1716 dark brown - *07-08*	7	9
R6346A	**GWR** 39320 dark grey + **GWR** container BC-1711 dark brown - *08-09*	7	10
X4852	**GWR** ? dark grey + **GWR** container ?ex-MO R1083L set - *08*	7	9

GWR 'Conflat' with furniture container [W5]

R6013	**LMS** N300465 pale grey + **LMS** container K37 maroon - *97-99*	6	8
R6241	**LMS** 4757 dark grey + **LMS** container K1 maroon - *04-05*	6	8
R6241A	**LMS** 4758 dark grey + **LMS** container K2 maroon - *05-06*	6	8
R6182	**SR** 39153 dark brown + **SR** container K599 green - *02*	6	8
R6182A	**SR** 39149 dark brown + **SR** container K596 green - *03-04*	6	8
R6182B	**SR** 39150 dark brown + **SR** container K592 green - *05-06*	6	8
R6318	**SR** 39168 dark brown + **SR** container K621 green - *06-07*	6	8
R6136	2001 dark grey + **'Hornby 2001'** container BK01 blue - *01*	6	6
R6036	**'Book Club** 20 Years' Sp Edn 2000 - *99*	12	15
(R1061)	black + **'EPS'** (Eddie Stobart) container ex-set - *05-06*	8	NA
R6294	black + **'EPS'** container 202 Sp Edn 500 (Eddie Stobart) - *05*	8	10
R6294A	as above but container numbered 204 * - *05*	8	10
R6294B	as above but container numbered 206 * - *05*	8	10
-	container - **GWR** BC1710 dark brown	2	NA
-	container - **GWR** BK1835 dark brown	2	NA
-	container - **LMS** K37 maroon	2	NA
R6175	set of above 3 containers - *02-05*	NA	5

* 500 were made for Eddie Stobart Ltd. with this number.

W6. 'Conflat L' with 3 'L' Type Containers (1962)

This was based on the BR 11T 'Conflat L' which was designed with locating brackets on the floor of the wagon to take three 'L' type containers. The model containers were produced carrying one of two numbers - L17253B or L17429B. The containers vary considerably in the shade of grey plastic used to mould them.

R340	**BR** B734259 red-brown + 3 containers - *62-72*	5	7

'Conflat L' with cement containers [W6]

R340	**BR** B734259 orange-brown + 3 containers - *?*	10	12

NB. Any with black containers will have received them from the girder flat wagon and so would not be authentic.

W7. Shunter's Truck (1973)

The model had side rails and used the short brake van's chassis. SS = Silver Seal wheels. The shunter's truck came with a grey plastic uncoupler.

R028	**Severn Tunnel Junc.** grey - *73-75*	5	7
R208	**Severn Tunnel Junc.** grey SS - *76-78*	5	7
R005	Carriage wagon red with car * - *82-83, 87-94*	8	12

* Minix car make and colour varies.

W8. 'Winkle' Plate Wagon (1972)

The large load fills the wagon whereas the small load fills only three quarters of the wagon.

R19	**BR** ED931972 dark green + large load - *72-73*	12	15
R19	**BR** ED931972 dark green + small load - *?*	12	15

W9. 'Girder Flat' (1974)

R133	red + boat load - *74*	25	30
R182	red + load of 4 black L type containers - *74*	12	14
R131	red + load of 4 wheel sets - *74-75*	10	12
R224	red + load of 4 wheel sets SS - *76*	10	12

W10. 'Bogie Steel AB' (1979)

R236	**BR** 400105 brown - *79*	6	8

'Bogie Steel AB' [W10]

R225	**BR** 400105 brown paint finish - *80-81*	9	11
R246	**BR Railfreight** 400105 grey+red - *81-83, 87-94*	6	8
R427	**BR Railfreight** 400044 grey+red - *96-98*	6	8
R6023	**BR** 400044 grey+yellow Engineer's - *97-98*	8	NA
R6209	**BR Railfreight** 40386 grey+red + 5 pipes - *03*	7	9
R6209A	**BR Railfreight** 40127 grey+red + 5 pipes - *04*	7	9
R6209B	**BR Railfreight** 40412 grey+red + 5 pipes - *05*	7	9
R6210	**BR Railfreight** 40223 grey+yellow + 12 rails - *03*	8	10
R6210A	**BR Railfreight** 40119 grey+red + 12 rails - *04*	8	10
R6210B	**BR Railfreight** 40101 grey+red + 12 rails - *05-06*	8	10
X5020	green+red with a resin Christmas trees load ex R1046 set - *04, 08*	9	NA
(R1107)	red + **'Bartellos Circus'** van ex-set (RailRoad) - *08-09*	10	NA
	Thomas Series		
R9214	grey + parts of a circus marquee - *05-09*	7	9
R9215	brown + tarpaulined circus load - *05-07*	7	9

W11. OTA Timber Carrying Wagon (2011)

R6469	**BR** ? blue - *11*	12	15
R6470	**BR** ? blue - *11*	12	15

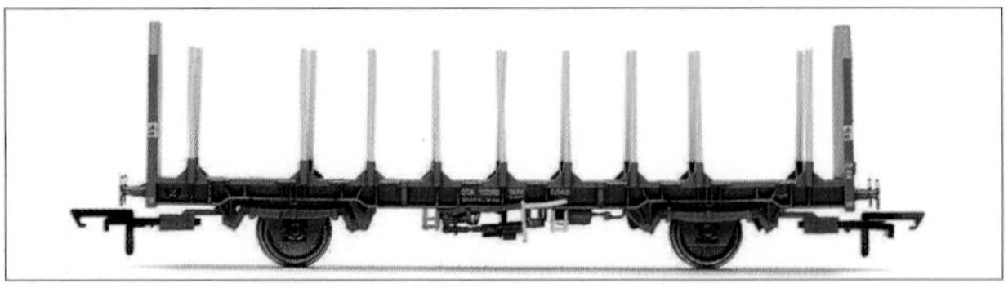

OTA timber carrier [W11] (Hornby)

R6471	**BR** ? blue - *11*	12	15
R6466	**EWS** ? maroon - *11*	12	15
R6467	**EWS** ? maroon - *11*	12	15
R6468	**EWS** ? maroon - *11*	12	15

Planked Open Wagons

W12. 3-plank Wagon (1995)

Originally introduced as a 'First' CAD designed wagon in 1995 but then absorbed into the general range. The chassis has a 9" wheelbase.

(R6190)	**'Babcock & Wilcox'** 334 grey Sp Edn 500 (Harburn Hobbies) ex-pack - *02*	8	NA
R6281	**'BQC Ltd'** 351 cream - *05-06*	5	7
R6439	**'BQC Ltd'** 360 red - *09-11*	5	8
R6167	**'Cammel Laird'** 630 red - *02*	5	7
R6167A	as above but numbered 631 - *03*	5	7
(R1092)	as above but numbered 633 ex-set - *07-08*	6	NA
(R6305)	as above 630 but weathered, ex-pack - *06*	6	NA
R6338	'James **Carter & Sons'** 172 grey - *07-09*	5	7
(R6450)	as above weathered ex-pack numbered 174 - *10*	6	NA
R6197	**'Ceiriog Granite Co.'** 195 brown - *03*	5	7
(R6306)	as above but weathered, ex-pack - *06*	6	NA
R6230A	**'Easter Iron Mines'** 5 brown - *04-06*	5	7
R6230	as above but numbered 4 - *04*	5	7
(R6278)	as above 4 but weathered - *05*	6	NA
R6298	'George K **Harrison'** 15 grey - *06-08*	5	7
R6231A	**'Imperial Chemical Industries Buxton Lime Firms'** 49 grey - *04-06*	5	7
R6231	as above but numbered 48 - *04*	5	7
(R6278)	as above 48 but weathered - *05*	5	NA

3-plank wagon - The Little Mill Brick Co. [W12]

R6490	'The **Little Mill Brick Co.**' 7 red - *10*	5	6
(R6190)	**'Robert McAlpine'** 112 blue Sp Edn 500 (Harburn Hobbies) ex-pack - *02*	8	NA
R6111	'William **Neave'** 6 grey - *00-01*	5	7
R151	'The **Patent Victoria Stone Co.'** 3 pale blue - *95-97*	5	7
R6008	**'Royal Dockyard Chatham'** 7 grey - *97-99*	5	7
R6133	**'SJ'** 32 light grey - *01-03*	5	7
R403	**'Trimsaran'** 51 red - *96-97*	5	7
R6337	as above reissued - *07-08*	5	7
(R6392)	as above but weathered ex-trio - *08-10*	6	NA
R041	'E **Turner & Son'** 26 cream - *95*	5	7
R6489	**E** LMS Engineers, 11442 grey Northampton - *10*	5	6

W13. 4-plank Wagon (1995)

Originally introduced as a 'First' CAD designed wagon in 1995 but then absorbed into the general range. The chassis has a 9" wheelbase.

R6492	**Abercriban Quarries Co.** 57 red - *10*	5	6
R6525	**'Bickershaw'** 624 maroon - *11*	5	7
R399	'The **Bold Venture Lime Co'** 24 grey - *96-97*	5	7
R6440	'The **Bold Venture'** Lime Co.' 24 grey - *09-11*	5	8
R131	**'Clee Hill Granite'** 331 grey - *95*	5	7
R6232	as above numbered 350 - *04-05*	5	7
R6232A	as above numbered 351 - *06-07*	5	7
R6232B	as above numbered 352 - *08-09*	5	8
(R1092)	as above numbered 327 ex-set - *07-08*	6	NA
(R6393)	as 350 weathered ex-trio - *08-09*	6	NA
R6198	**'Dutton Massey'** 41 black - *03-04*	5	7
(R6306)	as above but weathered ex-pack - *06*	6	NA
R6523	'Duxbury Park Colliery' 191 red - *11*	5	7
R6233	'The **Harts Hill Iron Co.'** 6 brown - *04*	5	7
(R6449)	'The **Harts Hill Iron Co.'** 7 brown W ex-pack - *09*	6	NA
R6009	**'Hensall Sand'** 2 red+white - *97-99*	5	7
R087	'H **Hotson'** 25 red - *95*	5	7
(R6191)	'William **Mitchell'** 37 red Sp Edn 500 (Harburn Hobbies) ex-pack - *02*	8	NA

4-plank - Ministry of Munitions [W13]

R6299	**'Ministry of Munitions'** 8535 dark grey - *06*	5	7
R6299A	as above numbered 8452 - *08-09*	5	8
R6339	**'New Cransley** Iron & Steel' 76 grey - *07-09*	5	8
(R6191)	'John **Nicolson**' 15 brown Sp Edn 500 (Harburn Hobbies) ex-pack - *02*	8	NA
R6282	**'Princess Royal Colliery Co.'** 56 dk.red - *05*	5	7
R6526	**'Scatter Rock Macadams**' 130 light grey - *11*	5	7
R6524	**'Stevens & Co.'** 103 maroon - *11*	5	7
R6134	**'Tarslag'** 605 grey - *01-03*	5	7
R6168	**'Teign Valley Granite'** 735 red - *02*	5	7
R6168A	as above numbered 736 - *03*	5	7
R6168B	as above numbered 737 - *04*	5	7
R6168C	as above numbered 738 - *05-06*	5	7
(R6290)	as above numbered 739 ex-Sp Edn wagon pack (Clifford James) - *05*	6	NA
R040	**'Tildesley* & Son'** 42 buff - *95*	6	8
R6112	'Mark **Williams'** 9 brown - *00-01*	5	7
(R6219)	as above W ex-wagon set - *03-04*	6	NA

* Spelt differently on the box.

W14. 5-plank Wagon (1973)

Although the body moulding remained the same, the chassis went through the usual modifications and included both 10' and 9' wheelbase versions.

R6030	**'Aberdeen'** 34 maroon Sp End 1500 (Harburn Hobbies) - *97*	8	12
-	'Nathl. **Atrill**'** 20 maroon	6	NA
-	as above numbered 24	6	NA
-	as above numbered 25	6	NA
R6115	set of above 3 wagons - *00-01*	NA	15
R116	'Amos **Benbow'** 29 pale blue - *83*	5	7
R096	**'Bestwood'** 655 black - *77-79*	5	7
R686	**'Burgess & Penfold'** 55 grey Sp Edn 1000 (Scale Rail) - *96*	8	12
R012	'A **Bodell'** 1 pale grey Sp Edn 19,000 (W.H.Smith) - *81*	5	7
R241	**'C&A'** (Australia) grey - *77*	10	12
R241	as above but black - *78*	10	12
R004	**'Colgate'** red - *82*	5	8

Original Hornby 5-plank wagon - 'Crook & Greenway' [W14]

R024	**'Crook & Greenway'** No.2 blue - *88-98*	5	7
-	**'Cumberland'** 22 black	6	NA
-	as above numbered 30	6	NA
-	as above numbered 38	6	NA
R6006	set of above 3 wagons - *97*	NA	15
R104	'AW **Day'** green 320 - *73-74*	5	7
R210	**'General Refractories'** 85 pale grey heat printed (thinner lettering) - *73-74*	5	7
R210	as above but tampo printed - *74-76*	5	7
R6066	**'Hamilton Palace'** 201 maroon Sp Edn 1160 (Harburn Hobbies) - *98*	8	12
R011	**'Hornby Railways 1992'** bright red Ltd Edn 3000 - *92*	8	12
R6089	**'Hornby Roadshow 1999'** red Ltd Edn 670 - *99*	8	12
R6118	**'Hornby Roadshow 2000'** red Ltd Edn 1000 * - *00*	8	12
R6149	**'Hornby Roadshow 2001'** red Ltd Edn 1000 - *01*	8	12
R149	**'Hunting'** 7 red - *94-99*	5	7
R222	**'Jif'** yellow - *83-87*	5	7
R014	**'Lucas'** bright green - *92-94*	5	7

-	**'Martin'** ** 25 grey	6	NA
-	as above numbered 26	6	NA
-	as above numbered 27	6	NA
R6087	set of above 3 wagons - *99*	NA	15
R6065	**'Morningside'** 270 brown Sp Edn 1200 (Harburn Hobbies) - *98*	8	12
R038	**'Pounsbery'** 1 green - *93-96*	5	7

One of a number of wagon designs that did not make it into production

R097	'Arnold **Sands'** red-brown - *77-79*	4	7
R717	as above with paint finish - *80-81*	5	7
R?	ditto unpainted orange-brown body - *?*	5	NA
R?	as above with no letter shading - *?*	5	NA
R?	ditto but black body - *84-85*	8	NA
R?	ditto but grey body with shading - *?*	8	NA
R716	**'Scarwood'** 13 grey, black moulding - *80-?*	3	7
R716	as above but grey moulding - *?-88*	6	7
R716?	**'Scarwood'** No.13 grey - *99-02*	5	NA
-	**'Spencer'** 22 red	6	NA
-	as above numbered 23	6	NA
-	as above numbered 24	6	NA
R6039	set of above 3 wagons - *98*	NA	15
R163	'M **Spiers'** 3 pale grey - *74*	5	7
R6102	**'Wilsden'** 420 dark grey Sp Edn 500 (The Model Railway Club) - *00*	8	12
R091	'JR **Wood'** 98 orange planned in 1975 - *not made*	NA	NA
R6018	**GW** 81791 dark grey - *97-01*	5	NA
R008	**BR** DM401274 brown Engineer's - *93, 97-98*	5	7
R119	**CIE** 11895 pale grey (Ireland) - *79*	12	NA
R120	**SLNC** 145 maroon (Ireland) - *79*	12	NA
R107	dark brown with face ex-Thomas Series *** - *85-10*	5	7

* This wagon may be found moulded from either black or light grey plastic. ** Also used in wagon packs.

W15. 5-plank Wagon (ex-Airfix) (1998)

R6053	'John **Allbutt'** 1 dark grey - *98-99*	5	7
(R1035)	'Wm **Barnard'** 23 grey ex-train set - *03-05*	6	NA
R6300	'S **Bookman'** 30 grey - *06-08*	5	7
(R6449)	'S **Bookman'** 31 grey W ex-wagon set - *09*	6	NA
R6520	'A **Bramley'** 6 brown - *11*	5	7
R?	'W **Butler'** 29 grey Sp Edn 500 (British Railway Modelling) - *08*	6	8
R6073	**'Candy & Co.'** 111 light grey - *99-00*	5	7
(R1070)	**'Crook & Greenway'** 5 blue - *07-10*	6	NA
R6235	as above but No.2 - *04-05*	5	7
(R6279)	as above but weathered - *05*	6	NA
R6199	**'Derby Co-operative'** 62 black - *03*	5	7

Former Airfix 5-plank wagon - 'Ellis & Everard' [W15]

R6121	'James **Durnford'** 37 black - *01*	5	7
R6442	**'Ellis & Everard'** 231 yellow - *09*	5	8

R6326A	'The **Fife Coal Co.**' 3224 red Sp Edn (Harburn Hobbies) - *06*	8	10
R6326B	as above numbered 3225 Sp Edn (Harburn Hobbies) - *06*	8	10
R6060	**'ICI (Lime) Ltd'** 3034 dark grey - *98-99*	5	7
(R6156)	as above W ex-wagon set - *02-03*	6	NA
R6491	'Thomas **Lant Roadstone Llanelwedd Quarries**' 223 black - *10*	5	6
(R1030)	'William **Lawson**' 2 red ex-set - *02-03*	6	NA
R6128	**'Lillishall Limestone'** 1750 brown - *01*	5	7
R6162	**'Lyle & Son'** 35 light grey - *02*	5	7
R6162A	as above but numbered 36 - *03*	5	7
R6493	'**Nook & Wyrley Collieries**' 113 black - *10*	5	6
R6072	**'Pontithel Chemical'** 7 maroon - *99-02*	5	7
(R6219)	as above W ex-wagon set - *03-04*	6	NA
(R6279)	as above W ex-wagon set - *05*	6	NA
R6521	'**Ralls & Son**' 51 light grey - *11*	5	7
R6283	'FH **Silvey**' 191 very dark brown - *05-06*	5	7
R6234	**'Somerset Trading Co.'** 56 red - *04*	5	7
(R6279)	as above but weathered - *05*	6	NA
R6522	'**Winstanley Collieries Co**.' 424 light grey - *11*	5	7
R6441	**NE** 629814 grey - *09-10*	5	8
R6340	**SR** 14131 dark brown - *07*	5	7
R6340A	**SR** 14133 dark brown - *08-10*	5	7
R6395	**BR** S14540 red-brown - *08*	5	7
R6395A	**BR** S14547 red-brown - *09-10*	5	8

W16. 6-plank Wagon (1995)

Originally introduced as a 'First' CAD designed wagon in 1995 but then absorbed into the general range. The chassis has a 9" wheelbase.

R6341	**'C&C Ayres'** 400 green+yellow - *07*	5	7
(R6393)	as above but weathered ex-trio - *08-10*	6	NA

6-plank wagon - 'C & C Ayres' [W16]

R6341A	**'C&C Ayres'** 406 green+yellow - *08-11*	5	8
R106	'Edwin W **Badland**' 57 dark maroon - *95*	5	7
(R1068)	**'Bessey & Palmer'** 743 Light grey ex-set - *06*	6	NA
R6301	**'Bute Merthyr'** 325 black - *06-08*	5	7
(R6393)	as above but weathered ex-trio - *08-10*	6	NA
R6519	'**Crook & Thompson**' 43 maroon - *11*	5	7
(R1036)	**'Evans & Bevan'** 482 black ex-set - *03-06*	6	NA
R128	**'Grassmoor'** 359 dark grey - *95*	5	7
R6435	**'Haymen'** 8324 red Sp Edn 1500 (ModelZone) - *09*	6	7
R454	'Henry **Heaven**' 1 brown - *96-97*	5	7
R6113	'Thomas **Meakins'** 48 red - *00-01*	5	7
R6237	'SJ **Moreland**' 1 blue+red - *04*	5	7
R6237A	as above numbered 2 - *05-06*	5	7
(R6290)	as above numbered 3 ex-Sp Edn wagon pack (Clifford James) - *05*	8	NA
R6169	**'Parkinson'** 39 dark blue - *02*	5	7
R6169A	as above numbered 36 - *03*	5	7
(R1092)	as above numbered 42 ex-set - *07-08*	6	NA
(R6305)	as 39 above but weathered ex-pack - *06*	6	NA
R6135	**'South Wales & Cannock Chase'** 774 red - *01-03*	5	7
R6236	**'Spiers'** 347 yellow - *04-06*	5	7
(R6450)	as above weathered ex-pk numbered 349 - *09-10*	5	NA
(R6290)	as above numbered 348 ex-Sp Edn wagon pack (Clifford James) - *05*	8	NA
R6200	**'Sneyd** 833 teak * - *03*	5	7
(R6305)	as above but weathered ex-pack - *06*	5	NA
R6010	'Richard **Weale**' 17 red - *97-99*	5	7
(R6156)	as above but weathered ex-pack - *02-03*	6	NA
R6356	**BR** Railfreight 2007 red - *07*	5	7
R6189	**'Hornby Roadshow 2002'** red Ltd Edn 1,000 - *02*	8	10
R6221	'**Hornby Roadshow 2003**' red Ltd Edn 1,000 - *03*	10	12
R6258	'**Hornby Roadshow 2004**' red Ltd Edn 1,000 - *04*	10	12

6-plank wagon - 'Sneyd' [W16]

R6285	'**Hornby Roadshow 2005**' red Ltd Edn 720 - *05*	10	12
R6322	'**Hornby Roadshow 2006**' red Ltd Edn 1,000 - *06*	8	10
R6356	'**Hornby Roadshow 2007**' red Ltd Edn 1,000 - *07*	8	10
R2426	'**Hornby Roadshow 2008**' red Ltd Edn - *08*	8	10
R6476	'**Hornby Roadshow 2009**' red Ltd Edn - *09*	6	8
R6501	'**Hornby Roadshow 2010**' red Ltd Edn - *10*	4	5

*The body of this wagon was made with the same teak effect plastic used for moulding LNER coach bodies.

W17a. 7-plank (1st Type) (ex-Trackmaster) (1952)

This was a simple 7-plank wooden type open wagon (designed by Pyramid Toys for their Trackmaster set) to which loads were later added to extend the range (see 1a and 1b below). The Trackmaster inscription on the underside of the wagon was replaced with 'TRI-ANG MADE IN ENGLAND'. A replacement body was tooled up in 1954 which was almost identical to the Trackmaster one but was inscribed 'Tri-ang R10/R13 MADE IN ENGLAND'. ** For those with Mk IIa couplings (as described above in the introduction) add £1-£2 to the value. SS = Silver Seal wheels.

R312	**'C&A'** black (Australia) - *74-75*	10	15
R100	**'Lancashire Coke Co.'** 322 red - *73-74*	5	8
R100	**'Northern United'** P284063 dark brown - *73*	150	NPG
R009	**'Ocean'** 921 maroon - *75*	7	9
R009	as above but dark brown - *75*	5	7
R204	as above but SS wheels - *76*	5	7
R090	**'Princess Royal'** 250 maroon - *75*	5	7
R209	as above but SS wheels - *76*	5	7
R010	**'Pugh & Co.'***** 380 red Sp Edn 120,000 - *79*	5	7
R010	as above but bottom plank black - *79*	15	17

Tri-ang 7-plank wagon - 'Pugh & Co.' [W17a]

R10	**GW** (thick or thin letters) 10836 brn - *52-54*	5	10
R10	as above but blue-grey - *52-54*	5	10
R10	as above but white - *52-54*	8	12
R10	**NE** 83610 brown - *52-53*	5	10
R10	as above but blue-grey - *52-53*	5	10
R10	as above but white - *52-53*	8	12
R10	**NE** (thin) 83670 brown - *53*	7	11
R10	as above but blue-grey - *53*	7	11
R10	as above but red - *53*	9	11
R10	**NE** (thick) ** 83670 brown -*54-55*	4	10
R10	as above but blue-grey - *54-55*	4	10
R10	as above but white - *54-55*	6	11
R10	as above but red - *54-55*	5	10
R10	as above but grey-green - *54-55*	4	10
R10	as above but light grey - *54-55*	8	10
R10	as above but orange - *54-55*	15	17
R10	as above but silver - *54-55*	18	20
R10	**NE** 22132 brown - *54*	4	10
R10	as above but blue-grey - *54*	4	10
R10	as above but red - *54*	4	10
R10	as above but white - *54*	5	10

R10	as above but grey-green - *54*	4	10
R10	as above but grey - *54*	6	11
R10	**NE** 76853 brown - *54*	4	10
R10	as above but blue-grey - *54*	4	10
R10	as above but grey-green - *54*	4	10
R10	**NE** 32075 brown - *55-56*	4	10
R10	as above but blue-grey - *55-56*	4	10
R10	as above but grey-green - *55-56*	4	10
R10	as above but mid-green - *55-56*	5	10
R10	**NE** 3207 dark-grey - *55*	10	12
R10	**NE** 47205 grey - *55-57*	4	10
R10	as above but brown - *55-57*	4	10
R10	as above but grey-green - *55-57*	4	10
R10	as above but translucent-grey - *55-57*	10	12
R10A	**SR** 12530 dark brown - *71-73*	4	10
R10A	as above but bright red - *74*	6	11

Tri-ang 7-plank wagons - SR in blue, red and grey [W17a]

R10A	as above but bright blue - *74*	7	11
R10A	as above but grey - *73*	20	NPG
R10	**BR** M2313 grey - *58*	8	12
R10	as above but brown - *58*	8	12
R10	as above but dark green - *58*	7	11
R10	as above but maroon - *58*	12	14
	W1005 number 10.5mm long		
R10	**BR** W1005 brown (shades) - *57-60*	4	10
R10	as above but grey - *57-60*	4	10
R10	as above but dark green - *57-60*	4	10
R10	as above but yellow-brown - *57-60*	6	11
R10	as above but maroon - *57-60*	10	12
	W1005 number 9.5mm long		
R10	**BR** W1005 grey - *60*	6	11
R10	as above but green - *60*	6	11
R10	as above but * pale brown - *60*	10	12
	W1005 number 8mm long		
R10	**BR** W1005 grey - *60*	6	11
R10	as above but brown - *60*	6	11
R10	as above but dark green - *60*	6	11
	W1005 number 7 mm long		
R10	**BR** W1005 grey (shades) - *61-70*	4	10
R10	as above but dark green - *61-70*	4	10
R10	as above but pale grey - *61-70*	5	10
R10	as above but green - *61-70*	4	10
R10	as above but dung-brown - *62*	10	12
R10	as above but maroon - *?*	10	12
R577	plain black converter wagon with Hornby Dublo coupling one end - *66-70*	10	15
R10NP	various colours ** but no printing ex-starter sets - *60-72*	4	NA

* Also known as Caramac brown. ** Colours known to exist include blue, maroon, orange brown, red and green. *** The lettering was usually white but often turned out light grey.

W17b. Coal Truck (ex-Trackmaster) (1952)

This was R13 and used the R10 open wagon with a single plastic moulding to give the effect of it being full of coal. As the moulding was loose, it tended to move round from wagon to wagon and so it is difficult to say in which versions of the open wagon they were originally used. Three different mouldings were used over the years, the earliest one being from the Trackmaster tools. For the coal wagon add £1 to the value of the open wagon according to which version has been used. The coal truck was available between 1952 and 1961.

W17c. Open Wagon with Planks or Drums (1960)

During 1960 and 1961 the open wagon was available with either a plank or drum load, in both cases these were represented by a single buff coloured plastic moulding. The wagon with oil drums was R245 and that with planks was R246. For either wagon add £2 to the value of the open wagon according to which version has been used.

W18. 7-plank Drop Door Wagon (1954)

This looked like the 1st type open wagon (above) but had a drop-down door either side.

R112A	**LMS** 12527 maroon - *71*	8	10
R112A	as above but bright red - *71-72*	5	10
R112A	as above but orange-brown - *72*	8	10

Tri-ang 7-plank drop-door wagons LMS in maroon, red and brown [W18]

R112	**NE** 83670 light grey - *54-55*	6	11
R112	as above but blue-grey - *54-55*	10	12
R112	**NE** 22132 grey - *54*	8	10
R112	as above but dark red - *54*	6	11
R112	as above but grey-green - *54*	10	12
R112	as above but bright red - *54*	10	12
R112	as above but SR-green - *54*	12	14
R112	**NE** 76853 grey - *54*	10	12
R112	**NE** 32075 grey - *55-56*	8	10
R112	as above but maroon - *55-56*	6	11
R112	as above but brown - *55-56*	12	14
R112	**NE** 47205 grey - *56*	8	10
R112	as above but maroon - *56-57*	6	11
R112	**BR** M2313 (10 mm) red - *56-60*	6	11
R112	as above but dark red - *56-60*	5	10
R112	as above but grey - *56-60*	8	10
R112	**BR** M2313 (6 mm) dark red - *60-70*	5	10

W19a. 7-plank Wagon (2nd Type) (1981)

This was very like the body of the 1st type of open wagon listed in (above) but had woodgrain effect on the planking

(R1121)	blue with black strapping ex-'Devon Flyer' set - *09-10*	4	NA
(R1015)	**'7 Up'** green ex-R1015 set - *99-02*	5	NA
R028	**'Beatties'** yellow Sp Edn 1960 (Beatties) - *95*	8	10
R206	**'Chance & Hunt'** 142 orange-brown - *85-00*	5	7
(R6116)	**'Cowham & Shearer'** 25 red - *00-01*	5	7
(R6116)	as above but numbered 26 - *00-01*	5	7
(R6116)	as above but numbered 27 - *00-01*	5	7
R6116	above 3 wagons - *00-01*	NA	15
R036	**'DCA'** 4981 brown - *93-98*	5	7
R056	**'Edinburgh'** 558 grey Sp Edn 1000 (Harburn Hobbies) - *94*	9	11
R118	**'Emlyn'** 813 dark green - *86-96*	5	7
R469	as above but red ex-train sets - *90-95*	5	NA
R142	**'Evans & Bevan'** 388 black - *89-96*	5	7
R135	**'Glasgow'** 962 brown Sp Edn 1500 (Harburn Hobbies) - *96*	8	10
R6382	**'Hamley's** 2007' yellow Sp Edn 1500 (Hamley's) - *07*	7	9
R6382W	**'Hamley's** 2007' yellow ex-MO R1108 set - *08*	6	NA
R6430	**'Hamley's** 2008' red Sp Edn (Hamley's) – *08*	8	10
R6480	**'Hamley's** 2009' blue Sp Edn (Hamley's) – *09*	7	8
R6502	**'Hamley's** 2010' red Sp Edn (Hamley's) - *10*	8	10
R6292	'**Hornby** Merry Christmas' 2005 red with a resin load parcels - *05*	10	12
R6324	'**Hornby** Merry Christmas' 2006 blue with a resin load parcels - *06*	9	11
R6380	'**Hornby** Merry Christmas' 2007 maroon with a resin load parcels - *07*	8	10
R6?	'**Hornby** Merry Christmas' 2008 red with parcels - *08*	7	9
R6479	'**Hornby** Merry Christmas' 2009 red with parcels - *09*	6	8
R6502/46	'**Hornby** Merry Christmas' 2010 red or green with parcels - *10*	8	12
(R1020)	**'Kilkenny'** yellow ex-R1020 set - *99*	8	NA
R6381	**'ModelZone'** red+black Sp Edn 1000 (ModelZone) - *07*	6	8
R6031	'C **Murrell'** 10 red Sp Edn 500 (Jane's Trains) - *97*	10	12
R094	**'Pilkington'** 1489 red Ltd Sp Edn 17,700 (WHSmith) - *81*	6	7
-	**'Rumbelow'** * 10 red	5	NA
-	as above but numbered 11	5	NA
-	as above but numbered 12	5	NA
R6086	above 3 wagons - *99*	NA	15

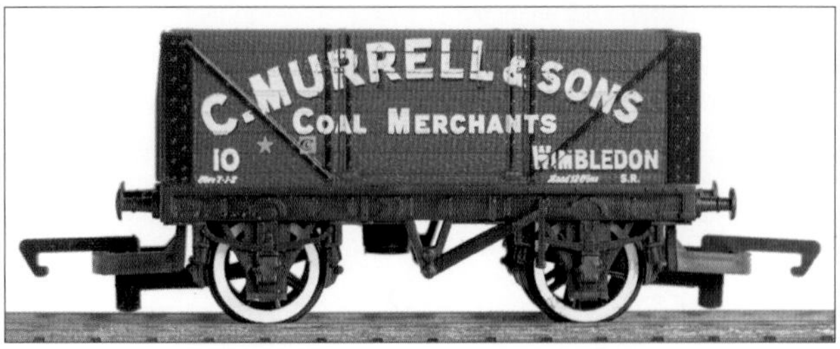

Hornby 7-plank wagon 'C.Murrell & Sons' [W19a]

Ex-Airfix 7-plank wagon - 'Breedon & Cloud Hill Lime Works' [W20]

R139	'Wm **Shaw**' 137 red - *84-86*	5	7
R031	**'Spiers'** 347 yellow - *92-96*	5	7
-	'Charles **Stott**' 78 brown	5	NA
-	as above but numbered 81	5	NA
-	as above but numbered 87	5	NA
R6005	above 3 wagons - *97*	NA	15
R208	**'Texas Homecare'** white - *85-86*	5	7
R155	**'Tudhope'** 40 black - *94-95*	5	7
-	'WE **Wise**' 18 black	5	NA
-	as above but numbered 19	5	NA
-	as above but numbered 21	5	NA
R6038	above 3 wagons - *98*	NA	15
(R1046)	red with a resin load parcels ex-R1046 set - *04, 08*	6	NA
	Thomas Series		
R9068	**'S C Ruffey'** grey+brown with face * - *03-10*	5	7
R9056	**'Sodor Scrap Co.'** blue * - *02-10*	5	7
R9234	red with black strapping - *06-10*	5	7
R9235	blue with grey strapping - *06-10*	5	7

* Also used in wagon packs.

W19b. Sheet Rail Wagon (7-plank) (1979)

R6211	**'Chance & Hunt'** 158 red W + tarpaulin - *03*	5	7
R6211A	as above but numbered 161 - *04-05*	5	7
R6211B	as above but numbered 162 - *04-05*	5	7

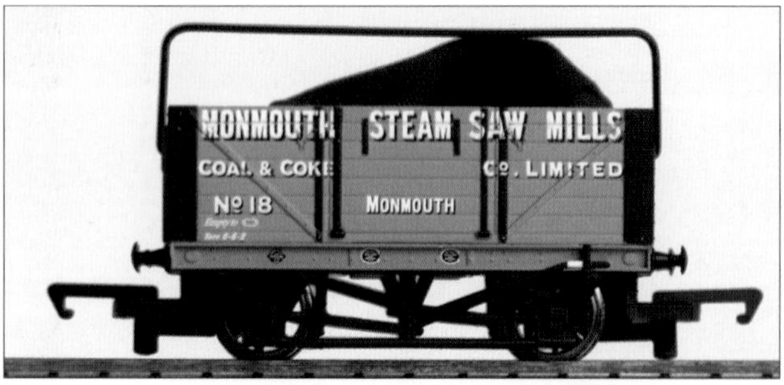

Sheet rail wagon - 'Monmouth Steam Saw Mills' [W19b]

R6297	**'Monmouth Steam Saw Mills'** 18 grey - *06*	5	7
R6297A	as above but numbered 17 - *07-09*	5	7
R016	**'Perfection'** 82 red - *82-83*	7	9
R240	**GW** 102971 grey - *79-81*	8	10

W20. 7-plank Wagon (ex-Airfix) (1998)

R6238	'IW **Baldwin & Co.**' 15 black - *04*	5	6
R6238A	as above but numbered 16 - *05-06*	5	6
(R6290)	as above but numbered 17 ex-Sp Edn wagon pack (Clifford James) - *05*	6	NA
(R6192)	**'Bannockburn'** 658 grey Sp Edn 500 (Harburn Hobbies) ex-pack - *02*	7	NA
R6068	**'Berthlwyd'** 385 dark green - *99-00*	5	7
(R6219)	as above but 'weathered' ex-wagon set - *03-05*	5	NA
R6164	**'Blidworth'** 2323 grey - *02*	5	7
(R1126)	**'Breedon & Cloud Hill Lime Works'** 21 cream (white chassis) ex-'Mixed Freight' set – *09-10*	10	9
R6516	**'Bullcroft Main Collieries'** 757 red-brown - *11*	5	7
R6513	**'City of Birmingham'** 1225 red - *11*	5	7
R6517	**'Coldendale Iron Co.'** 598 grey - *11*	5	7
R6494	**'Consolidated Steam Fishing & Ice Co.'** 403 red - *10*	5	6
(R1075)	'JL **Davies & Co.**' 121 red ex-set - *06-09*	5	NA
R6343	**'Firestone'** 2004 blue - *07*	5	7
(R6392)	as above but weathered ex-pack - *08-10*	5	NA
R6343A	**'Firestone'** 2008 blue - *08-11*	5	7
(R6192)	**'Forth & Clyde'** 249 red Sp Edn 500 (Harburn Hobbies) ex-pack - *02*	7	NA
R6067	**'Gedling'** 2598 red - *99-00*	5	7
(R1077)	**'Gellyceidrin'** 719 grey ex-set - *06-07*	5	NA
(R1097)	**'Gellyceidrin'** ? grey ex-set - *08-11*	5	NA
R6501	**'Hornby 2010'** red - *10*	5	6
R6427	**'Lambert & Cox'** 19 red Sp Edn 500 (*British Railway Modelling*) - *08*	5	7
R6129	**'Llewellyn Brothers'** 203 dark brown - *01*	5	7
R6302	'DR **Llewellyn**' 55 brown - *06-07*	5	7
(R6392)	as above but weathered ex-pack - *08-10*	5	NA
R6302A	'DR **Llewellyn**' 56 brown - *08-10*	5	7
R6518	**'Shelton Iron, Steel & Coal'** 1836 red-brown - *11*	5	7
R6201	'T **Threadgold**' 1915 red - *03*	5	7
(R6306)	as above but 'weathered' ex-pack - *06*	5	NA
R6059	**'Tredegar'** 5100 red - *98-99*	5	7
(R6156)	as above but 'weathered' ex-pack - *02-03*	5	NA
R6047	**'Wemyss'** 1997 grey - *98-99*	5	7
R6327A	as above but numbered 2866 Sp Edn (Harburn Hobbies) - *06*	7	9
R6327B	as above but numbered 2867 Sp Edn (Harburn Hobbies) - *06*	7	9
R6342	**LMS Loco Coal** 70170 grey - *07-11*	5	7
R6342A	**LMS Loco Coal** 7018 grey - *08-10*	5	7
R6394A	**BR Loco** M26347 light grey - *09-10*	7	9

Ex-Airfix 7-plank wagon - LMS Loco Coal [W20]

R6394	**BR Loco** M26333 red-brown - *08*	5	7
R6394A	**BR Loco** M26347 red-brown - *09-11*	5	8
	AB Gee ex-R2138 Sp Edn*		
(R2138)	**BR** M609546 grey - *99*	7	NA
(R2138)	as above but numbered M609580 - *99*	7	NA
(R2138)	as above but numbered M609585 - *99*	7	NA
(R2138)	as above but numbered M609600 - *99*	7	NA
(R2138)	as above but numbered M609601 - *99*	7	NA

* These were specially made for the A.B.Gee commissioned Colliery train pack (R2138) in 1999 and 1000 of each were made.

W21. Coke Wagon (7-plank) (1971)

This was similar to a 5-plank wagon but had its sides extended upwards with open bars.

R006	**'Barrow'** 1226 white - *82*	7	9
R719	as above but dark blue-grey - *80-81*	6	8
R6444	**'Bedwas Coke'** 331 red-brown - *09-10*	5	8
R6496	**'Carpenter & Sons'** 28 red - *10*	5	6

R6443	**'Coalite'** 401 red-brown - *09-10*	5	8
-	**'Dinnington'** 250 brown	5	NA
-	as above but numbered 254	5	NA
-	as above but numbered 258	5	NA
R6007	above 3 boxed set - *97*	NA	18
-	**'Gilbert'** * 211 grey W	5	NA
-	as above but numbered 212	5	NA
-	as above but numbered 213	5	NA
R6151	above 3 in boxed set - *02-04*	NA	16
-	**'Gilbert'** * 218 grey W	5	NA
-	as above but numbered 219	5	NA
-	as above but numbered 220	5	NA
R6151A	above 3 in boxed set - *03-04*	NA	16
R6063	**'Miller'** 19 grey Sp Edn 1200 (Harburn Hobbies) - *98*	8	10
R101	**'Plean Colliery**, **Bannockburn'** 4 grey heat print - *73-?*	5	7
R101	as above but tampo printed - *?-79*	8	10
R719	**'Roberts Davy'** 25 grey - *80*	7	9
R203	'Arther **H Stabler'** 21 grey - *95-00*	5	8
-	**'TWW'** 1690 brown	5	NA
-	as above but numbered 1692	5	NA
-	as above but numbered 1694	5	NA
R6037	above 3 in boxed set - *98*	NA	18

Coke Wagon - 'TWW' [W21]

R6495	**'TTW'** (Thos. W Ward) 1644A red - *10*	5	6
R6527	**GC** 06399 grey - *11*	5	7
R781	**NER** 52220 dark grey - *71-73*	6	8
R781	as above but rail blue - *?*	7	9
R781	as above but grey - *73*	8	10

* This appeared to have been misspelled 'Cilbert'. The models were based on wagons belonging to H Gilbert of Birmingham. ** Spelt 'Arthur' on the box.

W22. 8-plank End-Tipping Wagon (1982)

This wagon was introduced with the R515 and R528 operating tipper and conveyor sets but its value as a model in its own right was recognised in 1995 and it was released from then on in various guises without the tipping lever attached.

R6212	**'Adler & Allan'** 107 red - *03*	5	7
R6212A	as above but numbered 108 - *04*	5	7
R6212B	as above but numbered 112 - *05-06*	5	7
(R1085)	as above but numbered 112 - *07*	5	7
(R1070)	as above but numbered 117 - *07-10*	5	NA
-	**'Airedale'** 3434 black	5	NA
-	as above but numbered 3438	5	NA
-	as above but numbered 3440	5	NA
R6114	above 3 wagons - *00-01*	NA	15
-	**'Ammanford'** 15 brown *	5	NA
-	as above but numbered 16	5	NA
-	as above but numbered 18	5	NA
R6088	above 3 wagons - *99*	NA	15
R6344	**'Barkby Jolliffe'** 814 red - *07*	5	7
R6344A	as above but numbered 806 - *08-09*	5	7
R6303	'H.C. **Bull & Co.'** 101 red - *06-08*	5	7
R6345	**'Colman's'** 19 yellow - *07*	5	7
(R6450)	as above weathered ex-pack numbered 26 - *09-10*	5	NA
R6345A	as above but numbered 34 - *08*	5	7

8-plank end-tipping wagon - 'Colman's' [W22]

R?	**'East Valley Scrap Co**.' blue - *made?*	NPG	NPG
R6530	'George **Field & Son**' 15 grey - *11*	5	7
R003	**'Fife'** 963 brown So Edn 2,000 (Harburn Hobbies) - *95*	9	11
R199	**'Great Mountain'** 980 brown - *95-01*	5	7
R032	**'Hargreaves'** 455 grey tipping lever - *82-84*	5	7
R6323	**'Hornby Railway Co**.' 2006 red Ltd Edn 3,000 - *06*	5	7
R6445	**'Lunt'** 724 grey+black - *09*	5	8
R6529	**'Manton**' 6502 red - *11*	5	7
(R6449)	**'McKay'** 479 red W ex-wagon set - *09*	6	NA
R6239	**'McKay**' 477 red - *04*	5	7
R6239A	as above but numbered 478 - *05-06*	5	7
R6028	**'Newbattle'** 319 black Sp Edn 1,500 (Harburn Hobbies) - *97*	9	11

* This was also used in wagons packs.

W23. 8-plank LWB Open Wagon (2002)

(R1085)	yellow ex-set - *07-08*	4	NA
(R2669)	**'Berthlwyd**' 135 green (RailRoad) - *07-11*	4	NA
(R1127)	**'Beswick**' 996 red ex-'City Industrial' MO set - *09*	5	NA
(R2670)	**'Charringtons**' 7401 red (RailRoad) - *07-11*	NA	
(R1151)	**'Edinburgh Collieries Co.**' 760 grey ex-'Caledonian Belle' train set - *11*	4	NA
(R1121)	**'Highley Mining Company**' 425 red ex-set - *09*	4	NA
(R6482)	'DR **Llewellyn'** 55 red ex-RaiRoad wagon set - *10-11*	4	NA
(R1130K)	**'Lochgelly**' red ex various MO sets - *08*	4	NA
X0209	same as above ex-MO R1111KF set - *08*	4	NA

RailRoad set of open wagons [W23]

R?	**'Modern Transport**' 1206 grey - *09*	4	NPG
(R2669)	**'Parkinson**' 42 blue (RailRoad) - *07-11*	4	NA
R6370	**'Tredegar**' 5015 red (RailRoad) - *07-11*	4	5
(R6365)	same but numbered 5014 ex-pack - *07-11*	4	NA
(R6482)	'T.**Threadgold'** 1915 black ex-RailRoad wagon set - *10-11*	4	NA
X5786	**'?'** red ex-various MO sets - *08*	4	NA
X10231	same as above ex-MO sets - *08*	4	NA
(R6482)	**LMS** Loco Coal 70170 grey ex-RailRoad wagon set - *10-11*	4	NA
	Thomas Series		
R9053	grey with face - *02-10*	4	5
R9054	grey with different face - *02-10*	4	5

W24. Mixed Wagon Packs

In 1998, in order to clear old stocks of the 'First' Series of 9' wagons, Hornby introduced an assorted pack of three (R6035). This contained 6-plank, 4-plank and 3-plank wagons and 280 packs were assembled. This exercise was repeated in 2001 but with surplus wagons from triple wagon sets of two years earlier. There were also wagon packs commissioned by retailers which will be found here. Packs containing wagons all of the same type and finish, but with different running numbers will not be found in this table but are included in their appropriate table for that type. Most sets have a weathered finish.

R6002	**'Hotson'** + **'Turner'** + **'Badland'** in original boxes with outer sleeve Sp Edn 1500 (Toys R Us) - *98?*	NA	18

R6035	3 x standard 9' wheel base PO wagons (mixed) Sp Edn 240 - *98*	NA	18
R6113	3 x standard 10' wheel base PO wagons (mixed) - *01*	NA	18
R6117	3 x standard 10' wheel base PO wagons (mixed) - *01*	NA	18
R6190	2 x 3-plank '**Robert McAlpine**' + '**Babcock' & 'Wilcox'** Sp Edn 500 (Harburn Hobbies) - *02*	NA	12
R6156	3 wagons W - '**Tredegar**' + '**ICI (Lime) Ltd**' + '**Richard Weale**' - *02-03*	NA	15
R6191	2 x 4-plank '**John Nicolson**' + '**William Mitchell'** Sp Edn 500 (Harburn Hobbies) - *02*	NA	12
R6192	'**Forth & Clyde**' + '**Bannockburn**' Sp Edn 500 (Harburn Hobbies) - *02*	NA	12
R6219	3 wagons W - '**Berthlwyd**' + '**Pontithel Chemical Co**' + '**Mark Williams**' - *03*	NA	15

Mixed set of weathered wagons [W24]

R6226	3 wagons - large steel '**Glenhafod**', 'Monobloc' '**Shell**' black, small tank '**Castrol**' - *05*	NA	?
R6227	4 wagons - **BR** small yellow crane, **EW&S** HAA hopper wagon, **BR** ZKV Tippler grey+ yellow, **BR** van brown - *05*	NA	?
R6228	5 wagons - **GWR** 'Conflat' + container, '**Cammell Laird**' 3-plank, '**Parkinson**' 6-plank, **BR** Lowmac + '**ESG**' crate, '**Lyle**' 5-plank - *05*	NA	?
R6278	3 wagons W - '**Berthlwyd**' + '**Easter Iron Mines**' + '**Imperial Chemical Industries**' - *05*	NA	18
R6279	**'Crook' & 'Greenway+Somerset Trading Co'.+'Pontithel Chemical'** W set of 3 - *05*	NA	18
R6290	5 wagon pack - '**Spiers**' 6-plank, '**Teign Valley**' 4-plank, '**Englands Glory**' 6-plank, '**Baldwin**' 7-plank, **GWR** 'Toad' Sp Edn (Clifford James) - *05*	NA	30
R6305	3 wagons W - 6-plank '**Sneyd**', 6-plank '**Parkinson**', 3-plank '**Cammell Laird**' - *06-07*	NA	19
R6306	3 wagons W - 7-plank '**Threadgold**', 3-plank '**Ceirog**', 4-plank '**Dutton Massey**' - *06-07*	NA	19
R6392	3-plank '**Trimsaran**' 51, 7-plank '**Firestone**' 2004, 7-plank '**D R Llewwllyn**' 55 - *08-10*	NA	25
R6393	6-plank '**Bute**' 325, 6-plank '**C&G Ayres**' 400, 4-plank '**Clee Hill**' - *08-10*	NA	25
R6449	5-plank '**S Brookman**' 31, 8-plank '**McKay**' 479, 4-plank '**The Harts Hill Iron Co.**' 7 - *09*	NA	25
R6450	3-plank '**James Carter**' 174, 6-plank '**Spiers**' 349, 8-plank '**Colmans**' 26 - *09-10*	NA	25
	Thomas Series Wagon Packs		
R9090	2 x long 8-plank, '**Tidmouth**' milk tank - *05-09*	NA	23
R9091	'**Sodor**' tank, '**S C Ruffey**', tar tank - *05-10*	NA	23
R9092	5-plank, '**Sodor**' 7-plank, brake van - *05-10*	NA	23
R9093	3 x circus vans - *05-07*	NA	26
R9094	3 x circus vans - *05-10*	NA	26
R9095	Raspberry tank, ice cream van, cream tank - *05-09*	NA	23

W25. Large 9-plank Wagon (ex-Airfix) (1998)

R65/5	'**Denaby**' 3246 light grey - *11*	5	7
R6048	'The **Gas Light & Coke**' 766 grey - *98-99*	6	8
R6177	'**Hornby 2002**' grey - *02*	6	8
R6362	'**Hornby 2007**' SC50 ed - *07*	6	8
R6058	**NE** 30987 grey Loco - *98-99*	6	8
R6108	**BR** E30991 grey - *00-01*	5	7
R6108A	as above but numbered E30996 - *02*	5	7
R6108B	as above but numbered E30995 - *03-04*	5	7
R6108C	as above but numbered E30987 - *05*	5	7
R6108D	as above but numbered E30942 - *06*	5	7
R6108E	as above but numbered E30938 - *07-08*	5	7
R6108F	as above but numbered E157943 Loco - *09*	5	8
R6108G	as above but numbered E30911 - *09-11*	5	8

Ex-Airfix 9-plank wagon - BR [W25]

-	**BR** E61004 grey W	5	NA
-	as above but numbered E61005	5	NA
-	as above but numbered E61006	5	NA
R6218	above 3 wagons in a sleeve - *03-04*	NA	16
R6401	**BR** E157941 grey 'Loco' - *08*	5	7
R6401A	**BR** E157943 grey 'Loco' - *09-10*	5	8

W26. OAA/OBA Open Wagon (1979)

R235	**BRe Railfreight** 110003 brown - *79-81,87*	6	8
R248	**BRe Railfreight** Speedlink Distribution 110264 grey+red - *81-85, 87-90*	6	8
R209	**BRe Railfreight** Speedlink Distribution 110264 grey+red + 5 dice Sp Edn 3200 - *83*	20	35
R6348	**BRe Railfreight** 10098 grey+red OBA - *07-08*	8	10
R067	**BR Railfreight** 100005 dark grey OAA - *90-96*	6	8
R401	**BR Railfreight Distribution** 100027 grey OAA - *96-97*	6	8
R6383	**'Llanfairpwllgwyngyllgogerychwyrndrob-wllllantysiliogogogogch'** maroon Sp Edn 1500 (James Pringle Weavers*) - *08*	13	15

OBA wool mill promotional wagon [W26]

R6478	as above but yellow Sp Edn 1,000 (HCClub) - *09*	13	15
R035	**'Hornby Railways 1993'** red Ltd Edn 3600 - *93*	8	10

* This is a subsidiary of Edinburgh Woollen Mills Ltd and are based at the station.

Steel Open Wagons

W27. Drop-side Wagon (1954)

This was a low-sided steel type 13T wagon with both long sides hinged so that they could be dropped down. It was based broadly on LMS design. For 1966 the body moulding was altered to provide door stops to reduce the danger of the doors breaking off.

R113	**BR** B712 (2.7mm high) grey - *54*	10	12
R113	as above but maroon - *54*	6	8
R113	as above but grey-green - *54*	15	17
R113	**BR** B712 (2mm high) maroon - *54-56*	6	8
R113	as above but grey-green - *54-56*	13	15
R113	as above but bright red - *54-56*	12	14
R113	as above but orange-brown - *54-56*	15	17
R113	**BR** 8051 grey - *54*	20	22
R113	**BR** B4593 maroon flat top '3' - *57-65*	6	8
R113	as above but grey - *57-65*	8	10
R113	as above but pale brown* - *60*	10	12
R113	as above but dung-brown - *62*	12	14
R113	**BR** B4593 maroon round top '3' - *66-73*	6	8
R113	as above but grey - *66-73*	8	10
R113	**BR** B4596 - *?*	NPG	NPG
R113	**BR** B4597 maroon - *68-71*	6	8
R113	as above but bright red - *68?*	10	12
R113NP	maroon. no printing ex-starter sets - *c68*	8	NA
R113NP	bright red. no printing ex-starter sets - *c68*	8	NA

* Also known as Caramac brown.

Tri-ang drop-side steel wagon [W27]

W28. ZCA 'Sea Horse' Wagon

Long wheelbase, low-sided spoil conversion employing the OBA/OCA running gear. While planned for release in 2009, the high diversity of designs led to their being abandoned.

R6463	*? – not made*	NA	NA
R6464	*? – not made*	NA	NA
R6465	*? – not made*	NA	NA

W29. ZCA 'Sea Urchin' Wagon

Long wheelbase, low-sided spoil conversion employing the OBA/OCA running gear. While planned for release in 2009, the high diversity of designs led to their being abandoned.

R6469	*? – not made*	NA	NA
R6470	*? – not made*	NA	NA
R6471	*? – not made*	NA	NA

W30. Small Mineral Wagon (1960)

This was based on an all steel wagon with side and one end door and was initially offered with or without a coal load which was a black moulded plastic insert (R244). For these add £1 unboxed and £4 mint boxed.

R244	**'Beatties'** yellow four addresses (2 each side) Sp Edn 3000 (Beatties) - *73*	10	20

Tri-ang steel mineral wagon - 'Beatties' [W30]

R243	**BR** B75201 pale green-grey - *60-72*	5	7
R243	as above but stripes on wrong sides - *60-61*	7	10
R243	**BR** B75201 pale grey - *72-75*	5	7
R243	as above but very pale grey - *72*	12	14
R217	as above but slate-grey - *76-78*	5	7
R243NP	yellow no printing ex-starter sets - *c68*	8	NA
R243NP	bright blue no printing ex-starter sets - *c68*	8	NA

W31a. Tippler Mineral Wagon (1979)

R009	**'B&Q'** B388404 white - *92-96*	5	7
R501	**'Lion'** 221 black Ltd Edn 2560 - *91*	7	9
R?	**GW** 102971 grey - *79?*	6	NA
R239	**BR** B385760 brown 'Stone' - *79-86*	5	7
R6085	as above but numbered B385640 - *99-00*	5	7
R6085A	as above but numbered B386639 - *01*	5	7
R6085B	as above but numbered B385726 - *02*	5	7
R6085C	as above but numbered B386447 - *03-05*	5	7
R6085CW	as above but numbered B386447 ex-MO R1063 set - *08*	6	NA
R6085D	as above but numbered B386523 - *05-06*	5	7
R6085E	as above but numbered B385932 - *06-07*	5	7
R6085EW	as above but numbered B386447 ex-MO R1083L set - *08*	6	NA
R6085F	as above but numbered B388421 - *08-10*	5	7
(R1075)	as above but numbered B386337 - *06-09*	5	NA
-	**BR** B388435 brown	5	NA
-	as above numbered B388436	5	NA
-	as above numbered B388437	5	NA
R6473	set of above 3 wagons (RailRoad) - *09-11*	NA	12
-	**BR** B385641 brown W 'Stone'	5	NA
-	as above but numbered B385642	5	NA
-	as above but numbered B385643	5	NA
R6155	above 3 wagons - *02*	NA	15
-	**BR** B386001 brown W 'Stone'	5	NA
-	as above but numbered B386002	5	NA
-	as above but numbered B386003	5	NA
R6155A	above 3 wagons - 03	NA	15

'Tippler' wagon for stone traffic [W31a]

R6361	**BR** B386569 brown 'Stone' (logo) 7623 - *07-08*	5	7
R079	**BR** B388469 brown MSV - *87-01*	5	7
R6022	**BR** B433698 red+yellow ZKV - *97-02*	5	NA
R6107	**BR** DB389035 grey+yellow ZKV - *00-01*	5	7
R6107A	as above but numbered DB389040 - *02-05*	5	7
R6107B	as above but numbered DB388263 - *05-06*	5	7
R6107C	as above but numbered DB387631 - *05-09*	5	7
-	**BR** B? grey+yellow ZKV	5	NA
-	as above but numbered B?	5	NA
-	as above but numbered B?	5	NA
R6483	above 3 wagons (RailRoad) - *10-11*	NA	15
R081	**BR** B437000 grey 'Iron Ore' - *90-93*	5	7
R388	as above but numbered B388639 - *96-98*	5	7
R6000	as above but numbered B436192 - *97-98*	5	7
R6061	**'Hornby 1999'** grey Ltd Edn 2500 - *99*	8	11

W31b. 27T Iron Ore Tippler Wagon (2011)

This is a completely new wagon with a highly detailed body and chassis..

R6504	**BR** B747596 grey pre-TOPS - *11*	12	16
R6505	**BR** B383560 grey post-TOPS MSO - *11*	12	16
-	**BR** B383561 grey W pre-TOPS	12	NA
-	as above but numbered B383562	12	NA
-	as above but numbered B383563	12	NA
R6506	above set of 3 weathered wagons - *11*	NA	48

W32. Large Mineral Wagon (1972)

SS = Silver Seal wheels. nls = no letter shading.

R?	**'Black & Reoch'** 22 rail-blue - *?*	6	7
R021	as above but red - *82-84*	5	7
R021	as above but no letter shading - *82-84*	5	NA

Large steel mineral wagon 'Black & Reoch' [W32]

R136	**'Bolsover'** 6390 unpainted maroon - *78-79*	5	7
R136	as above but painted grey inside - *78-79*	5	7
R136	as before but no letter shading - *78-79*	6	NA
R136	as before but dark blue-grey moulding with a maroon paint finish - *80-81*	5	7
R136	as above but grey moulding - *80-81*	5	7
R?	as above but dark blue-grey nls - *84-85*	6	NA
R?	as above but rail-blue - *83-87*	6	NA
R?	as above but rail-blue nls - *83-87*	5	NA

R136	as above but black - *?*	6	NA
R?	as above but black nls - *?*	6	NA
R211	**'British Steel'** 20 blue - *85-00*	5	7
R22	'Wm **Cory'** 8008 maroon, transfers * - *72-74*	7	8
R22	'Wm **Cory'** 8008 maroon, tampo printed - *74*	6	7
R6163	**'Glenhafod'** 2277 black - *02-03*	5	7
R310	**'Miller'** (Australia) orange-brown - *74-75*	9	11
R386	**'Miller'** (Australia) orange-brown SS - *76-78*	9	11
R102	**'NCB'** 3471 black - *73-78*	5	7
R093	**'Norstand'** 480 blue - *75*	5	7
R220	**'Norstand'** 480 blue SS - *76-79*	5	7
R730	**'SC'** 25506 light olive-grey - *80-81*	6	7
R730	as above but olive-grey - *86-92*	5	7
R?	as above but red nls - *82*	8	NPG
R379	**'Hornby Railways 1996'** red Ltd Edn 3000 - *96*	6	10
R6372	**EWS** DB890224 maroon (RailRoad) - *07-11*	4	4
-	as above but DB890221 ex-pack	4	NA
-	as above but DB890222 ex-pack	4	NA
-	as above but DB890223 ex-pack	4	NA
R6367	above 3 wagons (RailRoad) - *07-11*	NA	11
R100	non-printed red+yellow	5	NA
R085	as above but blue+yellow	5	NA
R088	as above but yellow+red	5	NA
R102	above 3 wagons (Station Master) - *93-96*	NA	12
(R1031)	grey ex-starter set - *02*	5	NA
(R1031)	brown ex-starter set - *02*	5	NA

* The transfers on these were particularly vulnerable and ones in good condition are not easy to find.

W33. 21T Steel Mineral Wagon (ex-Airfix) (1998)

R6498	**'AAC Anthracite'** T300 black - *10*	5	6
R6051	**'Charringtons'** 7301 red - *98-99*	7	9
R6057	**'Cilely'** 12 black - *98-01*	6	8

Ex-Airfix 21T steel mineral wagon - 'Charringtons' [W33]

R6528	'**Consolidated Fisheries**' 600 black - *11*	5	7
R6071	'Richard **Thomas'** 23301 black - *99-00*	6	8
R6127	**'West Midlands'** 16 black - *01*	7	9
R6070	**BR** P339290K grey - *99-00*	5	7
R6161	**BR** B310312K brown - *02*	5	7
R6161A	as above but numbered B310824K - *03*	5	7
R6161B	as above but numbered B310796K - *04-05*	5	7
R6161C	as above but numbered B310437K - *05-06*	5	7
R6161D	as above but numbered B310192K - *06-07*	5	7
R6161W	as above but numbered ? ex-MO R1083L set - *08*	6	NA
(R1036)	as above but numbered B310799K - *03-06*	5	NA
R6400	**BR** B311281 red-brown MDV - *08*	7	9
R6400A	**BR** B312249 red-brown MDV - *09-10*	7	9

W34a. MHA 'Coalfish' Box Open (2003)

R6216	**EWS** 394119 maroon - *03-04*	6	8
-	**EWS** 394120 maroon W	7	NA
-	as above but numbered 394121	7	NA
-	as above but numbered 394122	7	NA
R6225	above 3 wagons - *03-05*	NA	30

W34b. MHA 'Coalfish' Box Open (2004)

New, more accurate body with reduced height, additional end ribs and an angled top lip.

R6216A	**EWS** 394123 maroon - *04-06*	9	13
R6216B	as above but numbered 394228 - *07-10*	9	14
-	**EWS** 394831 maroon W	9	NA
-	as above but numbered 394832	9	NA
-	as above but numbered 394833	9	NA
R6225A	above 3 wagons - *03-07*	NA	35

MHA 'Coalfish' box open wagon - EWS [W34b]

-	**EWS** 394587 maroon W	9	NA
-	as above but numbered 394589	9	NA
-	as above but numbered 394590	9	NA
R6225B	above 3 wagons - *08-10*	NA	39

W35. ZBA 'Rudd' Ballast Wagon (2008)

21T departmental ballast wagon converted from a coal hopper wagon. Only the chassis of the original wagon remains.

R6415	**BR** DB972007 grey+yellow - *08-11*	9	12
-	**BR** DB972004 grey+yellow W	9	NA
-	as above but numbered DB972005	9	NA
-	as above but numbered DB972006	9	NA
R6416	above 3 wagons - *08-11*	NA	34

W36. ZCV 'Clam' Ballast Wagon (2008)

21T departmental ballast wagon converted from a coal hopper wagon by Metro-Cammell in 1957.

R6417	**BR** DB973108 grey+yellow - *08-11*	9	12
-	**BR** DB973105 grey+yellow W	9	NA
-	as above but numbered DB973106	9	NA
-	as above but numbered DB973107	9	NA
R6418	above 3 wagons - *08-11*	NA	34

ZCV 'Clam' ballast wagon [W36]

Hopper Wagons

W37. Ore Hopper & Engineer's Wagon (1958)

This was the early grain wagon without the top section fitted. Most models were fitted with a working trapdoor triggered by a lever on the side but, for a while, they had a solid base.

R214	**'Consett Iron'** 1441 maroon - *75*	7	9
R232	as above but dark green - *76-79*	6	10
R732	as above but dark green paint finish - *80-82*	15	17
R214	**BR** B1402 pale green-grey - *60-63*	6	10
R214	as above but no black panel - *58-59*	10	14
R347	**BR** black Engineer's - *63-65*	6	10
R347	as above but thick letter 'E' - *63*	12	16
R347	**BR** dark green Engineer's - *66*	6	10
R347	as above but bottom hatch - *67-68*	6	10

W38. Large Hopper Wagon (1969)

This 35T wagon employed the bottom half of the large bulk grain wagon.

R103	**'Roberts'** 1100 black - *73-74*	7	12
R214	**BR** B35000 pale grey - *69-72*	6	10

W39. 20T Hopper (ex-Airfix) (1997)

R6017	**NE** 194720 dark grey - *97-00*	5	7
R6125	as above but numbered 193254 - *01*	5	7

R6125A	as above but numbered 194720 - *02-03*	5	7
R6125B	as above but numbered 193259 - *03-04*	5	7
R6125C	as above but numbered 193256 - *05*	5	7
R6125D	as above but numbered 414321 - *06-08*	6	8
R6125E	as above but numbered 193452 - *07-08*	6	8
(R1030)	as above but numbered 193265 - *02-03*	5	NA

Ex-Airfix 20T hopper wagon - LNER [W39]

R6016	**BR** B413161K grey - *97-01*	5	7
R6124	as above but numbered E252543K - *01*	5	7
R6124A	as above but numbered B414551K - *02*	5	7
R6124B	as above but numbered B414145K - *03-05*	5	7
R6124C	as above but numbered B414050K - *05*	5	7
R6124D	as above but numbered B193471K - *06*	5	7
R6124E	as above but numbered B414392K - *07-08*	6	8
(R1070)	as above but numbered B414087K - *07-10*	6	NA

W40a. PGA Aggregate Hopper (1988)

R004	**'BIS'** BIS7987 white - *91*	9	12

PGA aggregate hopper wagon - 'Caib' [W40a]

R6448	**'Caib'** 14445 pale grey+blue W + graffiti - *09-11*	9	14
-	**'ECC Quarries'** PR14367 blue	9	NA
-	as above but numbered PR14368	9	NA
-	as above but numbered PR14369	9	NA
R6332	above 3 wagons - *07-10*	NA	33
-	**'ECC Quarries'** PR14374 blue	9	NA
-	as above but numbered PR14375	9	NA
-	as above but numbered PR14376	9	NA
R6332A	above 3 wagons - *08-10*	NA	41
R026	**'Redland'** REDA14502 dull-green - *90-91*	8	10
-	**'Redland'** REDA14502 buff W	8	NA
-	as above but numbered REDA14503	8	NA
-	as above but numbered REDA14504	8	NA
R6254	above 3 wagons - *04*	NA	30
-	**'RMC'** PR14376 red W	8	NA
-	as above but numbered PR14377	8	NA
-	as above but numbered PR14378	8	NA
R6154	above 3 wagons - *02*	NA	30
-	**'RMC'** PR14365 red W	8	NA
-	as above but numbered PR14366	8	NA
-	as above but numbered PR14367	8	NA
R6154A	above 3 wagons - *03*	NA	30
R013	**'Tarmac'** TAMC14865 white+drab - *88-89*	8	9
R002	**'Tarmac QP'** TAM14869 dark green - *91-93*	8	10
R6217	as above but TAMC14863 very dark brown - *03-04*	8	10
R6217A	as above but TAMC14865 very dark brown - *05-07*	9	12
-	**'Tarmac QP'** TAMC14871 black W	8	NA
-	as above but numbered TAMC14872	8	NA
-	as above but numbered TAMC14873	8	NA
R6280	above 3 wagons - *05-06*	NA	30
R019	**'Tilbury'** TRB14521 red+white - *88-89*	8	10
R015	**'Yeoman'** PR14069 blue+silver - *88-96*	8	10
R6386	**'Yeoman Procor'** PR14180 blue+grey - *08*	9	NA

W40b. PGA Aggregate Hopper Wagon (ex-Lima) (2011)

This wagon was introduced by Lima in 1980 and last used in 1987.

R6487	**'Yeoman'** PR14130 pale grey+blue - *11*	7	9
R6534	**'Yeoman'** PR14181 pale grey+blue - *11*	7	9
-	**'Yeoman'** PR14108 pale grey+blue W	7	NA
-	as above but numbered PR14100	7	NA
-	as above but numbered PR14107	7	NA
R6486	above 3 wagons - *11*	NA	25
-	**'Yeoman'** ? pale grey+blue W	7	NA
-	as above but numbered ?	7	NA
-	as above but numbered ?	7	NA
R6511	above 3 wagons - *11*	NA	27

W41. HEA Hopper (ex-Dapol) (1998)

R6050	**EWS** 361870 maroon - *98*	5	7
R6084	as above but numbered 361866 - *99-00*	5	7
R6049	**Loadhaul** 361874 black+orange - *98*	5	7

HEA hopper wagon - EWS [W41]

R6083	as above but numbered 361876 - *99-02*	5	7
R6083A	as above but numbered 360695 - *03-05*	5	7
-	**Loadhaul** 361878 black+orange W	5	NA
-	as above but numbered 361879	5	NA
-	as above but numbered 361880	5	NA
R6152	above 3 wagons - *02*	NA	22
-	**Loadhaul** 360696 black+orange W	5	NA
-	as above but numbered 360697	5	NA
-	as above but numbered 360698	5	NA
R6152A	above 3 wagons - *03-07*	NA	22
-	**Loadhaul** 360699 black+orange W	5	NA
-	as above but numbered 360700	5	NA
-	as above but numbered 360701	5	NA
R6152B	above 3 wagons - *04-07*	NA	22
R6384	**Mainline** 363643 grey W - *08-10*	6	9
R6295	**Virgin Trains 'Warley 2005'** red+white Sp Edn 500 (Virgin Trains) - *05*	9	12

W42. 'Tope' Coal Hopper Wagon (2008)

Departmental ballast wagon.

R6419	**BR** DB970297 grey+yellow - *08-11*	9	12

'Tope' coal hopper wagon [W42]

-	**BR** DB970297 grey+yellow W	9	NA
-	as above but numbered DB970295	9	NA
-	as above but numbered DB970296	9	NA
R6420	above 3 wagons - *08-09*	NA	34

W43. ZFO/ZFP 'Trout' Ballast Hopper Wagon (2011)

Departmental ballast wagon.

R6544	? - *11*	13	17
R6545	? - *11*	13	17
-	? - *11*	13	NA
-	as above but numbered ?	13	NA
-	as above but numbered ?	13	NA
R6512	above 3 wagons - *11*	NA	50

W44a. HAA Merry-Go-Round Hopper (1980)

R238	**BR** 351540 silver+brown - *80-81*	6	8
R249	**BR Railfreight** 352556 silver+red - *81-03*	5	7
R039	**BR Railfreight** 351923 silver+yellow Coal - *88-90*	6	8
R033	**BR Railfreight** 350897 silver+yellow Coal (small) - *90-03*	5	7
R6041	**EW&S** 353397 maroon - *98-04*	5	7
R6041A	as above but numbered 354879 - *01-04*	5	7
-	**EW&S** 353390 maroon W	5	NA
-	as above but numbered 353391	5	NA
-	as above but numbered 353392	5	NA
R6150	set of above 3 wagons - *02*	NA	22
-	**EW&S** 352487 maroon W	5	NA
-	as above but numbered 352488	5	NA
-	as above but numbered 352489	5	NA
R6150A	above 3 wagons - *03-04*	NA	22

W44b. HAA 32.5t MGR Hopper (2003)

R6533	**BR** 355203 silver+brown - *11*	16	22
R6213	**BR** 355760 silver+red - *03-04*	10	12
R6213A	as above but numbered 355764 - *04-07*	10	12
-	**BR** 355761 silver+red W	10	NA
-	as above but numbered 355762	10	NA
-	as above but numbered 355763	10	NA
R6222	above 3 wagons - *03-05*	NA	33
-	**BR** 356732 silver+red W	10	NA
-	as above but numbered 356733	10	NA
-	as above but numbered 356734	10	NA
R6222A	above 3 wagons -	NA	33
-	**BR** 357570 silver+brown W	14	NA
-	as above but numbered 357571	14	NA
-	as above but numbered 357572	14	NA
R6222B	above 3 wagons - *08-10*	NA	58
R6331	**BR Mainline** 350469 silver+red - *07-08*	10	12

HAA 'Merry-go-round' hopper wagon [W44b]

-	**BR (Saltair)** 256710* silver+blue W Sp Edn 500 (Harburn Hobbies)	15	NA
-	as above but numbered 350801	15	NA
-	as above but numbered 354607	15	NA
R6429	above 3 Harburn Hobbies Saltair wagons - *08*	NA	45

*Possibly an incorrect number used (356710?)

W45a. HBA MGR with Hood (2002)

R6157	**BR** 350001 silver+red - *02*	7	10
R6157A	as above but numbered 350002 - *03-04*	7	10

W45b. HBA/HFA 32.5t MGR + Hood (2003)

There were errors with the first model in 2002 and so the following year an improved model appeared. The HBA and HFA are the same model but carry different classifications and tare weights.

R6333A	**BR** 358761 silver+brown HFA - *07-09*	12	20
R6333B	as above but numbered 356707 - *07-10*	12	20
R6333C	as above but numbered 356962 - *07-10*	12	20
R6215	**EWS** 368300 silver+red HBA - *03-04*	12	16
R6215A	as above but numbered 368304 - *05-06*	12	16
R6215B	as above but numbered 368340 - *06-08*	12	16
-	**EWS** 368301 silver+red W HBA	12	NA
-	as above but numbered 368302	12	NA
-	as above but numbered 368303	12	NA
R6224	above 3 wagons - *03-06*	NA	33

Bulk Grain & Powder Wagons

W46a. CDA China Clay Hopper (1988)

This was basically the HAA merry-go-round hopper wagon with a lid on it.

R052	**'ECC'** 353224 silver+blue - *88-92,97*	7	10

CDA china clay covered hopper wagon [W46a]

R6106	as above but numbered 375007 - *00-03*	7	10

W46b. CDA China Clay Hopper (2003)

R6214	**'ECC'** 375048 silver+blue - *03-04*	12	16
R6214A	as above but numbered 375052 - *05-06*	12	16
-	**'ECC'** 375049 silver+blue W	12	NA
-	as above but numbered 375050	12	NA
-	as above but numbered 375051	12	NA
R6223	above 3 wagons - *03-05*	NA	40
-	**'ECC'** 375125 silver+blue W	12	NA
-	as above but numbered 375126	12	NA
-	as above but numbered 375127	12	NA
R6223A	above 3 wagons - *06-07*	NA	40
R6334	**EWS** 375004 silver+maroon - *07-11*	12	20
R6387	**EWS** 375118 silver+maroon W - *08-11*	12	20
-	as above but numbered 375045	12	NA
-	as above but numbered 375046	12	NA
-	as above but numbered 375047	12	NA
R6385	above 3 weathered wagons - *08-11*	NA	54

W47. Grain Wagon (1958)

Most were fitted with a working trapdoor triggered by a lever on the side and the wagon had two sliding hatches in the roof.

R215	**BR** B85040 green - *58-59*	12	14
R215	as above but pale green-grey - *60-66*	6	12
R215	as above but no bottom hatch - *67-68*	6	12

W48. Trix/Tri-ang BRT Bulk Grain Wagon (1968)

These 35T BRT bulk grain vans were made, or part made, by Liliput for Trix and supplied by Trix to Rovex with Tri-ang couplings fitted. They were packaged in Tri-ang Hornby boxes. Due to production difficulties, few were supplied and some came as bodies only which Rovex fitted to their China Clay wagon chassis. The body of the Trix wagon was smaller than that of the Tri-ang Hornby model (below) which Rovex were forced to produce to meet mounting orders.

R647	**'Dewers'** blue - *68*	15	20
R650	**'Haig'** blue - *68*	15	20
R650	as above but (Trix body on Tri-ang chassis) - *68*	20	30
R648	**'Johnny Walker'** blue - *68*	15	20
R649	**'Vat 69'** blue - *68*	15	20

W49. Tri-ang BRT Bulk Grain Wagon (1969)

This slightly larger model was tooled-up when it was clear that Trix would be unable to meet their commitment to supply sufficient of their own model to meet the orders Rovex were receiving.

R023	**'BRT'** 7799 blue - *89-95*	10	14

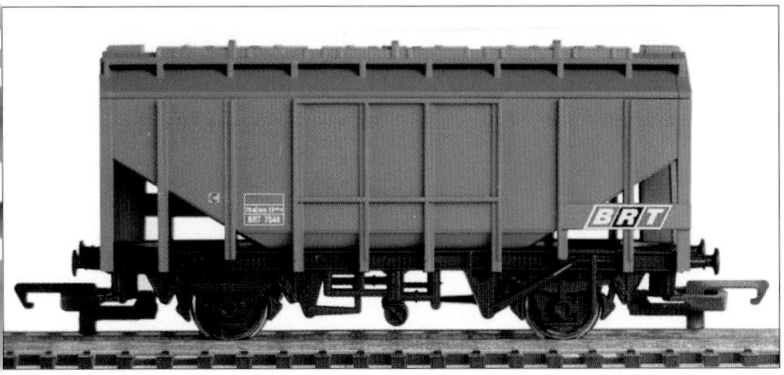

BRT bulk grain hopper wagon [W49]

R6353	**'BRT'** BRT7548 blue - *07-09*	8	10
R238	**'Heygates Grain'** 12 white - *86-87*	10	13
R648	**'Johnny Walker'** 5833 blue BRT - *69-73*	12	15
R649	**'Vat 69'** 5820 blue BRT - *69-71*	12	15

W50. Cement Wagon (1966)

SS = Silver Seal wheels.

R564	**'Blue Circle'** LA211 light grey - *66-71*	7	12
R564	**'Blue Circle'** yellow - *72-75*	5	10
R237	as above but SS wheels - *76*	5	10
R309	**'Readymix'** (Australia) pale grey - *74-75*	15	20
R385	as above but SS wheels - *76*	15	20

W51. 'Prestwin' Silo Wagon (1978)

As a result of a chassis change around 1983 the body moulding was altered to remove four projections on the footplate previously required to take locating lugs.

R011	**'Fisons'** B872001 white - *82-85*	7	10

'Prestwin' silo wagon - 'Bulk Powder' [W51]

R095	**'Bulk Powder'** B873740 buff - *89-90*	8	12
R125	**BR** B873001 brown 'Prestwin' - *78-79*	5	8
R723	as above but paint finish - *80-82*	7	10

W52. PCA 'Presflo' ('Vee Tank') (ex-Dapol) (1997)

R6126	**'Alcan'** BAHS10800 grey - *01*	7	10
R6389	**'Alcan'** ALCN11206 grey - *08-10*	7	10
R6335	**'Albright & Wilson'**/Tiger TRL10532 pale blue - *07*	6	8
R6335A	as above but numbered TRL9466 - *08*	6	8
-	**'Blue Circle'** 9343 grey	6	NA
-	as above but numbered 9344	6	NA
-	as above but numbered 9345	6	NA
R6253	above 3 wagons - *04*	NA	20
-	**'Blue Circle'** 9346 grey	6	NA
-	as above but numbered 9347	6	NA
-	as above but numbered 9348	6	NA
R6253A	above 3 wagons - *05*	NA	20
-	unbranded BCC10771 pale grey W	7	NA
-	as above but numbered BCC10779	7	NA
-	as above but numbered BCC10809	7	NA
R6388	above 3 wagons - *08-09*	NA	24
R6446	unbranded BCC10899 pale grey W 09 - *10*	7	10
R6027	**'Ketton Cement'** TLG9462 yellow - *97-99*	6	7
R6026	**'Lever Bros'** TRL10522 purple - *97-00*	6	7

'Presflo' PCA cement wagon [W52]

R6542	**'Rockware Glass'** Tiger TRL10552 light blue - *11*	9	12
R6160	**BR** 9202 grey - *02-04*	6	7
R6160A	as above but numbered 9288 - *03*	6	7
R6160B	as above but numbered 9236 - *05-07*	6	8
-	**BR** 9203 grey W	6	NA
-	as above but numbered 9204	6	NA
-	as above but numbered 9205	6	NA
R6153	above 3 wagons - *02*	NA	19
-	**BR** 9198 grey W	6	NA
-	as above but numbered 9199	6	NA
-	as above but numbered 9200	6	NA
R6153A	above 3 wagons - *03-05*	NA	20
-	**BR** 9113 grey W	6	NA
-	as above but numbered 9114	6	NA
-	as above but numbered 9115	6	NA
R6153B	above 3 wagons - *04-07*	NA	22
R6090	**'Hornby Collector'** black Sp Edn 7700 (HCC) - *99*	8	12

W53. Lime Wagon (1973)

This model used the 5-plank wagon body and had the pitched section added on top. The earlier models have a chassis with a 10' wheelbase but the chassis wheelbase on later ones was 9'.

R6458	**'Hornby 2009'** red+yellow Ltd Edn 3500 - *09*	5	9
R211	**'Minera Lime'** 125 brown heat printed - *73-75*	5	7
R211	as above but tampo printed - *76-78*	6	8

Lime wagon - 'SLB' [W53]

R6320	**'SLB'** 527 pale grey - *06-09*	6	9
R6243	**'Whitecliff Lime Co.'** 6 very pale grey - *04*	7	10
R6243A	as above but numbered 7 - *05-06*	6	8
	Thomas Series		
R9689	brown - *11*	7	10
R9688	light grey - *11*	7	10

Bulk Liquid Tank Wagons

W54. Slurry Tank Wagon (1969)

R668	**'Bowater's'** 1025 pale blue with blue gantry + broad ladder - *69*	15	18
R668	as above but blue gantry + narrow ladder - *70-73*	9	14

'Bowater's' slurry tank wagon [W54]

R668	as above but white gantry + narrow ladder - *72*	12	16

W55a. Small Tanker (1st Type) (1954)

This had the barrel made in three sections which plugged together and the tank cap was part of the centre moulding. Red solebars were usual on the silver tanker and black on the black and yellow ones but this did not always apply. tf = transfers.

R12	**'Shell'** + **'BP'** (opposite sides) silver tf - *54-57*	6	10
R12	as above but grey - *?*	10	12
R210	**'Shell BP'** black tf - *56-57*	6	12
R211	**'Shell Lubricating Oil'** yellow tf - *56-57*	6	10

W55b. Small Tanker (1st Type) with ladders (1954)

This was the same design as the tank wagon in the table immediately above but had a ladder each side.

R15	**'UD'** white, red heat printing - *54-57*	7	10

W56a. Small Tanker (2nd Type) (1957)

This improved tank wagon had the barrel and one end as a single moulding and the other end and the cap added afterwards. When the 'Shell BP' joint marketing company tanks no longer had 'Shell' on one side and 'BP' on the other, Tri-ang had both a 'Shell' and a 'BP' tank running simultaneously in their range but they shared the same 'R' number. The running numbers on these were sometimes swapped over. The solebars were usually red on the silver tanker but may be found unpainted (i.e. black). On the black and yellow tankers they are usually black. tf = transfers. st = stickers.

R12	**'Shell'** + **'BP'** tf (on opposite sides) silver - *57*	12	14
R12	as above but heat printed - *57-61*	5	10
R12	**'Shell'** 2 tf per side 5056 silver - *62-66*	5	10
R12	as above but numbered 5057 - *62-66*	10	12
R12	**'Shell'** 2 small logo tf per side 5056 silver - *?*	15	17
R12	**'BP'** 2 logo tf per side 5057 silver - *62-71*	5	10
R12	**'Shell'** 2 logo st per side 5056 silver - *67-71*	5	10
R12	as above but numbered 5057 - *67-71*	7	11
R12	**'Shell'** 2 logo st per side 5056 grey - *67-71*	5	10
R12	as above, numbered 5056 but grey - *67-71*	5	10
R210	**'Shell BP'** tf each side black - *57*	12	14
R210	as above but heat printed - *58-65*	5	10
R211	**'Shell Lubricating Oil'** tf yellow - *57*	12	14
R211	as above but heat printed - *58-68*	5	10
R12NP	silver no print ex-starter sets - *c68*	8	NA
R211NP	no printing ex-starter sets yellow - *c68*	8	NA

W56b. Small Tanker (2nd Type) with ladders (1957)

This was the same style of tank in the table immediately above but had a ladder each side. hp = heat printed. tp = tampo printed.

R108	**'Esso'** silver - *74-75*	7	9
R311	**'Peters Milk'** white - *74-75*	12	14
R15	**'UD'** white, transfers in red + black - *57*	12	14
R15	**'UD'** white, hp in red (narrow 'U') - *58*	10	12
R15	as above but wider 'U' - *59-73*	5	7
R015	**'UD'** white hp in red + black - *74*	12	14
R015	**'UD'** 101 white tampo in red + black - *74-75*	10	12
R15NP	white no print ex-starter sets - *c68*	8	NA

Type 2 small milk tank wagons [W56b]

W57a. Small Tanker (3rd Type) cross stays (1974)

This was similar to the 2nd type but had a retooled cradle and the tank had more lines of rivets. The cap was also smaller but the most noticeable difference was the stays that crossed in the middle of each side.

R?	**'BP Motor Spirit'** white (seen in an illustration in 2010 catalogue page 7) - *?*	NA	NA
(R1020)	**'Burmah'** red+ white - *99*	8	NA
R6064	**'Crichton's Oil Company Ltd'** 47 black Sp Edn 1200 (Harburn Hobbies) - *98*	8	10
R140	**'Duracell'** gold+black - *84-90*	10	12
R008	**'Esso'** (stickers) silver - *74-79*	5	7
R713	**'Esso** (printed) silver paint finish - *80-81*	6	8
R096	**'Esso'** (in red) white - *84-96*	5	NA
R096	as above but printed in blue - *84-91*	7	NA
R096	as above, printed in blue on pale grey - *?*	9	NA
(R1077)	**'Fothergill Brothers'** 2 maroon ex-set - *06-11*	7	NA
(R1097)	as above but numbered ? ex-set - *08*	7	NA
(R1015)	**'Pepsi'** dark blue - *99-02*	5	NA
R343w	**'Regent'** 15 red - *90-96*	7	NA
R6032	**'Scottish Oil Agency'** 24 red Sp Edn 1400 (Harburn Hobbies) - *97*	8	10
R6019	**'Shell'** 3 light grey+red - *97-02*	5	NA
R203	**'Trimite'** black - *85-88*	7	9
R086	**'Hornby Railways 1995'** red Ltd Edn 3300 - *95*	8	10
	Thomas Series		
R105	**'Tidmouth Milk'** (in blue) white * - *85-10*	4	6
R105	as above but printed in red - *85-96*	4	6
R305	**Tar** black - *89-94*	4	6
R9006	as above* - *99-10*	4	6
R9055	**'Sodor Fuel'** yellow * - *02-10*	4	6
R9204	Raspberry syrup tank deep pink - *05-09*	4	6
R9206	Cream tank pale cream, churns logo - *05-10*	4	6
R9233	**Oil** black W - *06-10*	4	6

* Also used in wagon packs.

W57b. Small Tanker (3rd Type) with ladders (1974)

This was the same style of tank in the table immediately above but had a ladder each side instead of the cross stays. SS = Silver Seal wheels.

R096	**'Esso'** (red) white - *not made*	NA	NA
R311	**'Peters Milk'** (Australia) white - *74-75*	12	14
R387	as above with SS wheels - *76-78*	12	14
R003	**'Polo'** green - *82-84*	8	10
R007	**'United Dairies'** white - *76-81*	4	6

W58. Small Tank Wagon (4th Type) (1980)

This was a much more detailed model with wire stays, ladders and gantry.

R6029	**'Anglo-Scottish Chemical Co Ltd'** 266 black Sp Edn 1480 (Harburn Hobbies) - *97*	9	11
R127	**'Castrol'** 65 green - *87-10*	5	7
R014	**'Esso'** 1800 silver - *82-83*	6	8
R221	**'National Benzol'** P93 buff - *81-83*	7	9

Type 4 small tank wagons [W58]

R129	**'Redline'** 245 blue - *87-90*	8	10
R025	**'Regent'** 101 silver - *88-90*	6	8
R245	**'Shell BP'** 4497 silver - *80*	6	8
R6262	**'Hornby 2005'** red - *05*	8	10

W59. 14T Tank Wagon (ex-Dapol) (1998)

This was a copy of the Mainline 12T tank wagon and tooled in China.

R6165	**'Berry Wiggins'** 116 silver - *02*	8	10
R6207	**'Esso'** 1634 buff Dalkeith - *03*	7	9
R6207A	as above but numbered 1635 - *04*	7	9
R6207B	as above but numbered 1636 - *05*	7	9
R6319	**'Esso'** 3060 silver - *06-07*	6	8
R6319A	as above but numbered 3065 - *07*	6	8
R6319B	as above but numbered 3063 - *08*	7	9
R6514	**'Esso'** 1164 buff - *11*	5	7
R6052	**'Lion Emulsion'** C.15 black - *98-99*	7	9
(R6193)	**'McEwan's'** 707107 buff - *02*	8	NA
(R6293)	as above but numbered 707108 - *02*	8	NA
R6193	above two models Sp Edn 500 (Harburn Hobbies) - *02*	NA	15
R6109	**'Royal Daylight'** 27258 orange-brown - *00-01*	6	8
R6069	**'Shell Electrical Oils'** SM3000 red-brown - *99-00*	6	8

W60. 20T Tank Wagon (ex-Airfix) (1997)

An old style tank wagon with a longer tank.

R6437A	**'Briggs Dundee'** 47 black Sp Edn (Harburn Hobbies) - *08*	8	10
R6437B	as above but numbered 48 Sp Edn (Harburn Hobbies) - *08*	8	10
R6122	'The **Distillers Company**' 226 buff - *01*	5	6

Ex-Airfix 20T tank wagons - 'Highland Bitumens' [W60]

R6325A	**'Highland Bitumens'** 3 black Sp Edn (Harburn Hobbies) - *06*	8	10
R6325B	as above but numbered 4 Sp Edn (Harburn Hobbies) - *06*	8	10
R6208	**'ICI'** 308 silver Methanol - *03*	5	7
R6208A	as above but numbered 309 - *04-05*	5	8
R6208B	as above but numbered 310 - *05*	5	8
R6208C	as above but numbered 315 - *06-07*	7	9
(R6289)	**'ICI'** 31 silver Methanol Sp Edn (Clifford James) ex-pack	8	NA
(R6289)	as above but numbered 32	8	NA
(R6289)	as above but numbered 33	8	NA
(R6289)	as above but numbered 34	8	NA
R6289	5 wagon pack - above 4 tanks + BR standard brake van Sp Edn (Clifford James) - *05*	NA	35
R6170	**'Shell'** Motor Spirit 1719 silver - *02*	5	6
R6012	**'United Oil Importers'** silver - *97-99*	7	9
R6360	**WD** 339 black Ammonia - *07*	6	7
R6360A	as above but numbered 341 - *08*	6	7
R6360B	as above but numbered 342 - *09-10*	6	8
R6011	'The **Yorkshire Tar Distillers**' 597 black - *97-99*	7	9

W61. 'Monobloc' Tank Wagon (1973)

These are 115mm long modern looking tanks with a gantry along the top and usually two ladders at the end although on some versions of the model these were left off. SS = Silver Seal wheels. tp = tampo printed. hp = heat printed.

R026	**'Albright & Wilson'** MD22 pale blue - *82-83*	6	8
(R6481)	**'Amoco'** 5684 red ex-RailRoad wagon set - *10-11*	4	NA
R6034	**'Beatties'** 97 black Sp Edn 1000 - *97*	6	10
R001	**'BP'** BPO60194 green TTA - *92-97*	5	7
(R1075)	**'BP'** BPO37192 green ex-set - *06-09*	7	NA
(R6481)	**'BP'** 9132 green ex-RailRoad wagon set - *10-11*	4	NA
R218	**'BP Chemicals'** CU2 grey - *86-97*	5	7
R6043	**BRT** 57650 grey - *98*	6	8
R6390	**BRT/Caib** BRT57503 grey Methanol - *08-10*	7	9
R6540	**'Carless'** NACCO NACO74007 pale grey - *11*	9	12
R143	**'Carlsberg'** white - *84*	5	8
R315	**'CIG'** white (Australia) - *74-75*	12	14
R391	as above but SS wheels - *76-78*	12	14

'Monobloc' tank wagon - 'BP' [W61] (RoadRail)

R071	**'Duckhams QXR'** dark blue - *87-88*	5	8
R181	**'Esso'** 500 silver sticker - *74*	6	NA
R6396	**'Esso'** 56085 grey W unbranded - *08*	7	9
(R6481)	**'Esso'** 7832 pale grey ex-RailRoad wagon set - *10-11*	4	NA
R115	**'Fina'** No.4 silver - *83-84*	6	8
R731	**'Gulf'** 731 grey+orange - *80-81*	5	7
R6001	'**Hornby Railways 1997**' red Ltd Edn 2500 - *97*	6	10
R6547	'**Hornby 2011**' red - *11*	5	7
R148	**'ICI Petrochemicals'** ICIA54360 white TTA black gantry - *94-97*	5	8
R148	as above but with a white gantry - *97-01*	5	8
R133	**'Milk Marketing Board'** MMB4028 chrome - *83-84*	6	10
R111	**'National Benzol'** 2020 black - *89-91*	5	7
R503	**'Norris Fertilizer'** 010 green Ltd Edn 2500 - *91*	7	10
R023	**'Pfizer'** green - *82*	6	8
R6255	**'RMC'** RC10045 orange PCA - *04*	5	7
R6255A	as above but numbered RC10046? - *04*	5	7
R6255B	as above but numbered RC10047 - *05-06*	6	9
R6255W	as above but numbered RC10047 ex-MO R1083L set - *08*	6	NA
R6421	**'RMC'** RC10045 orange PCA (RailRoad) - *08-10*	4	6
R020	**'Shell'** 500 grey 2 logos stickers* hp - *73-79*	4	6
R715	**'Shell'** 500 grey painted + 2 logos printed - *80-81*	5	7
R720	as above but yellow tank - *83-93*	5	NA
R132	**'Shell'** yellow 'Shell' + logo hp - *74*	4	6
R132	as above but tampo printed - *75*	4	6
R227	as above, tampo printed + SS wheels - *76-79*	4	6
R6044	**'Shell'** SUKO65537 black TTA - *98-08*	6	9
R6371	**'Shell'** RC65539 blk PCA (RailRoad) - *07-11*	4	6
(R6366)	as above but numbered RC65538 ex-RailRoad wagon pack - *07-10*	4	6
R119	**'Shell Oils'** SUKO65911 grey TTA - *91-98*	5	7
R6025	as above but numbered SUKO65905 - *97*	7	NA
R032	**'Shell Petrol'** SUKO67149 grey TTA - *92-96*	5	7

'Monobloc' tank wagon 'Tank Rentals' [W61]

R6021	as above but numbered SUKO67129 - *97-98*	6	NA
(R1126)	'**Tank Rentals**' A329 red ex-'Mixed Freight' set – *09-11*	10	NA
R184	**'Texaco'** 500 red - *75*	4	6
R231	as above but SS wheels - *76-82, 86-91*	4	6
(R6366)	**'Texaco'** 1627 red (RailRoad) ex-pack - *07-11*	4	6
R200	**'Texaco'** red (Station Master) - *93-96*	3	NA
R210	**'Think Tanker'** chrome Sp Edn 2200 - *83*	12	20
(R6366)	**'Total'** 407 grey (RailRoad) ex-pack - *07-11*	4	6
R6541	**'Total'** Caib PR58244 pale grey - *11*	9	12
R212	**'Vedette & Sentinal'** yellow Sp Edn 1000 - *84*	15	NA

R6194	**'Virgin Trains'** 2002 silver+red Sp Edn 500 (Virgin for Warley Show) - *02*	7	10
R6081	**Water** 56963 - *99-00*	5	8
R6275	**BR** BPO53756 pale grey 'Barrier Wagon' KBA - *05-10*	6	9

* These stickers vary in colour, and include: bright red and yellow, dark red and lemon, dark red and white.

W62. GWR 6-wheel Milk Tank (2007) (ex-Lima)

These use the Lima body on a chassis specially tooled by Hornby in GWR style. As the body belonged to the dairy and the chassis to the railway company, they each had their own numbering system, which explains why two numbers may be found on milk tank wagons.

R6377	**'Aplin & Barrett Ltd'** (GWR) 1951 grey - *07*	8	10
R6378	**'Express Dairy'** (GWR) 62/2583 dark blue - *07*	8	10
R6404	**'Express Dairy'** (LMS) 16/1999 dark blue - *08*	8	10
R6404A	as above numbered 25/44190 - *09-10*	9	11
R6404A	as above numbered 16/44190 - *not made*	NA	NA
R6499	graffiti covered ex-milk tank wagon ADW3035 white - *10*	8	10
R6405	**'Independent Milk Supplies '** (LMS) 44280 maroon - *08-10*	9	11
R6406	**'MMB Milk'** (GWR) dark grey - *08-09*	9	11

6-wheeled milk tank wagon 'United Dairies' [W62]

R6454	**'Satlink Western'** KDW2952 red+yellow ZRV - *09-10*	9	11
R6379	**'United Dairies (W) Ltd'** W1954 silver - *07*	8	10
R6453	**'United Dairies'** SR4423 silver - *09-10*	9	11
R6535	**'West Park Dairy Company'** 175 brown - *11*	10	12

Goods Vans

W63. 12T LMS Cattle/SR Sheep Wagon (1956)

Probably based on an LMS design, this was the longest surviving item of rolling stock in the range having originally been tooled up in 1955 and is still in production today in the Thomas series. The body is a single moulding, with the exception of the roof. The latter started white, changed to grey and returned to white in 1972 (late models had other coloured roofs).

R215	**'Harvey Bros.'** 12563 dark green - *86-89,96*	9	12
R022	**GW** 38901 grey - *82-84*	8	12
R122	**LMS** brown - *not made*	NA	NA
R470w	**LMS** 23716 grey - *90-93*	8	NA
R106	**SR** 51915 dark brown heat printed - *72-76*	5	9
R106	as above but tampo printed - *77-81*	5	9
R106	as above but black - *72?*	10	14
R097	as above but buff - *84-85*	9	NA
R?	as above but grey - *82*	12	NA
R122	**BR** M3712 orange-brown, cream * roof - *56*	12	16
R122	as above but grey roof - *56-71*	5	9
R122	as above but dung-brown - *62*	12	14
R122	**BR** M3713 orange-brown, grey roof - *59-71*	5	9

Tri-ang cattle wagon [W63]

R122	as above but dung-brown - *62*	10	12
R122	**BR** M3712 orange-brown white roof - *72*	7	11
R122	as above but black - *72*	10	14
R122	as above but dark brown - *72*	10	14
R122	**BR** B547 orange-brown grey roof - *?*	15	18
	Thomas Series		
R104	51915 buff - *86-90*	7	9
R9203	dark brown W unmarked - *05-10*	6	8
R9213	circus van 36 stock wagon yellow+red - *05-09*	6	7

* probably originally white.

W64a. GWR Horse Box (1956)

Based on a GWR design.

R094	**'Lord Derby Stables'** brown - *not made*	NA	NA
R123A	**GW** 505 dark brown - *72-74*	5	8
R123	**BR** M3713 grey - *not made*	NA	NA
R123	**BR** M3713 red - *56*	10	14
R123	as above but numbered M2313 - *56*	10	14
R123	**BR** B542 dark red nos. in white - *58-60*	7	11
R123	as above but nos. in yellow - *60-61*	5	9
R123	**BR** B547 maroon - *62-70*	5	9
R123	as above but white roof - *71*	15	18
R123	as above but dark brown, white roof - *72*	25	30
R578	**BR** B547 maroon converter wagon HD coupling one end - *67-68*	10	15

W64b. GWR Horse Box (2011)

This is a highly detailed model and does not have opening doors.

R6507	GWR 708 dark brown - *11*	15	19
R6507A	GWR ? dark brown - *11*	15	19

R6537	BR W713 maroon - *11*	15	19
R6537A	BR ? maroon - *11*	15	19

W65a. Closed Van (ex-Trackmaster) (1952)

This was a planked van designed by Pyramid Toys for their Trackmaster set, but the tools were bought from them to speed up the expansion of the Tri-ang Railways range. The Trackmaster inscription on the underside of the wagon was replaced with 'TRI-ANG MADE IN ENGLAND'. The body mould was also used as an 'Insulfish' and an Express Parcels van (see below). The body was retooled around 1954 when the inscription on the base was changed to 'Tri-ang R11/R14 MADE IN ENGLAND'. Roofs were more commonly plain early on but later rain strips were usual. Roofs could be grey or white (sometimes discoloured to cream).

R11	**GW** 62134 blue-grey - *52*	6	10
R11	as above but brown - *52*	6	10
R11	as above but white - *52*	9	13
R11	**GW** 43726 blue-grey - *52-53*	6	10
R11	as above but brown - *52-53*	6	10
R11	as above but white - *52-53*	9	11
R11	as above but red - *52-53*	8	10
R11	**GW** 43720 blue-grey - *53-54*	6	10
R11	as above but brown - *53-54*	6	10
R11	as above but grey-green - *53-54*	7	10
R11	as above but red - *53-54*	8	10
R11	as above but grey - *53-54*	8	10
R11	**GW** 10528 blue-grey - *54*	8	10

Tri-ang closed van - GW [W65a]

R11	as above but brown - *54*	8	10
R11	as above but grey-green - *54*	9	11
R11	as above but orange - *54*	15	17
R11	**GW** 87204 blue-grey - *54-55*	6	10
R11	as above but brown - *54-55*	6	10
R11	as above but grey-green - *54-55*	6	10
R11	**GW** 73628 blue-grey - *55-56*	6	10
R11	as above but brown - *55-56*	6	10
R11	as above but grey-green - *55-56*	6	10
R11	as above but grey - *55-56*	8	10
R11	as above but khaki - *55-56*	13	15
R11	**NE** 86203 brown - *52*	6	10
R11	as above but blue-grey - *52*	6	10
R11	**BR** N4301 blue-grey - *57*	10	12
R11	as above but brown - *57*	10	12
R11	as above but grey - *57*	10	12
	W8755 number 10mm long		
R11	**BR** W8755 brown - *57-60*	6	10
R11	as above but grey - *57-60*	6	10
R11	as above but dark green - *57-60*	6	10
R11	as above but light grey - *57-60*	8	10
R11	as above but pale brown* - *60*	10	12
	W8755 number 7mm long		
R11	**BR** W8755 grey - *60-?*	6	10
R11	as above but green - *60-68*	5	10
R11	as above but dark brown - *?*	10	12
R11	as above but dark green - *?*	8	10
R11	as above but black - *?*	10	12
R11	as above but dung-brown - *62*	10	12
R11NP	various colours ** no printing ex-starter sets - *65-72*	8	NA

* Also called 'Caramac' brown. ** Colours known to exist include blue, vermilion and khaki.

W65b. 'Insulfish' Van (1952)

This was a variation using the same body and roof tools as the closed van (above) but all carry the word 'Insulfish' on both sides. All early vans were supposed to be white but are frequently cream, either due to discoloration by sunlight or through use of a cream coloured plastic when white was not available. Both grey and white roofs may be found and they may be plain or with rain strips. As roofs have become swapped over during the years it is hard to say what came with what. 'White' plastics were sometimes cream.

R14	**BR** 14280 (small digits) white - *52-54*	7	10
R14	as above but larger digits - *53-54*	6	10
R14	**BR** 61745 white - *55*	10	12
R14	**BR** 28174 white - *54-57*	6	10
R14	**BR** N6307 (10.5mm) white - *57-58*	8	10

Tri-ang 'Insulfish' vans [W65b]

R14	**BR** N6301 (10mm) white - *58-60*	5	10
R14	**BR** N6301 (7mm) white - *61-65*	5	10
R14	as above but pale blue* - *66-73*	4	10
R14	**NE** N6301 (7mm) pale blue ** - *73*	45	50
R14	**BR** N6307 (7mm) pale blue * - *72-73*	4	10
R14NP	pale blue* no printing, ex-starter sets - *64-67*	5	NA
R14NP	pale blue no printing, NMRA couplings for export - *68*	15	NA

*Two shades of the pale blue body may be found, the warmer shade being the later of the two. ** This appears to have been an error at the time that the 'Insulfish' van production came to an end and the Hull & Barnsley NE van replaced it.

W65c. SPV Express Parcels Van (1971)

This used the tools of the closed van. It had a grey roof and sometimes was sold with the roof from the Hull & Barnsley van (see below).

R780	**BRe** E12080 rail-blue - *71-73*	6	10

W66. Hull & Barnsley Van (1972)

Hornby never professed to the model being based on a Hull & Barnsley Railway design but it clearly was. The van had distinctive panelled sides and large roof ventilators. SS = Silver Seal wheels.

R132	**'Baxters'** blue - *83-84*	5	8
R002	**'Birds'** yellow - *82*	7	9
R105	**'Birds Eye'** 14901 rail-blue - *74-79*	4	6
R134	**'Callard & Bowser'** white - *83*	8	10
R040	**'Eastbourne Models'** wht Sp Edn 4950 - *81*	7	9
R013	**'Fine Fish'** E81010 pale blue - *73-75*	4	6
R206	as above but with SS wheels - *76*	4	6
R206	as above but tampo printed* - *76-77*	6	8
R722	**'Kit-Kat'** red - *80-81*	6	8
R001	**'KP Nuts'** dark blue - *82-83*	5	7
R130	**'Lyons Maid'** white - *74*	9	11
R146	**'OXO'** blue - *84*	7	9
R149	**'Prima'** yellow - *84*	7	9
R162	**'Prime Pork'** E71011 green - *74-75*	4	6
R216	as above but SS wheels - *76*	4	6
R216	as above but tampo printed * - *76-79,82*	4	6
R042	**'Railmail'** light grey Sp Edn 5000 - *81*	8	10
R038	**'Redgates'** yellow Sp Edn 3500 - *81*	7	9
R135	**'Smiths'** white - *78-79*	4	6
R725	as above but paint finish - *80-81*	6	8
R725	as before but pale grey plastic - *?*	8	10
R043	**'Taylor & Mckenna'** orange Sp Edn 5000 - *81*	7	9
R728	**'Weetabix'** yellow - *80-81*	6	8
R728	**'Weetabix'** yellow with advert characters - *86-89*	5	NA
R205	**'Van Houten's'** Cocoa dark brown - *95-96*	5	10
R111	**'Yorkshire Pudding'** yellow Edn 2500 - *82*	7	9
R?	**GW** 102971 rail-blue ex-set - *?*	7	9
R?	as above but electric-blue ex-set - *?*	8	10
R21	**NE** 7901 white 'Refrigerator' - *72*	6	8
R502	**SR** 50643 buff 'Banana' Ltd Edn 2500 - *91*	8	10
R108	dark brown Thomas with face - *85-90*	5	7

* Tampo printed wagons have the printing crossing the door frames unbroken.

Hull & Barnsley van - 'Weetabix' [W66]

W67. 12T Ventilated Van Sliding Doors (1968)

Based on one of only 6 vans of this type built at Derby in 1962, the van had two doors each side that could be opened. SS = Silver Seal wheels.

R11A	**BR** B784287 brown, grey roof - *68-75*	6	8
R11A	as above but pale grey roof - *68-75*	6	8
R205	as before but with SS wheels - *76-78*	6	8

W68. 12T VEA/Vanwide Ventilated Van (1979)

R147	**'Hornby Railways 1994'** bright red Ltd Edn 3160 - *94*	8	10
R?	**'Mighty White'** white - *88-91*	9	NA
R6099	**'Pendle Forest MRS'** 35 bright red Sp Edn 500 (Pendle Forest MRS) - *99*	8	10
R243	**'Rest Assured'** cream - *86-87*	7	9
(R1015)	**'Tango'** black+orange ex-set - *99-02*	10	NA
R063	**'Yellow Pages'** yellow - *87-88*	8	10
R242	**BR** B784690 brown, brown roof - *79-80*	7	9

VEA rail stores van [W68]

R242	as above but white roof - *81-82*	5	7
R115	**BRe** ADB778246 grey+light blue 'Rail Stores' - *91-92*	7	9
R010	**BR** B783396 brown 'Vanfit' - *93-94*	7	9
R045	**BR** DW107897 bright red 'Tool Van', Eastleigh black roof - *93-98*	6	8
R213	**BR** B882356 brown 'Banana' - *95-98*	6	8
R6178	**BR** B784837 red-brown **'R Silcocks'** - *02-04*	5	7
R6178W	**BR** B784837 red-brown **'R Silcocks'** ex-MO R1083L set- *08*	6	NA
(R1092)	as above but numbered B784842 - *07-08*	6	NA
R117	**BRe** Railfreight 230062 grey+red VEA (red moulding) - *83-85*	5	7
R117	as above but grey moulding - *87-94*	6	8
R6352	**BRe** Railfreight 230117 grey+red - *07-08*	6	8
R034	**BR** Rft 230069 dark grey VEA yellow ends - *90-92*	7	9
R6179	**BR** Railfreight 230377 olive grey+yellow - *02-03*	5	7
(R1020)	**CIE** 2004 brown ex-set - *99*	8	NA

W69. 12T GWR Ventilated Van (ex-Dapol) (1997)

This van was designed and tooled by Dapol. Hornby bought the tools in 1996.

(R1035)	**'Welsh Tin Plate & Metal Stamping Co.' Ltd** 4 brown-red ex-set - *03-05*	6	NA
R6272	**GW** 114497 dark grey - *05*	5	7
R6272A	as above but numbered 11622 - *06-07*	6	8
(R1077)	**GW** 11582 very dark grey ex-set - *06-07*	6	NA
(R1097)	**GW** ? very dark grey ex-set - *08-11*	6	NA
(R2670)	**GW** No.56 brown (RailRoad) ex-train pack - *07-11*	4	NA
R6422	**NE** 2606 very dark grey (RailRoad) - *08-11*	4	6
(R2669)	**BR** W18402 very dark grey (RailRoad) ex-train pack - *07-11*	4	NA
R6003	**BR** B763295 grey - *97-98*	5	7
R6003A	as above but numbered B762430 - *99*	4	6
R6147A	**BR** B759180 brown Sp Edn 250 * - *00*	5	9
R6147B	as above but B759186 Sp Edn 250 * - *00*	5	9
R6147C	as above but B760429 Sp Edn 250 * - *00*	5	9
R6147D	as above but B763281 Sp Edn 250 * - *00*	5	9
R6147E	as above but B764100 Sp Edn 250 * - *00*	5	9
R6186A	**BR** B777387 red-brown - *02*	5	7
R6186B	as above but numbered B777327 - *02*	5	7
R6271	**BR** W14574 red-brown - *05*	5	7
R6271A	as above but numbered W124480 - *06-07*	6	8
R6271W	as above but numbered ? ex-various MO sets - *08*	6	NA
(R1029)	**BR** DB756126 red ex-set - *02-03*	6	NA

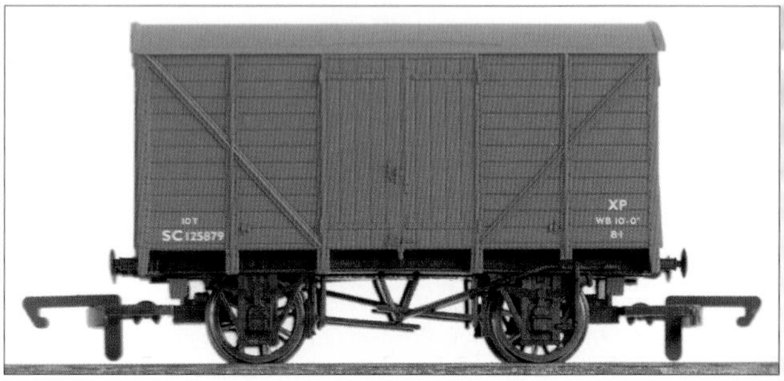

Ex-Airfix GWR ventilated van - BR Scottish Region [W69]

X10239	brown ? ex-MO R1111KF set - 08	6	NA
(R1126)	**BR** SC125879 brown ex-'Mixed Freight' set - *09-11*	9	NA
(R1127)	**BR** W43892 brown ex-'City Industrial' MO set - *09*	8	NA
(R1130K)	**BR** 43892 grey ex-'Highland Rover' Argus set - *09*	10	NA
(R1147)	grey-green W ex-'Codename Strike Force' set - *10*	5	NA
	Thomas Series		
R9238	light grey van - *06-10*	5	9
R9239	red oxide van - *06-09*	5	9

* These originally appeared in the AB Gee commissioned train pack of which 1000 were made. The last 250 packs were broken up, the wagons individually boxed by Hornby and the entire stock sold to the Trafford Model Centre in Manchester.

W70. 12T GWR 'Mogo' Van (ex-Dapol) (1998)

This van was based on the Mainline 'Mogo' van and tooled in China. The tools were bought by Hornby in 1996.

R6056	**GW** 126336 dark grey - *98-99*	6	9
R6080	as above but numbered 124000 - *99-00*	6	9
R6402	as above but numbered 126345 - *08*	6	9
R6402A	as above but numbered 126352 - *09-10*	8	11
	Thomas Series		
R9207	Circus Van (4) red+yellow - *05-10*	4	NA
(R9094)	Circus Van (8) blue+red - *06-07*	4	NA
R9209	Circus Van (12) red+yellow – *05-10*	4	NA

W71. 12T SR Box Van (ex-Airfix) (2005)

(R1068)	**MSLR** 1452 brown ex-set - *06*	7	NA
R6268	**SR** 44395 dark brown - *05*	6	7
R6268A	as above but numbered 44399 - *06-10*	6	11
R6267	**BR** S44431 light grey - *05*	6	7
R6267A	as above but numbered S44437 - *06-07*	6	7
(R1075)	**BR** M16485 grey ex-set - *06-09*	7	NA

W72. 10T BR Meat Van (ex-Dapol) (2002)

Based on 100 vans built at Wolverton Works in 1952.

R6185A	**BR** B870006 red-brown (1,200 made) - *02*	10	15
R6185B	**BR** B870012 red-brown (1,270 made) - *02-03*	10	15

Hard to find ex-Dapol meat van [W72]

W73. 8T LNER Refrigerator Van (1982)

Although mainly used by Hornby for fictitious private owner liveries, it was based on an LNER design of 1926 which had a 9' wheelbase.

R015	**'Canterbury Lamb'** buff - *82*	8	12
R200	**'ETC'*** 314 white - *85-86*	7	10
R214	**'Gamleys'** white Sp Edn 2000 - *84*	6	10
R009	**'Golden Shred'** red - *82-84*	7	10
R722	**'Kit Kat'** red - *85?*	7	NA
-	**'Pendle Forest'** blue Sp Edn 50 - *85*	30	35
-	as above but white Sp Edn 100 - *89*	20	25
R201	**'Terry's'** 254 grey - *85-86*	6	8
R114	**'Wimpy'** 151275 red - *83-85*	6	8
R241	**'Yorkshire Dales Railway'** dark brown Sp Edn 1000 (YDR) - *85*	7	10
R147	**NE** 151275 white - *84-87*	7	10
R147	as above but paint finish - *?*	7	10
R6180	**NE** 151276 white - *02-03*	7	10

LNER refrigerated van - 'Bartellos Circus' [W73]

R6181	**NE** 439848 white - *02-03*	5	7
(R1107)	**'Bartellos Circus'** red+yellow ex-set (RailRoad) - *08-09*	7	NA

Thomas Series

-	Circus Van (1) blue+yellow	6	NA
-	Circus Van (2) red+blue	6	NA
-	Circus Van (5) red+yellow	6	NA
R9093	above 3 Circus Vans - *05-07*	NA	26
-	Circus Van (3) blue+yellow	6	NA
-	Circus Van (7) red+yellow	6	NA
-	Circus Van (8) blue+red **	6	NA
R9094	above 3 Circus Vans - *05-10*	NA	26
R9208	Circus Van (6) red - *05-10*	6	8
R9210	Circus Van (9) - *not made*	NA	NA
R9211	Circus Van (10) - *not made*	NA	NA
R9212	Circus Van (11) - *not made*	NA	NA
R9205	Circus Ice Cream van, cream, cone logo - *05-09*	6	8

* ETC stands for E T Carfrae - Tom Carfrae was the designer at Hornby! ** This was a Mogo van instead.

W74. Long Wheelbase Van (Freelance) (1974)

R217	**'Anglian'** cream - *86-87*	5	9
R056	**'Astra Fireworks'** yellow - *87-88*	5	9
R109	**'Cadburys'** 476 white+purple - *74-75*	6	10
-	**'Coca Cola'** red - *?*	NPG	NPG
R321	**'Cox Brothers Circus'** red - *94-96*	5	12

Long wheelbase van showing proposed and actual livery [W74]

R021	**'Harvester Restaurants'** yellow - *92-93*	5	8
R134	**'Heinz'** emerald-green - *74*	7	10
R183	**'Kelloggs'** white outlined in red - *74*	5	8
R222	as above but no outline - *76*	4	6
R222	**'Kelloggs'** blue large head small eye - *77*	4	6
R222	as above but small head large eye - *77*	4	6
R137	**'McVities'** blue - *78-79*	4	6
R727	as above but with paint finish - *80-81*	4	6
R202	**'Reconafork'** cream+brown - *85-86*	7	9
R145	**'Red Arrows'** light blue design different on either side - *84-91*	5	8
R596w	**Red Star Parcels** yellow - *91-95*	6	NA
?	**'Riplas'** white Sp Edn (Rittas Plastics Machinery Co.) - *?*	15	20
R?	**'Rollei Cameras'** * silver - *77*	NPG	NPG
R6474	**'Sheaf Materials Handling'** 25624 maroon (RailRoad) - *09-11*	3	4
R138	**'Silver Spoon'** blue - *84*	8	12
R008	**'Yellow Pages'** yellow - *86*	10	12
R317	Australian markings (1975) - *not made*	NA	NA
R121	**CIE** 2007 white Insulated Container - *79*	30	NA

* Very little is known about this wagon other than it was seen in an exhibition in 1977. It may have been a Code 3 model.

W75a. 45T VDA/ZRA Long Wheelbase Van (1980)

Many of these larger vans were built for BR in the 1970s.

R234	**BRe Railfreight** 210304 brown - *80-81*	8	10
R247	**BRe Railfreight** 210218 grey+red, red moulding - *81-83*	8	10
R247	as above but with a grey moulding - *87-94*	6	8
R237	**BRe Railfreight** 210218 grey+red Speedlink Distribution on roof Sp Edn 4000 - *83*	15	25
R6349	**BRe Railfreight** 200650 grey+red - *07-08*	8	10
R016	**BR Railfreight** 200706 light grey yellow - *89*	8	10
R017	**BR Railfreight** 200659 dark grey+yellow - *90-94*	6	8
R156	**BR** DC200514 grey+yellow - *94-95*	6	8
R404	**BR Railfreight** 200895 light grey+yellow - *96-97*	6	8
R6042	**EWS** 200896 maroon - *98*	5	7
R6042A	as above but numbered 210238 - *01*	5	7
R6042W	as above but numbered 210238 ex-MO R1063 set - *08*	5	NA
R6042B	as above but numbered 200991 - *02*	5	7
R6042C	as above but numbered 200731 - *03-04*	5	7

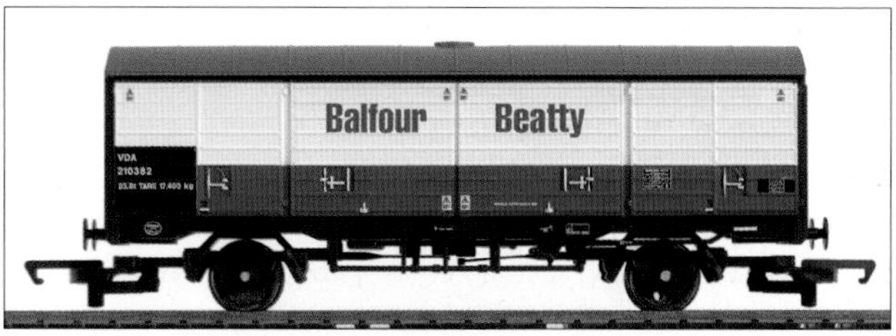

VDA van - 'Balfour Beatty' [W75a]

R6074	**BRe Civilink** 200660 grey+yellow - *99-00*	5	7
R6188	**BRe Civilink** DC200660 grey+yellow - *02*	5	7
R6452	**'Balfour Beatty'** 210382 dark blue+white - *09*	7	10
R6264	**Bombardier Prorail** 200759 blue REA - *05-08*	7	10
R6265	**NSE Satlink** KDC210280 red+yell ZXA - *05*	7	10

R6265A	**NSE Satlink** KDC200879 red+yell ZXA - *06-09*	7	10
(R2437)	**Serco** 210238 red+grey VDA ex-R2437 Serco Railtest train pack - *05-07*	8	10
R6138	**Transrail** Enterprise 210195 grey - *01*	5	7
R6260	**'Virgin Trains'** 2004 Rail Bicentenary red+white Sp Edn 500 (Virgin) - *04*	6	8

W75b. PVA/PVB/ZRA Curtain-Sided Van (1984)

Although curtain sided vans were made, this model involves a lot of compromise.

R097	**Caib** PR6917 red+white - *91-92*	8	10
R141	**'Campbells'** BRT6117 red - *84-85*	9	11
R6101	**'Eddie Stobart'** green Sp Edn 1000 (Trafford Model Centre) - *00*	15	18
R6046	'**Hornby 1998**' white Ltd Edn 2500 - *98*	8	10
R216	**Procor** PR6915 blue - *86-88*	8	10

Curtain-sided van - 'Railiner' [W75b]

R043	**'Railiner'** TRL6950 yellow - *93-96*	8	10
R6187	**'Railiner'** TRL6950 yellow - *02*	9	11
R6137	**EWS** DC201008 maroon ZRA - *01*	7	9

W76. VIX Ferry Van (1970)

400 of these vans were built between 1962 and 1964. The model is based on a Pressed Steel Co. Ltd design used on the Harwich-Zeebrugge Ferry. It is fitted with a pair of 2-wheel bogies and had sliding doors. Early models (probably up to the end of 1974) had their bogies linked by a rubber band under tension. When the model was re-released in 1978 the bogies had flexible plastic projections, trapped in hoops, to self-centre the wheels.

R787	**'Ford'** blue+white - *73*	15	NA
R786	**'Fyffes'** white+yellow - *73*	15	NA
R6414	**'Hornby 2008'** blue 70 Years of Hornby - *08*	10	12
R742	**'Interfrigo'** 0286184.3 white - *72-73*	11	16
R741A	**'Transfesa'** 0286184.3 bright blue - *72-74*	12	17
R738	**BR** GB787102 maroon rubber band tensioned bogies - *70-72*	10	15
R738	**BR** GB787102 maroon plastic tensioned bogies - *78-79*	10	15
R740	**BR** GB787102 maroon paint finish - *80-81*	18	22
R6159	**BRe** 240157-5 brown - *02*	11	15
R6159A	**BRe** 2380-393/5 brown - *03*	11	15
R027	**BRe Speedlink** 'Railfreight International'2380 393.5 grey+red - *82-83, 87-90*	15	18
R6263	**BR Railfreight** DB768980 grey+yellow ZSX - *05-07*	9	11
R6304	**BRe Railfreight** 2380 203-6 grey+red VIX - *06-07*	9	11
R6351	**BRe Railfreight International** 2390 249-7 grey+red VIX - *07-08*	10	12
R6403	**BRe Railfreight International** DB787011 grey+red + graffiti ZSX - *08*	10	12

W77. BR CCT Van (ex-Lima) (2006)

R6314	**BR** M94149 maroon - *06*	7	9
R6364	**BR** E94586 lined maroon - *07*	7	9

Ex-Lima CCT van [W77]

R6315	**BR** M94883 blue - *06*	7	9
R6315A	as above but numbered M94453 - *07-08*	8	10
	Thomas Series		
R9236	**'Sodor Mail'** maroon - *06-09*	7	10
R9237	utility van cream - *06-09*	7	10
R9690	works unit van brown - *11*	11	15

W78. 6-wheeled Van (1976)

Based on two vans built by the GWR at Swindon in 1936. npf = non-paint finish

(R6291)	**'Clifford James'** white Sp Edn (Clifford James) - *05-07*	12	NA
R6259	**'Hornby 2004'** red - *04*	8	10
R670	**'Palethorpes'** maroon npf - *76-79*	6	9

6-wheeled Palethorpes vans of 1976 and 1980 [W78]

R733	as above but with paint finish - *80-82*	9	12
R6158	**GWR 'Palethorpes'** 2802 dark brown - *02-04*	6	8
R6158A	as above but numbered 2801 - *05*	6	8
R671	**LMS** 3855 white 'Insulated Milk' npf - *76-79*	6	9
R734	as above but with paint finish - *80-81*	9	12
R6242	**LMS** 38553 maroon 'Insulated Milk' - *04*	6	9
R6242A	as above but numbered 38554 - *05*	6	8
R6242B	as above but numbered 38551 - *06-07*	7	9
R6317	**BR 'Palethorpes'** M38732M brown - *06-07*	7	9

Brake Vans

W79. Short Brake Van (1st Type) (1953)

This was the first wagon to be designed by Rovex and used the former Trackmaster chassis. It had a verandah at each end and was used in many sets as well as being sold solo. Initially, it had stamped metal running boards which hooked over the chassis but later a special chassis casting, incorporating the boards, was made. Likewise, it had its own plastic chassis when these were introduced in the early '60s.

R16	**NE** 16083 light grey - *53*	9	15
R16	as above but brown - *53*	8	15
R16	**NE** (thin) 129085 light grey - *53*	5	12
R16	as above but brown - *53*	5	12
R16	as above but grey - *53*	6	12
R16	as above but red - *53*	8	15
R16	**NE** 129085 brown - *53-54*	7	14
R16	as above but grey - *53-54*	7	14
R16	**NE** 129803 - *54*	8	15
R16	**NE** 129083 light grey - *54*	8	15
R16	**NE** 129083 brown - 54	8	15
R16	**NE** 748936 light grey - *54*	6	12
R16	as above but pale blue-grey - *54*	6	12
R16	as above but brown - *54*	5	12
R16	as above but red - *54*	8	15
R16	**NE** 138224 light grey - *54-55*	6	12
R16	as above but brown - *54-55*	5	12
R16	**NE** 573684 light grey - *54-56*	6	12
R16	as above but brown - *54-56*	5	12
R16	**NE** 650432 light grey - *56*	8	15
R16	as above but brown - *56*	7	12
R16	**NE** 13326 light grey - *?*	10	16
R16	**NE** 73684 grey - *56-57*	6	12
R16	as above but brown - *56-57*	6	12
R16	**BR** N53612 brown - *57*	7	12
R16	as above but grey - *57*	7	12
R16	**BR** M73031 (12mm) grey - *57-62*	4	10
R16	as above but brown - *57-62*	4	10
R16	as above but blue-grey - *57-62*	6	12
R16	**BR** M73031 (7mm) brown - *62-67*	4	10
R16NP	brown no printing, for starter sets - *60-72*	5	12

W80. GWR Brake Van (1st Type) (1956)

R124A	**GW** GW57740 light grey - *71-74*	5	10
R124	as above but LMS roof with rain strips - *74-75*	6	10
R124	**BR** W.6297 (10mm) or-brown - *56-60*	7	12

R124	as above but white roof - *56*	12	18
R124	**BR** W6297 (8mm) orange-brown - *60-70*	5	10
R124	as above but dung-brown - *62*	10	15

1st & 2nd Series Tri-ang GWR brake vans [W80/81]

W81. GWR Brake Van (2nd Type) (1976)

New 1976 body with more accurate profile being narrower than the type 1 brake van. It was also fitted with a red light at the back, with or without a means of lighting it.

R018	**GW** 114925 light grey 20T 'Saltney' - *77-79*	7	10
R018	as above but '20Tons' - *76*	9	12
R714	**GW** 114925 dark grey 20T 'Saltney' paint finish - *80-02*	8	11
R402	**GW** 114775 dark grey 'Neath' - *96-00*	7	10
R6020w	**GW** 56261 dark grey 'Reading' - *97-98*	9	NA

W82. GWR Brake Van (ex-Airfix) (1999)

R6077	**GW** 114775 dark grey 'Worcester' - *99-03*	5	7
R6077A	as above but numbered 56683 - *04*	5	7
R6077B	**GW** 36515 dk.grey 'Old Oak Common' - *05*	5	7
(R6290)	as above now numbered 114862 ex-Sp Edn wagon pack (Clifford James) - *05*	6	NA
(R1037)	**GW** 114763 dark grey 'Worcester' ex-set - *03-04*	5	7
R6316	**GW** 114800 dark grey 'Rhymney' - *06*	6	8
R6347	**GW** 68898 dk.grey 'Dowlais Caeharris' - *07*	6	8
R6347A	**GW** 114990 dk.grey 'Bordesley Junction' - *08-09*	7	9
R6076	**BR** B950572 grey - *99-00*	5	7
R6146	**BR** W68870 brown 'Tavistock Junc' - *01*	5	7
R6146A	as above but numbered W17441 - *02*	5	7
R6220	**BR** W114854 brown - *03*	5	7
R6257	**BR** W17274 brown 'Birkenhead' - *04-07*	6	8
R6257A	**BR** W114873 brown - *06-08*	7	9
R6195	**'Hornby 2003'** yellow Ltd Edn 3000 - *03*	5	7
	Thomas Series		
R9200	**GW** 56831 dark brown with face (Toby) - *05-09*	6	8

* Box label wrongly shows 'Worcester'.

W83. LMS Brake Van (1974)

R107	**LMS** 730386 brown, working light, silver handrails - *74-76*	8	10
R098	**LMS** 730386 brown thin 'S' white handrails - *77-79*	4	6
R718	as above with paint finish - *80-96*	7	9
R201	yellow (Station Master) - *93-96*	3	5

W84. LMS Brake Van (ex-Airfix) (1999)

R6079	**LMS** 730670 light grey - *99-00, 09*	5	7
R6079A	as above but numbered 730450 - *02-03*	5	7
R6079B	as above but numbered 723484 - *03-04*	5	7
R6079C	as above but numbered 732310 - *05*	5	7
(R1125)	**LMS** 732310 light grey ex-set - *09-10*	7	NA
(?)	**BR** M730708 grey ex-set - *99*	5	7
R6296	**BR** M730119 light grey - *06-07*	6	8
R6296A	as above but numbered M732478 - *08-10*	7	9
R6409	**BR** DM732346 light grey ZTO - *08-10*	7	9
R6410	**BR** DM732540 yellow+black stripe ZTO - *08-10*	7	9

Ex-Airfix LMS brake van in BR brown [W84]

R6145	**BR** M730708 brown - *01-02*	5	7
R6145A	as above but numbered M730106 - *03-04*	5	7
R6145B	as above but numbered M730202 - *05-07*	6	8
(R1092)	as above but numbered M730198 - *07-08*	7	NA
R6078	**BR** DM730767 dark olive - *99-00*	5	7

W85. LBSC Brake Van (1980)

Glazed unless marked 'ug'.

R019	**LBSC** 43 grey ug - *80-82*	10	12
R029	**SR** (large) 55918 dark brown ug - *82-90*	9	11
R6321	**SR** (large) 55916 brown - *06-07*	5	7
R6321A	as above but numbered 55914 - *08-09*	7	9
R6144	**SR** (small) 55920 dark brown - *01*	5	7
R6144A	as above but numbered 55925 - *02-03*	5	7

Ex-LBSC brake van in SR livery [W85]

R6144B	as above but numbered 55910 - *04-05*	5	7
R6144C	as above but numbered 55897 - *05-07*	6	8
R6266	**BR** (small) S55926 light grey - *05-07*	6	8
R6266A	as above but numbered S55924 - *06-07*	6	8
R6266B	as above but numbered ? - *not made*	NA	NA
R6266C	as above but numbered S55908 - *09-10*	9	11

W86a. Short Brake Van (2nd Type) (1973)

R215	**NE** 178595 grey (also R114) - *73-76*	4	6
R215	as above but tampo printed (larger digits) - *76-79*	7	9

W86b. BR(ER) Brake Van (1st Type) (1967)

This was made to fit the chassis of the Western Region brake van (which was 2' too short to be correct) but the body was also used to make a short brake van using a 10' chassis (see below). The roof was initially grey but, for a while, a white one was fitted. The original version was catalogued as R636, R16A, R16 and R218 the last being when Silver Seal (SS) wheels were fitted.

R636	**BR** B952698 brown, grey roof - *67*	5	8
R16A	as above but new catalogue number - *67-72*	5	8
R016	as above but white roof - *73-75*	5	8
R218	as above but grey roof and SS - *76-79*	5	8
R729	as above but paint finish - *80-82*	7	10
(R1017)	**BR** B952564 brown ex-set - *99-02*	8	NA
(R1030)	**BR** B808733 brown ex-set - *02-03*	8	NA
(R1121)	**BR** B952010 brown ex-'Devon Flyer' set - *09-10*	6	NA
R6368	**BR** B952042 brown (RailRoad) - *07-11*	4	5
(R6365)	as above but (RailRoad) ex-wagon pack - *07-11*	4	NA
(R2670)	**BR** B952004 light grey (RailRoad) ex-train pack - *07-11*	4	NA
	Thomas Series		
R109	**BR** B952698 brown paint finish - *85-96*	4	5
R109	as above but numbered B952564 - *?*	4	5
R109	as above but numbered B952566 * - *97-10*	6	10
R9202	**BR** dark brown W no markings - *05-10*	6	10
	Made for Australia		
R313	**NSWR** maroon - *74-75*	10	12
R389	as above but with SS wheels - *76-78*	10	12
R314	**VR** blue - *74-75*	12	14
R390	as above but with SS wheels - *76*	12	14

* Also used in wagon packs.

W86c. BR(ER) Brake Van (2nd Type) (1982)

R031	**LNER** 157838 grey - *82-84*	5	7
R6307	**LNER** 260922 brown (brown roof) - *06-07*	6	8
R6307A	as above but numbered 271943 - *07-09*	7	9
R030	**BR** B951480 brown - *82-84*	5	7
R048	**BR Railfreight** B954817 CAR grey+red - *87-92*	5	7

R6500	**London Underground** B955151 grey - *10*	7	9
R6350	**BR** D8955196 * RAR grey+red+yellow - *07-08*	7	9

BR standard brake van in use on London Underground [W86c]

R089	**BR** Service Department B872163 grey+ yellow ZTR - *89-90*	6	8
R6407	**BR** LBD954219 olive green ZTR Electrification - *08-10*	7	9
R6408	**BR** KDB954164 red+yellow ZTR S&T - *08-09*	7	9
R049	**BR** Railfreight B954603 CAR grey - *90-91*	6	8
R6459	**BR Railfreight Distribution** B954989 CAR dark green - *09*	6	10
R264	**BR** Engineer's DB950436 grey+yellow ZTV - *94-96*	5	6
R6062	**BR** B452516 brown - *98*	5	6
R6148	**BR** B950866 brown Sp Edn 250 boxed (Trafford Model Centre) - *00*	7	10
R6119	**BR** B952005 brown - *01-03*	4	6
R6119A	as above but numbered B952008 - *04*	4	7
R6119B	as above but numbered B952006 - *05-06*	6	8
R6119C	as above but numbered B952004 - *07-10*	7	9
(R1036)	as above but numbered ? - *03-06*	6	NA
(R1061)	as above but numbered ? - *05-06*	6	NA
(R1070)	as above but numbered B952045 - *07-10*	7	NA
(R1085)	as above but numbered B952016 - *07-10*	7	NA
(R6289)	as above now numbered B952013 ex-Sp Edn wagon pack (Clifford James) - *05*	8	NA
R6206	**BR Railfreight** B954779 grey+red W - *03*	5	7
R6206A	as above but numbered B954780 - *04-06*	6	8
R6308	**NSE** ADB955009 blue - *06-07*	6	8

* error: the number 'D8955196' should really be 'DB955196'. Also, the box shows 'B8955196' which is also incorrect.

W87. BR Standard Brake Van (3rd Type) (2011)

This is a very accurate scale model.

R6508	**BR** B951410 brown - *11*	13	17
R6509	**BR** DB954032 grey ZTO - *11*	13	17
R6510	**BR** B654779 grey+red CAR - *11*	13	17

W88. ZUV/ZUA 'Shark' Brake Van (2008)

Short wheelbase brake van fitted fore and aft with ballast ploughs. Built between 1956 and 1960. Super-detailed model.

R6411	**EWS** DB993753 maroon ZUV - *08*	12	14
R6412	**BR** DB993782 grey+yellow ZUV - *08*	12	14

'Shark' ballast train brake van - EWS [W88]

R6433	**BR** DB993795 grey+yellow ZUV - *08*	12	14
R6456	**BR** DB993738 grey+yellow W ZUV - *09-11*	12	17
R6413	**Loadhaul** DB993715 black+orange ZUA - *08*	12	14
R6457	**Loadhaul** DB993876 black+orange W ZUA - *09-11*	12	17
R6432	**BR** DB993789 black - *08*	12	14
R6434	**BR** DB993792 olive green ZUV - *08*	12	14
R6455	**BR** DB993834 olive green W ZUV - *09-11*	12	17

Mobile Cranes

W89. Small Mobile Crane (1962)

This has a specially made heavy diecast chassis and was based on a Cowans Sheldon 10T crane used in railway yards. It used the 2nd type bolster wagon as a match truck. The hook was diecast and the chain brass.

R127	No.127 brown - *62-70*	9	12
R385	as above but CKD kit - *66-71*	NA	35
R127	as before but red - *71-79*	10	12
R142	yellow no markings - *84*	10	12
R6004	No.101 yellow Eng. Dept. Crane - *97-11*	14	24

W90. Cowans-Sheldon Breakdown Crane (1971)

Based on a design by Cowans-Sheldon Co. Ltd it represented a 75T mobile rail-crane and came with three trucks. Two of these were short and were both spacers and the third was a jib runner. Early versions of the model used an integral low sided wagon from the starter sets as the jib runner but for later versions the plate wagon was used, modified to provide a cradle in the centre of the wagon.

R6183	**BRb** black W DS1580 Ransomes & Rapier - *02-04*	30	35
	Stratford District - Red		
R739	**BR** DB966111 original jib runner * - *71-81*	18	25
R197	**BR** DB998617 Cowans-Sheldon - *95-99*	20	25
R6104	**BR** DB966111 + DB998617 W - *00-02*	22	30
(R1029)	as above but ex-set - *00-02*	22	NA
	Stratford District - Yellow		
R749	**BRe** DB966111 original jib runner * - *82-84*	22	30
R749	as above but with new jib runner * - *88-94*	24	30
R6204	**BRe** ADB141 + ADB998538 yellow W Eastleigh - *03-10*	28	45
	Thomas Series		
R306	drab from Thomas Series - *89*	35	40
R9216	as above but reissued - *05-08, 10*	30	38

* The jib runner was originally a former integral type flat wagon from a late 60s starter sets but, from 1988, the 'Winkle' plate wagon was converted and used.

W91. 35T Large Mobile Crane (ex-Lima) (2007)

This Continental style rail crane was first released by Lima in 1977. The crane has 8 wheels and the jib-carrier has two 4-wheeled bogies. There are two plug-in hand winders for controlling the jib and hook.

R6369	**BR** ADRC 96709 yellow - *07-11*	10	13
(R6365)	**BR** ADRC 96708 yellow ex-RailRoad wagon pack - *08-11*	10	NA

Ex-Lima - Large mobile crane [W91]

	Thomas Series		
R9691	brown - *11*	12	16

Bogie Wagons

W92a. Bogie Bolster Wagon (1st Type) (1953)

The body started as a rather crude moulding but over the years, detail was added. It was also used as a flat bed for other wagons the most famous of which was the rocket launcher. The earliest examples had the bogies from the ex-Rovex 6" LMS coach.

R110	**BR** 129085 grey Rovex bogies - *53-54*	10	16
R110	as above but with TC bogies - *54*	8	14
R110	**BR** 129803 grey Rovex bogies - *53-54*	10	16
R110	as above but with TC bogies - *54*	8	14
R110	**BR** 129083 grey Rovex bogies - *53-54*	15	21
R110	as above but with TC bogies - *54*	10	16
R110	**BR** 708924 grey (number on either end) - *55*	7	13

R110	**BR** M13127 grey TC bogies - *56?*	10	16
R110	**BR** M13127 grey - *56-59*	7	13
R110	as above but blue-grey - *?*	10	16
R110	as above but orange - *?*	20	26
R110	as above but orange-brown - *?*	20	26
R110	**BR** M13071 (12mm) grey - *59-60*	6	12
R110	**BR** M13071(7mm) grey - *60-61*	6	12
R110	as above but light grey (+ log) - *60-61*	6	12

W92b. **Bogie Bolster** (1st Type) with Log Load (1957)

This used the bogie bolster wagon (above) with a log set between the bolster pins.

R212	**BR** M13127 grey - *57-59*	15	21
R212	**BR** M13071 (12mm) grey - *59-60*	15	21
R212	**BR** M13071 (7mm) grey - *60-61*	15	21

Rocket Launcher - *see Battle Space Series*

W93. **Bogie Bolster** (2nd Type) and Loads (1961)

This was more delicate looking and much more realistic being made from completely new tools. The bolsters were now part of the body moulding. The underframe was particularly vulnerable to damage.

R110	**BR** B940052 grey, pins - *61-66*	10	15
R565	**BR** B940052 pale brown + 2 'Freightliner' containers - *67-69*	15	NA
R563	as above but + 3 Minix Ford vans - *67-72*	22	30
R569	as above but + 3 Minix cars - *68*	18	NA
R110NP	as above but no printing + 3 Minix cars ex-starter sets - *c68*	15	NA
R579	**BR** B940052 light grey black printing + 2 cti containers - *?*	20	25
R1210	**BR** B940052 light grey, pins reversed to hold steel rail load (Canada) - *71*	15	25
R023	**BR** DB996821 black Engineer's 'Salmon' + track load - *72-73*	15	20
R244	brown BCV planned for 1986 - *not made*	NA	NA

W94. **GWR 'Macaw H' Bogie Bolster** (ex-Airfix) (1997)

R6015	**GW** 107285 dark grey 'Macaw H' - *97-00*	5	7
R6477	**GW** 107285 dark grey 'Macaw H' - *09*	6	8

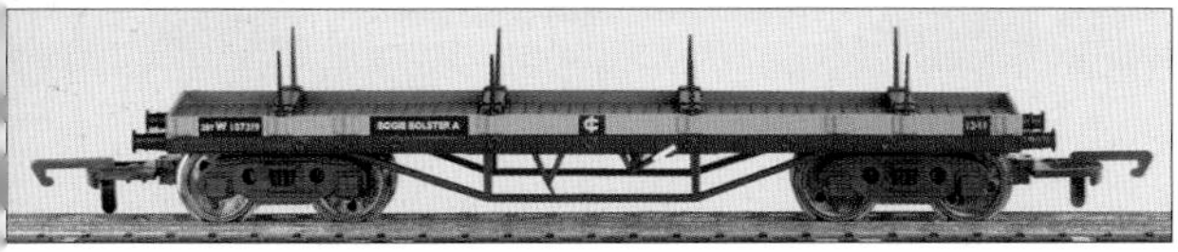

Ex-GWR 'Macaw H' bogie bolster wagon [W94]

R6477A	**GW** 84428 dark grey 'Macaw H' - *09*	6	8
R6123	**BR** W107259 grey 'Bogie Bolster A' - *01-02*	6	8
R6123A	as above but numbered W107363 - *03*	6	8
R6123B	as above but numbered W107293 - *04*	6	8
R6123C	as above but numbered W107365 - *05*	6	8
R6123D	as above but numbered W107288 - *06*	6	8
R6123E	as above but numbered W107319 - *07-08*	6	8

W95. **Bogie Timber Wagon** with Log Load (ex Life-Like) (2005)

This is a model borrowed from the Life-Like range and has a tipping mechanism.

(R1061)	**'Forest Lumber Co.'** yellow - *05-07*	8	NA

W96. **Bogie Gravel Tipper** (ex Life-Like) (2005)

This is a model borrowed from the Life-Like range and has a tipping mechanism.

(R8134)	**'McKeesport Coal Co.'** 291 yellow - *05-07*	8	NA
R8134WA	**'McKeesport Coal Co.'**? 291? yellow ex-MO R1063 'Gravel Tipper Freight' set - *08*	8	NA

W97a. **Well Wagon** *(see also Battle Space)* (1960)

The model consisted of a single plastic moulding slung between two standard issue diamond bogies. Later the basic model was a popular subject for spin-offs both as a load carrier and also as a flatbed to which structures could be fitted. It was also used in the Transcontinental range (included in this table) and these models usually had the metal buffers missing. During its long life, the body moulding tool was modified on a number of occasions. Early examples had no fixing pegs underneath. These were added in 1957. The number R213 was added beneath soon afterwards.

R118	**BR** 41913 brown - *60-63*	10	16
	41917 number 13mm long		
R118	**BR** dark blue - *55-56*	8	14
R118	as above but grey-green - *55-56*	7	13
R118	as above but orange - *55-56*	7	13
	41917 number 10mm long		
R118	**BR** dark blue - *56-59*	8	14
R118	as above but grey-green - *56-59*	6	12

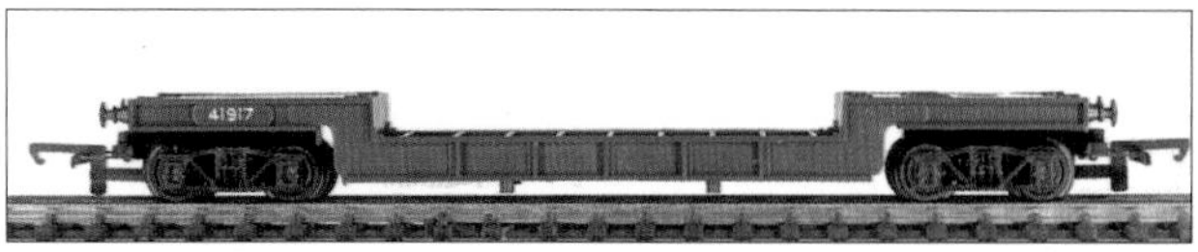

Tri-ang well wagon [W97a]

R118	as above but orange - *56-59*	6	12
R118	as above but grey - *56-59*	5	11
R118	as above but maroon - *56-59*	10	16
	41917 number 10mm long		
R118	**BR** grey - *56-67*	7	14
	41917 number 8.5mm long		
R118	**BR** grey - *59-67*	5	11
R118	as above but green - *59-67*	4	10
R118	as above but brown - *59-67*	6	12
	41917 number 8.5mm long		
R118	**BR** grey - *59-67*	5	11

W97b. **Well Wagon with Crane Load** (1957)

This used the standard well wagon with a mobile crane from the Minic Push-and-Go range.

R213	41917 (8.5mm long) blue or green + Minic Push & Go crane with red base and cream top - *57-61*	30	40
R213	as above but crane with cream base and red top	30	40
R213	as above but crane with white base and red top	30	40
R213	as above but crane with orange base and top	30	40
R213	as above but crane with red base and top	30	40
R213	as above but crane with blue base and top	30	40
R213	as above but crane with green base and top	30	40
R213	as above but crane with beige base and top	30	40

Well Wagon with Tank *(see Battle Space series)*

W98. **55T 'Trestrol' Trolley** (1961)

The real wagons were built by Teeside Bridge & Engineering in 1950. The model consisted of a single moulded body slung between two six-wheel bogies. The wagon, in khaki or green, was used as the basis of a number of military or Battle Space wagons which are listed towards the end of this section.

R242	**BR** B901600 grey 'Trestrol E C' on right, number in centre - *61*	10	15
R242	**BR** B901600 grey 'Trestrol E C' in centre, number on right, 3 black panels - *64*	12	17
R242	as above but 2 black panels - *65*	10	15
R242	**BR** B901600 pale green-grey 'Trestrol E C' in centre, number on right - *62*	8	13
R242	as above but number on left - *62-63*	8	13
R242	as above with number on right but 3 black panels - *64*	10	15
R242	as above but 2 black panels - *65*	10	15
R242	**BR** B901600 dark blue-grey 'Trestrol E C' in centre, number on left + girder load - *72-73*	15	25

W99a. **Freightliner Container Flats** (3 x 20') (1967)

The long flat Freightliner wagon that carried the containers was sometimes rail blue and sometimes black. It is difficult to be accurate as to which colour was used with which containers. Where they were known to be blue they are marked with a 'B'. ATT = ones made for American Train & Track and boxed by them in their own packaging.

R633	+ 3 x **'Freightliner'** 05B41, 05B71, 05B17 pale grey+red - *67-69*	15	20
R633	+ 3 x **'Freightliner Limited'**, 05B41, 05B71, 05B17 pale grey+red B - *71-74*	15	20

Freightliner container flat + containers [W99a]

R633	+ 3 x **'Freightliner Limited'** pale grey+red, no numbers B - *77-81*	15	20
R035	+ 3 x **'Freightliner'** 09L91 white+red - *82-83*	15	20
R022	+ 3 x **'Freightliner'** 82L04 red+yellow B - *92-94*	15	20
R632	+ 3 x open containers pale grey - *69-73*	15	20
R635	+ 3 x **'BP Chemicals'** tanks white+green BP transfers B - *69?*	25	30
R635	as above but BP stickers B - *69-72*	15	20
R637	+ 3 x **'Harold Wood**' tanks yellow+buff B - *69-72*	18	25
R678	+' **Freightliner Limited'** + open + '**BP Chemicals'** B - *70-71*	15	20
R6331	+ 3 x **'Canadien National'** silver - *70*	30	45
R6331	as above but pale grey - *68*	25	40
R6331	as above but pale grey marked 05B17 - *68*	30	45
R7340	+ 3 x **'cti'** (export) red - *69-71*	25	35
R820	+ 3 x **'Santa Fe'** (ATT) silver - *68*	30	45
R821	+ 3 x **'Flexi-Van**' (ATT) silver - *68*	30	45
R839	+ 3 x **'ACT**' (Australia) white+blue - *70-72*	25	NA
R839	as above but silver+blue - *70*	35	NA
R204	+ **'Royal Mail Lines'** 10082 red + **'Scan Dutch'** 203241 white + **'OCL'** 261830 blue B - *85-87*	15	20
R010	+ 3 x **'Business Pages'** GBX430 yellow B - *86*	20	NA
R010	as above but white containers B - *86*	25	NA
R010	as above but mixed yellow & white containers B - *86*	20	NA
R020	+ **'P&O'** 086155 dark blue + **'Royal Mail Parcels'** 300216 red + **'MB'** 151470 dark blue B - *88-91*	15	18
X3716	+ **'P&O'** 086155 dark blue + **'Hamburg Sud'** 522400 red + **'CGM'** 222020 white - *98*	15	NA
R6141	+ **'Seaco'** SCZU718063[1] blue + **'CGM'** CGMU222020 [2] white + **'Hamburg Sud'** 522400 red - *01*	12	15
R6142	+ **'P&O'** 035756 blue + **'MOL'** 2880955 white + **'Med Tainer Line'** SCKU293417[7] yellow - *01*	12	15
R6172	+ **'CMA CGM'** 113815[7] dark blue + **'Uniglory'** 852416[0] red + **'UASC'** 302792[8] very dark green - *02-04*	13	17

Container flat with mixed containers 3x20' [W99a]

R6100	3 x **'Eddie Stobart**' containers ex-R1026 set RF438, RF439, RF440 green - *01*	20	NA
R6203	+ **'NSCSA'** NSAU207785[7] turquoise + **'Cronos'** CRXU252411[3] brown + **'Contship'** CSQU308474[7] black - *03-05*	13	17
	Containers only		
(R6174)	**'Seaco'** SCZU718063[1] blue	2	NA
(R6174)	**'CGM'** CGMU222020 [2] white	2	NA
(R6174)	**'MedTainer Line'** SCKU293417[7] yellow	2	NA
R6174	set of 3 above containers - *02-08*	NA	6

* For the Canadian market.

W99b. Frieghtliner Container Flats (2 x 30') (1969)

The long flat freightliner wagon that carried the containers was sometimes rail blue and sometimes black. It is difficult to be accurate as to which colour was used with which containers. Where they were known to be blue they are marked with a 'B'.

R634	+ **'Pickfords'** dark blue + **'Containerway'** red B - *69-72*	15	20
R719	+ **'Sainsbury's'** grey + **'Ford'** wht B - *69-72*	15	20
R677	+ **'Fyffes'** yellow + **'Manchester Liners**' red B - *69-71*	15	25
R7352	+ 2 x **'Canadian Pacific'** yellow B - *69-71*	25	35
R7360	+ 2 x **'Canadian Pacific Sea'** yellow B - *69-71*	25	35
R7370	+ 2 x **'Manchester Liners'** red B - *69-71*	18	25
R7353	+ 2 x **'CP Ships'** grey B - *not made*	NA	NA
R036	+ **'CP Ships'** green + **'IFF'** IFF8010 silver B - *82-84*	15	20
R006	+ **'Hapag-Lloyd'** 406189 orange + **'Evergreen'** 120842 green B - *91*	16	21
R030	+ 2 x **'Fletcher'** blue B - *92-94*	15	20
R387	+ **'Haulmark'** 425528 dark blue + **'Maersk'** 2365746 silver - *96-98*	10	15
X3350	+ 2 x **'Haulmark'** 425528 dark blue - *96-97*	12	NA
X3348	+ 2 x **'Maersk'** 2365746 silver - *96-97*	12	NA
X3349	+ 2 x **'ECL'** dark grey - *96-97*	12	NA
X3463	+ 2 x **'Ferryline'** light blue - *97*	12	NA
X3462	+ **'Ferryline'** light blue + **'Maersk'** 2365746 silver - *98*	12	NA
X3712	+ **'Hyundai'** 426091 red + **'MSco'** 381276 yellow - *98*	15	NA
X3714	+ **'Hanjin'** 717359 dark blue + **'Yang Ming'** grey - *98*	15	NA
R6100	+ 2 x **'Eddie Stobart**' green Sp Edn 1400 (Trafford Model Centre) - *99*	20	25
(R1026)	as above numbered RF538 & RF916 - *01*	20	NA
(R1026)	as above numbered RF539 & RF917 - *01*	20	NA
(R1026)	as above numbered RF540 & RF918 - *01*	20	NA
R6139	+ **'Hyundai'** HDCU426091[8] red + **'IFF'** IFFU890478[4] blue - *01*	12	15
R6140	+ **'IBC'** IBCU560570[9] red + **'Yang Ming'** 4471607 grey - *01*	12	15
R6171	+ **'Waterfront'** 970127[9] red + **'Linea Mexicana'** 232731[3] dark blue - *02*	12	17
R6202	+ **'Evergreen**' EMCU519644[4] white + **'Di Gregorio'** IRNU400318[8] orange - *03-05*	12	17
(R1054)	+ **'Hyundai**' HDCU426091[8] red + **'Yang Ming'** YMLU4471907 grey ex-SP Edn set (Toys R Us) - *05*	15	NA
R6425	+ **'IBC' Bulk'** IBCU550570[4] maroon + **'IFF'** IFFU890478[4] blue (RailRoad) - *08-11*	12	15

Container flat with 2x30' containers [W99b]

	Containers only		
-	**'Tartan Arrow'** red+white sold with container depot - *70-74*	8	NA
-	**'IBC'** IBCU550570[9] red	3	NA
-	**'IFF'** IFFU890478[4] blue	3	NA
R6173	set of above 2 containers - *02-09*	NA	6

* For the Canadian market.

W100. KFA Container Wagon (2011)

Each wagon includes a 40' container and a 20' container.

R6484	**Tiphook Rail** TIPH93478 blue + grey **Maersk Sealand** 40' container MSK618758[0] + white **Stolt** tank 20' container SNTU400404[4] - *11*	24	30
R6485	**Tiphook Rail** TIPH93482 blue + blue **P&O** 40' container OCLU152154[2] + pale grey **NOL** 20' container NOSU228694[0] - *11*	24	30
R6536	**Tiphook Rail** TIPH93482 blue + blue **LYS-Line** 40' container OCLU152154[2] + pale grey **Hoyer** tank 20' container SNTU400404[4] - *11*	25	33

W101. Bogie 'Carflat' (1977)

R126	**BR** orange plain deck + 3 Triumph 2000 - *77-81*	15	18
R124	**BR** vermilion painted deck + 3 Triumph 2000 - *82-85*	15	18
R124	as above but no railings - *86-89*	15	18
R124	**BR** vermilion painted deck + 3 Triumph 2000 - *90*	15	18
R126	as above but 3 Ford Sierras - *91-00*	15	17
R6143	**BR** B748698 yellow 'Carflat' + 3 Ford Sierras - *01-08*	15	17
R6398	**BR** B748721 yellow 'Carflat' + 3 Mini vans * - *08-09*	16	21

'Tierwag' car transporter [W102]

W102. 'Tierwag' Car Transporter (Car-a-Belle) (1965)

The wagon had a lifting lower deck and a flap at each end of the upper deck which could be let down to bridge the gap between wagons. It came with six Minix cars (mixed).

R342	pale green-grey 'No Hump Shunting' - *65-?*	15	20
R342	as above but Acho couplings (France) - *67*	45	50
R342	pale grey 'No Hump Shunting' - *?-74*	15	20
R3421	**'Canadian National'** CN700184 blk - *65-71*	30	35
R3423	**'CPRail'** black - *70-73*	30	35
R373	as above but different 'R' number - *73*	30	35

* Van colours are pale grey, white and light green.

W103. 'Motorail' 'Cartic' Car Transporter (1970)

The model was sold in a large end flap-box along with the Minix cars still in their normal individual packaging. The prototype was a four wagon articulated unit but Rovex did not model the two shorter inner wagons. The Tri-ang Hornby model therefore consisted of two identical wagons, a separate bogie to join them and the cars.

R666	**'Silcock Express'** 90510 orange + 16 Sunbeam Alpine cars PJA - *89-90*	30	40
R018	**'Silcock Express'** 90510 orange + 12 Ford Sierra cars PJA - *91*	30	40
R666	**BRe** blue 'Motorail' + 16 mixed cars - *70*	50	270*
R666	as above but 12 mixed cars - *71-73*	40	200*
R6397	**BRe** blue Motorail B909300/B909400 dark blue+ 12 Ford Anglias ** (SkaleAutos) - *08-09*	28	38

*These figures take account of the fact that the boxed cars themselves sell for at least £5 each and sometimes quite a bit more.** The colours of the cars are various.

W104. Car Transporter (ex-Lima) (2008)

This model was introduced by Lima in 1984.

R6423	**RailRoad** blue + 6 cars (RailRoad) - *08-10*	14	17

W105. 50T Bogie Brick Wagon (1959)

The 50T brick wagon was based on a GNR design and body and chassis were moulded as one. Initially it was offered with or without a load which was a salmon coloured moulded insert representing individually stacked bricks - obviously before the days of bulk handling!

R219	**'London Brick'** red - *70-73*	7	9
R219	as above but chassis not painted - *70-73*	9	11
R219	**'London Brick'** brown - *70*	15	20
R219	**BR** E451004 brown narrow 'R' and larger number digits - *59*	12	17
R219	**BR** E451004 brown - *60-67*	8	15

Tri-ang bogie brick wagon [W105]

R219	as above but + brick load - *59-61*	10	16
R2193	**'CPRail'** CP342826 red - *71*	25	30
R219NP	red no printing ex-starter sets - *c68*	6	NA
R219NP	as above but pale brown - *c68*	6	NA
R219NP	as above but brown - *c68*	6	NA
R219NP	**'M-T Express'** (Canada) black - *67*	30	NA

W106. PTA 102T Bogie 'Tippler' (ex-Lima) (2008)

This model was introduced by Lima in 1983.

R6424	**'ARC'** PR26805 mustard yellow (RailRoad) - *08-10*	7	9

W107a. YGB Bogie 'Seacow' Ballast Hopper (2005)

This model is based on the 1981 welded type of 'Seacow'.

R6286A	**EWS** DB980238 maroon - *05*	15	18
R6286B	as above but numbered DB980239 W - *05*	15	18
R6286C	as above numbered DB980240 W - *05*	15	18
R6286D	as above numbered DB980241 - *06-07*	15	18
R6286E	as above numbered DB980242 W - *06-08*	17	21
R6286F	as above numbered DB980243 W - *06-09*	17	25
R6287A	**Mainline** DB980052 blue - *05*	17	21
R6287B	as above numbered DB980053 W - *05-11*	17	25
R6287C	as above numbered DB980054 W - *05-10*	17	25
R6287D	as above numbered DB980055 - *06-10*	17	25
R6287E	as above numbered DB980056 W - *06-10*	17	25
R6287F	as above numbered DB980057 W - *06-10*	17	25
R6288A	**BR Eng**. DB980153 grey+yellow - *06*	15	18
R6288B	as above numbered DB980154 W - *06*	15	18
R6288C	as above numbered DB980155 W - *06*	15	18
R6288D	as above numbered DB980156 - *06-08*	17	21
R6288E	as above numbered DB980157 W - *06-11*	17	25
R6288F	as above numbered DB980158 W - *06-11*	17	25

W107b. YGH Bogie 'Sealion' Ballast Hopper (2006)

This model is based on the former Lima model but with additional detail.

R6328A	**BR** DB892637 olive green - *06-09*	17	25
R6328B	as above numbered DB892638 W - *06-09*	17	25
R6328C	as above numbered DB892639 W - *06-09*	17	25
R6329A	**BR Eng**. DB892782 grey+yellow - *06-08*	17	21
R6329B	as above numbered DB892783 W - *06-08*	17	21

YGH 'Sealion' ballast hopper wagon in Loadhaul livery [W108]

R6329C	as above numbered DB892784 W - *06-08*	17	21
R6330A	**Loadhaul** DB892582 black+orange - *06-08*	17	21
R6330B	as above numbered DB892583 W - *06-09*	17	25
R6330C	as above numbered DB892584 W - *06-08*	17	21

W108. PDA/JCA Bogie 'Presflo' (ex-Lima) (2006)

R6311	**'Blue Circle'** 20180 pale grey - *06*	15	20
R6311A	as above numbered 20182 - *07-11*	15	24
R6312	**'Croxton &Garry'** CG9528 pale grey - *06-08*	15	20
R6313	**'Lloyds & Scottish'** 9732 pale grey - *06-08*	15	20

W109. Bogie Caustic Liquor Tank Wagon (1962)

R247	**'ICI'** 357 red - *62-67*	10	15
R2470	as above but blue (Export) - *70*	25	35

ICI bogie caustic soda tank wagon [W109]

R349	**'Murgatroyd's'** T227 white - *63-70*	10	15
R349	as above but white+cream - *?*	15	20
R349	as above but cream - *?*	10	15
R3490	**'Polysar'** (Export) * white+blue, white top - *71*	25	35
R3490	as above but black top * - *70-71*	25	35
R3490	as above but white+rail-blue * - *70-71*	35	40

* Mainly exported to Canada but some probably went to Australia.

W110. 100T Bogie Tank Wagon (1970)

R667	**'BOC'** 0005 white Liquid Oxygen - *72-74*	12	18
R007	**'BP'** BPO87566 green - *91*	15	18
R216	**'BP'** BPO87460 grey - *95-96*	12	15
R6246	**'BP'** BPO7461 grey - *04-05*	13	15
R6110	**'Elf'** ELF82307 pale grey - *01*	12	15
R028	**'Esso'** 20027 grey+red - *88-89*	12	15
R6336	**EWS** EWS870201 grey L4BF - *07*	14	17
R6132	**'Fina'** pale grey - *01*	12	14
R236	**'Gulf'** GL815 dark blue - *86-87*	15	18
R144	**'Jet Conoco'** grey - *84-85*	12	15
R6045	**'Murco'** PR85300 red+blue - *98-99*	12	15
R6166	**'Murco'** MURCO30827 grey - *02-03*	15	17
R6472	**'Murco'** GERS89019 red W - *09*	17	23
R6543	**'Merco'** Caib PR85309 red+blue - *11*	20	26
R6284	**'Petroplus'** VTG83106 bright red - *05-06*	12	19
R669	**'Shell'** 2309 pale grey - *70-72*	12	18
R669	as above but white plastic - *72*	20	25
R669	**'Shell BP'** 2264 grey - *82-83*	12	15
R6391	**'VTG'** VTG88126 red W - *08-10*	15	19

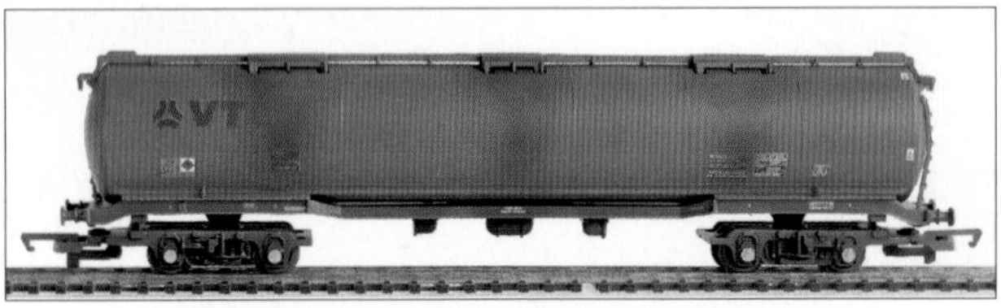

TEA 100T bogie tank wagon - 'VTG' [W110]

R6693	**'CPRail'** CP382920 off white - *not made*	NA	NA
R6103	**'Hornby 2000'** HH2000 chrome - *00*	14	20

W111. 14T 'Siphon G' (ex-Airfix) (1998)

GWR milk van with corridor connections built in 1926.

R6055	**GW** 1359 dark brown - *98*	12	15
R6055A	as above but numbered 1447 - *99-00*	12	15
R6538	as above but numbered 1269 - *11*	16	22

W112. 14T 'Siphon H' (ex-Airfix) (1998)

GWR milk van with end doors and built in 1919.

R6054	**BR** W1422 maroon - *98*	12	15
R6054A	as above but numbered W1428 - *99-01*	12	15
R6539	as above but numbered W1432 - *11*	16	22

W113. PWA Procor 'Palvan' (ex-Lima) (2007)

R6359	**'Kemira Fertilisers'** SSTR7044 deep blue - *07-09*	12	15
R6358	**'UKF'** SSTR7301 brown+cream - *07-08*	12	15

STARTER SET WAGONS

These are mainly of little value but some starter sets contained unique container wagons which are now much sought after. These include, Tri-ang Toys, Scalextric, Frog and Coca-Cola. With the exception of the two 'Primary Series' vehicles, they were sold only in sets. Wagons from the standard British and Transcontinental ranges were also used in a non-printed form and these will be found within the appropriate tables of those sections.

Cat No.	Company, Number, Colour, Dates	£	£

WP1. 'Primary' Truck (1959)

Based on a Continental steel open wagon, the model had an integral chassis and was used in 'Primary' train sets in the late 1950s and early 1960s.

R217	grey - *59-62*	4	14
R217	as above but pale grey - *59-62*	5	15

WP2. 'Primary' Van (1959)

Based on a Continental van, the model had an integral chassis and was used in 'Primary' train sets in the late 1950s and early 1960s.

R218	blue-green with grey roof - *59-62*	4	14
R218	as above but with black roof - *59-62*	10	20
R218	as before but yellow-green - *59-62*	5	15

WP3. Canadian Rocket Launcher (1965)

This was sold in starter sets in Canada and consisted of the rocket firing turret from the Battle Space range fitted to a standard 10' chassis.

R570CN?	khaki green + 4 Red Eye rockets - *65*	15	NA

WP4. Canadian Radar Tracking Car (1965)

We have not seen an example of this but believe that it consists of the radar tracking turret mounted on a small wagon chassis.

R567CN?	? - *c65*	30	NA

WP5. 'Integral' High-Sided Wagon (1969)

Single body/chassis moulding with just wheels and couplings attached. It was produced in vast quantities and was also listed at times as R710NP. Playtrains wheels were large flangeless wheels for use with the Playtrains track. MkIII = standard MkIII tension-lock couplings. Integral = couplings integral with the body/chassis moulding with a hook at one end and a loop at the other.

R710	MkIII red - *69-71*	2	NA
R710	as above but maroon - *69-71*	3	NA
R710	as above but blue - *69-71*	2	NA
R710	as above but violet-blue - *69-71*	4	NA
R710T	NMRA couplings for ATT (US) - *69*	15	NA
R710	MkIII red, bulge * - *71-72?*	3	NA
R710	Integral red, with pinpoint wheels - *73-?*	3	NA
R710	as above but light blue - *73-?*	3	NA
R710	Integral blue - *73-98*	2	NA
R710	as above but red - *73-98*	2	NA
R710	as above but green - *73-98*	3	NA
R710	as above but yellow - *73-98*	3	NA
R710	Integral blue with Playtrains wheels - *86-98*	2	NA
R710	as above but red - *86-98*	2	NA
R710	as above but yellow - *86-98*	2	NA
R710	as above but green - *86-98*	2	NA

* Presumably Rovex experienced complaints of the coupling boss in the moulding breaking off and strengthened it by putting a bulge in the wall above it. These were also fitted with the fine scale wheels.

WP6. 'Integral' Low-Sided Wagon (1969)

Single body/chassis moulding with just wheels and couplings attached. It was also listed at times as R712NP. Playtrains wheels were large flangeless wheels for use with the Playtrains track. MkIII = standard MkIII tension-lock couplings. Integ = couplings integral with the body/chassis moulding with a hook at one end and a loop at the other. Prone to breaking, the coupling join was later strengthened with a bulge in the body. These were also fitted with the fine scale wheels.

R712	MkIII yellow - *69-71*	2	NA
R712	as above but translucent pale lemon - *69?*	5	NA
R712	as above but dark green - *69?*	3	NA
R712	as above but blue - *69-71*	2	NA
R712T	NMRA couplings, dark green? for ATT (US) - *69*	15	NA
R713CN	MkIII dark green + Minix car+caravan for Canada - *69*	10	NA

Integral low-sided wagon with car and caravan [WP6]

R888	as above but with Minix Ford van - *70*	6	NA
R878	as above but with Minix car + caravan - *71*	10	NA
R877	as above but + 20' **'Frog Kits'** container - *71*	35	NA
R887	MkIII blue + Minix car - *71-72*	6	NA
R876	MkIII + 20' **'Tri-ang Toys'** container - *71-72*	40	NA
R712	MkIII bulge lemon-yellow - *71-72?*	5	NA
R712	as above but blue - *71-72?*	3	NA
R712	as above but black - *71-72?*	7	NA
R712	as above but black - *71-72?*	7	NA
R712	as above but red - *71-72?*	7	NA
R712	Integral yellow - *83-84*	4	NA
R712	as above but blue - *83-84*	4	NA
R712	Integral yellow, Playtrains wheels - *86-94*	2	NA
R712	as above but red, - *90-98*	3	NA

WP7. 'Integral' Tank Wagon (1969)

Single body/chassis moulding with just wheels and couplings attached. It was also listed at times as R712NP. Integral = couplings integral with the body/chassis moulding with a hook at one end and a loop at the other.

R711	MkIII couplings yellow no printing - *69-71*	4	NA
R711T	NMRA couplings yellow for ATT (US) - *69*	15	NA
R711	Integral **'Shell'** yellow heat printed - *73-77*	2	NA
R711	as above but tampo printed - *78-91*	2	NA
R711	Integral **'Tidmouth Milk'** white - *86-98*	3	NA

WP8. 'Integral' Long Low-Sided Wagon (1970)

Single body/chassis moulding with just wheels and couplings attached. It had sides but these were lower than those of the Integral Low-Sided Wagon but the wagon was longer and designed to take the 30' container. Colours seen include red, yellow, blue and violet blue.

R880	MkIII couplings with 30' **'Tri-ang Toys'** container - *70*	40	NA
R875	as above with 30' **'Coca-Cola'** container red+white - *71-72*	45	NA
R875	as above with 30' **'Coca-Cola'** container red+yellow+blue - *71-72*	45	NA
R?	as above with 30' **'Scalextric'** container - *?*	45	NA

WP9. 'Integral' Long Flat Wagon (1970)

Single body/chassis moulding with just wheels and couplings attached. It was long and had no sides but had four pegs to hold a 30' container in place. The only examples we have seen were yellow and were illustrations in the 1970 Trade Catalogue and it is possible that the model described in the Integral Long Low-sided Wagon table (above) was released instead.

R879	MkIII couplings yellow + 30' **'Coca-Cola'** container - *70*	NPG	NA
R880	MkIII couplings yellow + 30' **'Tri-ang Toys'** container - *70*	NPG	NA

Coca-cola container [WP9]

R881	MkIII couplings yellow + Minix car+caravan - *70*	NPG	NA
R889	MkIII couplings yellow + Minix car - *70*	NPG	NA

BATTLE SPACE & OTHER MILITARY WAGONS

The Battle Space series was available during the second half of the 1960s and consisted of a range of standard models adapted for military purposes and turned out in a khaki green coloured plastic. It had been preceded by a rocket launching wagon and tank transporter in the late 1950s and some green NATO wagons in the mid 1960s.

The Battle Space range was quite large and for the first two years proved to be popular. After that, it experienced a lingering death until all the initial stocks had cleared the storeroom in the early 1970s. It was during its death-throes that, what is today, the rarest wagon was made - the Q Car.

Two of the vehicles were based on Transcontinental passenger stock (Command Car and Ambulance Car) and these are listed above under their respective coach model type headings in the Transcontinental section.

Packaging - The range of packaging used for the comparatively small Battle Space series was surprisingly large. While a few were sold in standard Tri-ang Hornby boxes, most had specially designed Battle Space wrappings which ranged from simple end flap boxes to elaborate display trays. The latter are particularly sought after, especially if they still have their outer sleeve and this type of box can add £5-£10 to the prices quoted below.

'K' Suffixes - While most of the Battle Space range were given 'K' suffixes to their 'R' number, these were sometimes dropped.

Cat No.	Company, Number, Colour, Dates	£	£

B1. Rocket Launcher (1957)

The model was based on the bogie bolster wagon to which a rocket launcher from the Minic 000 Push-and-Go Series was fixed. The rubber tipped plastic rockets were fired by hand when a lever was used to release tension in a coil spring. The wagons originally had bolsters but these were later dropped.

R216	M13127 grey, clear plastic rocket, yellow launcher - *57*	25	30
R216	as above but with silver rocket - *58*	25	30

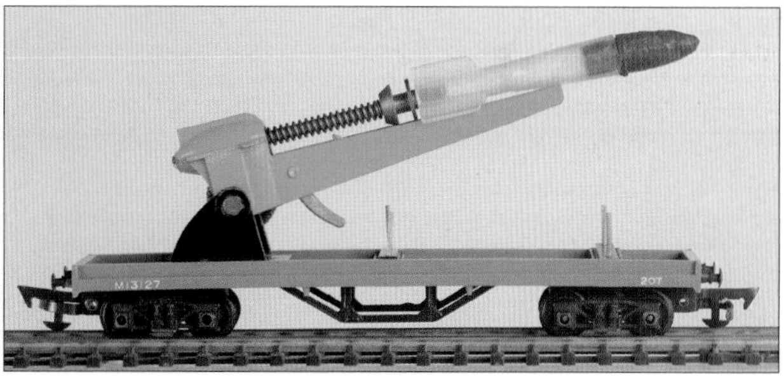

Rocket-launcher [B1]

R216	as above but with red rocket - *58-62*	12	20
R216	same with blue launcher - *63-65*	12	20
R216K	khaki, red rocket, khaki launcher + 7 commandos - *66-71*	25	35
-	as above without commandos	15	NA
R216F	as above with Acho couplings - *67-68*	40	55
R216F	M13071 grey, red rocket and blue launcher, with Acho couplings (France) - *65*	35	50

B2. Well Wagon + Tank (1960)

This used the standard grey, green or brown well wagon with a green 'Conqueror' tank from the Minic Push-and-Go range.

R241	41917 green, grey or brown with green or grey tank - *60-63*	30	40
R241	41913 green, grey or brown with green tank - *60-63*	30	40
R241	TR1371 light blue with grey tank - *60-63*	30	40

B3. Helicopter Car (1962)

Based on a Lionel design, the wagon used the Transcontinental flat car to which were added a clockwork spring mechanism below the body and a spun mounting block above. When the spring was released the block spun.

R128	**NATO** TR7301 grey, red helicopter - *62-63*	15	25
R128	as above but green wagon - *63-65*	15	25
R128F	as above but with Acho couplings - *65*	35	50
R128K	khaki, red helicopter + commandos - *66*	25	35
-	as above without commandos	15	NA
R128F	as above but with Acho couplings - *67-68*	35	50
R128K	khaki, yellow helicopter + commandos - *66-68,70*	25	35
-	as above without commandos	15	NA
R128K	khaki, maroon helicopter + men - *69*	25	35
-	as above without commandos	15	NA
R128K	khaki, green helicopter + commandos - *71*	25	35
-	as above without commandos	15	NA
R128	yellow, red helicopter - *not made*	NA	NA
(R579)	white, yellow helicopter - *82*	30	NA
R165	red helicopter only - *62*	12	40

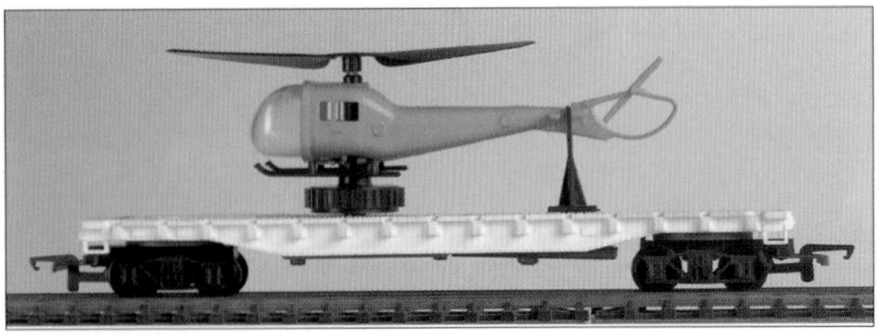

Helicopter car [B3]

B4. Bomb Transporter (1962)

The model utilised the 'Trestrol' wagon and the Red Arrow Bomb from the Minic Maximus range: indeed, some examples of the bomb were heat stamped 'Tri-ang Minic' in silver. The nose of the bomb had an compression cap for firing caps.

R239	**NATO** TR7190 green + red bomb - *62-65*	30	40
R239K	khaki + red bomb + commandos - *66-71*	35	45
-	as above without commandos	25	NA

B5. Antiaircraft Searchlight Wagon (1963)

This was another wagon that used the 'Trestrol' as its base. The superstructure was tooled up specially for the model.

R341	**NATO** TR7192 green, searchlight - *63-65*	20	30
R341K	khaki, searchlight + commandos - *66-71*	25	35
-	as above without commandos	15	NA
R341	**NATO** TR7191 green, searchlight - *63-65*	30	40

B6. Exploding Car (1963)

This was based on a design by Lionel. The sides and roof were carefully balanced and would stand the normal vibrations of movement but if hit by a rocket, the van would disintegrate.

R249	9841 red 'Warheads' - *63-65*	12	20
R249F	as above but with Acho couplings - *65*	30	35
R249K	9841 khaki 'Warheads' + men - *66-71*	25	35
-	as above without commandos	15	NA
R249F	as above but with Acho couplings - *67-68*	35	50
(R579)	455 red 'Rockets' - *82*	15	NA

B7. 4-rocket Launcher (1963)

This was another wagon that used the 'Trestrol' as its base. The superstructure was tooled up specially for the model but was used on other models. The four Red-eye missiles were plastic with metal tips and each was forced down onto one of the four turret mounted firing pins and this tensioned a spring ready for firing. Replica missiles are available.

R343	**NATO** TR191 green + 4 red tipped 'Red-eye' missiles - *63*	20	30
R343	as above but black tipped missiles - *63-65*	20	30
R343	khaki + 4 black tipped missiles + commandoes - *66-71*	25	35
-	as above without commandos	15	NA

B8. Plane Launching Car (1966)

This was another wagon that used the 'Trestrol' as its base. The ramp superstructure was tooled up specially for the model. The plane was the least realistic item in the whole series as it had to fly when fired by an elastic band.

R562	**NATO** green + plane - *66*	35	45
R562	khaki + plane + commandos - *66-71*	30	40
-	as above without commandos	15	NA

B9. Satellite Launching Car (1966)

This was one of two wagons that supplied the 'space' side of Battle Space. It was based on the 'Transcontinental' flat car, using the launch mechanism from the helicopter car and superstructure from the searchlight car. Only the satellite was new - and the colour scheme!

R566	red+blue + satellite + commandos - *66-71*	25	25
-	as above without commandos	15	NA

Satellite launching car [B9]

B10. Radar Tracking Car (1966)

This was a 4-wheel vehicle which used a metal brake van chassis and a superstructure borrowed from the searchlight car. The radar scanner turned by means of a drum beneath the model which was revolved by a rubber band driving off the wheel axles. A domed light also flashed as it moved along.

R567	blue + commandos - *66-71*	25	35
-	as above without commandos	15	NA

B11. Assault Tank Transporter (1966)

This model used the well wagon and the tank with a new turret that carried twin 'Red-eye' missile firing mechanisms. Two missiles were provided with it.

R568	khaki + khaki twin missile tank + commandoes - *66-71*	35	45
-	as above without commandos	20	NA
R673	assault tank on its own + 2 missiles + commandos - *67-71*	30	40
(R589)	sand coloured wagon and tank - *82*	10	NA

B12. POW Car (1967)

Based on the 'Transcontinental' stock car.

R630	334 khaki + commandos - *67-71*	25	40
-	as above without commandos	15	NA

B13. Sniper Car (1967)

This is a slightly modified giraffe car from the 'Transcontinental' range.

R639	D-459 khaki + commandos + actuating rails + trigger - *67-71*	30	45
-	as above without commandos	20	NA

B14. Tank Recovery Car (*see also WT16*) (1967)

This was another well wagon but this time with the small crane fixed to its base and a bolster from the early bolster wagon fitted at one end.

R631	901 khaki + commandos - *67-71*	30	40
-	as above without commandos	20	NA

Tank recovery car [B14]

B15. 'Q' Car (1968)

2,700 of these 'Q' Cars were made in 1968 and it used the body of exploding car to conceal the turret of the assault tank with its two 'Red-eye' missiles.

R571	G-10 khaki + commandos + 2 missiles - *68*	150	200
-	as above without commandos	140	NA

B16. Twin Missile Site (1967)

The main part was made of expanded polystyrene painted green onto which had been fitted the turret of the assault tank with its two 'Red-eye' missiles.

R670	green + commandos + 2 missiles - *67-71*	75	100
-	as above without commandos	65	NA

B17. **Multiple Missile Site** (1967)

Very similar to B16 (above) but fitted with the turret of the 4 rocket launcher with its 4 'Red-eye' missiles.

R671	green + commandos + 4 missiles - *67-71*	75	100
-	as above without commandos	65	NA

B18. **Honest John Pad** (1967)

The launcher was from the rocket launcher car and the rocket is thought to have been supplied by Meccano Ltd.

R672	5261 grey + commandos + 'Honest John' rocket - *67-71*	100	125
-	as above without commandos	90	NA

Commando Car (1967)

See under **CT2. Mail Car** in the section on coaches.

TRANSCONTINENTAL FREIGHT STOCK

The TC range contained some very attractive freight cars produced principally for the Canadian market. They started to arrive in 1954 and throughout the rest of the 1950s they carried the road name 'Tri-ang Railways'. In the early 1960s this was changed to 'Transcontinental' and by the middle of the decade, overseas customers were demanding (and got) authentic road names. The greatest number of these were Canadian, but Australian and American ones added to the variety. More than any other British manufacturer of a model railway system, Tri-ang catered for the overseas market.

'R' Number Changes - Many of those freight cars made for the Canadian market appeared under several different 'R' numbers although the model itself did not change during this time. Initially they had suffixes to the standard model's number and then they were given a four figure number and finally, when the new computer would not handle this, they were given a completely new three figure 'R' number. It is not feasible for us to record all these changes here.

Cat No.	Company, Number, Colour, Dates	£	£

WT1. **Short Box Car** (1954)

R114	**TR** TR22831 brown, white lettering - *?*	20	25
R114	as above but yellow, transfers - *54-56?*	9	12
R114	as above but orange, transfers - *54-56?*	9	12

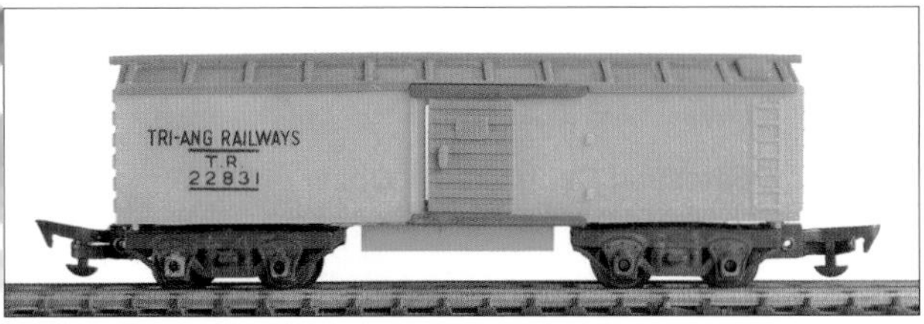

Short box car [WT1]

R114	as above but yellow, heat print - *56?-59*	5	8
R114	as above but orange, heat print - *56?-59*	5	8
R114	as above but yellow, modified - *59-60*	6	9

WT2. **Caboose** (1954)

hs = heat stamped.

R115	**TR** 7482 red transfers - *54-55?*	9	12
R115	as above but maroon, transfers - *c55-56*	8	11
R115	as above but maroon hs - *56?-61*	5	8
R115TR	**TR** shield TR7482 maroon - *62-68*	4	8
R1150	as above but numbered TR2742 - *69-70*	4	8
R115CN	**CN** CN79184 soft-orange - *65-66*	12	18
R115CN	as above but bight orange - *67-68*	12	18
R1151	**CN** 7482 orange - *68-69*	15	20
R1151	as above but maroon - *69-71*	10	15
R1151	as above maroon but with shortened steps (also R270) - *72-73*	10	15
R1152	**CP** 346346 orange-brown - *69-71*	15	20
R1153	**CPRail** CP35644 yellow - *70-72*	12	18
R1153	as above but shortened steps - *72-74*	12	18
R115NP	**M-T** (sticker) orange - *67*	20	NA
R115NP	yellow no printing ex-starter sets (boxed as R1150) - *71*	12	18

WT3. **Gondola** (1954)

ED = 'Express Delivery'. tf = transfers. hp = heat printed.

R1160	**'Rock Island Line'** pale grey - *70-74*	10	15
R116	**TR** TR3576 translucent-blue tf - *54-55*	9	12
R116	as above but grey tf - *54-55*	20	23
R116	as above but VR-blue tf - *54-55*	8	11
R116	as above but green tf - *54-55*	8	11

Gondola [WT3]

R116	as above but red tf - *54-55*	12	15
R116	as above but VR-blue hp - *55-59*	5	8
R116	as above but green hp - *55-59*	5	8
R116	**TR ED** TR3576 VR-blue - *59-61*	6	9
R116	as above but green - *59-61*	6	9
R116	as above but dull-red - *59-61*	10	13
R116	**ED TR** shield TR3576 VR-blue - *61-63*	7	10
R116	as above but green - *61-63*	7	10
R1161	**CN** CN141101 brown (also R116CN) - *66-74*	12	18

WT4. **Hopper Car** (1955)

These were fitted with an automatic unloading device. A trigger would release a trapdoor in the bottom of the hopper.

R111	**TR** 174421 orange - *55-61*	8	12
R111	as above but dark green - *55-61*	10	15
R111	as above but red - *55-61*	8	12
R111	**TR** shield TR174421 red - *62-66*	9	13
R1111	**CN** CN98103 orange-brown (also R111CN) - *67*	15	20
R1111	as above but base hatch plated over - *68-74*	12	18

WT5. **Oil Tanker** (1955)

tf= transfers. hp = heat printed.

R1170	**'BP'** yellow square logos tf (also R323) - *69-73*	8	12
R117	**'Shell'** SCCX333 dull-red tf - *55-58*	12	17
R117	as above but yellow tf - *55-58*	9	14
R117	as above but grey-green tf - *55-58*	15	20
R117	as above but blue tf - *55-58*	9	14
R117	as above but blue hp - *58-62*	7	12
R117	**'Shell'** (square logos) VR-blue hp - *62-66*	8	12
R1170	as above but yellow tf (also R323) - *69-73*	8	12
R1171	**CN** CGTX20044 blue - *68*	20	NPG
R1171	as above but black, logos always to the right (also R117CN) - *65-73*	6	9
R1171	as above but black, logos both the same end - *72-73*	8	12

WT6. **Stock Car** (1957)

R126	**TR** shield (white) TR742 green - *57*	20	25
R126	as above but blue - *57*	20	25
R126	as above but maroon - *57*	20	25

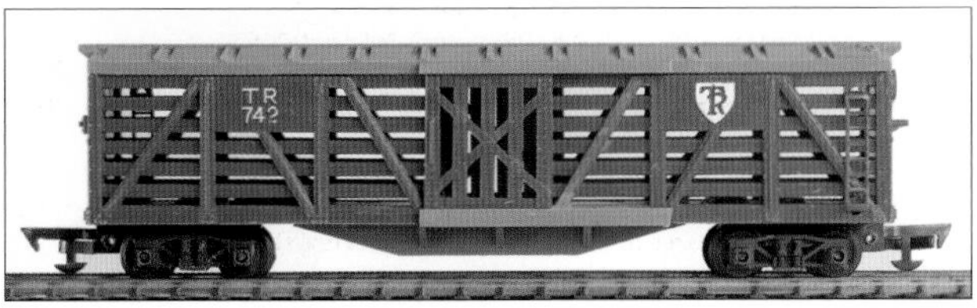

Brown stock car [WT6]

Depressed-centre car with cable drums [WT12d]

R126	as above but brown - *57-78*	15	20
R126	as above but yellow - *58-61*	8	12
R126	**TR** narrow shield (red) TR2742 yell - *62-71*	7	10
R126	**TC** TC1260 yellow - *70*	12	15
R1261	**Canadian National** CN172350 orange-brown (also R126CN) - *65-68*	15	20
R1261	**CN** CN172350 orange-brown (also R271) - *69-74*	15	20
R1262	**CP** CP503588 yellow (also R126CP) - *69-71*	15	20

WT7. Refrigerator Car (1957)

R1290	**C&O** C&O5500 white - *69-74*	12	17
R1330	**'Eat More Beef'** white beef car - *73-74*	12	15
R1350	white newsprint car with names of newspapers (also R275) - *73*	12	15
R1291	**CN** CN211429 silver (also R129CN and R272) - *66-68, 71-74*	10	15
R1291	as above but white - *69-70*	12	17
R1292	**CP** - *70*	NPG	NPG
R1293	**CPRail** CP288138 silver (also R273) - *70-74*	13	18
R1353	**CPRail** CP81030 green newsprint car (also R276) - *70*	15	20
R129	**TR** shield TR2690 white letters in black * - *57-61*	7	10
R129	as above but letters in blue* - *?*	9	12
R129	**TR** shield (slim) TR2690 white letters in black * - *62-73*	7	10

* Roof and underframe either grey or black.

WT8. Long Box Car (1965)

R136CN	**CN** CN523976 brown - *65-68*	15	20
R1361	as above but vermilion (also R277) - *69-74*	15	20
R1362	**CP** CP258599 brown (also R136CP) - *69-73*	15	20
R1363	**CPRail** CP202199 red (also R278) - *70*	15	25
R1363	as above but maroon (also R278) - *71-72*	15	20
R1343	**CPRail** CP35644 yellow (also R274) - *71-73*	15	20
R1353	**CPRail** CP81030 green - *71-74*	15	20
R136	**TR Speedy Service** TR2703 brown - *58-?*	12	15
R136	as above but grey - *58-?*	14	17
R136	as above but pink - *58-66*	10	13

WT9. Cement Car (1958)

These were fitted with an automatic unloading device. A trigger would release a trapdoor in the bottom of the hopper.

R1370	**'Wabash'** WAB31627 grey - *69*	12	15
R1370	as above but darker roof - *71-74*	12	15
R1371	**CN** CN11 3000 grey (also R137CN) - *66-67*	25	30
R1371	as above but base plated over - *68-69*	25	30
R137	**TR** TR2127 grey - *58-61*	12	15
R137	as above but pale green-grey - *?*	15	18
R137	as above but pale blue - *c60?*	20	25
R137	**TR** shield (slim) TR2127 grey - *62-68*	15	18

Cement car [WT9]

WT10. Snow Plough (1958)

R138CN	**CN** brown - *66-68*	20	30
R1381	**CN** green+grey (also R279) - *69-73*	20	30
R138	**TR** TR53437 green+black - *58-68*	15	20

WT11. Pickle Car (1959)

R1390	**'Heinz Pickles'** green - *70-73*	30	40
R139	**'Westwood Pickles'** TR63551 yellow+cream - *59-69*	12	20
R139	as above but white+red, grey roof - *59-69*	12	20
R139	as above but white+red white roof - *?*	20	25

WT12a. Depressed Centre Car (1961)

This was the well wagon from the British range but with the buffers missing.

R236	**TR** TR2132 dark green - *61-63*	8	10
R236	as above but VR-blue - *61-63*	8	10
R236	**TR** TR2371 VR-blue - *61-63*	8	10
R236	as above but blue - *61-63*	8	10
R236	**TR** TR1371 VR-blue - *61-63*	8	10
R236	as above but light blue - *61-63*	10	12
R236	as above but grey-green - *61-63*	8	10
R236	**TR** TR2313 dark green - *61-63*	8	10

WT12b. Depressed Centre Car + Plane (1958)

The metallic coloured Avro Delta plane was from the Minic Push-and-Go Series and consisted of a body and two separate wings parcelled together with rubber bands. The model was used in the RSX military set sold in Canada.

R?	**TR** + Avro Delta (Canada) - *58*	20	NA

WT12c. Depressed Centre Car + Dozer (1960)

The low-loader and dozer were from the Minic Push-and-Go Series. Colours of the load varied according to what was supplied.

R237	**TR** green + mechanical horse + low-loader + dozer various colours - *60-61*	25	50

WT12d. Depressed Centre Car + Cable Drums (1960)

The large size cable drums used on this model were from the Mechanical Horse and Cable Drum Trailer in the Minic Push-and-Go Series. The drums were usually moulded in a cream coloured plastic but blue ones may be found.

R238	blue + 2x **'BICC'** large cable drums - *60-61*	18	35
R238	as above but **'British Insulated Callenders Cables'** drums - *60-61*	18	35

WT13. Flat Car (1960)

The flat car had 10 iron retaining pins that came in a cellophane packet in the box and are almost always missing! Without them the model is of little value. The model (minus pins) was used as the basis for a number of other freight cars, the most successful of which was the pulp wood car.

R234CN	**CN** CN655309 brown 10 metal retaining pins - *67-68*	25	30
R1200	as above but black + 3 logs (also R1201) - *71-73*	30	35

R1200	as above but grey + 3 logs (also R1201) - *71-73*	30	35
R234	**TR** TR3471 grey 10 metal retaining pins - *60-63*	20	25

WT14. Pulp Wood Car (1960)

This was based on the flat car but with bulkheads added and a load of logs, the latter being a single hollow moulding.

R2354	**'International Logging'** 2350 vermilion - *72-73*	15	20
R2354	as above but with Acho couplings - *?*	40	50
R2351	**CN** CN655309 brown (also R235CN) - *66-72*	15	20
R2351	as above but black - *68*	17	22
R235CP	**CP** CP520047 black - *69-70*	20	30
R2353	**CPRail** CP304318 vermilion - *71-72*	20	25
(R824)	**L&N** 25780 black (US) ATT boxes - *68-70*	30	45
(R824)	as above but in Model Power boxes - *70-72*	30	45
(R822)	**Northern Pacific** 621381 black (US) ATT boxes - *68-70*	30	45
(R822)	as above but in Model Power boxes - *70-72*	30	45
(R823)	**Southern** 43271 black (US) ATT boxes - *68-70*	30	45
(R823)	as above but in Model Power boxes - *70-72*	30	45
R2350	**TC** TC2350 vermilion - *71-72*	12	27
R235	**TR** TR3471 grey - *60-66*	10	15
R235	as above but numbered TR4415 - *60-70*	8	13

WT15. Track Cleaning Car (1961)

This model used the body of the short box car when that was replaced by a more accurate model. The doors were no longer sliding but fixed in place and it contained a felt pad which was impregnated with Carbon Tetrachloride (until 1965) which was supplied in plastic capsules (6 to a box - RT528).

R3441	**CN** dark green (also R344CN) - *69-70*	25	30
R344NP	**'M-T Express'** orange-brown (Canada) - *67*	25	NA
R344	TR9372 black - *61-65*	4	6
R344*	as above but dark green - *66-70*	4	6
R344	as above but red - *72-76*	4	6

* When Carbon Tetrachloride could no longer be used, remaining stocks of the wagon were sold abroad numbered R344E.

WT16. Crane Car (see also B14) (1962)

This was physically identical to the Tank Recovery Car in the Battle Space Series, consisting as it did of the well wagon (without buffers) and the small mobile crane.

R560	**TR** 41917 green+brown - *62-70*	20	35
R5600	as above but black+yellow - *not made*	NA	NA
R560	**TR** 23127 green+brown - *62-70*	20	35

WT17. Side-Tipping Car (1965)

This model came in an attractive presentation box with its grey ramp and dark brown bin. The latter was missing when the model returned in 1974.

R345	**TR** TR2549 salmon + 3 plastic logs + ramp + bin - *65-69*	20	50
R345	red + 3 plastic pipes + ramp - *74-75*	15	40

WT18. Old Time Caboose (1965)

This was a small 4-wheel model.

R449	**Transcontinental** TR449 red - *65-68*	30	50

Old time caboose [WT18]

WT19. Giraffe Car (1965)

Based on the stock car (but with fixed doors), this was an idea borrowed from Lionel and is remembered by many with affection. It came in an attractive presentation box.

R348	**TR** TR937 yellow Giraffe Car, mast, rail, clips - *65-72*	20	60

WT20. Fourgon (Continental Brake Van) (1963)

R262	**SNCF** M921452 brown - *63-65*	30	45

WT21. Australian Z Brake Van (1977)

R331	**VR** 739ZL orange (Australia) - *77*	10	15
R331	**VR** 683ZL maroon (Australia) - *77*	18	25

DATE WAGONS

Every year since 1992, Hornby have produced a wagon with their name on it and the year it was issued. Known as 'date' wagons, they are a collecting line of their own. The following is a list of those produced so far, together with their catalogue number and colour:

1992 - 5-plank open wagon (R011) red
1993 - 45 ton OAA open wagon (R035) red
1994 - ventilated van (R147) red
1995 - 3rd type small tank wagon (R086) red
1996 - large mineral wagon (R379) red
1997 - Monobloc tank wagon (R6001) red
1998 - curtain sided van (R6046) white
1999 - tippler mineral wagon (R6061) grey
2000 - 100 ton bogie tank wagon (R6103) chrome
2001 - Conflat wagon and container (R6136) blue
2002 - 9-plank mineral wagon (R6177) grey
2003 - GWR Toad brake van (R6195) - yellow
2004 - 6-wheeled van (R6259) - red
2005 - 4th type small tank wagon (R6262) red
2006 - 8-plank wagon (R6323) red
2007 - 9-plank mineral wagon (R6362) - red
2008 - ferry van (R6414) - blue
2009 - Lime wagon (R6458) - red+yellow
2010 - 7-plank wagon (R6501) - red

ACCESSORIES

Rovex, more than any other British manufacturer, supported their trains with plenty of lineside accessories so that a complete scene could be created. Once again it would be impossible to list them all here but the following are particularly sought after:

Water troughs (£100), pack of double space sleepers (£20), metal badge (£35), Pullman train boards (£50), Golden Arrow coach stickers and headboard (£50), coach train boards (£20), railway sounds record (£25), former Hornby-Dublo covered station (£200), extension to covered station (£220), former H-D island platform (re-boxed) (£50), track packs (£10-£35), olive green footbridge, river bridge or level crossing (£20 each), early footbridges or station buildings with uncommon posters (£10), Arkitex Ultra Modern Station (£300), pack of unpainted passengers and staff (£15), brown large girder bridge (£150), orange-red small girder bridge (£10), orange-red catenary mast (£8), brick bridge with graffiti, (£20), freight depot (ex-Minic) (£20), home maintenance kit (£25), power cleaning brush (£20) and service boxes (£100).

SETS

Since 1952 about 500 sets have been released by this company. Most of these worth only as much as their contents but a few are worth more as sets. Here are some of them:

Original Rovex set picture box (£250) label box (£200), No.4 or No.5 set (£150), Gamages Rovex set, (£500), Gamages Tri-ang set (£450), Blundells set (£320), Old Smoky set (£200), Dutch Primary sets (£200 each), Canadian assembled sets (£150-£250), Miniville sets (£100), clockwork toy train wholesale sets (£100), R6 Rich Uncle set (£500), RF EMU set (£200), R3P and R3Q sets (£150 each), RS7 unlisted set (£100), RS8 or RS28 large *Lord of the Isles* set (£250), RS16 and RS17 Battle Space sets (£150 each), RS30 Crash Train set (£180), RS36 Highwayman set (£450), RS37 The Frontiersman (£150), RS38 Snow Rescue set (£180), RS48 *Lord of the Isles* set (£100), RS44 The Picador (£200), RS47 Monster Double set (£200), RS62 Car-a-Belle set (£120), RS65 The Conqueror (£150), RS74 export military set (£200), RS105 Diesel Freight set (£100), R346 *Rocket* presentation pack (£150), French version (£250), RS602 Senior Freightliner set (£120), RS603 Local Diesel set (£100), RS606 Express Goods set (£100), RS607 Local Passenger set (£180), RS615 *The Railway Children* set (£150), French version of the R640 *Lord of the Isles* presentation set (£250), RMA, RMB, RMC (£450) and RMD Motorail sets (£120). This list is not exhaustive.

Hornby Princess Elizabeth from computer artwork by Robbie McGavin

Skytrex (SMR)

The tables in this chapter have been renumbered.

HISTORY

Skytrex Ltd had been making metal models, including military subjects, for over 30 years and have also produced a 1:148 finescale N gauge range of model railway products which is now marketed by Fleetline Road 'n' Rail.

In 2004, they launched a major marketing campaign to sell the first series of ready-to-run, authentic, 0 gauge, 1:43 scale, British wagons with moulded resin bodies. A series of coaches in the same scale was started in 2005. These are all sold under the name Skytrex Model Railways (or SMR).

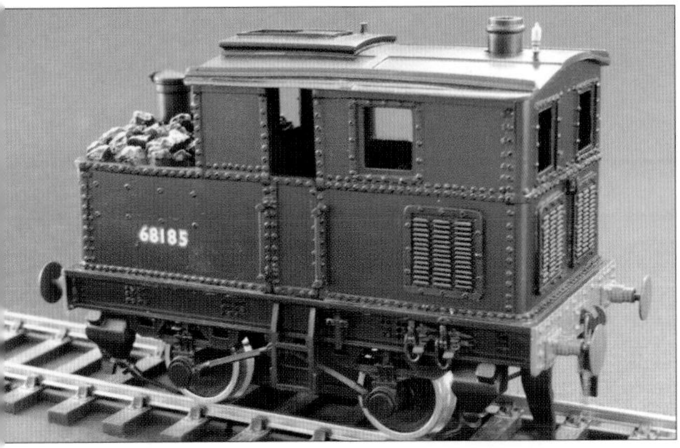

LNER Y3 Setinel steam 0-4-0 shunter [L1] (SMR)

The move into 0 gauge came about because managing director, John Hammond, was planning a garden railway. Having cut his teeth on Hornby tinplate 0 gauge back in the 1950s, he had decided that the garden should have an 0 gauge line. He discovered an absence of ready-to-run 0 gauge rolling stock, a problem confirmed by other 0 gauge enthusiasts, so he put Skytrex designers on to modelling some.

The first five wagons were released at the Gauge 0 Guild show at Telford in September 2004, since then the range has expanded quickly.

The models are available fully finished and most are also available in undecorated form for those who prefer to finish the models themselves. There is also a growing range of loads, containers and other accessories.

Skytrex Ltd are based at Unit 1A, Charnwood Business Park, North Road, Loughborough in Leicestershire.

The models are produced in batches according to demand. Production methods allow for detail and livery variations, if required, and the company is always pleased to quote for particular finishes.

Initially concentration was on the 1947-66 period of British railway history. By September 2005, models from the 1967-94 period had been produced with post-privatisation period models following in 2006.

Running Numbers - The running numbers listed in the following tables are ones seen on models illustrated in catalogues and advertisements. The models are sent out with running numbers already in place, but with a sheet of alternative numbers and insignia decals for customers to change them if they wish.

LOCOMOTIVES

The larger diesels are fitted with two power bogies to increase their power. They should be able to pull either 10 coaches or 50 vans. They have good slow running ability.

Cat No.	Company, Number, Colour, Dates	£	£

L1. Class Y3 Sentinel Steam 0-4-0 Shunter (2007)

The Sentinel Y3 steam shunting locomotive was sold to the LNER and to private industry. They were in service from 1927 to the end of BR steam in the 1960s. A few survive on preserved railways as their economy and practicality are still of value today.

SMR400	**68185** BRb black - *07*	150	250

L2. Class Y6 Steam 0-4-0 Tram Engine (2007)

This is immediately recognised as the subject on which the Rev,W,Awdry based the character Toby in his books.

SMR401	brown - *07*	200	250

L3. Class 02 Diesel Shunter (2008)

The 02 Shunter had a brief 10 year lifespan with BR, spanning blue and green liveried periods. However, most were taken up by private industry and had much longer lifespans in very varied colours. Latterly several have been refurbished for use on preserved lines. Provided with alternative numbers and decals.

SMR402	**D2857** BRc green - *08*	200	250

BR Class 0-4-0 diesel shunter [L3] (SMR)

SMR402	**02001** BRe blue - *08*	200	250

L4. Class 24 Diesel

The model is provided with alternative numbers and decals.

SMR402	BRc green - *?*	NPG	250
SMR402A	BRe blue - *?*	NPG	250

L5. Class 25 Diesel

Provided with alternative numbers and decals.

SMR?	BRc green – *?*	NPG	NPG
SMR?	BRe blue – *?*	NPG	NPG

L6. Class 31 Diesel (2009)

SMR427	**D5504** BRc green with grey bands 31/0 - *09*	350	420
SMR427C	as above but with 2 power bogies - *09*	400	475
SMR427A	**31041** BRe blue 31/0 - *09*	250	420
SMR427B	as above but with 2 power bogies - *09*	400	475
SMR428	**D5545** BRc green, roof fitted headcode boxes 31/1 - *09*	350	420
SMR428B	as above but with 2 power bogies - *09*	400	475
SMR428A	**31117** BRe blue 31/1 - *09*	300	395
SMR428C	as above but with 2 power bogies - *09*	400	475
SMR429	BRc green 31/4 - *09*	350	435

L7a. Class 37/0 Co-Co Diesel (2008)

Single or two powered bogies with all-wheel drive and power pick-up. Decals provided for alternative numbers. Split headcodes, end doors and valances,

SMR420	BRc green - *08*	280	340
SMR420B	as above but with 2 power bogies - *09*	370	425
SMR421	BRc green non-powered - *08*	200	260
SMR420A	BRe blue - *08*	280	340
SMR420C	as above but with 2 power bogies - *09*	370	425
SMR421A	BRe blue non-powered - *08*	200	260

L7b. Refurbished Class 37/5 Co-Co Diesel (2009)

Refurbished freight version with new bogies and electric train heating. Decals provided for alternative numbers. Smooth noses.

SMR422	BRe green - *09*	320	395

SMR422A	BRe blue - *09*	320	395

BR refurbished Class 37 [L7b] (SMR)

SMR423	BRe blue with yellow cabs - *09*	280	340
SMR423A	as above but with 2 power bogies - *09*	350	425
SMR424	BRe ? ? 37/9 - *09*	280	320

L8. Class 40 Diesel (2008)

With front access doors and indicator discs. sh = split headcodes.

SMR434	**D213** BRc green - *08*	350	420
SMR434B	as above but with 2 power bogies - *09*	400	495
SMR434A	**40051** BRe blue - *08*	350	420
SMR434C	as above but with 2 power bogies - *09*	400	495
SMR434B	BRc green sh – *?*	NPG	NPG
SMR434C	BRe blue sh – *?*	NPG	NPG

L9. Class 43 'HST'

SMR580A	BR I-C blue+grey power car – *?*	NPG	350
SMR580B	BR I-C blue+grey powered rear car – *?*	NPG	350
SMR580U	BR I-C blue+grey non-powered car – *?*	NPG	280
SMR588A	BR I-C grey power car – *?*	NPG	350
SMR588B	BR I-C grey powered rear car – *?*	NPG	350
SMR588U	BR I-C grey non-powered car – *?*	NPG	280

L10. Class 44 Diesel

SMR440	**D1 *Scafell Pike*** BRc green – *?*	NPG	NPG
SMR440A	BRe blue – *?*	NPG	NPG

L11. Class 45 Diesel (2011)

With split headcodes.

SMR444	BRc green – *11*	NPG	425
SMR444A	BRe blue – *11*	NPG	425

L12. Class 46 Diesel

SMR448	BRc green – *?*	NPG	425
SMR448A	BRe blue – *?*	NPG	425

L13. Class 55 'Deltic' Diesel (2009)

SMR450	**D9001 *St Paddy*** BRc green - *09*	400	475
SMR450A	**D9011** BRc 2-tone green - *10?*	360	420

BR Class 55 'Deltic' [L13] (SMR

SMR450B	as above but ith 2 power bogies - *10?*	440	495
SMR450C	**D9003** BRc 2-tone green, white window surrounds - *10?*	390	450
SMR450D	as above but with 2 power bogies - *10?*	470	525
SMR450E	**9001** blue - *10?*	360	420
SMR450F	as above but with 2 power bogies - *10?*	440	495
SMR450A	**55014 *Tulyar*** BRe blue - *09*	400	475

L14. Class 60 Diesel (2011)

SMR?	? - *11*	NPG	NPG
SMR?	? - *11*	NPG	NPG

L15. Class 66 Diesel (2011)

SMR?	? - *11*	NPG	NPG
SMR?	? - *11*	NPG	NPG

L16. Class 101 DMU (2009)

With interior detail.

SMR600A	**BR** early green with whiskers power car - *09*	310	370
SMR600B	**BR** early green centre car - *09*	200	250
SMR600C	**BR** early green non-powered trailer car - *09*	220	280
SMR601A	**BR** late green power car with yellow panel - *09*	310	370

BR Class 101 DMU [L16] (SMR)

SMR601B	**BR** late green centre car - *09*	200	250
SMR601C	**BR** late green non-powered trailer car with yellow panel - *09*	220	280
SMR602A	**BR** blue power car with yellow front - *09*	310	370
SMR602B	**BR** blue centre car - *09*	200	250
SMR602C	**BR** blue trailer non-powered car with yellow front - *09*	220	280
SMR603A	**BR** blue+grey power car with yellow front - *10*	310	390
SMR603B	**BR** blue+grey centre car - *10*	200	280
SMR603C	**BR** blue+grey trailer non-powered car with yellow front - *10*	220	300
	2-Car Sets		
SMR603D	**BR** early green (SMR600A+SMR600C) - *10*	500	550
SMR603E	**BR** late green (SMR601A+SMR601C) - *10*	500	550
SMR603F	**BR** blue (SMR602A+SMR602C) - *10*	500	550
SMR603G	**BR** blue+grey (SMR603A+SMR603C) - *10*	520	575

COACHES

These have resin based bodies, internal fittings and metal underframe detailing. The bogies are from the Eazi-build range.

Cat No.	Company, Number, Colour, Dates	£	£

BR Mk1 Suburban Coaches

C1a. Mk1 Suburban 63.5' Composite (2005)

Based on a 63.5' BR 1950s design diagram 312.

SMR500C	**BR** crimson - *05*	180	230
SMR502G	**BR** green - *05*	180	230
SMR504B	**BR** blue - *05*	180	230

C1b. Mk1 Suburban 63.5' Brake 2nd (2005)

Based on a 63.5' BR 1950s design diagram 372.

SMR501C	**BR** crimson - *05*	180	230
SMR503G	**BR** green - *05*	180	230

SMR508B	**BR** blue (also listed as SMR505B) - *05*	180	230

C1c. Mk1 Suburban 63.5' All 2nd (2005)

Based on a 63.5' BR 1950s design diagram 327.

SMR506C	**BR** crimson - *05*	180	230

Mk1 suburban all-2nd coach [C1c] (SMR)

SMR507G	**BR** green (also listed as SMR503G) - *05*	180	230
SMR505B	**BR** blue (also listed as SMR508B) - *05*	180	230

C1d. Mk1 Suburban 57' Composite (2008)

Based on a 57' BR design diagram 311.

SMR509C	**BR** crimson - *08*	180	230
SMR509G	**BR** green - *08*	180	230
SMR509B	**BR** blue - *08*	180	230

C1e. Mk1 Suburban 57' Brake 2nd (2008)

Based on a 57' BR design diagram 371.

SMR512C	**BR** crimson - *08*	180	230
SMR512G	**BR** green - *08*	180	230
SMR512B	**BR** blue - *08*	180	230

C1f. Mk1 Suburban 57' All 2nd (2008)

Based on a 57' BR design diagram 326.

SMR511C	**BR** crimson - *08*	180	230
SMR511G	**BR** green - *08*	180	230
SMR511B	**BR** blue - *08*	180	230

C1g. Mk1 Suburban 57' 2nd Open (2008)

Based on a 57' BR design diagram 328.

SMR510C	**BR** crimson - *08*	180	230
SMR510G	**BR** green - *08*	180	230
SMR510B	**BR** blue - *08*	180	230

BR Mk1 Main Line Coaches

C2a. Mk1 Corridor 2nd SK (2008)

Based on a 63.5' BR 1950s design diagram 146.

SMR510M	**BR** maroon - *not made*	NA	NA
SMR520C	**BR** crimson - *08*	200	250
SMR520G	**BR** green - *08*	200	250
SMR520BC	**BR** red+cream - *09*	200	250
SMR520CC	**BR** brown+cream - *09*	200	250

C2b. Mk1 Open 2nd SO (2008)

Based on a 63.5' BR 1950s design diagram 89.

SMR511M	**BR** maroon - *made?*	NPG	NPG
SMR521C	**BR** crimson - *08*	200	250
SMR521G	**BR** green - *08*	200	250

Mk1 SO [C2b] (SMR)

SMR521BC	**BR** red+cream - *09*	200	250
SMR521CC	**BR** brown+cream - *09*	200	250

C2c. Mk1 Open 2nd SO

Based on diagram 94.

SMR522	**BR** red+cream - *?*	NPG	250
SMR522C	**BR** crimson - *?*	NPG	250

C2d. Mk1 Open 2nd TSO

Based on diagram 93.

SMR522	**BR** red+cream - *?*	NPG	250
SMR522C	**BR** crimson - *?*	NPG	250

C2e. Mk1 Corridor 1st FK

Based on a 63.5' BR 1950s design.

SMR525M	**BR** maroon - *?*	NPG	250
SMR525G	**BR** green - *?*	NPG	250
SMR525BC	**BR** red+cream - *?*	NPG	250
SMR525CC	**BR** brown+cream - *?*	NPG	250

C2f. Mk1 Open 1st FO

Based on a 63.5' BR 1950s design.

SMR524M	**BR** maroon - *?*	NPG	250
SMR524G	**BR** green - *?*	NPG	250
SMR524BC	**BR** red+cream - *?*	NPG	250
SMR524CC	**BR** brown+cream - *?*	NPG	250

C2g. Mk1 Corridor Brake 2nd. BSK (2008)

Based on a 63.5' BR 1950s design.

SMR512M	**BR** maroon - *not made*	NA	NA
SMR526C	**BR** crimson - *08*	200	250
SMR526G	**BR** green - *08*	200	250

Mk1 corridor brake 2nd (SMR)

SMR526BC	**BR** red+cream - *09*	200	250
SMR526CC	**BR** brown+cream - *09*	200	250

C2h. Mk1 Corridor Brake Composite BCK

Based on diagram 171.

SMR522	**BR** red+cream - *?*	NPG	250
SMR522C	**BR** crimson - *?*	NPG	250

C2i. Mk1 Restaurant RUO (2009)

Based on a 63.5' BR 1950s design diagram 61.

SMR513M	**BR** maroon - *not made*	NA	NA
SMR523C	**BR** crimson - *09*	200	275
SMR513G	**BR** green - *not made*	NA	NA
SMR523BC	**BR** red+cream - *09*	200	275
SMR513?	**BR** brown+cream - *not made*	NA	NA

C2j. Mk1 Restaurant 2nd Open RSO

Based on diagram 60.

SMR522	**BR** red+cream - *?*	NPG	275
SMR522C	**BR** crimson - *?*	NPG	275

C2k. Mk1 Full Brake BG (2009)

SMR530	**BR** red+cream - *09*	160	200
SMR530C	**BR** crimson - *09*	160	200
SMR530B	**BR** blue - *09*	160	200

C2l. Mk1 57' Super BG Full Brake

SMR340	**RES Royal Mail** red+dark grey - *?*	NPG	200

Mk1 full brake [C21] (SMR)

C2m. Mk1 57' GUV

SMR312C	**BR** crimson - ?	NPG	200
SMR312B	**BR** blue Express Parcels - ?	NPG	200

BR Mk3 Coaches

C3a. Mk3 Corridor 1st

SMR560	**BR** blue+grey buffers fitted - ?	NPG	280
SMR581	**BR** I-C blue+grey without buffers - ?	NPG	280
SMR563	**BR** grey buffers fitted - ?	NPG	280
SMR589	**BR** grey without buffers - ?	NPG	280

C3b. Mk3 Corridor 2nd

SMR561	**BR** blue+grey buffers fitted - ?	NPG	280
SMR582	**BR** I-C blue+grey without buffers - ?	NPG	280
SMR564	**BR** grey buffers fitted - ?	NPG	280
SMR590	**BR** grey without buffers - ?	NPG	280

C3c. Mk3 Buffet Car

SMR583	**BR** I-C blue+grey without buffers - ?	NPG	280
SMR591	**BR** grey without buffers - ?	NPG	280

C3d. Mk3 Brake End

SMR583	**BR** I-C blue+grey without buffers - ?	NPG	280
SMR591	**BR** grey without buffers - ?	NPG	280

WAGONS

These have plastic bodies, full underframe detail, sprung buffers, 3-link couplings and blackened metal wheels. They are made in batches of 250 and the running number is changed with each batch. We have listed ones we have seen evidence of but others will exist.

Cat No.	Company, Number, Colour, Dates	£	£

W1. BR 10T Single Bolster Wagon (2005)

SMR20	**BR** M772736 grey - *05*	42	50

BR single bolster wagon [W1] (SMR)

SMR20A	**BR** M722043, M11114 brown - *05*	42	50

W2. BR 'Conflat A' (2005)

SMR30	**BR** B739600 brown - *05*	45	55
SMR30A	**BR** B739600 brown + container (various) - *05*	NPG	NPG

W3. 'Lowmac' 25T Machinery Wagon (2008)

Built to diagram 2/242

SMR38	**BR** B? brown - *08*	45	55

W4. BR Steel 'Lowfit' Open Wagon 10ft (2008)

SMR36	**BR** B451236, B451660 brown - *08*	45	55

W5. BR PFA with Coal Container (2007)

SMR307	**BR** black + 87101? red **'British Fuels'** Container - *07*	70	85
SMR307A	**BR** black + yellow **'Cawoods'** container - *07*	70	85

W6. 1-plank 12T Wagon 9ft (2005)

SMR19	**BR** M209346 grey - *05*	32	40
SMR19A	**BR** M210401 brown - *05*	32	40
SMR39	**BR** M209346 grey + tarpaulined load - *05*	38	45
SMR39A	**BR** M210401 brown + tarpaulined load - *05*	38	45

W7. BR 3-plank 12T Wagon 9ft (2005)

SMR18	**BR** M26818 grey - *not made*	NA	NA
SMR18A	**BR** M110282, M210401 brown - *not made*	NA	NA
SMR40	**BR** M26818 grey + tarpaulined load - *05*	38	45
SMR40A	**BR** M110282 brown + tarpaulined load - *05*	38	45

W8. BR 3-plank 13T Drop-side Wagon 10ft (2005)

13T medium goods wagon to diagram 1/017.

SMR32	**BR** B457351 brown - ?	42	50

W9. 5-plank 10T Wagon 9ft (2005)

SMR21	**BR** P19950 grey - *05*	35	45
SMR21A	**BR** P94782 brown - *05*	35	45

BR 5-plank wagon [W9] (SMR)

SMR28	**BR** P19840 grey + tarpaulin ** - *05*	42	50
SMR28A	**BR** P94918 brown + tarpaulined load * - *05*	42	50

* 5 different tarpaulined loads were produced to provide variety. ** 2 different.

W10a. 5-plank 13T Wagon (wooden ends) **10ft** (2005)

High goods wagon to diagram 1/032.

SMR33	**BR** B475021 brown - ?	42	50
SMR43	**BR** B475021 brown + tarpaulined load - *05*	42	50

W10b. 5-Plank 13T Wagon (steel ends) **10ft** (2008)

High goods wagon.

SMR34	**BR** B492867 brown - *not made*	NA	NA
SMR44	**BR** brown + tarpaulined load - ?	42	50

W10c. 5-Plank 13T High Bar Wagon 10ft

High goods wagon, timber sides, steel ends and a sheet rail..

SMR34A	**BR** brown - ?	45	55
SMR43	**BR** brown with tarpaulin cover - ?	NPG	NPG

W10d. 5-Plank 13T Drop-side Wagon 10ft

High goods wagon.

SMR	**BR** brown - ?	45	55

W11. 5-plank China Clay Wagon (2006)

Wagon, ropes and hood are a single moulding. It is based on their existing 5-plank wagon and so lacks end doors which a clay wagon would have had. W = weathered

SMR41	**BR** B483814 brown W with blue hood - *06*	45	55

W12. 13T RCH 8-plank Wagon 9ft (2004)

W = weathered

SMR2	'HC **Bull & Co. Ltd**' 101 grey - *04*	23	30

8-plank wagon - 'H.C.Bull & Co.' [W12] (SMR)

SMR2W	'HC **Bull & Co. Ltd**' 101 grey W - *04*	23	30
SMR1	**'Phorpres Bricks'** 988 grey - *04*	23	30
SMR1W	**'Phorpres Bricks'** 988 grey W - *04*	23	30
SMR17	**BR** P110156, P102546 grey - *05*	37	42

W13. 13T RCH Coke Wagon 9ft (2004)

This is an 8-plank wagon with an additional 2-plank extension.

SMR10	**'Suncole'** 5162? black - *04*	25	30
SMR11	**'Modern Transport Company'** 110 black - *04*	25	30
SMR12	**BR** P110239, P387946 grey - *05*	40	50

W14. BR OBA Open LWB Wagon

SM309	**BR** Railfreight ? red+grey - *not made*	NA	NA

W15. BR 13T Steel 'Highfit' Open Wagon 10ft (2005)

SMR35	**BR** B483198 brown - *05*	42	50
SMR44	**BR** B4676?? brown + tarpaulined cover - *08*	37	42

W16. BR 16.5t MCV Steel Mineral Wagon 10ft (2005)

SMR37	**BR** B596260, B552483 grey - *05*	45	55
SMR37A	**BR** B596250, B552463 brown - *05*	45	55
SMR37AW	**BR** B506??7 brown W MCV - *not made*	NA	NA

W17. MTA Steel Low-sided Open Box Wagon (2008)

SMR305	**EWS** 395274? maroon+yellow - *08*	NPG	75

W18. POA 33T Steel Box Wagon (2008)

SMR304	**'Yeoman'/'Tiger'** TRL5157 grey - *08*	NPG	75

W19. HAA MGR Hopper Wagon (2005)

SMR300	**BR** 358027 silver+brown early markings - *05*	NPG	85

BR HAA merry-go-round hopper wagon [W19] (SMR)

SMR300A	**BR** 355203 silver+red later markings - *05*	NPG	85
SMRL18	coal load for the above - *05*	4	5

W20. HBA MGR Hopper Wagon (with hood) (2005)

SMR301	**BR**358017? silver+brown early markings - *05*	NPG	95
SMR301A	**BR** 355203? silver+red later markings - *05*	NPG	95

W21. CDA Bulk Powder Hopper Wagon

SMR302	**ECC** ? silver+blue - *not made*	NA	NA
SMR302A	**EWS** ? silver+maroon - *not made*	NA	NA

W22. PCA 'Presflo' Bulk Powder Wagon (2007)

This is a depressed centre tank. This is supplied devoid of logos and with a sheet of decals for 'Blue Circle' and 'Alcan'.

SMR306	**'Blue Circle Cement'** very pale grey - *07*	70	85

PCA bulk powder tank wagon [W22] (SMR)

SMR306	**'Alcan'** ? very pale grey - *07*	70	85

W23. TTA 'Monobloc' Tank Wagon (2007)

This was supplied devoid of logos and with a sheet of decals for Shell and BP. Design as modified in 1984.

SMR303	**'Shell'** very pale grey - *07*	90	95
SMR303	**'BP'** very pale grey - *07*	90	95
SMR303B	**'Shell'** black - *08*	90	95
SMR303G	**'BP'** green - *08*	90	95
SMR?	**'Shell/BP'** ? very pale grey - *not made*	NA	NA
SMR?	**'Shell'** ? very pale grey - *not made*	NA	NA
SMR?	**'BP'** ? very pale grey - *not made*	NA	NA

W24a. 10T Salt Van (side hinge doors)

SMR26	**'Saxa Salt'** 238 yellow - *not made*	NA	NA

W24b. 10T Salt Van (drop down doors)

SMR27	**'Saxa Salt'** 207 yellow - *not made*	NA	NA

W25. MR 8T Goods Van (2005)

Planked timber ends with single sliding doors.

SMR7A	**LMS** 78172 light grey - *05*	45	55
SMR7	**BR** M32385 light grey - *05*	45	55

W26. LMS 12T Single Vent Van (2005)

Corrugated steel ends and planked sides with sliding doors.

SMR22	**BR** M506875 brown - *05*	45	55

W27a. SR Ventilated Box Van (planked sides) (2008)

Double doors.

SMR46	**BR** S59123 brown - *08*	45	55

Ex-SR ventilated van [W27a] (SMR)

W27b. SR Ventilated Box Van (plywood sides) (2008)
Double doors.

SMR45	**BR** B752496 brown - *08*	45	55

W27c. SR Box Van (planked sides)
Unventilated.

SMR45	**BR** B752456? brown - *not made*	NA	NA

W28a. BR 10T Insulated Ale Van (2005)
With planked sides, corrugated steel ends.

SMR23	**BR** B872094 brown 'Ale' - *05*	45	55

W28b. BR 10T Insulated Meat Van (2005)
With planked sides, corrugated steel ends and double doors.

SMR24	**BR** B872095, B872056? white 'Insulated' - *05*	42	50

W29. BR 10T Ventilated Meat Van (2005)
With planked sides, corrugated steel ends and double doors, 4 louvre end vents.

SMR29	**BR** B470006? brown - *05*	45	55

W30a. BR 12T Vent Standard Fruit Van (2005)
Double doors and corrugated steel ends with four louvers and side vents. Double doors.

SMR5	**BR** B785753 brown - *05*	45	55

BR standard 12T ventilated van [W30a] (SMR)

W30b. BR 12T Plywood Sided Vent Fruit Van (2005)
Double doors and corrugated steel ends with four louvers and side vents. Double doors.

SMR5A	**BR** B785753 brown - *05*	45	55

W31. BR 12T Planked Single Vent Van (2005)
Double doors, steel ends. Picture shows plywood sides!

SMR25	**BR** B785753, B755922? brown - *05*	45	55

W32. BR 12T 'Vanwide' Van (2008)
Double sliding doors. Diagram 1/217.

SMR48	**BR** B743159? brown - *08*	45	55

W33. BR VEA 10T Airbraked Van

SMR325	**BR** Railfreight 230427 red+grey - *not made*	NA	NA

W34. BR 12T 'Palvan' (2008)
Double side hinged doors to the left of the side to allow loading of pallets.

SMR49	**BR** B773142? brown - *08*	45	55

W35. BR VDA 25t LWB Airbraked Van

SMR325	**BR** Railfreight 700715? red+grey - *?*	NPG	NPG

W36. BR VGA 28t LWB Van

SMR335	**BR** Railfreight ? grey - *?*	NPG	NPG

W37. BR CCT
Standard BR metal bodied covered carriage truck.

SMR310	**BR** ? blue - *?*	NPG	NPG

W38. SR CCT
SR style wooden bodied covered carriage truck.

SMR311	**BR** ? green - *?*	NPG	NPG

W39. BR 20T Standard Brake Van (2006)

SMR42	**BR** B952104 brown - *06*	80	100
SMR42A	**BR** B951481 grey - *06*	80	100
SMR42B	**BR** DB950746? grey+yellow - *06*	80	100

W40. 30T Bogie 'Macaw B'/'Bolster C' (2005)

SMR31	**GWR** 70247 dark grey 'Macaw B' - *05*	110	135
SMR31A	**BR** B940154 grey low bolsters 'Bogie Volster C' - *05*	110	135

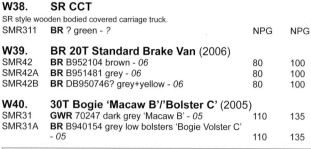

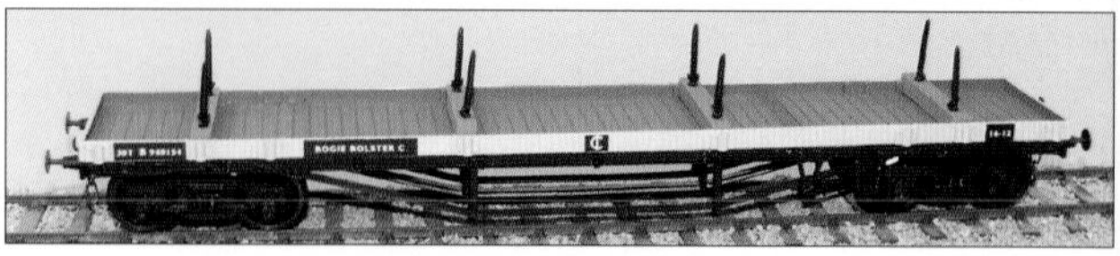
BR 30T bogie bolster wagon [W40] (SMR)

SMR31B	**BR** B945117 grey high bolsters 'BCO' - *05*	110	135
SMR31C	**BR** B924439 brown high bolster + modern bogies 'BCV' - *05*	110	135

W41. FGA Container Wagon

SMR331	**Freightliner**? grey+red - *?*	NPG	NPG

W42. HTA 102T Bogie Coal Hopper Wagon

SMR308	**EWS** 210670? maroon+yellow - *?*	NPG	NPG

W43. TEA 100t Bogie Oil Tanker

SMR310	**'Shell'** grey - *?*	NPG	125

W44. IWB Bogie Van

SMR333	**'Blue Circle Cement'** ? yellow+blue - *?*	NPG	NPG
SMR334	**?** ? grey+blue - *?*	NPG	NPG

The Skytrex Factory

Production of your model starts here with talented designers making the original patterns

Tri-ang Big Big

(including Novo and Red Rocket)

HISTORY

Big Big was the idea of W Moray Lines, then Chairman of Lines Bros. Ltd, and was developed at the Tri-ang Research Centre at Canterbury, then handed to Rovex Scale Models Ltd for tooling and production.

The idea was to involve children in copious play participation which could involve the outdoors as well as in the house.The plan was that the track could be laid from the house into the garden and a child could send trains outside while staying indoors himself even if it was raining. With this in mind, the system was designed to withstand all weathers. This principle was illustrated in the 4 page coloured leaflet produced to launch the system, which showed children playing with a set in this way.

Freelance 0-4-0 steam locomotive [L1]

In July 1966 the model railway press carried advertisements for Big Big under the heading 'Model or Toy'.They extolled its virtues, referring to safety, authentic detail and suitability for outdoor use. Apparently its pliable polypropylene track took the ups and downs of a garden layout in its stride.The trip switch, which would automatically reverse the direction of drive at the end of the line, was illustrated, as were the two sets available at that time; one had the *Blue Flyer* and two trucks and the other the *Blue Flyer* and four trucks. In attempting to appeal to children, the bright colours were not to everyone's taste, but the serious modeller could always paint them.

Big-Big was discontinued in 1972. In the final years, various new models were considered using parts for which tools already existed. One of these was a low steel wagon with two cable drums and another was a steel covered wagon. A pre-production sample of a GWR 'Prairie' tank engine was made bur not put into production. Whilst a nice product, Big-Big was not really profitable, due to the heavy tooling costs. Although large quantities were exported, these had a low profit margin - a common problem with exporting.

Eventually the tools were sold to Russia and used to make the Novo train sets that were available in the UK in the late 1970s.

Ruston diesel shunter 0-4-0 [L3]

Novo - Dunbee-Combex-Marx, who had acquired Rovex Ltd at the break-up of the Lines Group in 1971, entered into an agreement with the Soviet Ministry of Light Industries in 1975, under which various factories in the Soviet Union would manufacture kits and toys using tools and materials supplied by DCM. The finished products would be packaged under the Novo name and be delivered to DCM without charge in payment for the tools. Amongst the tools cleaned up and test run for this deal were Frog aircraft kits, Tri-ang TT and Tri-ang Big Big.

Novo Toys Ltd was set up in 1975 by DCM as a British company, based in Peterborough, with the sole purpose of handling this business. Once the agreed number of Novo kits, toys etc. had been delivered, the tools became the property of the Russians and no further toys would be supplied.

With the demise of Dunbee-Combex-Marx in 1980, Novo Toys Ltd went first into receivership and then was wound up when a buyer for the company could not be found.

Lima - While the system had a reasonable reception in the UK it sold well on the Continent. In 1967 the concept was sold to Lima in exchange for a deal to supply Wrenn with N gauge trains. Lima tooled up their own version of Big Big under the name 'Jumbo'. Later they went onto a more realistic 0 gauge model railway system using power from the track.

AMF - Big Big was also sold to the American Machine & Foundry Co. (AMF) who tooled up their own version. This was where the idea for the caboose came from.

Red Rocket - Yet another version was made in Hong Kong for an Australian store but this was a pirate. It was sold as the 'Red Rocket Set' possibly in the early 1980s. The set included the Hymek in red with a white roof and carrying raised white letters giving the name *Red Rocket* in the same style as the original *Blue Flier*. The cab windows, unlike those on the Tri-ang and Novo versions, were glazed. The other contents were mineral wagons, side tipping wagons, switches and an oval of track in dark blue plastic instead of red. The couplings were the Peco type and the only inscription carried on the parts was 'Made in Hong Kong'. The mineral wagons differed from the Rovex ones in having domed buffers.

The box was white with the train flying out of a scenic picture circled in track. The box carried a sticker with the name 'Artin' on it and a racing car logo.

Couplings - The models were fitted with couplings similar to the Peco type used on the Hornby-Dublo locos and rolling stock. They were at first attached with a brass screw into a type of heli-coil fixed to the chassis. In 1968 the type of fixing changed to the more familiar brass eyelet.

'Red Rocket' Hymek locomotive [L4]

Packaging - Big-Big solo models were packed in yellow cardboard boxes. Initially, these were individually printed with a picture of the contents and the name 'Big-Big Trains' between two heavy black lines. Later, the boxes depicted the contents only on the end flaps and the logo took on a different style with the heavy lines being dropped.

With an uncertain future, in 1971 a number of models were sold in other yellow boxes with a label stuck over the printing or in temporary white boxes when stocks of the normal packaging ran out.

These had a printed label stuck on the box ends describing the contents; the labels being produced on a small printing machine in the factory.

Dates: The ones quoted in the tables below are mostly those when factory records indicate that batches of the models were made or, in the case of Novo products, when stock entered the factory store.

LOCOMOTIVES

The locomotives were all powered by batteries placed inside each model rather than within a remote control module.

Cat No.	Company, Number, Colour, Dates	£	£
L1.	**Freelance Small Tank Engine 0-4-0T** (1968)		
Powered by four 1.5v HP11/U11 batteries.			
RV276	red - *68-69*	10	20
RV276	yellow - *68-69*	10	20
RV276A	blue - *70-71*	10	20
L2.	**USA Class Tank 0-6-0T** (1971)		
Powered by four 1.5v HP11/U11 batteries.			
RV262	green - *71-72*	20	30

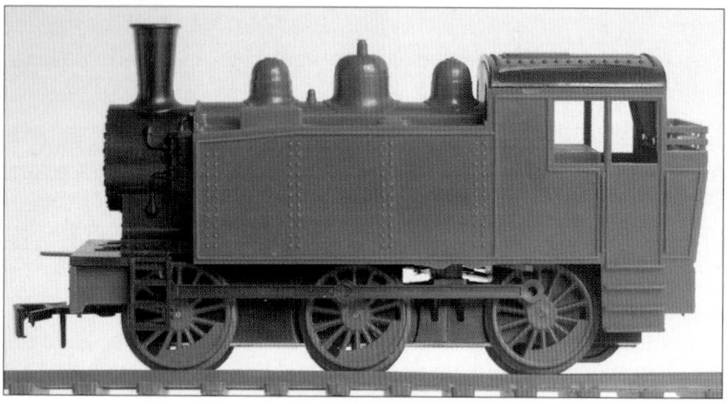

USA Class 0-6-0 tank engine [L2]

Cat No.	Company, Number, Colour, Dates	£	£
RV262	yellow - *71-72*	40	50
L3.	**Ruston Diesel Shunter 0-4-0DS** (1967)		
Powered by four 1.5v HP11/U11 batteries.			
RV272	yellow - *67-69*	10	20
RV272A	blue - *70-71*	10	20
L4.	**'Hymek' Diesel Hydraulic Bo-Bo** (1967)		
Powered by four 1.5v HP2/U2 batteries.			
RV256	***Blue Flier*** blue with white roof - *67-69*	10	20
RV256A	yellow with black roof - *70-71*	25	30
-	blue with white roof (Novo) - *75-80*	10	NA
-	***Red Rocket*** red with white roof * - *?*	40	NA

** See 'History' notes above.*

COACHES

Cat No.	Company, Number, Colour, Dates	£	£
C1.	**Mk2 Composite** (1968)		
RV257	blue + white - *68-71*	8	15

MK2 coach [C1]

Cat No.	Company, Number, Colour, Dates	£	£
RV257	blue + white (Novo) - *75-80*	8	15
C2.	**US Style Coach** (1968)		
This was the same as the Mk2 coach but had corrugated sides.			
RV274	yellow - *68-71*	20	25

WAGONS

Cat No.	Company, Number, Colour, Dates	£	£
W1.	**Steam Roller Wagon** (1967)		
A flat wagon with depressions in the deck to take the steam roller from the Minic range.			
RV275	red + blue steam roller - *67-68, 71*	15	25
RV275	red + pink steam roller - *?*	15	25
W2.	**Cable Drum Wagon**		
This would have been a steel open wagon with two cable drums from the Minic Push-and-Go Series.			
?	*planned but not made*	NA	NA
W3.	**Steel Mineral Wagon** (1967)		
RV258	green - *67-70*	10	14
RV258	red - *67-70*	8	12

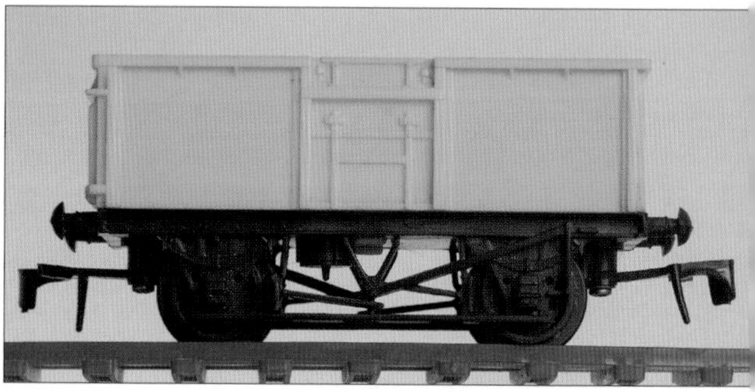

Steel mineral wagon [W3]

Cat No.	Company, Number, Colour, Dates	£	£
RV258	blue - *70-71*	8	12
-	yellow (ex-Red Rocket set) - *?*	15	NA
W4.	**Covered Steel Wagon**		
This was the steel mineral wagon with a top making it look like a 'Presflo' wagon.			
?	*planned but not made*	NA	NA
W5.	**Side Tipping Wagon** (1966)		
RV273	red - *66-71*	6	10
RV273	green - *66-71*	6	10
-	green (Novo) - *75-80*	6	NA
-	green (ex-Red Rocket set) - *?*	7	NA
W6.	**Zoo Cage Wagon** (1971)		
A 4-wheel flat wagon carrying a circus cage containing an animal.			
RV283	red cage with yellow roof - *71*	15	25
W7.	**Crane Truck**		
It was intended that this wagon would carry the Dinky Toys crane.			
?	*planned but not made*	NA	NA
W8a.	**Caboose** (1970)		
A 4-wheel vehicle.			
RV298	green - *70-71*	10	15
W8b.	**Message Carrier** (1972)		
Based on the caboose, it had a slot in the roof for posting letters.			
RV330	green - *72?*	20	30
W9.	**Bogie Zoo Cage Wagon** (1971)		
A bogie flat wagon carrying two circus cages each containing a free-standing animal.			
RV?	red cages with yellow roofs - *71*	25	NPG

Bogie 200 cage wagon [W9]

W10. Gondola (1971)

American style bogie steel open wagon without buffers. Some are inscribed 'Made in England' and others have this blanked out.

RV259	blue (3 shades - light, mid and dark) - *67-71*	8	12
RV259	yellow - *67-71*	8	12
RV259	red - *67-71*	12	15

W11. 3-section Change-a-truck

This was a kit of bits which made a bogie wagon out of three 10' base sections joined together and various tops added.

RV297	in sets only - *?*	15	25

W12. 4-section Change-a-truck (1970)

This was a kit of bits which made a bogie wagon out of four 10' base sections joined together and various tops added.

RV277	various colours - *70-71*	20	30

SETS

There was a good range of train sets in Tri-ang Big Big and the following may be found along with the dates when they were made:

RV266	Train Set No1 (2 trucks)	*66*
RV267	Train Set No2 (4 trucks)	*67?*
RV278	Yellow Shunter Train Set (freight)	*67-68*
RV279	Blue Flier Train Set No.3 (freight)	*67-68*
RV280	Big-Big Passenger Set	*68-70*
RV281	Mixed Traffic Train Set	*68-70*
RV282	Goods Train Set	*68-70*
RV320	Express Train Set	*70-71*
RV321	Lumber Camp Train Set	*70-71*
RV322	Goods Train Set	*70*
RV323	Mining Depot Train Set	*70-71*
RV324	Freight Yard Train Set	*70-71*
RV325	Zoo Train Set	*71*
RV326	Local Goods Train Set	*71*

Mining Depot Action set (Vectis)

Hornby A3 Galtee More from computer artwork by Robbie McGavin

Scales and Gauges

'Scale' refers to the linear scale of the model, for example: 4mm to 1 foot (the OO scale measurement). Gauge referes to the distance between the running rails of the track, listed here are a few of the more common scales and gauges.

Gauge name	Scale	Gauge distance
'N' (British)	2mm to 1 foot	9mm
'OOO'	2mm to 1 foot	9.5mm
'TT' (British)	3mm to 1 foot	12mm
'H0'	3.5mm to 1 foot	16.5mm
'OO'	4mm to 1 foot	16.5mm
'EM'	4mm to 1 foot	18mm
'O' (British)	7mm to 1 foot	32mm
'No.1'	10mm to 1 foot	45.45mm
'No.2'	7/16inch to 1 foot	51mm
'No.3'	12/32", 1/2" or 14mm to 1 foot	63.5mm

The illustrations below are only approximately to scale to give some idea of the difference in size between the various gauges.

'N' gauge 9mm | **'OOO' 9.5mm** | **'TT' gauge 12mm**

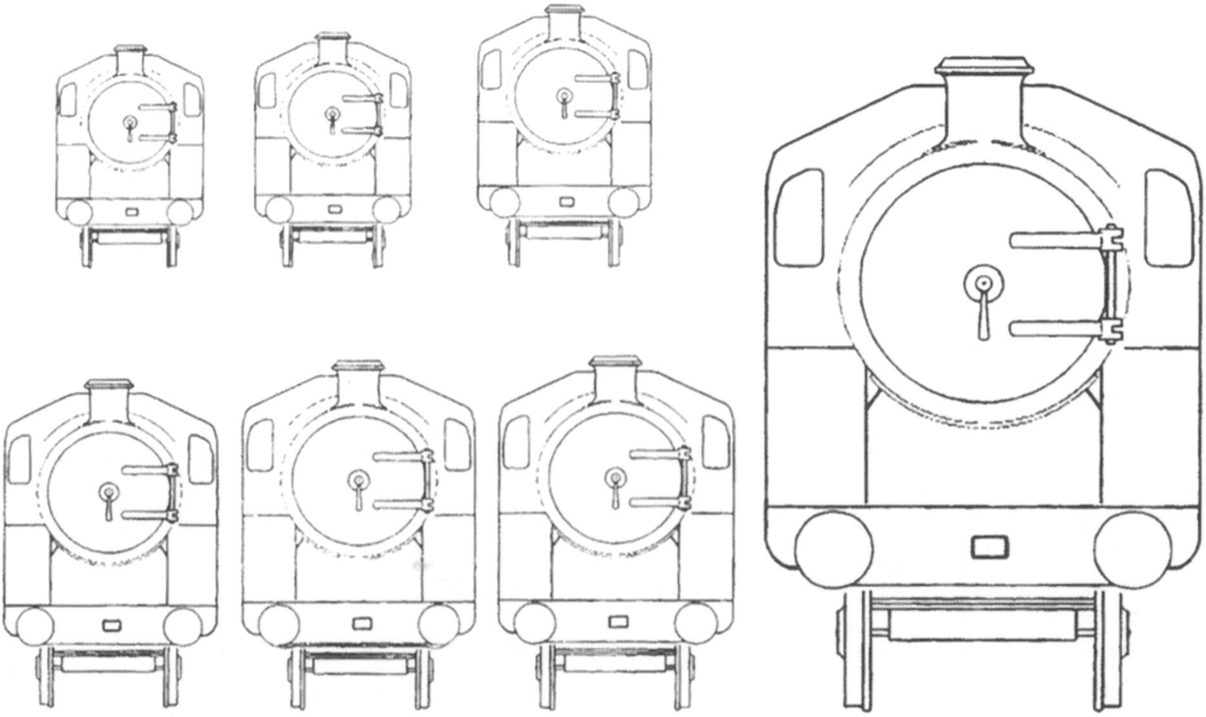

'H0' gauge 16.5mm | **'OO' gauge 16.5mm** | **'EM' gauge 18mm** | **'O' gauge 32mm**

Tri-ang TT

HISTORY

In the 1930s there had been experiments in 2.5mm:1' scale on 12.2 mm gauge track but, while the gauge was successful, the scale was found to be too cramped.

Milestones

1951 Rokal TT imported into Britain.
1953 Lines Bros. examine a Wesa TT set.
1954 Work on a Tri-ang TT system has started.
1957 Tri-ang TT launched at Toy Fair.
1959 'Merchant Navy' model launched.
1959 B type track introduced.
1960 'Britannia' released.
1961 Gold plated set appears.
1962 Production of Continental range of Tri-ang TT starts in France.
1963 French tools transferred to Margate.
1964 Last catalogue is released.
1967 A special run of models made.
1967 A few blue and grey coaches made.
1968 Wrenn acquire outstanding TT stock.

Following the Second World War, HP of America produced a TT system in 2.5 mm scale and in 1950 the German Rokal system was developed in a slightly larger scale. Rokal was imported into Britain in 1951 and this rekindled interest in TT scale in Britain. While Peco produced their 'Minilay' track, few others responded. It needed a major company to show its faith in the scale.

Ex-GWR Prairie tank [L2]

In 1953, Walter Lines, chairman of the toy manufacturing giant Lines Bros. Ltd, returning from a trip to the Continent, brought back a train set manufactured by Wesa of Switzerland. He gave instruction that Rovex Scale Models Ltd., who were manufacturing the Tri-ang Railways 00 system, were to start work immediately on a Tri-ang TT system.

The command from above was not well received at Rovex, where management were struggling to keep their heads above water with the staggering success of their 00 system. Despite this, someone was put on TT development as soon as the Company moved into its new factory at Margate in the Summer of 1954.

Many of the TT tools were made in the factory at Margate and the system was launched at the Toy Fair in the Spring of 1957, where the first two sets were displayed.

All locomotives and rolling stock were fitted with tension-lock couplings which had not yet appeared on the Tri-ang Railways 00 system. To distinguish it from the larger gauge system, the new TT products were packaged in yellow boxes with red printing and these would soon become a very familiar sight in model shops. Sets were available either with a battery box or a mains controller. The latter carried an 'X' suffix to their code.

Ex-GWR 'Castle' Class Tintagel Castle [L3]

At last the market had the impetus it needed to see TT taken as a serious scale for modelling. Other manufacturers quickly jumped on the band wagon, producing accessories in the scale. For many this meant just producing smaller versions of existing models, but track, card buildings, wagon kits and lineside accessories quickly appeared. Peco even produced a more detailed 10' chassis and, supplied with Tri-ang bodies by Rovex, sold their TT chassis with a Tri-ang body fitted.

As with many of their ventures, Lines Bros. were determined to give their new baby a fighting chance. This meant producing a sizeable range of models to demonstrate their confidence in the system. Only by doing this could they persuade both the public and retailers that Tri-ang TT was here to stay and therefore worth buying.

1962 saw models of French prototypes added to the TT range. In order to access the European Common Market, which Britain had not yet joined, Lines Bros. built a factory in Calais. Various toy ranges were transferred there and one which the Company hoped to introduce to France was Tri-ang Railways TT. While other product lines from the Calais factory succeeded, the TT venture was not a success and the Continental tooling was sent to the Margate factory to be used there.

Tri-ang's eighth edition TT catalogue showed a system in decline with a number of models now missing from the range. Sales of the TT system had been falling sharply since 1960 and in just two years the sales figures for sets halved. By 1964, total sales were just one sixth of what they had been in 1960.

By 1968, G&R Wrenn, who were another member of the Lines Group, had acquired the remaining stock of Tri-ang TT and were selling it as Wrenn Table Top Railways. According to a tool inventory, carried out in the early '90s, the bulk of the tools for the TT system stayed at Margate or, at least, those for the British range did.

Thus passed Britain's only TT scale system, but it was not the end of TT. It has remained one of the scales still modelled today and much of this success should be laid at the door of the 3mm Society who have concentrated their energies on the production of models and materials to meet their members' needs.

BR 0-6-0 diesel shunter [L6]

Further Reading

There is, as yet no definitive book on this subject, although there is coverage in the first volume of Pat Hammond's trilogy, *The Rovex Story*. The book concerned is *Volume 1 - Tri-ang Railways*. There are a few additional notes in *Volume 2 - Tri-ang Hornby*. The subject was also covered in a three part article in the *Model Railway Collector* magazine Volume 7 numbers 2-4 (February-April 2000).

Collectors Club

We would also like to recommend the Tri-ang Society which caters for collectors of a wide range of Tri-ang toy products. The Society has a quarterly newsletter, called *Tri-ang Telegraph*, which contains a number of original articles by well known collectors. Details of the Tri-ang Society may be obtained from Miles Rowland, Tel: 0161 9765059. Tri-ang TT is also sometimes covered in the magazine of the Train Collectors Society (details at the front of the book).

Dates - It is difficult to be completely accurate with production dates and those given should be treated as a guide, only.

Listing - The locos are listed in order of size starting with tank engines followed by tender locos and ending with diesels and multiple units. Wagons are listed in the order of: flats, open wagons, hoppers, tanks, vans, brake vans and bogie stock.

LOCOMOTIVES

Transfers - Early models had forward facing lions on their BR decals but on later ones the lions all faced to the left.

Cat No.	Company, Number, Colour, Dates	£	£

British Locomotives

L1. LMS 'Jinty' Class 3F 0-6-0T (1957)

There were two similar but different body moulds used at the same time. It could have been a two impression mould producing two bodies with each shot.

T90	**34171** BRc unlined black, plastic centre wheels, number transfers - *57*	30	35
T90	as above but heat printed - *58*	20	25
T90	as above but all metal wheels - *59-61*	20	25

Early and late examples of the 'Jinty' 0-6-0T [L1]

T90S	**4171** BRc lined black + smoke - *62*	40	55
T90	As above without smoke - *62-68*	25	30

L2. GWR 'Prairie' Class 61XX 2-6-2T (1961)

This used a modified 'Castle' chassis and wheels. Both solid and open spoke wheels may be found on this models, the latter being introduced in 1964. The numbers were usually in yellow but white ones exist.

T99	**6157** BRc lined black, copper chimney top and dome - *61-67*	55	65
T99	**6157** BRc lined black, unpainted chimney top and dome - *61-64*	55	65
T99	The same with open spoke wheels - *64-65*	60	70

L3. GWR 'Castle' Class 4-6-0 (1957)

Both solid and open spoked (introduced in 1964) wheels may be found on *Tintagel Castle*. Early locos were gloss green.

T91/92	**4082 *Windsor Castle**** BRc green versions plastic centre wheels - *57*	35	40
T91/92	as above but all metal wheels - *58-61*	35	40
T91/92	**5011 *Tintagel Castle*** BRc green, black nameplate - *62-64*	40	45
T91/92	**5011 *Tintagel Castle*** BRc green, green nameplate - *62-64*	40	45
T91/92	The same with open spoke wheels - *64-65*	50	60

* Two different fonts were used for the nameplate.

L4. SR Non-Rebuilt 'Merchant Navy' 4-6-2 (1959)

The model had metal nameplates.

T93/94	**35028 *Clan Line*** BRc green* - *59-64*	50	55

'Gold plated' 'Merchant Navy' Class loco [L4]

(T43)	BRc gold from Ltd Edn T43 Kays set - *61*	80	NA

* Lining varies in shade between yellow and orange and both gloss (early) and matt finishes may be found.

L5. BR 'Britannia' Class 4-6-2 (1960)

T97/98	**70000 *Britannia*** BRc green - *60-61*	50	55
T97/98	as above with open spoke wheels - *67*	65	80
T97S/98	**70036 *Boadicea*** BRc green + smoke generator - *62-64*	70	75
T97/98	as above but no smoke - *62-64, 67*	55	70
T97/98	as above with open spoke wheels - *64*	65	80

L6. Diesel Shunter 0-6-0DS (1959)

This used the 'Jinty' chassis.

T95	**13007** BRc green - *59-61*	25	30
T95	**D3115** BRc green - *62-67*	25	30
T95	**D3117** BRc green - *62-67*	25	30

L7. Class 31 Diesel A1A-A1A (1959)

Early models had brass gears but plastic ones were used later. Early examples had wire handrails but later models had moulded ones. The blue version came in a box marked 'Loco Electrique Habille Bleu'.

T96	**D5501** BRc green, wire handrails - *59-?*	30	35
T96	**D5501** BRc green moulded rails - *?-68*	30	35
T96	**D5501** BRc blue made in France - *67?*	400	500

L8. Class 104 Birmingham RC&W Co. DMU (1963)

T190	**M50421** BRc green power car - *63-67*	35	40
T137	**M59133** green centre car - *63-67*	30	35

BR Class 104 DMU [L8]

T136	**M50425** BRc green trailer car - *63-67*	25	30

Continental Locomotives

L9. Continental 0-6-0T (1963)

T590	**4711** black - *63-64*	80	120
T590	**4711** black unpainted rear lights - *63-64*	80	120

L10. Est Class 231D 4-6-2 (1962)

Both solid and open spoke wheels may be found on these models, the latter being introduced in 1964.

T591	**1401** AL S16 black - *62-68*	60	80
T591S	**1401** AL S16 black + smoke - *62-68*	80	100

L11. Continental EMU

T594/595	silver - *not made*	NA	NA

COACHES

The body was a single moulding with a separate roof, underframe, bogies and buffers and the window glazing was strips or sheets of clear plastic inside the coach. Most of the coaches fell into two categories - suburbans and main line. From January 1960, roofs were screw fixed and interior units could be bought and added. Examples with seats usually sell for £2-3 more. Early suburban coaches had roundish windows while late ones had squarer ones and are rarer. The rarest and most sought after main line coaches are blue and grey. There are a lot of minor variations in common main line coaches including different running numbers, class lines and shades of plastic used in their construction.

Cat No.	Company, Number, Colour, Dates	£	£

C1a. Mk1 Suburban Composite (1957)

sfr = screw fixed roof. ov = oval windows. sq = squared windows. rn = raised number (others are heat printed).

T80	**BR** M41006 maroon ov rn - *57-58*	8	12

T80	**BR** M41007 maroon ov - *58-60*	10	15
T80	**BR** 41007 maroon ov sfr - *60-61*	10	15
T80	**BR** 41007 maroon sq sfr - *62-65*	10	15
T130	**BR** S3153S green ov - *59-61*	10	15
T130	**BR** S3153S green ov sfr - *61*	10	15
T130	**BR** S3153S green sq sfr - *62*	15	20

C1b. Mk1 Suburban Brake 2nd (1957)

sfr = screw fixed roof. ov = oval windows. sq = squared windows. rn = raised number (others are heat printed).

T81	**BR** M34000 maroon ov rn - *57-58*	8	12
T81	**BR** M53171 maroon ov - *58-60*	10	15
T81	**BR** 53171 maroon ov sfr - *60-61*	10	15
T81	**BR** 53171 maroon sq sfr - *62-65*	10	15

Mk1 suburban brake 2nd [c1b]

T131	**BR** S4718S green ov - *59-61*	10	15
T131	**BR** S4718S green ov sfr - *61*	10	15
T131	**BR** S4718S green sq sfr - *62*	15	20

C2a. Mk1 Main Line Composite (1957)

From January 1960, roofs were screw fixed and interior units could be bought and added. Examples with seats usually sell for £2-3 more. sfr = screw fixed roof. cl = yellow class line over 1st class section.

T82	**BR** W.15732 bright maroon - *57*	8	12
T82	**BR** W15732 bright maroon - *57-59*	8	12
T82	**BR** 24011 bright maroon - *59*	8	12
T82	**BR** 24011 maroon sfr - *60*	8	12
T82	**BR** 24010 maroon sfr - *60-63*	8	12
T82	**BRc** 24010 maroon sfr cl - *63-66*	8	12
T132	**BR** S15021 green - *59*	8	12
T132	**BR** S15021 green sfr - *60-62*	8	12
T132	**BRc** S15021 green sfr - *63-64*	8	12
T182	**BR** W15773 brown+cream - *59*	8	12
T182	**BR** W15773 brown+cream sfr - *60-63*	8	12
T182	**BR** W15772 brown+cream sfr - *60-63*	8	12
T182	**BRc** W15772 brown+cream sfr cl - *60-63*	8	12
T87	**BR** S15021 blue+grey sfr - *67-68*	35	40

C2b. Mk1 Main Line Brake 2nd (1957)

From January 1960, roofs were screw fixed and interior units could be bought and added. Examples with seats usually sell for £2-3 more. sfr = screw fixed roof.

T83	**BR** W.53111 bright maroon - *57*	8	12
T83	**BR** W53111 bright maroon - *57-59*	8	12
T83	**BR** 34001 bright maroon - *59*	8	12
T83	**BR** 34001 maroon sfr - *60-66*	8	12
T133	**BR** S4718S green - *59*	8	12
T133	**BR** S34245 green - *59*	8	12
T133	**BR** S4718S green sfr - *60*	8	12
T133	**BR** S34245 green sfr - *60-62*	8	12
T133	**BRc** S34245 green sfr - *63-64*	8	12
T183	**BR** W21134 brown+cream - *59*	8	12
T183	**BR** W34150 brown+cream sfr - *60-63*	8	12
T183	**BRc** W34150 brown+cream sfr - *60-63*	8	12
T88	**BR** S34245 blue+grey sfr - *67-68*	35	40

C2c. Mk1 Restaurant Car (1958)

The restaurant cars had blue (bc) or white (wc) curtains.

T84	**BR** W307 bright maroon bc - *58-59*	8	12
T84	**BR** 11005 bright maroon bc - *59-66*	8	12
T84	**BRc** 11005 maroon wc - *59-66*	8	12
T134	**BR** S1771 green bc - *59-64*	8	12

BR Mk1 restaurant car [C2c]

T134	**BR** S1771 green wc - *59-64*	8	12
T184	**BR** W301 brown+cream bc - *59-63*	8	12
T184	**BR** W301 brown+cream wc - *59-63*	8	12
T89	**BR** S1771 blue+grey - *67-68*	35	40

C3. Mk1 Sleeping Car (1961)

T86	**BR** 2510 maroon - *61-65*	13	15
T86	**BR** 2510 dark maroon - *61-65*	13	15

C4. SR Utility Vans (1961)

T85	**BR** 46205 maroon - *61*	20	25
T135	**BR** 46205 green - *61*	20	25
T85	**BR** S224S maroon - *61*	13	15
T85	**BR** S227S maroon - *61*	13	15
T135	**BR** S2278 green - *61-67*	13	15
T135	**BR** S227S green - *61-67*	13	15

C5. DMU Centre Car (1963)

The roof (painted grey) and sides were a single moulding. The underframe and bogies were from the DMU power cars.

T137	**BRc** M59133 green centre car - *63-67*	30	35

C6. Pullman Cars (1961)

These were 1st class kitchen cars. The screw-fixed roof was a separate moulding which was usually cream but white ones may be found. The printed curtains were blue and it was always sold with an interior unit.

T185	***Snipe*** brown+cream - *61-67*	30	35
T185	***Falcon*** brown+cream - *61-67*	30	35
T185	***Eagle*** brown+cream - *61-67*	30	35

C7. Continental Stock (1962)

Special bogies were made for the Continental coaches.

T580	stainless steel car, silver - *62-65*	25	30
T581	generator/baggage blue - *not made*	NA	NA
T582	**Wagon-Lits** blue sleeper - *not made*	NA	NA

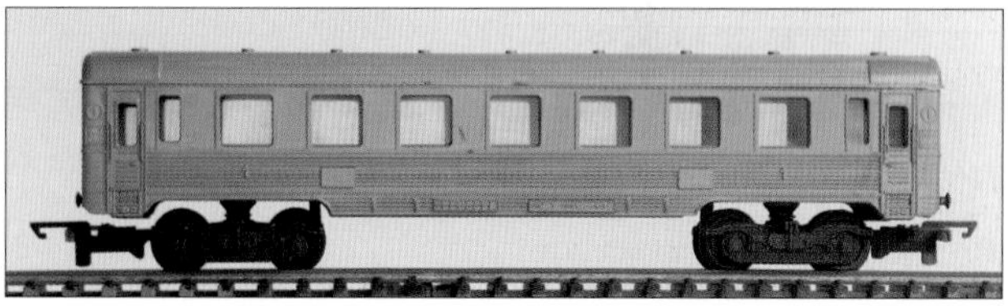

French stainless steel car [C7]

T583	**Wagon-Lits** Pullman car blue+cream - *not made*	NA	NA
T584	**SNCF** 1471 forestiere green - *65?*	45	60

WAGONS

These had diecast chassis with moulded plastic bodies. They were joined together by four pins on the casting which located in four holes in the moulding. There are examples of unusual plastic colours that are worth looking out for and these often sell at much higher rates. Some colours, such as grey, brown and maroon, turn up in a range of different shades. As it is practically impossible to determine which shade was available when, the period during which it may have occurred is given.

Peco fitted their more detailed 10' chassis to four Tri-ang TT bodies supplied by Rovex. These were the 13T steel low-sided wagon, mineral wagon, cattle wagon and 12T goods van.

Loads: It seems that each of the mouldings for the loads was produced in a twin impression mould, resulting in there being two versions of each load to be found in equal quantities and in each colour variation.

Two of the wagons sold fitted to Peco chassis

Cat No.	Company, Number, Colour, Dates	£	£

British Wagons

W1. 14T 'Conflat L' + 3 'L' Type Containers (1960)

The 'L' type containers (3 per wagon) may be a dark greenish grey or a paler translucent grey.

T276	**BR** B530258 red-brown + load - *60-67*	8	10
T276	**BR** B530258 dark brown + load - *60-67*	8	10

W2. 12T 6-plank Open Truck (1959)

Timber loads, of which there were two versions, were cream or tan and drum loads were black, maroon, brown, grey or cream. The heat printing was white.

T176	**BR** 17351 green - *59-67*	25	30
T176	**BR** 17351 yellow brown - *59-67*	5	7
T176	**BR** 17351 red-brown - *59-67*	5	7
T176	**BR** 17351 dark yellow brown - *62*	8	10
T176	**BR** 17351 maroon - *59-67*	8	10
T177	any of the above + timber - *59-61*	8	10
T178	any of the above + drums - *59-61*	8	10

W3. 13T Steel Low-Sided Wagon (1958)

plank = planked interior. plain = plain interior. The load was a plastic moulding representing granite chips. Two different mouldings of this exist.

T172	**BR** B9325 grey plank - *58-67*	5	7
T273	as above with load - *60-61*	8	10
T172	**BR** B9325 light grey plank - *58-67*	5	7
T273	as above with load - *60-61*	8	10
T172	**BR** B9325 grey plain - *58-67*	5	7
T273	as above with load - *60-61*	8	10
T172	**BR** B9325 light grey plain - *58-67*	5	7
T273	as above with load - *60-61*	8	10
-	BR grey fitted to Peco chassis - *58-62*	10	20

W4. 16T Mineral Truck (1957)

This had raised numbers etc. and two versions of the coal/ore load moulding may be found. Quite a variety of shades of grey exist.

T70	**BR** B44821 grey - *57-68*	5	7
T179	As above + coal - *59-61*	8	10
T270	The same + iron ore - *59-61*	8	10
T70	**BR** B44821 light grey - *57-68*	5	7
T70	**BR** B44821 translucent grey - *57*	7	9
T70	**BR** B44821 duck egg blue - *59-61*	15	20
T179	as above + coal - *59-61*	15	20
T270	the same + iron ore + ore - *59-61*	15	20
-	BR B44821 fitted to Peco chassis - *57-62*	10	20

W5. BR 21T Ore Wagon (1958)

On some, the number was printed directly onto the moulded body but later it was printed onto a black panel. The body was also printed in white with 'Bulk Ore'.

T170	**BR** light grey no markings - *58-59*	5	7
T170	**BR** B41429 light green-grey - *59-68*	5	7
T170	**BR** B41429 blue-grey - *59-68*	5	7
T271	any above + bauxite load - *59-61*	8	10
T274	any above + iron ore load - *60-61*	8	10

BR ore wagon with load [W5]

T170	**BR** B41429 green - *?*	25	30

W6. BR 20T Bulk Grain Wagon (1958)

This model used the body of the ore wagon with a matching top and was produced in similar shades to the ore wagon. On some, the number was printed directly onto the moulded body but later it was printed onto a black panel. The position of this panel varies: A = last section on left, B = first section in on left.

T171	**BR** B85040 A grey - *58-59*	5	7
T171	**BR** B85040 A grey - *60-64*	5	7
T171	**BR** B85040 B grey - *60-64*	5	7

W7. BR 20T 'Presflo' (1961)

The printing on both was white.

T278	**BR** B887812 red, Cement - *61-64*	10	12
T279	**BR** B888185 dark green, Salt - *61-64*	10	12

W8. Tar Tank Track Cleaning Wagon (1963)

This had a special diecast lwb chassis incorporating an internal tank to hold the cleaning fluid. A felt strip was used as a wick to transfer the liquid to the track. The body was printed in white - 'Permanent Way Dept'.

T146	**BR** DS4020 black tar tank - *63-66*	12	15

W9a. Tank Wagon (1957)

The silver tank wagon originally had heat printed red 'Shell' on one side and a green 'BP' on the other. A later version had four Shell logos - two on each side and a red line on the chassis side. T75 was heat printed in white and T76 in red and black.

T73	**'Shell BP'** silver black solebar - *57-61*	5	7
T73	**'Shell BP'** silver red solebar - *57-61*	5	7
T73	**'Shell'** 5056 silver logos - *62-67*	18	20

'Shell' lubricating oil tank wagon [W9a]

T75	**'Shell BP'** black fuel oil - *57-64*	5	7
T76	**'Shell Lubricating Oil'** yellow - *57-66*	5	7

W9b. Milk Tank Wagon (1957)

Physically this was the same as W9a but had a ladder each side. It was heat printed in red.

T74	**'UD'** white - *57-64*	5	7

W10. BR 8T Cattle Wagon (1958)

This used the roof from the goods van and this was either white or cream coloured.

T77	**BR** B3778 yellow-brown - *58-64*	5	7
T77	**BR** B3778 red-brown - *58-64*	5	7

T77	**BR** B3778 green - *58-64*	25	30
-	**BR** brown fitted to Peco chassis - *58-62*	10	20

W11. GWR Horse Box (1958)

The position of the inscription 'Return to Depot' varies: A below door, B below door window and C on upper door, These are sometimes found with grey roofs. Printing was in yellow.

T78	**BR** W2483 maroon A - *58-64*	5	7
T78	**BR** W2483 maroon B - *58-64*	5	7
T78	**BR** W2483 maroon C - *58-64*	5	7

W12. GWR Fruit Van (1958)

This model had white or yellow lettering and a cream or white roof.

T79	**BR** W2460 yellow brown - *58-64*	5	7
T79	**BR** W2460 dark yellow brown - *62*	8	10
T79	**BR** W2460 maroon - *?*	16	20

W13. BR 12T Goods Van / Meat Van (1957)

The same moulding was used for the goods van and the meat van. It had raised numbers etc.. The roof of the van was white.

T71	**BR** B875550 dark grey - *57-68*	5	7
T71	**BR** B875550 brown - *57?*	8	10
T71	**BR** B875550 green-grey - *57-68*	6	8

BR meat van [W13]

T71	**BR** B875550 light grey - *58-66*	8	10
T175	**BR** B875550 white - 58-66	5	7
-	**BR** B875550 fitted to Peco chassis - *57-62*	10	20

W14. GWR 16T 'Toad' Brake Van (1961)

This used the same chassis as the standard BR brake van and printing was white.

T370	**BR** W56423 greenish grey - *61-64*	10	12
T370	**BR** W56423 grey - *61-64*	10	12

W15. BR Standard Brake Van (1957)

This had a special chassis made for it which had decked platforms at both ends. Some platforms have a patterned surface and the sides had full-length step boards. It usually had a white roof.

T72	**BR** B9514 brown - *57-68*	5	7
T72	**BR** B9514 red brown - *57-68*	5	7
T72	one of the above but grey roof - *57-68*	8	10

W16. SR Bogie Well Wagon (1958)

Single body moulding with coach buffers attached and cast bogies. Printed in white.

T173	**BR** S61077 dark grey - *58-64*	5	7
T173	**BR** S61077 light grey - *58-64*	6	8
T173	**BR** S61077 green* - *58-64*	25	30

* Southern coach green.

W17. BR 30T 'Bogie Bolster C' (1958)

The timber load was a single cream coloured moulding.

T174	**BR** B940050 grey - *58-61*	5	7

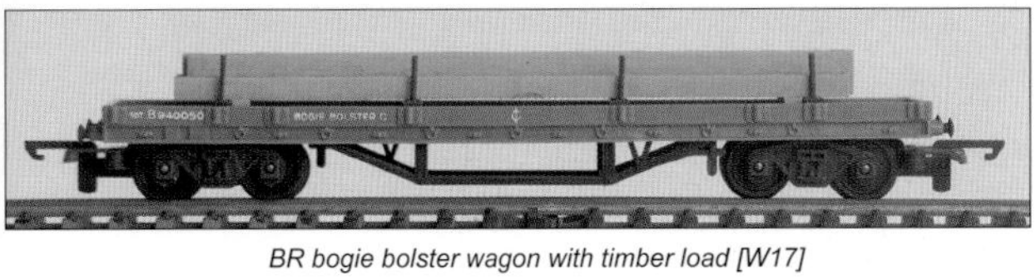

BR bogie bolster wagon with timber load [W17]

T277	**BR** B940050 grey + timber - *60-65*	8	10

W18. Bogie Caustic Tank Wagon (1959)

This had plastic body and frame and metal bogies.

T272	**'ICI'** 355 bright red - *59-65*	8	10
T272	**'ICI'** 355 darker red - *59-65*	8	10
T275	**'Liquid Chlorine'** T204 cream - *60-65*	12	15
T275	**'Murgatroyds'** T27 white - *60-61*	15	18
T275	**'Murgatroyds'** T227 white - *62-65*	14	17

Continental Wagons

A special diecast long wheelbase chassis (with no hand brake handle) was tooled up for these wagons. The fixing of the body to the chassis was the same as for the British wagons. Unlike the British range, the Continental wagons had no identification markings on the underside of the body.

W19. French Mineral Wagon (1962)

Heat printed in white.

T574	**SNCF** 76923 brown - *62-64*	25	30

W20. French Grain Wagon (1963)

Heat printed in red and white.

T571	**SNCF** T502/84 **CTC** grey - *63-65*	22	28

W21. French Petrol Tank Wagon (1963)

T572	**'Primagaz'** white - *63-64*	20	25

W22. French Cattle Wagon (1963)

The roof was bonded to the body and heat printing was white.

T573	**SNCF** K dark blue - *63-64*	25	30
T573	**SNCF** K black - *63-64*	25	30

W23. French Brake Van (Fourgon) (1963)

Heat printing was in white except for the tail lights which were red.

T570	**SNCF** 92145 black - *63-65*	22	28

French fourgon [W23]

ACCESSORIES

The Tri-ang TT system had the benefit of a good range of attractive lineside accessories. The station was available both as the T31 main set (£30-35) and T32 island set (£25-30) and as loose items (£1 to £10 depending what they are). Other accessories included signal boxes and water towers (£8-10), engine and diesel sheds (£10-12), level crossings (£5-6), fuelling depots (£20-25), goods sheds (£65-70), girder bridges (£15-18), girder bridge presentation sets (£30-35), cattle docks (£40-70), signal gantries (£65-70), track foundations, incline pier sets, high levels supports, telegraph poles (all £2-3), lineside hut sets (£9-10), footbridges (£7-8) and signals (£3-5). The rarest item in the British range is the rubber tunnel (made by associate company Young & Fogg) for which we have no example of a price. The French accessories consisted of a signal box, water tower, engine shed and goods depot all of which are rare and for which we have no established prices.

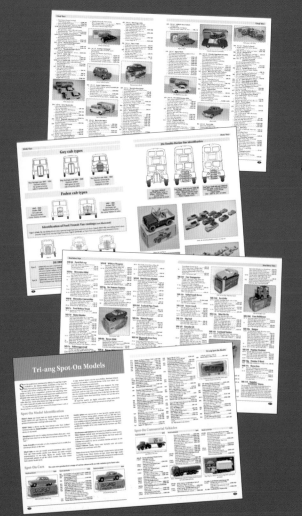

Trix (British)

This includes Trix Twin Railway, British Trix, Trix Trains and Liliput UK.

HISTORY

The history of the Trix model railway system is very complicated and, with its twists and turns, is a fascinating one to study. It started out as a 3-rail 14V AC coarse scale system and finished up 2-rail fine scale with 12V DC operation. At times its owners could not decide whether it was 00 or H0 scale and the confusion did nothing to improve sales. The company changed hands many times and the product was renamed on almost as many occasions. The story is further complicated by its links with the German Trix system and Liliput of Austria.

Ex-LNER 'Hunt' Class 4-4-0 No.62750 Pytchley [L6] (Vectis)

Milestones

1928 Stephan Bing buys Andreas Fortner.
1930 Trix construction toy launched.
1932 Trix Ltd formed in UK. with W J Bassett-Lowke as a director.
1932 Franz Bing joins Trix Ltd.
1935 Trix Express is launched in Germany and imported and sold by Trix Ltd.
1936 Trix Twin, made by Winteringham Ltd, is launched by Trix Ltd.
1937 Wholesale expansion of Trix Twin on the back of early high volume sales.
1937 First issue of The TTR Gazette printed.
1938 First 'Pacific' locomotives arrive.
1938 Launch of Hornby Dublo hits sales.
1940 Death of Stephan Bing.
1941 Trix Ltd and Winteringham Ltd form Precision Models Ltd.
1942 Trix Ltd take control of Precision Models Ltd.
1946 Post-war production starts.
1948 Models designed for the American market.
1950 BR liveries introduced.
1950 First post-war edition of The TTR Gazette.
1951 Winteringham Ltd wound up.
1952 German company sells its Trix Ltd shares.
1953 Death of W J Bassett-Lowke.
1955 The first 12V DC train set is produced.
1957 Ewart Holdings Ltd buy Trix.
1957 Fibre base track introduced.
1958 Ewart Holdings bankrupt and Trix and PML assets are acquired by Dufay Ltd.
1958 Trix Products Ltd formed.
1960 Trix production moved to Birmingham.
1961 Ernst Rozsa joins Trix Products Ltd.
1961 Production of Trix ceases.
1963 Trix sold to British Celanese Ltd and moved to Wrexham.
1965 Courtaulds offer Trix to Lines Bros..
1967 Production of British Minitrix starts at Wrexham.
1968 Trix sold to German Trix and production restarted at Wrexham through Thernglade Ltd.
1971 Decision taken to phase out Trix production.
1973 Thernglade factory closes. Rozsa acquires British Trix spares and stock, Liliput buy tooling.
1973 Rovex Ltd take over marketing of British outline Minitrix models as Hornby Minitrix.
1974 Rozsa forms Liliput Model Railways (UK) Ltd.
1992 Ernst Rozsa ceases production.
1993 Kader buy Liliput and thereby acquire Trix Trains tools.
1995 Upgraded former Trix Class A4 re-released as a Bachmann model.

The Trix Twin Railway took its name from the fact that one could operate two trains on the same piece of track. This was achieved by having three rail track with the centre rail acting as a common return. The left-hand outer rail was then used by one locomotive to collect current and the right outer rail by another loco. When overhead catenary was introduced it became possible to run three trains on the same track!

Repainted SR 'Schools' Class 4-4-0 No.911 Dover [L7] (Vectis)

Trix was a system invented and initially made in Germany but, soon afterwards, made in Britain through the involvement of W J Bassett-Lowke.

Stephan Bing left the famous family toy making firm and, in 1928, purchased the toy making business of Andreas Fortner. Bing brought to his new venture a number of colleagues including Siegfried Kahn who became his general manager and designer of his new range of toys. A construction toy, along the lines of Meccano, was launched in 1930 under the name of Trix and proved very successful. In order to make this system in Britain, Trix Ltd was formed in 1932.

The actual manufacture took place at Winteringham Ltd; an associate company of Bassett-Lowke Ltd. The MD at the factory was James Mackenzie and he had as his assistant Robert Bindon Blood, a keen model railway man who was responsible for the design of some of the finest locomotives made by Bassett-Lowke Ltd.

In 1932 Stephan Bing's son Franz emigrated to Britain and joined the fledgling company, organising sales. About this time Mettoy Ltd, another toy manufacturer who would later be remembered for Corgi toys and Playcraft model railways, started up in the basement of Winteringham Ltd with Winteringham doing the manufacturing for them. In 1935, a new 00 scale model railway system called Trix Express was launched in Germany by Stephan Bing and, by the end of the year, was being imported to the UK by Trix Ltd. Initially it was sold here as 'Bassett-Lowke Twin-Train Table Railway' and production of a British version was soon started at Winteringham Ltd in Northampton and launched by Trix Ltd in time for Christmas 1936.

Diesel Flyer [L14A] (Vectis)

Like the German version, design was built around an 0-4-0 14V AC electric mechanism. The locomotives had diecast bodies while rolling stock was tinplate and wood was largely used for lineside buildings.

1937 saw considerable expansion of the Trix Twin Railway and, to keep the public informed, The TTR Gazette was published from late 1937. The first Pacific locomotives arrived in 1938 but this was the year the rival Hornby Dublo system was launched with its better looking models.

Anti-Semitic legislation in Germany forced Stephan Bing and his partners to sell their German company. Their associate Ernst Voelk, who had also bought the Distler toy company in Nuremberg, purchased it. The partners and Kahn emigrated to Britain.

War halted production as Winteringham Ltd transferred its attention to the war effort. In 1941, Winteringham Ltd got together with Trix Ltd and formed Precision Models Ltd to take over the production of the Trix range. The following year, Trix Ltd took a controlling interest in Precision Models Ltd and effectively separated the former Winteringham factory from Bassett-Lowke's control.

The Trix trains were not to reappear until 1948 and by then had the Peco-type automatic couplings fitted. It was at this time that the fateful decision was made to stick with 14V AC 3-rail operation and coarse wheels, for the sake of existing customers; a decision that was to condemn Trix to a very slow death and bankrupt companies along the way.

Export was the first priority after the war and American outline models were produced. However, shortage of materials was the company's biggest problem. Ahead of their rivals, Trix adopted the new BR liveries in 1950 but the public wanted more realism in model design. They were getting it from Hornby Dublo and Tri-ang but not from Trix. In 1952 the German company decided it was time to pull out of its involvement with Trix Ltd and sold its shares. The following year WJ Bassett-Lowke resigned from the boards of both Trix Ltd and Precision Models Ltd.

Trix Ltd limped along, but with very low profits as there was no money to invest in the new models needed to reform the system. They managed to produce a 12V DC junior train set in 1955, but a complete 12V DC system was needed. By the end of 1956 the financial problems peaked and there was no way out but to sell the company. In February 1957 the Trix group was bought by Ewart Holdings Ltd.

From 1957 both Trix Ltd and Precision Models Ltd had a completely new board of Directors and a fresh start was feasible. The conversion to 12V DC continued, fibre base track was introduced and an excellent range of new locomotives was designed. The only problem was: they were to be in the smaller H0 scale! Furthermore, 3-rail operation was retained and so too were those horrible coarse wheels.

BR Standard Class 4-6-2 Britannia [L18] (Vectis)

New models needed new capital and money was borrowed. With insufficient money coming in the financial position worsened and in 1958 Ewart Holdings collapsed. A major creditor was Dufay Ltd who in November 1958 acquired the assets of Trix Ltd and Precision Models Ltd. Trix Products Ltd took over the design and marketing of the Trix range and in 1960 Dufay moved Trix production to Birmingham.

In 1958 Ernst Rozsa had established a company to import Liliput models from Austria. His company was called Miniature Constructions and assembled some of the Austrian models in the UK. He persuaded Liliput to make an 00 model of the Class AL1 E3000 for them. Rozsa joined Trix in 1961 and took with him the E3000 model.

Poor sales in 1960 and 1961 lead to Dufay closing down Trix production in order to save damaging the rest of their group and Trix was prepared for sale. In 1962 the company was sold to Alvus Investments & Trading Ltd, who planned to restart production of Trix in High Wycombe but only the coach moulding tools were made. At about this time it was reported that Trix models were produced to a scale of 3.8mm to the foot.

In April 1963 British Celanese (part of the Courtaulds Group) formed British Trix Ltd and purchased the goodwill and patents of Trix Products Ltd for £1 and a production base was set up at the British Celanese factory in Wrexham. Ernst Rozsa was placed in charge of design and development but later took full responsibility for production. The decision was taken to dump the stocks of tinplate and 14V AC models and they were buried in a large hole on the Wrexham factory site.

To swell the range quickly, a lot of models were bought in from Continental manufacturers and repackaged. 1964 was a good year, but by 1965 Courtaulds were inviting Lines Bros. to take Trix off their hands. Lines Bros. turned down the offer. Kit locomotives and rolling stock were introduced that year and sold well and in 1967 N gauge Minitrix models for the British market were being made in the Wrexham factory.

Despite a number of successes, the financial problems continued and at the end of 1967 the plug was once again pulled. Quickly, the German Trix company acquired the assets of British Trix and a company called Thernglade Ltd was acquired to take over production. Rozsa was a Director of the new company and the product was renamed 'Trix Trains'. This period was famed for the excellent LNER 'Pacific' locomotives they produced in 00 scale.

London Transport 0-4-0 electric loco [L13] (Vectis)

A number of German toy company ownership changes lead to a decision to phase out model railway production at Wrexham from 1971. The Minitrix tools were bought by the German Trix company and in 1973 Rovex Ltd became the importers of the range which was renamed Hornby Minitrix. Meanwhile Thernglade continued toy production until the factory closed in 1973.

Rozsa had salvaged the model railway side of the business and purchased stock and spares. He set up a mail order business under the name Berwyn Hobbies Supplies, while Liliput of Austria purchased the British model tools owned by Trix of Germany. In 1974 Rozsa formed Liliput Model Railways (UK) Ltd and continued to assemble former British Trix models from parts supplied by Liliput. This continued until 1992 when the supply of parts finally dried up. Some parts and tools were acquired by Dapol Ltd and others were retained by Liliput which was bought by Kader in 1993. Kader, a Chinese company who owned the American Bachmann company, had established Bachmann Industries Europe Ltd in Britain to market British outline models made from the former Mainline Railways tools which it owned. With the Liliput tools now in their possession, the former British Trix A4 model formed the basis of the Class A4 models currently sold by Bachmann, although much improved.

As we said at the beginning, Trix has a very complicated history!

Further Reading

The excellent book *The History of Trix H0/00 Model Railways in Britain* by Tony Matthewman, which formed the basis of the above potted history, is strongly recommended to anyone wishing to study the subject. It was published by New Cavendish Books (ISBN 0-904568-76-8).

Collectors Clubs

The Trix Twin Railway Collectors Association (TTRCA) was founded in 1975 and caters for enthusiasts of Trix Twin, Trix Express, Trix Trains and the models of Liliput UK. It publishes a quarterly magazine called *Trix Twin Gazette* and offers a spares service to its members. For enquiries concerning membership, telephone: 0116 271 5943.

Couplings - These provide a means of distinguishing between pre- and post-war models. The pre-war coupling (referred to as 'PW' in the tables) was non-automatic and consisted of a cast (or tinplate) hook and a wire loop. The post-war couplings came into use in 1948 and were the Peco style automatic ones also used by Meccano Ltd on Hornby Dublo stock. Pre-war couplings were used after the war during 1946 and 1947 but only small quantities of certain models were being made.

Ruston Hornby 0-6-0DS and shunter's track [L20] (Vectis)

Dates - Where a model was available with a variety of numbers, it is hard to say which numbers were being carried at any one time. The dates quoted in the following tables, therefore, normally apply to the model form and not the number.

Listing - The locos are listed in order of size in each section starting with tank engines followed by tender locos and ending with diesels, electrics and multiple units. Wagons are listed in the order of: flats, open wagons, hoppers, tanks, vans, brake vans and bogie stock.

LOCOMOTIVES

White Numbers - A lot of people are mystified by the white numbers printed on the underside of locomotives (and other electrical equipment) made after 1948. These numbers indicate the month and year that the model was made. The months were lettered 'A' for January, 'B' for February, and so on, while the year was represented by the last digit (sometimes last two digits). Thus 'C3' was March 1953. This provides us with a very useful way of dating much post-war Trix electrical equipment up until 1960 when the system was dropped. Incidentally the letter 'I' was not used and so September was 'J'.

A single 'R' on a chassis means that it went back to the factory at some time for a repair and 'M' was applied to chassis in 1948, indicating modification.

Voltage - The Trix Twin Railway system initially operated on a 14V AC power supply but later manufacturers used 12V DC as it was more controllable. Trix were tied to their AC system but eventually had to change over to 12V DC as the market demanded. The DC system was introduced in 1956. Some of the locomotives listed below were made only for an AC supply and some only for DC. Four models may be found with either AC or DC mechanisms and these are clearly marked in the respective tables. The models that were available only with AC mechanisms are those listed in tables L1, L4-L15 unless otherwise stated.

Scale - With the exception of the AL1 electric locomotive, the A1, A2 and A4, which were all 4mm scale, all the post-1958 introductions were to a 3.8mm scale which was neither 00 nor H0.

Cat No.	Company, Number, Colour, Dates	£	£

1st Series of Locomotives

L1. Freelance 0-4-0 Tank (1936)

Tank engines bearing the wording on the back of the bunker 'Patents TTR Pending' were made before mid-1937 while those with 'British TTR Patents 465168 469656 Patented Abroad' were made between 1937 and circa 1950. They were not to be found on BR models.

Cat No.	Company, Number, Colour, Dates	£	£
	Pre-war couplings		
2/510	**91, 121, 141, 191** LMS lined black - *36-39,46*	30	50
2/515	**5, 20, 31, 91, 121** LMS unlined black - *36-39,46*	30	50
2/515	**39, 58, 62** LMS unlined blk - *36-39,46*	40	60
2/515	**58** LMS lined black - *36-39,46*	40	60
2/515	**11** LMS unlined black - *47-52*	30	50
4/510	**2901, 9276** LNER lined black - *36-39,46*	50	70
4/515	**2901, 6178, 7693, 8403** LNER unlined black - *36-39,46*	50	70
5/510	**520** Southern lined green - *37-39,46*	150	200
5/515	**951** Southern lined black - *37-39,46*	150	200
	Post-war couplings		
2/515	**5, 11, 20, 31** LMS unlined black - *47-52*	30	50
2/515	**30, 62** LMS unlined black - *47-52*	40	60
2/515	**63** LMS lined black - *47-52*	40	50
2/515	**68** LMS unlined black - *47-52*	40	50
2/515	**91** LMS lined or unlined black - *47-52*	30	40
2/515	**97** LMS unlined black - *47-52*	25	35
2/515	**98** LMS unlined black - *47-52*	40	45
2/515	**781, 914, 1109** LMS unlined black - *47-52*	35	40
4/510	**396** LNER lined black - *47-52*	40	60
4/515	**298, 605, 7693, 8403** LNER unlined black - *47-52*	40	60
5/510	**1923** Southern lined green - *47-52*	150	200
5/515	**91** Southern lined or unlined black - *47-52*	100	150
1/510	**40, 63** BRb lined black - *47-52*	30	40
1/510	**63** BRb unlined black - *47-52*	30	40
1/510	**48, 50, 85** BRb lined black - *50-55*	25	35

Freelance 0-4-0T in BR lined black livery [L1] (Vectis)

L2. Freelance 0-4-0 Tank with Plastic Body (1956)

Distler motor.

Cat No.	Company, Number, Colour, Dates	£	£
1/510	**59, 85** BRb lined black 14vAC - *56-57*	35	45
1/515	**84** BRb unlined black 14vAC - *56-57*	35	45
1/510	**85** BRc lined black 14vAC - *56-57*	35	45
1/515	**98, 30951** BRc unlined black 14vAC - *56-57*	35	45

Freelance 0-4-0T with plastic body [L2] (Vectis)

210	**84** BRc unlined black 12vDC - *55-61*	25	35
210	**30951, 41218** BRc unlined black 12vDC - *58-61*	25	35
210	**67611** BRc unlined black 12vDC - *58-61*	40	60

L3. Freelance 2-4-2 Tank

This was planned for 1940 based on the German 2-4-2 chassis but was dropped because of the war.

2/514	LMS - *not made*	NA	NA
4/514	LNER - *not made*	NA	NA
5/514	Southern - *not made*	NA	NA

L4. Freelance 0-4-0 with Tender (1936)

This was the first loco in the Trix range being originally released with 'Trix Express' on the tender. PW = pre-war couplings. dlt = double lining on tender. slt = single lining on tender.

-	**5391** TRIX EXPRESS lined green, disc wheels - *36*	500	NPG
-	**5391** TRIX EXPRESS unlined black, disc wheels - *36*	500	NPG
-	TRIX TWIN on tender unlined green demonstration model PW - *46?*	600	NPG
-	TRIX TWIN on tender unlined black demonstration model PW - *46?*	600	NPG
	Pre-war couplings		
2/520	**5647, 5670, 5724 , 6138, 6200** LMS lined maroon - *36-39,46*	80	100
2/525	**5049, 6138, 8046, 8067, 8209** LMS lined black - *36-39,46*	60	80
4/520	**2581** LNER lined light green - *36-39,46*	80	100
4/520	**4472** LNER lined light green - *36-39,46*	60	80
4/525	**2394, 3451** LNER lined black - *36-39,46*	40	60
4/525	**4472** LNER lined black - *36-39,46*	80	100
5/520	**763** Southern lined green - *37-39*	200	250
5/525	**498** Southern lined black tender - *37-39,46*	180	250
	Post-war couplings		
2/520	**5647** LMS lined maroon - *47-52*	80	100
2/520	**6138** LMS lined very dark maroon - *47-52*	80	100
2/525	**6138, 8209** LMS lined black front boiler band and tender - *47-52*	40	60
2/525	**6138** LMS lined black front boiler band - *47-52*	40	60
2/525	**5124** LMS unlined black - *47-52*	40	60
2/525	**8032** LMS unlined black - *47-52*	30	50
4/520	**2876** LNER lined light green - *47-52*	80	100
4/520	**2876** LNER lined dark green - *47-52*	80	100
4/520	**693** LNER lined light green, black cylinders - *47-52*	80	100
4/520	**103, 447, 465** LNER lined green - *47-52*	100	120

Freelance 0-4-0 loco in BR 'Express' blue [L4] (Lacy, Scott & Knight)

4/520	**2876** LNER lined green - *47-52*	80	100
4/525	**2394, 3451** LNER lined black - *47-52*	40	60
4/525	**2394, 3451** LNER lined black on tender only - *47-52*	40	60
4/525	**4472** LNER lined black on tender only - *47-52*	80	100
4/525	**103**, **620, 693** LNER unlind black - *47-52*	60	80
4/525	**4472** LNER unlined black - *47-52*	80	100
4/525	**5124, 8032** LNER unlined black - *47-52*	60	80
5/520	**763** Southern lined green - *48-50?*	250	NPG
5/525	**498** Southern lined black tender - *47-52*	180	220
1/520	**46231** BRb lined light blue - *50-51*	100	120
1/520	**46256**, **60100** BRb light blue lined - *50-51*	80	100
1/520	**46256**, **60100** BRb dark blue lined - *51-52*	80	100
1/520	**30782, 46256, 46258**, **60089** BRb lined green dlt black cylinders - *52-58*	40	60
1/520	**60100** BRb lined green dlt green cylinders - *51-52*	60	70
1/520	**73029** BRb lined green dlt green or black cylinders - *52-53*	60	70
1/520	**30782, 60089** BRb lined green slt black cylinders - *52-58*	40	60
1/520	**46258** BRb lined green slt black cylinders - *52-58*	30	50
1/525	**48427** BRb lined black front boiler band and cylinders - *52-58*	30	50
1/525	**48152** BRb lined black front boiler band only - *52-58*	30	50
1/525	**2750, 6201** BRb unlined black - *50-58*	30	50
1/525	**30846, 31829** BRb unlined black - *50-58*	25	40
1/525	**46201** BRb unlined black - *50-58*	50	70
1/525	**48427** BRb unlined black - *50-58*	30	50
1/525	**63950** BRb unlined black - *50-58*	25	40

L5. LMS Midland 'Compound' 4-4-0 (1939)

dlt = double lined tender. slt = single lining on tender.

2/536	**1168** LMS lined maroon PW - *39,46*	250	350
2/536	**1168** LMS lined black PW - *39,46*	150	250
2/536	**1168** LMS lined maroon - *47-52*	300	400
2/536	**1168** LMS lined matt black - *49-52*	100	200
2/536	**41062 41128 41135** BRb black dlt - *50-56*	80	120
2/536	**41162** BRb black dlt - *50-56*	60	90

LMS Black 'Compound' No.1168 [L5] (Vectis)

2/536	**41128** BRb black slt - *50-52?*	80	120
2/536	**41162** BRb green dlt - *53*	400	600
2/536	**62750** BRb green dlt, factory mistake (only one) - *53*	NPG	NPG
2/536	**41135** BRc black dlt - *56-58*	80	120
2/536	**41162** BRc black dlt - *56-58*	60	90
F101	**1168, 41168** BRc black 12vDC - *59-60*	120	150

L6. LNER 'Hunt' Class 4-4-0 (1939)

dlt = double lining on tender. slt = single lining on tender.

	Pytchley		
4/536	**298** LNER lined green PW 14vAC - *39*	400	500
4/536	**298** LNER lined green 14vAC - *47-48*	500	600
4/536	**2750** LNER lined green 14vAC - *48-52*	500	600
4/536	**2750** LNER lined matt black 14vAC - *49-52*	200	300
4/536	**62750**, **62750** BRb green dlt 14vAC - *53-58*	80	100
4/536	**62750** BRb black dlt 14vAC - *50*	120	150
4/536	**62750** BRb black slt 14vAC - *50*	120	150
230	**62750** BRc green 12vDC - *57-60*	80	100
235	**62750** BRc black 12vDC - *57-60*	80	100

L7. SR 'Schools' Class 4-4-0

The 'Schools' Class locomotive was planned for 1940 and an order placed but the war intervened. The project was then shelved until the late 1950s when it was released as a 12v DC model with a new casting.

5/536	**911 *Dover*** Southern green - *not made*	NA	NA
5/364	**911 *Dover*** Southern green set in wooden presentation box with 3 coaches - *not made*	NA	NA
F100	**30911 *Dover*** BRc green 12vDC - *59-60*	200	300

L8. LMS 'Princess' 4-6-2 (1938)

The chassis were made in Germany. The tooling became damaged beyond economic repair and so the model was not reintroduced after the war.

2/540	**6201 *Princess*** LMS maroon - *38-39*	375	475

LMS 4-6-2 Princess No.6201 [L8] (Vectis)

2/344	**6201 *Princess*** LMS maroon set in wooden presentation box with 3 coaches - *38-39*	525	1000

L9. LMS 'Coronation' 4-6-2 (1939)

After the war, with the streamlining being removed from the real locomotives, the model was thought to be out of date and not worth reintroducing.

	6220 *Coronation*		
2/542	LMS maroon - *39*	600	800
2/347	LMS maroon set in wooden presentation box with 3 coaches - *39*	800	1500
2/347	LMS maroon set in dark green wooden presentation box with 3 coaches - *39*	800	1500

L10. LNER A3 4-6-2 (1938)

The chassis were made in Germany. PW = pre-war couplings. dlt = double lined tender.

	4472 *Scotsman*		
4/540	LNER green PW - *38-39*	600	800
4/344	LNER green in wooden presentation box with 3 coaches PW - *38-39*	800	1000
4/540	LNER green PW black cylinders - *39*	600	800
4/540	LNER black PW - *c42?*	NPG	2000

Ex-LNER A1 60103 Scotsman [L10] (Vectis)

1/540	BRb dark blue single lined tend - *51-52*	300	400
1/540	BRb green single lined tender - *52-53*	300	375
1/540	BRb green dlt silver nameplate - *53-54*	300	375
1/540	BRb green dlt orge nameplate - *55-58*	300	375

L11. American 0-4-0 with Tender (1948)

This looked similar to the next model but had a larger square backed tender and a hooded lamp in the centre of the smokebox door. Trix Twin on tender

9/519	**4638, 4762** black no light - *48-49*	60	80
9/520	**4826** black - *48-49*	60	80
9/520	**4638, 4762, 5986, 8612** black - *50-56*	60	80

L12. American 0-4-0 Switcher with Tender (1948)

This looked similar to the last model but had a smaller tender with a sloping back and a lamp above the smokebox door. Both were produced as part of a post-war export drive.

9/524	**3747, 3812, 5986, 8612** black no light - *48-49*	60	80
9/525	**2690, 4681** black - *48-49*	60	80
9/525	**3747, 3812, 4701, 5647, 5986, 8612** black - *50-56*	60	80
81/50	kit for export with DC motor - *51*	100	160
81/51	kit without lamp - *51*	100	160

L13. LT 0-4-0 Electric (1937)

This was an adaptation from a German model with pantographs removed etc.

7/530	**19** London Transport maroon - *37-38*	350	450
7/530	**17** London Transport maroon - *not made*	NA	NA

L14. 'Meteor' Diesel Express (1955)

377	**1394** red 3-car 14vAC - *55-58*	140	200
277	**1394, 2602** red 3-car 12vDC - *57-61*	140	200
277	**2602, 2782** blue 3-car 12vDC - *58-61*	160	220

L14A. 'Diesel Flier' (1939)

Based on the 'Flying Hamburger'. Very few were finished in this Oxford-Bletchley-Cambridge colour scheme.

?	LMS silver+vermilion 2-car 14vAC - *39*	200	400

L15. Southern EMU (1937)

This model was made in Germany with the exception of the tinplate body which was produced in the UK. Several shades of green may be found.

5/375	**11081** Southern Railway green 3-car set - *37-39*	400	700

Southern Railway EMU power car [L15] (Vectis)

5/530	**11081** Southern Railway green power car only - *37-39*	200	400

2nd Series of Locomotives

L16. SR Class E2 0-6-0T (H0) (1961)

1107	**32103** BRc black 2-rail (F107) - *61-72*	20	25
1108	**32103** BRc black 3-rail (F107) - *61-66*	20	25

L17. GWR Collett Class 5600 0-6-2T (H0) (1959)

This was wrongly called a Class 66XX by Trix. conw = convertible wheels. sw = 'scale' wheels.

F103B	**6664** BRc black 3-rail conw (1101) - *59-63*	40	60
F103B	**6664** BRc black 2-rail conw - *59-60*	45	60
F103B	**6664** BRc black 2-rail sw (1102) - *60-64*	45	60
F103G	**6664** BRc green 3-rail conw (1105) - *59-63*	50	75
F103G	**6664** BRc green 2-rail conw - *60*	50	75
F103G	**6664** BRc green 2-rail sw (1106) - *60-64*	50	75

L18. BR 'Britannia' Class 4-6-2 (H0) (1959)

'Scale' wheels fitted from 1960 had smaller flanges so that they could run on 2-rail track but the wheels were still thick. Many, however, were converted to run on universal tack, after purchase.

	70000 *Britannia* - green		
236	BRc coarse wheels - *59*	60	90
1109	BRc 'scale' wheels 2/3-rail - *60-65*	60	90
1110	BRc 'scale' wheels 3-rail - *63*	60	90
1111	BRc 'scale' wheels 2-rail - *63-65*	60	90
2111	Footplateman construction kit - *66,69*	60	90

L19. BR Standard Class 5 4-6-0 (H0) (1959)

'Scale' wheels fitted from 1960 had smaller flanges so that they could run on 2-rail track but the wheels were still thick. Many, however, were converted to run on universal tack, after purchase. sw = 'scale' wheels. cw = coarse wheels. The Footman kits were unlined.

237G	**73000** BRc green cw - *59*	70	100
237G	**73001** BRc green cw - *59*	100	150
237B	**73000** BRc black cw - *59*	60	90
1115	**73000** BRc green sw 2/3-rail (also 237G) - *60-65*	70	100
1112	**73000** BRc black sw 2/3-rail (also 237B) - *60-66*	60	90
1117	**73000** BRc green sw 2-rail - *63-65*	70	100
1114	**73000** BRc black sw 2-rail - *63-66*	60	90
1113	**73000** BRc green sw 3-rail - *63-64*	70	100
1116	**73000** BRc black sw 3-rail - *63-64*	60	90
2113	**73000** green Footplateman kit - *66,69*	NPG	110
2116	**73000** black Footplateman kit - *66,69*	NPG	110

BR Standard 5 [L19] & 'Warship' diesel [L21] (Vectis)

L20. Ruston Hornsby 0-6-0DS + Shunter's Truck (H0) (1958)

244	green - *58-61*	85	110

L21. 'Warship' Diesel Hydraulic B-B (H0) (1960)

Vanguard had red nameplates while the others had black ones. conw = convertible wheels. sw = 'scale' wheels.

	D801 *Vanguard*		
1119	BRc green 2-rail conw (F106) - *60-64*	50	65
1120	BRc green 2-rail sw (F106) - *60-71*	50	65
1118	BRc green 3-rail sw (F106) - *60-66*	50	65
1122	BRc maroon 2-rail sw - *66-69*	70	90
1119	BRc maroon 3-rail sw - *66*	70	90
1123	BRc blue 2-rail sw - *67-71*	70	90
	D809 *Champion*		
1120	BRc green 2-rail sw - *66-70*	70	90
1118	BRc green 3-rail sw - *66*	70	90
1122	BRc maroon 2-rail sw - *66-69*	70	90

1119	BRc maroon 3-rail sw - *66*	70	90
1123	BRc blue 2-rail sw - *67-71*	70	90
	D811 *Daring*		
1120	BRc green 2-rail sw - *66-70*	70	90
1118	BRc green 3-rail sw - *66*	70	90
1122	BRc maroon 2-rail sw - *66-69*	70	90
1119	BRc maroon 3-rail sw - *66*	70	90
1123	BRc blue 2-rail sw - *67-71*	70	90
	D828 *Magnificent*		
1120	BRc green 2-rail sw - *66-70*	90	110
1118	BRc green 3-rail sw - *66*	90	110
1122	BRc maroon 2-rail sw - *66-69*	80	110
1119	BRc maroon 3-rail sw - *66*	80	110
1123	BRc blue 2-rail sw - *67-71*	80	110
	D844 *Spartan*		
1120	BRc green 2-rail sw - *66-70*	70	90
1118	BRc green 3-rail sw - *66*	70	90
1122	BRc maroon 2-rail sw - *66-69*	70	90
1119	BRc maroon 3-rail sw - *66*	70	90
1123	BRc blue 2-rail sw - *67-71*	70	90

L22. EM1 Bo-Bo (H0) (1959)

conw = convertible wheels. sw = scale wheels.

F105B	**26010** BRc black conw (1122) - *59-63*	100	170
F105B	**26010** BRc black 2-rail sw (1123) - *60-64*	100	170
F105G	**26056 *Triton*** BRc green conw - *60-61*	120	200
F105G	**26056 *Triton*** BRc green 2-r sw - *60-61*	120	200

BR Class EM1 electric loco [L22] (Vectis)

F105G	**26056** BRc green conw (1125) - *62-63*	120	190
F105G	**26056** BRc green 2-rail sw (1125) - *62-64*	120	190

3rd Series of Locomotives

L23. 0-4-0 Southern Tank

Illustrated in the 1964 catalogue but not made.

1165	black 2-rail - *not made*	NA	NA
1166	black 3-rail - *not made*	NA	NA

In 1965, a 'Royal Scot', a 'Black 5' and a 9F were planned but none of these came to fruition.

L24. LNER Class A2 4-6-2 (1970)

This used a Trix Express/International chassis made in Germany with other parts manufactured by Liliput of Austria but assembled by Thernglade Ltd at Wrexham in Wales. The body tool was made by British Lego which was another member of the Courtaulds Group. From 1974 these models were Liliput UK products (see 'History' above). The model was not released in 3-rail versions but they could be made to order as too could ones with Trix coarse scale wheels. A small batch of A2 kits was released by Ernst Rosza in 1995. Today the tools that remained in the UK are owned by Dapol Ltd. Some very late A2s were released in plain white boxes but stamped with the Liliput UK name and address.

	LNER 525 *AH Peppercorn*		
1186	green - *70-73*	90	140
1060	green - *74-92*	90	140
1062	green tender drive - *78-92*	90	140
1160	green EMS equipment fitted - *82-84*	NPG	NPG
1187	***532 Blue Peter**** LNER green as preserved loco - *?*	185	NPG
	NE *AH Peppercorn*		
1064	wartime black - *82-92*	160	200
1065	wartime black tender drive - *82-92*	160	200
	BRc 60525 *AH Peppercorn*		
1185	green - *71-73*	100	165
1061	green - *74-92*	100	165
1063	green tender drive - *78-92*	100	165
1161	green EMS equipment fitted - *82-84*	NPG	NPG

Class A2 LNER No.525 A H Peppercorn [L24] (Lacy, Scott & Knight)

* Twelve models of this were made specially for the BBC *Blue Peter* programme when it featured a model railway layout. Those not used were released onto the market and it is thought that 10 still exist.

L25. LNER Class A3 4-6-2 (1686)

The body was tooled by British Lego and the model manufactured by Liliput of Austria but assembled by Thernglade Ltd at Wrexham in Wales. From 1974 these models were Liliput UK products. Production of 3-rail models ceased in 1970 although they were available by special order until 1972.

	LNER 4472 *Flying Scotsman*		
1180	very pale apple green - *68*	50	90
1180	correct apple green 2-rail - *68-70*	50	90
1181	as above 3-rail - *68-70*	60	80
1180	green, front handrails on tender 2-rail - *70-73*	60	100
1181	as above 3-rail - *70*	70	90
1180	green, motor in tender - *70-73*	50	70
1071	green, static model - *75,90*	NPG	NPG
1130	green, EMS equipment fitted - *82-84*	NPG	NPG
1180DT	2 tenders very pale apple green coal top on both tenders - *68*	50	100
1180DT	as above but apple green 2-rail - *68-70*	50	100
1181DT	as above 3-rail - *68-70*	50	100
1180DT	green 2 tenders, water tender now with correct top and front handrail fitted to both tenders 2-rail - *70-73*	70	90

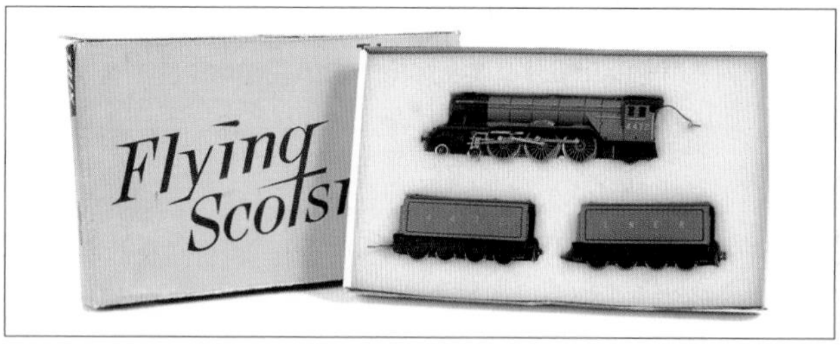

Preserved Flying Scotsman with 2 tenders [L25] (Vectis)

1181DT	as above 3-rail - *70*	70	90
1035	green, 2 tenders - *74-87*	50	90
1075	green, 2 tenders static model - *75,90*	NPG	NPG
1183	NER black, red buffer beams and running plate edges Ltd Edn - *69?*	NPG	NPG
1183	***Flying Scotsman*** black, red buffer beams and running plate edges 2-rail - *69-73*	90	110
1183	as above motor in tender - *70-73*	90	110
1039	as above without lights - *74-87*	90	110
1035	**4472** LNER water tender in apple green on		
1071	its own - *76,79*	20	30
1070	water tender black fitted with red snow plough on its own - *78-87*	100	220
	BRc 60103 *Flying Scotsman*		
1182	green 2-rail - *70-73*	90	110
1182/3	as above 3-rail - *70*	100	120
1182	green motor in tender - *70-73*	90	110
1030	green (also 1037) - *74-87*	90	110
1031	green without lights (also 1038) - *74-75*	90	110
1078	green static model - *75,90*	NPG	NPG
1137	green EMS equipment fitted - *82-84*	NPG	NPG

L26. LNER Class A4 4-6-2 (1970)

Tooled and manufactured by Liliput of Austria but assembled by Thernglade Ltd at Wrexham in Wales. From 1974 these models were Liliput UK products. 3-rail versions were not available. v = with valances down over the wheels. op = optional name to order.

	4468 *Mallard*		
1190	LNER blue v - *70-73*	60	90
1045	LNER blue v - *74-87*	60	90
1085	LNER blue v static model - *75,90*	NPG	NPG
1045	LNER blue v with fire glow - *78*	80	100
1140	LNER blue v EMS equip fitted - *82-84*	NPG	NPG
1046	NE wartime black - *78-87*	120	160
1046	NE wartime black with fire glow - *78*	120	160
	2509 *Silver Link*		
1188	LNER grey v - *71-73*	60	90
1040	LNER grey v - *74-87*	60	90
1080	LNER grey v static model - *75,90*	NPG	NPG
1040	LNER grey v with fire glow - *78*	80	100
1145	LNER grey v EMS equip fitted - *82-84*	NPG	NPG
	60027 *Merlin*		
1195	BRc green - *71-73*	50	75
1050	BRc green - *74-87*	50	75
1090	BRc green static model - *75, 90*	NPG	NPG
1050	BRc green with fire glow - *78*	70	90
1150	BRc green EMS equip fitted - *82-84*	NPG	NPG
	Various		
1047	**4498 *Sir Nigel Gresley*** LNER blue v op - *74-87*	NPG	NPG
1048	***7 Sir Nigel Gresley*** LNER blue op - *74-87*	NPG	NPG
1041	**2512 *Silver Fox*** LNER grey v op - *74-87*	NPG	NPG
1042	**2511 *Silver King*** LNER grey v op - *74-87*	NPG	NPG
1043	**2510 *Quicksilver*** LNER grey v op - *74-87*	NPG	NPG
1051	**60025 *Falcon*** BRc green op - *74-87*	NPG	NPG

LNER A4 Class No.2509 Silver Link [L26] (Vectis)

1052	**60030 *Golden Fleece*** BRc green op - *74-87*	NPG	NPG
1053	***Golden Shuttle**** BRc green op - *74-87*	NPG	NPG
1054	***Kestrel**** BRc green op - *74-87*	NPG	NPG
1055	**60033 *Seagull*** BRc green op - *74-87*	NPG	NPG

* No BR liveried real A4s carried these names!

L27. Class 47 Brush-Sulzer Type 4 Co-Co

1170	green - *not made*	NA	NA
1171	blue - *not made*	NA	NA

L28. Class 52 'Western' Diesel Hydraulic C-C (1965)

This H0 model was developed and tooled by Liliput in Austria to a design by Ernst Rozsa. Route codes on these models vary as the model was supplied with a sheet of self-adhesive labels as well as yellow cab front panels (with earlier releases) for the purchaser to apply. All models made after 1966 were 2-rail. From 1974 these were Liliput UK models, manufactured in Austria and assembled in Wales.

	D1002 *Western Explorer*		
1165	BRc green 2-rail - *65-73*	55	75
1166	BRc green 3-rail - *65-66*	55	75
1011	BRc green yellow cab fronts - *74-87*	55	75
1013	BRc green yellow cab fronts no lights - *77-87*	55	75
1017	BRe green yellow cab fronts 2 motor bogies - *79-81*	80	100
1163	BRe blue - *67-73*	55	75
1010	BRe blue yellow cab fronts - *74-87*	55	75
	D1004 *Western Crusader*		
1165	BRc green 2-rail - *65-73*	55	75
1166	BRc green 3-rail - *65-66*	55	75
1011	BRc green yellow cab fronts - *74-87*	55	75
1013	BRc green yellow cab fronts no lights - *77-87*	55	75

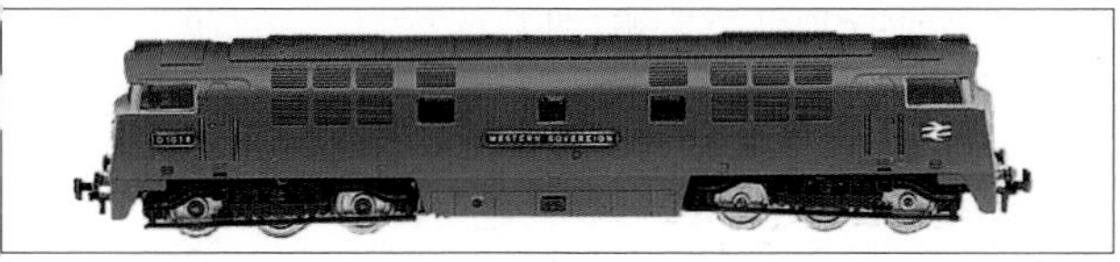

BR 'Western' diesel No.D1038 Western Soveriegn [L28] (Vectis)

1017	BRe green yellow cab fronts 2 motor bogies - *79-81*	80	100
1163	BRe blue - *67-73*	55	75
1010	BRe blue yellow cab fronts - *74-87*	55	75
	D1000 *Western Enterprise*		
1164	BRc maroon 3-rail 2 motor bogies - *65-66*	80	100
1167	BRc maroon 2-rail - *65-73*	55	75
1168	BRc maroon 3-rail - *65-73*	55	75
1169	BRc maroon 2-rail 2 motor bogies - *65-73*	80	100
1012	BRc maroon yellow cab fronts - *74-87*	55	75
1009	BRc sand changing lights - *79-87*	160	200
1163	BRe blue - *67-73*	55	75
1010	BRe blue yellow cab fronts - *74-87*	55	75
	D1069 *Western Vanguard*		
1164	BRc maroon 3-rail 2 motor bogies - *65-66*	55	75
1167	BRc maroon 2-rail - *65-73*	55	75
1168	BRc maroon 3-rail - *65-68*	55	75
1169	BRc maroon 2-rail 2 motor bogies - *65-73*	80	100
1012	BRc maroon yellow cab fronts - *74-87*	55	75
1013	BRc maroon fitted with track cleaning device - *82*	200	300
1163	BRe blue - *67-73*	55	75
1010	BRe blue yellow cab fronts - *74-87*	55	75
	D1038 *Western Sovereign*		
1167	BRc maroon 2-rail - *65-73*	55	75
1168	BRc maroon 3-rail - *65-68*	55	75
1169	BRc maroon 2-rail 2 motor bogies - *65-73*	80	100
1164	BRc maroon 3-rail 2 motor bogies - *65-66*	80	100
1012	BRc maroon yellow cab fronts - *74-87*	55	75
1163	BRe blue - *67-73*	55	75
1010	BRe blue yellow cab fronts - *74-87*	55	75
	D1045 *Western Viscount*		
1167	BRc maroon 2-rail - *65-73*	55	75
1168	BRc maroon 3-rail - *65-68*	55	75
1169	BRc maroon 2-rail 2 motor bogies - *65-73*	80	100
1164	BRc maroon 3-rail 2 motor bogies - *65-66*	80	100
1012	BRc maroon yellow cab fronts - *74-87*	55	75
1163	BRe blue - *67-73*	55	75
1010	BRe blue yellow cab fronts - *74-87*	55	75
	Various		
1013	BRc maroon yellow ends no lights - *77-87*	55	75
1017	BRe maroon yellow cab fronts 2 motor bogies - *79-81*	80	100
1014	BRe blue yellow cab fronts kit - *74-76*	55	75
1015	BRe blue yellow cab fronts 2 motor bogies - *74-81*	55	75
1016	BRe blue yellow cab fronts changing lights - *75-77*	55	75
1013	BRe blue yellow ends no lights - *76-87*	55	75
1110	EMS various equipment fitted - *82-83*	55	75
-	various unmade kits of these models	NA	200

Many other variations were advertised but only those known to have been made are listed above.

L29. Class 81 (AL1) Bo-Bo Electric (1963)

This 00 model was initially manufactured and partly finished by Liliput in Austria and imported by Miniature Construction Ltd who fitted the Stone-Favieley pantographs and put it on the market in 1960. In 1962, Trix bought the model from Miniature Construction Ltd to adapt and sell as a Trix product. From 1974 they were assembled and sold by Liliput Model Railways (UK) Ltd. After 1966, all models were 2-rail.

	E3001 - blue		
1128	BRd (moulding) 2-rail - *63-64*	100	150
1127	BRd (moulding) 3-rail - *63-64*	100	150
1128	BRd (transfers) 2-rail improved pantograph yellow panels - *64-72*	100	150

BR Class 81 AC electric loco No.E2001 (detailed) [L29] (Vectis)

1127	as above but 3-rail - *64-66*	100	150
1130	BRd (transfers) 2-rail 2 motors - *65-68*	100	150

1129	as above but 3-rail - *65-66*	100	150
2128	BRd 2-rail Footplateman kit - *65-71*	NA	120
2127	as above but 3-rail - *65-66*	NA	120
1128	BRd one pantograph - *72*	100	150
1001	BRd one pantograph - *74-76*	100	150
1002	ditto but changing headlights - *74-83*	100	150
1003	ditto but no lights - *74-88*	100	150
1004	BRd kit - *not made*	NA	NA
1002	BRd 2 motor bogies - *76-82*	100	150
1001/0	BRd 2 pantographs - *84-88*	100	150
1001	BRd 1 pantograph - *84-88*	100	150
1001/0	**E3012** BRd blue 2 pants - *84-88*	100	150
1001	as above but 1 pantograph - *84-88*	100	150
1001/0	**E3018** BRd blue 2 pants - *84-88*	100	150
1001	as above but 1 pantograph - *84-88*	100	150
1005	**81007** BRe blue yellow front - *77-88*	100	150
1005	**81014** BRe blue yellow front - *77-88*	100	150
1100	various models fitted with EMS train control blue - *82-85*	100	150

L30. Class 124 'Trans-Pennine' DMU (H0) (1966)

Based on BR 6-car units built at Swindon for the Hull-Manchester route, the model was partly tooled by Liliput of Austria with a German Trix motor bogie fitted. A choice of headcodes and front yellow panels were provided for the purchaser to attach. From 1974 the model was assembled and sold by Liliput UK and these models may be identified by grey (instead of cream) interiors. No 3-rail versions were made after 1970.

	Green NE51953/NE51954		
1178	BRc 2-rail 2 car set - *66-73*	100	120
1179	BRc 3-rail 2 car set - *66-70*	100	120
1175	BRc 2-rail 2 car without lights - *67-73*	100	120
1176	BRc 3-rail 2 car without lights - *67-68*	100	120
1125	BRc 2 car EMS equipment fitted - *82-85*	100	120

BR Intercity Class 124 'Trans-pennine' unit [L30] (Vectis)

1025	BRe 2 car without lights - *74-88*	100	120
1025	BRe 2 car with route lights - *74-88*	100	120
1027	BRe 2 car with route lights 2 motors - *74-88*	100	120
	Blue and Grey 51960/51960		
1174	BRe 2-rail 2 car without lights - *67-73*	100	120
1177	BRe 2-rail 2 car with lights - *67-73*	100	120
1173	BRe 3-rail 2 car without lights - *68-70*	100	120
1173/3	BRe 3-rail 2 car with lights - *68-73*	100	120
1020	BRe 2 car without lights - *74-84*	100	120
1021	BRe 2 car with route lights - *74-84*	100	120
1022	BRe 2 car with route lights 2 motors - *74-84*	100	120
1120	BRe 2 car EMS equipment fitted - *82-85*	100	120

COACHES

Trix coaches fall into two distinct categories - tinplate and plastic.

Cat No.	Company, Number, Colour, Dates	£	£

Tinplate Coaches

The very first coaches sold in Britain were Trix Express ones. The British range of tinplate coaches, which were made from the start of Trix Twin Railway production until the early 1960s, came in three sizes. The smallest were short 4-wheeled suburban stock which were shorter than the Trix Express ones, available in LNER or LMS livery and were available in composite and brake versions.

The standard coaches were short bogie main line stock of three types - composite (all 3rd for SR), brake end and restaurant car and in three pre-nationalisation liveries and three BR ones. These were made up to the end of 1939 and resumed for two years in 1946 before the Peco coupling was introduced.

For the 'scale' models such as the *Scotsman, Princess* and *Coronation* there were tinplate bogie coaches of nearer scale length (8.5" long) and in a similar range of liveries except that when it came to producing BR versions, BR(SR) green ones were not produced but BR(WR) chocolate and cream coaches later were. Late in the day, interiors were fitted greatly improving their appearance. Post-war LNER scale coaches had elliptical roofs giving them a Gresley appearance.

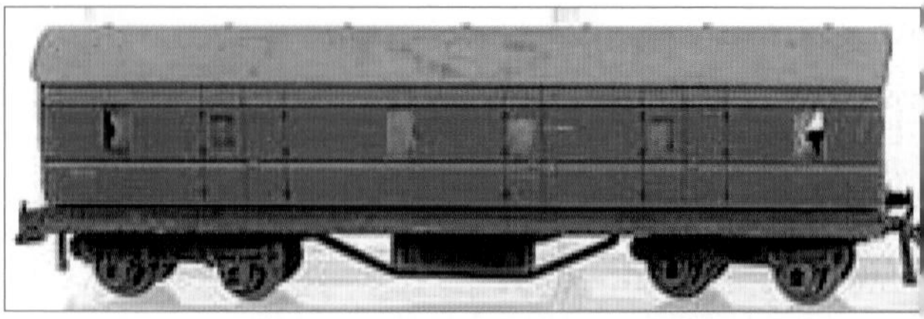

Parcels van fitted with a whistle [C3a] (Vectis)

For the 'Coronation' train set, 'scale' coaches were specially liveried for 'The Royal Scot'. There was also a Pullman parlour car which carried 'TRIX TWIN' on its sides in place of a name, although authentic parlour car names were adopted in the early '60s.

Pre-war coaches all had diecast and wire non-automatic couplings (PW) while those made after the war had the Peco type fitted. All coaches were glazed but, with time, the celastoid glazing strips have shrunk. This glazing had window dividing bars printed on them up until 1937, but from then on the printing could be found on only the 'scale' coaches (even these were non-printed in 1948 for one year only).

C1a. 4-Wheel Suburban Coach (1936)

2/550	**LMS** 3012 maroon PW - *36-39*	20	30
4/550	**LNER** 3120 teak PW - *36-39*	25	35
5/550	**SR** green - *not made*	NA	NA

LMS + LNER 4-wheeled coaches [C1] (Vectis)

C1b. 4-Wheel Suburban Luggage Van (1936)

2/555	**LMS** 7401 maroon PW - *36-39*	20	30
4/555	**LNER** 3316 teak PW - *36-39*	25	35
5/555	**SR** green - *not made*	NA	NA

C2a. Short Coach 1st (1936)

-	**TTR** 1st, 2nd or 3rd class green demonstration coach - *46?*	35	50
-	as above but later couplings - *48*	40	60
2/560	**LMS** 7495 maroon PW - *36-47*	15	20
2/560	**LMS** 7495 brown - *48-49*	8	12
2/560	**LMS** 7495 maroon - *50*	10	15
4/560	**LNER** 1134 gloss teak PW - *36-47*	15	20
4/560	**LNER** 1134 matt teak - *48*	8	12
4/560	**LNER** 1134 gloss teak - *49-50*	10	15
5/560	**SR** 12232 gloss green PW* - *37-48*	25	30
1/560	**BR** 4135 red+cream dull - *51*	5	8
1/560	**BR** 4135 red+cream - *52-58*	8	12
1/561	**BR** 4135 maroon - *57-62*	8	12
5/560	**BR** green no markings - *59*	30	NPG
5/560	**BR** green markings no number - *60*	30	NPG
5/560	**BR** S31595 (transfer) green - *61-62*	30	NPG

* some were made with PW couplings in 1946-47 for export only.

C2b. Short Brake 3rd (2nd) (1936)

2/570	**LMS** 5542 maroon PW - *36-47*	15	20
2/570	**LMS** 5542 brown - *48-49*	8	12

2/570	**LMS** 5542 7495 maroon - *50*	10	15
4/570	**LNER** 1263 gloss teak PW - *36-47*	15	20
4/570	**LNER** 1263 matt teak - *48*	8	12
4/570	**LNER** 1263 gloss teak - *49-50*	10	15
5/570	**SR** 11012 gloss green PW* - *37-48*	25	30
1/570	**BR** 27104 red+cream dull - *51*	5	8
1/570	**BR** 27104 red+cream - *52-58*	8	12
1/571	**BR** 27104 maroon - *57-62*	8	12
5/570	**BR** green no markings - *59*	20	25
5/570	**BR** green markings no number - *60*	20	25
5/570	**BR** S31595 (transfer) green - *61-62*	20	25

* some were made with PW couplings in 1946-47 for export only.

C2c. Short Dining/Restaurant Car (1936)

This used the same body pressing as the 1st class coach.

2/580	**LMS** 2074 maroon PW - *36-47*	15	20
2/580	**LMS** 2074 brown - *48-49*	8	12
2/580	**LMS** 2074 7495 maroon - *50*	10	15
4/580	**LNER** 1433 gloss teak PW - *36-47*	15	20

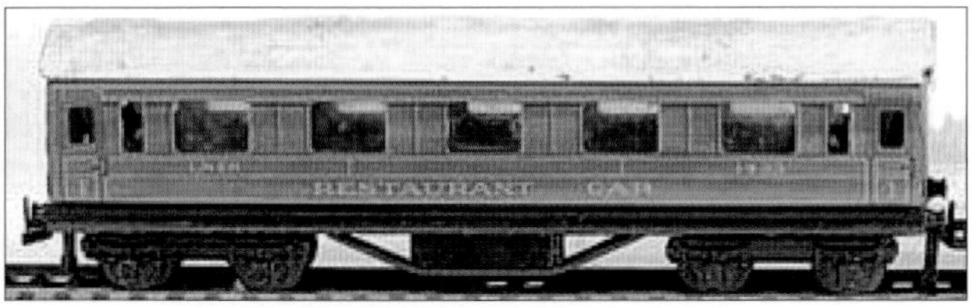

Short teak restaurant car [C2c] (Vectis)

4/580	**LNER** 1433 matt teak - *48*	8	12
4/580	**LNER** 1433 gloss teak - *49-50*	10	15
4/580	**SR** 7621 gloss green PW* - *37-48*	25	30
1/580	**BR** 19 red+cream dull - *51*	5	8
1/580	**BR** 19 red+cream - *52-58*	8	12
1/581	**BR** 19 maroon - *57-62*	8	12

* some were made with PW couplings in 1946-47 for export only.

C2d. Short All 3rd (1937)

This used the same body pressing as the 1st class coach.

5/590	**SR** 10055 green PW - *37-39*	25	30

C3a. Parcel Van/Whistle Coach (1955)

1/557	**BR** 7055 red - *55-57*	12	15
1/558	**BR** 7055 maroon - *57-62*	12	15
(274)	**BR** 7055 red + whistle without windows in end ex-set - *55*	18	NA
(274)	**BR** 7055 red + whistle with windows in end ex-set - *56-58*	15	NA

C3b. Bogie Suburban Composite Coach (1955)

Aluminium underframe and roof. The Engineer's coach was made by respraying surplus red or maroon ones.

1/553	**BR** 6301 red - *55-59*	12	15
1/554	**BR** 6301 maroon - *57-62*	12	15
1688	**BR** Engineer's ED94528 black - *61-63*	25	30
1688	as above but blue - *not made*	NA	NA

C4a. Scale 1st Coach (1938)

2/567	**LMS** 7652 maroon PW - *38-39*	30	40
2/567	**LMS** 7652 maroon - *48-51*	25	35
4/567	**LNER** 31876 teak PW - *38-39*	30	40
4/567	**LNER** 31876 pale matt teak - *48*	25	35
4/567	**LNER** 31876 gloss teak - *49-51*	25	35
5/567	**SR** green - *not made*	NA	NA
1/567	**BR** 3963 red+cream - *51-52*	20	25
1/568	as above + lights - *53-60*	25	30

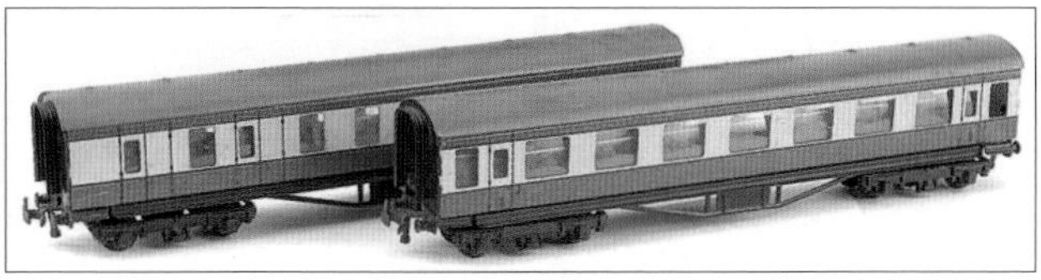

'Scale' BR coaches [C4a+b] (Vectis)

1/569	**BR** 3963 maroon + lights - *57-61*	25	30
1/562	**BRc** as above + interior - *60-62*	25	30
FL1/562	as above + lights + interior - *60-62*	30	35
1/569	**BR** brown+cream + lights - *59-60*	30	35
1/563	**BRc** as above + interior - *60-62*	30	35
FL1/563	as above + lights + interior - *61-62*	35	40

C4b. Scale Brake 3rd (2nd) (1938)

2/577	**LMS** 5772 maroon PW - *38-39*	30	40
2/577	**LMS** 5772 maroon - *48-51*	25	35
4/577	**LNER** 4942 teak PW - *38-39*	30	40
4/577	**LNER** 4942 pale matt teak - *48*	25	35
4/577	**LNER** 4942 gloss teak - *49-51*	25	35
5/577	**SR** green - *not made*	NA	NA
1/577	**BR** 27316 red+cream - *51-52*	20	25
1/578	as above + lights - *53*	25	30
1/578	as above + tail light - *54-58*	30	35
1/579	**BR** 27316 maroon + lights - *57-61*	25	30
1/572	**BRc** as above + interior - *60*	25	30
1/572	as above but with luggage in guard's section - *61-62*	25	30
FL1/572	as above + lights + interior - *60-62*	30	35
1/579	**BR** brown+cream + lights - *59*	25	30
1/573	**BRc** as above + interior - *60-62*	30	35
FL1/573	as above + lights + interior - *61-62*	35	40

C4c. Scale Restaurant Car (1938)

2/587	**LMS** 243 maroon PW - *38-39*	30	40
2/587	**LMS** 243 maroon - *48-51*	25	35
4/587	**LNER** 3587 teak PW - *38-39*	30	40
4/587	**LNER** 3587 pale matt teak - *48*	25	35
4/587	**LNER** 3587 gloss teak - *49-51*	25	35
1/587	**BR** 23 red+cream - *51-52*	20	25
1/588	as above + lighting - *53-58*	25	30
1/589	**BR** 23 maroon + lights - *57-62*	25	30
1/582	as above + interior - *60-62*	25	30
FL1/582	as above + lights + interior - *60-62*	30	35
1/583	**BRc** brown+cream + interior - *60-62*	30	35
FL1/583	as above + lights + interior - *61-62*	35	40

C5. Pullman Car (1939)

598	***Trix Twin*** dark brown+cream PW - *39*	40	50
598	as above post-war couplings grey roof, heavy poor printing - *50-52*	20	25
599	as above but + lights and improved fine printing, white roof - *53-59*	25	35
599	as above + interior, no lights - *60-61*	25	30
FL599	as above + interior + lights - *60*	30	35

Tinplate Pullman car [C5]

599	***Zena*** as above no lights - *61-62*	35	40
599	***Sheila*** as above no lights - *61-62*	35	40
599	**No.34** as above no lights - *61-62*	35	40

C6a. LMS 'Coronation' Coach (1939)

2/568	**LMS** 56001 maroon+yellow PW - *39*	80	120
2/568	**LMS** 56001 very dark maroon+yellow PW - *39*	80	120

C6b. LMS 'Coronation' Brake End (1939)

2/578	**LMS** 56501 maroon+yellow PW - *39*	80	120
2/578	**LMS** 56501 very dark maroon+yellow PW - *39*	80	120

C7. 'Meteor' Centre Car (1956)

597	red - *56-63*	20	30

Plastic Coaches

With new locomotives like *Britannia* and the 'Standard 5' in 3.8mm scale, and the intention of offering the new coaches in the German Trix Express catalogue, when it came to designing the new range of plastic coaches in 1961, it was decided to produce them in a scale of 3.8mm to the foot. This proved to be an unfortunate decision as it tied Trix to the less popular scale for subsequent models. The coaches were very attractive, all having interior units, and quickly replaced the tinplate ones. They were also available in kit form.

Some coaches were also used as trailer cars for the Trans-Pennine DMU and, as such, were released in Brunswick green and in blue and grey. These had printing on the solebars until around 1970 after which the solebars were left non-printed.

Less attractive was the later use of the coaches in pre-Nationalisation liveries including GWR and LMS during the Liliput UK period. The Trix LMS and GWR coaches may be found with black or white roofs but Liliput (UK) ones had white on the GWR and black on the LMS coaches. During the Trix period the coaches had self coloured plastic but during the Liliput UK days they were moulded in black plastic and sprayed the required colour.

Plastic coaches (Vectis)

An unfurnished (no interior unit) range was advertised in 1962 and 1963 but these were never made; nor were the interior units sold on their own as planned. Coaches with a space between the prefix letter of the running number and the number itself date from 1966 where as those without the gap probably predate that. Composite brakes carrying the words 'Load 1 Ton Evenly Distributed' were made during 1965. Light grey roofs were moulded during the Liliput (UK) period when Trix roofs had run out.

C8a. BR Mk1 Composite Corridor (1962)

1935	**GWR** 2017 brown+cream - *71-72*	8	12
1235	as 1935 by Liliput (UK) - *74-87*	8	12
1932	**LMS** 1670 maroon - *71-72*	8	12
1232	as 1932 by Liliput (UK) - *74-83*	8	12
1911	**BRc** W16198 brown+cream - *62-71*	10	15
1915	as above + lights 2-rail - *65-67*	15	20
1918	as above + lights 3-rail - *66-67*	15	20
1211	as 1911 by Liliput (UK) - *74-88*	12	18
1921	**BRc** S15900 green - *64-72*	10	15
1925	as above + lights 2-rail - *65-67*	15	20
1928	as above + lights 3-rail - *66-67*	15	20
1221	as 1921 by Liliput (UK) - *74-88*	12	18
1901	**BRc** M16171 maroon - *64-72*	8	12
1905	as above + lights 2-rail - *65-67*	13	17
1908	as above + lights 3-rail - *66-67*	13	17
1201	as 1901 by Liliput (UK) - *74-88*	10	15
1951	**BRc** M16171 blue+grey - *66-72*	12	18
1251	as 1951 by Liliput (UK) - *74-88*	12	18
1971	**BRc** NE59766 dark green DMU trailer- *67-72*	15	20
1271	as 1971 by Liliput (UK) - *74-88*	15	20
1291	as above + lights - *78-85*	20	25
1975	**BR** NE59766 blue+grey DMU trailer - *67-71*	15	20
1275	as 1975 by Liliput (UK) - *74-88*	15	20
1295	as above + lights - *78-85*	20	25

BR (WR) composite [C8a]

'Coachbuilder' kits

1944	**BRc** W16198 brown+cream - *65-72*	10	15
1947	**BRc** S15900 green - *65-72*	10	15
1941	**BRc** M16171 maroon - *65-72*	8	12
1954	**BR** S15900 blue - *68-70*	20	25
1959	**BRc** W? blue+grey - *68-69*	NPG	NPG
1956	**BRc** M16171 blue+grey - *66-72*	12	18

'Coachbuilder De Luxe' kits

1961	**BRc** M16171 maroon - *67-68*	8	12
1966	**BRc** M16171 blue+grey - *67-68*	12	18

C8b. BR Mk1 Composite Brake End (1962)

1936	**GWR** 3148 brown+cream - *71-72*	8	12
1236	as 1936 by Liliput (UK) - *74-79*	8	12
1933	**LMS** 5531 maroon - *71-72*	8	12
1233	as 1933 by Liliput (UK) - *74-79*	8	12
1912	**BRc** W21194 brown+cream - *62-71*	10	15
1916	as above + lights 2-rail - *65-67*	15	20
1919	as above + lights 3-rail - *66-67*	15	20
1212	as 1912 by Liliput (UK) - *74-88*	12	18
1922	**BRc** S2301 green - *62-71*	10	15
1926	as above + lights 2-rail - *65-67*	15	20
1929	as above + lights 3-rail - *66-67*	15	20
1222	as 1922 by Liliput (UK) - *74-88*	12	18
1902	**BRc** M21240 maroon - *64-72*	8	12
1906	as above + lights 2-rail - *65-67*	13	17
1909	as above + lights 3-rail - *66-67*	13	17
1981	**BRc** M21240 maroon + tail light - *67*	NPG	NPG
1202	as 1902 by Liliput (UK) - *74-88*	10	15
1952	**BRc** M21240 blue+grey - *66-72*	12	18
1252	as 1952 by Liliput (UK) - *74-88*	12	18
1982	as above + tail light* - *67*	NPG	NPG
1972	**BRc** NE57976 dark green DMU trailer - *67-72*	15	20
1272	as 1972 by Liliput (UK) - *74-88*	15	20
1293	as above + lights - *78-85*	20	25
1976	**BR** NE51970 blue+grey DMU trailer - *67-72*	15	20
1276	as 1976 by Liliput (UK) - *74-88*	15	20
1297	as above + lights - *78-85*	20	25
1252	**BR** M16171 blue/grey - *74-88*	15	20

'Coachbuilder' kits

1945	**BRc** W21194 brown+cream - *65-72*	10	15
1948	**BRc** S2301 green - *65-72*	10	15
1942	**BRc** M21240 maroon - *65-72*	8	12
1955	**BR** S2301 blue - *68-70*	20	25
1957	**BRc** M21240 blue+grey - *66-72*	12	18

'Coachbuilder De-Luxe' kits

1963	**BRc** M21240 maroon - *67-68*	8	12
1967	**BRc** M21240 blue+grey - *67-68*	12	18

* very rare as only a handful were made due to the high cost of the Trix Express light units used.

C8c. BR Mk1 Miniature Buffet (1962)

1913	**BRc** W1816 brown+cream - *62-71*	10	15
1917	as above + lights 2-rail - *65-67*	15	20
1920	as above + lights 3-rail - *66-67*	15	20
1213	as 1913 by Liliput (UK) - *74-88*	12	18
1923	**BRc** S1852 green - *62-71*	10	15
1927	as above + lights 2-rail - *65-67*	15	20
1930	as above + lights 3-rail - *66-67*	15	20
1223	as 1923 by Liliput (UK) - *74-88*	12	18
1903	**BRc** M1820 maroon - *64-72*	8	12
1907	as above + lights 2-rail - *65-67*	13	17
1910	as above + lights 3-rail - *66-67*	13	17
1203	as 1903 by Liliput (UK) - *74-88*	10	15
1953	**BRc** M1820 blue+grey - *66-72*	12	18
1253	as 1953 by Liliput (UK) - *74-88*	12	18

BR buffet car [C8c]

1973	**BRc** NE59774 dark green DMU trailer - *67-72*	15	20
1273	as 1973 by Liliput (UK) - *74-88*	15	20
1977	**BR** NE59744 blue+grey DMU trailer - *67-72*	15	20
1277	as 1977 by Liliput (UK) - *74-88*	15	20
	'Coachbuilder' kits		
1946	**BRc** brown+cream - *65-72*	10	15
1949	**BRc** green - *65-72*	10	15
1943	**BRc** maroon - *65-72*	8	12
1958	**BRc** blue+grey - *66-71*	12	18
	'Coachbuilder De-Luxe' kits		
1964	**BRc** maroon - *67-68*	8	12
1968	**BRc** blue+grey - *67-68*	12	18

C9. BR Mk1 Pullman 1st Class Kitchen Car (1962)

	Pullman brown+cream		
1931	'Pullman' printed on + interior, names also printed on - *62-?*	20	25
1931	as above but blank + sheet of names supplied - *?-70*	15	20
1931	as above but 'Pullman' now also applied as transfers - *71-72*	15	20
1938	as 1931 but with lights - *66-67*	25	30
1278	as 1931 by Liliput (UK) - *74-85*	20	25
1950	Coachbuilder Series kit - *65-72*	15	20
	Pullman grey+blue		
1960	'Coachbuilder' Series kit - *68-72*	20	25
1978	342 assembled - *71-72*	25	30
1279	as 1978 by Liliput (UK) * - *74-85*	25	30
	Names carried by Pullman cars		
	Adrian, Aries, Carina, Eagle, Hawk, Heron, Ibis, Joan, Lydia, Orion, Raven, Plato, Robin, Snipe, Wren	-	-

* E3000 loco roof plugs fitted as table lamps in later ones.

C10. BR Mk2 Stock

These were planned in 1968.

1906	**BR** 2nd open blue+grey - *not made*	NA	NA
1907	**BR** M5070 blue+grey - *not made*	NA	NA

C11. BR Mk1 Grey & Blue Pullman Stock

These were planned in 1968.

1933	**BR** parlour car 1st class - *not made*	NA	NA
1934	**BR** parlour brake car - *not made*	NA	NA
1935	**BR** parlour kitchen car - *not made*	NA	NA

WAGONS

Like the coaches, the wagons started life as tinplate models and plastic was not adopted until the 1960s; and even then the transition was gradual. Originally most wagons were on a short wheelbase with a slightly longer one for brake vans, tanks and cattle wagons. They were initially printed with large company lettering but, even pre-war, changed to small letters in the bottom left hand corner of the wagon side. The open wagon also appeared quite early on in a private owner liveries as well as those of 'Trix' and 'Bassett-Lowke'. The most striking wagon was the breakdown crane which consisted of two short four wheel trucks one of which contained a working diecast crane and the other a jib cradle.

Shell tank wagon [W5]

After the war the wagon range looked very much the same and by 1948 was being fitted with Peco style couplings. These simple tinplate wagons adopted BR liveries around 1951, received a diecast chassis in 1954 and had cheap versions made of some of them, of which some were made for Cadet starter sets from 1957. A very attractive 'Weltrol' wagon was released in 1953 with a variety of well designed loads. This was diecast as were the lighted brake van and the tipping hopper wagon that were released about the same time.

The 1960s we saw the introduction of plastic for wagon production but unlike Meccano Ltd with their Hornby Dublo range, Trix did not initially appreciate the possibilities of the new material. The first series of plastic wagons had embossed numbers and looked little better than the tinplate wagons they replaced. This quickly changed when the first private owner open wagons appeared, followed by a series of plastic tank wagons and the BRT bulk grain wagon with a large range of adverts. Some wagons were also available in kit form. From 1974 the wagon range was reintroduced under the Liliput UK name and many remained available until the mid '80s.

Cat No.	Company, Number, Colour, Dates	£	£

Tinplate Wagons

The tinplate series of wagons started with the launch of the system in the mid 1930s and survived into the 1960s. Around 1954 the tinplate chassis used for most wagons was replaced with a diecast (die1) one, with tinplate brake gear, in an attempt at improving the appearance of the models. This itself was replaced with another diecast chassis around 1960. The new chassis had cast brake gear but as a new range of plastic wagons came in at the same time, very few tinplate wagons received the new chassis (die2). The Cadet set wagons introduced in 1957 had tinplate chassis but with no axlebox detail.

W1. Timber Wagon (1936)

662	flat + 29 plank load with cross strapping PW - *36-37*	10	14
662	same without cross-strapping - *37-38*	10	14
662	flat + 25 plank load with 2 card straps PW - *38-39*	10	14
657	post-war couplings - *48-50*	8	12

W2a. 3-plank Platform Truck (1937)

600	**LMS** 472870 dark brown PW - *37-39*	15	20
600	**LMS** 472870 dark brown - *48-51*	10	15
600	**BR** 49736 grey - *51-53*	NPG	NPG
600	**BR** 481760 red-brown - *51-53*	8	12
600	**BR** 481760 grey - *51-59*	5	7
630	as above but die1 chassis - *54-59*	6	9
-	as above but Cadet chassis - *57-61*	5	NA

W2b. 3-plank Container Wagon (1938)

612	**LMS** 472870 dark brown PW + **'Carter Paterson'** container - *38-39*	18	22
612	**LMS** 472870 dark brown + **'Carter Paterson'** container - *48-51*	15	20

LMS 3-plank wagon with container [W2b] (Unknown)

612	**BR** 481760 grey + **'Carter Paterson'** container - *48-51*	8	12

612	**BR** 481760 red-brown + **'Carter Paterson'** container - *48-51*	10	14
639	as above but die1 chassis - *55-59*	10	14

W3a. 4/5-plank Open Wagon (1936)

Pre-war open wagon

2/601	**LMS** 247185 grey PW - *36-38*	15	20
2/601	**LMS** 33550 dark brown PW - *37-39*	15	20
4/601	**NE** 140721 red-brown PW - *36-38*	15	20
4/601	**NE** 174651 red-brown PW - *37-39*	15	20

Pre-war wagon with ballast

609	any wagon + grey load PW - *37-38*	18	22
609	same but blue-grey load - *38-39*	18	22

Post-war open wagon

2/601	**LMS** 33550 dark brown - *48-51*	8	12
4/601	**NE** 174651 red-brown - *48-51*	8	12
1/601	**BR** 183724 red-brown - *51-59*	5	7
623	same but die1 chassis - *54-60*	5	7

Post-war wagon with coal

608	**LMS** 33550 dark brown + coal - *48-51*	10	14
608	**NE** 174651 red-brown + coal - *48-51*	10	14
608	**BR** 183724 red-brown + coal - *51-54*	6	9

Post-war wagon with ballast

609	**LMS** 33550 dark brown + ballast - *48-51*	10	14
609	**NE** 174651 red-brn + ballast - *48-51*	10	14
609	**BR** 183724 red-brown + ballast - *51-54*	6	9
638	same but die1 chassis - *54-59*	6	9

W3b. Tarpaulin Wagon (1936)

5-plank wagon

660	**LMS** 33550 dark brown PW + tarpaulin **LMS** 304721 - *37-39*	18	22
660	same with post-war couplings - *48-51*	12	15
660	**NE** 140721 red-brown PW + tarpaulin NE 270341 - *36-39*	18	22

BR tarpaulined wagons [W3b]

660	same with post-war couplings - *48-51*	12	15
660	**BR** 183724 red-brown + tarpaulin - *51-54*	10	14
662	as above but die1 chassis - *54-60*	10	14

7-plank wagon

660	**LMS** 604707 dark brown + tarpaulin LMS 304721 - *48-49*	12	15
660	**NE** 10687 grey + tarpaulin NE 270341 - *48-51*	12	15
660	**BR** 168723 grey + tarpaulin - *51-54*	10	14
662	same but die1 chassis - *54-60*	10	14
660	**BR** 12738 grey + tarpaulin - *51-54*	10	14
662	same but die1 chassis - *54-60*	10	14

BR tarpaulin numbers: 278304, 287430, 317420, 317521 and 321704

W4. 6/7-plank Open Wagon (1936)

While of the same dimensions, some were printed as 6-plank wagons and others as 7-planks.

Pre-war open wagon

604	**'Trix'** 7372 yellow PW - *36-39*	30	35
605	**'Bassett-Lowke'** 6285 grey+yellow PW - *36-37*	25	30
605	same but dark grey + yellow - *37-39*	25	30
607	**'Hinchliffes'** 236 red PW - *37-39*	15	20

High-sided open wagons - 'Trix' & 'Bassett-Lowke' [W4] (Vectis)

607	**'Charringtons'** 451 red PW - *37-39*	15	20
2/603	**LMS** 93631 grey Loco PW - *36-38*	15	20
2/603	**LMS** 604707 dark brown PW - *38-39*	15	20
2/603	**LMS** 53084 dark brown Loco PW - *38-39*	15	20
4/603	**NE** 142690 grey PW - *36-38*	15	20
4/603	**NE** 171312 grey PW - *38-39*	15	20
4/603	**NE** 10687 grey PW - *38-39*	15	20
5/603	**SR** 40037 dark brown PW - *37-39*	15	20

Pre-war wagon with ballast

609	**LNER** + blue-grey load PW - *38-39*	18	22

Pre-war wagon with coal

606	any wagon + coal PW - *36-39*	18	22

Post-war open wagon

607	**'Hinchliffes'** 236 red - *48-54*	8	12
607	**'Charringtons'** 451 red - *48-54*	8	12
2/603	**LMS** 604707 dark brown - *48-49*	8	12
2/603	**LMS** 53084 dark brown Loco - *49-50*	8	12
4/603	**NE** 171312 grey - *48-51*	8	12
4/603	**NE** 10687 grey - *48-51*	8	12
5/603	**SR** 40037 dark brown - *48-51*	12	15
1/603	**BR** 168732 grey - *51-59*	5	7
634	same but die1 chassis - *54-59*	6	8
634	same but Cadet chassis - *57-61*	5	NA
1/603	**BR** 12738 grey - *51-59*	5	7
634	same but die1 chassis - *54-59*	6	8

Post-war wagon with ballast

609	**NE** 171312 grey + ballast - *48-51*	10	14
609	**NE** 10687 grey + ballast - *48-51*	10	14
609	**BR** 168732 grey + ballast - *51-59*	6	9
638	same but die1 chassis - *54-59*	7	10
609	**BR** 12738 grey + ballast - *51-59*	6	9
638	same but die1 chassis - *54-59*	7	10

Post-war wagon with coal

2/606	any wagon + coal - *48-54*	10	14
606	**BR** 12738 grey + coal - *51-59*	6	9
606	**BR** 168732 grey + coal - *51-59*	6	9
637	same but die1 chassis - *54-59*	7	10

W5. Small Tank Wagon (1936)

Pre-war

640	**'Esso'** yellow PW small black cap - *36-38*	15	20
640	same but large yellow cap - *38-39*	15	20
643	**'Shell Oil'** red PW small black cap - *36-38*	15	20
643	same but large red cap - *38-39*	15	20
645	**'UD'** green PW small black cap - *36-38*	15	20
645	same but large green cap - *38-39*	15	20

Post-war

640	**'Esso'** yellow large yellow cap - *48-49*	8	12
640	same but black cap - *49-50*	8	12
640	**'Esso'** 1591 silver - *51-53*	12	15
640	**'Esso'** 2591 silver - *53*	6	9
641	same but die1 chassis - *54-59*	7	10
-	same but Cadet chassis - *57-61*	5	NA
P646	same but die2 chassis* - *60-65*	10	14

Small tank wagon - 'Shell Lubricating Oil' [W5]

643	**'Shell Oil'** red large red cap - *48-49*	8	12
643	same but black cap - *49-54*	8	12
646	same but die1 chassis - *57-60*	8	12
-	same but Cadet chassis - *57-61*	6	NA

P641	same but die2 chassis* - *60-65*	10	14
643	**'Shell'** silver - *51-54*	6	9
643	same but die1 chassis - *54-59*	5	7
-	same but Cadet chassis - *57-61*	5	NA
P644	same but die2 chassis* - *60-65*	10	14
645	**'UD'** green large black cap - *48-51*	12	15

* These were strictly speaking in the plastic wagon series and although they had the old tinplate tank barrel, they now had a plastic gantry (of sorts) on top.

W6. Cattle Truck (1937)

627	**LMS** 14549 dark brown PW - *37-39*	15	20
627	same but post-war couplings - *49-50*	5	7
627	**BR** 15263 red-brown white roof - *50-51*	7	10
636	same but grey - *50-51*	7	10
627	same but red brown and die 1 chassis - *54-60*	7	10
627	**BR** 14263 grey, grey roof - *52-59*	6	9
627	same but red-brown - *52-59*	6	9
636	as above but die 1 chassis - *54-60*	7	10

W7a. Covered Van (1936)

2/621	**LMS** 91548 grey PW - *37-38*	18	22
2/621	**LMS** 61253 dark brown PW - *38-39*	18	22
2/621	same but post-war couplings - *48-51*	12	15
4/621	**NE** 24296 red-brown PW - *36-39*	18	22

W7b. Refrigerator Van (1936)

661	**SR** 50165 cream PW - *36-39*	18	22

W8. LMS/LNER Goods Brake Van (1936)

	Pre-war		
2/650	**LMS** 134900 grey PW - *36-37*	15	20
2/650	**LMS** 730274 dark brown PW - *38-39*	15	20
4/650	**NE** 140351 red-brown PW - *36-37*	15	20
4/650	**NE** 141578 red brown PW - *38-39*	15	20
	Post-war		
2/650	**LMS** 730274 dark brown grey roof - *48-49*	6	8

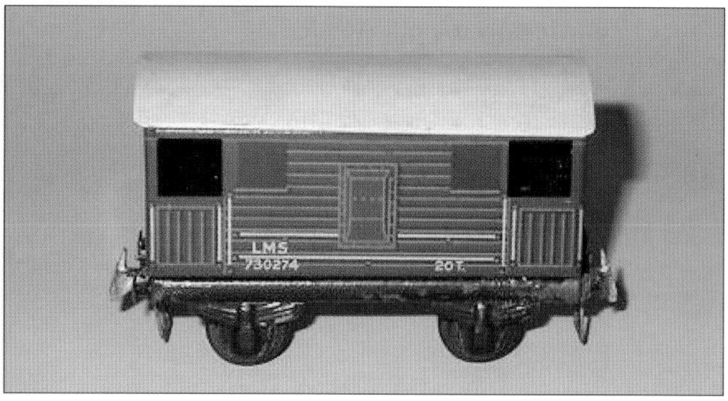

LMS brake van [W8] (Unknown)

2/650	same with white roof - *49-51*	8	10
4/650	**NE** 141578 red brown - *48-51*	6	8
1/650	**BR** 743126 grey - *51-59*	5	7
651	same but die1 chassis* - *54-59*	5	7
1/650	same but red-brown - *51-59*	5	7
651	as above but die1 chassis* - *54-59*	5	7
-	as above but Cadet chassis - *57-61*	5	NA

* no brake gear fitted to these models.

W9. SR Goods Brake Van (1937)

5/650	**SR** 56130 dark brown PW - *37-39*	18	22
5/650	same with post-war couplings - *48-50*	12	15

W10a. 20T Bogie Bolster Wagon (1938)

671	6713 black PW - *38*	12	15
671	46713 black PW - *39*	12	15
671	no number black - *48-50*	8	12
671	46713 black - *54-59*	10	15
671	58209 black - *54-59*	10	15
671	59382 black - *54-59*	10	15
671	no number black embossed sides (later 1671) - *59-63*	8	10

W10b. Bogie Timber Wagon (1938)

673	6713 black + 20 planks PW - *38*	15	20
673	46713 black + 25 planks PW - *39*	15	20
673	no number black +20 planks - *48-54*	10	14
673	46713 black +20 planks - *54-59*	12	15
673	58209 black +20 planks - *54-59*	12	15
673	59382 black +20 planks - *54-59*	12	15
673	no number black embossed sides black +20 planks (later 1673) - *59-63*	8	12

W11a. Bogie Brick Wagon (1938)

675	**NE** 163551 red-brown PW - *38-39*	20	25
675	same with post-war couplings - *48-50*	12	15

BR bogie brick wagon [W11a]

675	**BR** 164132 red-brown - *51-62*	12	15

W11b. 30T Bogie High Capacity Wagon (1938)

676	**LMS** 10468 dark brown PW - *38-39*	20	25
676	same with post-war couplings - *48-50*	12	15
676	**BR** 12640 grey - *51-59*	12	15

W12. Breakdown Crane (1939)

This consisted of two tinplate 3-plank wagons, one carrying a diecast crane and the other acting as the match truck with a jib rest.

615	**Eng Dept** 83610/49736 dark grey - *39*	25	30
615	sprayed dark grey no markings - *46-48*	25	30
615	**Eng Dept** 8361O/49736 dark grey - *48-52*	15	20
615	**Eng Dept** 8361O/49736 grey - *52-55*	15	20
615	same but die1 chassis - *56-61*	15	20

Diecast Wagons

W13. 20T Tipping Hopper Wagon (Dump Car) (1953)

666	**BR** grey - *53-63*	12	15

W14. Goods Brake Van (1953)

This model had an internal light and tail lamp. die = diecast chassis.

653	**BR** 31595 grey tinplate chass - *53-61*	9	12
P621	same but die2 chassis - *60-62*	10	14
P622	as above but red-brown - *60-62*	15	20

W15. 'Weltrol' Bogie Well Wagon (1953)

677	**BR** 41900 grey - *53-54*	10	14
677	**BR** 41900 black orange print - *53-54*	9	13
677	same with white print - *53-54*	8	12
677	**BR** 41900 black - *55-65*	8	12
678	**BR** 41900 grey + boiler - *53-54*	15	20

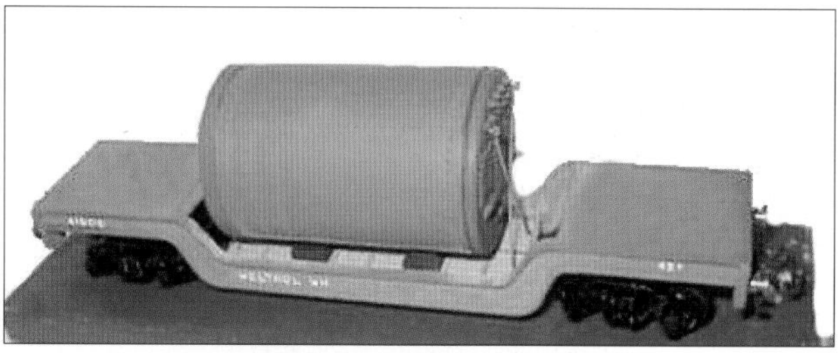

'Weltrol' well wagon [W15] (Unknown)

678	same but black - *54-65*	13	18
679	**BR** 41900 black + transf'mer - *54-60*	13	18
680	**BR** 41900 grey + cable drum - *53-54*	15	20
680	same but black - *54-65*	13	18
P674	**BR** 41900 black + granite - *60-63*	20	25

Plastic Wagons

With the new plastic wagons which started to arrive at the end of the 1950s came a new design of diecast chassis (die2) marked 'TTR made in England'. This was available in two sizes and with or without a vacuum tank beneath. In 1964 a plastic chassis came into use. Where there is no indication of chassis type in the following tables, it should be assumed that the 4-wheel models have plastic chassis. In 1974, Liliput Model Railways UK took over stock and tools for the Trix range and once stocks of parts were used up, new supplies were produced. Plastic chassis with the Trix name removed will have been produced by Liliput UK. From 1978 the earlier plastic wagons were made to order only.

'L' in the following tables means that the model was assembled by Liliput UK and sold in their packaging.

W16. Container Flat A (1960)

P616	**BR** B735103 brown die 2 - *60-64*	6	8
P617	**BR** B735103 brown + maroon standard container die 2 - *60-64*	7	9
P618	same but white container - *60-64*	7	9
1617	**BR** B735103 brown + maroon standard container - *65-71*	7	9
1618	same but white container - *65-72*	7	9
2017	**BR** B735103 brown + maroon standard container kit - *65-71*	NA	10
2018	same but white container - *65-71*	NA	10

W17. Container Flat B (1960)

P619	**BR** B740367 brown + 2 **'Birds Eye'** containers die 2 - *60-64*	8	10
1619	**BR** B740367 brown + 2 **'Birds Eye'** containers - *65-69*	8	10

BR 'Conflat' with 2 'Birds Eye' containers [W17]

2019	same but kit - *66-69*	NA	12
1623	**BR** B740367 brown + **Speedfreight** container - *66-71*	8	10
2023	same but kit - *68-69*	NA	12

W18a. 3-plank Platform Truck (1959)

die1 = first style diecast chassis.

630	**BR** B457434 light grey die1 - *59*	7	9
630	same but medium grey - *60*	7	9
P601	**BR** B457434 brown die2 - *60-64*	6	8
P602	same but light grey - *60-64*	6	8
2001	**BR** B457434 brown kit - *65-66*	NA	10
2002	same but light grey - *65-66*	NA	10
1301	**BR** B457434 brown L - *74-88*	9	12
1302	same but light grey L - *74-88*	9	12

W18b. Plate Wagon (1964)

P603	**BR** B457434 light grey die2 + trestle + plate - *60-64*	10	15

W19. Shunter's Truck (1958)

620	**BR** grey die 1 - *58-62*	8	12
1620	same but die 2 - *63-65*	8	12

W20. 7-plank Wagon (1967)

1669	**'Abbott'** 3510 black - *67-72*	8	10
2069	same but kit - *68-71*	NA	12
1369	same but L - *74-78, 84-88*	9	12
1666	**'Blue Circle'** 173 yellow - *67-71*	8	10
1366	same but L - *74-78, 84-88*	9	12
1667	**'Charringtons'** 257 brown - *67-72*	8	10
1367	same but L - *74-83*	9	12
1671	**'Chubb'** 181 brown - *68-72*	8	10
1371	same but L - *74-78, 84-88*	9	12
1664	**'Hall & Co.'** 510 grey - *67-72*	8	10
2064	same but kit - 68-71	NA	12
1364	same but L - *74-78, 84-88*	9	12
1665	**'ICI'** 326 red - *67-72*	8	10
2065	same but kit - *68-71*	NA	12
1365	same but L - *74-83*	9	12
1668	**'Isaac Wilkinson'** 35 red - *67-72*	8	10
1368	same but L - *74-83*	9	12
1658	**'Maltby'** 11 brown - *67-72*	8	10
1358	same but L - *74-83*	9	12
1675	**'Nicholsons'** 1 black - *68-72*	8	10
1375	same but L - *74-78, 84-88*	9	12
1662	**'Ocean'** 17107 black - *67-72*	8	10

7-plank wagon - 'Young' [W20] (Peter Richardson)

2062	same but kit - *68-70*	NA	12
1362	same but L - *74-83*	9	12
1673	**'Roberts Jenks'** 100 black - *68-72*	8	10
1373	same but L - *74-78, 86-88*	9	12
1659	**'Salter'** 122 brown - *67-72*	8	10
1359	same but L - *74-83*	9	12
1657	**'Spiers'** 347 yellow - *67-71*	8	10
2057	same but kit - *68-70*	NA	12
1357	same but L - *74-83*	9	12
1670	**'Stewart & Lloyds'** 6534 dark green - *67-71*	8	10
1370	same but L - *74-78*	9	12
1674	**'Sutton Manor'** 1075 grey - *68-72*	8	10
1374	same but L - *74-84*	9	12
1672	**'Wm Gordon Jamesons'** 51 yellow - *68-72*	8	10
1372	same but L - *74-78, 84-88*	9	12
1661	**'Young'** 25 dark brown - *67-72*	8	10
2061	same but kit - *68-71*	NA	12
1361	same but L - *74-78*	9	12
1631	**LMS** 259484 brown - *71-72*	12	15
1346	same but L - *75-76*	9	12
1632	**GWR** 109453 v.light grey - *71-72*	12	15
1348	same but L - *75-76*	9	12
1632	**GWR** 109453 medium grey - *71-72*	12	15
1633	**SR** 32277 medium grey - *71-72*	12	15
1633	same but very light grey - *71-72*	12	15
1349	as above L - *75-76*	9	12
1634	**NE** 91528 brown - *71-72*	12	15
1347	same but L - *75-76*	9	12
1656	no number matt black - *72*	12	15
1356	same but L - *74-85*	9	12

W21. 20T Pig Iron Wagon (1960)

P604	**BR** B744083 brown die 2 - *60-64*	7	9
P605	same but grey - *60-64*	7	9
2004	**BR** B744083 brown kit - *65-66*	NA	10
2005	same but grey - *65-66*	NA	10

W22a. 16T Mineral Wagon (1960)

	Open wagon		
P606	**BR** B68174 grey die 2 - *60-64*	6	8
P607	same but brown - *60-64*	6	8
1606	**BR** B68174 grey - *65-71*	7	10
1606	same but no diag lines - *71-72*	8	10
1607	**BR** B68174 brown - *65-72*	8	10
2006	same but grey kit - *65-70*	NA	10
2007	same but brown kit - 65-71	NA	10

Two BR steel mineral wagons [W22a] (Vectis)

1307	**BR** B68174 grey L - *74-85*	9	12
1306	same but brown - *74-?*	9	12
1306	same but grey painted brown - *?-85*	12	15
	Open wagon with coal		
P608	**BR** B68174 grey + coal die2 - *60-64*	6	8
P612	same but brown - *60-64*	6	8
2008	same but grey kit - *65-66*	NA	10
	Open wagon with iron ore		
P609	**BR** B68174 grey + ore die 2 - *60-64*	6	8
2009	same but kit - *65-66*	NA	10
	Open wagon with ballast		
P611	**BR** B68174 brown + ballast die 2 - *60-64*	6	8
2011	same but kit - *65-66*	NA	10
2011	**BR** B68174 brown or grey + load kit - *68-70*	NA	10

W22b. Tarpaulined Mineral Wagon (1960)

P660	**BR** B68174 grey die 2 - *60-64*	8	10
	BR tarpaulin numbers: 278304, 287430, 317420 and 321704		

W23a. Open Hopper Wagon (1967)

This was formed from the bottom of the bulk grain wagon (below).

1692	**BR** grey - *67-68*	15	20

W23b. BRT Bulk Grain Hopper Wagons (1967)

This wagon was made for British Trix by Lilliput who retained the tooling. The later passed to Kader when they brought Lilliput in 1993 and the wagon was added to the Bachmann Branchline range the following year.

1690	**'Abbot's Choice'** any numbers blue - *67-71*	9	12
2090	same but kit - *68-69*	NA	12
1390	same but L - *74-83*	9	12
1686	**'Crawfords'** 5899 blue - *67-71*	9	12
2086	same but kit - *68-69*	NA	12

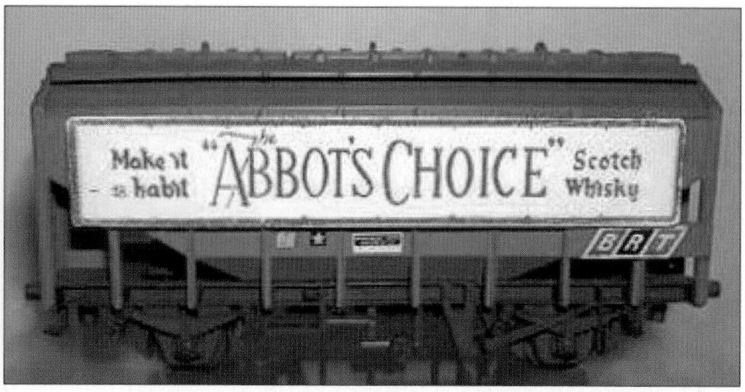

BRT bulk grain wagon - 'Abbot's Choice' [W23b] (Unknown)

1386	same but L - *74-85*	9	12
1685	**'Dewer's'** 5810, 5811, 5812, 5838 blue - *67-72*	9	12
2085	same but kit - *68-69*	NA	12
1385	same but L - *74-85*	9	12
1681	**'Haig'** 5815, 5823, 5826, 5830, 5834, 5839, 5843, 5862, 5863, 5864, blue - *67-72*	9	12
2081	same but kit - *68-69*	NA	12
1381	same but L - *74-83*	9	12
1688	**'Jamie Stuart'** any numbers blue - *67-72*	9	12
2088	same but kit - *68-69*	NA	12
1388	same but L - *74-85*	9	12
1680	**'Johnnie Walker'** 5817, 5820, 5822, 5825, 5829, 5833, 5837, 5842, 5846, 5847, 5850, 5853, 5854, 5857, 5858, 5859, 5860, 5861 blue - *67-72*	9	12
2080	same but kit - *68-69*	NA	12
1380	same but L - *74-83*	9	12
1684	**'King George IV'** 5816, 5878 blue - *67-69*	9	12
2084	same but kit - *68-69*	NA	12
1384	same but L - *74-85*	9	12
1689	**'The Maltsters Association of Great Britain'** any numbers yellow - *67-72*	9	12
2089	same but kit - *68-69*	NA	12
1389	same but L - *74-83*	9	12
1683	**'Vat 69'** 5814, 5819, 5824, 5827, 5831, 5835, 5840, 5844, 5848, 5851 blue - *67-69*	9	12
2083	same but kit - *68-69*	NA	12
1383	same but L - *74-85*	9	12
1687	**'White Horse Whisky'** 5813, 5818, 5821, 5828, 5832, 5836, 5841, 5845, 5849, 5852, 5855, 5856 blue - *67-72*	9	12
2087	same but kit - *68-69*	NA	12
1387	same but L - *74-83*	9	12
1691	**BR** any numbers grey - *67-71*	9	12
2091	same but kit - *68-69*	NA	12
1391	same but L - *74-85*	9	12

W24. Small Tank Wagon (1966)

1645	**'BP'** green - *66-72*	10	12
1646	same but black - *66*	12	14
2030	same but black kit - *66*	NA	12
1345	same but L - *74-83*	10	12
1644	**'Esso'** silver - *66-72*	10	12
1643	same but black - *66*	12	14
2026	same but black kit - *66*	NA	12
1344	same but silver L - *74-83*	10	12
1647	**'Fina'** silver - *66-69*	10	12
1670	same but black - *66*	12	14

Small plastic tank wagons [W24] (Vectis)

2027	same but black kit - *66*	NA	12
1649	**'Mobil'** silver - *66-69*	10	12
2029	same but black - *66*	12	14
1638	**'Regent'** grey - *66-69*	10	12
1639	same but black - *66*	12	14
1640	**'Shell'** silver - *66*	12	14
1340	**'Shell'** red L - *74-83*	10	12
1641	**'Shell BP'** red - *66-72*	10	12
1642	same but black - *66*	12	14
2025	same but black kit - *66*	NA	12
1648	**'Total'** grey - *66-71*	10	12
2028	same but kit - *66-71*	NA	12
2024	**'Total'** or **'Regent'** black kit - *67-71*	NA	14
2025	**'Shell BP'**, **'Fina'**, **'Esso'** or **'Mobil'** black kit - *67-71*	NA	15

W25. 12T Covered Van with Sliding Doors (1960)

P613	**BR** B753500 brown die 2 - *60-64*	6	8
P614	same but grey - *60-64*	6	8
1613	**BR** B753500 brown - *65-72*	6	8

1614	same but grey - *65-72*	6	8
2013	**BR** B753500 brown kit - *65-71*	NA	10
2014	same but grey - *65-70*	NA	10
1313	**BR** B753500 brown L - *74-84*	9	12
1314	same but grey L - *74-84*	9	12

W26. Goods Brake Van (1960)

P621	**BR** M731528 grey die 2 - *60-64*	6	8
P622	same but brown - *60-64*	6	8
1621	**BR** M731528 grey - *65-72*	6	8
1622	same but brown - *65-72*	6	8
1653	**BR** M731528 grey + lights 2-rail - *66-69*	10	12
1654	same but brown + lights 3-rail - *66*	10	12
2021	**BR** M731528 brown kit - *66-71*	NA	10
2022	same but grey - *66-71*	NA	10
1321	**BR** M731528 brown L - *74-90*	9	12
1322	same but grey - *74-90*	9	12

Plastic goods brake van [W26]

W27. Breakdown Crane (1961)

615	2 plastic bodied 3-plank wagons grey - *61-62*	18	20
615	same but brown - *61-62*	18	20

ACCESSORIES

The first lineside buildings were made of wood and painted cream with grey roofs and red bases. Most impressive of these was a terminus station with all-over glazed cover. The footbridges had very steep steps. The buildings developed into the Many-Ways station system which reflected WJ Bassett-Lowke's interest in modern architecture. The building was modular, allowing the modeller to make up any one of a number of complex designs. Some parts were diecast and heavy, especially the central clock tower. Others, including water towers, gantry signal boxes, engine and carriage sheds, remained in wood until they were dropped from the range. The stations over-all roof and windows were printed acetate sheet.

Trix bought in some items including station figures, luggage and platform accessories from Britains and containers for trucks from Kenlow who manufactured similar ones for MasterModels. An attractive and popular lineside accessory in pre- and post-war years was the derelict coach hut which used the body of the 4-wheel coach, in either teak or maroon finish, mounted on a base. Other small accessories included diecast signs, telegraph poles and yard lamps; the last two being mounted on similar large square bases. Single, double and junction signals were made and a tinplate signal box which concealed a whistle.

The most famous of all the Trix lineside accessories was the working coal conveyor which allowed tipping hopper wagons to dump coal in a bin from which it was carried up an elevator onto a conveyor belt and emptied into another waiting truck - all operated electrically. The largest accessory came in the '50s and was a ready wired table top, which was covered with green flock and made by the furniture manufacturers Vono Ltd.

SETS

The first train sets were copies of the German Trix Express sets but with British coloured coaches. These had long shiny red boxes in which trains included either three coaches or four wagons. They also contained an oval of Bakelite track and a square power controller. Another feature was the bottle of Trix Shell oil and the brass plugs for fitting onto the end of the connecting wire to attach the controller to the track.

The near square hinged lid set box came in after the war and survived through the 1950s . A feature of it was the space marked as being for your second train. They were really train packs rather than train sets as they contained no track or controls. This would have kept the cost down making an otherwise expensive system look better against rival makes which did include track, etc.

At the end of the '50s the sets changed again to include track and incorporate cheaper boxes with lift-off lids and a more attractive printed top. These were redesigned in the '60s with the introduction of plastic coaches; the box top picture showing 'family involvement'.

There was a large range of train sets and train packs made over a period of 35 years and these are sought by some collectors. The most common, and therefore the least interesting, are those in the red hinged top boxes of the 1950s.

Union Mills

HISTORY

Union Mills is run by Colin Heard from his base at Union Mills Models, 5 Union Mills Trading Estate, Braddan, Isle of Man IM4 4AB. He designs and hand-builds the precision models himself and produces them in small batches. He produces mainly LNER steam locomotive models along with some LMS and SR subjects. This means that they are in stock for only short periods He occasionally re-releases earlier ones and sometimes retools them.

As will be seen from the table below, we are missing a number of dates. If you can supply these and any additional information, we look forward to hearing from you.

LOCOMOTIVES

The model locomotives are sold ready-to-run and have metal bodies for both the engine and tender, which give them weight for good pulling power. The handrails are cast integrally and cabs are unglazed. The locos all have powerful tender drives using a can motor driving trhough two worms and worm wheels onto the front and rear sets of wheels. All the subjects chosen to model are of fairly simple design with no outside cylinders and with simple liveries. The models have traction tyres and have pick-ups down one side of the loco and down the other side of the tender. They are fitted front and rear with standard Arnold Type N gauge couplings. The numbers and insignia are pad printed onto each model. The wheels are nickel plated brass and forced onto splined steel axles and the connecting rods are photo etched nickel silver. All reports say that they perform very well.

Cat No.	Company, Number, Colour, Dates	£	£
L1.	**LMS Class 2P 4-4-0** (1994)		
	A Deeley design taken over by Fowler and used on light expresses.		
	S&DJR dark blue - *94*	65	77
	700 LMS red - *94*	65	77
	LMS black - *94*	60	72
	BR black - *94*	60	72
L2.	**LNER Class D20 4-4-0** (1996)		
	Introduced by the NER in 1899 as their express R Class.		
	2024 LNER green - *96*	65	77
	BR black - *96*	60	72
L3.	**SR Class T9 4-4-0** (2008)		
	SR black - *08*	65	75
	BR black (wrong number) - *08*	58	69
L4.	**LMS Class 3F 0-6-0**		
	LMS black - *?, 06*	58	69
	BR black - *?, 06*	58	69
L5.	**GCR/LNER Class J11 0-6-0** (2006)		
	Robinson's ex-GCR 'Pom Pom' Class.		
	4354 LNER black - *06*	50	59
	BR black - *06*	50	59
L6.	**LNER Class J25 0-6-0**		

LNER J25 [L6] (David Wild)

	LNER black - *?*	60	69
	BR black - *?*	60	69
L7.	**LNER Class J26 0-6-0**		
	A Worsdell design for the NER dating from 1904 and taken over by the LNER.		
	LNER black - *?*	60	69
	65775 BRb black - *?*	60	69
L8.	**LNER Class J27 0-6-0**		

Ex-LNER J27 [L8] (Unknown)

	LNER black - *?*	60	69
	65785 BRb black - *?*	60	69
L9.	**LNER Class J38 0-6-0** (2006)		
	A Gresley design for the LNER and first released in 1926.		
	5919 LNER black - *06*	50	59
L10.	**LNER Class J39 0-6-0** (1994)		

LNER J39 [L10] (David Wild)

	2943 LNER green - *06*	65	74
	LNER black - *94*	60	69
	BR black - *94*	60	69
L11.	**SR Class 700 0-6-0** (2008)		
	SR black - *08*	60	69
	BR black - *08*	60	69
L12.	**LNER Class B12 4-6-0** (1999)		

LNER B12 [L12] (Vectis)

	LNER green - *99, 06*	65	79
	BR black - *99, 06*	63	76
L13.	**LMS Class 7F 0-8-0** (2006)		
	LMS black - *06*	60	72
	BR black - *06*	60	72
L14.	**LMS Class G2 0-8-0** (2004)		
	This shows the G2 in its final form with a Belpaire firebox and Webb pattern wheel spokes.		
	9032 LMS black - *04*	60	72
	49078 BRb black - *04*	60	72
L15.	**LNER Class Q2 0-8-0**		
	LNER black - *?*	60	72
	BR black - *?*	60	72

Collectors Corner

HORNBY BACHMANN FARISH VITRAINS AIRFIX MAINLINE PECO GAUGEMASTER

CLASSIX OXFORD | DAPOL WILLS

Aspire Gifts & Models

SHOP OPENING TIMES: Mon 2pm-5pm Tues, Wed, Thurs 10am-5pm

New & Pre-Owned Railways MAIL ORDER CREDIT CARDS WELCOME

Come and see our OO , 009, N Gauge Railways, Circus & Model Fairground Layouts Under Construction

Unit 9. Court Farm Business Park, Buckland Newton. Nr Dorchester, Dorset. DT2 7BT Telephone: 01300 345355

email:edward.aspire@btinternet.com www.aspiregiftsandmodels.co.uk

METCALFE SUPERQUICK KNIGHTWING KESTREL MODELSCENE FALLER RATIO

TAMLYN AND SON

AUCTIONS OF ALL GAUGES OF RAILWAY

Locomotives, Rolling Stock, Accessories, Lay-Outs etc Early or Modern. Catalogues mailed and on line www.tamlyns.co.uk

For further information contact: Claire Rawle, Tamlyns Auction Rooms, Market Street, Bridgwater, Somerset TA6 3BN. Tel: 01278 445251

JACKSONS MODELS & RAILWAYS

33 NEW STREET WIGTON, CA7 9AL Tel: 01697 342 557

www.jacksonsmodels.co.uk

Stocking Model Railways by Hornby, Bachmann, Farish, Peco, Dapol, Metcalfe, Superquick, Corgi, Oxford, Classix etc. Railway Scenery by Gaugemaster, Woodland Scenics, Javis, Busch, Expo, etc.

Opening Times: Mon, Tue, Fri 9-5, Late night Thurs to 7.00pm, Sat 10-3 Closed Wed & Sun

---

TENNENTS Trains

Shop 1, 130 Hagley Road, Hayley Green, Halesowen, B63 1DY

0121 550 1266 www.tennentstrains.co.uk

Open Mon-Wed, Fri & Sat 11am - 5pm (Closed Thurs & BH Mon & Tues)

"We deal in trains of all sorts"

Special: Lionel O Gauge tinplate track for good quality running with a traditional look. Also modern style O Gauge 3 rail track. or for details

---

MARCWAY MODELS & HOBBIES

47 Years

HORNBY & SCALEXTRIC MAIN AGENTS

Secondhand Equipment Bought & Sold in all gauges G to Z. Controls, Scenics, Kits, Tools, Paints, etc, etc.

VAST SELECTION OF CONSTRUCTION KITS, DIECAST, ETC

598-600 ATTERCLIFFE ROAD SHEFFIELD S9 3QS

Tel 0114 2449170 Fax 2619729

www.marcway.com and www.modelrailways.me.uk

SITUATED 2 MILES FROM M1 JUNC 34 (Meadowhall Exit) 200 yds from Attercliffe Tram Stop

---

TRAINS and BOATS and PLANES

www.trainsandboatsandplanes.co.uk

High St., Bognor Regis, W.Sussex, PO21 1EH

A Traditional Shop for Model Railways in all Gauges, Repairs, Garden Railways, Live Steam, Mamod etc. Plastic and Wooden kits - Slot Cars Radio Control Aeroplanes and Model Boats Model Boat Accessories, Meccano, Model Maker's Supplies, Tools & Much More Collectibles & Secondhand Bought and Sold

The South Coast Model Centre **01243 864727**

Millennium Models

Hornby, Bachmann, Peco and more.

New and Secondhand stock

Jarvis, Dapol, Metcalfe, Corgi, Oxford

67 Queen Street, Morley, Leeds LS27 8EB

Tel: 0113 2189286 www.millennium-models.co.uk

BACHMANN BRANCH-LINE | HORNBY

TRAINS ON TIME

Model Trains | Train Sets | Accessories

Unit 4, Abercorn Street Ind. Est, Abercorn Street, Paisley PA3 4AY

www.trainsontime.co.uk

Stockists of Hornby, Bachmann & Tomix, Thomas the Tank Engine ranges

0141 889 6677

MORRIS MODELS

NORTH LANCING

80 Manor Road, N. Lancing, W. Sussex BN15 0HD

Tel / Fax: 01903 754850

info@morrismodels.co.uk www.morrismodels.co.uk

Open 9.30am – 5pm Mon – Sat except Bank Holidays

British and Continental Model Railways

Hornby, Bachmann, Peco, Graham Farish, Dapol, Fleischmann, Roco, Trix, Brawa, LGB, Marklin. Associated Scenics and model road vehicles.

Z Gauge to Garden Gauge: New & good quality second-hand

In shop Digital demonstration layout

We are between Brighton & Worthing, *just off the A27 – easy free parking*

Huge ranges from the top names in

HOBBY AND MODELS

OO and N gauge in stock

www.austins-uk.com

AUSTINS

Toy Store

Wolborough Street

Newton Abbot

Devon

01626 333444

RON LINES

Wanted your model railways!

Good prices paid, send us a list of your items.

332 Shirley Road, Southampton, SO15 3HJ

02380 772 681 www.ronlines.co.uk

VINTAGE RAILWAYS NORWICH.COM

acetrains | BASSETT-LOWKE | DARSTAED

O-GAUGE TRAINS

VISA | Digital plus by Lenz | ETS

Tel : 01508 483 854

sales@vintagerailwaysnorwich.com

DURHAM TRAINS OF STANLEY

MORE THAN JUST A MODEL SHOP

Free P&P on all orders over £100 in the UK

Open Mon-Sat 09.30 - 17.00

Over 3000 products

We stock: ✓ Bachmann ✓ Hornby ✓ Farish ✓ Peco ✓ Vi-Trains ✓ Heljan ✓ N, 00, 0 Gauges ✓A large range of Scenics ✓ A range of Secondhand items

6 Station Road, Stanley, County Durham, DH9 0JL

Tel: 01207 232545 Email: sales@durhamtrainsofstanley.co.uk

Website: www.durhamtrainsofstanley.co.uk

HASLINGTON MODELS

134 Crewe Road, Haslington, Crewe CW1 5RQ

Telephone/Fax 01270 589079

email: sales@haslingtonmodels.co.uk

Appointed Stockists of

Bachmann, Farish, Hornby, Peco, Gaugemaster, Dapol, Vi-Trains, Heljan, Humbrol, etc. • FREE Parking

OPEN MON-SAT 10.00-1630 CLOSED WED/SUN

ViTrains

HISTORY

Following the demise of the Lima Group in Italy there were many redundancies, so some of the former Lima and Rivarossi employees came together in 2005 to form a new company, based in Vicenza,Northern Italy, where Lima had once been made.

ViTrains principally makes H0 models for the Italian market but has its sights on a world market. The models are handmade and produced in low volume. Production is done in Italy.

In 2006, work started on a British 00 scale model to be marketed through The Hobby Company, who had previously marketed Lima models in Britain.

LOCOMOTIVES

The locomotives are built to the high standard demanded by modellers today. ViTrains models feature a wealth of additional detail parts to add according to choice.Some of these are plastic, whilst others are etched metal, some being designed for static display only.

The models boast a detailed scale body with etched brass radiator fan grille, flush glazing, sprung buffers, metal lamp irons, windscreen wipers and more. They have a 5-pole centrally-mounted motor in a heavy cast chassis frame driving the outer two axles of each bogie. The locomotive are ready for fitment of a digital command control decoder if desired.They have NEM coupling pockets and removable slim tension-lock couplings.

The first British model they produced was a Class 37/4 and this was followed in the summer by a 37/0.

Cat No.	Company, Number, Colour, Dates	£	£

L1. Class 37 Co-Co Diesel (2007)

All models feature working directional lights and are fitted with DCC Decoder socket and five pole centrally mounted motors. DC8 = DCC 8-pin socket fitted.

Cat No.	Company, Number, Colour, Dates	£	£
V2037	**37131** BRe blue Ltd Edn 1000 - *07*	42	50
V2026	**37156 *British Steel Hunterston*** Civil Engineers grey+yellow 37/0 - *07*	42	50
V2038	**37201** Railfreight Metals triple grey 37/0 - *08*	45	60
V2030	**37216/D6916 *Great Eastern*** BR green DC8 37/0 - *08*	50	78
V2028	**37229 *Jonty Jarvis*** BR green DC8 - *08*	50	60
V2048	**37371** Mainline blue - *08*	45	60
V2027	**37378** Railfreight Red Stripe grey - *08*	45	60
V2021	**37401 *Mary Queen of Scots*** BReLL blue - *07*	42	50
V2029	**37402 *Bont Y Bermo*** EWS light & very dark grey 37/4 DC8 - *08*	45	60
V2014	**37403 *Glendarroch*** Rft Distribution triple grey - *07*	42	50
V2032	**37403 *Isle of Mull*** BReLL blue Sp Edn 250 (Rails/Allisons) - *07*	45	60
V2073	**37405** EWS maroon+yellow 37/4 - *08*	45	60
V2033	**37406 *Saltire Society*** BReLL blue Sp Edn 250 (Rails/Allisons) - *07*	45	60
V2016	**37411 *Caerphilly Castle/Castell Caerffili*** BR green - *07*	42	50
V2034	**37412 *Loch Lomond*** BReLL blue Highland motif Sp Edn 250 (Rails/Allisons) - *07*	45	60
V2035	**37413 *Loch Eil Outward Bound*** BReLL blue Sp Edn 250 (Rails/Allisons) - *07*	45	60
V2017	**37414 *Cathays C&W Works 1846-1993*** Regional Railways - blue+grey Ltd Edn 800 - *07*	42	50
V2074	**37415** EW&S maroon DC8 37/4 - *08*	50	78
V2052	**37417 *Highland Region*** IC triple grey Sp Edn 250 (Kernow MRC) - *08*	50	65
V2049	**37417 *Richard Trevithick*** EWS maroon DC8 37/4 - *08*	50	78
V2036	**37418 *East Lancashire Railway*** EWS maroon+yellow 37/4 DC8 - *08*	50	66
V2051	**37420 *The Scottish Hosteller*** IC triple grey Sp Edn 250 (Kernow MRC) - *08*	50	65
V2022	**37421 *Strombidae*** BR Railfreight Petroleum triple grey Immingham motif 37/4 - *07*	42	50
V2020	**37422 *Carfiff Canton*** EWS maroon - *07*	42	50
V2015	**37423 *Sir Murray Morrison*** IC grey - *07*	42	50
V2019	**37427 *Bont Y Bermo*** EW&S - maroon+yellow - *07*	42	50
V2005	**37428 *David Lloyd George*** BReLL blue Ltd Edn 800 - *07*	42	50

BR Class 37 No27428 David Lloyd George [L1] (ViTrains)

Cat No.	Company, Number, Colour, Dates	£	£
V2023	**37429 *Eisteddfod Genedlaethol*** Rft Construction grey 37/4 - *07*	42	50
V2024	**37430 *Cwmbran*** Transrail triple grey - *07*	42	50
V2018	**37461** EW&S Royal Scotsman maroon - *07*	50	78
V2076	**37512 *Thornaby Demon*** BReLL grey with yellow cabs DC8 - *08*	50	78
(V2053)	**37505** ICs grey DC8 ex-pack 37/5 - *08*	50	NA
V2082	**37682** DRS (compass) dark blue 37/5 - *09*	50	78
(V2053)	**37685** ICs grey DC8 ex-pack 37/5 - *08*	50	NA
V2053	two locos - *08*	NA	146
V20??	**37703** EWS maroon+yellow DC8 37/7 - *09*	50	78
V2080	**27706** West Coast maroon 37/7 - *09*	50	78
V20??	**37709** Mainline triple grey DC8 37/7 - *09*	50	78
V2077	**37710** Loadhaul black+orange DC8 37/7 - *08*	50	66
(V2088)	**37712** West Coast maroon ex-pack with Cl47 Ltd Edn 250 - *10*	65	NA
V2071	**37800 *Glo Cymru*** Railfreight Coal 37/7 - *09*	65	90
-	**97302** Network Rail yellow 97/3	50	NA
-	**97304 *John Tiley*** Network Rail yellow 97/3	50	NA
V2031	above two locos Lt Edn 800 sets - *09*	NA	50

L2. Class 47 Co-Co Diesel (2008)

All models feature working directional lights and are fitted with 8-pin DCC decoder socket and five pole centrally mounted motors.

Cat No.	Company, Number, Colour, Dates	£	£
V2097	**47237** Avenza Freight blue - *09*	65	90
V2061	**47370 *Andrew A Hodgekinson*** Avenza Freight - *09*	65	90
V2098	**47375** Advenza Freight blue - *10*	70	95
V2058	**47401 *North Eastern*** BReLL blue - *08*	65	90
V20??	**47501 *Craftsman*** DRS (compass) dark blue Sp Edn (*Model Rail* magazine) - *09*	65	93
V2060	**47519** BRc 2-tone Heritage green - *10*	70	95
(V20??)	**47727 *Rebecca*** Colas yellow+orange 47/7 Sp Edn (*Rail Express Modeller*) - *09*	65	NA
V2084	**47739 *Robin of Templecombe*** Colas yellow+ orange - *09*	65	90
(V20??)	**47749 *Demelza*** Colas yellow+orange 47/7 Sp Edn (*Rail Express Modeller*) - *09*	65	NA
V20??	above two locomotives - *09*	NA	160
V2039	**47768 *Resonant*** RES red+dark grey - *08*	65	90
V2095	**47787** West Coast maroon - *09*	65	90
(V2088)	**47760** West Coast maroon ex-pack with Class 37 Ltd Edn 250 - *10*	65	NA
V2099	**47802 *Pride of Cumbria DRS*** (compass) - *09*	65	90
V2063	**47805 *Pride of Toton*** Virgin red+black - *10*	70	95
V2065	**47810 *Captain Sensible*** Cotswold Rail grey - *10*	70	95
V2067	**47828 *Severn Valley Railway*** Virgin red+black - *09*	70	90
V2094	**47828 *Joe Strummer*** Cotswold Rail pale grey - *09*	65	90
V2096	**47839 *Pegasus*** Riviera Trains blue 47/8 - *10*	70	95
V2059	**47844 *Derby & Derbyshire Chamber of Commerce & Industry*** Intercity Swallow grey - *08*	65	90
V2086	**47848 *Titan Star*** Riviera Trains blue - *09*	65	90

Collectors Corner

Advertisers Index *complied by Warners Group Publications*

Wrenn 00

HISTORY

George and Richard Wrenn established their company, G&R Wrenn, at Lee Green near Blackheath, London, in the 1950s making track for railway modellers, not satisfied with existing proprietary brands.They were later to be joined by their brother Cedric. In 1955 they moved to an industrial unit at 11 Honeywood Road, Basildon, Essex, where they had room to expand their activities. By the early 1960s they were offering at least 120 items of 00 and TT track and had developed their own slot-car racing system called Formula 152, which had been launched in 1960.

Milestones

1950s G&R Wrenn established as track makers.
1955 The Company moves to Basildon.
1960 Formula 152 racing system launched.
1964 Lines Bros. take over Meccano Ltd.
1964 Lines Bros. buy control of the Company.
1966 Wrenn purchase former Hornby Dublo tools.
1966 Wrenn advertise their first ex-Hornby Dublo product - *Cardiff Castle*.
1967 First Wrenn locos released.
1967 Wrenn enter into an agreement to market Lima N gauge in Britain.
1968 First Tri-ang Wrenn wagons released.
1968 The company sells-off remainder of Tri-ang TT stock.
1971 Wrenn buy back their share 1972 The product is renamed Wrenn Railways.
1972 The product is renamed Wrenn Railways.
1973 Wrenn take over the marketing of their own products from Rovex and release first full-colour catalogue.
1980 First new locomotive.
1984 Last new locomotive launched.
1992 George Wrenn retires and sells his business to Dapol Ltd in 1993.
1995 Dapol restart Wrenn production at Llangollen.
2001 G&R Wrenn Ltd bought by Mordvale Ltd.
2002 First Cheshunt model.
2004 Publication of Maurice Gunter's book on Wrenn.

Class N2 0-6-2T in LMS livery [L3] (Special Auction Services)

They had developed a number of other mechanical toys and one, a unique design of motor, caught the eye of a representative of the giant toy makers, Lines Bros. Ltd., better known for their Tri-ang trade mark. Lines bought a controlling interest in G&R Wrenn in the early 1960s and thus it became part of the Lines Bros. Group and was placed under the wing of Rovex Scale Models Ltd who made Tri-ang Railways.

Following the take-over of Meccano Ltd. by Lines Bros. in 1964, George Wrenn successfully purchased some of the redundant Hornby-Dublo tools from the Meccano factory in Liverpool in 1966. He re-launched the system under the name Tri-ang Wrenn and for the next few years felt the benefit of the large Tri-ang sales network. On the break-up of the Lines Bros. empire in 1971, he bought back from the receiver the shares in his company that had been held by Lines and changed the name of his railway system to Wrenn Railways. From the start of 1973 Wrenn was no longer marketed by Rovex and by the mid 1970s Airfix and Palitoy were providing a new higher quality product being demanded by modellers. Wrenn's sales were also affected by Hornby's development of new models of better quality which included competing subjects such as the A4 and 'Duchess'.

The range of models produced by Wrenn in the '70s and '80s was quite considerable and included four new model locomotive designs. However, the volumes produced were low and getting lower. By the late '80s many short runs and limited editions reached the market and Wrenn had become manufacturers of collectables.

In 1992 George Wrenn retired and closed down production. The following year he sold his equipment, stock and the Wrenn intellectual assets to Dapol. However, a quirk of fate at this time was to make Wrenn models even more highly collectable.

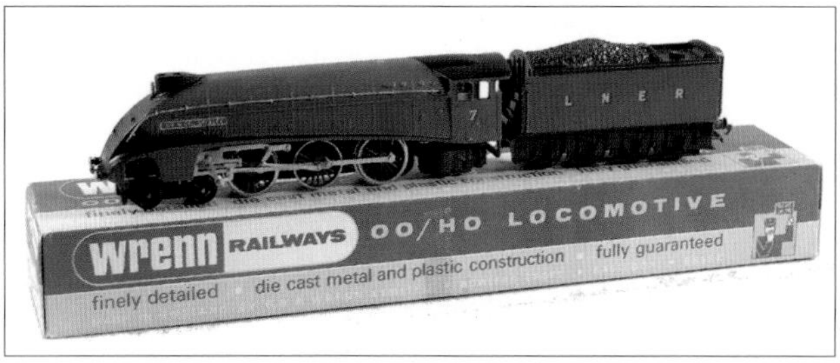

LNER Class A4 No7 Sir Nigel Gresley [L10] (Special Auction Services)

As we have seen, demand for Wrenn had been falling during the 1980s and various limited edition locomotives rarely received enough orders to require completion of the proposed batch. Added to this George Wrenn's dogged determination to clear the decks as far as possible before he left the business, many unfinished models were produced in the final days in order to use up the stock of parts.This meant, for example, normally lined locomotives going out with only a part or none of their lining. Thus, in a few weeks many future 'rarities' were produced and these more than anything else drew the interest of collectors in the years ahead. This phenomenon was further extended by Dapol who assembled further models from parts that they inherited.

A disastrous fire at the Dapol headquarters at Winford destroyed or damaged much of the paperwork and pre-production models causing Dapol to abandon plans to open a Wrenn museum. No new Wrenn locomotive models have been produced since then except, perhaps, from the stock of parts acquired with the company, but Dapol absorbed a number of the former Wrenn wagon models into their own range, giving them new chassis.

Having extracted from the Wrenn tooling those items that Dapol felt were commercially viable, the remainder of the tooling, outstanding stock of parts and the surviving Wrenn archive were sold, in 2001, along with the intellectual assets of G&R Wrenn Ltd. The new owner was a company set up by three Wrenn collectors and this became G&R Wrenn Ltd. It has continued the production of new limited edition models from the old tooling and formed a collectors club.

Further Reading

With the company archives in his hands, Maurice Gunter has written a history of the company with comprehensive details of the Wrenn range of models. The book was published by Irwell Press (ISBN 1903266424) early in 2004 and is called *The Story of Wrenn*. It is currently out of print but second-hand copies may be available. The book includes production numbers and values.

Packaging: More than with any other make of model, the value of Wrenn items depends on the packaging they are in and the above book describes the models under the different phases of box used. Thus any model may appear several times in the book with the value changing according to the box it is in. In quoting prices we have chosen the lowest in each case but the same model in a rarer box could increase its value by as much as three times. This also means that there is a far larger difference in price between boxed and unboxed examples.

Prices: Since the fourth edition of the book the prices have been based on those quoted in Maurice Gunter's book (see above), but since then I have been advised that prices have been falling and several people have questioned the adherence to the levels shown in the 6th Edition. Since that was published I have acquired the results of an independent survey of eBay prices carried out between 2002 and 2008. This survey was extensive and has the advantage over other auction sources in that wagons on Ebay are sold individually, whereas in the auction room they are sold in batches. For example we know that 572 examples of the 'Lowmac' wagon were sold on eBay during this period of the survey and the differing conditions were separated out and individually listed. Thus we know how many of each type, boxed and unboxed, were sold and what the average price was in each category. This also emphasises the difference in value of boxed and unboxed examples, as referred to above, which is far greater than we previously thought.

0-6-0DS in LMS black livery [L14] (Special Auction Services)

Some of the rarer models have gone up in value.

Collecting Club

We are indebted to the Wrenn Railways Collectors Club for their considerable help with advice and proof reading during the original preparation of this section. Anyone interested in further information about this organisation should contact Barry Fentiman Tel: 01628 488455 or visit the Club's website at http//www.wrennrail.freeserve.co.uk

More recently the official Wrenn Collectors Club was formed by the G&R Wrenn company and offers its members concessions. All details available on the company website at www.gandr-wrenn.co.uk

Dates - Providing dates to indicate availability of Wrenn models has always been difficult, as they were produced in small batches sometimes with breaks between. Introduction dates were also convoluted as new models were frequently added to the catalogue and price list several years before they were ready for release. Dates quoted here have been mostly taken from Maurice Gunter's book. A span of dates should not be interpreted as meaning that the model was made, or even available, every year between those dates.

In the case of wagons, it is often not possible to date when plastic shades or stock numbers changed and so the dates covering the run of a model irrespective of any changes have been put against just one of the variations and question marks against the others. If anyone has more precise information about when variations occurred, the editor would be interested to hear from them.

Numbers Made - Only where the quantity of a model made is small have they been quoted in the text. However, this information is not known in all cases. The numbers quoted are not always the complete picture as production figures are missing from the archive for at least three years. However, with such small numbers produced in each batch, the missing information should not dramatically change the result.

Limited Editions - Only official limited editions are marked as such although these were sometimes larger in quantity than some of the batches of models released towards the end of Basildon production. Official limited editions usually came with a stand on which to display the model.

Listing - The locos are listed in order of size starting with tank engines followed by tender locos and ending with diesels, electrics and multiple units. Wagons are listed in the order of: flats, open wagons, hoppers, tanks, vans and brake vans.

SR BB Class No.21C155 Fighter Pilot for the 'Golden Arrow' service [L11] (Special Auction Services)

LOCOMOTIVES

Late Issues - Locomotives produced late in the history of the Basildon based company are usually scarcer than those produced in the early years and it is useful to be able to recognise them. The boxes were generally a darker grey or even green-grey (make sure that this was not due to exposure to sunlight). The contents description on the end of the box could be either rubber stamped, or on a sticky label with typed print. The last five locos made (W2312 to W2316) had typed labels. The base of the box was stamped with a five or six figure code; two of the figures indicating the year of production (in 1990 and 1991 it was the first two figures but in 1992 this changed to the last two).

The models themselves received improvements which included better lining and larger driving wheels.

Suffixes - Some models were later fitted with 5-pole motors and these generally received a 'M2' or '5P' suffix to their catalogue number and, on the whole, at auction fetch a higher price (as do any of the later models).

Mk1 and Mk2 Chassis - The Hornby Dublo A4 and 'Duchess' had undersize wheels and so when Wrenn revised these chassis to take the 5-pole motor from 1983, they took the opportunity to also change the wheels using the larger ones from the 'Castle'. At the same time they did away with the flangeless centre wheels and used flanged ones instead. This was called the Mk2 chassis and there were other improvements on the Mk2 such as more power collectors. In the case of the 'Duchess', there was added cab detail. 'M2' meant a Mk2 chassis, however, not all A4s and 'Duchesses' with Mk2 chassis are fitted with 5-pole motors although these are the exception. The locos fitted with Mk2 chassis could not negotiate 1st radius curves and so A4s and 'Duchesses' with Mk1 chassis remained in production.

LMS 'Duchess' No.62235 Princess Alice [L8] (Vectis)

Flaking Paint - Due to a bad lot of varnish used in the factory, some of the last models made (including some of the rarest) suffer from flaking paint. This makes them a questionable investment.

'Khaki' Models - Around 1984/85, a number of locomotives, supposedly BR Brunswick green, were sold with correct coloured tenders but with the paintwork on the loco body in different shade. This was a khaki green and may have resulted from over cooking in the stove enamelling oven. Paradoxically, these faulty models are now worth more than correct ones.

Cat No.	Company, Number, Colour, Dates	£	£

L1. LSWR Adams Tank 4-4-2

W3003	**52** LSWR light green - *not made*	NA	NA

L2. SE&CR Class R1 Tank 0-6-0T (ex-H/Dublo) (1968)

This loco shared a chassis block with the 2-6-0T but the tool for this was lost in 1990 and, as a result, few R1 tanks were produced after 1989.

-	GWR clear plastic body Sp Edn as display item - *?*	500	NA
W2204	**7420** LMS red - *74-89*	20	35
W2207	**1127** Southern green - *72-90*	25	35
W2207A	**1152** Southern green 156 made - *86-92*	55	115
W2410	**1047** Southern olive green Ltd Edn 71 with stand - *89-92*	110	685
W2205A	**31047** BRb black 210 made - *85-88*	60	115
W2206	**31337** BRb dark green - *?*	250	300
W2206A	**31128** BRb green 95 made - *85-88*	NPG	285
W2205	**31337** BRc black - *68-92*	35	50
W2205	**31340** BRc black - *68-71, 91-92*	27	45
W2206B	**31337** BRc black - *79-82*	20	35
W2206	**31337** BRc green - *68-88*	NPG	160
W2206	**31340** BRc green also W2206(G) - *69-71*	20	45
W2206A	**31340** BRc green also W2206(G) - *77-78*	20	45
W2201	**38** 'Esso' blue 336 made - *80*	45	120
W2201	as above but unfinished body * - *92-93*	NPG	NA
W2202	**56** 'NTG' (North Thames Gas) yellow c600 made - *79-80*	45	85
W2202	as above but unfinished body * - *92-93*	NPG	NA
W2201	**69** SE&CR green 241 made - *88-92*	140	200

SE&CR Class R1 0-6-0T [L2] (Vectis)

W2203	'Shell' silver - *78-83*	45	55
W2408	non-powered 24ct gold plated Jubilee tank Ltd Edn 149 with stand - *88-89*	NPG	285
W2500	***George Wrenn*** silver (body only) Ltd Edn 30 - *?*	NPG	45
W2501	as above but black - *?*	NPG	45
W2502	***Richard Wrenn*** black (body only) - *08?*	NPG	NPG
W2206C	chassis and motor only - *69-76*	NA	125

* Maurice Gunter's book suggests that these were not officially released by the factory but were unfinished bodies sold by Dapol and fitted to a chassis by the purchaser.

L3. LNER Class N2 Tank 0-6-2T (ex-H/Dublo) (1969)

This loco shared a chassis block with the 0-6-0T but with a rear bogie added. The tool for this was lost in 1990 and, as a result, few N2 tanks were produced after 1989.

W2280	**8230** GWR green 98 made - *88-89*	NPG	485
W2214	**2274** LMS plain red - *78-87*	40	85
W2215	**2385** LMS plain black - *72-87*	30	65
W2217	**9522** LNER light green - *69-89*	30	50
W2217A	**2690** LNER plain black (number on tank) c130 made - *82-84*	220	280
W2217A	**2690** LNER plain black (number on bunker) 43 made - *88*	450	600
W2292	**2752** SR olive green 25 made - *90*	NPG	590
W2292	**2752** SR malachite green 23 made - *89*	NPG	620
W2216A	**69496** BRb black 111 made * - *85-88*	NPG	340
W2216	**69550** BRc lined black - *69-92*	30	60
W2216	as above but no boiler bands - *84-85*	180	250
W2216	**69550** BRc maroon - *?*	500	620

* Two types of transfer used (with serifs and san-serifs).

L4. GWR 'Prairie' Class 45XX Tank 2-6-2T

W3001	**4528** GWR green - *not made*	NA	NA

L5. BR 4MT Standard Tank 2-6-4T (ex-H/Dublo) (1967)

W2246	**2085** CR lined blue - *79-89*	115	245
W2246	**2079** CR lined blue - *not made*	NA	NA
W2220	**8230** GWR green - *73-92*	65	120

BR Standard 4MT 2-6-4T in LMS livery [L5] (Special Auction Services)

W2219	**2679** LMS lined maroon - *72-90*	50	75
W2219	**2679** LMS maroon bright yellow lining c50 made - *91-92*	200	225
W2219	**2679** LMS unlined maroon c15 made - *91*	1000	1100
W2219	**2642** LMS maroon - *not made*	NA	NA
W2271	**9025** LNER lined green 144 made - *83-89*	250	500
W2271	**9025** LNER partially lined or unlined green 20 made - *92*	950	1000
W2245	**1927** SR lined green - *78-88,*	95	115
W2245	**1927** SR unlined green 20 made - *92*	NPG	700
W2279/5P	**80151** BRb lined black 518 made - *87-92*	155	200
W2307	**80079** BRb unlined black 59 made - *91-92*	NPG	710
W2406	**80120** BR lined black Ltd Edn 283 with stand - *88-89*	NPG	210
W2218A	**80064** BR lined black c560 made - *85-92*	90	145
W2218	**80079** BR lined black - *84*	40	145
W2270	**80135** BRc lined green c630 made - *83-92*	115	215
W2218	**80033** BRc lined black, numbers various shades of yellow - *67-92*	35	50
W2218	same but, gold+red transfers - *late 70s*	60	95
-	**2679** maroon specially inscribed with transfers Silver Jubilee 1977 Basildon Sp Edn 51 * (Basildon Development Corporation) - *77*	2500	3000

* Released in standard box with an explanatory sticker on the lid in three languages.

L6. GWR 'Castle 'Class 4-6-0 (ex-Hornby Dublo) (1967)

W2247	**7029 *Clun Castle*** Great()Western green (number on buffer beam) - *78-80, 83-92*	65	130
W2222	**7002 *Devizes Castle*** G()W green - *71-77,84*	50	70
W2222	**7002 *Devizes Castle*** G()W green improved lining - *82-84*	70	100
W2221	**5023 *Brecon Castle*** BRb experimental light green - *74-82*	100	150
W2221B	**5023 *Brecon Castle*** BRb experimental light green - *91-92*	95	180
W2223	**4082 *Windsor Castle*** BRb blue - *75-82*	60	95
W2400	**7007 *Great Western*** BRb green Ltd Edn 250 with stand 150 Anniversary headboard - *85-87*	80	290

Ex-GWR 'Castle' Class No.5023 Brecon Castle in experimental livery [L6] (Vectis)

W2417	**5034 *Corfe Castle*** BRb green Ltd Edn 132 with stand - *91-92*	NPG	485
W2247A	**7029 *Clun Castle*** BR green (number on smokebox door) 104 made - *86-87, 91-92*	NPG	365
W2284	**5090 *Neath Abbey*** BR green 139 made - *90-92*	NPG	495

W2221K	**4075 *Cardiff Castle*** BRc green kit - *69-70*	NA	745
W2221	**4075 *Cardiff Castle*** BRc green - *67-71, 76-89*	45	70
W2221	**4075 *Cardiff Castle*** BRc green in white temporary packaging - *67*	NA	500
W2221	**4075 *Ludlow Castle*** BRc green Cardiff Castle number (an error but about 50 made) - *69?*	110	245
W2221A	**7013 *Bristol Castle*** BRc green improved lining c350 made - *80-82, 88-89*	80	210

L7. LMS 'Royal Scot' Class 6P 4-6-0 (1981)

This was an un-rebuilt 'Royal Scot' with parallel boiler.

LMS Maroon

W2260	**6100 *Royal Scot*** (cat. error W3002) - *81-92*	135	200
W2260/5P	**6100 *Royal Scot*** 80 made - *86-88*	NPG	310
W2260A	**6141 *Caledonian*** Ltd Edn c250 made - *82-90*	180	330
W2274/5P	**6125 *Lancashire Witch*** c300 made - *84-92*	175	370

LMS Black

W2261	**6102 *Black Watch*** - *81-92*	130	210
W2261	**6102 *Black Watch*** 4 boiler bands - *?-91*	NPG	NPG
W2261/5P	**6102 *Black Watch*** 61 made - *86-87*	NPG	215
W2261A	**6160 *Queen Victoria's Rifleman*** lined c200 made - *82-83*	145	405
W2293	**6141 *Caledonian*** unlined gloss - *89-92*	NPG	965
W2293	**6141 *Caledonian*** unlined matt - *89-92*	NPG	965
W2403	**6146 *The Rifle Brigade*** Ltd Edn 243 with stand - *87-90*	260	355

BR Green

W2262	**46110 *Grenadier Guardsman*** BRb - *81-92*	160	250
W2262	'khaki model' (see notes) - *84-85*	280	320
W2262/5P	**46110 *Grenadier Guardsman*** BRb 86 made - *86-87*	NPG	560
W2262A	**46148 *The Manchester Regiment*** BR c200 made - *82-83*	NPG	455
W2262A/5P	**46148 *The Manchester Regiment*** BR 72 made - *89*	270	420
W2288	**46159 *The Royal Air Force*** BRb blue 112 made - *89-92*	185	388

Ex-LMS 'Royal Scot' Class No.46159 The Royal Air Force [L7] (Vectis)

W2298	**46100 *Royal Scot*** BR - *89-92*	190	600
W2273	**46159 *The Royal Air Force*** BRb blue c150 made - *83-92*	NPG	750

L8. 'Duchess' Class 8P 4-6-2 (ex-Hornby Dublo) (1969)

Large wheels on locos with 3-pole motors were introduced around 1986/87. In 1989 all 'Duchesses' received the larger driving wheels on both Mk1 and Mk2 chassis.

LMS Experimental Grey

W2294	**6234 *Duchess of Abercorn*** 151 made - *90-92*	NPG	680

LMS Maroon

W2242	**6247 *City of Liverpool*** - *78-92*	90	130
W2242	as above but larger wheels - *89-92*	220	350
W2242	**6247 *City of Liverpool*** extended lining on tender - *90-92*	245	300
W2242	**6247 *City of Liverpool*** no lining on tender 26 made - *89*	245	300
W2285	**6221 *Queen Elizabeth***, Mk1 chassis with large wheels, 243 made - *89-92*	NPG	380
W2401	**6223 *Princess Alice*** Ltd Edn 345 with stand Mk2 chassis, usually a 3-pole motor - *86-87*	230	365

LMS Black

W2227	**6254 *City of Stoke on Trent*** lined - *70-76, 79-89*	70	100
W2227	as above but Mk2 chassis - *90-92*	460	500
W2227A	**6256 *Sir William Stanier*** lined c500 made - *80-83, 88-92*	160	220

LMS 'Duchess' Class No.6229 Duchess of Hamilton [L8] (Vectis)

W2227AM2	**6256 *Sir William Stanier*** lined Mk2 chassis c100 made - *84-87*	NPG	825
W2241	**6229 *Duchess of Hamilton*** lined no smoke deflectors - *77-86*	85	115
W2241	**6229 *Duchess of Hamilton*** lined Mk1 but large wheels 10 made - *92*	950	1000
W2241M2	**6229 *Duchess of Hamilton*** 123 made Mk2 chassis - *87-92*	NPG	340
W2241A	**6225 *Duchess of Gloucester*** lined c150 made - *82-85*	145	375
W2241AM2	**6225 *Duchess of Gloucester*** Mk2 chassis 122 made - *86-92*	NPG	390

BR Black

W2286	**46252 *City of Leicester*** ex-LNWR black, 182 made - *89-92*	255	435
W2414	**46251 *City of Nottingham*** BRb ex-LNWR black, Ltd Edn 182 with stand - *90-92*	NPG	680
W2311	**46244 *City of Leeds*** BRb unlined, 69 made - *91-92*	NPG	830
W2311	**46244 *City of Leeds*** BRc unlined, very few made - *91-92*	NPG	NPG

BR Blue

W2229A	**46246 *City of Manchester*** BRb 360+ made - *80-84*	130	280
W2229	**46242 *City of Glasgow*** BRb - *73-81*	75	125
W2229	**46242 *City of Glasgow*** BRc - *not made*	NA	NA

BR Green

W2316	**46242 *City of Glasgow*** 22+ made - *92*	NPG	850
W2312	**46245 *City of London*** 40+ made, larger wheels - *92*	NPG	1200
W2313	**46234 *Duchess of Abercorn*** 10+ made - *92*	NPG	750
W2299	**46221 *Queen Elizabeth*** BRc 145 made - *91-92*	NPG	540
W2228	**46235 *City of Birmingham*** BRc - *73-91*	75	115
W2228M2	**46235 *City of Birmingham*** BRc Mk2 chassis c100 made - *84-86*	NPG	360
W2228A	**46241 *City of Edinburgh*** BRc 400+ made - *80-84*	115	230
W2228AM2	**46241 *City of Edinburgh*** BRc Mk2 chassis 87 made - *87-90*	NPG	290
W2314	**46256 *Sir William Stanier*** BRc 26+ made - *92*	NPG	785
W2405	**46231 *Duchess of Atholl*** BRc Ltd Edn 249 with stand - *88*	310	355

BRc maroon

W2226	**46245 *City of London*** - *69-80, 86-90*	60	120
W2226	**46245 *City of London***, lined tender - *?*	210	250
W2226M2	**46245 *City of London*** Mk2 chassis 118 made - *88-89*	145	760
W2226	**46245 *City of London/City of Birmingham*** factory error, different name on each side - *?*	310	350
W2226A	**46238 *City of Carlisle*** 322 made - *80-88*	185	270
W2226AM2	**46238 *City of Carlisle*** Mk2 chassis 168 made - *85-88*	NPG	380
W2315	**46242 *City of Glasgow*** 43+ made - *92*	NPG	600
W2264	**46229 *Duchess of Hamilton*** c300 made (many variations to this model) - *81-86*	350	375
W2264	**46229 *Duchess of Hamilton*** Mk1 chassis but large wheels, 10 made - *92*	250	365
W2304	**46244 *King George VI*** with optional ***Leeds City*** etched metal plates 166 made - *91-92*	NPG	440

L9. 'Coronation' Class 8P 4-6-2 (1983)

These used the Mk2 chassis with whitemetal loco and tender bodies produced by N&KC Keyser Ltd.

W2300	kit with R-T-R chassis - *not made*	NA	NA
W2301	**6221 *Queen Elizabeth*** LMS blue 200 made - *83-87*	700	810
W2301A	**6220 *Coronation*** LMS blue 80 made - *86-87*	NPG	1220

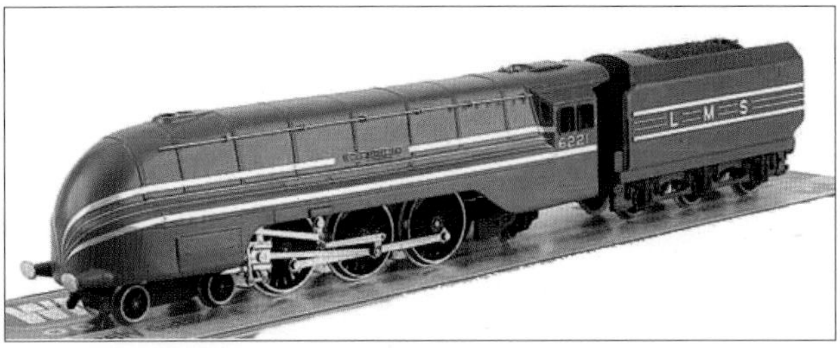

LMS 'Coronation' No.6221 Queen Elizabeth [L9] (Vectis)

W2302	6244 ***King George VI*** LMS maroon c200 made - *83-87*	NPG	550
W2302A	6228 ***Duchess of Rutland*** LMS maroon c100 made - *86-87*	NPG	910
W2303	6237 ***City of Bristol*** LMS unlined black c15 made by Dapol, sold unboxed - *c85*	850	NA

L10. Class A4 4-6-2 (ex-Hornby Dublo) (1969)

From 1989 all A4s received the larger driving wheels on both Mk1 and Mk2 chassis. The M2 versions listed below did not have a cab interior. Models with 3-pole motors and larger wheels are scarce.

W2283	4489 ***Woodcock*** LNER workshop grey Mk1 with large wheels 173 made - *89-92*	500	865
	LNER Green		
W2209	4482 ***Golden Eagle*** - *78-92*	80	115
W2209A	4495 ***Great Snipe*** c420 made - *80-92*	125	215
W2209AM2	4495 ***Great Snipe*** Mk2 chassis c60 made - *87-88*	380	810
W2413	4464 ***Bittern*** Ltd Edn 142 with stand - *90-92*	NPG	600
	LNER Garter Blue		
W2210AM2	4495 ***Golden Fleece*** Mk2 chassis, etched brass nameplate 118 made - *88-90*	195	300
W2212A	4498 ***Sir Nigel Gresley*** - *79-89*	70	120
W2212AM2	4498 ***Sir Nigel Gresley*** Mk2 chassis 170 made - *87-90*	NPG	340
W2310	4498 ***Sir Nigel Gresley*** (as preserved) 53 made - *91-92*	NPG	1000
W2212	7 ***Sir Nigel Gresley*** - *70-92*	60	75
W2295M2	4489 ***Dominion of Canada*** 90 made Mk2 chassis - *90-92*	NPG	850
W2404	4468 ***Mallard*** etched metal plates, Mk2 chassis but usually a 3-pole motor Ltd Edn 252 with stand - *88*	170	280
W2210	4468 ***Mallard*** - *79-85*	80	100
	LNER Wartime Black		
W2213	4903 ***Peregrine*** - *74-90*	70	120
W2213	as above but larger wheels - *90-92*	75	130

LNER Class A4 No.4900 Gannet in war-time black [L10] (Vectis)

W2213A	4900 ***Gannet*** - *80-89*	NPG	245
W2282	4463 ***Sparrow Hawk*** Mk1 with large wheels c100 made - *89-92*	NPG	585
	BR Green		
W2211A	60014 ***Silver Link*** c550 made - *80-92*	110	210
W2211	60022 ***Mallard*** BRc - *69-79, 83-91*	60	90
W2306	60010 ***Dominion of Canada*** BRc 76 made - *91-92*	NPG	480

L11. Streamlined Bulleid 'Pacific' 4-6-2 (1982)

Although a model of the smaller WC/BB light 'Pacifics', Wrenn also applied names/numbers from the larger, heavier Merchant Navy Class 'Pacifics. The late streamlined Bulleid 'Pacifics' have a satin sheen paintwork and are lined with a finer orange/black/orange lining (as opposed to a pale yellow lining). In 1990, some were released with old lining on the loco and new lining on the tender.

	Southern Green		
W2265A	21C155 ***Fighter Pilot*** Golden Arrow c550 made - *84-90*	205	400
W2265A	as above but with later lining - *90-92*	330	470
W2265AX	21C155 ***Fighter Pilot*** c250 made - *84-90*	NPG	400
W2265AX	as above but with later lining - *90-92*	300	440
W2266	21C103 ***Plymouth*** - *82-90*	150	275
W2266	as above but with later lining - *90-92*	220	335
W2222/5P	21C103 ***Plymouth*** - *?*	NPG	NPG
W2305	21C107 ***Wadebridge*** 93 made - *91-92*	NPG	685
W2407	21C111 ***Tavistock*** Ltd Edn 248 with stand - *88-89*	NPG	390
W2407	as above but with later lining - *90-91*	315	470
W2407	as above but Golden Arrow version - *?*	NPG	1420
W2276	21C101 ***Exeter*** 50 made - *89*	470	800
W2276/5P	21C101 ***Exeter*** Golden Arrow, 103 made - *86-89*	NPG	670
W2276X/5P	21C101 ***Exeter*** 185 made - *86-89*	NPG	560
W2278A	21C13 ***Blue Funnel Line*** 83 made - *88-89*	NPG	680
W2278A	as above but Golden Arrow version - *?*	800	1000
W2290	21C5 ***Canadian Pacific Line*** c60 made - *89-90*	500	750
W2290	as above but with later lining - *90-92*	620	770
W2290	21C5 ***Canadian Pacific Line*** unlined tender c40 made - *89*	NPG	635
	SR Wartime Black		
W2278	21C13 ***Blue Funnel Line*** 346 made - *85-91*	280	455
W2278	as above but with later lining - *90-92*	400	550
W2289	21C5 ***Canadian Pacific Line*** c100 made - *89-90*	NPG	540
W2289	as above but with later lining - *90-92*	500	750
	BR Blue		
W2267	35026 ***Lamport and Holt Line*** BRb (cat. error W3000) c850 made - *82-85*	250	325
W2268	34004 ***Yeovil*** BRb c230 made - *83-89*	NPG	460
W2268/5P	34004 ***Yeovil*** '5 Pole Motor' on box 57 made - *87-88*	NPG	545
W2411	35003 ***Royal Mail Line*** BRb Ltd Edn 248 with stand - *89-92*	280	510
W2411	as above but with later lining - *90-92*	500	700
	BR Green		
W2268A	34004 ***Yeovil*** BRb 165 made - *88-92*	355	670
W2291	34010 ***Sidmouth*** BRb 165 made - *89-90*	NPG	480
W2291	as above but with later lining 35 made - *90-92*	355	525
W2412	34020 ***Seaton*** BRb Ltd Edn 196 with stand - *89-92*	NPG	525
W2277	34066 ***Spitfire*** 140 made - *86-91*	310	545
W2266AX	34092 ***City of Wells*** BRc c650 made - *85-92*	NPG	330
W2266AX	as above but with later lining - *90-92*	265	410
W2266AX	'khaki model' (see notes) - *84-85*	380	500
W2267A	35026 ***Lamport and Holt Line*** BRc 82 made - *88-89*	280	730
W2268A	34004 ***Yeovil*** BRc, later lining, 12 made - *92*	1100	1200
W2275/5P	34065 ***Hurricane*** BRc, c300 made - *84-90*	280	510
W2275/5P	as above but with later lining - *90-92*	530	700
W2275/5P	'khaki model' (see notes) - *84-85*	NPG	400
W2416	34057 ***Biggin Hill*** BRc Ltd Edn 171 with stand - *90-92*	NPG	630
W2265	34051 ***Winston Churchill*** BRc - *82-90*	NPG	320

SR Class MN No.21C5 Canadian Pacific [L11] (Wallis & Wallis)

W2265	as above but with later lining - *90-92*	300	400
W2265	'khaki model' (see notes) - *84-85*	380	480
W2266A	34092 ***City of Wells*** BRc 'Golden Arrow' c800 made - *85-90*	235	345
W2266A	as above but with later lining - *90-92*	260	400
W2266A	'khaki model' (see notes) - *84-85*	380	480

* This was not a standard issue and may have been made to order or from a 'Golden Arrow' kit that was available.

L12. Rebuilt Bulleid 'Pacific' 4-6-2 (ex-HDublo) (1968)

Although a model of the smaller WC/BB light 'Pacifics', Wrenn also applied names/numbers from the larger, heavier Merchant Navy Class 'Pacifics. The late rebuilt Bulleid 'Pacifics' have a satin sheen paintwork and are lined with a finer orange/black/orange lining (as opposed to a pale yellow lining). On some, the green paint on the sides of the footplate runs the entire length of the loco instead of ending at the smoke deflectors (as was the case even with the earlier Hornby Dublo locomotives).

Southern Malachite Green

W2237	**21C109 *Lyme Regis*** - *73-90*	75	135
W2237	**21C109 *Lyme Regis*** transfers more orange 58 made - *91-92*	950	1000
W2237	**21C109 *Lyme Regis*** SR blue over green - *?*	265	400

BRb Black

W2309	**34036 *Westward Ho*** unlined, beware of repaints, no smoke deflectors, 34 made - *91-92*	560	850

BRc Green

W2238	**35015 *Rotterdam Lloyd*** planned for '76 but replaced by *Clan Line*	NA	NA
W2269	**34053 *Hurricane*** 'Golden Arrow' planned for '83 - *not made* **	NA	NA
W2235	**34005 *Barnstaple*** - *68-92*	70	110
W2236	**34042 *Dorchester*** - *70-92*	80	110
W2236A	**34016 *Bodmin*** black nameplates - *80*	NPG	395
W2236A	**34016 *Bodmin*** red nameplates - *80-88*	NPG	345
W2236A	'khaki model' (see notes) - *84-85*	300	400
W2238	**35028 *Clan Line*** - *77-88*	80	130
W2238	**35028 *Clan Line*** etched brass nameplates - *88-92*	NPG	180

BR MN Class No.35028 Clan Line [L12] (Special Auction Services)

W2239	**34028 *Eddystone*** - *79-88, 92*	110	170
W2239	as above but centred nameplate - *?*	NPG	175
W2269	**34053 *Sir Keith Park*** 'Golden Arrow' 512 made - *84-92*	185	355
W2269	as above but with later lining - *90-92*	270	400
W2269X	**34053 *Sir Keith Park*** 270 made - *83-92*	250	360
W2269X	'khaki model' (see notes) - *84-85*	400	550
W2287	**34036 *Westward Ho*** 280 made - *89-92- 90-92*	NPG	335
W2296	**34021 *Dartmoor*** gold+black lining * 141 made - *90-92*	NPG	500
W2296	**34021 *Dartmoor*** orange-red +black lining* - *92*	110	400
W2297	**35010 *Blue Star Line*** 152 made - *90-92*	325	425
W2309	**34036 *Westward Ho*** unlined 280 made - *89-92*	NPG	1350
W2402	**34090 *Sir Eustace Missenden*** Ltd Edn 250 with stand - *87-88*	250	370
W2415	**34052 *Lord Dowding*** Ltd Edn 182 with stand - *90-92*	NPG	410

* A total of 300 of both types made but how many of each is not known. ** This was demonstrated at the 1983 Toy Fair before it was discovered that *Hurricane* was not rebuilt!.

L13. Class 8F 2-8-0 (ex-Hornby Dublo) (1967)

W2225	**8042** LMS plain black - *70-80*	45	65
W2225A	**8233** LMS plain black, transfers gold shaded red, c400 * made - *80-89*	65	135
W2225A	as above but unshaded yellow transfers	90	155
?	**8431** LMS plain black - *84-88*	330	500
W2272	**8016** LMS maroon c270 made - *83-92*	NPG	260
W2281	**302** WD grey 207 made - *88-92*	125	550

War department Class 8F No.302 [L13] (Wallis & Wallis)

W2281	as above but grey front end and smaller transfers, 8 made - *92*	900	1000
W2240	**3144** LNER plain black, gold transfers shaded red - *77-79*	30	125
W2240	as above but yellow transfers - *78-80*	50	95
W2224	**48109** BR plain black - *67-69*	65	200
W2224A	**48290** BR plain black c450 made - *83-92*	85	170
W2224	**48073** BRc plain black - *67-81*	40	70
W2409	**48102** BRc plain black Ltd Edn 151 with stand - *89-91*	NPG	320
W2308	**48290** BRc plain green 58 * made - *91-92*	NPG	870
W2308	as above but numbered **48102** - *91-92*	NPG	NPG

* this figure includes the version below it.

L14. Class 08 0-6-0DS (ex-Hornby Dublo) (1975)

This model's body was retooled by Wrenn as Meccano Ltd had altered the original tool to produce their 0-4-0 diesel shunter. The two bodies differ in that the Wrenn one has no manufacturer's name inside. A quantity of bodies were taken over by Dapol and these may account for a number of unusual variations, including part finished ones, which turn up.

W2233	**7124** LMS black - *76-88*	40	65
W2233	**7124** LMS green - *92*	260	300
W2232	**D3464** BRe blue - *75-90*	25	40
W2232	**D3523** BRe blue - *86*	280	60
W2232NP	**D3523** BRe blue non-powered 55 made - *82-85*	100	320
W2231	**D3763** BRc green - *75-90*	35	40
W2231	**D3768** BRc green - *86*	125	200
W2231NP	**D3768** BRc green non-powered 57 made - *82-85*	250	375
W2232A	**08 762** BRe blue - *made?*	NPG	NPG
W2234	**72** 'NCB' red * - *78-80*	40	70
W2243	**'Dunlop'** yellow c400 made - *80*	55	105
W2231NP	black non-powered - *82?*	250	370

* Some have moulded red plastic bodies while others have black ones sprayed red.

L15. Class 20 Diesel Bo-Bo (ex-Hornby Dublo) (1977)

It seems that the Hornby Dublo body tool was not available and a new tool had to be made for this model. This would explain why it was a late addition to the range. In the 1980s, press-fitted bogie side-frames were gradually replaced by screw fitted ones.

W2230	**8003** BRe blue - *77-89*	35	55

BR Class 20 diesel No.D8017 [L15] (Vectis)

W2230NP	**8003** BRe blue non-powered - *?*	40	85
W2230NP	**D8010** BRc green non-powered 323 made - *80-87*	75	165
W2230BNP	**D8015** BRe blue non-powered 415 made - *80-88*	85	125
W2230BNP	**D8015** BRe blue non-powered - *?*	NPG	80
W2230	**D8017** BRc green - *77-89*	30	45
W2230NP	**D8017** BRc green - *?*	80	135
W2230	**20 008** BRe blue - *88-89*	45	70
W2230B	as above but different number on box	145	225
W2230NP	**20 008** BRe blue non-powered - *?*	*NPG*	125
W2230RF	**20 132** BReLL grey early Railfreight livery 116 made - *88-89*	130	320

L16. Pullman EMU 'Brighton Belle' (1980)

Tooling subsequently bought by Mordvale in 2001.

Blue + Grey

W3005	**S291S** BRe dummy car 9 made - *80-81*	NA	NPG
W3004/5	**S290S+S291S** * BRe 2-car set - *80-92*	200	230
	as above but sold in 2 loco boxes - *91-92*	NA	450
W3004/5A	**S290S+S291S** * BRe 2-car set in 2 loco boxes 150 Years 1841-1991 Ltd Edn 11 made - *92*	500	750
W3006/7A	as above but wrong catalogue number	NA	1500

Brown + Cream

W3007	**91** dummy car sold singly 40 made - *80-81*	NA	350
W3006/7	**3052 (90+91)** 2-car set brown tables - *79-85*	200	250

BR 'Brighton Belle' Pullman power cars [L16] (Vectis)

W3006/7	as above but white tables - *86-91*	255	310
W3006/7	same packed in 2 loco boxes - *91-92*	NA	535
W3006/7	same packed in 2 coach boxes - *92*	NA	320
W3006/7A	**3051 (88+89)** 2-car set, 246 made - *80-83*	380	575
W3006/7A	same packed in 2 coach boxes - *92*	NA	500
W3006/7A	**3051 (90+89)** 2-car set in 2 loco boxes, '150 years 1841-1991', Ltd Edn 40 - *91-92*	500	750

* Some of the blue and grey power cars were differently numbered on each side with S290S on one side and S291S on the other.

L17. Class 501 EMU (ex-Hornby Dublo)

W3008/9	**65320** BRc maroon - *not made*	NA	NA
W3010/11	**S66238?** BRc green - *not made*	NA	NA

COACHES

The Wrenn range of coaches was limited to those that could be produced from the former Hornby-Dublo tools for the Pullman cars. Those produced included some impossible liveries, namely those of the LMS and the Southern Railway. However, there was a case for Pullman cars in both crimson lake and in green livery. The former were cars run on both the Metropolitan line and the SE&CR. The latter were the result of Pullman cars being painted green by BR to run as restaurant cars on certain central and eastern section trains on the Southern Region.

In the mid 1980s detailing changed to tampo printing and at this time the coat-of arms on the brown and cream Pullmans changed to full colour.

There had been the intention to produce some of the tinplate coaches and the 'Stove' was even illustrated in one catalogue but these were not proceeded with.

Cat No.	Company, Number, Colour, Dates	£	£

C1a. Pullman Cars (ex-Hornby Dublo) (1976)

These were based on 1928 vehicles built for LNER use. The prototypes were transferred to steam-hauled services on the Southern Region in the 1950s. bt = brown tables. wt = white tables. White table versions tend to attract a higher price and so it is important to be sure that they have been painted white in the factory. Tooling subsequently bought by Mordvale in 2001.

Pullman Brown + Cream

W6001	No 73 2nd bt - *77-86*	10	17
W6001	No 73 2nd wt c560 made - *86-92*	22	35
W6001C	No.83 parlour car Ltd Edn 350 - *91-92?*	55	80
W6001AG	*Agatha* parlour c600 made wt - *86-92*	30	74
W6001S	*Sheila* parlour c150 made wt - *91-92*	85	140
W6001U	*Ursula* parlour c110 made wt - *90-91*	95	160
W6002	*Aries* 1st bt - *79-86*	8	15
W6002	*Aries* 1st wt c570 made - *86-92*	20	35
W6002B	*Belinda* 1st kitchen 150 made wt - *91-92*	100	160
W6102E	*Evadne* 1st kitchen wt Ltd Edn 84 sold - *90*	NPG	260

Limited edition Pullman car Evadne [C1a] (Vectis)

W6002E	*Evadne* 1st kitchen wt * 6 sold - *92*	NPG	435
W6102C	No.83 parlour wt Ltd Edn 88 sold - *90*	70	175
W6001C	No.83 parlour wt * 13 sold - *92*	NPG	220
W6002C	*Carina* 1st kitchen 100 made wt - *91-92*	65	250

'Brighton Belle' Brown + Cream

W6001A	No.87 parlour 3052 c330 made bt - *82-86*	30	50
W6001A	No.87 parlour 3052 c500 made wt - *86-92*	30	60
W6001/B	No.86 parlour 3051 bt - *83-86*	25	45
W6001/B	No.86 parlour 3051 wt - *86-92*	30	60
W6002A	*Audrey* 1st 3052 bt - *79-86*	30	45
W6002A	*Audrey* 1st 3052 c650 made wt - *86-92*	60	80
W6002A	*Vera* 1st 3052 bt - *79-81*	32	50
W6002V	*Vera* 1st 3052 c360 made bt - *81-86*	NPG	NPG
W6002V	*Vera* 1st 3052 c600 made wt - *86-92*	44	90
W6002/D	*Doris* 1st 3051 c270 made bt - *82-86*	30	90
W6002/D	*Doris* 1st 3051 c460 made wt - *86-92*	38	88
W6002/H	*Hazel* 1st 3051 c230 made bt - *82-86*	55	90
W6002/H	*Hazel* 1st 3051 c500 made wt - *86-92*	NPG	70

'Golden Arrow' Brown + Cream

W6012	*Pegasus* (+ alternative name transfers) 1st c750 made bt - *82-86*	20	42
W6012	*Pegasus* (+ alternative name transfers) 1st c325 made wt - *86-92*	33	75
-	*Perseus* transfer on the above - *86-84*	30	NA
-	*Phoenix* transfer on the above - *86-84*	30	NA
-	*Cygnus* transfer on the above - *86-84*	30	NA
W6012A	*Cecilia* 1st 400 made wt - *85-92*	32	100
W6012B	*Aries* 1st 270 made wt - *86-92*	18	110
W6012C	*Cygnus* 1st parlour c100 made wt - *91-92*	NPG	185
W6105P	*Phoenix* Ltd Edn 60 - *02*	56	150

BR Blue + Grey

W6004	S302S 2nd wt - *76-81, 87-92*	25	35
	as above but no number **	NPG	NPG

'Brighton Belle' Blue + Grey

W6004A	S287S parlour car wt - *76-81, 85-92*	35	42
W6004A	S302S parlour car wt - *76-92*	100	120

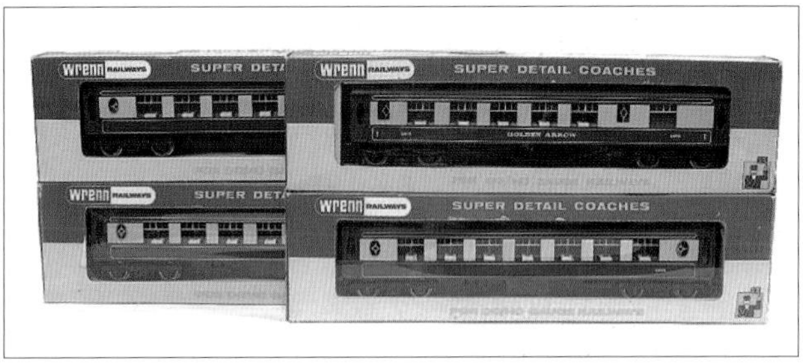

Pullman cars in blue & grey livery [C1a] (Vectis)

W6005A	S280S 1st wt - *79-81, 90-92*	40	70
W6005A	S284S 1st wt - *79-81, 90-92*	33	50

'Golden Arrow' Blue + Grey

W6005	S301S 1st wt - *79-80, 90-92*	18	25
W6005	S280S 1st wt - *79-80, 90-92*	100	150

Non-Authentic Liveries

W6007	**SR** 2523 green 2nd wt - *78-84*	22	40
W6008	**SR** 1245 green 1st wt - *78-84*	20	26
W6010	**LMS** 3459 red 2nd class wt - *78-84*	18	32
W6011	**LMS** 1046 red 1st class wt - *78-84*	25	36

* These were limited edition coaches which did not sell and so were re-boxed and sold as non-limited editions. ** Possibly made from unfinished body at end of production.

C1b. Pullman Brake 2nd (ex-Hornby Dublo) (1972)

These were based on 1928 vehicles built for LNER use. The prototypes were transferred to steam-hauled services on the Southern Region in the 1950s. bt = brown tables. wt = white tables. White table versions tend to attract a higher price and so it is important to be sure that they have been painted white in the factory. Tooling subsequently bought by Mordvale in 2001.

Pullman

W6000	No 77 brown + cream bt - *72-86*	11	17
W6000	No 77 brown + cream wt, c600 made - *86-92*	17	24
W6000A	No 79 brown + cream wt, 390 made wt - *88-?*	15	60
W6003	S308S blue+grey wt - *76-80, 90-92*	15	20
	as above but no number	NPG	NPG

Pullman car in ficticious SR green livery [C1b] (Vectis)

Non-Authentic Liveries

W6006	**SR** 1708 green wt - *78-84*	23	34
W6009	**LMS** 2370 red wt - *78-84*	22	33

C2. BR Mk1 Coaches (ex-Hornby Dublo)

W6006	**BR** maroon+cream corridor composite - *not made*	NA	NA
W6007	**BR** maroon+cream corridor brake 2nd - *not made*	NA	NA
W6008	**BR** maroon corridor comp - *not made*	NA	NA
W6009	**BR** maroon corridor brake 2nd - *not made*	NA	NA
W6010	**BR** green suburban brake 2nd - *not made*	NA	NA
W6011	**BR** green suburban comp - *not made*	NA	NA
W6012	**BR** maroon suburban brake 2nd - *not made*	NA	NA
W6013	**BR** maroon suburban comp - *not made*	NA	NA
W5014	**BR** maroon M32598 stove 6-wheel brake - *not made*	NA	NA

WAGONS

A large range of wagons was produced and these may be quickly distinguished from Hornby Dublo ones by their tension-lock couplings.

Special Edition wagon bodies released through the Wrenn Railways Collectors Club were supplied by Dapol and appear in the Dapol wagon listing.

Wrenn wagons sold after 1993 were produced by Dapol in their factory in Llangollen and will be found in the Dapol section of this catalogue. Those numbered with a 'WR1' prefix were sold in Wrenn boxes but all others had Dapol packaging.

Wagons made by the 'new' G&R Wrenn, from 2001, are included here.

Great care should be taken in buying supposedly rare models as they may have been assembled in the Dapol factory from leftover parts or by others.

Cat No.	Company, Number, Colour, Dates	£	£

W1. 'Lowmac' Machine Wagon (ex-Hornby Dublo) (1970)

Tooling subsequently bought by Mordvale in 2001.

W4652P	**'Auto Distributors'** BR brown + Minix Ford Anglia car and caravan - *70-79*	67	155
W4652A	**GW** 43260 grey 'Loriot' dark axle-hangers - *81- 90*	12	20
W4652A	as above but nickel axle-hangers * - *90-92*	7	11
W4652A	**GW** 43260 brown 'Loriot' dark axle-hangers - *81- 90*	41	75
W4652A	as above but nickel axle-hangers - *90-92*	130	200
W4652	**BR** B904631 brown 'Lowmac WBB' dark axle-hangers - *73-92*	5	11
W4652	as above but nickel axle-hangers - *82-92*	30	30
W5103	**BR** B904631 brown dark axle hangers + Cement body load 174 made - *89-92*	NPG	140
W5103	**BR** B904631 brown bright axle hangers + Cement body load 98 made - *89-92*	115	175
W5512	plain brown wagon with red Wrenn Series 152 racing car Ltd Edn - *05*	NPG	120
W5512	as above but green car Ltd Edn 20 - *06*	NPG	120
W5512	as above but blue car Ltd Edn 20 - *06*	75	120
W5512	as above but yellow car Ltd Edn 20 - *08?*	NPG	NPG
W5512	as above but black car Ltd Edn 20 - *08?*	NPG	NPG
W5515	as above but gold car Ltd Edn 50 - *07*	NPG	95
W5514	as above but silver car Ltd Edn 25 - *08?*	NPG	NPG

* The last ones made were brown mouldings painted grey.

'Lowmac's' with racing cars [W1] (G8R Wrenn)

W2. Low-sided Wagon (1980)

W5059	**'Auto Spares'** 115 red-brown load of 4 large tyres - *80*	11	22
W5060	**BR** B459325 grey - *80-81*	7	13
W5060	**BR** B459325 grey Ltd Edn 10 - *02-?*	25	35

W3. 5-plank Open Wagon (ex-Hornby Dublo) (1968)

W5067	**'Amos Benbow'** 3 grey + coal - *81-90*	10	21
W5043	**'Ayr Co-op'** 67 black - *77-87*	6	15
W5500	**'Barnsley Collieries'** 350 brown + load Ltd Edn 314 - *89-91*	13	105
W5109	overrun of W5500 (above) - *92*	NPG	300
W5074	**'Bassetts'** painted dark grey + coal 696 made - *82-88*	8	25
W5000	**'J Bly'** dark green + coal - *71-74, 86-92*	7	14
W5096	'A **Bramley'** 6 brown + coal 413 made- *88-92*	NPG	65
W5096	As above but black shading missing ** - *92*	65	95
W5069	**'British Soda'** 14 red + grey load 679 made - *82-88*	10	37
W5069	as above but white load ** - *89-92*	35	50
W5069	**'British Soda'** 14 red + grey load Ltd Edn 14 - *02-?*	NPG	35
W5069	**'British Soda'** 14 red + white load 10 made - *02-?*	NPG	35
W5069	**'British Soda'** 14 red + black load brown top edge to wagon sides Ltd Edn - *02-08*	NPG	25
W5107	**'Consolidated Fisheries'** 76 grey + load 140 made - *91-92*	NPG	135
W5107	**'Consolidated Fisheries'** 76 grey, brown top edge to wagon sides Ltd Edn 40 - *02-?*	NPG	135

5-plank wagon 'Cranston' [W3] (Oakleafomx)

W5048	**'Cranston'** 347 red-brown + coal - *78-83*	5	9
W5008	**'S Harris'** 14 black + coal - *71-92*	8	16
W4635P	**'Higgs'** 85 beige + coal, cream and thick red letters - *70-71*	NPG	19
W4635P	same with white and thin red letters - *70-71*	30	45
W4635P	**'Higgs'** 85 dark brown + coal - *69-71*	9	18
W4635P	**'Higgs'** 85 dark grey + coal - *69-71*	5	10
W4635P	**'Higgs'** 85 light grey + coal - *69-85, 92*	12	18
W4635P	**'Higgs'** 85 grey + coal, also W4635 - *73-80*	12	18

W4635P	**'Higgs'** 85 blue-green + coal - *70-80*	27	38
W4635	**'Higgs'** 85 grey - *02-08?*	NPG	25
W4660P	**'Twining'** 95 beige - *68-71*	3	16
W4660P	**'Twining'** 95 red-brown - *68-72* *	4	11
W5075	**'Twining'** 95 dark brown shaded black letters + coal 759 made *82-92*	NPG	11
W5075	as above but shading missing **- *82-92*	50	75
W5097	**'Webster'** 47 grey 378 made - *88-92*	10	40
W5032	**LMS** 314159 red + white load - *?*	NPG	NPG
W5032	**LMS** 24361 red + white load - *74-77*	6	10
W5032	**LMS** 24361 orange-red + black load - *74-77*	12	18
W?	**BR** B478038 grey - *?*	NPG	NPG

*pre-production model seen at 1968 Toy Fair. **production figures included in the figure above.

W4. High-sided Wagon (1991)

This was the body of the gunpowder van without a roof.

W5106	**'Hughes Minerals'** 29 grey 129 made - *91-92*	NPG	234

W5. Steel-sided Wagon (ex-Hornby Dublo) (1973)

Tool bought in 1972.

W5073	**'BAC'** 4253 red-brown 461 made - *82-92*	10	45
W5073	**'BAC'** 4253 red-brown Ltd Edn 16 - *02-?*	10	45

Steel-sided wagon - 'NTG' [W5] (Special Auction services)

W5034	**'NTG'** B486863 yellow + load - *74-79*	5	14
W5034	**'NTG'** B486863 buff + load - *73-80*	7	13
W5034	as above with white edged transfers - *80*	NPG	9
W4660	**'Twining'** B486865 brown - *not made*	NA	NA
W4640	**BR** B466865 brown - *73-92*	5	10
W4640	**BR** B466865 red-brown - *73-92*	4	13
W4640	**BR** B466865 buff - *73-80*	17	23
W4640	**BR**? brown Ltd Edn 13 - *07?*	NPG	30

W6. 16T Mineral Wagon (ex-Hornby Dublo) (1974)

Tool bought in 1972.

W5051A	'Esso' blue or silver 357 made - *88-89*	14	54
W5026	**'Park Ward'** 7 brown - *74-80, 87*	4	8
W5051	**'Shell'** silver - *78-79*	9	18
W5029	**GW** 110265 dark grey - *74-78*	5	10
W5029L	**GW** 110265 dark grey + mineral load - *74-79*	6	11
W5029	**GW** 110265 light grey - *87-88*	55	85
W4655	**BR** B54884 grey - *78-92*	5	11
W4655	**BR** B54884 grey - *02-08*	NPG	25
W4640	**BR** B54884 grey + coal - *79-82*	5	11
W4655A	**BR** B550200 brown * - *81-88*	6	14
W4655A	**BR** B54884 brown 260 made - *88-92*	9	24

* Early examples were grey mouldings painted brown.

W7. 21T Hopper Wagon (ex-Hornby Dublo) (1973)

Tools bought in 1972. Tooling subsequently bought by Mordvale in 2001.

W5088	**'British Gas'** 142 dark grey 488 made - *87-92*	10	52
W5098	**'British Steel'** 28 brown 358 made - *88-92*	15	46
W5068	**'Charringtons'** B421818K grey 696 made - *82-90*	12	50
W5036	**'Hoveringham'** 230 red-brown - *83*	8	18
W5036	as above but no number - *80-86*	15	19
W5036	**'Hoveringham'** 230 red-brown - *02-08*	NPG	35
W5512	**'Lawrence'** light green board Ltd Edn 13 - *07*	NPG	70
W5512	**'Lawrence'** dark green board Ltd Edn 27 - *07*	NPG	70
W5035	**'NCB'** 128 dark grey + load - *86-92*	10	13
W5035	**'NCB'** 128 dark grey - *02-08*	NPG	35
W5035	**'Simpson'** 72 light grey - *not made*	NA	NA
W5082	**'Sykes'** 7 light grey 451 made - *87-90*	17	40
W5056	**'Tarmac'** M82 beige - *79-92*	10	14

Hopper wagon - 'Tarmac' [W7] (S&D Models)

W5056	**'Tarmac'** M82 beige - *02-08*	NPG	35
W5502	**'Weaver Transport'** 152 brown + load Ltd Edn 277 - *89-91*	NPG	125
W5111	overrun of W5502 (above) - *92*	140	225
W5079	**NE** 174369 dark grey 679 made- *83-92*	12	32
W5079	**NE** 174369 light grey * - *83-92*	13	35
W4644	**BR** B413021 light grey - *81-92*	NPG	36
W4644	**BR** B413021 dark grey - *81-92*	NPG	54
W4644	**BR** B414029 light grey - *73,78-92*	10	15
W4644L	**BR** B414029 light grey + load - *78-83*	13	20

* production figures included in the figure above.

W8a. Hopper Wagon (grain wagon body)

W5078	**'Wilton Quarry'** 95 red-brown + load - *not made*	NA	NA

W8b. Grain Wagon (ex-Hornby Dublo) (1973)

Tools bought in 1972.

W5071	**'Bass Charrington'** 24 maroon 296 made - *82-83*	9	32
W5020	**'Kelloggs'** B885040 grey - *74-76*	5	11
W5020	as above but no numbers - *74-84*	12	18
W5045	**'Quaker Oats'** red-brown - *77-80*	5	17
W4625	**BR** B885040 light grey - *73-92*	6	10

W9a. Ore Wagon ('Presflo' body) (1969)

This was the 'Presflo' without its top and is thought to be fictitious.

W5025	'Wm.**Carter**' 7 black + gravel - *74-81*	5	8
W4600P	**'Clay Cross'** light grey, grey board - *69-70*	5	10
W4600P	as above but orange board - *70-?*	12	18
W5503	**'Clay Cross'** black Ltd Edn 175 - *90-91*	18	95
W5112	overrun of W5530 (above) - *92*	140	225
W5015	**'Hinchley'** 14 blue + chalk - *74-80*	5	9
W5015	**'Hinchley'** 14 grey + chalk - *?*	NPG	NPG
W5017	**'Pycroft Granite'** black, black boards + granite load - *74-83*	5	11
W5017	**'Pycroft Granite'** light green, green boards + granite load - *73-80*	5	11
W5006	**'Southdown'** 17 grey, green board + chalk load - *71-80, 88-90*	17	25
W5006	same but green label on grey boards *71-82*	4	8
W5006	same but yellow label 200 made - *88*	7	17
W5006	**'Southdown'** 17 blue + chalk - *?*	NPG	NPG

W9b. 'Presflo' Wagon (ex-Hornby Dublo) (1968)

YbG = yellow background on grey plastic boards, YbB = yellow background on blue plastic boards, BbB = blue background on blue plastic boards.

W4626P	**'Blue Circle'** dark grey YbG - *68-71*	13	20
W4626P	as above but grey BbB - *70-71*	17	25
W4626P	as above but pale grey YbG - *68-69*	6	11
W4626P	as above but dark blue-green YbB - *68-69*	17	25

'Presflo' - 'Blue Circle Cement' [W9b] (Oakleafomx)

Salt van - 'Saxa Salt' [W11] (Oakleasomx)

W4626P	as above but dark blue BbB - *70-71*	22	35
W5016	**'Blue Circle'** pl. yellow paper labels - *73-80*	7	15
W5016	as above but darker colours on boards	7	15
W5016	**'Blue Circle'** dark yellow paper labels - *74-82*	7	15
W5016	**'Blue Circle'** painted bright yellow with tampo detail 251 made - *90-92*	NPG	45
W5072	**'Blue Circle'** grey 'Bulk Loaded' - *82-89*	11	20
W5072	**'Blue Circle'** bright yellow 'Bulk Loaded' - *90-92*	NPG	85
W5084	**'Bulk Cement'** 52 red-brown c550 made - *87-92*	9	43
W5084	**'Bulk Cement'** 52 buff c20 made - *92*	115	175
W4627P	**'Cerebos Salt'** blue-black also W4627 - *68-71* *	27	40
W4626P	as above but dark blue-green	NPG	13
W4626P	as above but grey	6	11
W5021	**'Cerebos Salt'** red - *74-79*	5	14
W5021	as above but tampo printed - *86-92*	NPG	50
W5092	**'Ready Mix'** 68 grey 413 made - *88-91*	13	41
W5080	**'Rugby'** 17 grey - *85-92*	12	42
W5080	**'Rugby'** 17 light grey - *85-92*	37	50
W5005	**'Tunnel Bulk'** grey, red board paper label - *71-92*	6	9
W5005	the same tampo printed - *85-92*	10	28
W5005	**'Tunnel Bulk'** red - *?*	NPG	NPG
W5081	**BR** 72 brown 'Presflo' - *86-92*	9	28
W5005X	grey 20T 12-17 - *72-76*	5	12
W5005X	same but no markings at all - *72-76*	20	30
W5510	72 black 'Presflo' Ltd Edn 92 - *02*	NPG	75

* pre-production model seen at 1968 Toy Fair.

W10. 'Prestwin' Silo Wagon (ex-Hornby Dublo) (1971)

Tooling subsequently bought by Mordvale in 2001.

W4658	**'Fisons'** B873000 red-brown - *71-84*	5	11
W4658X	**BR** B873000 brown-red 466 made - *87-92*	8	35

W11. Salt Van (ex-Hornby Dublo) (1968)

This was the old salt wagon with a pitched roof.

W5024	'Jas. **Colman'** 15 pale green, white lettering - *74-79*	NPG	48
W5024	same with black lettering - *74-79*	8	15
W5024	'Jas. **Colman'** 15 yellow - *73-80*	7	32
W5024	'Jas. **Colman'** 15 pale yellow - *73-80*	NPG	32
W5070	**'DCL'** 87 blue mouldings painted grey 388 made - *82-83*	17	36
W5070	**'DCL'** 87 grey mouldings 200 made - *84-90*	17	36
W5101	**'ICI Bulk Salt'** 25 light grey 377 made - *89-91*	23	68
W5101	same but brown body painted grey * - *91-92*	23	68
W4665P	**'Saxa Salt'** 248 dark orange - *68-92*	5	12
W4665P	**'Saxa Salt'** 248 light orange - *68-71*	5	12
W4665P	**'Saxa Salt'** 248 pale lemon - *73-81*	6	9
W4665P	**'Saxa Salt'** 248 pale lemon (darker red) - *73-80*	10	15
W4666	**'Sifta Table Salt'** 125 blue - *71-77*	6	15
W4666	as above but bright blue - *73-77*	NPG	30
W5018	**'Star Salt'** 105 red, white letters - *74-84*	5	12
W5018	**'Star Salt'** 105 red, black letters - *74-80*	5	20

* production figures included in the above figure.

W12. Short Tank Wagon (1980)

W5501	**'British Sugar'** 23 red Ltd Edn 284 - *89-91*	30	70
W5110	overrun of W5501 (above) - *92*	140	225
W5104	**'Bulk Flour'** 20 white 187 made - *90-92*	NPG	100
W5039	**'Esso'** 3300 dark blue green star and writing - *80-90*	13	27
W5039	as above but yellow star and writing - *80-90*	13	48
W5042	**'Esso'** silver large emblems - *80-81*	12	24
W5042	as above small emblems 66 made - *91-92*	80	125
W5093	**'ICI Chlorine'** 163 black 520 made - *88-92*	36	50
W5041	**'Mobil'** red - *80-92*	13	30
W5041	**'Mobil'** red - *02-08*	NPG	40
W5076	**'Power Ethyl'** green 576 made - *82-91*	11	33
W5062	**'Royal Daylight'** black - *81-92*	19	34
W5040	**'Shell'** yellow small star 896 made - *80-90*	11	20
W5040	as above but large star * - *80-90*	30	45
W5040	as above but with white background to the star * - *90-92*	26	47
W5040	**'Shell'** yellow, white missing from printing - *80-86*	NPG	NPG
W5040	as above but with white background to Shell - *02-08*	NPG	45
W5061	**'Shell BP'** Motor Spirit 1265 stone - *80-84*	13	25
W5077	**'United Molasses'** 18 purple-brown 487 made - *82-91*	18	40
W5517	**'Wrenn'** silver Ltd Edn 75 - *07*	NPG	80

* production figures included in the figure quoted above.

W13. 6-wheel Tank Wagon (ex-Hornby Dublo) (1970)

Tooling subsequently bought by Mordvale in 2001.

W5086	**'Co-op'** 172 white 650 made - *87-92*	26	50
W5044	**'Double Diamond'** red-brown - *77-78*	9	19
W5095	**'Express Dairies'** 50 blue 469 made - *88-92*	45	57
W5003	**'Guinness'** silver paper label - *71-81*	8	15

6-wheeled tank wagon - 'Guinness' [W13] (Oakleafomx)

W5003	same tampo printed - *90-92*	NPG	70
W5023	**'Milk Marketing Board'** blue - *74-92*	10	20
W5511	as above but matt black Ltd Edn 50 - *03*	NPG	60
W5511	as above but satin black Ltd Edn 50 - *03*	NPG	60
W5013	**'St Ivel'** white+orange - *73-83*	7	16

W5013	**'St Ivel'** white+red-brown - *80-86*	22	35
W5013	**'St Ivel Gold'** white - *91-92*	32	74
W5066	**'Skol Lager'** red 675 made - *81-82*	16	31
W4657	**'UD'** white also W4657P - *70-92*	11	16
W5091	**'Unigate'** 220 white 427 made - *88-92*	35	57

W14. **Gunpowder Van** (ex-Hornby Dublo) (1968)

W5009	**'BSA'** B887002 red brown - *71-75*	9	16
W5009	**'BSA'** B887002 brown - *71-75*	9	16
W4313P	**'Standard Fireworks'** B887002 brown - *68-70* *	22	38
W4313	as above but no letter shading	50	75
W4313	as above but cream lettered name	50	75
W4313	as above but name missing	20	30
W4313P	**'Standard Fireworks'** B887002 dark green - *68*	18	42
W5057	**GW** W105780 black red X - *79-92*	13	18
W4313	**BR** B887002 brown - *68?*	37	55
W5102	**BR** B887002 brown 192 made - *90-91*	NPG	120
W5102	**BR** W105780 brown only about 5 made - *91*	335	500

* pre-production model seen at 1968 Toy Fair.

W15. **Cattle Wagon** (ex-Hornby Dublo) (1971)

Tools bought in 1972.

W5504	**'Manor Farm'** brown 50 Ltd Edn 226 - *90-91*	34	88
W5113	overrun of W5504 (above) - *92*	140	225
W4630A	**GW** 103240 grey - *87-92*	11	24
W4630	**BR** B893344 brown - *71-92*	5	8

W16. **BR Horse Box** (ex-Hornby Dublo) (1970)

Tooling subsequently bought by Mordvale in 2001.

W4315P	**'Roydon Stables'** E96435 SR green 'Foxhunter Championships Oct 6-11 Wembley' - *70-71, 74-90*	18	25
W4315P	same but lime green label	35	50
W4315	**'Roydon Stables'** E96435 green 'Foxhunter Championships' - *81-90*	60	90

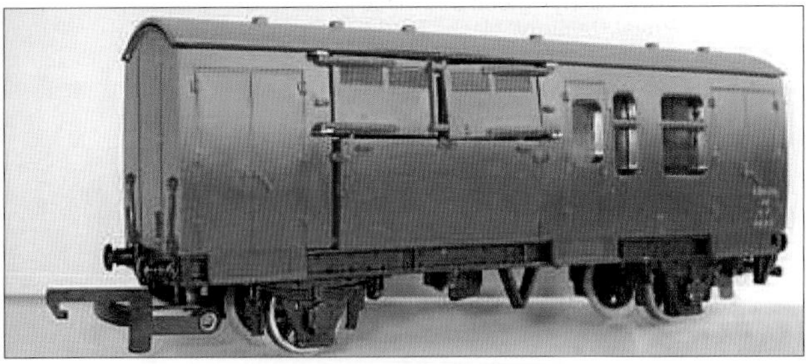

BR horse box [W16] (Oakleafomx)

W5002	**'Selsdon Stables'** E96435 maroon 'Foxhunter Championships Oct 6-11' Wembley - *71-74*	13	20
W4315X	**BR** E96435 green 'Foxhunter Championships' 193 made - *90-92*	80	125
W4315X	same but no poster * - *90-92*	36	50
W4316	**BR** E96435 maroon no label - *72-90*	15	25

* The number made is included in the figure above.

W17. **8T Fruit Van** (1980)

This model represents one of 130 cattle vans converted to fruit vans by the GWR in 1939.

W5058	**GW** 38200 light grey - *80-92*	5	16
W5058	**GW** 38200 dark grey - *80-92*	22	35
W5083	**BR** B872181 brown 680 made - *86-92*	17	26
W5083A	**BR** B872181 grey 25 made - *91-92*	NPG	190

W18. **Passenger Fruit Van** (ex-Hornby Dublo) (1970)

Tooling subsequently bought by Mordvale in 2001.

W4305P	**'Babycham'** maroon * W2910 - *70-74, 79-80*	7	17
W4305P	as above but paper labels for advert	18	25
W5300	**'WCC 2007'** pink Sp Edn (Wrenn Collectors Club)- *07*	NPG	50
W5516	**'Wrenn'** black Ltd Edn 100 - *07*	NPG	75
W5049	**GW** (yellow) 27614 dark brown - *78-86*	7	17
W5049	**GW** (white) 27614 dark brown - *88-92*	15	36
W4305X	**BR** W2910 maroon (shades) - *74-92*	7	11
W4305X	as above but no numbers	30	45

Passenger fruit van - Wrenn club wagon [W18] (G&R Wrenn)

W5055	**BR** W28720 blue - *79-92*	6	10
W5108	**BR** B517112 grey 75 made - *91-92*	53	135

* Roof colour varies.

W19. **'Yellow Spot' Banana Van** (ex-H/Dublo) (1968)

W4301P	**'Fyffes'** B881867 brown also W4301 - *68-71* *	7	13
W4301P	**'Fyffes'** B881867 green - *68-?*	6	16
W5022	**'Fyffes'** B881867 pale yellow - *73-80*	NPG	40
W5022-	**'Fyffes'** B881867 yellow - *73-80*	6	12
W5022	**'Fyffes'** B881867 dark yellow - *86-92*	30	45
W5022	**'Fyffes'** B87023 yellow - *74-79, 86-88*	NPG	NPG
W5022A	**'Fyffes'** B881867 brown 426 made - *87-90*	5	75
W5518	**'Fyffes'** blue Ltd Edn 25 - *07*	NPG	60
W5518	**'Fyffes'** green Ltd Edn 25 - *07*	NPG	60
W5007	**'Geest'** B881867 brown - *71-88*	6	12
W5007	as above but khaki spot - *71-80*	13	20
W5007	as above but no yellow spot - *71-80*	10	15
W5007	**'Geest'** B881902 brown - *90-92*	NPG	50
W5007A	**'Geest'** B881902 grey 171 made - *90-92*	NPG	127
W5105	**'Jaffa'** B881902 grey 124 made - *91-92*	107	268
W5063	**'Tropical Fruits'** M40 grey - *80-84*	6	26
W5063	**'Tropical Fruits'** M40 grey - *02-08*	NPG	25
W5028	**NE** 159611 grey - *74-76*	5	9
W5033	**SR** 41596 dark brown - *74-81*	6	11
W5007X	**BR** B881867 brown - *81-92*	50	75
W5007X	**BR** B881867 brown no yellow spot - *81-92*	5	12
W5007X	**BR** B881902 brown no yellow spot - *81-92*	NPG	70

* pre-production model seen at 1968 Toy Fair.

W20. **Ventilated Van** (ex-Hornby Dublo) (1968)

W5047	**'Bisto'** 25 beige - *77-84*	5	15
W5047	**'Bisto'** 25 dark brown - *87-88*	7	60
?	**'Cinzano'** white displayed at 1968 Toy Fair - *not made*	NA	NA
W5054	**'Decca'** DE545543 yellow - *79-80*	7	22

Ventilated van - 'Dunlop' [W20] (Oakleafomx)

W5004	**'Dunlop'** DE545543 yellow - *71-81*	5	12
W5004	**'Dunlop'** DE545523 dark yellow - *73-84*	5	12
W5004	**'Dunlop'** DE545523 dark yellow slogan reversed - *73-80*	27	47
W5004	**'Dunlop'** B757051 pale yellow - *73-80*	5	12
W5004	**'Dunlop'** B757051 yellow - *73-80*	10	15
W4325P	**'OXO'** DE545533 white - *68-72* *	5	12

W4325P	same but no running no. - *?*	NPG	60
W4325P	**'OXO'** DE545523 white - *70-?* *	7	24
W4318P/A	**'Peak Frean's'** DE545533 brown - *71-90*	30	45
W4318	**'Peak Frean's'** B757051 brown - *81*	40	60
W4318P/A	**'Peak Frean's'** 757051 brown - *73-80*	13	20
W4318P/A	**'Peak Frean's'** DE545523 brown - *68-72* *	5	16
W4318P/A	**'Peak Frean's'** DE545523 dark grey - *68-?*	12	18
W4318P/A	**'Peak Frean's'** DE545533 dark grey - *70-?*	30	45
W4318P/A	as above but blue-grey - *70-?*	NPG	12
W4318P/A	**'Peak Frean's'** B757051 grey - *?*	NPG	NPG
W5010	**'Robertson's'** DE545533 blue-grey - *?*	15	23
W5010	**'Robertson's'** B757051 light grey, white roof - *73-80*	7	12
W5010	same with grey roof - *73-80*	30	45
W5010	**'Robertson's'** B757051 blue-grey, grey roof - *71-83*	28	40
W5010	**'Robertson's'** B757051 dark grey - *73-80*	7	12
W5010	**'Robertson's'** B757051 brown - *73-80*	8	16
W5010	**'Robertson's'** 57 brown - *02-08*	NPG	30
W5010	**'Robertson's'** 57 brown - *73-80*	6	12
W5010	**'Robertson's'** B545533 dark brown - *?*	NPG	NPG
W5046	**'Walls'** Bacon 57 dark brown - *78-84*	8	16
W5046	**'Walls'** Bacon B757051 red-brown - *78-83*	5	16
W5046	**'Walls'** Bacon DE545523 brown - *78-83*	5	12
W4318	**'Walls'** DE545523 red - *68-72* *	9	12
W5011	**'Watney's'** B757051 red - *73-77*	6	12
W5011	**'Watney's'** B881867 red - *?*	NPG	NPG
W5100	**'Wrenn Railways'** W145207 grey 532 made - *89-92*	10	67
W5100A	**'Wrenn Railways'** W145207 brown 89 made - *90-92*	NPG	170
W4318X	**BR** B757051 brown also W5011X - *73-92*	8	10
W4318X	**BR** 57 brown - *80-92*	6	23
W4318X	**BR** B545523 brown - *80-92*	3	11
W4318X	**BR** DE545533 bright red - *?*	NPG	NPG
W5011X	**BR** DE545533 red - *73-75*	6	14
W5011X	**BR** B757051 bright red - *?*	NPG	NPG
W5007X	**BR** B881902 brown - *81-92*	50	75
W5007X	**BR** B881867 brown - *81-92*	50	75
W5094	**BR** W145207 grey 453 made - *89-92*	21	33
W5094	**BR** W145207 painted grey on a red moulding - *92*	65	100
W5030	**LMS** 59673 red - *74-76*	5	12
W5030	**LMS** 59673 red - *02-08*	NPG	25
W5033	**SR** 41596 dark brown - *74-81*	6	11
W5033	**SR** 41596 dark brown - *02-08*	NPG	25

* pre-production model seen at 1968 Toy Fair.

W21. SR Utility Van (ex-Hornby Dublo) (1970)

W4323P	**SR** S2380S green yellow letters - *70-90*	11	18
W4323P	as above but white letters - *70-90*	15	46
W4323	**SR** S2371S green - *91*	NPG	106
W4323	**BR** S2380S green no lettering - *80-90*	NPG	33
W4324	**BR** S2380S blue - *73-90*	6	11
W4324	**BR** S2371S blue - *91-92*	NPG	80
W5053	**BR** E37232 brown - *79-90*	10	15
W5085	**BR** M527071 maroon 543 made - *56-89*	11	32

W22. 6T 'Mica B' Van (ex-Hornby Dublo) (1968)

Tooling subsequently bought by Mordvale in 2001.

W5065	**'Birds Eye'** 312 blue - *80-90*	10	25

'Mica B' van - 'Eskimo' [W22] (Oakleafomx)

W5027	**'Carr & Co.'** pale green W59850 - *73-90*	5	12
W4320P	**'Eskimo'** W59850 white also W4320 - *68-81**	7	12
W5052	**'Young's'** 78 white - *79-92*	6	16
W5052	**'Young's'** 78 white Ltd Edn 15 - *02-08*	NPG	30
W5019	**GW** 59828 white 'Mica B' - *74-92*	5	12
W5019X	**BR** W145207 white 'Mica B' c200 made - *88-92*	NPG	140
W5019X	**BR** W59850 white 'Mica B' 96 made - *87*	120	175
W4320X	**BR** W59850 white 'Mica B' - *73-75*	7	153
W5089	**BR** 105721 white 512 made - *87-92*	17	80
W5089	**BR** 105720 grey Vent-Insul-Meat - *?*	40	60

* pre-production model seen at 1968 Toy Fair.

W23. 'Blue Spot' Fish Van (ex-Hornby Dublo) (1969)

W4300P	**'Findus'** E87231 white also W4300 - *69-71*	5	9
W5050	**'North Sea Fish'** E67840 blue - *78-81*	7	11
W5001	**'Ross'** E87231 cream or white - *72-92*	7	12
W5012	**BRe** E87003 blue 'Express Parcels' - *73-89*	5	9
W5001X	**BR** E87231 white 'Insulfish' - *73-86*	6	13
W5001X	**BR** E87502 white 'Insulfish' - *88-91*	25	80
W5064	**BRe BRT** E67840 beige - *80-84*	10	12
W5087	**BR Red Star** E87003 blue 580 made - *87-92*	8	44

W24. WR Goods Brake Van (ex-Hornby Dublo)

Tools bought in 1972. Mould faulty listed 1974-77.

W5037	**GW** 17575 grey - *not made*	NA	NA
W4312	**BR** W35247 brown - *not made*	NA	NA

W25. LMS Goods Brake Van (ex-Hornby Dublo) (1969)

Tooling subsequently bought by Mordvale in 2001.

W4311P	**LMS** M730973 brown * also W4311- *69-90*	4	9
W4311X	**BR** M730973 brown - *78-90*	4	12
W4311X	**BR** M730973 grey - *?*	13	20
W5090	**BR** B950127 grey 338 made - *88-92*	55	80
W5090	**BR** M730012 grey - *88-94*	10	65
W5513	**BR** B950130 grey - *07*	NPG	65

* Roof colour varies.

W26a. BR Goods Brake Van (ex-Hornby Dublo) (1970)

Tools bought in 1972. Tooling subsequently bought by Mordvale in 2001.

W5038	**SR** 32831 dark brown - *74-80*	5	17
W4310	**BR** B950350 grey - *70-*	5	10

SR brake van [W26a] (Rails of Sheffield)

W4310	**BR** B950350 brown - *73-92*	NPG	NPG
W4310	**BR** B932103 brown - *81-91*	12	18

W26b. BR Goods Brake Van (short) (ex-H/Dublo) (1974)

W5031	**NE** 128105 light grey - *74-77*	4	8
W5099	**BR** B950231 brown 263 made - *89-92*	30	45
W5099A	**BR** B932103 grey 321 made - *89-92*	26	44

ACCESSORIES

Of particular interest to collectors are the diesel horn sets made by Wrenn in the late 1960s. These contained either a Hymek or a Class 37 diesel locomotive, supplied by Rovex from their Tri-ang Hornby range, and a Wrenn horn sound unit. One sold at auction in 1998 for £260.

SETS

Initially Wrenn made up train sets to use up the remnant stocks of Hornby-Dublo that they acquired in the mid '60s. After that there were three Wrenn sets numbered 001 to 003. The first two sell at around £250 each while 003 could cost you about twice that.